JAPANESE COLLEGES and UNIVERSITIES

Supervised by **Monbusho**
(The Ministry of Education,Science and Culture)

Compiled and Edited by
The Association of International Education, Japan

MARUZEN

Japanese Colleges and Universities 1991

5-29, Komaba 4-chome, Meguro-ku, Tokyo, 153 Japan
Published by MARUZEN COMPANY, LTD.
3-10, Nihonbashi 2-chome, Chuo-ku, Tokyo, 103 Japan

Address orders to:
MARUZEN COMPANY, LTD.
Export & Import Department
P.O. Box 5050, Tokyo International, 100-31 Japan.

ISBN 4-621-03599-1 C1502

Preface

International exchanges in the fields of education and research are crucial to promoting further understanding and friendship among peoples of different countries. Exchanging students, more than anything else, is very important as it not only broadens the students' vision but also contributes greatly to the enhancement of educational levels in all countries concerned. More importantly, it provides a strong foundation for building international cooperation in the future, which is a fact proven by history.

In recognition of such a significance of student exchanges, Japan has set a political goal to accept 100,000 foreign students by the beginning of the 21st century. Under this futuristic policy, we are making constant efforts to increase the number of foreign students coming to study in Japan on Japanese Government Scholarships. We are also making the best efforts to beef up academic guidance systems in universities and other institutions, and improve necessary measures for self-financed foreign students in Japan.

Such a goal will not be implemented easily by only improving domestic systems and measures. For example, foreign students, wishing to pursue further studies in Japan, need to be well informed about Japanese institutions of higher education and what requirements they need to meet in order to realize their personal desire. In other words, they need to be provided with correct and latest information so that they can make proper decisions accordingly before coming to Japan.

This guide was first published in 1985, and has been updated every other year thereafter. This latest revision is designed to provide foreign students with fuller and more recent information. In addition, it divides Japan into nine regional blocks and introduces all of the national, local public and private universities and colleges in each block to ensure a greater ease of use. I hope that non-Japanese students wishing to study in Japan will find it helpful and convenient. I am certain also that this guide will reflect continued efforts of improvement each time it is published.

Finally, I wish to express my deepest appreciation to the Association of International Education, Japan who edited this guide, and universities and colleges that provided valuable information which was put into the guide.

Tokyo, March 1991

Yoshikazu Hasegawa, Director-General
Science and International Affairs Bureau,
The Ministry of Education, Science and Culture

Preface

International exchanges in the fields of education and research are crucial to promoting further understanding and friendships among peoples of different countries. Exchanging students, more than anything else, is very important as it not only broadens the students' vision but also contributes greatly to the enhancement of educational levels in all countries concerned. More importantly, it provides a strong foundation for building international cooperation in the future, which is a fact proven by history.

In recognition of such a significance of student exchange, Japan has set a political goal to accept 100,000 foreign students by the beginning of the 21st century. Under this futuristic policy, we are making constant efforts to increase the number of foreign students coming to study in Japan on Japanese Government scholarships. We are also making the best efforts to beef up academic guidance systems in universities and other institutions, and improve necessary measures for self-financed foreign students in Japan.

Such a goal will not be implemented easily by only improving domestic systems and measures. For example, foreign students wishing to pursue further studies in Japan need to be well informed about Japanese institutions of higher education and what requirements they need to meet in order to realize their personal desire. In other words, they need to be provided with correct and latest information so that they can make proper decisions accordingly before coming to Japan.

This guide was first published in 1985 and has been updated every other year thereafter. This latest revision is designed to provide foreign students with fuller and more recent information. In addition, it divides Japan into nine regional blocks and introduces all of the national, local public and private universities and colleges in each block to ensure a greater ease of use. I hope that non-Japanese students wishing to study in Japan will find it helpful and convenient. I am certain also that this guide will reflect continued efforts of improvement each time it is published.

Finally, I wish to express my deepest appreciation to the Association of International Education, Japan who edited this guide and universities and colleges that provided valuable information which was put into the guide.

Tokyo, March 1991

Yoshikazu Hasegawa, Director-General,
Science and International Affairs Bureau,
The Ministry of Education, Science and Culture

Editor's Preface

Japan is taking various steps to achieve its target of increasing the number of foreign students in the country to 100,000 by the beginning of the next century. The Association of International Education, Japan implements these steps with the guidance and assistance of the Ministry of Education, Science and Culture. The AIEJ assists foreign students in Japan, organizes examinations for foreigners wishing to enter a Japanese institute of higher education, and provides information and advice on study in Japan both in this country and overseas.

The number of foreign students in Japan has increased tremendously in recent years and now stands at about 41,000. Unfortunately, the amount of information on Japanese institutes of higher education available to people desiring to study in Japan is far from adequate. To close the gap, the AIEJ in 1985 began to publish this guide, which initially covered only the national and local public universities but later came to include also private universities around the country. With each new edition, we have expanded the guide's contents.

This latest edition provides up-to-date information on national, local public, and private universities in Japan. To make the information easy to understand and to let students know the characteristics of each region, it divides Japan into nine areas—Hokkaido, Tohoku, Kanto, Chubu, Kinki, Chugoku, Shikoku, Kyushu, and Okinawa—and area's national, local public, and private universities. It also has an index of major subject areas. In addition, to help readers better understand the general atmosphere and academic environment of each university, the guide lists the number of foreign students in each university by major and by department.

I sincerely hope that foreign students wishing to study in Japan find this guide useful. Since we will be revising it again in the future, we would be grateful to receive suggestions for further improvement.

Finally, I would like to thank all those who have worked so hard on this project, which has resulted in the publication of a most valuable reference book.

Nakao Ishida
President
Association of International Education, Japan

Acknowledgements

Appreciation is extended to all institutions listed herein for their cooperation in providing their program information.

In addition, Kokuritsu Daigaku Kyokai (Association of National Universities), Koritsu Daigaku Kyokai (Association of Public Universities) and Nihon Shiritsu Daigaku Dantai Rengokai (Federation of Japanese Private Colleges and Universities Associations), all gave their full support to the project and were most helpful in promoting their member institutions' cooperation in this undertaking.

Contents

Introduction

Criteria for Inclusion and Data Collection

"Japanese Colleges and Universities" is the most comprehensive single-volume reference on institutions of higher education accredited by the Ministry of Education, Science and Culture in Japan. The guide is organized into three major sections: studying in Japan; institutional profiles, containing detailed information on 507 colleges and universities grouped by geographical location; and includes appendixes, listing scholarships and financial aid for foreign students, preparatory Japanese language programs at universities, Japan Studies Program (Study Abroad Program), and indexes to majors in undergraduate and graduate programs for all institutions, arranged alphabetically by name in Japanese and English.

Questionnaires were mailed to appropriate officials at each of the institutions, and the overall response rate was over 90%. All returned questionnaires go through a rigorous process of editing, proofing, and error checking to ensure that the data are as complete, accurate, and up-to-date as possible. The omission of an item from a profile listing signifies either that the item is not applicable to that institution or that the information was not available. While every effort has been made to ensure the accuracy and completeness of the data, information is sometimes unavailable, and changes may occur after the deadline for publication.

The Association of International Education, Japan

The Association of International Education, Japan (AIEJ) was established as a foundation in March 1957 with the objective of carrying out various activities relating to international educational exchange and thereby contributing to international cooperation and friendship between Japan and other countries in line with government policies. As the central organization involved in providing welfare and assistance to foreign students in Japan, the AIEJ undertakes a wide range of activities in close cooperation with the Ministry of Education, Science and Culture.

The activities of the Association include the following:

1. Providing of information on study in Japan and overseas—Information Center
   (a) For foreign students wishing to study in Japan
   (b) For Japanese students wishing to study overseas
   (c) Publication of a monthly newsletter
2. Administering of examinations—Testing Division
   (a) Japanese Language Proficiency Test
   (b) General Examination for Foreign Students
   (c) Japanese Language Teaching Competency Test
3. Welfare and assistance for foreign students in Japan—Student Affairs Division
   (a) Assistance for medical expenses
   (b) Scholarships for privately-financed foreign students
   (c) Assistance for schools that reduce or waive tuition fees for foreign students
   (d) Assistance for the construction of dormitories for foreign students
   (e) Meeting foreign students on Japanese Government Scholarships on their arrival in Japan and paying allowance money
   (f) Assistance with accommodation expenses
   (g) Foreign student houses—Komaba, Kansai, and Soshigaya Foreign Student Houses
4. Follow-up support for foreign students who have studied in Japan—Student Exchange Division
   (a) Short training courses for students who have returned home
   (b) Distribution of research materials
5. Promotion of international exchange—Student Exchange Division
   (a) Inter-university student seminars
   (b) Assistance for Japanese students studying overseas

Part I　Studying in Japan

Colleges and Universities in Japan

(1) School education system in Japan

The Japanese school system can be divided into four stages; pre-school education, primary education, secondary education, and higher education. Elementary and junior high school are compulsory, lasting a total of nine years. Further education is voluntary.

In addition, there are special schools that give physically or mentally handicapped children education adapted to their individual needs. There are schools for the blind, schools for the deaf, and schools for those with other handicaps.

(a) Pre-school education

Kindergartens

Kindergartens are noncompulsory schools for children aged from 3 to 5, intended to help children develop their minds and bodies. Children can attend for one, two, or three years.

(b) Primary education

Elementary school

All children who have reached the age of 6 are required to attend a six-year elementary school. Elementary schools provide children from 6 to 12 with general elementary education suited to their stage of mental and physical development.

(c) Secondary education

Junior high school

After completing elementary school, all children are required to attend a three-year junior high school.

Senior high school

There are three types of high school courses: full-time, part-time and correspondence. The full-time course lasts three years, while the part-time and correspondence courses require three years or more. Part-time courses are further divided into day and evening courses. The majority are evening courses.

Education System in Japan

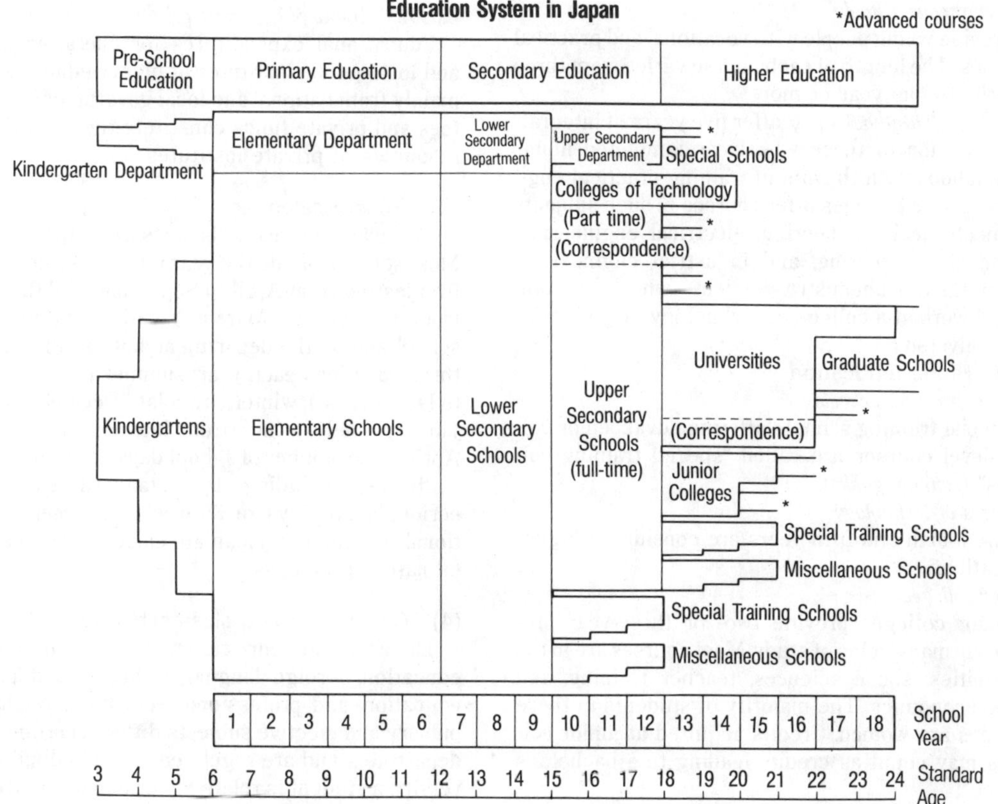

In 1988 "credit system" high schools began to offer a new type of part-time and correspondence education. Students graduate from these schools not on the basis of the length of their enrollment, but on the number of credits they earn.

In terms of the content of the teaching provided, high school courses can be divided broadly into two categories: general and vocational.

General courses offer comprehensive education with an emphasis on academic subjects, while vocational courses are designed to provide vocational, technical or other specialized education in such fields as agriculture, industry, business, fisheries, home economics, nursing, mathematics, physical education, music, art, and English.

In addition to regular schools, there are a number of special training schools and miscellaneous schools at high school level.

Special training schools

Offer programs that develop the abilities required for work, for daily life, or to increase the student's level of general education. In this category, schools offering high school level courses are called "upper secondary special training schools" (*koto-senshu-gakko*). There are also many general courses open to anyone, regardless of their educational qualifications. The length of each course is one year or more, usually with over 800 yearly teaching hours. Since 1986, students who have completed a 3-year course in a government-designated special training school are entitled to apply to universities.

Miscellaneous schools

Provide young people with vocational and practical courses. The length of each course varies from three months to one year or more.

Colleges of technology They offer five years of integrated education to those who have completed junior high school, with the aim of training practical engineers. These colleges offer courses in such subjects as mechanical engineering, electrical engineering, chemical engineering, and industrial engineering, and industrial chemistry. Students who have completed work at a college of technology may transfer to a university.

(d) Higher education

Special training schools

Special training schools offering advanced or college-level courses are called "special training colleges" (*senmon-gakko*).

Colleges of technology

The fourth and fifth years are considered higher education.

Junior colleges

Junior colleges provide two- or three-year programs in many fields of study. Most courses are in the humanities, social sciences, teacher training, and home economics. The majority of students in these colleges are women. Credits acquired at junior colleges may count as credits leading to a bachelor's degree.

Universities

Universities are divided into faculties or colleges and are then subdivided into departments and/or courses. Universities offer four-year undergraduate programs leading to a bachelor's degree. Medical, dental and veterinary courses last six years.

Graduate schools

A university may set up a graduate school offering advanced studies in a variety of fields leading to graduate degrees. More than half of the universities in Japan have graduate schools offering two-year master's courses and three-year doctoral courses. Some universities offer a five-year doctoral course that combines both degrees.

Number of Institutes of Higher Education by Type
(As of May 1, 1991)

	Special training schools	Colleges of technology	Junior colleges	Universities	Graduate schools
National	153	54	41	96	95
Local public	170	4	54	39	23
Private	2408	4	498	372	195
Total	2731	62	593	507	313

(2) Administration

Institutes of higher education can be divided into national, local public and private.

Educational expenditures for operating national and local public institutes of higher education come mainly from national and local governments. Student fees and private funds constitute the main financial resources of private institutes.

(3) School calendar

The academic year in Japan is from April to March. Most schools divide the year into two semesters, the first lasting from April to September and the second from October to March. Vacations differ by the school and by the department, but usually there are three vacations each year: summer (from early July to late August), winter (from late December to early January) and spring (from late February to early April). The number of school days per year in higher institutes, including the standard examination period, is 210 days, or 35 weeks. In general, educational institutes in Japan are closed on Sundays and on national holidays.

(4) Curriculum and class schedules

The university curriculum is divided into general education, foreign languages, health and physical education, and professional education. While compulsory and elective subjects differ according to the department and are regulated by the individual university, a student is relatively free to select from the available subjects those that are of interest. Class selection must also be within the guidelines of the student's major, which must be declared at the time of application. Some universities allow students to declare a major after the second year, and most allow for some flexibility with regard to changing majors. However, this can be a complicated procedure and it is rarely done by Japanese students. General subjects, foreign languages, and physical education classes are generally taken in the first and second years. These classes are usually large and are held in an auditorium. Major subjects are usually taken in the third and fourth years. These classes are relatively small. They generally take the form of seminars, laboratory sessions, study projects, or practical sessions.

A typical class at a university meets once a week and last 90 minutes. There is a 10-minute interval between classes and a 50-minute lunch period.

Classes are held every day from Monday through Saturday. In general, a student's workload is four to five hours a day and 20 to 25 hours a week.

(5) Credits, examinations and grades

Except for schools of dentistry, medicine and veterinary science, universities follow the credit system. Students complete the required study and exams for each course and receive credits.

Since Japanese universities operate on a semester system, exams are usually held before or after the summer vacation, and again in December or January, before or after the winter vacation. These are usually formal exams, but at the discretion of the professor, reports or short papers may be submitted in lieu of the test.

Grades are based on the results of written work and exam scores, with attendance also taken into consideration. Grades given are excellent, good, passing, or failure, i.e., A, B, C, or F. Usually, A=100%–80%, B=79%–70%, C=69%–60%, F=59%–0%. No credit is given for an F.

(6) Conferment of degrees

Undergraduate course

To graduate from an undergraduate course, a student must study at a university for four years (six years for medicine, dentistry and veterinary medicine) and acquire the necessary number of credits. Most universities require at least 124 credits (excluding medicine and dentistry). University graduates earn a bachelor's degree and are given a diploma and certificate of graduation. In Japan, over 78.6% of all students entering university complete a bachelor's degree. This degree is not conferred on graduates of any other institute of higher education.

Postgraduate course

The conditions for completing a graduate program are different from master's and doctor's courses. To earn a master's degree a student must complete two years or more in the master's program, accumulate at least 30 required credits in the major subject, and successfully pass the thesis exam and final exams. A doctorate requires an additional three years of study after a master's (four years for those in medicine and dentistry after bachelor's), completion of the required courses, passing final exams and the completion of a dissertation. In general, it is considered difficult to get a master's or doctorate degree in Japan, but for foreign students it is much more encouraging. (See Table below.) Furthermore, while graduate thesis generally must be written in Japanese, some advisory professors have recently allowed thesis to be submitted in English.

Master's and Doctrate Degrees Conferred on Foreign Students (1989)

Field	Master's course			Doctor's course		
	Completed	Degree conferred	%	Completed	Degree conferred	%
Humanities and social sciences	780	688	88	122	45	37
Natural sciences	796	767	96	593	557	94
Interdisciplinary sciences	60	60	100	45	45	100
Total	1636	1515	93	760	647	85

(7) Non-degree students (research students and auditors)

Generally speaking, programs for research students and auditors are regulated by each university, not by law. Consequently, the status and treatment of auditors and researchers vary not only with each university, but also with each faculty or college within the same university.

A university admits non-degree students only when it has the capacity to accommodate them without impeding the academic progress of full-time degree students. Credits accumulated by auditors and research students cannot be transferred to fulfill the requirements of a degree course.

(8) Transfer students

Transferring credits from one university to another is not a common practice in Japan. Occasionally, junior college graduates, students who have completed one or two years of general education at a university, and graduates of four-year universities transfer to another university in order to change their field of study. Transfer student acceptance policies differ with each university; some universities do not accept transfer students at all. A graduate of a special training school can never transfer to a junior college or a university.

Although the number is small, there are a few universities that will accept foreign students who have completed two or three years of education at a foreign university as second- or third-year students.

Studying in Japan

(1) Foreign students statistics

Transition of the Number of Foreign Students in Japan

(As of May 1 annually)

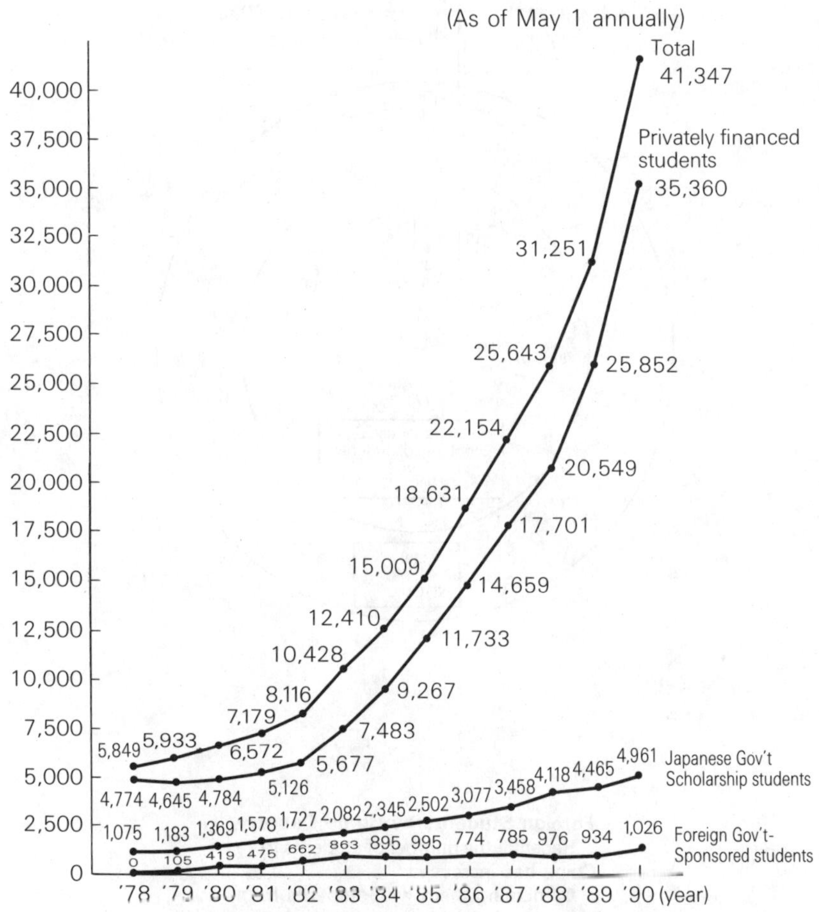

Note: Foreign gov't-sponsored students refers to students from China, Indonesia and Malaysia.

Source: Wagakuni no Ryugakusei Seido no Gaiyo (Outline of Japan's Exchange Student Program). 1991, Ministry of Education, Science and Culture.

Foreign Students by Home Area

The rate of students from Asian countries is increasing. They account for 91.7% of all foreign students in Japan.

Foreign Students by Home Area

(As of May 1, 1990)

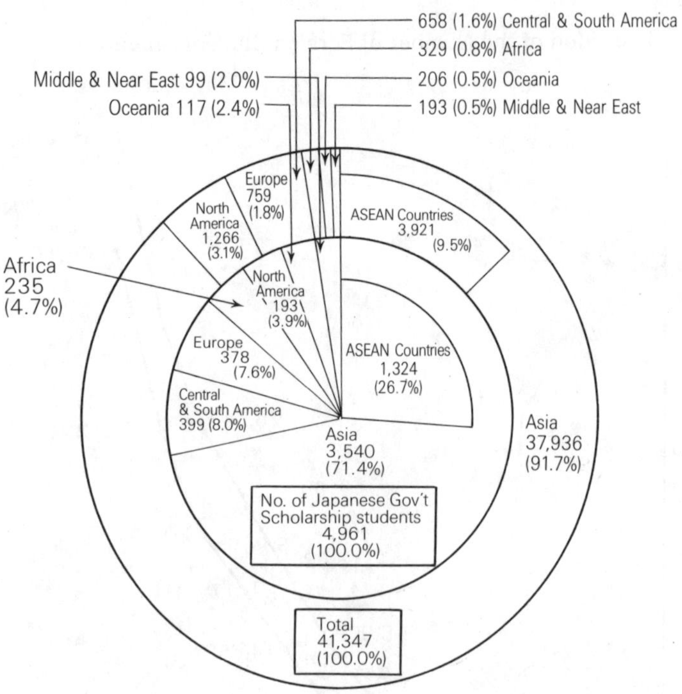

Percentage in ( )

Foreign Students by Home Country

Recently, the number of students from China has increased.

Combining them with students from Korea and Taiwan, they account for 78.9% of all foreign students in Japan.

(As of May 1, 1990)

Country	Number of students	Ratio (%)
China	18,063	43.7
South Korea	8,050	19.5
Taiwan	6,484	15.7
Malaysia	1,544	3.7
United States	1,180	2.9
Indonesia	948	2.3
Thailand	856	2.1
Philippines	479	1.2
Hong Kong	422	1.0
Bangladesh	394	0.9
Others	2,927	7.0
Total	41,347	(100.0)

Foreign Students by School Type/Academic Level

A look at the percentage of foreign students by school level shows that the undergraduate level (including two-year junior colleges) has not changed much from the previous year. However, the percentage at the graduate level has decreased, while the percentage at Special-training schools (Specialized courses) has increased.

Foreign Students by School Type/Academic Level

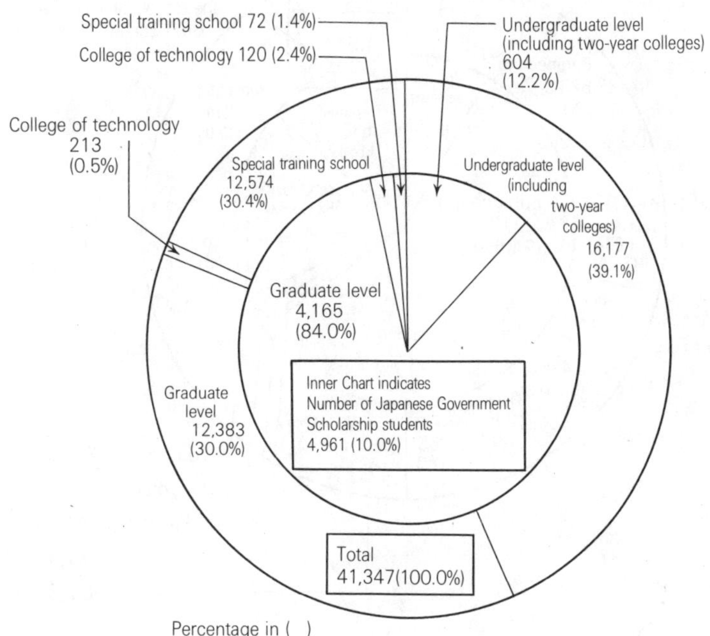

Number of Foreign Students by School Category and Academic Level
(As of May 1, 1990)

	Under-graduate	Graduate	Junior college	College of technology	Special training school	Total
National univ.	4,300	9,128	11	209	3	13,651
Local Public univ.	471	513	31	0	0	1,015
Private univ.	10,324	2,742	1,040	4	12,571	26,681
Total	15,095	12,383	1,082	213	12,574	41,347

Foreign Students by Major Field

The majority of students study in the fields of social sciences, humanities and engineering.

Foreign Students in Japan by Field of Specialization

(As of May 1, 1990)

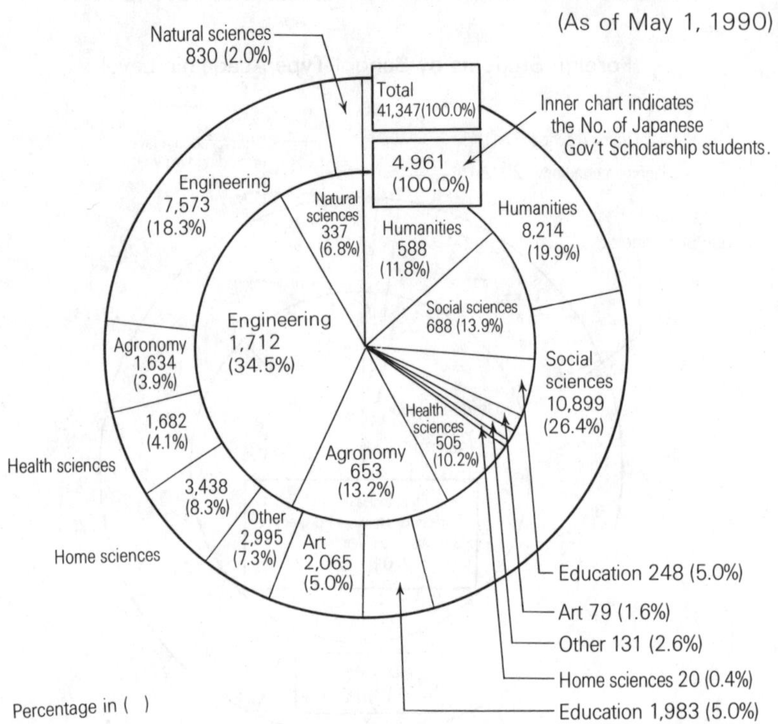

Foreign Students by Region and Prefecture

(As of May 1, 1990)

Region	Number of students	Prefecture	Number of students
Hokkaido	503 (1.2%)	Hokkaido	503
Tohoku	1,191 (2.9%)	Aomori	39
		Iwate	51
		Miyagi	702
		Akita	106
		Yamagata	89
		Fukushima	204
Kanto	26,206 (63.4%)	Ibaraki	1,215
		Tochigi	283
		Gumma	221
		Saitama	1,189
		Chiba	994
		Tokyo	20,403
		Kanagawa	1,901
Chubu	3,463 (8.4%)	Niigata	340
		Toyama	135
		Ishikawa	140
		Fukui	93
		Yamanashi	119
		Nagano	266
		Gifu	189
		Shizuoka	266
		Aichi	1,915
Kinki	6,617 (16.0%)	Mie	144
		Shiga	65
		Kyoto	1,859
		Osaka	3,409
		Hyogo	911
		Nara	201
		Wakayama	28
Chugoku	1,105 (2.7%)	Tottori	58
		Shimane	37
		Okayama	312
		Hiroshima	576
		Yamaguchi	112
Shikoku	303 (0.7%)	Tokushima	69
		Kagawa	74
		Ehime	113
		Kochi	47
Kyushu	1,959 (4.7%)	Fukuoka	771
		Saga	103
		Nagasaki	222
		Kumamoto	219
		Oita	183
		Miyazaki	53
		Kagoshima	108
		Okinawa	300
Total	41,347 (100.0%)		41,347

Note: Foreign students at a university with campuses located in more than one prefecture are counted in the prefecture where the main administration office is located.

(2) Information gathering and selecting a school

Foreign students wishing to study in Japan have different motivations. Their desired methods of study, periods of study, and educational institutions also differ. Some students wish to obtain a degree, some do not. Others wish to continue with another course of study. Whatever the case, it is important for a student to give careful consideration to his or her motivation and objectives. Why do you want to study in Japan? What is the most appropriate time and length of study? What career do you wish to pursue in the future?

(a) Time and length of study: When do you wish to begin studying in Japan, and how long do you want to stay?
(b) Level: What kind of educational institution do you wish to enter?
(c) Major field: What do you want to study?
(d) Degree: Do you wish to obtain a degree or not?

When selecting a school, it is very important for you to clarify your study plans and gather as much information as possible. Without such preparation, you run the risk of entering a school that does not offer courses in your chosen field of study. You may also have to pay extra expenses. Collecting the most up-to-date, reliable information is essential.

(a) Japanese embassies and consulates

Japanese embassies and consulates provide information on study in Japan. They may have guidebooks, AIEJ publications, and video tapes introducing study in Japan. Some may even offer individual consultation by appointment.

(b) Local study abroad information centers and friendship organizations

You may find in your area a study abroad information center or a friendship organization with an academic exchange program in Japan.

(c) People who have studied in Japan and alumni associations

People who have studied in Japan and their alumni associations can be another source of valuable information. They can provide a foreign student's point of view on life in and out of school, including things overlooked by native Japanese.

(d) Reference books, guidebooks on study in Japan

There are several books that provide a general overview of study in Japan. Guides to individual schools, textbooks for the Japanese language exams required by universities, and others are also available.

(e) School catalogues and application guidelines

Catalogues and application guidelines can be obtained by contacting the institution that you wish to attend. These materials outline the school's academic programs, providing you with valuable information when deciding on a school. These catalogues or brochures are usually printed in Japanese, but some institutions offer editions in other languages.

(f) Japan Education Fairs

In 1991 the AIEJ held "Japan Education Fairs" in Indonesia, Malaysia, Thailand, and Republic of Korea to provide students with firsthand information on study in Japan. The Association plans to organize similar fairs in other countries in the future.

After confirming that an educational institution offers courses in your chosen field, you should use the following criteria and bear in mind your objectives and ability. Different individuals will place different degrees of emphasis on the following points, according to what they wish to study, their budget, their academic records, their ability in Japanese, and whether they can obtain a scholarship. But if you give careful consideration to the criteria and keep in mind your plans for the future, you should have no difficulty finding the most appropriate school.

(a) Curriculum content
(b) Quality of the institution and teaching staff
(c) Research facilities
(d) Scholarships
(e) Tuition and other expenses
(f) Accommodation facilities
(g) Entrance examination
(h) Japanese-language program
(i) Special program for foreign students
(j) Location

(3) Qualifications for admission

Students wishing to enter a university, junior college, or special training school in Japan must have completed 12 years of school in their home country and must have completed secondary school.

Students from countries where school up to the secondary level lasts for 10 or 11 years are considered on a par with students who have completed 12 years of school if they study Japanese for one year at the Japanese language schools attached to the International Students Institute in either Tokyo or Osaka. Most universities accept the International Baccalaureate granted to students over 18 years of age.

Students wishing to gain admission to a master's course must have completed 16 years of school and graduated from a four-year university or be recognized as having academic ability at this level or higher. To gain admission to a doctor's course, a student must have a master's degree or be recognized as having academic ability at this level or higher.

(4) Admission

(a) Application procedures

Each educational institution has its own application procedures, so first ask the institution of your choice for a catalogue and application forms.

Deadlines for submitting school applications in Japan differ by the school. Some are as early as

August or September, some are as late as January or February. When sending an application from overseas, bear in mind the postal situation in your country and give yourself plenty of time to meet the deadline.

(b) Entrance examinations for universities

To enter a Japanese university, a student must meet that university's entrance requirements.

The examinations that foreign students must take differ by the university. In most cases, they are a combination of two or more of the examinations explained below. Recently, more and more universities have adopted separate procedures for selecting foreign students, but most still require applicants to sit for examinations in Japan. An increasing number of universities base their selection on the Japanese Language Proficiency Test and the General Examination for Foreign Students, discussed below. Only a few universities accept foreign applications on the basis of overseas documentation alone.

For information about university entrance requirements, either contact the university of your choice directly or refer to the *Shihi Gaikokujin Ryugakusei no tameno Daigaku Nyugaku Annai* (Guide to University Entrance for Privately-Financed Foreign Students), published in Japanese every November by the AIEJ.

Japanese Language Proficiency Test

This test evaluates and certifies a foreign student's proficiency in the Japanese language. It is organized by the AIEJ in Tokyo, Nagoya, Osaka, and Fukuoka and by the Japan Foundation in 41 cities in 21 countries and regions around the world. There are four different tests, each with a different level of difficulty. Level 4 is the easiest, Level 1 is the most difficult. Each level is made up of three categories; writing and vocabulary, listening comprehension and reading comprehension and grammar. About 90% of national and 70% of local public universities and 50% of private universities consider these results when admitting foreign students. Applicants to Japanese universities must choose Level 1. The results are sent to the prospective universities. Certificates of proficiency are given to those who pass the test. However, the degree of importance attached to the results of the examination differs by university. Some universities emphasize a student's results on this examination, while others consider the results along with the student's results on the school's own examination. Applicants who would like to take the test in Japan should contact the Testing Division of the AIEJ. Applicants who intend to take the test outside Japan should contact the Japanese Language Division of the Japan Foundation (address: Park Bldg., 3-6 Kioi-cho, Chiyoda-ku, Tokyo 102, Japan. Tel: 03-3263-4501).

Level	Criteria (approximate number)		
	No. of kanji	Vocabulary	Total hours of study
1 Advanced	2,000	10,000	900
2 Intermediate	1,000	6,000	600
3 Elementary II	300	1,500	300
4 Elementary I	100	800	150

General Examination for Foreign Students

About 90% of national and 80% of local public universities and about 30% of private universities use this examination to evaluate students. The AIEJ administers the test every December in Tokyo, Nagoya, Osaka, and Fukuoka. The results are sent to the university indicated by the student, and the university uses the results in deciding whether or not to accept the student. As with the Japanese Language Proficiency Test, universities attach different degrees of importance to this examination.

Major field of examinee	Subject
Humanities and social sciences	Mathematics World history English
Natural sciences	Mathematics Science (two subjects chosen from physics, chemistry, and biology) English

Examination of the National Center for University Entrance Examination

Japanese applicants for all national and local public universities and some private universities must take this examination. Most universities exempt foreign students, but some universities, mainly medical schools and education departments, insist that foreign students also take this examination.

Other examinations

Other methods used by universities to select foreign students include screening of required documentation, university-set scholastic ability tests, interviews, short written examinations or essays, and competence and aptitude tests. University departments differ in their methods of selection.

(c) Entrance examination for graduate schools

To enter a master's or doctor's program at a graduate school, a foreign student must pass that graduate school's entrance examination. A few graduate schools accept students on the basis of the documents they submit, but usually a student must sit for an entrance examination in Japan.

Graduate school entrance examinations usually

consist of a screening of required documentation, a short written examination, and an oral exam, mainly on the student's chosen field of study. Some graduate schools also have written tests in Japanese, English, or other subjects. Though the date of the examination differs by university, most graduate schools hold their entrance examinations between August and October. Some graduate schools, especially those for liberal arts, hold their exams in February or March.

Research students whose purpose in entering graduate school is not to obtain a degree are admitted on the basis of the documents they submit.

Usually foreign students who wish to enter graduate school to obtain a degree gain admission to the school as research students for up to a year, during which time they make the necessary preparations to take the entrance examination for admission as a full-time degree student.

(5) Japanese Language Institutes

With only a few exceptions, classes in higher education are conducted in Japanese. Foreign students must be prepared to spend a year or more studying Japanese so they can follow lectures, take exams, and participate in class discussions.

As international exchange between Japan and foreign countries grows, the number of foreign students in Japan continues to increase. People overseas are now taking a greater interest in Japan, its culture, and its language. Accordingly, in the past few years there has been a remarkable increase in the number of Japanese language institutions in Japan. While there are many excellent institutions, there are also some that operate under substandard educational conditions and with poor facilities and management. This can create problems for unwitting foreign students. Be sure to choose a Japanese language school carefully.

Preparatory Japanese language courses for university entrance are offered by universities, junior colleges, special training schools, and other schools.

In May 1989 the Association for the Promotion of Japanese Language Education was established to set national standards for assessing Japanese language institutes (except courses associated with universities and colleges), to provide in-service training for teachers, and to carry out relevant research to raise the standards of Japanese language education. As of December 1990, 436 institutes had been accredited by the association.

The first thing to do when choosing a Japanese language institute other than one run by a university is to check which ones are accredited by the Association for the Promotion of Japanese Language Education. Visas are not granted for study at unauthorized institutions. Since the authorized institutions and their profiles are described in "Japanese Language Institutes in Japan," published by the association, the next step will be to refer to this handbook, keeping the following points in mind. Of course, obtaining additional information from each institution's catalogue and from current or former students also will be helpful.

(a) Program objectives: What are the main objectives of the program? Does the program have a course that suits your goals?

(b) Grouping of students: Are students divided into groups according to their knowledge of Japanese, so each can receive lessons suited to his or her ability? Is there a placement test for this purpose?

(c) Other subjects: Does the institute offer lessons in other subjects required for entrance examinations (English, mathematics, physics, chemistry, social studies, etc.)?

(d) Educational environment: Are the location and other aspects of the educational environment satisfactory?

(e) Accommodations: Does the institute provide accommodations? If it does not have accommodations of its own, will it help you find an apartment or lodging?

(f) Guidance on further education and living in Japan: Does the institute offer advice and counseling on further education? Does it provide counseling services related to the problems of living in Japan?

(g) Language of instruction: In what language are the classes conducted?

(6) Tuition and fees

Students are required to pay a nonrefundable application fee when they apply to a school and take the entrance examination. School expenses for first-year students include an admission fee, tuition, and other fees, such as laboratory fees, facilities fees, and student activities fees. Fees at private and public schools vary according to the school and the faculty or department. The table below shows the average cost of admission to an institute of higher education in Japan.

Average Cost of First Year of Education

(As of April 1991) (Unit: yen)

Graduate Schools	
National Universities	545,000
Local Public Universities	
Dentistry	739,000
Medicine	668,000
Law	601,000
Engineering	591,000
Social studies	575,000
Literature, humanities, and foreign languages	572,000
Economics, Business, Commerce	572,000
Arts and Music	566,000
Science	564,000
Home economics	556,000
Pharmacy	498,000
Agriculture/Fisheries	466,000
Private Universities	
Agriculture/Fisheries	1,347,000
Arts and Music	1,247,000
Engineering	1,112,000
Dentistry	1,105,000
Veterinary science and animal husbandry	1,069,000
Education	1,069,000
Science and Engineering	1,015,000
International Relations	979,000
Science	977,000
Physical education	883,000
Home economics	825,000
Economics, Business, Commerce	800,000
Law	795,000
Medicine	770,000
Literature, humanities, and foreign languages	769,000
Social studies	756,000
Pharmacy	690,000

Universities (Undergraduate)	
National Universities	545,000
Local Public Universities	752,000
Private Universities	
Dentistry	9,257,000
Medicine	9,133,000
Pharmacy	2,049,000
Veterinary science and animal husbandry	1,862,000
Health and hygiene	1,700,000
Arts and music	1,284,000
Science and Engineering	1,246,000
Physical education	1,227,000
Agriculture/Fisheries	1,215,000
Computer and Information Science	1,168,000
International Relations	1,130,000
Home economics	1,127,000
Education	1,126,000
Literature, humanities, and foreign languages	1,037,000
Social studies	972,000
Law	969,000
Economics, Business, Commerce	964,000

(7) Scholarships and financial aid for foreign students

The following organizations offer scholarships for foreign students. For details and application procedures, please refer to the appendix.

(a) Japanese government (The Ministry of Education, Science and Culture)
(b) Local governments
(c) Private foundations
(d) Educational institutions

Most scholarships are for students and research students at the university level or above. There are few scholarships for students attennding special training schools, and almost none for students studying at Japanese language institutes. Most scholarships cover only a part of a student's education and living expenses; only a few cover all expenses. Students should check the cost of studying in Japan carefully and plan their stay accordingly, without relying on a scholarship.

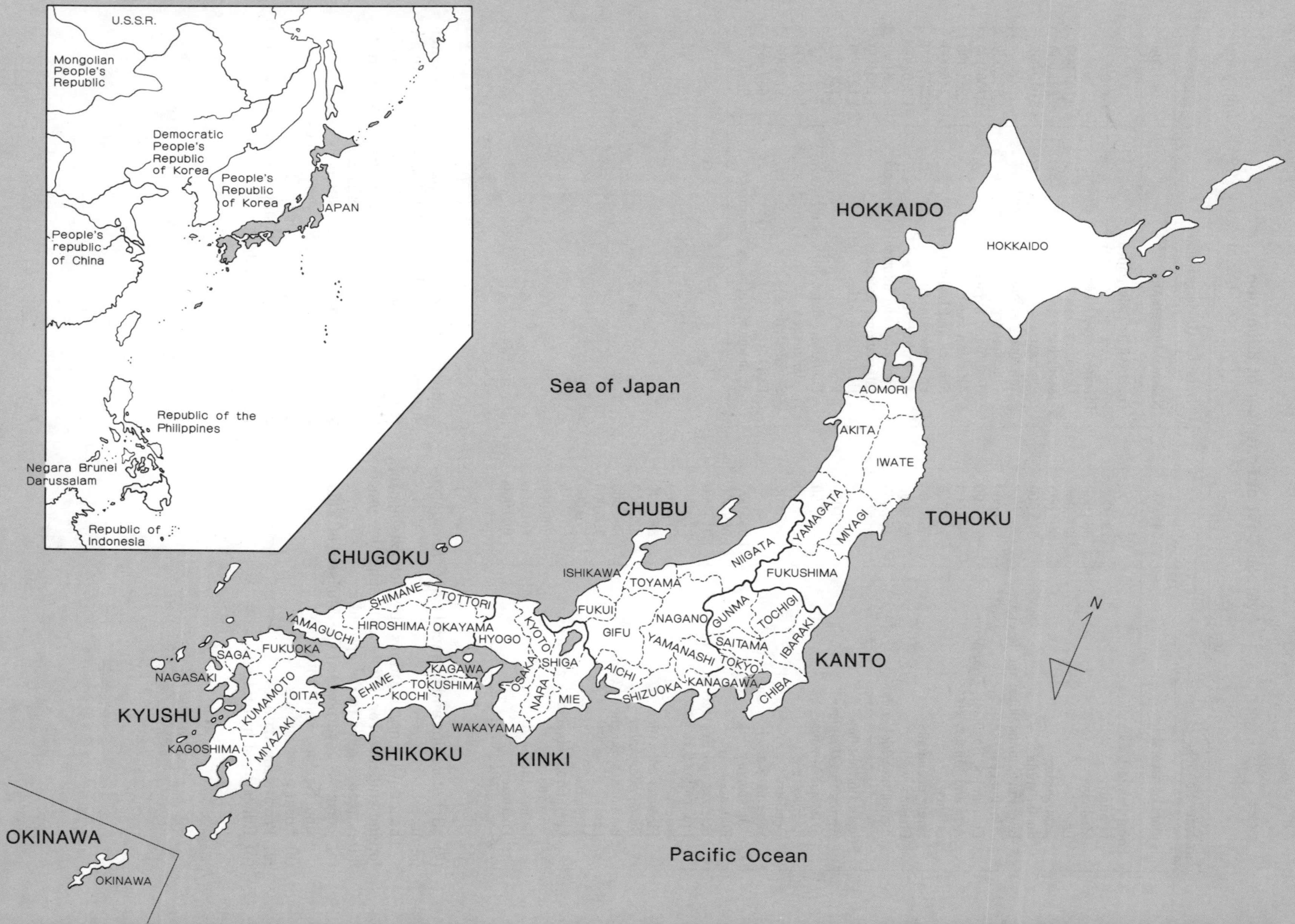

U.S.S.R.
Mongolian People's Republic
Democratic People's Republic of Korea
People's Republic of Korea
JAPAN
People's republic of China
Republic of the Philippines
Negara Brunei Darussalam
Republic of Indonesia

HOKKAIDO
HOKKAIDO
Sea of Japan
AOMORI
AKITA
IWATE
YAMAGATA
MIYAGI
TOHOKU
CHUBU
NIIGATA
FUKUSHIMA
ISHIKAWA
TOYAMA
FUKUI
NAGANO
GUNMA
TOCHIGI
IBARAKI
GIFU
YAMANASHI
SAITAMA
TOKYO
KANAGAWA
CHIBA
AICHI
SHIZUOKA
KANTO
N
CHUGOKU
SHIMANE
TOTTORI
YAMAGUCHI
HIROSHIMA
OKAYAMA
HYOGO
KYOTO
OSAKA
SHIGA
NARA
MIE
WAKAYAMA
KINKI
KAGAWA
TOKUSHIMA
EHIME
KOCHI
SHIKOKU
SAGA
FUKUOKA
NAGASAKI
KUMAMOTO
OITA
MIYAZAKI
KAGOSHIMA
KYUSHU
OKINAWA
OKINAWA
Pacific Ocean

Part II Institutional Profiles

How to Use the Institutional Profiles

The schools are divided into nine regions from north to south—Hokkaido, Tohoku, Kanto, Chubu, Kinki, Chugoku, Shikoku, Kyushu and Okinawa—then by administration into national, local public, and private, and are listed in alphabetical order by name.

Each profile contains under the following sections:

Institutional heading:

The heading of each profile contains the institution's full name in Japanese (Kanji and Roman letters) and its English name, address, and main telephone and facsimile numbers.

General information:

This section contains basic institutional data (as of May 1, 1990) and characteristics, divided into the following items.

Founded:

The year the institution came into existence or was chartered as an educational entity, regardless of subsequent mergers or other organizational changes.

Professors:

The number of professors in the institution.

Associate Professors:

The number of associate professors in the institution.

Assistant Professors (Tenured):

The number of assistant professors and lecturers working full-time.

Assistant Professors (Non-tenured):

The number of assistant professors and lecturers working part-time.

Research Assistants:

The number of research assistants in the institution.

Undergraduate Students/Foreign Students:

The number of students enrolled in the undergraduate programs. The numbers in parentheses show the total number of students and the number of foreign students.

Graduate Students/Foreign Students:

The number of students enrolled in graduate programs. The numbers in parentheses show the total number of students and the number of foreign students.

Library:

The number of books, references, periodicals, etc.

Contact:

The name of the section handling admissions. The address is given if it is different from that mentioned in the Institutional heading.

Educational philosophy:

The institution's philosophy of education, the school motto, and a summary of its founding spirit.

Foreign students:

Policies or programs for receiving foreign students and words of welcome.

Environment:

Natural, geographical, historical, and cultural environment, location, transportation, population.

Facilities:

Library, research facilities, gymnasiums, computer labos, etc.

Student activities:

School events, extracurricular activities, sports, etc.

Academic programs for foreign students:

Special academic programs designed for foreign students such as supplemental Japanese language classes, tutoring system.

Services:

Services for foreign students as well as for students in general such as counseling, housing, part-time employment, homestays, home visits, cultural exchange programs.

Undergraduate programs:

This section lists all the faculties and departments offering undergraduate programs. The numbers in parentheses show the total number of students and the number of foreign students.

Graduate programs:

This section lists all the graduate schools, divisions and classes. The numbers in parentheses show the total number of students and the number of foreign students. M stands for master's course, D for doctoral course.

HOKKAIDO

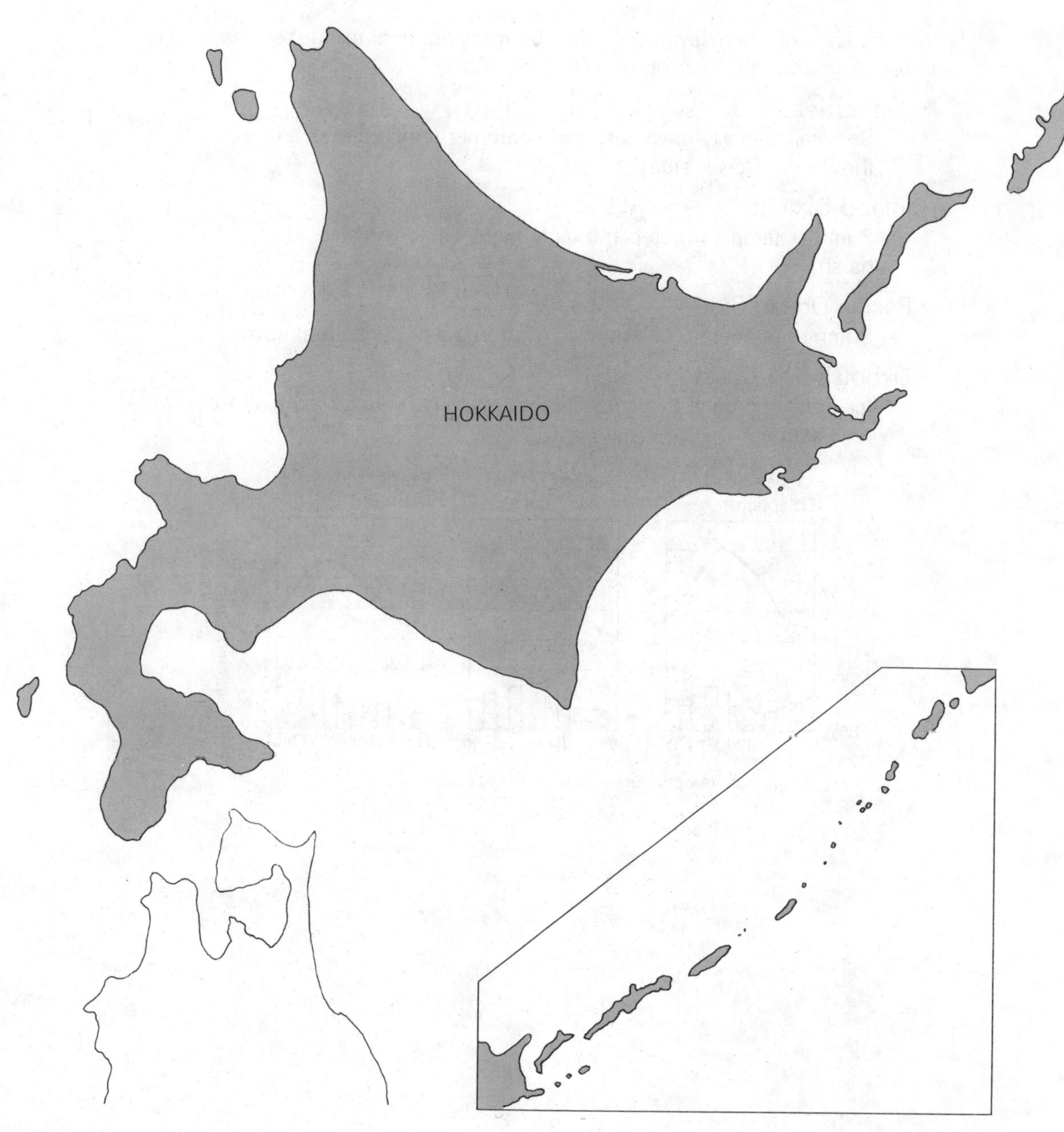

HOKKAIDO REGION CLIMATE

Winters are long, and severely cold. Summers are cool throughout, with little impact from the rainy season or typhoons.

- Japan Sea Side
  Snowfall is heavy in winter, while summer temperatures are higher than the Pacific Ocean side.
- Inland District
  Summer temperatures climb fairly high, while winter cold is particularly harsh.
- Pacific Ocean Side
  Summer temperatures are cool, with frequent dense fogs (over the sea).
- Okhotsk Sea Coast
  Ice drifts approach this area in winter, with harbors forced to close down until spring.

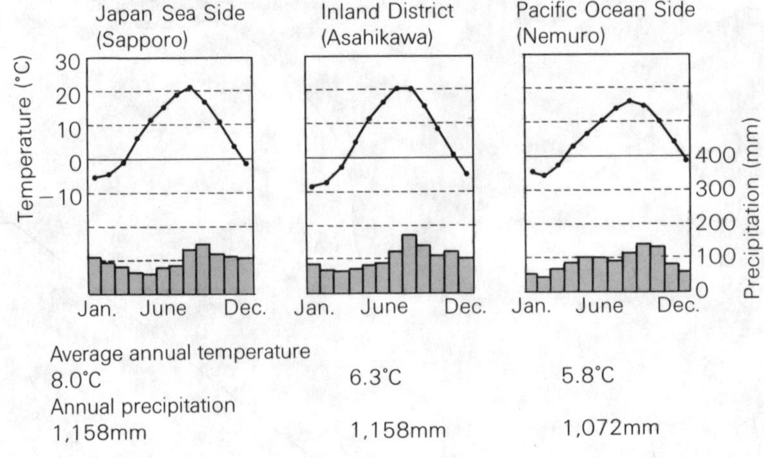

National Universities

旭川医科大学
(Asahikawa Ika Daigaku)
Asahikawa Medical College

4-5 Nishikagura, Asahikawa-shi, Hokkaido 078
☎ 0166-65-2111

Founded 1973
Professors 37
Associate Professors 26
Assistant Professors(Tenured) 38
Assistant Professors(Non-tenured) 134
Research Assistants 136
Undergraduate Students/Foreign Students 703/0
Graduate Students/Foreign Students 72/0
Library 103, 154 volumes
Contact: Admission Office Student, Affairs Section

Educational philosophy 1. To train doctors and medical researchers to understand the medical code and medical ethics and to respect human life above all else.
2. To contribute to the advance of medical knowledge and social welfare.
Foreign students Foreign students can enjoy a rewarding experience in our college, and can contribute a great deal to the promotion of mutual understanding and the development of firendly relations.
Environment Asahikawa Medical College founded in 1973 is a completely new college. Set in an area of outstanding natural beauty located in the northeast of Japan adjacent to Sapporo it is within easy reach of the ski slopes and landscapes at all seasons of the year.
Facilities Seminar Room, Chashitsu (tatami-matted room for tea ceremony), Gymnasium, Budo Gymnasium (gymnasium for Kendo, Judo and Karate), Kyudo Gymnasium, Athletic Sports Field, Baseball Field, Tennis Courts
Student activities There are 35 sporting clubs and 27 cutural clubs. Campus events include College sports, college festival, freshmen welcome party, etc. Skiing trip is held as a special extra-curricular activity once a year.
Academic programs for foreign students Tutoring system

Undergraduate Programs

School of Medicine(703/0)
Medical Course

Graduate Programs

Graduate School of Medical Research(D 72/0)
Div. of Cells and Organs(D 8/0)
Div. of Defence Mechanism(D 8/0)
Div. of Human Ecology(D 0/0)
Div. of Integrative Control of Biological Function (D 56/0)
Anatomy, Physiology, Biochemistry, Pharmacology, Pathology, Bacteriology, Hygiene, Public Health, Parasitology, Legal Medicine, Internal Medicine, Psychiatry and Neurology, Pediatrics, Surgery, Orthopedics, Dermatology, Urology, Ophthalmology, Otorhinolaryngology, Gynecology and Obstetrics, Radiology, Anesthesiology, Neurosurgery, Laboratory Medicine, Dentistry and Oral Surgery

北海道大学
(Hokkaidô Daigaku)
Hokkaido University

Nishi 5 Kita 8, Kita-ku, Sapporo-shi, Hokkaido 060
☎ 011-716-2111 FAX 011-746-9488

Founded 1876
Professors 557
Associate Professors 524
Assistant Professors(Tenured) 156
Assistant Professors(Non-tenured) 977
Research Assistants 765
Undergraduate Students/Foreign Students 5, 779/18
Graduate Students/Foreign Students 2, 628/305
Library 2, 765, 817 volumes
Contact: Foreign Students Office, International Affairs Section Admininistration Bureau

Educational philosophy The founding principle of the university,'frontier spirit' has been inherited until today with our motto, 'lofty ambition.' The university aims at teaching and studying up-to date high-level art and science to develop intellectual, moral and applied abilities so students may contribute much to cultural betterment and social improvement.
Foreign students We believe that foreign students can enjoy a rewarding experience in our university, and can contribute a great deal to promoting mutual understanding and the development of friendly relations.
Environment The main campus of the university is situated in the center of Sapporo, whose population is 1, 613, 000; it is 5 munites' walk from Sapporo JR station, but blessed with splendid environment in 450 acres of rich green land as a backcloth to the campus. There is Mt. Teine noted for its panoramic views of the city and its excellent ski grounds.
Facilities General library, Gymnasium, Student Center, Center for Extracurricular Activities, Computer Center, etc.
Student activites Popular campus events includes freshmen welcome party, homecoming, school festival, sports games like `Ekiden'. There is a wide variety of extracurricular activities including fine art, orchestra, choral groups, baseball, ice hockey, archeries, moun-

taineering, etc.
Academic programs for foreign students Supplemental Japanese language classes, tutoring system
Services for foreign students Health clinic, personal/psychological counseling, housing information, part-time job information, home stay-visit, cultural exchange programs, etc.

Undergraduate Programs

Faculty of Agriculture(525/0)
Dept. of Agricultural Biology(30/0)
Dept. of Agricultural Chemistry(110/0)
Dept. of Agricultural Economics(75/0)
Dept. of Agricultural Engineering(98/0)
Dept. of Agronomy(64/0)
Dept. of Animal Science(43/0)
Dept. of Forest Products(57/0)
Dept. of Forestry(48/0)
School of Dentistry(331/0)
Dept. of Dentistry(331/0)
Faculty of Economics(418/2)
Dept. of Business Administration(284/2)
Dept. of Economics(134/0)
Faculty of Education(131/0)
Dept. of Education(131/0)
Faculty of Engineering(1, 538/4)
Dept. of Applied Chemistry(75/0)
Dept. of Applied Physics(97/0)
Dept. of Architecture(103/0)
Dept. of Chemical Process Engineering(107/0)
Dept. of Civil Engineering(198/0)
Dept. of Electrical Engineering(119/2)
Dept. of Electronic Engineering(95/0)
Dept. of Information Engineering(82/0)
Dept. of Mechanical Engineering(91/1)
Dept. of Mechanical Engineering II(91/1)
Dept. of Metallurgical Engineering(99/0)
Dept. of Mineral Resources Development Engineering(76/0)
Dept. of Nuclear Engineering(93/0)
Dept. of Precision Engineering(79/0)
Dept. of Sanitary Engineering(133/0)
Faculty of Fisheries(425/0)
Dept. of Biology and Aquaculture(89/0)
Dept. of Chemistry(88/0)
Dept. of Fishing Science(162/0)
Dept. of Food Science and Technology(86/0)
Faculty of Law(525/0)
Faculty of Letters(434/0)
Dept. of Behavioral Science(128/0)
Dept. of History(81/0)
Dept. of Literature(132/0)
Dept. of Philosophy(93/0)
School of Medicine(474/0)
Dept. of Medicine(474/0)
Faculty of Pharmaceutical Sciences(177/0)
Dept. of Pharmaceutical Chemistry(88/0)
Dept. of Pharmaceutical Sciences(89/0)
Faculty of Science(635/0)
Dept. of Biology(67/0)
Dept. of Chemistry(72/0)
Dept. of Chemistry II(93/0)
Dept. of Geology and Mineralogy(70/0)
Dept. of Geophysics(57/0)
Dept. of Mathematics(119/0)
Dept. of Physics(77/0)
Dept. of Polymer Science(80/0)
Faculty of Veterinary Medicine(166/0)
Dept. of Veterinary Medicine(166/0)

Graduate Programs

Graduate School of Agriculture(M 131/14, D 80/28)
Div. of Agricultural Economics(M 8/3, D 10/4)
Agricultural Policy, Farm Management, Agricultural Development, Agricultural Co-operation, Agricultural Marketing
Div. of Agricultural Biology(M 22/2, D 21/6)
Plant Pathology, Plant Virology & Mycology, Crop Physiology, Applied Zoology, Entomology, Sericology
Div. of Agricultural Chemistry(M 41/1, D 14/4)
Soils, Plant Nutrition, Biochemistry, Food & Nutrition Science, Utilization of Agricultural Products, Agricultural Organic Chemistry, Applied Microbiology, Microbial Technology
Div. of Agricultural Engineering(M 10/2, D 5/5)
Land Improvement, Agricultural Physics, Soil Amelioration, Agricultural Machinery, Agricultural Prime Mover, Agricultural Process Engineering
Div. of Agronomy(M 17/2, D 8/3)
Food Crops, Industrial Crops, Plant Breeding, Horticulture (Fruit Trees & Vegetable Crops), Floriculture & Landscape Architecture
Div. of Animal Science(M 14/3, D 6/2)
Animal Breeding, Animal Nutrition & Feeding, Meat & Dairy Science & Technology, Leather Science & Technology
Div. of Forestry(M 13/1, D 10/3)
Forest Management, Silviculture, Erosion Control Engineering, Forest Policy
Div. of Forest Products(M 6/0, D 6/1)
Wood Physics, Chemical Technology of Forest Products, Timber Engineering, Wood Chemistry
Graduate School of Dentistry(D 46/4)
Div. of Basic Dentistry(D 7/1)
Oral Anatomy, Oral Physiology, Oral Biochemistry, Oral Pathology, Oral Microbiology, Pharmacology, Dental Materials & Engineering, Preventive Dentistry, Operative Dentistry, Periodontics & Endodontics, Prosthetic Dentistry, Oral Surgery, Orthodontics, Pediatric Dentistry, Dental Radiology
Div. of Clinical Dentistry(D 39/3)
Graduate School of Economics(M 8/3, D 17/6)
Div. of Business Administration(M 3/2, D 7/3)
Business Administration, Accounting, Personnel Management, Industrial Management, Marketing, Business Organization, Cost Accounting, Financial Management
Div. of Economics(M 5/1, D 10/3)

Theory of Economics, Economic History, Public Finance, Comparative Study of National Economics, Applied Economics

Graduate School of Education(M 19/1, D 16/2)

Div. of Education(M 13/1, D 8/0)

Educational Planning, History of Education, Adult Education, Industrial Education, Special Education/Clinical Psychology, Educational Sociology, Didactics/Curriculum Making & Instruction Theory, Educational Administration, Developmental Psychology

Div. of Education System(M 6/0, D 8/2)

Graduate School of Engineering(M 717/21, D 124/33)

Div. of Applied Chemistry(M 43/0, D 33/2)

Chemical Engineering Unit Operations, Fuel Technology & Coal Chemistry, Industrial Organic Chemistry, Cellulose Chemistry & Polymer Science, Ceramic Science, Industrial Inorganic Chemistry

Div. of Applied Physics(M 54/1, D 8/0)

Mathematical Physics, Instrumentation Physics, Applied Optics, Crystal Physics, Molecular Engineering, Applied Diffraction Crystallography

Div. of Architecture(M 34/1, D 4/1)

General: Nuclear Engineering Physics, Nuclear Reactor Engineering, Nuclear Reactor Materials, Applied Hydrodynamics, Physical Chemistry, Mathematical Electrical Engineering, Optical Engineering Science, Physical Fluid Mechanics, Applied Mathematical Science

Architecture: Building Construction, Building Materials, Architectural Planning, Environmental Engineering of Building, Earthquake Engineering, Housing

Div. of Biomedical Engineering(M 40/1, D 8/0)

Div. of Chemical Process Engineering(M 52/2, D 7/2)

Chemical Process Instrumentation, Chemical Reaction Engineering, Organic Chemistry & Organic Synthesis, Polymer Chemisty, Material Science, Chemical Process Design

Div. of Civil Engineering(M 64/2, D 4/2)

Structural Mechanics, Bridge Engineering, Concrete Engineering, Structural Engineering, Harbor Engineering, River Engineering, Disaster Prevention Engineering, Transportation & Traffic Planning, Transportation & Traffic Engineering, Highway Engineering, Foundation Engineering, Soil Mechanics

Div. of Electrical Engineering(M 56/1, D 18/6)

Electrical Machines, Automatic Control, Electric Power Engineering, Applied Electricity, Electricity & Magnetism, Electric Circuit, Electrical Materials Engineering

Div. of Electronic Engineering(M 55/3, D 22/3)

Electron Physics, Electromagnetic Waves & Transmission, Electronic Circuits, Computer & Signal Processing, Solid State Electronics, Applications of Electromagnetic Waves

Div. of Information Engineering(M 57/2, D 14/4)

Mathematical Science & Engineering for Information, Language & Information, Information Processing, Systems Engineering, Applied Computer Engineering, Intelligence and Information Engineering

Div. of Mechanical Engineering(M 45/3, D 7/3)

Strength of Materials, Fluid Mechanics, Heat Engines, Combustion Engineering, Mechanical Technology, Heat Energy Conversion

Div. of Mechanical Engineering Ⅱ(M 36/0, D 2/0)

Machine Design, Dynamics of Machines, Plastic Working, Engineering Materials for Machinery, Heat Transfer, Fluid Mechanics

Div. of Metallurgical Engineering(M 37/1, D 4/1)

Nonferrous Extractive Metallurgy, Ferrous Metallurgy, Ferrous Materials & Foundry Metallurgy, Fundamental Aspects of Physical Metallurgy, Electrometallurgy, Mechanical Metallurgy, Welding & Foundry

Div. of Mineral Resources Development Engineering(M 21/0, D 9/6)

Rock Mechanics, Mining Engineering, Machinery for Engineering, Mineral Processing, Economic Geology, Safety Engineering

Div. of Nuclear Engineering(M 45/4, D 2/0)

Radiation Source, Energy Conversion Engineering, Quantum Instrumentation, High Vacuum Engineering, Applid Radiation & Radioactivity, Nuclear Reactor Safety

Div. of Precision Engineering(M 36/0, D5/0)

Precision Machining, Precision Mechanics, Automatic Control Engineering, Engineering Physics

Div. of Sanitary Engineering(M 42/0, D 5/3)

Water Works, Sewage Works Engineering, Water-Quality Engineering, Process Equipment for Sanitary Engineering, Industrial Health Engineering, Urban Environmental Engineering, Solid-Wastes Control, Air Pollution Control

Graduate School of Environmental Science(M 88/5, D 33/6)

Div. of Environmental Conservation(M 22/2, D 8/1)

Biosystem Management, Frost Heaving Section, Floriculture and Landscape Architecture, Analytical Chemistry

Div. of Enivironmental Planning(M 23/2, D 2/2)

Regional Planning, Structural Engineering, Urban Design and Planning, Urban Environmental Engineering

Div. of Environmental Structure(M 20/0, D 5/0)

Fundamental Research, Meterology, Systematic Botany, Systematic Zoology

Div. of Social Environment(M 23/1, D 18/3)

Environmental Medicine, Hygiene and Preventive Medicine, Social Laws, Agricultural Policy

Graduate School of Fisheries Science(M 100/2, D 50/11)

Div. of Biology & Aquaculture(M 29/0, D 27/4)

Marine Botany, Embryology & Genetics, Marine Zoology, Physiology & Ecology, Planktology, Fresh Water Fish Culture, Mariculture

Div. of Chemistry(M 27/0, D 9/1)

Biopolymer Chemistry, Marine Lipid Chemistry, Marine Chemistry, Analytical Chemistry, Chemical Engineering

Div. of Fishing Science(M 24/0, D 9/4)

Principles of Fishing Ground, Oceanography & Meteorology, Biology of Fish Population, Fishing Navigation, Operational Technology of Fishing, Fishing Gear Engineering, Mechanical Engineering for Fishing, Instrument Engineering for Fishing, Engineering of Fishing Boats, Fishing Boat Seamanship, Fisheries Business Ecnomics

Div. of Food Science & Technology(M 20/2, D 5/2)
Food Chemistry, Biochemistry, Microbiology, Marine Food Technology

Graduate School of Law(M 15/5, D 15/0)

Div. of Private Law(M 3/0, D 5/0)
Education Division: Public Law, Private Law, Social Law, Jurisprudence, Political Science, Research Division: Comparative Law, History of Law, Sociology of Law, Philosophy of Law

Div. of Public Law(M 12/5, D 10/0)

Graduate School of Letters(M 72/2, D 58/3)

Div. of Asian History(M 3/0, D 3/0)
History: Japanese History, Asian History, Western History, Literature: Japanese Linguistics, Japanese Literature, Chinese Literature, English Linguistics, English & American Literature, German Linguistics, German Literature, Russian Literature, Linguistics, General: Foundational Studies of Culture, Synthetic Studies of Culture, Human Behavioristics

Div. of Behavioral Science(M 18/0, D 15/0)
Cognitive Information Studies, Comparative Behavioral Studies, Study of Social Behavior, Dynamic Sociology, Mathematical Studies in Behavioral Science, Social Ecology, Social Psychology

Div. of Chinese Literature(M 3/0, D 1/0)

Div. of Eastern Philosophy(M 3/0, D 5/0)

Div. of English & American Literature(M 8/0, D 5/0)

Div. of German Literature(M 5/0, D 5/0)

Div. of Japanese History(M 6/2, D 1/0)

Div. of Japanese Literature(M 9/0, D 9/3)

Div. of Linguistics(M 5/0, D 1/0)

Div. of Philosophy(M 9/0, D 12/0)
Western Philosophy, Chinese Philosophy, Indian Philosophy, Ethics, Science of Religion

Div. of Western History(M 3/0, D 1/0)

Graduate School of Medicine(D 154/15)

Div. of Internal Medicine(D 50/0)
Anatomy, Physiology, Biochemistry, Pathology, Microbiology, Pharmacology, Legal Medicine, Hygiene & Preventive Medicine, Public Health, Internal Medicine, Cardiovascular Medicine, Surgery, Orthopedic Surgery, Obstetrics & Gynecology, Ophthalmology, Pediatrics, Otolaryngology, Dermatology, Urology, Psychiatry & Neurology, Radiology, Nuclear Medicine, Anesthesiology, Neurosurgery, Plastic Surgery, Laboratory Medicine

Div. of Pathology(D 32/9)

Div. of Physiology(D 12/2)

Div. of Social Medicine(D 6/1)

Div. of Surgery(D 54/3)

Graduate School of Pharmaceutical Sciences(M 90/1, D 25/3)

Div. of Pharmaceutical Chemistry(M 36/0, D 11/1)
Pharmaceutical Synthetic Chemistry, Pharmaceutical Organic Chemistry, Chemical Microbiology, Biological Chemistry, Plant Chemistry, Physical Chemistry & Biophysics

Div. of Pharmaceutical Sciences(M 54/1, D 14/2)
Pharmaceutical Chemistry, Analytical Chemistry, Pharmacognosy, Synthetic & Industrial Chemistry, Hygienic Chemistry, Pharmaceutics, Pharmacology

Graduate School of Science(M 271/7, D 154/13)

Div. of Botany(M 10/0, D 16/2)
(Botany): Plant Physiology, Systematic Botany, Plant Morphology, Cell Biology
(Zoology): Systematics & Taxonomy, Morphology & Genetics, Animal Physiology, Cell Biology

Div. of Chemistry(M 51/1, D 37/6)
Physical Chemistry, Inorganic Chemistry, Analytical Chemistry, Organic Chemistry, Biological Chemistry, Environmental Chemistry

Div. of Chemistry Ⅱ (M 40/1, D 18/2)
Quantum Chemistry, Structural Chemistry, Genetic Biochemistry, Liquid State Chemistry, Solid Chemistry, Bioorganic Chemistry, Coordination Chemistry, Mechanistic Organic Chemistry

Div. of Geology & Mineralogy(M 18/1, D 7/1)
Petrology, Stratigraphy, Economic Geology, Mineralogy, Coal & Petroleum Geology

Div. of Geophysics(M 36/0, D 24/2)
Hydrology, Seismology & Volcanology, Meteorology, Applied Geophysics, Physical Oceanography

Div. of Mathematics(M 24/1, D 11/0)
Functional Analysis, Geometry, Theory of Partial Differential Operators, Algebra, Theory of Manifolds, Function Theory, Number Theory, Applied Mathematics

Div. of Physics(M 52/0, D 23/0)
Solid State Physics, Mathematical Physics, Theoretical Nuclear Physics, Theoretical Physics, Experimental Physics

Div. of Polymer Science(M 28/3, D 1/0)
Solid Polymer Physics, Polymer Solution Physics, Polymer Physical Chemistry, Polymer Chemistry, Biopolymer Science

Div. of Zoology(M 12/0, D 17/0)

Graduate School of Veterinary Medicine(D 40/16)

Div. of Morphology-Function(D 15/5)
Veterinary Medicine: Veterinary Internal Medicine, Veterinary Surgery, Veterinary Hygiene & Microbiology, Comparative Pathology, Veterinary Anatomy, Veterinary Physiology, Veterinary Public Health, Veterinary Biochemistry, Epizootiology, Veterinary Pharmacology, Theriogenology, Parasitology, Radiation Biology, Laboratory Animal Science

Div. of Prophylaxis-Therapeutics(D 25/11)

One-Year Graduate Programs

Fisheries Course
Fisheries Major
Deep-sea Fishery Major

北海道教育大学
(Hokkaidô Kyôiku Daigaku)
Hokkaido University of Education

5-3-1-3 Ainosato, Kita-ku, Sapporo-shi, Hokkaido 002
☎ 011-778-8811 FAX 011-778-8840

Founded 1949
Professors 180
Associate Professors 173
Assistant Professors(Tenured) 44
Assistant Professors(Non-tenured) 379
Research Assistants 20
Undergraduate Students/Foreign Students 5, 351/0
Library 795, 944 volumes
Contact: Hokkaido University of Education
Sapporo Campus 5-3-1-5 Ainosato, kita-ku, Sapporo-shi 002 ☎ 011-778-8811
Hakodate Campus: 1-2 Hachiman-cho, Hakodate-shi 040 ☎ 0138-41-1121
Asahikawa Campus: 9 Hokumon-cho Asahikawa-shi 070 ☎ 0166-51-6151
Kushiro Campus: 1-15-55 Shiroyama Kushiro-shi 085 ☎ 0154-41-6161
Iwamizawa Campus: 2-34-1 Midorigaoka, Iwamizawa-shi 068 ☎ 0126-22-1470

Educational philosophy The main objectives of the University are in comformity with Article 52 of the School Education Law. Further, as a university of education, it seeks to ensure that the students gain a deeper insight into the meaning and practice of education.

Foreign students The University expects to promote cross-cultural understanding by receiving students from foreign countries. Students must have a good command of the Japanese language, for it is the language used in teaching.

Environment The University consists of five campuses, each located in a principal city of Hokkaido: Sapporo (a population of approximately 1. 61 million), Hakodate (310, 000), Asahikawa (360, 000), Kushiro (210, 000) and Iwamizawa (80, 000). Hokkaido is a land full of potential and energy in terms of the quality of life and the natural environment.

Facilities Besides the five campuses, the University has its Library, Research and Guidance Center for Teaching Practice, Health Administration Center, and other facilities.

Student activities Extracurricular activities and organizations of each campus include student government association; orchestra; a variety of clubs, such as drama, puppet play, flower arrangement, tea ceremony, judo, karate, tennis, soccer. Campus festival, sports meet, welcoming of new students are among popular campus events.

Academic programs for foreign students As a principle, no special programs are provided for foreign students, except for some supplementary tutoring or lecturing.

Service for foreign students Foreign students can receive the following services from the University: psychological and personal counselling, assistance for medical costs, homestay arrangement.

Undergraduate Programs

Faculty of Education (Sapporo Campus) (1, 124/0)
- **Course of Art and Culture**(120/0)
- **Course for Elementary School Teachers**(396/0)
- **Course for Junior High School Teachers**(360/0)
- **Course for Nurse Teachers**(166/0)
- **Course for Teachers of Schools for Mentally Handicapped Children**(82/0)

Faculty of Education (Hakodate Campus) (1, 271/0)
- **Course for Elementary School Teachers**(625/0)
- **Coures of Integrated Arts and Sciences**(146/0)
- **Course for Junior High School Teachers**(298/0)
- **Course for Kindergarten Teachers**(120/0)
- **Course for Teachers of Schools for Mentally Handicapped Children**(82/0)

Faculty of Education (Asahikawa Campus) (1, 274/0)
- **Course for Elementary School Teachers**(578/0)
- **Course for Junior High School Teachers**(291/0)
- **Course for Kindergarten Teachers**(118/0)
- **Course for Nurse Teachers**(227/0)
- **Course of Sports and Health Sciences**(60/0)

Faculty of Education (Kushiro Campus) (936/0)
- **Course for Elementary School Teachers**(521/0)
- **Course of Integrated Arts and Sciences**(33/0)
- **Course for Junior High School Teachers**(264/0)
- **Course for Kindergarten Teachers**(118/0)

Faculty of Education (Iwamizawa Campus) (746/0)
- **Course for Elementary School Teachers**(716/0)
- **Course of Social Education**(30/0)

北見工業大学
(Kitami Kôgyô Daigaku)
Kitami Institute of Technology

165 Koen-cho, Kitami-shi, Hokkaido 090
☎ 0157-24-1010 FAX 0157-25-8200

Founded 1960
Professors 34
Associate Professors 45
Assistant Professors(Tenured) 11
Assistant Professors(Non-tenured) 15
Research Assistants 28
Undergraduate Students/Foreign Students 1, 524/4

Graduate Students/Foreign Students 38/1
Library 129, 642 volumes
Contact: School Affairs Division, School Affairs Section

Educational philosophy As a national industrial higher education organization, our main goal is to provide knowledge about technology so that students may become engineers adaptable to rapidly advancing technology. We also aim to contribute to the progress of the international community through our contributions to industrial prosperity.
Foreign students We are a new industrial college established in 1960, and we are young and full of energy. We are looking forward to educating young people from the world over who want to become engineers full of human vitality.
Environment The city of Kitami, with a population of about 110, 000, is located on the Sea of Ohotsuku side of Hokkaido and enjoys an excellent natural environment with many national parks nearby. It is about a 40–minute drive to Memanbetsu Airport, which has direct flights to and from Tokyo.
Facilities Attached Library, Natural Energy Laboratory, Kussharo Training Center, Gymnasium, Hall for practicing the martial arts, Ball Park, Sports Field, Data Processing Center.
Student activities Facilities include a Health Maintenance Center, a restaurant, a store, a bookstore, and a barbershop. There are 32 extracurricular activities such as baseball, tennis and soccer clubs. Campus events include the College Festival and sports competitions.
Academic programs for foreign students A four–hour Japanese lesson is given per week for foreign students.
Services for foreign students A " Foreign Students Exchange " is set up for exchanging views and establishing friendships among foreign students, Japanese students and the teaching staff, Compare notes about learning and campus life and to deepen understanding of different cultures and customs.

Undergraduate Programs

Faculty of Engineering(1524/4)
Dept. of Applied Mechanical Engineering(185/1)
Dept. of Civil Engineering(176/0)
Dept. of Developmental Engineering(179/0)
Dept. of Electrical Engineering(191/0)
Dept. of Electronic Engineering(192/0)
Dept. of Environmental Engineering(182/0)
Dept. of Industrial Chemistry(195/2)
Dept. of Information Engineering(40/0)
Dept. of Mechanical Engineering(184/1)

Graduate Programs

Graduate School of Engineering(M 38/1)
Div. of Chemical Environmental Engineering(M 8/0)
Reaction Chemistry, Environmental Control Engineering, Industrial Inorganic Chemistry, Synthetic Organic Chemistry, Chemical Reaction Engineering
Div. of Developmental Civil Engineering(M 4/1)
Structural Engineering, Cold Regions Developmental Engineering, Soil Engineering and Geotechnics, Water and Wastewater Engineering, Excavation Engineering and Rock Mechanics
Div. of Electrical and Electronic Engineering(M 6/0)
Electric Fundamentals, Electronic Circuits Engineering, Electric Power Engineering and Electrical Machinery and Apparatus, Electrical and Electronic Material Science and Technology, Applied Electronics
Div. of Mechanical Engineering(M 20/0)
Mechanical Dynamics and Applied Mechanics, Thermodynamics and Heat Transfer, Fluid Mechanics, Metals Machining, Metarial Processing

---

室蘭工業大学
(Muroran Kôgyô Daigaku)
Muroran Institute of Technology

27–1 Mizumoto–cho, Muroran–shi, Hokkaido 050
☎ 0143–44–4181 FAX 0143–45–1381

Founded 1949
Professors 72
Associate Professors 72
Assistant Professors(Tenured) 8
Assistant Professors(Non–tenured) 65
Research Assistants 36
Undergraduate Students/Foreign Students 2, 803/4
Graduate Students/Foreign Students 272/24
Library 231, 172 volumes
Contact: Instruction Division

Educational philosophy The goal of our teaching is to develop high level engineering and technological abilities with wider view of the society and the humanity in order to contribute to the betterment of local as well as international communities.
Foreign students The faculty and the students all welcome foreign students to join in our educational and research activities. We believe international exchange contributes much to our educational experience here. Local community is also very active in receiving foreign students.
Environment Our campus is located in the suburbs of Muroran, the largest technological center of Hokkaido. The city is practically surrounded by rich natural resources, the Shikotsu–Toya National Park and the Pacific Ocean. Access from Sapporo City and Sapporo Airport is within one and half hours.
Facilities Library, Medical Service Center, Center for Cooperative Research and Development, Education-

al Center for Information Processing, Gymnasium, Judo and Kendo Gymnasium, Students Center, Dormitory, Book Shops and Restaurants

Studen activities Popular campus events includes Homecoming, Sports Festival, Open Day of Institute, Open Day of the Dormitory. Extra curriculum activities are active in Baseball, Soccer, Kyudo, Archery, Amateur Radio, Photography, etc.

Academic programs for foreign students Supplemental Japanese language calsses (8 credits), Tutoring system with the assistance by graduate students.

Services for foreign students Medical Service Center, Dormitory for Foreign Students, Information Service for Housing and Accommodation, Homestay Program, Home Visit Program, Cultural Exchange Program, Visit to Winter Resort

Undergraduate Programs

Faculty of Engineering(2, 803/4)
Dept. of Applied Chemistry(418/1)
Dept. of Civil Engineering and Architecture(486/0)
Dept. of Computer Science and Systems Engineering(288/0)
Dept. of Electrical and Electronic Engineering (586/2)
Dept. of Materials Science and Engineering(411/0)
Dept. of Mechanical System Engineering(614/1)

Graduate Programs

Graduate School of Engineering(M 251/22)
Div. of Applied Chemistry(M 48/1)
Fundamental Chemistry, Bioengineering, Chemical Procrss Engineering
Div. of Civil Engineering and Architecture(M 31/5)
Structural Engineering, Urban Environmental Planning, nvironmental Engineering
Div. of Computer Science and Systems Engineering(M 31/3)
Information Processing Engineering, Instrument and Mathematical Engineering, Knowledge Engineering
Div. of Electrical and Electronic Engineering(M 44/5)
Electrical Engineering, Electric Engineering, Electron Device Engineering
Div. of Materials Science and Engineering(M 42/2)
Applied Physics, Materials Process Engineering, Meterials Properties and Performance
Div. of Mechanical Systems Engineering(M 55/6)
Thermal and Fluids Engineering, Basic Engineering for Production, Design and Control Engineering
Graduate School of Engineering(D 21/2)
Div. of Chemical and Materials Engineering(D 6/0)
Applied Materials Science, Materials Chemistry and Design, Chemical Engineering
Div. Civil and Environmental Engineering(D 6/0)
Environmental Planning, Structural Engineering, Geotechnology
Div. of Production and Information Systems Engineering(D 9/2)
Instrumentation and Control Engineering, Production Systems Engineering, Thermal Energy Conversion and Fluid Systems Engineering, Electrical and Computer Engineering

---

帯広畜産大学

(Obihiro Chikusan Daigaku)

Obihiro University of Agriculture and Veterinary Medicine

Nishi 2-11, Inada-cho, Obihiro-shi, Hokkaido 080
☎ 0155-48-5111

Founded 1941
Professors 46
Associate Professors 49
Assistant Professors(Tenured) 8
Assistant Professors(Non-tenured) 31
Research Assistants 39
Undergraduate Students/Foreign Students 1, 192/0
Graduate Students/Foreign Students 58/14
Library 132, 614 volumes

Educational philosophy Obihiro University is not so large as major national universities, but the university is unique in its education and research for the emphasis on animal and agricultural sciences and veterinary medicine. We aim to send out graduates as front-line specialists in the fields mentioned above.

Foreign students We are continuing to welcome foreign students and academic exchanges. We believe that they can enjoy academic and personal life in our campus. We will fully support their study abroad.

Environment Obihiro, with a population of approximately 170, 000 and located in the center of Hokkaido is recognized as an ideal area for dairy farming, thus providing an excellent environment for the various specialities. It takes 90 minutes by jet plane from Tokyo. The area is rich in natural sightseeing spots.

Facilities Library, Farm, Veterinary Hospital, Computer Center, Research Center of Protozoan Molecular immunology, Radioisotope Center, Health Care Center, International House, Sports Training Center, Gymnasium, Auditorium, etc.

Student Facilities Popular campus events include university festival, dormitory festival, freshmen welcome party, sport day. There is a wide variety of extra curricular activities including student council, clubs such as karate, judo, ice hockey, skiing, horseback riding, agri-

cultural problem studies, etc.
Academic programs for foreign students The university has special courses for Japanese language and Japanese affairs and tutoring system.
Service for foreign students Health clinic, personal/psycological counseling, International House, housing information, part-time job information, homestay, home visits, ski, excursion, some cultural exchange programs.

Undergraduate Programs

Faculty of Agriculture and Veterinary Medicine (1, 192/0)
Dept. of Agro-environmental Science(98/0)
Dept. of Animal Production and Agricultural Economics(75/0)
Dept. of Bioresource Chemistry(53/0)
Dept. of Veterinary Medicine(242/0)

Graduage Programs

Graduate School of Agriculture(M 57/11)
Div. of Agricultural Chemistry(M 8/1)
Agricultural Processing Machinery, Applied Biochemistry, Food Chemistry, Forest Products Chemistry
Div. of Agricultural Economics(M 6/3)
Agricultural Economics and Marketing, Agricultural Policy, Farm Accounting and Statistics, Farm Business Management
Div. of Agricultural Engineering(M 2/1)
Farm Power and Tractors, Field Machinery, Machinery for Animal Husbandry, Soil and Water Engineering
Div. of Agro-environmental Chemistry(M 24/1)
Environmental Chemistry, Environmental Botany, Environmental Entomology, Wildlife Resource Ecology
Div. of Animal Science(M 12/4)
Animal Breeding, Animal Husbandry, Animal Nutrition, Dairy Chemistry, Meat Animal Production, Meat Animal Reproduction
Div. of Grassland Science(M 5/1)
Forage Crops, Grassland Ecology, Grassland Production, Grassland Utilization
The United Graduate School of Veterinary Science (D 3/0)
Div. of Veterinary Science(D 3/0)
Applied Veterinary Science, Basic Veterinary Science, Clinical Veterinary Science, Veterinary Science of Pathogenesis

小樽商科大学

(Otaru Shôka Daigaku)

Otaru University of Commerce

3-5-21 Midori, Otaru-shi, Hokkaido 047
☎ 0134-23-1101 FAX 0134-22-0467

Founded 1910
Professors 38
Associate Professors 53
Assistant Professors(Tenured) 6
Assistant Professors(Non-tenured) 40
Research Assistants 8
Undergraduate Students/Foreign Students 1, 816/0
Graduate Students/Foreign Students 5/2
Library 310, 844 volumes
Contact: Admission Office, Student Division ☎ ext. 535

Educational philosophy With the single Faculty of Commerce, our academic programs are characterized by a strong unity among the faculty members and students who share their interests in social sciences.
Foreign students A faculty advisor is appointed to each foreign student to make his/her stay a rewarding and pleasant experience.
Environment Anyone will enjoy scenic views of the Ishikari Bay and Otaru Harbor from our campus, located on the western highland of Otaru, a city 22 miles north of the city of Sapporo, with a population of 170,000 and long history.
Facilities University Library, Institute for Economic Research, Information Processing Center with Campus LAN, Language Laboratory, Gymnasia, Indoor Swimming Pool and others
Student activities Besides their academic programs, most students are enthusiastic about extra curricular activities such as yachting, skiing, tennis, chorus, PCs, etc.
Foreign students Supplementary classes of Japanese language are offered at the Language Laboratory by arrangement. Tutoring system.
Services for foreign students A variety of services such as academic counseling, career guidance, financial aids, health care, housing, and personal counseling.

Undergraduate Programs

Faculty of Commerce(1, 816/0)
Dept. of Commerce(739/0)
Dept. of Economics(335/0)
Dept. of Management Science(222/0)

Graduate Programs

Graduate School of Commerce(M 3/2)

Div. of Business Administration(M 3/2)
Statistics, Economics, Economic History, Economic Policy, Public Finance, International Economics, Finance, International Finance, Science of Commerce, International Marketing, Transportation Insurance, Securities Market, Business Administration, Management, International Business Administration, Introductory Accounting, Financial Accounting, Managerial Accounting, Public Law, Civil Affairs Law, Commercial Law, Antitrust Law, Social Law, International Law, International Economic Law, Management Science, Electronic Data Processing in Accounting, Applied Mathematics, Computer Sciences

Local Public Universities

釧路公立大学
(Kushiro Kôritsu Daigaku)

Kushiro Public University of Economics

4-1-1 Ashino, Kushiro-shi, Hokkaido 085
☎ 0154-37-3211 FAX 0154-37-3287

Founded 1988
Professors 17
Associate Professors 7
Assistant Professors(Tenured) 11
Assistant Professors(Non-tenured) 26
Undergraduate Students/Foreign Students 802/0
Library 44, 316 volumes
Contact: Administration Office

Educational philosophy We aim at establishing an open university with a good connection with the community, and placing a special emphasis on internationalism, while combining theories and practices properly.
Foreign students Our university has just been opened in 1988 and is at the first stage of laying its foundation. Therefore, we will not accept any students from overseas for the time being.
Environment Our university is located about 5 kilometers north of the center of Kushiro City, with a population of about 210, 000 one of the core cities of Eastern Hokkaido, while it is right next to Kushiro Marshland National Park and is surrounded by the beauties of nature.
Facilities University library, Gymnasium, Computer center, Computer taining room, Audio-visual room, Language laboratory, Clubrooms, Cafeteria, Coffee shop, School store, etc.
Student activities Our campus events of the year include field day, school festival, etc. There are about 40 club activities, which are now very active, including baseball, tennis, ice hockey, light music, art, tea ceremony, etc.

Undergraduate Programs

Faculty of Ecnomics(802/0)
Dept. of Ecnomics

札幌医科大学
(Sapporo Ika Daigaku)
Sapporo Medical College

South 1 West 17, Chuo-ku, Sapporo-shi, Hokkaido 060
☎ 011-611-2111 FAX 011-612-8561

Founded 1950
Professors 43
Associate Professors 44
Assistant Professors(Tenured) 67
Assistant Professors(Non-tenured) 143
Research Assistants 149
Undergraduate Students/Foreign Students 631/0
Graduate Students/Foreign Students 80/1
Library 150, 914 volumes
Contact: Student Affairs and Research Section

Educational philosophy We aim at teaching and studying medical philosophy and high-level medical science to bring up creative doctors with great capabilities and humanity so that they can continue progressive medical practice and contribute much to regional and international societies.
Environment Sapporo Medical College was founded in 1950 by Hokkaido Government and the graduate school was established in 1956 and the pre-medical course in 1958. The campus is located within easy access to the central area of the city and a short-walk distance of various cultural institutions.
Facilities College Hospital, Cancer Research Institute, Marine Biochemical Institute, Library, Medical Museum, gymnasium, tennis court, baseball ground, soccer ground, lodge, dormitory, auditorium.
Student activities Popular campus events are college festival, sports festival, College Memorial Day, culture festival, and other intercollegiate students activities such as Hokkaido intercollegiate sports festival, sports, meetings of medical students in eastern Japan. We have 24 sports clubs (ski, skate, etc.), and 14 culture clubs (E.S.S., picture, etc.).

Undergradute Programs

Faculty of Medicine(631/0)

Graduate Programs

Graduate School of Medicine(D 80/1)
Anatomy, Physiology, Biochemistry Pathology, Microbiology, Pharmacology, Hygiene, Public Helth, Legal Medicine, Internal Medicine, Surgery, Orthopedic Surgery, Neurological Surgery, Obstetrics and Gynecology, Pediatrics, Ophthalmology, Dermatology, Urology, Otolaryngology, Neuropsychiatry, Radiology, Anesthsiology, Oral Surgery

Private Universities

旭川大学
(Asahikawa Daigaku)
Asahikawa University

3-23-113 Nagayama, Asahikawa-shi, Hokkaido 079
☎ 0166-48-3121 FAX 0166-48-8718

Founded 1968
Professors 20
Associate Professors 9
Assistant Professors(Tenured) 2
Assistant Professors(Non-tenured) 50
Undergraduate Students/Foreign Students 1275/0
Library 100, 000 volumes
Contact: General affairs section

Educational Philosophy We aim to teach and study the social sciences with the philosophy: to build higher education that is rooted in our regional community and is useful to develop our regional community, and to make our college open to the regional community.
Foreign students We welcome foreign students who are interested in learning about Japanese society, economy, and culture in order to promote mutual understanding and better relations.
Environment The city of Asahikawa, with a population of about 360, 000, is located in the central part of Hokkaido, the northernmost island of Japan. Our campus gives students a chance to learn and enjoy in the best environments with four distinct beautiful seasons.
Facilities Library, Regional Research Institute, Educational Institute for Information Processing and Audio/Visual Materials, Auditorium, College Hall, Gynasium, etc.
Student activities Campus events include a freshmen study excursion, mountaineering tour, campus festival, ski tour. There are many extra curricular, including Music, Photograph, Sign Language, Kendo, Judo, Baseball, Soccer, American Football, Tennis, Skiing, etc.
Academic programs for foreign students Every student is required to take a small group seminar to enable him or her to ask the instructor's assistance.
Services for foreign students Health care program, Personal counselling, Housing information, Part-time job infromation, etc.

Undergraduate Programs

Faculty of Economics(1, 275/0)
  Dept. of Economics(1, 275/0)

道都大学
(Dôto Daigaku)
Dohto University

7 Ochiish-cho, Mombetsu-shi, Hokkaido 094
☎ 01582-4-8101 FAX 01582-4-6311

Founded 1978
Professors 17
Associate Professors 19
Assistant Professors(Tenured) 13
Assistant Professors(Non-tenured) 7
Research Assistants 1
Undergraduate Students/Foreign Students 1, 263/5
Library 39, 984 volumes
Contact: Admission Office

Educational philosophy We aim at training students to become a " backboned industrial man " under the spirits of " ever onward " and " service to others " which develope youths who go forward coping with every difficulty and never giving up.

Foreign studens Mombetsu, with a population of 31, 000, is located in Hokkaido which is in the northernmost part of Japan. The city has been successful in the fishing industry and also in the international exchanges with its sister cities including Fairbanks and Newport in U.S.A.

Environment As Dohto is a relatively small university foreign students should enjoy the personal attention and respect as well as wonderful natural environment that are so seldom found today.

Facilities Northern Welfare Research Institute, Northern Design Research Institute, Marine Biology Research Institute, High-Tech Art Room, Library, Gymnasium

Student activities Volunteer activities including puppet shows and concerts are especially featured and highly reputated. We have fine athletic teams such as baseball, judo, rugby, basket ball which have been ranked first in Hokkaido.

Academic programs for foreign students Social supplemental Japanese language program.

Services for foreign students Provide students with general assistance and counseling program. Regular exchange programs with local community.

Undergraduate Programs

Faculty of Fine Arts(395/4)
Dept. of Architecture(199/1)
Dept. of Design(196/3)
Faculty of Social Welfare(868/1)
Dept. of Social welfare

藤女子大学
(Fuji Joshi Daigaku)
Fuji Women's College

North16 West 2, Sapporo-shi, Hokkaido 001
☎ 011-736-0311 FAX 011-709-8541

Founded 1961
Professors 23
Associate Professors 1
Assistant Professors(Tenured) 2
Assistant Professors(Non-tenured) 51
Undergraduate Students/Foreign Students 548/0
Library 195, 117 volumes

Educational philosophy The philosophy of the College is based to envision the full personal development of each student, with the hope that each grows in staunch independence of mind and in generous commitment to service of God, society, and fellow humans.

Environment The City of Sapporo is the capital city of Hokkaido, with a population of 1, 671, 000, but also rich in the natural beauties of mountains, forests, and rivers. The main campus is in the urban area, near the center of the city, and the large second campus lies in the suburbs of the city, surrounded by nature.

Facilities In Main Campus: Library, Auditorium, Gymnasium, In Second Campus: Seminar House, Tennis courts, Athletic grounds

Student activities All year round, students enjoy each of the annual campus events such as freshmen welcome party, sports meeting, college festival, memorial service, Christmas gathering, graduation party, etc. And they also have a wide range of choice for the extra-curricular activities both of sports and culture.

Undergraduate Programs

Faculty of Literature(548/0)
Dept. of English Literature(284/0)
Dept. of Japanese Literature(264/0)

函館大学
(Hakodate Daigaku)
Hakodate University

51-1 Takaoka-cho, Hakodate-shi, Hokkaido 042
☎ 0138-57-1181 FAX 0138-57-0298

Founded 1965
Professors 10
Associate Professors 4
Assistant Professors(Tenured) 15
Assistant Professors(Non-tenured) 30
Undergraduate Students/Foreign Students 1, 293/2

Library 90, 197 volumes
Contact: Admission Office

Educational philosophy Our first purpose and aim is to provide vocational education through which we promote learning. True learning is to develop enriched intelligence, emotion, and will. Accordingly, learning and virtue are not considered separately, but rather, together. No true learning can be attained without development of virtue. Learning is, on the whole, a total acquisition of intelligence, emotion, and will. In other words, learning is "trust."

Foreign students As one of the educational principles, our university emphasizes and nurtures internationality. Since 1973, in our international trade, short-term study trips abroad have been undertaken every year. Based on the success of these foreign excursions, in April 1983 through various negotiations. Our university became affiliated with Hawaii Loa College, located on the island of Oahu, near Kaneohe. Hawaii Loa College has since been designated as our "sister school."

This program surely help to enhance our growing sense of internalization further and further. The community of Hakodate has likewise encouraged this exchange from its beginning.

Environment Our univesity is located in Hakodate, a city of 320, 000 peole in the southernmost part of Hokkaido. The climate is mild. With four beautiful seasons in a scenic, natural environment. Hakodate is a cultural and sight-seeing attraction, with our university located in its educational district. Hakodate continues to grow and to flourish, especially with completion of the Aomori-Hakodate Seikan Tunnel (undersea length: 23 km) linking the islands of Honshu and Hokkaido.

Academic programs for foreign students Basic Japanese intermediate Japanese

Services for foreign students Boarding house or homestay, counseling once a week, learning Kendo

Undergraduate Programs

Faculty of Commercial Science(1, 293/2)
Dept. of Business administration

東日本学園大学
(Higashi Nippon Gakuen Daigaku)

Higashi-Nippon-Gakuen University

1757 Kanazawa, Tobetsu-cho, Ishikari-gun, Hokkaido 061-02
☎ 01332-3-1211 FAX 01332-3-1669

Founded 1974
Professors 47
Associate Professors 30
Assistant Professors (Tenured) 26
Assistant Professors (Non-tenured) 141
Research Assistants 112
Undergraduate Students/Foreign Students 1, 385/0
Graduate Studetns/Foreign Students 57/0
Library 99, 500 volumes
Contact: Admission Office

Educational philosophy The conceptional purpose is to provide students with scientific and warm-hearted education, in medical fields to a high level, and to foster such ability as to support human health and welfare.

Foreign students We have never received undergraduate foreign students, but we are preparing for graduate foreign students.

Environment The campus is located in the country town of Tobetsu which is 35 km to the north of the city of Sapporo and has a population of 16, 000 with distinct seasons giving students a good environment.

Facilities Center for Radioisotope Studies, Center for Experimental Animals, Medical Herb Garden, Center for Instrumental Analysis, Electron Microscope Laboratory, University Library, Dental Hospital

Student activities Campus events: Tree-Planting Festival, school festival, athletic festival, etc.
Student activities: tennis, Karate, Kendo, baseball, skiing, basketball, rowboat, rugby football, popular music, fine art, photography, Igo-Shogi, science fiction studies, botany studies, etc.

Undergraduate Programs

Faculty of Pharmaceutical Sciences(640/0)
Dept. of Pharmaceutical Sciences(328/0)
Dept. of Hygienic Pharmaceutical Sciences(312/0)
School of Dentistry(744/0)
Dept. of Dentistry

Graduate Programs

Graduate School of Pharmaceutical Sciences(M 30/0, D 0/0)
Graduate School of Dentistry(D 27/0)

One-Year Graduate Programs

Pharmacy Course
Pharmacy Major

北海道情報大学
(Hokkaidô Jôhô Daigaku)

Hokkaido Information University

59-2 Nishinopporo, Ebetu-shi, Hokkaido 069
☎ 011-385-4411 FAX 011-384-0134

Founded 1989
Professors 20
Associate Professors 9
Assistant Professors(Tenured) 15
Assistant Professors(Non-tenured) 5
Research Assistants 3
Undergraduate Students/Foreign Students 513/0
Library 20, 000 volumes

Educational philosophy The HIU amis at teaching and studying a new learning of Business Administration combined with Information Science to develop abilities so students may contribute to promoting the highly advanced information society.

Foreign students Foreign students will be welcomed in the near future because our university was just opened in 1989 and facilities for receiving foreign students were not enough yet right now.

Environment Our university is in the suburbs of Ebetsu City, about 40 minutes drive from Sapporo City, Hokkaido. The campus is located in the symbol zone of the RTN park, an innovation area called "Forest of Intelligence", and adjacent of our campus there is the famous Nopporo natural Forest park.

Facilities Computer room (main computer, terminals, personal computers etc.), library, sports training center

Student activities Popular campus events include school festival, freshman welcome party, athletic meeting. There is a wide variety of extra curricular activities for sports, music, volunteer work and hobby, etc.

Undergraduate Programs

Faculty of Business Administration And Information Science(513/0)
Dept. of Business Administration(259/0)
Dept. of Information Science(254/0)

北海道薬科大学
(Hokkaidô Yakka Daigaku)

Hokkaido Institute of Pharmaceutical Sciences

7-1 Katsuraoka-cho, Otaru-shi, Hokkaido 047-02
☎ 0134-62-5111 FAX 0134-62-5161

Founded 1974
Professors 17
Associate Professors 11
Assistant Professors(Tenured) 6
Assistant Professors(Non-tenured) 16
Research Assistants 36
Undergraduate Students/Foreign Students 850/0
Graduate Studetns/Foreign Students 11/0
Library 49, 676 volumes
Contact: Admission Office

Educational philosophy We aim at contributing to the public welfare through research and education in pharmaceutical sciences.

Foreign students We believe that foreign students can have a worthwhile experience in our school, and can contribute a great deal to promoting mutual understanding and the development of friendly relations.

Environment Our campus is located on a hill halfway between Otaru (a main seaport) and Sapporo (the fifth largest city in Japan) in the western part of Hokkaido. The campus is especially blessed with natural beauty and tranquility, accompanied by a fine view of Ishikari Bay in the Japan Sea.

Facilities Library, Herbal Garden, Laboratory Animal House, Radio-Isotope Center, Gymnasium.

Student activities Popular campus events includes freshmen welcome party, school festival, X'mas Party, thank-you party for the teachers.
There is a wide variety of extra curricular activities, including American football, baseball, light music, folk song, etc.

Undergraduate Programs

Faculty of Pharmaceutical Sciences(850/0)
Dept. of Pharmacy(513/0)
Dept. of Biopharmacy(337/0)

Graduate Programs

Graduate School of Pharmaceutical Sciences(M 11/0, D 0/0)
Analytical Chemistry, Medicinal Chemistry, Organic Chemistry, Pharmaceutics, Pharmacognosy, Pharmacology, Radiobiology, Biochemistry, Chemical Hygiene, Clinical Biochemistry, Environment Hygiene, Microbiology, Toxicology

---

北海道工業大学
(Hokkaidô Kôgyô Daigaku)

Hokkaido Institute of Technology

419-2 Teine-Maeda, Teine-ku, Sapporo-shi, Hokkaido 006
☎ 011-681-2161 FAX 011-681-3622

Founded 1967
Professors 60
Associate Professors 37
Assistant Professors(Tenured) 22
Assistant Professors(Non-tenured) 81
Research Assistants 16
Undergraduate Students/Foreign Students 3, 486/1
Graduate Studetns/Foreign Students 18/1
Library 96, 923 volumes
Contact: Student admission section of student admission office ☎ ext. 550

Educational philosophy Our institute, based on the founding spirit of our institute—To set our goals higher and respect them—, brings up students to be creative, learned, useful characters and it is also the fundamental idea of the institute that it should be devoted to the development of industry and society.
Foreign students During their stay in our institute they are expected to study their fields and to be interested in Japanese whole society as well in order to dedicate themselves to international friendship in the future.
Environment Our institute is located in the western part of Sapporo City that has a population of 1,670,000. It is situated in Ishikari Plains, enjoys fine environment and overlooks Ishikari Bay and Teine mountains. It is a twenty-five-minute train ride or a fifty-minute bus ride from the center of the city.
Facilities We have the Computer Center, the Cold Region General Research Center, along with 200 big and small laboratories. We also have audio-visual facilities in the library.
Student activities Activities: Freshmen welcome party, school festival, school sport, graduation party
Clubs: Baseball, Ski, Karate, Archery, Japanese achery, Art, Camera, Jazz, Rover scout, Aviation, Computer, Car, etc.
Academic programs for foreign students We can give Japanese or Japanese affairs instead of some general science courses.
Services for foreign students We can reduce the tuition fee by certain degree for the students who pay their expenses by themselves when they meet the condition specified by the institute.

Undergraduate Programs

Faculty of Engineering(3, 486/1)
Dept. of Applied Electronics(405/0)
Dept. of Architecture(648/0)
Dept. of Civil Engineering(673/0)
Dept. of Electrical Engineering(423/1)
Dept. of Industrial Engineering(661/0)
Dept. of Mechanical Engineering(676/0)

Graduate Programs

Graduate School of Engineering(M 18/1)
Div. of Electrical Engineering(M 3/1)
Energy and Control Engineering, Electrical Materials and Devices Engineering, Electrical Circuits and Communication Engineering, Systems and Information Engineering
Div. of Applied Electronics(M 7/0)
Biomedical Electronics and Bio-system Engineering, Light-/Radio-wave Applications and Information Processing Engineering, Information Transmission and Electronics Equipment, Materials Sciences and Engineering
Div. of Architecture(M 8/0)
Urban Planning and Design, Environmental Engineering in Cold Climate, Building Structural Engineering, Building Construction

北海道東海大学
(Hokkaidô Tôkai Daigaku)

Hokkaido Tokai University

5-1-1-1 Minami-sawa, Minami-ku, Sapporo-shi, Hokkaido 005
☎ 011-571-5111 FAX 011-571-7879

Founded 1977
Professors 60
Associate Professors 34
Assistant Professors (Tenured) 22
Assistant Professors (Non-tenured) 79
Research Assistants 5
Undergraduate Students/Foreign Students 1, 746/0
Graduate Studetns/Foreign Students 4/1
Library 120, 052 volumes
Contact: Phone and address indicated above. Also, Office of Academic Affairs 224 Chuwa, Kamui-cho, Asahikawa, Hokkaido 070 ☎ 0166-61-5111 FAX. 0166-62-8180

Educational philosophy The philosophical foundation of Hokkaido Tokai University is to educate students based upon humanism and respect for the individual personality, not upon a world view of materialism and the materialistic conception of history.
Foreign students We welcome youth who are broad-minded and can love others, their society, their country, and even the whole world, and we do not welcome whose who are selfish, exclusive, and narrow-minded.
Environment Sapporo is the fifth largest city in Japan and the center of politics, economics, education and culture of the province of Hokkaido, with a population of 1.6 million. The city of Asahikawa, about 86 miles from Sapporo, is also very fascinating place to study.
Facilities General Research Center, Research Institute of Life in Northern Japan. Two libraries, Computer, Experimental Aquarium, Skiing ground, Baseball stadium, Arboretum, Bio-Experimental Farm, etc.
Student activities Popular campus events include freshman welcome party, university festival, athletic games, Christmas party. There are a number of clubs for extra-curricular activities including baseball, skiing, volleyball, soccer, Intermusika (classic music), popular music, etc.
Academic programs for foreign students We give special Japanese language and culture programs for the students of Earlum College (U.S.A.) and Univ. of Stockholm (Sweden), based upon the agreements between these institutions.
Services for foreign students We provide teaching staff, and also program associates who arrange and give advice for various activities for these students. Housing information, particularly that of homestay is readily available.

Undergraduate Programs

Faculty of Art and Technology(756/0)
 Dept. of Architecture(374/0)
 Dept. of Design(382/0)
Faculty of International Cultural Relations(427/0)
 Dept. of International Cultural Relations(427/0)
 (Comparative Cultures Major, Intercultural Communications Major)
Faculty of Engineering(563/0)
 Dept. of Bioscience and Technology(136/0)
 Dept. of Electronic and Information Engineering(283/0)
 Dept. of Marine Sciences and Technology(144/0)

Graduate Programs

Graduate School of Arts(M 4/1)
 Course of Design(M 4/1)

北海学園大学
(Hokkaigakuen Daigaku)
Hokkaigakuen University

4-1-40 Asahi-machi, Toyohira-ku, Sapporo-shi, Hokkaido 062
☎ 011-841-1161 FAX 011-824-3141

Founded 1950
Professors 111
Associate Professors 29
Assistant Professors(Tenured) 10
Assistant Professors(Non-tenured) 267
Research Assistants 2
Undergraduate Students/Foreign Students 7, 778/0
Graduate Studetns/Foreign Students 18/1
Library 400, 000 volumes
Contact: Adimission Office

Educational philosophy We aim at educating and studying with "Pioneer Spirits"
Foreign students Foreign students, studying with "Pioneer Spirits" will be welcome.
Environment Located in the central area of Sapporo (with a population of 1, 650, 000), the cultural and economic city in Hokkaido.
Facilities Center for Development Policy Studies, Library (including Hokuga Collection), Electronics Research Laboratory, Natural Science Laboratory, Sports traingin center, etc.
Student activities School festival, Freshmen welcome party. There is a wide variety of extra curricular activities, including many voluntary works, sports club, etc.
Services for foreign students Health clinic, personal counseling, housing information, etc.

Undergraduate Programs

Faculty of Economics(4, 185/0)
 Dept. of Business Administration(2, 098/0)
 Dept. of Economics(2, 087/0)
Faculty of Engineering(1, 353/0)
 Dept. of Architectural Engineering(464/0)
 Dept. of Civil Engineering(452/0)
 Dept. of Electronic and Information Engineering(437/0)
Faculty of Law(2, 240/0)
 Dept. of Law

Graduate Programs

Graduate School of Economics(M 4/1)
 Div. of Economic Policy
Graduate School of Law(M 14/0)
 Div. of Law

北海学園北見大学
(Hokkaigakuen Kitami Daigaku)
Hokkai-Gakuen University of Kitami

235 Hokko, Kitami-shi, Hokkaido 090
☎ 0157-22-2721 FAX 0157-22-2729

Founded 1977
Professors 15
Associate Professors 6
Assistant Professors(Tenured) 4
Assistant Professors(Non-tenured) 24
Undergraduate Students/Foreign Students 956/1
Library 80, 014 volumes
Contact: Entrance Examination Section

Educational philosophy The university aims to provide a high level of education, building character and developing to the fullest the individual potential of young people who will create and support the society of the future.
Foreign students Kitami university welcomes students from other countries. The small size at the university enables foreign students to mix easily with Japanese students.
Environment The university was established in Kitami City, in eastern Hokkaido in 1977. 107, 000 people live in Kitami. Kitami is an important point on the transportation network connecting central and eastern Hokkaido near the sea of Okhotsk and Akan National Park.
Facilities Library, Computer room, Japanese Tea House, Gymnasium, Guest House, Accommodation House for Foreign students
Student activitites University Festival, Sports Fes-

tival, A range of sports and cultural clubs including Baseball, Soccer, Kendo, Archery, Trampoline, Tea Ceremony, Koto music, Science Fiction, Photography
Academic programs for foreign students Supplementary Japanese language tutoring program
Services for foreign students College housing, Housing information, Part-time job information, City cultural exchange activities

Undergraduate Programs

Faculty of Commerce(956/1)
Dept. of Commerce

北星学園大学
(Hokusei Gakuen Daigaku)

Hokusei Gakuen University

Oyachi Nishi 2, 3-1, Atsubetsu-ku, Sappro-shi 004
☎ 011-891-2731 FAX 011-892-6097

Founded 1962
Professors 40
Associate Professors 26
Assistant Professors(Tenured) 5
Assistant Professors(Non-tenured) 126
Research Assistants 1
Undergraduate Students/Foreign Students 2,556/2
Library 132, 000 volumes
Contact: Admission Office

Educational philosophy Founded on Christian principles, we are committed to the pursuit of the development of the individual, of society, and of internationalism. We believe that in an age of materialism, only education based on the Bible can provide students with deeper resources and values restore their true humanity.
Foreign students Hokusei is a place where a warm friendly atmosphere prevails. We welcome foreign students to this rather small college community in which close contacts with faculty and students can be expected. We believe that foreign studetns are great resource persons for promoting international understanding.
Environment Hokusei is located in a residential area on the southern side of Sapporo, Capital of Hokkaido with a population of 1, 600, 000. It is at the Oyachi exit of the Hokkaido Express Way and a seven minute walk form the Oyachi subway station. It enjoys a convenient location which allows easy access to Chitose Airport and to the inner city area well.
Facilities Library, Computer, Center, Gymnasium, Language Center, International Center, Training Room, student Club Building, College Hall, College Retreat House
Student activities Major all-campus events include Hokusei Festival, freshman welcome party and Sports Festival. A variety of extra-curricular activities goes on daily on and off campus centering around 67 sport/non-sports clubs.
Services for foreign students Health clinic, personal counseling, housing information, part-time job information, cultural exchange programs

Undergraduate Programs

Faculty of Economics(1, 385/2)
Dept. of Economics(931/1)
Dept. of Management Information(454/1)
Faculty of Literature(1, 171/0)
Dept. of English Literature(548/0)
Dept. of Social Work(623/0)

One-Year Graduate Programs

Literature Course
English Literature Major
Social Work Major
Economics Course
Economics Major

酪農学園大学
(Rakunô Gakuen Daigaku)

Rakuno Gakuen University

582-1 Bunkyodai-Midorimachi, Ebetsu-shi, Hokkaido 069
☎ 011-386-1112 FAX 011-386-1214

Founded 1950
Professors 59
Associate Professors 31
Assistant Professors(Tenured) 22
Research Assistants 9
Undergraduate Students/Foreign Students 2, 544/2
Graduate Students/Foreign Students 16/2
Library 170, 000 volumes
Contact: Admission Office, Examination Section, Instruction Department

Educational philosophy The instruction at our university features 'education through practical studying'-learning practiacl knowledge, and 'San'ai Spirit' (love of God, humanity and earth) based on Christianity.
Foreign students We believe that foreign students can enjoy friendly fellowship in our university, and can contribute agreat deal to promoting mutual understanding and fellowship.
Environment At our extensive verdant campus, land area 142 hectares situated in the suburbs of Sapporo (population 1.5 million), in the modern city Ebetsu having the natural forest park.
Facilities Rakuno Gakuen Hall, Library, Extension Center, Computer center, Gymnasium
Student activities University festival, freshmen welcome party. There is a wide variety of extra curric-

ular activities, including many cultural clubs and sports clubs.

Services for foreign students Health clinic, personal counseling, University–students–residence Housing information, Dairy exchange program in Extension Center

Undergraduate Programs

Faculty of Dairy Science(2, 544/2)
Dept. of Dairy Science(815/2)
Dept. of Agricultural Economics(564/0)
Dept. of Food Science(294/0)
Dept. of Veterinary Medicine(868/0)

Graduate Programs

Graduate School of Dairy Science(M 17/1)
Div. of Dairy Science
Graduate School of Veterinary Medicine(D 2/1)
Div. of Veterinary Medicine

札幌学院大学
(Sapporo Gakuin Daigaku)
Sapporo Gakuin University

11 Bunkyodai, Ebetsu–shi, Hokkaido 069
☎ 011–386–8111 FAX 011–386–8115

Founded 1946
Professors 63
Associate Professors 32
Assistant Professors(Tenured) 8
Assistant Professors(Non–tenured) 132
Undergraduate Students/Foreign Students 4, 879/2
Library 244, 516 volumes
Contact: Educational Affairs Department

Educational philosophy Some of the major features of our university are expressed in its ideals about learning: academic freedom, creative research, and respect of individuals.

Foreign students We do not have a program for Japanese language studies. Foreign students are welcome to enroll as regular students at our university, but must have already reached proficiency in Japanese.

Environment The University is located in the city of Ebetsu from which you can quickly reach the city of Sapporo, by bus, train, or car within half an hour. Ebetsu, with a population of 96, 000, is in the center of the Ishikari Plain, and is crisscrossed by rivers.

Facilities Library, sports training center, computing center, room for archeological exhibitions, language lab, audio–visual rooms, stadium for track and field events, baseball stadium, tennis courts, etc.

Student activities Popular campus events include the short trip during Freshmen Orientation and the School Festival. There is a wide variety of extracurricular activities and cultural clubs, including the Freshmen Welcome Party, volunteer work, the brass band, drama, baseball, football and soccer.

Undergraduate Programs

Faculty of Commerce(2, 704/1)
Dept. of Commercial Sciences(1, 464/1)
Dept. of Economics(1, 240/0)
Faculty of Humanities(872/0)
Dept. of Human Sciences(576/0)
Dept. of English Language and Literture(296/0)
Faculty of Law(944/1)
Dept. of Jurisprudence

札幌大学
(Sapporo Daigaku)
Sapporo University

1–3; 3–7 Nishioka, Toyohira–ku, Sapporo–shi, Hokkaido 062
☎ 011–852–1181

Founded 1967

Undergraduate Programs

Faculty of Business Administration
Dept. of Business Administration
Faculty of Economics
Dept. of Economics
Faculty of Foreign Languages
Dept. of English
Dept. of Russian

TOHOKU

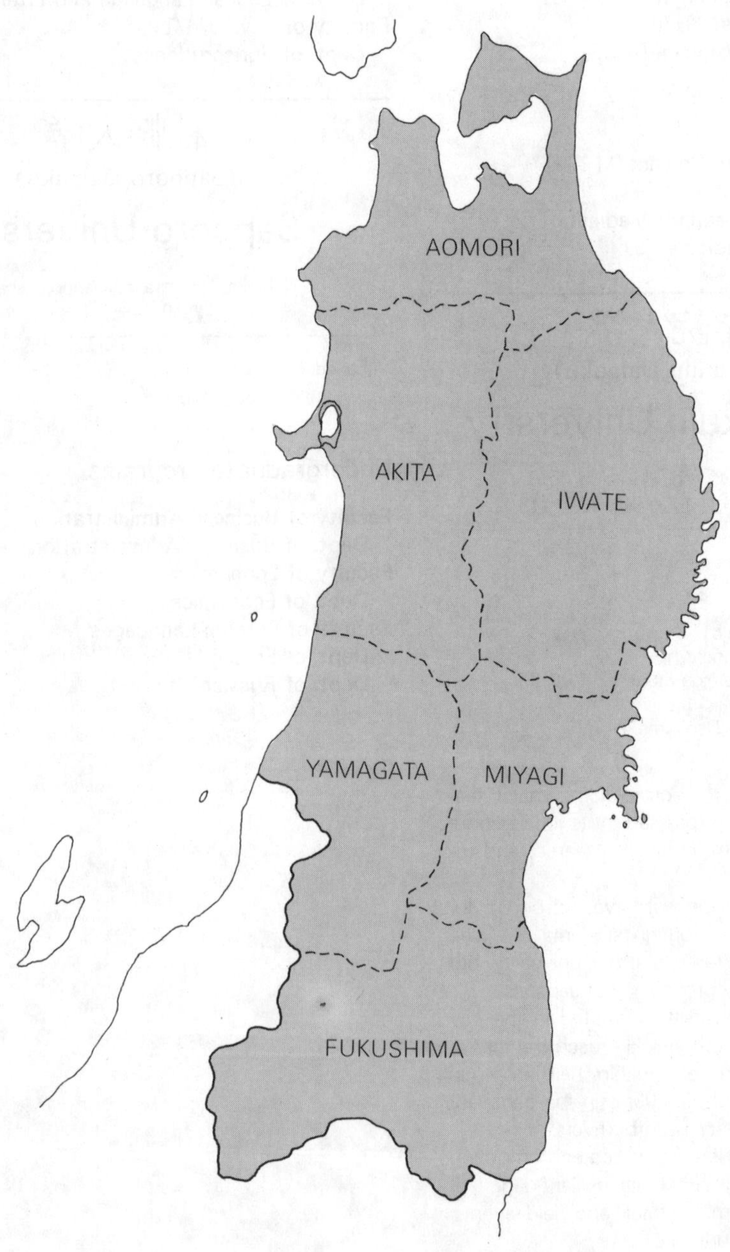

TOHOKU REGION CLIMATE

Generally cool, with broad temperature differences between northern and southern districts.

- Japan Sea Side

  Heavy snow accumulation in winter, ranking with Hokuriku as heavy snowfall region.

- Pacific Ocean Side

  Winter snowfall comparatively light, with summer cooler than Japan Sea side.

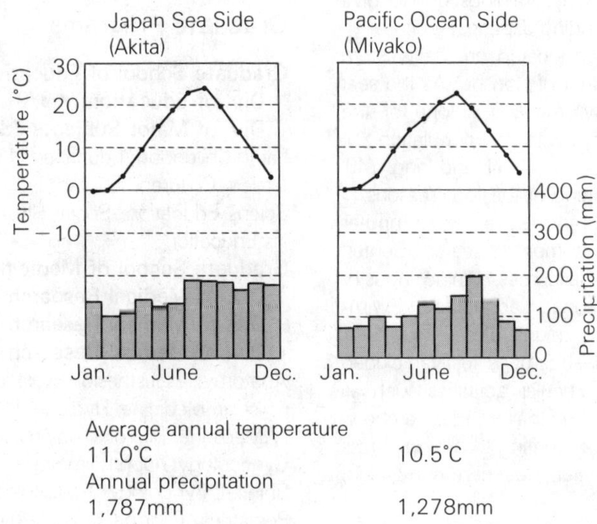

Average annual temperature

11.0°C 10.5°C

Annual precipitation

1,787mm 1,278mm

National Universities

秋田大学
(Akita Daigaku)

Akita University

1-1 Tegata-Gakuen-machi, Akita-shi, Akita 010
☎ 0188-33-5261 FAX 0188-32-5364

Founded 1, 949
Professors 136
Associate Professors 139
Assistant Professors(Tenured) 75
Assistant Professors(Non-tenured) 309
Research Assistants 151
Undergraduate Students/Foreign Students 4, 038/23
Graduate Students/Foreign Students 280/13
Library 412, 222 volumes
Contact: Student Office

Educational philosophy The aim of our university is not only to train scientists, technologists and other professiolnals but to educate young men and women so that they will become good citizens of the world.

Foreign students We heartily welcome all eager foreign students who want to share our educatinal philosophy. Our motto of receiving foreign students is not only to provide proper academic trainings but to give them every help for understanding Japanese culture.

Environment Akita City is located on the western side of the North-Eastern district of Honshu. As the seat of the Akita Prefectural Goverment, it is one of the major cities of the district with a pupulation of 300,000. The city is situated at lat. 40. N. and long. 140. E. and enjoys a marked changing of the four seasons.

Facilities University Library, University Computer center, Heath Center, Radioisotope Research Center, Research Institute of Natural Resources, Mining Industry Museum, Center for Educational Technology, Swimming Pool, Gymnasium, Tennis courts, etc.

Student activities Annual campus festival, ekiden race, ski trek, other extra curricular activities such as baseball, rugby football, basketball, judo, archery, kendo, row boat, yachting, mounting climbing, brass band, chorus group, magic club, tea ceremony club, etc.

Academic programs for foreign students Japanese language and culture courses for foreign students, tutorimg, system for foreign students, credit unit transfer system

Services for foreign students University Internatinal Students House, housing Information service, advices homestay programs and cultural exchanges

Undergraduate Programs

Faculty of Education(1, 359/2)

- **Course of Elementary School of Teacers Program**(753/0)
- **Course of Junior High School Program**(397/2)
- **Course of Kindergarten Teachers Program**(125/0)
- **Course of Special School Teachers Program**(84/0)

Faculty of Medicine(638/6)

- **Dept. of Medicine**

Faculty of Mining(2, 041/15)

- **Dept. of Chemical Engineering for Resources**(143/1)
- **Dept. of Civil Engineering**(201/1)
- **Dept. of Electrical Engineering**(210/3)
- **Dept. of Electronic Engineering**(209/6)
- **Dept. of Fuel Chemistry**(144/0)
- **Dept. of Geosciences, Mining Engineering and Materials Processing**(101/0)
- **Dept. of Information Engineering**(40/0)
- **Dept. of Materials Engineering and Applied Chemistry**(119/0)
- **Dept. of Mechanical Engineering**(212/3)
- **Dept. of Mechanical Engineering for Production**(201/1)
- **Dept. of Metalic Engineering for Materials**(143/0)
- **Dept. of Metallurgy**(121/0)
- **Dept. of Mining Engineering**(132/0)
- **Dept. of Mining Geology**(65/0)

Graduate Programs

Graduate School of Education(M 28/0)

- **Div. of Education**(M 9/0)
- **Div. of Major Subjects Education**(M 19/0)

Early Childhood Education, Education of Mentaly Retarded Children, English Education, School Education, Sciens Education, Social Studies Education, Mathematics Education

Graduate School of Medicin(D 102/2)

- **Div. of Medical Research Program Ⅰ**(D 2/0)
- **Div. of Medical Research Program Ⅱ**(D 4/1)
- **Div. of Medical Research Program Ⅲ**(D 4/1)

Anatomy, Anesthesiology, Biochemistry, Dermatology, Forensic Medicine, Hygiene, Internal Medicine, Laboratory Medicine, Microbiology, Neurosurgery, Obstetrics and Gynecology, Ophthalmology, Orthopedicsurgery, Oto-Rhino-Laryngology, Parasitology, Pathology, Pathology, Pediatrics, Pharmacology, Physirogy, Psychiatry, Public Health, Radiology, Urology

Graduate Shool of Mining(M 280/13)

- **Div. of Chemical Engeneering for Resources**(M 24/1)
- **Div. of Civil Engeneering**(M 13/0)
- **Div. of Electrical Engineering**(M 17/0)
- **Div. of Electronic Engineering**(M 18/2)
- **Div. of Fuel Chemistry**(M 18/0)
- **Div. of Mechanical Engeneering**(M 10/2)
- **Div. of Mechanical Engineering for Production**(M 11/0)

Div. of Metaric Engineering for Metarics(M 9/0)
Div. of Metallagy(M 7/1)
Div. of Mining Engineering(M 10/3)
Div. of Mining Geology(M 13/2)

Advanced Materials, Applied Earth Sciences, Applied Electrical Engineering, Applied Electronics, Applied Information Engineering, Chemical Process Engineering, Computer Engineering, Concrete Engineering, Control Engineering for Machinery, Dynamics of Machinery, Electric Machinery, Electornic Circuits, Electornic Instruments, Electric Power, Fluid Engineering, Function Molecular Chemistry, Fundamental Electrical Engineering, Fundamental Electronics, Highway Engineering, Hydraulic Engineering, Manufacturing Technology, Materials Process Enghineering, Materials Production Engineering, Mechanical Material Technology, Mechanics of Materials, Mining and Excavation Engineering, Pnysics and Chemistry of Materials, Resourse System Engineering, Structural Engineering, Thermal Engineering, Thermo–Fulid Engineering

One–Year Graduate Programs

Special Education course
Education for Mentally Retarded Children Major

福島大学
(Fukushima Daigaku)
Fukushima University

2 Sugumichi, Asakawa, Matsukawa–machi, Fukushima–shi, Fukushima 960–12
☎ 0245–48–5151 FAX 0245–48–3180

Founded 1949
Professors 125
Associate Professors 103
Assistant Professors(Tenured) 15
Assistant Professors(Non–tenured) 88
Research Assistants 6
Undergraduate Students/Foreign Students 4, 217/26
Graduate Students/Foreign Students 50/6
Library 553, 104 volumes
Contact: The Chief of Academic Affairs,
The Faculty of Adiministration and Social Sciences ☎ ext. 2705
The Faculty of Economics, ☎ ext. 2507
The Faculty of Education, ☎ ext. 2311

Educational philosophy We highly esteem students' autonomy and liberalism. We also eagerly hope their enterprising spirit and development of our university. We earnestly attempt to upbring graduates of merits. And we creatively establish an advanced institute open to local district.

Foreign students We heartily welcome foreign students who learn Japanese society, culture, education, and economics. Our expectation stems from wishes for their advancement in knowledge and world peace through cross–cultural communication.

Environment Fukushima City, located in southern Tohoku, has a population of 280, 000. It takes one hour and half by Shinkansen from Tokyo. It has Culture Center, Concert Hall, Art Museum and Libraries. Fukushima University has been spread over the site of 420, 000m^2, surrounded by nature, since 1981.

Facilities We have Information Processing Center, Attached Library, Research and Guidance Center of Teaching Practice, Gymnasiums, Intensive Training Centers, Fields and Tracks, Dormitories, University Hall, Dispensary, Center of Regional Studies.

Student activities Popular campus events include Welcome Festival for Freshmen (April), University Festival (October–November), Ski Training Camps (February–March), and a wide variety of extra–curricular activities: 46 circles for cultural activities and 41 circles for physical activities.

Academic programs for foreign students We open courses, " Japanese Language " and " Things Japnese ". We also adopt a tutorial system. Tutors and foreign students advisers help foreign students for their social and academic life.

Services for foreign students Dormitories are available for undergraduate foreign students through a screening, though we have no foreign students hall yet. Advisers arrange rooms and side–jobs for them. University holds a few parties and sightseeing tours.

Undergraduate Programs

Faculty of Administration and Social Sciences (828/0)
Dept. of Law and Administration(562/0)
Dept. of Applied Sociology and Social Sciences (266/0)

Faculty of Economics(1, 796/22)
Dept. of Business Administration(413/9)
Dept. of Economics(671/0)

Faculty of Education(1, 593/4)
Elementary School Teachers Course(810/0)
Junior High School Teachers Course(417/3)
Kindergarten Teachers Course(121/1)
Senior High School Teachers Course (for Health and Physical Education) (163/0)
Teachers Course for Mentally and Physically Handicapped Children(82/0)

Graduate Programs

Graduate School of Economics(M 17/3)
Div. of Business Science(M 7/1)

Business Science, Commerce, Financial Accounting, Management, Management, Accounting

Div. of Economics(M 10/2)

Economic Dynamics, Economic History of Foreign Countories, Economic Policy, Economic Statisties, Economic Systems, Finance, History of Political Economy, Industorial Economy, International Economics, Japanese Economy, Local Public Finance, Political Economy, Public Finance, Regional Economics, Social Problems, Theoretical Economics

Graduate School of Education(M 33/3)

Div. of School Education(M 11/0)

School Education

Div. of School Subject Education(M 22/3)

English Language Education, Home Economics Education, Japanese Language Education, Natural Science Education, Social Studies Education

One-Year Graduate Programs

Special Research Course

Health and Physical Education Major

弘前大学

(Hirosaki Daigaku)

Hirosaki University

1 Bunkyo-cho, Hirosaki-shi, Aomori 036

☎ 0172-36-2111 FAX 0172-37-6594

Founded 1949
Professors 167
Associate Professors 164
Assistant Professors(Tenured) 84
Assistant Professors(Non-tenured) 439
Research Assistants 155
Undergraduate Students/Foreign Students 5, 092/0
Graduate Students/Foreign Students 334/10
Library 700, 029 volumes
Contact: Student Affairs Bureau

Educational philosophy Hirosaki University, in accordance with the spirit of The Basic Law of Education, seeks to foster in the members of its community a broard range of knowledge, a deep understanding of a specialized discipline, the ability to put one's learning and moral principles into practice, as well as the intelligence and vision to enable them to contribute to human culture.

Foreign students To elevate the levels of educational research in Japan and throughout the world. In line with the objectives of the Japanese Government, the goal of the university is to create a spirit of cooperation in the training of persons of talent, to promote international mutual understanding and friendship, and to open its doors to as many international students as possible.

Environment The campus is located Hirosaki City (population about 176, 000), which until 1868 was the castle town of the Tsugaru, Clan. Hirosaki is the center of culture and education in the Tsugaru area and noted for both its old shrines and temples built in the Edo period and for its western style buildings and churches of the Meiji period. Hirosaki is Japan's leading apple producer, as well.

Facilities Universtiy Library, Seismological and Volcanological Observatory, University Hospital, Institute of Neurological Diseases, Farm Institute for Experimental Animals, Information Processing Center

Student activities Presently, there are 52 cultural and 43 sports clubs active on campus. Students are free to join the club of their choice. Special events include the national inter-university athletic meet, the university ski meet, and various public performances given by the cultural clubs. The university festival is held in the fall, bringing together students from different faculties and disciplines. It also serves to introduce the university to the surrounding community.

Academic programs for foreign students Japanese language instruction is provided in the Faculty of Education. In April, 1991, the College of Liberal Arts will begin offering international students courses in " Japanese Language. Japanese Studies " which can be taken as partial fulfillment of either the general distribution requirement or the foreign language requirement. Those international students who qualify under the government's tutorial program will be provided with tutors.

Services for foreign students Students may use the Health Care Center in case of emergency illness, accident or for psychological counseling. The university also provides introductions and procedural help in securing housing. The university also sponsors field trips and other social gatherings for international students. In addition, it is possible to participate in a number of cultural exchange activities sponsored by organizations outside of the university.

Undergraduate Programs

Faculty of Agriculture(612/0)

Dept. of Agricultural Science(55/0)

Dept. of Agricultural System Engineering(40/0)

Dept. of Science of Bioresource(50/0)

Faculty of Education(1, 555/0)

Training Course for High School Teachers of Nursing(81/0)

Training Course for Junior High School Teachers(405/0)

Training Course for Kindergarten Teachers(118/0)

Training Course for Primary School Teachers(710/0)

Training Course for School Nurse Teachers(160/0)

Training Course for Teachers of the Mentally Handicapped(81/0)

Faculty of Humanities(1, 331/0)

Dept. of Economics(740/0)

Dept. of Humanities(591/0)

School of Medicine(705/0)

Dept. of Medicine

Faculty fo Science(889/0)

Dept. of Biology(134/0)

Dept. of Chemistry(152/0)

Dept. of Earth Science(141/0)

Dept. of Information Science(160/0)
Dept. of Mathematics(146/0)
Dept. of Physics(156/0)

Graduate Programs

Graduate School of Agriculture(M 26/1)
Div. of Agricultural Engineering(M 1/0)
Agricultural Machinery, Agricultural Power, Irrigation and Drainage Engineering, Land Reclamation Engineering, Agricultural Structures and Constructions Engineering
Div. of Agronomy(M 5/0)
Crop Science, Plant Breeding, Agricultural Economics, Zoo-Technical Animal Science, Agricultural Marketing, Agricultural Managerial Economics
Div. of Horticultural Chemistry(M 13/0)
Utilization of Horticultural Products, Food Science, Biological Chemistry, Soil Science and Plant Nutrition
Div. of Horticultural Science(M 7/1)
Pomology, Vegetable Crops and Floriculture, Phytopathology, Applied Entomology
Graduate School of Humanities(M 25/5)
Div. of Fundamentals of Culture(M 6/1)
Philosophy, Cultural Anthropology, Social Studies
Div. of International and Area Studies(M 19/4, D 19/0)
Japanese Studies, Oriental Studies, Western Studies
Graduate School of Medicine(D 229/4)
Div. of Internal Medicine(D 58/0)
Internal Medicine, Pediatrics, Neuropsychiatry, Radiology, Dermatology, Department of Neurology (Institute of Neurological Disease)
Div. of Pathology(D 24/1)
Department of Pathologic Physiology (Institute of Neurological Disease), Pathology, Parasitology, Bacteriology
Div. of Physiology(D 41/1)
Anatomy, Physiology, Biochemistry, Pharmacology
Div. of Social Medicine(D 22/0)
Department of Neuropathology (Institute of Neurological Disease), Hygience, Public Health, Legal Medicine
Div. of Surgery(D 84/2)
Surgery, Orthopedic Surgery, Obstetrics and Gynecology, Anesthesiology, Neurosurgery, Clinical Laborator Medicine, Dentistry and Oral Surgery, Department of Rehabilitation Medicine (Institute of Neurological Disease)
Graduate School of Science(M 54/0)
Div. of Biology(M 14/0)
Physiology and Developmental Biology, Systematics and Morphology, Environmental Biology, Cytology, Genetics and Physiological Chemistry
Div. of Chemistry(M 10/0)
Physical Chemistry, Inorganic Chemistry, Organic Chemistry, Analytical Chemistry
Div. of Earth Science(M 15/0)
Physics of Earth's Interior, Ocean and Atmosphere, Seismology and Volcanology, Geology and Petrology, Geochemistry and Mineralogy
Div. of Mathematics(M 6/0)
Algebra, Geometry, Analysis, Applied Mathematics
Div. of Physics(M 9/0, D 9/0)
Quantum Physics, Atomic Physics, Electromagnetism, Solid State Physics

One-Year Graduate Programs

Humanities Course
Economics Major
Education Course
Education Major

岩手大学
(Iwate Daigaku)
Iwate Universtiy

3-18-8 Ueda, Morioka-shi, Iwate 020
☎ 0196-23-5171 FAX 0196-54-9010

Founded 1949
Professors 157
Associate Professors 167
Assistant Professors(Tenured) 41
Assistant Professors(Non-tenured) 161
Research Assistants 55
Undergraduate Students/Foreign Students 5, 423/11
Graduate Students/Foreign Students 228/15
Library 605, 277 volumes
Contact: ☎ ext. 2241

Educational philosophy We aim at teaching and studying up-to-date high-level art and sciences to develop intellectual, moral and applied abilities so students may contribute much to cultural betterment and social improvement.
Foreign students The university thus extends a hearty welcome to foreign students to join with us in making friends through study and recreation.
Environment The whole campus strikes us as a wilderness park with woods and apple orchards around it where we often see squirrels playing. It takes, however, only ten minutes to go downtown on foot. You will be able to enjoy a sense of fulfilment in the student life guaranteed by the best possible environment one can imagine in Northern Japan.
Facilities Botanical Garden, Computer Center. Electron Microscope Room. Memorial Hall of Agriculture, Environment Control Center, Experimental Farm, Experimental Forest, Natural Energy Greenhouse, Laboratory for Remote Sensing Date Analysis, Mass Spectrometer Laboratory, etc.
Student activities Popular campus events includes Homecoming, school festival, freshmen welcome party. There is a wide variety of extra curricular activities, including volunteer work, choral groups, marching band, student news paper, drama, baseball, football, soccer, etc.
Academic programs for foreign students Sup-

plemental Japanese language class, Tutoring system, As a regular event, the Seminar for Cultural Exchange for foreign students is held once or twice a year, and this always includes a bus trip to a major industry and a famous sight of Japan.

Services for foreign students Health clinic, personal/psychological counseling, part-time job information, vocational guidance Homestay, Home visit, cultural exchange program

Undergraduate Programs

Faculty of Agriculture(1, 039/2)
Dept. of Agricultural Chemistry(143/0)
Dept. of Agricultural Engineering(147/2)
Dept. of Agricultural Machinery(123/0)
Dept. of Agronomy(144/0)
Dept. of Animal Husbandry(138/0)
Dept. of Forestry(130/0)
Dept. of Veterinary Medicine(214/0)
Faculty of Education(1, 448/0)
Arts and Crafts Education(126/0)
Elementary Education(822/0)
Secondary Education(422/0)
Special Education(78/0)
Faculty of Engineering(2, 001/8)
Dept. of Applied Chemistry(203/0)
Dept. of Civil Engineering(188/0)
Dept. of Computer Science(201/1)
Dept. of Electrical Engineering(214/3)
Dept. of Electronic Engineering(209/2)
Dept. of Mechanical Engineering(203/2)
Dept. of Metallurgical Engineering(191/0)
Dept. of Mechanical Engineering II (192/0)
Dept. of Mineral Development Engineering(199/0)
Dept. of Resource Chemistry(201/0)
College of Humanities and Social Sciences(924/1)
Dept. of Humanities and Social Sciences

Graduate Programs

Graduate School of Agriculture(M 55/7)
Div. of Agronomy(M 9/2)
Crop Science, Pomology, Olericulture and Floriculture, Plant Breeding, Plant Pathology, Applied Entomology, Agricultural Economics
Div. of Agricultural Chemistry(M 18/1)
Soil Science, Plant Nutrition, Food Science and Technology, Applied Microbiology, Biochemistry, Nutritional Biochemistry
Div. of Forestry(M 8/0)
Forest Policy, Silviculture, Forest Management, Erosion Control Engineering, Forest Operations and Techniques, Wood Science and Technolgy, Wood Chemistry
Div. of Animal Husbandry(M 10/1)
Animal Breeding, Animal Reproduction, Animal Nutrition and Management, Feeds and Feeding, Grassland Improvement
Div. of Agricultural Engineering(M 2/0)
Farm Land Reclamation Technology, Land Improvement, Land Planning, Agricultural Hydrotechnics, Agricultural Construction Engineering, Agricultural Systems Engineering
Div. of Agricultural Machinery(M 8/3)
Farm Machinery, Farm Land Reclamation Machinery, Agricultural Environmental Engineering, Agricultural Process Engineering
Graduate School of Agricultural Sciences(D 12/3)
Science of Bioproduction(D 4/1)
Science of Bioresources(D 3/1)
Science of Biotic Environment(D 5/1)
Graduate School of Engineering(M 132/5)
Div. of Mechanical Engineering(M 20/2)
Applied Mechanics, Manufacturing Technology, Fluid Engineering, Thermal Engineering
Div. of Mechanical Engineering(M 12/0)
Precision Engineering, Instrumentation and Control Engineering, Heat Power Engineering, Machine Elements Design
Div. of Electrical Engineering(M 16/0)
Basic Electricity, Electrical Power Engineering, Electrical Power Application Engineering, Electrical Communication Engineering
Div. of Electronic Engineering(M 12/0)
Applied Electronics, Electronic Materials and Measurements, Electron Tubes and Electronic Circuits, Fundamentals of Electronics
Div. of Computer Science(M 19/2)
Fundamentals of Computer Science, Computer Systems, Computer Machinery, Applied Computer Science
Div. of Mineral Development Engineering(M 6/0)
Geological Engineering, Mineral Engineering, Excavation Engineering, Mineral Processing and Water Treatment
Div. of Civil Engineering(M 7/0)
Hydraulic Engineering and Materials of Construction, Structural Mechanics and Traffic Engineering, Sanitary Engineering, Planning in Civil Engineering
Div. of Metallurgical Engineering(M 15/1)
Non-Ferrous Metallurgy, Ferrous Metallurgy, Metallography, Metal Materials
Div. of Applied Chemistry(M 16/0)
Industrial Inorganic Chemistry, Synthetic Organic Chemistry and Technology, Polymer Chemistry and Technology, Chemical Engineering
Div. of Resource Chemistry(M 9/0)
Inorganic Resource Chemistry, Organic Resource Chemistry, Chemical Reaction Engineering, Applied Physical Chemistry
Graduate School of Humanities and Social Sciences(M 14/0)
Program in Area Studies(M 6/0)
Program in Social Sciences(M 8/0)

One-Year Graduate Programs

Pedagogy Course
Arts & Crafts Major
Pedagogy Major

Special Education Course
Special Education (Handicapped) Major

宮城教育大学
(Miyagi Kyôiku Daigaku)
Miyagi University of Education

Aramaki, Aoba, Aoba-ku, Sendai-shi, Miyagi 980
☎ 022-222-1021

Founded 1965
Professors 72
Associate Professors 57
Assistant Professors(Tenured) 1
Assistant Professors(Non-tenured) 171
Research Assistants 7
Undergraduate Students/Foreign Students 1, 850/1
Graduate Students/Foreign Students 62/3
Library 249, 971 volumes

Educational philosophy Our university was founded with the view of producing good and promising teachers and educators, and contributing much to the cultural development of the natoin by mastering academic profundity.
Foreign students Our university is prepared to receive foreign students. Our staff and students think it a valuable experience to have social, cultural and academic relations with foreign students. We hope this will continue to be realised.
Environment The campus is located in the west of the town and on a hill surrounded by forests. Students study, take part in extracurricular activities and relax among academic buildings, green wood and grounds of 211, 000 square meters overlooking the city of Sendai. Sendai has a population of 900, 000.
Facilities Attached Library, Health Service Center, Research Institute for Science Education, Teacher's Center, Swimming Pool, Gymnasium, Auditorium.
Student activities Annual campus events include freshmen week, a students' festival, residential spring, summer and winter seminars, skiing and swimming, etc. We have 29 circles or and 27 sports clubs.
Academic programs for foreign students Supplemental Japanese Language Class, Tutoring system.
Services for foreign students Housing information, Homestay, Cultural exchange program.

Undergraduate Programs

Faculty of Education(1, 850/1)
Course for Teachers of Elementary School(911/0)
Course for Teachers of Jr. High School(381/1)
Course for Teachers of Kindergarten School(64/0)
Course for Teachers of Special Subject (Mathematics) (125/0)
Course for Teachers of Special Subject (Science) (121/0)
Course for Teachers of School for Blind Children (69/0)
Course for Teachers of School for Mentally Handicapped Children(106/0)
Course for Teachers of Orally Handicapped Children(73/0)

Graduate Programs

Graduate School of Education(M 62/3)
Div. of School Education(M 14/2)
School Education
Div. of Education of Handicapped Children(M 10/0)
Education of Handicapped Children
Div. of Education of Subjects(M 38/1)
Japanese Education, Mathematics Education, Science Education, Music Education, Art Education, Health and Physical Education, English Education

One-Year Graduate Programs

Special Education Course
Education for the physically handicapped children Major

東北大学
(Tôhoku Daigaku)
Tohoku University

2-1-1 Katahira, Aoba-ku, Sendai-shi, Miyagi 980
☎ 022-227-6200(ext. 2236) FAX 022-221-6032

Founded 1907
Professors 566
Associate Professors 510
Assistant Professors(Tenured) 160
Assistant Professors(Non-tenured) 881
Research Assistants 1, 069
Undergraduate Students/Foreign Students 5, 813/23
Graduate Students/Foreign Students 2, 563/315
Library 2, 918, 810 volumes
Contact: Admission Office International Exchange Section General Affairs Division

Educational philosophy Since its foundation, we have been very progressive and liberal with an " open-door " attitude to edcation. It was the first Japanese university to admit women students, and conferred degrees on foreign graduates as long as 1911. We are also known for its " Research First " principle, believing that where there is good research, there is good education.
Foreign students We believe that foreign students

can get advanced knowledge in various fields of education and researches. We can also contribute a great deal to promoting mutual understanding and the development of liternational friendly relations.

Environment Sendai is about 300 kilometers north of Tokyo and the center of the Tohoku district. It is called " mori no miyako ", the city of trees, since most of the major streets in the city are lined with trees. It is also referred to as the city of universities and schools. There are some ten colleges and universities here.

Facilities Library, University Hospital, Health Center, Research Center for Applied Information Science, Cyclotron and Radioisotope Center, Education Center for Information Processing, Institute of Genetic Ecology, Computer Center and numerous other educational and research institutions.

Student activities We have some events like study excursions for foreign students, farewell party, home visit, university festival, the international festival, etc. On the other hand, we have many other events sponsored by private groups like excursions, speech contest, dinner party, flower arrangement class, and Japanese language school.

Academic programs for foreign students Special Course for Foreign Students (ex, Lecture of Science Language, Japan's Cultural Backgrounds, etc.), Tutorial System

Services for foreign students Counselling for immigration, a support system to medical expenses, personal/psychological counselling, housing information, presenting information on the part-time job, home visit

Undergraduate Programs

Faculty of Agriculture(361/2)
Dept. of Agricultural Chemistry(80/0)
Dept. of Agronomy(82/0)
Dept. of Animal Science(71/0)
Dept. of Fishery Science(54/0)
Dept. of Food Chemistry(74/2)
Faculty of Arts and Letters(426/2)
Dept. of History(98/0)
Dept. of Japanese(35/1)
Dept. of Literature(139/1)
Dept. of Philosophy(50/0)
Dept. of Social Science(104/1)
Faculty of Dentistry(261/0)
Dept. of Dentistry(261/0)
Faculty of Economics(572/1)
Dept. of Business Management(128/1)
Dept. of Economics(444/0)
Faculty of Education(180/0)
Dept. of Educational Psychology(80/0)
Dept. of Educational Science(100/0)
Faculty of Engineering(1, 923/12)
Dept. of Applied Physics(101/0)
Dept. of Architecture(131/1)
Dept. of Civil Engineering(138/1)
Dept. of Electrical Communications(511/4)
Dept. of Electrical Engineering(511/4)
Dept. of Electronic Engineering(511/4)
Dept. of Information Engineering(511/4)
Dept. of Materials Processing(253/0)
Dept. of Materials Science(253/0)
Dept. of Metallurgy(253/0)
Dept. of Mechanical Engineering(129/0)
Dept. of Mechanical Engineering II (153/0)
Dept. of Biochemistry and Engineering(222/4)
Dept. of Molecular Chemistry and Engineering (222/4)
Dept. of Nuclear Engineering(92/1)
Dept. of Precision Engineering(136/1)
Dept. of Resources Engineering(57/0)
Faculty of Law(610/1)
Dept. of Law(610/1)
Faculty of Medicine(496/3)
Dept. of Medicine(496/3)
Faculty of Pharmacy(329/1)
Dept. of Pharmaceutical Science
Dept. of Pharmaceutical Technology
Faculty of Science(656/1)
Dept. of Astronomy(21/0)
Dept. of Biology(84/0)
Dept. of Chemistry(76/0)
Dept. of Chemistry II (77/0)
Dept. of Geography(21/0)
Dept. of Geology and Paleontology(20/0)
Dept. of Geophysics(46/0)
Dept. of Mathematics(98/1)
Dept. of Mineralogy, Petrology and Economic Geology(30/0)
Dept. of Physics(92/0)
Dept. of Physics II (91/0)

Graduate Programs

Graduate School of Agriculture(M 128/6, D 38/25)
Div. of Agricultural Chemistry(M 29/0, D 12/3)
Plant Nutrition, Biochemistry, Applied Biochemistry, Applied Microbiology, Pesticide and Bioorganic Chemistry, (Institute of Genetic Ecology): Soil Microbiology, (Gene Research Center): Advanced Gene Research
Div. of Agronomy(M 32/1, D 12/9)
Crop Science, Horticulture, Plant Breeding, Plant Pathology, Soil Science, Farm Management, Food Policy Research, Entomology, Farm Work Technology, (Institurte of Genetic Ecology): Ecological Physiology, Plant Variation and Adaptation, Genetically Engineered Organisms
Div. of Animal Science(M 24/1, D 9/4)
Animal Reproduction, Animal Nutrition, Grassland Science, Animal Breeding, Animal Physiology, Animal Histology, Animal Microbiology, Animal Products Chemistry, Animal Husbandry Management
Div. of Fishery Sciences(M 15/0, D 7/5)
Aquacultural Biology, Fisheries Biology, Oceanography, Fisheries Chemistry, Fish Genetics
Div. of Food Chemistry(M 28/4, D 8/4)
Lipid Chemistry, Analytical Chemistry, Food Protein Chemistry, Nutritional Biochemistry and Physiology, Ma-

rine Food Poisoning, Food Biotechnology

Graduate School of Arts and Letters(M 128/19, D 125/24)

Div. of Aesthetics and History of Fine Arts(M 6/1, D 4/1)

Aesthetics and History of European Fine Arts, History of Oriental and Japanese Fine Arts

Div. of Chinese Studies(M 9/1, D 6/0)

Chinese Literature, Chinese Philosophy, Comparative Studies Section I

Div. of English Literature, English Linguistics, and Linguistics(M 16/1, D 13/2)

English Literature, English Linguistics, Linguistics, Interlinguistics, Comparative Studies Section II

Div. of European History(M 3/0, D 6/1)

European History

Div. of French Literature and French Linguistics(M 3/0, D 7/0)

French Literature

Div. of German Literature and German Liguistics(M 6/0, D 5/0)

German Literature

Div. of Indology, and History of Buddhism(M 8/0, D 7/0)

Indian Philosophy, Indology and History of Buddhism

Div. of Japanese History(M 17/1, D 12/0)

Japanese History, Archaeology, Fundamental Studies

Div. of Japanese Literature, Japanese Linguistics, and History of Japanese Thoughts(M 33/14, D 34/20)

Japanese Literature, Japanese Linguistics, Modern Japanese, Teaching of Japanese as a Foreign Language, History of Japanese Thoughts

Div. of Oriental History(M 6/1, D 1/0)

Oriental History

Div. of Philosophy(M 6/0, D 7/0)

Modern Philosophy, European Philosophy

Div. of Practical Philosophy(M 5/0, D 9/0)

Ethics, Science of Religion and History of Religions

Div. of Psychology(M 8/0, D 7/0)

Psychology, Social Psychology

Div. of Sociology(M 2/0, D 7/0)

Theoretical Sociology, Applied Sociology, Behavioral Science

Graduate School of Dentistry(D 34/2)

Div. of Basic Dental Science(D 8/2)

Oral Anatomy, Oral Physiology, Oral Biochemistry, Oral Pathology, Oral Bacteriology, Pharmacology, Dental Materials Science

Div. of Clinical Dental Science(D 26/0)

Preventive Dentistry, Endodontics and Periodontics, Operative Dentistry, Oral and Maxillofacial Surgery, Prossthetic Dentistry, Orthodontics, Pediatric Dentistry, Oral Diagnosis and Dental Radiology Dental Hospital (Preventive Dentistry, Endodontics and Periodontics, Operative Dentistry, Oral and Maxillofacial Surgery, Prosthetic Dentistry, Orthodontics, Pediatric Dentistry, Oral Diagnosis and Dental Radiology, Clinics for Oral-Maxillo Facial Disorders, Clinic for the Disabled)

Graduate School of Economics(M 12/5, D 10/4)

Div. of Business Management(M 6/4, D 5/4)

Business Administration, Accounting, Management Sciences, Business Policy

Div. of Economics(M 6/1, D 4/0)

Economic Theory, Economic History, Economic Policy, Economic Statistics, Contemporary Economy

Graduate School of Education(M 24/3, D 42/6)

Div. of Educational Psychology(M 10/2, D 24/0)

Psychology of Personality and Learning, Psychology of Childhood and Adolescence, Speech Pathology and Audiology, Visual Defectology, Mental Retardation Research

Div. of Pedagogy(M 14/1, D 18/6)

Philosophy of Education, History of Education, Sociology of Education, Adult Education, Educational Administration, School Administration, School Curriculum and Teaching Method, Center for University Extension

Graduate School of Engineering(M 1, 001/59, D 167/118)

Div. of Architecture

Architectural History and Design, Building Materials Science, Structural Mechanics, Structural Engineering, Disaster Proof Engineering, Urban Planning, Architectural Planning, Environmental Engineering

Div. of Applied Chemistry

Industrial Inorganic Chemistry, Organic Resources Chemistry, Electrochemical Science and Technology, Organic and Bioorganic Synthesis, Organic Chemistry, (Chemical Research Institute of Non-Aqueous Solution): Inorganic Chemistry, Organic Reaction Chemistry, Synthetic Organic Chemistry, Physical Chemistry, Coal Chemistry Laboratory

Div. of Applied Physics

Applied Mathematical Physics, Solid State Physics, Magnetism and Magnetic Materials, Pico-Second Spectroscopy, Piezoelectricity and Ferroelectrics, Low Temperature Physics, Engineering Mechanics, (Institute for Materials Research): Low Temperature Condensed State Physics, Physics of Electronic Materials, (Research Institute for Scientific Measurements): Section of Solid State Physics, VUV/X-ray Optics and Spectroscopy, Laboratory of Soft X-ray Multilayers

Div. of Chemical Engineering

Applied Chemistry of Dimensionally Functional Materials, Transport Phenomena, Reaction Engineering, Process System Engineering, Bioprocess Engineering, Inorganic and Physical Chemistry, The Research Institute of Combustion Engineering for Effective use of Energy, (Chemical Research Institute of Non-Aqueous Solution): High Pressure Chemistry, Chemical Engineering, Surface Engineering

Div. of Civil Engineering

Mechanics of Materials, Bridge Engineering and Structures, Infrastructure Planning, Fluvial and Coastal Engineering, Environmental Pollution Control Engineering, Concrete Engineering, Soil Engineering, Applied Hydraulics and Hydrodynamics, Road Engineering, Water Supply Engineering, Structural Engineering

Div. of Electrical and Communication Engineering

Electromagnetic Theory, Acoustic Measurements and

Imaging, Electrical Machine Engineering, High Voltage Engineering, Electric Power Engineering, Applied Electrical Engineering, Control Systems Theory, Network Theory, Electrical Communication Systems, Antennas and Optical Wave Transmission Electroacoustics, Instrumentation Electronics, Applied Radio Physics, Mathematics, Electrical Engineering Science, (Research Institute of Electrical Communication): Section of Electroacoustics, Section of Electrical Communication Systems, Section of Microwave Transmissions, Section of Information Recordings, Section of Applied Ultrasonics, Section of Elasticwave Circuits, Section of Control Engineering, Section of Acoustoelectronics

Div. of Electronic Engineering

Plasma Physics and Gaseous Electronics, Electron Devices, Solid State Electronics, Solid State Physics, Electronic Control Systems, Electronic Circuits, Mathematics, (Research Institute for Scientific Measurements): Section of Solid State Electronics, Section of Electron Devices, Section of Solid State Physics, Section of Electric and Magnetic Materials, Section of Optical Communications, Section of Opto–Electronic Conversion, Section of Vacuum Electronic Devices, Section of Ultrahigh Vacuum Electronics, Section of Quantum Electronics, Section of Plasma Electronics, Section of Molecular Electronics, Division of Microfabrication

Div. of Information Engineering

Foundation of Information Science, Knowledge Engineering, Linguistic Information Processing, Computer Engineering, Information Transmission Systems, Information Systems Engineering, Neurophysiology and Bioinformation Science,(Research Institute of Electrical Communication): Section of Information Theories, (Research Center for Applied Information Sciences): Program Systems

Div. of Materials Chemistry

Analytical Chemistry, Advanced Ceramic Materials, Macromolecular Chemistry, Fluid Materials Design, Molecular Thermodynamics, Applied Biochemistry, Biofunctionnal Chemistry, Basic Physical Chemistry, (Chemical Research Institute of Non–Aqueous Solution): Coal Treatment Chemistry

Div. of Materials Processing

Materials Systems, Deformation Mechanics, Foundry Engineering, Welding Engineering, Powder Processing, Materials Evaluation, (Institute for Materials Research): Materials Processing and Characterization, Deformation Processing

Div. of Materials Science

Applied Solid Physics, Solid Surface Science, Microstructure Science, Structural Materials, Electronic Materials, (Institute for Materials Research): Chemical Physics of Non–Crystalline Materials, Surface Materials Chemistry, Non–Equilibrium Materials, High Purity Metallic Materials, Material Design via Computer, High Temperature Materials Science, Structural Science of Non–Stoichiometric Compound, Facility for Developmental Research of Advanced Materials

Div. of Mechanical Engineering

Hydraulics Machinery, Fluid Mechanics, Heat and Thermodynamics, Properties of Materials and Manufacturing, Dynamics of Machines and Machine Design, Solid Mechanics, Combustion Engineering, Instrument and Control Engineering, Science and Technology of Materials Working, Production Engineering, Mechanical Engineering Science, (Institute of Fluid Science): Section of Low–Density Gas, Section of Ultra–High Speed Flow, Secton of Heat Transfer Control, Section of Structural System Control, Section of Fluid Control, Section of Compound Fluids, Shock Wave Research Center

Div. of Mechanical Engineering II

Strength and Fracture of Materials, Elasticity and soid Mechanics, Plasticity and Solid Mechanics, Fluid Mechanics and Flow, Robotics and Control Engineering, Theory of Machine and Mechanical Design Analysis, Basic Thermodynamics and Heat Transfer, Division of Fracture Physics and Chemistry, Division of Crustal Rock Fracture Mechanics, (Institute of Flued Science): Section of Molten Geomaterials Science, Section of Cryogenic Fluid Flow, Section of Computer Simulation, Section of Nonequilibrium Magnetofluiddynamic Flow, Section of Reactive Fluids, Section of Thermophysical Properties of Fluids

Div. of Metallurgy

Chemical Metallurgy, Metallurgical Electrochemistry, Metallurgical Engineering, Extractive Metallurgy, Ferrous Process Metallurgy, Applied Metallurgical Chemistry, (Institute for Materials Research): Analytical Science, (Research Institute of Mineral Dressing and Metallurgy): Ironmaking, Steelmaking Hydrometallurgy, Pyrometallurgy, Electrometallurgy and Materials Science, Direct Ironmaking, Metallurgical Engineering, New Metallurgical Resources

Div. of Nuclear Engineering

Nuclear Reactor Engineering, Nuclear Instruments and Measurements, Reactor Physics, Nuclear Chemical Engineering, Nuclear Fuel Engineering, Nuclear Material Engineering, Plasma Physics and Fusion Engineering, (Institute for Materials Research): Radiochemistry of Metals, Nuclear Materials Science, Nuclear Materials Engineering, Irradiation Research of Nuclear Materials, (Research Institute of Mineral Dressing and Metallurgy): Nuclear Fuel Metallurgy, Metallurgy of Radioelements, (Cyclotron and Radioisotope Center): Radiation Protection

Div. of Precision Engineering

Measurement and Instrumentation, Precision Measurement, Automatic Control, Machine Elements, Precision Machinery, Workability and Strength of Materials, Plastic Forming, Precision Machining, Applied Mechanics, (Institute for Materials Research): Magnetic Materials, (Research Institute for Scientific Measurements): Section of Solid State Ionics, Section of Surface Science

Div. of Resources Engineering

Information Geology, Geomechanics, Energy Resources Engineering, Mineral Science, Exploitation Machinery, Geotechnical Instrumentation, Resources Systems Engineering, (Research Institute of Mineral Dressing and Metallurgy): Applied Mineralogy, Mineral Processing, Chemical Processing for Minerals

Graduate School of Law(M 15/3, D 11/1)

Div. of Foundations of Law(M 3/0, D 0/0)
Anglo-American Law, Jurisprudence, Japanese Legal History, European Legal History

Div. of Political Science(M 5/1, D 2/1)
Political Theory, History of Political Theory, International Politics, Comparative Politics

Div. of Private Law(M 4/1, D 1/0)
Civil Law, Commercial Law, Labor Law and Social Welfare Law, Civil Procedure, Debtor-Creditor Law, Private International Law

Div. of Public Law(M 3/1, D 8/0)
Constitutional Law, Comparative Constitutional Law, Administrative Law, Criminal Law, Criminal Procedure, Criminology, International Law

Graduate School of Medicine(D 171/12)

Div. of Internal Medicine(D 75/3)
Internal Medicine, Psychiatry and Neurology, Dermatology, Pediatrics, Radiology, Clinical and Laboratory Medicine, Clinical Therapeutics Neurology, University Hospital (First Department of Internal Medicine, Second Department of Internal Medicine, Third Department of Internal Medicine, Gerontology, Psychiatry and Neurology, Dermatology, Pediatrics, Radiology, Psychosomatic Medicine, Neurology, Central Clinical Laboratories, Division of Clinical Radiology, Division of Blood Transfusion), Narugo Branch Hospital (Internal Medicine, Dermatology, Pediatrics) (Research Institute for Tuberculosis and Cancer): Internal Medicine, Pediatraics, Radiology and Nuclear Medicine, Clinical Cancer Chemotherapy, Medical Engineering and Cardiology (The Hospital attached to the Research Institute for Tuberculosis and Cancer): Internal Medicine, Clinical Cancer Chemotherapy, Pediatrics, Radiology and Nuclear Medicine, Cyclotron Nuclear Medicine

Div. of Medical Science(D 25/0)
Biochemical Genetics, Neurological Sciences, Neurophysiology, Clinical Biology and Hormonal Regulation, Biochemistry, Pharmacology, Pathology, Surgery, (Research Institute for Tuberculosis and Cancer): Cancer Chemotherapy and Prevention, Immunology

Div. of Pathology(D 11/1)
Pathology, Bacteriology, Institute of Experimental Animals, University Hospital (Pathology Laboratories), (Research Institute for Tuberuculosis and Cancer): Pathology, Cell Biology, Experimental Oncology, Cancer Cell Repository

Div. of Physiological Sciences(D 11/0)
Anatomy, Pharmacology, Physiology, Biochemistry, Applied Physiology, Radiation Research, Radioisotope Center, University Hospital (Pharmacertical Science), (Research Institute for Tuberuculosis and Cancer): Biochemistry, Pharmacology, (Research Center for Applied Information Sciences): Applied Biological Information

Div. of Social Medicine(D 4/1)
Environmental Health, Forensic Medicine, Public Health, Hospital and Medical Care Administration

Div. of Surgery(D 45/7)
Surgery, Thoracic and Cardiovascular Surgery, Pediatrics Surgery, Orthopedic Surgery, Obstetrics and Gynecology, Urology, Ophthalmology, Otorhinolaryngology, Anesthesiology, Clinical Kinesiology and Neuro-Rehabilitation, Neurosurgery, University Hospital (First Department of Surgery, Second Department of Surgery, Thoracic and Cardiovascular Surgery, Pediatrics Surgery, Orthopedic Surgery, Obstetrics and Gynecology, Urology, Ophthalmology, Otorhinolaryngology, Anesthesiology, Plastic Surgery, Neurosurgery, Central Operating Theater, Intensive Care Unit, Division of Perinatology, Division of Emergency Medicine), Narugo Branch Hospital (Surgery, Orthopedic Surgery, Rehabilitation), (Research Institute for Tuberculosis and Cancer): Surgery, (The Hospitatl attached to the Research Institute for Tuberculosis and Cancer): Department of Surgery

Graduate School of Pharmacy(M 89/5, D 23/1)

Div. of Pharmaceutical Science(M 49/4, D 11/0)
Pharmaceutical Chemistry, Analytical Chemistry, Oraganic Chemistry, Pharmacognosy, Hygienic Chemistry, Pharmaceutics, Pharmacology, Botanical Garden for Medicinal Plants

Div. of Pharmaceutical Technology(M 40/1, D 12/1)
Physical Chemistry, Synthetic Organic Chemistry, Natural Products Chemistry, Structural Chemistry, Biochemistry, Heterocyclic Chemistry, (Cyclotron and Radioisotope Center): Pharmaceutical Chemistry Division

Graduate School of Science(M 336/3, D 209/19)

Div. of Astronomy(M 12/0, D 4/0)
Theoretical Astronomy, Astrophysics

Div. of Biology(M 30/0, D 21/2)
Animal Physiology, Animal Ecology, Plant Taxnomy, Developmental Biology, Plant Ecology, Plant Physiology, The Marine Biological Station

Div. of Chemistry(M 52/1, D 33/3)
Inorganic Chemistry, Organic Chemistry, Theoretical Chemistry, Analytical Chemistry, Quantum Chemistry, Radiochemistry, Organosilicon Research Laboratory, (Institute for Materials Research) : Crystal Chemistry, Solid State Chemistry Under High Pressure, (Research Institute for Scientific Measurements): Surface Science, (Chemical Research Institute of Non-Aqueos Solution): Magnetochemistry, Tropoid Reaction Chemistry, Tropoid Synthetic Chemistry, Structural Chemistry

Div. of Chemistry II(M 38/0, D 21/1)
Synthetic Organic Chemistry, Bio-organic Chemistry, Physical Organic Chemistry, Coordination Chemistry, Organic Reactions, Analytical Organic Chemistry, (Chemical Research Institute of Non-Aqueous Solution): High Polymer Chemistry, Ploymer Structure (Research Institute for Scientific Measurements): VUV/X-ray Optics and Spectroscopy

Div. of Gelogy and Paleontology/Mineralogy, Petrology and Economic Geology/Geography(M 28/0, D 23/1)
Geology, Historical Geology, Paleontology, Mineralogy, Petrology and Geochemistry, Economic Geology and Geochemistry, Experimental Petrology, Human Geography, Physical Geography

Div. of Geophysics(M 36/1, D 23/3)
Seismology, Earth and Space Electrodynamics, Meteorology, Physical Oceanography, Laboratory of Funda-

mental Geophysics, Upper Atmosphere and Space Research Laboratory, Observation Center for Prediction of Earthquakes and Volcanic Eruptions, Nihonkai Observatory for Earthquakes and Volcanoes, Research Center for Atmospheric and Oceanic Variations

Div. of Mathematics(M 27/0, D 7/2)
Complex Analysis, Algebra, Geometry, Functional Analysis, Real Analysis, Probability and Statistics, Numerical Analysis, Differential Equation, Manifold Theory

Div. of Nuclear Physics(31/0, D 26/3)
Experimental Nuclear Physics, Experimental High Energy Physics, Theoretical Nuclear Physics, Electron Linac Research Section, Electro-Nuclear Reaction Research Section, Pulse Beam Stretcher R & B Section Bubble Chamber Physics Laboratory, (Cyclotron and Radioisotope Center): Accelerator Research Division, Instrumentation Research Division

Div. of Physics(M 49/0, D 25/2)
Photoemission and Surface Physics, Optical Properties of Solids, Theoretical High Energy Physics, Theoretical Solid State Physics, Theoretical Nuclear Physics, Theoretical Solid State Physics, Optical Properties of Solids, Magnetic Property of Solid, (Institute for Materials Research): Section of Soild State Physics, Section of Crystal Physics, Section of Physics of Crystal Defects, Section of Magnetism, Section of Diffraction Crystallography, Section of Solid State Physics with Radiation, Section of Low Temperature Physics, High Field Laboratory for Superconducting Materials (Research Institute for Scientific Measurements): Section of Soild State Ionics, Section of Solid State Physics, Section of Surface Science

Div. of Physics Ⅱ (M 33/1, D 26/2)
Optical properties of Solids, Biophysics, Theoretical Solid State Physics, Magnetic Properties of Solids, Theoretical Condensed Matter Physics, Electron Diffraction, Low Temperauture Physics, Neutron Diffraction, Ultra-Small Energy Physics Laboratory

---

山形大学
(Yamagata Daigaku)
Yamagata University

1-4-12 Kojirakawa-machi, Yamagata-shi, Yamagata 990
☎ 0236-31-1421 FAX 0236-31-1893

Founded 1949
Professors 223
Associate Professors 230
Assistant Professors(Tenured) 84
Assistant Professors(Non-tenured) 386
Research Assistants 211
Undergraduate Students/Foreign Students 7, 604/10
Graduate Students/Foreign Students 431/28
Library 812, 027 volumes
Contact: Educational Affairs Section, Student Bureau

Educational philosophy As an academic and research center, we provide wide knowledge and aim at teaching and studying professional high-level art and sciences to develop intellectual, moral and applied abilities so students may contribute much to the formation of a democratic and peace-loving nation and to cultural betterment and industrial development.

Foreign students We wish to extend a warm welcome to students from all parts of the world. You will experience a cultural and academic environment which is probably very different from your home country. It will be challenging to you, and we sincerely hope that you will find your experience enjoyable and rewarding as well.

Environment The University has four campuses. Each of campuses is surrounded by magnificent mountains and clean, clear rivers. They are blessed by beautiful natural surroundings which make them ideal for physical fitness as well as for the concentration academics demand.

Facilities University Library & Museum, Research & Guidance Center for Teaching Practice, Laboratory Animal Center, Macromolecular Research Laboratory, University Farm & Experimental Plantation, Information Processing Center, Gymnasium, Athletic fields, Baseball grounds.

Student activities Popular campus events includes freshmen welcome weeks and campus festivals. There is a wide variety of extra curricular activities, including chorus groups, ESS, volunteer work, drama, Bible, baseball, football, soccer, etc.

Academic programs for foreign students Tutoring system. Supplemental Japanese language class (in preparation)

Services for foreign students Health clinic, personal/psychological counseling, Housing information, part-time job information, Home visit, cultural exchange programs.

Undergraduate Programs

Faculty of Agriculture(683/1)
- **Dept. of Agricultural Chemistry**(181/0)
- **Dept. of Agricultural Engineering**(121/0)
- **Dept. of Agriculture**(140/1)
- **Dept. of Forestry**(103/0)
- **Dept. of Horticulture**(138/0)

Faculty of Education(1, 295/1)
- **Dept. of Training Course for Elementary School Teacher**(748/0)
- **Dept. of Training Course for Junior High School Teacher**(345/1)
- **Dept. of Training Course for Special Subject (Music) Teacher**(123/0)
- **Dept. of Training Course for Handicapped Children's School Teacher**(79/0)

Faculty of Engineering(3, 022/10)
- **Dept. of Materials Science and Engineering** (1, 242/1)
- **Dept. of Mechanical System Engineering**(694/4)
- **Dept. of Electrical and Information Engineering**

(1, 086/5)
Faculty of Literature and Social Sciences(1, 178/3)
Dept. of Economics(426/2)
Dept. of Law(368/1)
Dept. of Literature(384/0)
School of Medicine(677/0)
Dept. of Medical Science(677/0)
Faculty of Science(749/0)
Dept. of Biology(145/0)
Dept. of Chemistry(144/0)
Dept. of Earth Sciences(139/0)
Dept. of Mathematics(166/0)
Dept. of Physics(155/0)

Graduate Programs

Graduate School of Agriculture(M 44/1)
Div. of Agricultural Chemistry(M 26/0)
Applied Microbiology, Biological Chemistry, Chemistry of Agricultural Products, Food and Nutritional Chemistry, Soil Science and Fertilizer Science
Div. of Agricultural Engineering(M 3/1)
Agricultural Machinery, Irrigation and Drainage, Reclamation and Melioration, Soil Mechanics
Div. of Agriculture(M 10/0)
Agricultural Economics, Applied Zoology, Crop Breeding, Crop Science and Farm Management, Phytopathology, Zootechnical Science
Div. of Forestry(M 1/0)
Forest Engineering, Forest Management, Forest Policy, Forest Utilization and Chemical Technology of Forest Products, Silviculture
Div. of Horticulture(M 4/0)
Horticlutural Breeding and Propagation, Pomology, Post–harvest Horticulture, Vegetable Crop Science
Graduate School of Engineering(M 258/27)
Div. of Applied Chemistry(M 34/2)
Dyestuff Chemistry, Industrial Inorganic Chemistry, Industrial Organic Chemistry, Inorganic Material Chemistry, Organic Material Chemistry, Synthetic Chemistry, Technical Analytical Chemistry
Div. of Chemical Engineering(M 28/3)
Chemical Reaction Engineering, Fluid Flow and Heat Transfer, Mass Transfer, Mechanical Operation, Process Control and Instrumentation
Div. of Electrical Engineering(M 27/3)
Applied Electricity, Electric and Electronic Machinery, Electric Energy Engineering, Electric Power Engineering, Information and Computer Engineering, Theory of Electricity, Transmission and Communication Engineering
Div. of Electronic Engineering(M 30/3)
Applied Electronics, Electronic Circuits, Electronic Devices, Instrument and Control Engineering, Physical Electronics
Div. of Information Engineering(M 20/6)
Applied Informatics, Computer Engineering, Fundamental Informatics, Information Processing, Information System, Intelligence System
Div. of Mechanical Engineering(M 27/4)
Engineering Materials, Engineering Thermodynamics and Heat Transfer, Fluid Mechanics and Fluid Machinery, Mechanism and Machine Design, Production Machine System, Strengty of Materials, Thermal Engineering
Div. of Polymer Chemistry(M 34/1)
Applied Polymer Chemistry, Fundamental Polymer Chemistry, Polymer Synthesis, Structural Properties and Processing of Polymers, Technology of Dyeing and Finishing
Div. of Polymer Materials Engineering(M27/2)
Applied Polymer Physics, Functional Polymer Materials, Fundamental Polymer Materials, Materials Application, Materials Design, Materials Dynamics
Div. of Precision Engineering(M 31/3)
Control Engineering, Materials and Processes of Precision Manufacturing, Precision Instrument and its Design, Precision Measurement, Technology of Plasticity
Graduate School of Medical Sciences(D 75/3)
1 st Cluster of Study (Control Organism of a Living Body)
2 nd Cluster of Study (Function of a Living Body and Its Morbid State)
3rd Cluster of Study (Specialization and Formation of Living Body)
4 th Cluster of Study (Reciprocal Action of a Living Body and Its Circumstance)
Anatomy, Anestheia, Bacteriology, Biochemistry, Dentistry and Oral Surgery, Dermatology, Forensic Medicine, Hygiene and Preventive Medicine, Internal Medicine, Laboratory Medicine, Molecular and Pathological Biochemistry, Neuropsychiatry, Obstetrics and Gynecology, Ophthalmology, Orthopaedics Otolaryngology, Parasitology, Pathology, Pediatrics, Pharmacology, Physiology, Public Health, Radiology, Surgery, Surgical Neurology, Urology
Graduate School of Science(M 54/3)
Div. of Biology(M 17/0)
Cytology, Embryology, Environmental Biology, Physiology
Div. of Chemistry(M 13/1)
Analytical Chemistry, Inorganic Chemistry, Organic Chemistry, Physical Chemistry
Div. of Earth Sciences(M 9/1)
Applied Geology, Crustal Evolution, Petrology, and Mineralogy, Physical Geology
Div. of Mathematics(M 6/0)
Algebra, Anlysis, Applied Mathematics, Geometry
Div. of Physics(M 9/1)
Applied Physics, Classical and Quantum Mechanics, Electromagnetism, Solid State Physics

One–Year Graduate Programs

Literature and Social Science Course
Literature Major
Education Course
Music Major
Education Major

Local Public Universities

福島県立医科大学
(Fukushima Kenritsu Ika Daigaku)

Fukushima Medical College

1 Hikarigaoka, Fukushima-shi, Fukushima 960-12
☎ 0245-48-2111

Founded 1952

Undergraduate Programs

Faculty of Medicine
Dept. of Medicine

Graduate Programs

Graduate School of Medicine
Div. of Internal Medicine
Div. of Pathological Studies
Div. of Physiological Studies
Div. of Social Medicine
Div. of Surgery

Private Universities

秋田経済法科大学
(Akita Keizai Hôka Daigaku)

Akita University of Economics and Law

46-1 Mamorisawa, Sakura, Shimokitate, Akita-shi, Akita 010
☎ 0188-36-1341 FAX 0188-36-3321

Founded 1964
Professors 23
Associate Professors 15
Assistant Professors (Tenured) 10
Assistant Professors (Non-tenured) 46
Undergraduate Students/Foreign Students 2, 724/1
Library 10, 527 volumes
Contact: Office of Department of Academic Affairs

Educational philosophy We aim at teaching and studying up-to-date high-level art and sciences to develop intellectual and personal, practical and applied abilities so students may contribute much to cultural and social improvement.
Foreign students We believe that foreign students can enjoy a satisfying campus life in our school, and can contribute a great deal to promoting mutual understanding and the development of friendly relations.
Environment The city of Akita, with a population of 300, 000, is located in scenic northwest in the Tohoku District, and is on the coast of Sea of Japan. Though located in a rural area, Akita has a good service of plants and trains. Akita is cold in winter, but hot in summer. It is famous for its producing rice, Japanese sake and belles.
Facilities Library, Auditorium, Sports Training Center, Gymnasium, Computer Center, Economics, Research Institute, Law and Politics Research Institute, Institute for the Collection of Folk Material in Snowy Lands
Student activities Popular campus events include school festival, athletic meeting, freshman welcome party, 40-kilometer walking over night. There is a wide variety of extra curricular activities, including volunteer work, choral groups, drama, fine arts, baseball, basketball, soccer, rugby football, judo, etc.
Academic programs for foreign students Tutoring system
Service for foreign students Health clinic, Personal counseling, Dormitory, Housing information, Part-time job information, Cultural exchange program, Home visit, Vocational guidance

Undergraduate Programs

Undergraduate Programs

Faculty of Commerce
Dept. of Commercial Science

八戸工業大学
(Hachinohe Kôgyô Daigaku)

Hachinohe Institute of Technology

88–1 Obiraki, Myo, Hachinohe-shi, Aomori 031
☎ 0178–25–3111 FAX 0178–25–2769

Founded 1972
Professors 36
Associate Professors 45
Assistant Professors (Tenured) 12
Assistant Professors (Non-tenured) 43
Research Assistants 3
Undergraduate Students/Foreign Students 2, 871/3
Library 65, 197 volumes
Contact: Admissions Office

Educational philosophy We aim at teaching and studying arts and sciences with emphasis on engineering to develop moral, intellectual and applied abilities and contributing to world peace, cultural betterment, and the development of the community in which our school exists.

Foreign students We place emphasis on the education of engineers. In order to meet the recent development of technology, we introduce new subjects to the curriculum. We believe that foreign students can gain technical knowledge and training at our school and can contribute to the development of their home countries.

Environment The city of Hachinohe, located in the southern part of Aomori Prefecture, is famous as an industrial city and a fishing port, with a population of 250, 000. It takes about 4 hours and a half to travel from Tokyo to Hechinohe by train. In the recreation area offering sea bathing, fishing and camping.

Facilities Library, Laboratory of Food Technology, Laboratory of Information and System Engineering, Computer Center, baseball ground, football ground, running track, swimming pool, tennis court, sports training room, gymnasium, etc.

Student activities Campus events include freshmen welcome party, orientation for freshmen, school festival, school sports. The range of extracurricular activities is wide, including cultural activities such as art, wireless communication and athletics such as baseball, tennis, aikido.

Academic programs for foreign students The following subjects are offered to foreign students:Culture of Japan and Japanese Language. A student who has completed each subject will receive 4 credits for a regular general education subject in the field of humanities and social sciences and in the field of languages.

Services for foeign students Housing information, part-time job information

Undergraduate Programs

Faculty of Engineering (2, 871/3)
Dept. of Architectural Engineering (556/0)
Dept. of Civil Engineering (576/0)
Dept. of Electrical Engineering (589/1)
Dept. of Energy Engineering (568/0)
Dept. of Mechanical Engineering (582/2)

弘前学院大学
(Hirosaki Gakuin Daigaku)

Hirosaki Gakuin College

13–1 Minori-cho, Hirosaki-shi, Aomori 036
☎ 0172–34–5211 FAX 0172–32–8768

Founded 1886
Professors 7
Associate Professors 7
Assistant Professors (Tenured) 4
Assistant Professors (Non-tenured) 48
Contact: International Exchange Committee

Educational Philosophy We aim to provide an education in the humanities for women based on Christian principles, with the goal of developing good character and the skills and knowledge for coping in the modern world.

Foreign students We feel that the intimate atmosphere of our school lends itself to providing valuable interactions between foreign students and our own, enhancing, international understanding and sympathy.

Environment Hirosaki, where our college is located, is accessible by the Tohoku Expressway and Aomori Airport and is the cultural center of Aomori Prefecture and the Tsugaru Region. It's population of 170, 000 guarantees all necessary services, yet it retains the congenial rural atmosphere of this apple producing region.

Facilities Institute for the Study of Regional Culture, Library, Gymnasium, Mountain Retreat House, Missionary House (Important Cultural Property), Japanese Archery Range

Student activities Campus events include the annual school festival, sports festivals, excursions and concerts. There are many extra curricular activities including the chamber orchestra, sports clubs, traditional culture clubs and involving more modern interests.

Acdemic programs for foreign students Japanese language tutoring, independent study guidance, cultural activities

Services for foreign students College housing, housing information, part-time job information, homestay, home visit, foreign exchange program

Undergraduate Programs

Faculty of Literature(430/0)
Dept. of English and American Literature(209/0)
Dept. of Japanese Literature(221/0)

石巻専修大学
(Ishinomaki Senshû Daigaku)

Ishinomaki Senshu University

1 Minamisaki Shinmito, Ishinomaki-shi, Miyagi 986
☎ 0255-22-7711 FAX 0255-22-7170

Founded 1989
Professors 41
Associate Professors 32
Assistant Professors(Tenured) 7
Assistant Professors(Non-tenured) 27
Research Assistants 14
Undergraduate Students/Foreign Students 875/0
Library 54, 489 volumes
Contact: Admission Office

Educational philosophy Founding sprit of I. S. U. is to educate and train young people to serve the cause of the public good in a spirit of gratitude, forlitude, sincerity and industry.
Foreign students Now we are making plan for international exchange program and it's curriculum. So we do not put in practice on accepting a foreign students this year.

Undergraduate Programs

Faculty of Buisiness Administration(493/0)
Dept. of Business Administration
Faculty of Science and Engineering(382/0)
Dept. of Basic Science(121/0)
Dept. of Mechanical Engineering(87/0)
Dept. of Electrical Materials(87/0)
Dept. of Biological Technology(87/0)

いわき明星大学
(Iwaki Meisei Daigaku)

Iwaki Meisei University

5-5-1 Chuodai-Iino, Iwaki-shi, Fukushima 970
☎ 0246-28-5415

Founded 1987

Undergraduate Programs

College of Humanities
Dept. of English and American Literature
Dept. of Japanese Literature
Dept. of Sociology
College of Science and Engineering
Dept. of Electronic Engineering
Dept. of Fundamental Science
Dept. of Materials Science
Dept. of Mechanical Engineering

岩手医科大学
(Iwate Ika Daigaku)

Iwate Ika University

19-1 Uchimaru, Morioka-shi, Iwate 020
☎ 0196-51-5111 FAX 0196-51-8055

Founded 1928
Professors 67
Associate Professors 57
Assistant Professors(Tenured) 89
Assistant Professors(Non-tenured) 303
Research Assistants 260
Undergraduate Students/Foreign Students 1, 015/3
Graduate Students/Foreign Students 183/0
Library 194, 902 volumes
Contact: Admission Office

Educational philosophy This university prepares young men and women of dedication in the liberal arts and medical and dental sciences so that they can serve both humanity and their respective disciplines as clinicians and reserchers.
Foreign students We believe that foreign students can contribute a great deal to promoting mutual understanding in our schools. However, those who plan to enroll in our six-year program must take the same entrance examination as Japanese students do.
Environment Our-school is located in Morioka, the capital of Iwate-ken (prefecture). Morioka, with a population of 240, 000, is one of the key urban centers of the norht-eastern Japan. It was the site of the Nambu Castle and is rich in nature surrounded by moutains famous for their ski slopes.
Facilities Attached medical and dental hospitals; Cyclotron Center; Two libraries; Student Center; Gymnasiums; Soccer and Rugby Football Field; Baseball Field; Tennis Courts; Archery and Kyudo (Traditional Archery) Ranges; Riding Ground, etc.
Student activites A wide variety of extracurricular activities can be enjoyed. Approximatetly 30 athletic and 15 non-athletic clubs are run by students.
Academic programs for foreign students Special non-credit course in Japanese as a foreign language is offered during the first two years (two hours

per week). Otherwise, foreign students must take the same courses as Japanese students do, which are conducted in Japanese.

Services for foreign students Currently no special counselling service for foreign students is available. Nor is a home-stay program offered now, but those who want to live in the University-supported housing are welcome. Approximately 10% of our students are living in it.

Undergraduate Programs

Faculty of Dentistry(505/2)
Dept. of Dentisry
Faculty of Medicine(510/1)
Dept. of Medicine

Graduate Programs

Graduate School of Dentistry(D 49/0)
Div. of Dentistry
Oral Anatomy, Oral Physiology, Biochemistry, Oral Pathology, Microbiology, Pharmacology, Dental Techonology, Hygiene and Dental Public Health, Operative Dentistry, Endodontics, Periodontology, Fixed prosthodontics, Removable Prosthodontics, Oral Surgery, Orthodontics, Pedodontics, Dental Radiology
Graduate School of Medicine(D 134/0)
Div. of Physiology(D 23/0)
Anatomy, Physiology, Biochemistry, Pharmacology
Div. of Pathology(D 12/0)
Pathology, Bacteriology
Div. of Social Medicine(D 2/0)
Hygiene and Public Health, Legal Medicine
Div. of Internal Medicine(D 43/0)
Internal Medicine, Neurology, Pediatrics, Dermatology, Radiology, Psychiatry and Neourology, Clinical Pathology
Div. of Surgery(D 54/0)
Surgery, Neurosurgery, Orthopedic Surgery, Plastic and Reconstructive Surgery, Ophthalmology, Obstetrics and Gynecology, Urology, Otorhinolaryngology, Anesthesiology

---

郡山女子大学
(Kôriyama Joshi Daigaku)

Koriyama Women's College

3-25-2 Kaisei, Koriyama-shi, Fukushima 963
☎ 0249-32-4848 FAX 0249-33-6748

Founded 1947
Professors 31
Associate Professors 29
Assistant Professors(Tenured) 18
Assistant Professors(Non-tenured) 99
Research Assistants 16
Undergraduate Students/Foreign Students 453/3
Library 60, 000 volumes
Contact: General Management Office

Educational philosophy Our college's goal is to educate students that will fulfill their highest aspirations and become citizens who will realize peace and prosperity in their community, in their country, and in the world.

Foreign students We believe that foreign students can enjoy a rewarding experience in our college, and can develop intellectual abilities and contribute much to promoting mutual understanding.

Environment The city of Koriyama, 300, 000 population, is located in scenic northern Japan, just 80 minutes by train from Tokyo. Though life styles and culture are not so different from Tokyo's, Koriyama is surrounded by beautiful nature.

Facilities Establishment Memorial Hall, General Education Park, Seminar House, Computer Center, Language Laboratory, Library, Tea-Ceremory House, House for Communication of Students and Faculty, Gymnasium, etc.

Student activities There are various school events; main events are extra-curricular freshmen orientation, Bandai highland school, school sports meet, fall school festival, special art appreciation and culture courses. There is a wide variety of club activities.

Academic programs for foreign students One to two advisors, assigned in each course to give advice on research and school life, become great helpers for foreign students. The international exchange and education committee tutors them.

Services for foreign students Health clinic, Personal/Psychological counseling, College housing, Housing information, Part-time job information, Vocational guidance, Homestay, Home visit, Cultural exchange program

Undergraduate Programs

Faculty of Home Economics(453/3)
Dept. of Human life(327/3)
Dept. of Food and Nutrition(126/0)

宮城学院女子大学
(Miyagi Gakuin Joshi Daigaku)

Miyagi Gakuin Women's College

9-1-1 Sakuragaoka, Aoba-ku, Sendai-shi, Miyagi 981
☎ 022-279-1311 FAX 022-279-7566

Founded 1886

Educational philosophy Miyagi Gakuin was founded in 1886 by Japanese Christians and young missionary women from the USA. This school was founded to " educate women in the spirit of Christianity ", later continued to grow into the largest institution for the higher education of women in northern Japan.

盛岡大学
(Morioka Daigaku)

Morioka College

808 Sunagome, Takizawa, Iwate 020-01
☎ 0196-88-5555 FAX 0196-88-5577

Founded 1981
Professors 23
Associate Professors 24
Assistant Professors(Tenured) 10
Assistant Professors(Non-tenured) 65
Research Assistants 7
Undergraduate Students/Foreign Students 2, 029/0
Library 82, 699 volumes
Contact: Admission Office

Educational philosophy Education at Morioka College is based on Christian principle which attempts to promote the intellectual, spiritual, and social growth through academic and character building programs. Students-faculty communications are highly evaluated.
Foreign students We welcome students from abroad who are willing to study Japanese language and culture through the heritage of Tohoku area, the significant region of nature and human.
Environment The main campus is located in the suburb of Morioka City. Thirty minutes ride of bus takes the students into an open and clean atmosphere surrounded by greenly woods, spectacle mountains in the distance, streams in the middle. The land of heritage.
Facilities The Research Center for Studies of Comparative Cultures, Library Auditorium, Language Laboratory, Computer practice room, Athletic field, Gymnasium, Cafeteria
Student activities Popular campus events: freshmen welcome party, Athletic meeting, College festival Chapel program: Mother's day service, Thanks giving service, Christmas service, Student activities: chorus, drama, fine arts, baseball, tennis, volleyball, rugby, etc.
Services for foreign students Personal/psychological counseling, Dormitory, Homestay, cultural exchange program

Undergraduate Programs

Faculty of Humanities(2, 029/0)
Dept. of English Literature(615/0)
Dept. of Japanese Literature(442/0)
Dept. of Juvenile Edcation(972/0)

奥羽大学
(Ôu Daigaku)

Ohu University

31-1 Misumido, Tomita-machi, Koriyama-shi, Fukushima 963
☎ 0249-32-8931 FAX 0249-33-7372

Founded 1972
Professors 48
Associate Professors 19
Assistant Professors(Tenured) 33
Assistant Professors(Non-tenured) 63
Research Assistants 67
Undergraduate Students/Foreign Students 1, 270/3
Graduate Students/Foreign Students 43/0
Library 135, 645 volumes
Contact: the instruction division

Educational philosophy The educational core of Ohu University is to cultivate fine human characters. We aim at bringing up young characters with broad humanity, as well as with expertise so students may contribute to cultural betterment, social improvement and desirable human communications.
Foreign students Though we have received few foreign students, we have made utmost efforts for them to enjoy a rewarding experience in developing mutual understanding and acquiring satisfactory expertise.
Environment The city of Koriyama, with a population of 310, 000, is located in the heartland of Fukushima Prefecture; the center of the traffic network of the District as well. The City, surrounded by fine natural scenes, has made a remarkable development as prefectural center of commerce and distribution.
Facilities Pathological laboratory, Auditorium, Annexed hospital, Library, Gymnasium, Martial arts hall, Tennis courts, Computer center, Electronics reserch labo., Audio-visual classroom, etc.
Student activities Popular campus events include school festival, diverse academic meets, freshmen's orientation tour, etc.. There is a wide variety of extra curricular activities, including inter-college communication party, yacht, archery, American football, rugby, tea ceremony, international communication club, and so on.
Academic programs for foreign students We are now ready to make every possible programs for receiving foreign students.
Services for foreign students We are now planning out a structure for accepting foreign students with the help of our counselling staff, well-experience in staying abroad.

Undergraduate Programs

Faculty of Dentistry(734/2)
Dept. of Dentistry

Faculty of Literature, Linguistics and Culture Studies(536/1)
Dept. of English language and literature(259/0)
Dept. of French language and literature(128/0)
Dept. of Japanese language and literature(149/1)

Graduate Programs

Graduate School of Dentistry(D 43/0)
Div. of Dentistry
Oral Anatomy, Oral Physiology, Oral Biochemistry, Oral Pathology, Oral Bacteriology, Dental Pharmacology, Dental Materials Science, Preventive Dentistry, Clinical Periodontology, Endodontics, Crown and Bridge Prosthodontics, Removable Prosthodontics, Oro-Maxillo-Facial Surgery, Orthodontics, Dental Anesthesiology, Dental Radiology, Pedodontics

---

仙台大学
(Sendai Daigaku)
Sendai College

Minami 2, 2-18 Funaoka, Shibata-machi, Shibata-gun, Miyagi 989-16
☎ 0224-55-1121

Founded 1967

Undergraduate Programs

Faculty of Physical Education
Dept. of Physical Education

東北薬科大学
(Tôhoku Yakka Daigaku)
Tohoku College of Pharmacy

4-4-1 Komatsushima, Aoba-ku, Sendai-shi, Miyagi 981
☎ 022-234-4181 FAX 022-275-2013

Founded 1939
Professors 19
Associate Professors 17
Assistant Professors(Tenured) 29
Assistant Professors(Non-tenured) 24
Research Assistants 41
Undergraduate Students/Foreign Students 1, 788/0
Graduate Students/Foreign Students 35/0
Library 55, 610 volumes

Educational philosophy Our college was developed, based upon the principle that every teaching staff and student should have the desire to seek after truth with mutual respect; " Portas veritais aperiamus (Let us open the door to the truth) "
Environment Our college is located, surrounded by natural beauty, in the northern part of Sendai, one of the most beautiful cities in Japan. Students are very comfortable with the verdant trees which can be seen everywhere on our campus. This environment promotes an atmosphere ideal for academic life.
Facilities Cancer Research Institute, Radioisotope Center, Center for Laboratory Animal Sciences, Drug Plant Garden, Waste-water Treatment Center, C.A.I. Room, Library, Gymnasium, Auditorium, Takayanagi Memorial
Student activities Students enjoy Homecoming and many exciting interclass matches of baseball, softball, volleyball, soccer, etc. every year.

Undergraduate Programs

Faculty of Pharmaceutical Sciences
Dept. of Pharmacy
Dept. of Environmental and Hygienic Chemistry
Dept. of Pharmaceutical Technochemistry

Graduate Programs

Graduate School of Pharmaceutical Sciences(M 30/0, D 5/0)
Pharmaceutical Chemistry, Pharmaceutical Analytical Chemistry, Synthetic Organic Chemistry, Biochemistry, Hygienic Chemistry & Public Hygiene, Pharmaceutics, Pharmacognosy, Pharmacology

---

東北福祉大学
(Tôhoku Fukushi Daigaku)
Tohoku Fukushi University

1-8-1 Kunimi, Aoba-ku, Sendai-shi, Miyagi 400
☎ 022-233-3111 FAX 022-273-5322

Founded 1962
Professors 42
Associate Professors 23
Assistant Professors(Tenured) 11
Assistant Professors(Non-tenured) 109
Research Assistants 7
Undergraduate Students/Foreign Students 4, 413/8
Graduate Students/Foreign Students 17/1
Library 140, 000 volumes
Contact: The Instruction Department

Educational philosophy Traditionary the University has a spirit of Education regarding " fukushi " in Japanese which means " welfare " or " human service " in English. The sprits is rooted in Zen Buddhism and human nature.
Foreign students The undergrauduate program

and graduate program are offered for foreign students, but qualifications for Foreign transfer student is as follows; 1) A student who finished the course not less than fourteen years formal schooling or with attainments equal or higher than the former. 2) A student who has graduated from a university, or left a university before graduation. 3) Students must meet the requirment for literacy of Japanese language to follow lectures.

Environment Main campus of the University is located on a hill overlooking Sendai City, which has been the castle town of the famous Feudal Lord Date since the begining of Seventeenth Century Present time the city with beautiful and calm environments is nicknamed " Wooden metropolis " or " Academic City ". The city has a population of 900, 000, and is about 220 miles north of Tokyo, but it is only two hours distance by the Bullet Train " Tohoku Shinkansen ".

Facilities University campuses are well equipped as institutions for research, learning, fieldwork, athleties and cultural activities. The university library is going on computerization. Serizawa Keisuke Art & Craft Museum at the main campus open to the general public.

Student activites A proverb saying " A sound mind in a sound body. " is also an important guiding principle for students. The University Stresses physical education and intercollegiate sports. Many of its teams, especially baseball, volleyball and table tennis, have placed high in national competitions. And physical education for aged and physical handicapped people are student's matters of concern. Many voluntary groups and cultural clubs have been well organized by students.

Undergraduate Programs

Faculty of Social Welfare(4, 413/8)
- **Dept. of Industrial Wefare**(663/0)
- **Dept. of Social Education**(995/3)
- **Dept. of Social Welfare**(2, 371/8)
- **Dept. of Welfare Psychology**(384/1)

Graduate Programs

Graduate School of Social Welfare(M 15/0)
- **Div. of Social Welfare**

The princeples of Social Welfare, Fieldwork, Sociology, Foundamental theory, Methodology of Social Welfare, Social Casework, Clinical Training of Social Welfare, Social Group Work, Special Lecture on Metholology of Social welfare, Community Organization.

東北学院大学
(Tôhoku Gakuin Daigaku)
Tohoku Gakuin University

1-3-1 Tsuchitoi, Aoba-ku, Sendai-shi, Miyagi 980
☎ 022-264-6411 FAX 022-264-3030

Founded 1886
Professors 193
Associate Professors 118
Assistant Professors (Tenured) 41
Assistant Professors (Non-tenured) 175
Research Assistants 4
Undergraduate Students/Foreign Students 12, 236/3
Graduate Students/Foreign Students 53/2
Library 614, 500 volumes
Contact: International Center Office ☎ 022-264-6425

Educational philosophy Tohoku Gakuin University is dedicated to an educational approach which is deeply rooted in Christian values. It seeks to provide its students with a deep understanding of the sprit of sacrifice and a feeling of awe toward God. It also endeavors to enrich their personalities and intelligence so that they may devote themselves to the welfare of society and all humankind. As an expression of this spirit in which the shcool was founded, chapel services held every morning, well-attended by students, faculty and other staff workers.

Foreign students In 1990 Tohoku Gakuin University revised the fundamental school regulations to send students to study abroad and to accept foreign students on a long-term basis. We sincerely hope to welcome foreign students wishing to study together with the Japanese students and to share cross cutural experiences.

Environment Tohoku Gakuin University is located in Sendai, with over 900, 000 population, capital of Miyagi Prefecture. Developed as a castle town, Sendai is very modernized city and plays an important role as educational, cultural and economic center in the northern Japan. The JR Bullet train links Sendai Tokyo with a less than two hours ride.

Facilities We have three campuses, namely Tsuchitoi, Izumi and Tagajo, each has its own up-to-date chapel, library, gymnasium, student hall, computer information center, sporting facilities, etc.

Student activities Student clubs number over 230 and vary from sporting groups, like baseball, soccer, American football, judo, kendo, and sumo, to cultural groups, such as the English Speaking Society, chorus, choir, tea ceremony, social welfare service and various study groups.

Undergraduate Programs

Faculty of Economics(3, 372/1)
- **Dept. of Commerce**(1, 397/0)

Dept. of Economics(2, 475/1)
Faculty of Engineering(2, 070/0)
Dept. of Applied Physics(368/0)
Dept. of Civil Engineering(581/0)
Dept. of Electrical Engineering(565/0)
Dept. of Mechanical Engineering(556/0)
Faculty of Law(1, 558/0)
Dept. of Law(1, 558/0)
Faculty of Liberal Arts(433/0)
Dept. of Human Science(155/0)
Dept. of Information Science(129/0)
Dept. of Linguistic Science(149/0)
Faculty of Literature(2, 587/2)
Dept. of Christian Studies(24/2)
Dept. of English(1, 522/0)
Dept. of History(1, 041/0)

Graduate Programs

Grduate School of Economics(M 1/0, D 3/0)
Div. of Economics
Graduate School of Law(M 1/0, D 0/0)
Div. of Law
Graduate School of Literature(M 11/0, D 3/0)
Div. of English Language and Literature(M 11/0, D 3/0)
Graduate School of Engineering(M 29/1, D 5/1)
Div. of Applied Physics(M 8/0, D 1/0)
Div. of Civil Engineering(M 3/0, D 0/0)
Div. of Electrical Engineering(M 13/1,D 3/1)
Div. of Mechanical Engineering(M 5/0, D 1/0)

東北工業大学
(Tôhoku Kôgyo Daigaku)
Tohoku Institute of Technology

35-1 Kasumicho, Yagiyama, Taihaku-ku, Sendai-shi, Miyagi 982
☎ 022-229 1151 FAX 022-228-1813

Founded 1964
Professors 54
Associate Professors 47
Assistant Professors(Tenured) 17
Assistant Professors(Non-tenured) 87
Research Assistants 54
Undergraduate Students/Foreign Students 3450/1
Library 123, 370 volumes
Contact: Admission Office

Educational philosophy The school aims to graduate well-educated, well-balanced individuals who can make positive contributions to society. As the academic center of technological learning in northern Japan, we particularly strive to provide our students with both a grounding in the humanities and a high level of technical knowledge in their area of specialization.

Foreign students We have had only a few foreign students in the past and would like to see their number increase. We encourage foreign students to apply in the belief that their participation in the life of the school would foster a truer understanding of internationalization.

Environment Sendai (pop. 1 million) combines big city conveniences with traditional Tohoku hospitality. Capital of Miyagi Prefecture, it is the economic and cultural center of northern Japan, and can be reached from Tokyo, 350 km to the south, in two hours by bullet train. Renowned for its scenic beauty, Sendai is nicknamed " the city of trees ".

Facilities TIT library, Informatics Laboratory, Workshop, Student Hall, Gymnasium, Auditorium

Student activities Popular campus events include School festival, freshmen orientation. There is a wide variety of extra curricular activities, including baseball, soccer, karate, judo, rugby, American football, folksong, photograph, brass, cinema, etc.

Undergraduate Programs

Faculty of Engineering(3450/1)
Dept. of Architecture(743/0)
Dept. of Civil Engineering(738/1)
Dept. of Communication Engineering(741/0)
Dept. of Electronics(749/0)
Dept. of Industrial Design(479/0)

東北生活文化大学
(Tôhoku Seikatsu Bunka Daigaku)
Tohoku Living Culture College

1-18 Nijinooka, Izumi-ku, Sendai-shi, Miyagi 981
☎ 022-272-7511 FAX 022-272-7516

Founded 1957
Professors 7
Associate Professors 3
Assistant Professors(Tenured) 15
Assistant Professors(Non-tenured) 44
Research Assistants 2
Undergraduate Students/Foreign Students 426/0
Library 51, 360 volumes
Contact: Instruction Department ☎ ext. 281

Educational philosophy We aim at educating the heart of being fond of " beauty " and teaching of scientific thinking of living life and, we at promoting persons of creative heart.

Foreign students We believe that foreign students can a rewarding experience in our school, and can contribute a great deal to promoting mutual understanding and the development of friendly relations.

Environment Our campus is located in scenic north in the city of Sendai with a population of about 1,000,000. Our compus is convenient to the urban area. The area is rich in the establishments of culture.
Facilities Library, Training Room, Gymnasium, Swimming pool, Computer Research instiltion.
Student activities Popular campus events includes freshmen welcome party, college festival and physical culture festival, There is a variety of extra curricular activities.

Undergraduate Programs

Faculty of Domestic Science(426/0)
Dept. of Domestic Science(212/0)
Dept. of Living Art(214/0)

東北女子大学
(Tôhoku Joshi Daigaku)
Tohoku Women's College

1-2-1 Toyohara, Hirosaki-shi, Aomori 036
☎ 0172-33-2289

Founded 1969

Undergraduate Programs

Faculty of Home Economics
Dept. of Child Science
Dept. of Living Science

Faculty of Economics(1, 408/1)
  Dept. of Economics
Faculty of Law(1, 316/0)
  Dept. of Law

青森大学
(Aomori Daigaku)
Aomori University

248 Abeno, Kobata, Aomori-shi, Aomori 030
☎ 0177-38-2001 FAX 0177-35-4617

Founded 1978
Professors 29
Associate Professors 24
Assistant Professors(Tenured) 10
Assistant Professors(Non-tenured) 16
Undergraduate Students/Foreign Students 1, 434/4
Library 73, 157 volumes
Contact: Administrative Bureau

Educational philosophy The motto is to help every student to be a person who can contribute to the society and be actively involved with a changing world without losing spiritual virtue, through our educational philosophy, integrity, dilligence, purity, and blithe spirit.
Foreign students A pleasant atmosphere for studying and conducting a daily life for foreign students exists. We hope that they can be a friendly bridge between Japan and their country after the graduation.
Environment Located on the top of the hill from which the entire Aomori city can be seen to the north, and to the south, the beautiful Towada national park makes the environment beautiful and very convenient. Population of Aomori City is about 300, 000.
Facilities There are many facilities such as the library, sport arena, computer room, institule of industrial study, institute of integrated local study, institute of information study, and open collage.
Student activities There are variety of events and activities such as a freshman orientation, sports event, educational rally, Nebuta festival, university festival, and ski school.

Undergraduate Programs

Faculty of Business management(745/4)
  Dept. of Business management
Faculty of Sociology(689/0)
  Dept. of Sociology

富士大学
(Fuji Daigaku)
Fuji College

450-3 Shimoneko, Hanamaki-shi, Iwate 025
☎ 0198-23-6221 FAX 0198-23-5818

Founded 1965
Professors 22
Associate Professors 10
Assistant Professors(Tenured) 7
Assistant Professors(Non-tenured) 15
Undergraduate Students/Foreign Students 902/0
Library 60, 508 volumes
Contact: Admission Office.

Educational philosophy Our aim is to build up students well-balanced in intellctual, moral and physical abilities through our small seminar system, so, on the basis of understanding of ecnomics and liberal arts, they will contribute to the development of the society as capable citizens.
Foreign students We are ready to accept today's view of " internationalization " and welcome foreign students to our campus. We are sure we can foster our friendly relations.
Environment The city of Hanamaki, with population of 70, 000 is located on a fertile plain in the heart of Iwate Prefecture. Though located in a rural area, Hanamaki is convenient to the urban area (about 30 km south of Morioka), famous for hot springs and historical sites.
Facilities College Library (60, 000 books), Lecture Theater (audiovisual), Sport Training Center (Kendo, Judo, Karate, Baseball, etc.), Gymnasium, Auditorium.
Student activities Campus events include Freshman Camp, Softball Tournament (interseminar), College Festival, Study Tour Abroad, Extra curricular activities include Cheering Party, Baseball, Soccer, Kendo, Judo, Karate ,Ski, Economics, Asian Philosophy, Go, Tea Ceremony, etc.

Undergraduate Programs

Faculty of Economics(902/0)
  Dept. of Economics

八戸大学
(Hachinohe Daigaku)
Hachinohe University

13-98 Mihono, Hachinohe-shi, Aomori 031
☎ 0178-25-2711

Founded 1981

KANTO

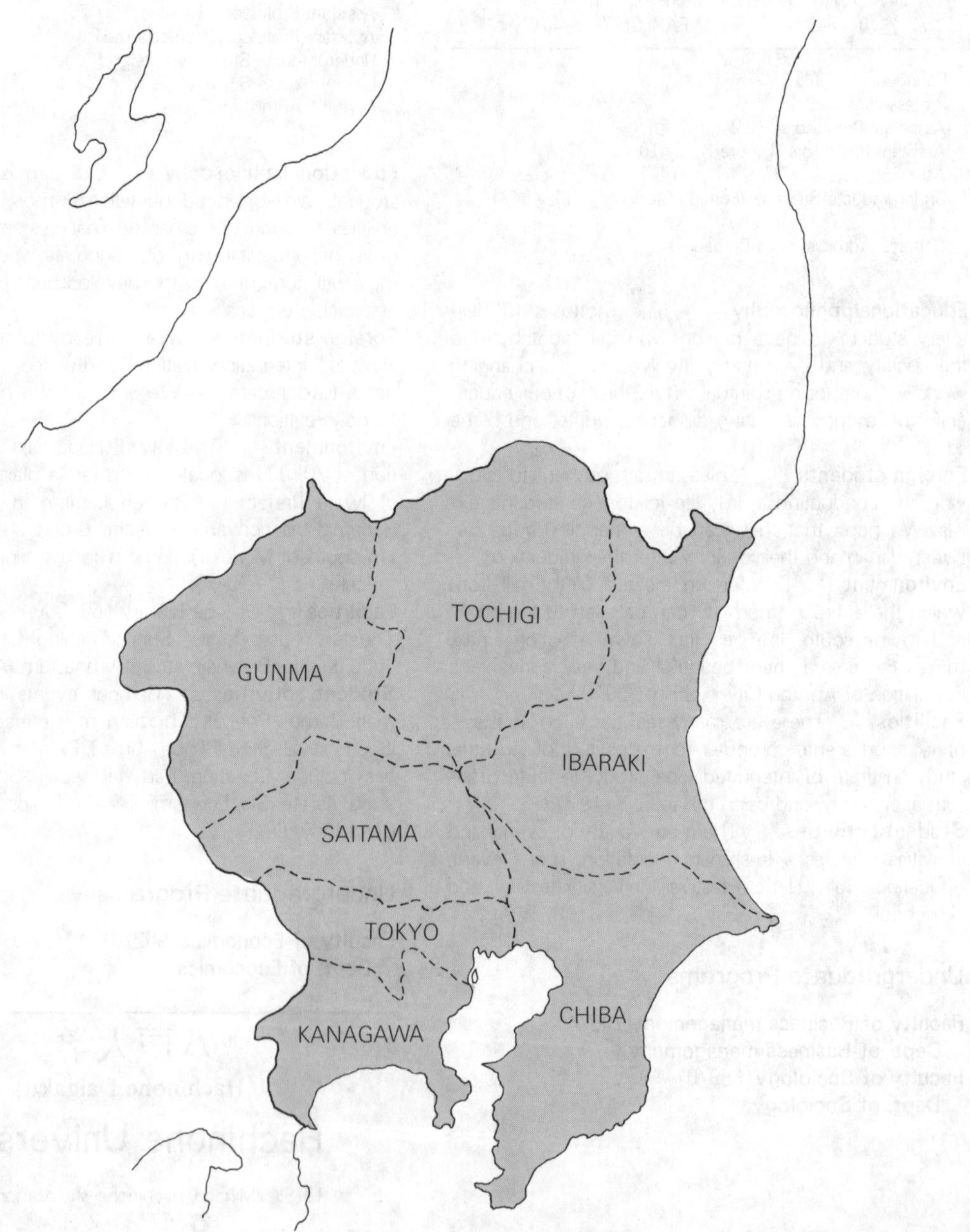

KANTO REGION CLIMATE

Summers are warm with considerable rainfall, with clear weather continuing through winter.

- Inland District
  Fierce winter cold, with fairly broad summer-winter temperature differences.
- Coastal District
  Winters warm, with only rare frosts.

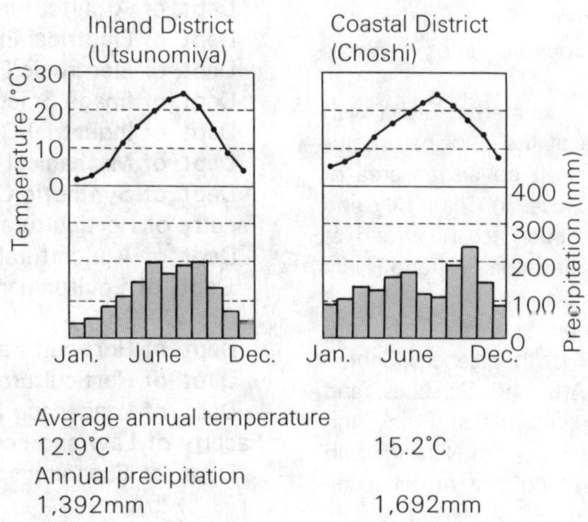

Average annual temperature
12.9°C 15.2°C
Annual precipitation
1,392mm 1,692mm

National Universities

千葉大学
(Chiba Daigaku)

Chiba University

1–33 Yayoi–cho, Chiba–shi, Chiba 260
☎ 0472–51–1111 FAX 0472–55–7983

Founded 1949
Professors 369
Associate Professors 303
Assistant Professors(Tenured) 130
Assistant Professors(Non–tenured) 1, 156
Research Assistants 351
Undergraduate Students/Foreign Students 11, 781/117
Graduate Students/Foreign Students 1, 110/144
Library 1, 115, 009 volumes
Contact: Educational Affairs Division, Student Bureau

Educational philosophy Education at Chiba University is directed toward a wide range of interdisciplinary knowledge along with intensive academic training, encouraging students to develop their personal autonomy and problemsolving ability and to enhance their competency for the current internationalized society.

Foreign students Great emphasis is placed on international exchange at our University. Hence our readiness to welcome students from other parts of the globe. At present more than four hundreds overseas students are enrolled.

Environment Our University, located in Chiba with a mild oceanic climate, in one of the principal institutions in the Greater Tokyo Area. It covers an area of 860, 000m², including two campuses in Chiba City and one in Matsudo City. Japan is open to the world at Chiba because of the presence of Chiba Port and Narita International Airport.

Facilities The main campus in Nishi–Chiba has Central Library, University Hall, Health Sciences Center, six Faculties and College of Arts and Sciences, and many other facilities including Information Processing Center. School of Medicine and School of Nursing, with University Hospital, are located at Inohana Area Faculty of Horticulture and affiliated farms are at Matsudo.

Student activities Students may join any of the athletic or cultural clubs (" circles "). The Circle Hall and other facilities are available for students activities. The annual " Daigakusai " (Student Festival) and bus tour for freshmen are organized. Parties for international students are held on various occasions.

Academic programs for foreign students Courses in Japanese Language and various aspects of Japan are provided for undergraduates at College of Arts and Sciences. Supplementary courses in Japanese Language for graduate students are also available. Tutors are ready to help freshmen.

Services for foreign students The Forein Students' Dormitory accomodates 169 inmates. Foreign Student Advisors help them with their studies and personal problems. Occasional meetings with local inhabitants are organized to promote international cultural exchanges.

Undergraduate Programs

Faculty of Education(2, 468/10)
- **Training Program for Elementary School Teachers**(1, 568/1)
- **Training Program for Junior High School Teachers**(524/8)
- **Training Program for Teachers of Handicapped Children**(85/0)
- **Training Program for Kindergarten Teachers** (130/1)
- **Training Program for School Nurses**(161/0)

Faculty of Engineering(3, 468/38)
- **Dept. of Applied Chemistry**(107/2)
- **Dept. of Architecture**(319/4)
- **Dept. of Electrical and Electronics Engineering** (239/4)
- **Dept. of Image Science**(404/4)
- **Dept. of Industrial Design**(390/2)
- **Dept. of Information and Computer Sciences** (134/3)
- **Dept. of Materials Science**(65/0)
- **Dept. of Mechanical Engineering**(406/8)
- **Dept. of Architectural Engineering**(188/4)
- **Dept. of Electrical Engineering**(177/3)
- **Dept. of Electronic Engineering**(166/4)
- **Dept. of Image Science and Technology**(285/0)
- **Dept. of Industrial Chemistry**(231/0)
- **Dept. of Mechanical Engineering II** (151/0)
- **Dept. of Synthetic Chemistry**(206/0)

Faculty of Horticulture(997/9)
- **Dept. of Agricultural Chemistry**(150/3)
- **Dept. of Environmental Studies for Open Space** (211/1)
- **Dept. of Horticultural Economics**(179/5)
- **Dept. of Horticultural Science**(239/0)
- **Dept. of Landscape Architecture**(218/0)

Faculty of Law and Economics(1, 956/34)
- **Dept. of Economics and Business Administration** (995/25)
- **Dept. of Law and Politics**(961/9)

Faculty of Letters(779/16)
- **Dept. of Behavioral Sciences**(290/9)
- **Dept. of Historical Sciences**(159/3)
- **Dept. of Literature**(330/4)

School of Medicine(660/8)
- **Dept. of Medicine**(660/8)

School of Nursing(353/0)
- **Dept. of Nursing**(353/0)

Faculty of Pharmaceutical Sciences(327/0)
- **Dept. of Pharmaceutical Sciences**(327/0)

Faculty of Science(773/2)
- **Dept. of Biology**(102/0)

Dept. of Chemistry(169/1)
Dept. of Earth Sciences(171/0)
Dept. of Mathematics(163/0)
Dept. of Physics(168/1)

Graduate Programs

Graduate School of Education(M 133/7)
Div. of Art Education(M 10/1)
Painting, Sculpture, Creative Design, Theory in Formative Arts, Art Education
Div. of English Education(M 6/0)
English Linguistics, English and American Literature, Teaching of English
Div. of Health and Physical Education(M 12/2)
Physical Education, Physical Exercise, School Hygiene, Basic Medical Science, Clinical Medical Science and Nursing, Science of Health Education, Teaching of Health and Physical Education
Div. of Japanese Language Education(M 9/1)
Japanese Language, Japanese Literature, Chinese Classics, Calligraphy, Teaching of Japanese
Div. of Music Education(M 12/1)
Vocal Music, Instrumental Music, Composition, Teaching of Music
Div. of Mathematical Education(M 12/0)
Algebra and Geometry, Analysis and Applied Mathematics, Teaching of Mathematics
Div. of School Education(M 26/1)
Science of Education, Curriculum and Method of Teaching, History of Education, School Management, Educational Sociology, Educational Psychology, Developmental Psychology, Social Education, Education of Handicapped Children, Psychology of Handicapped Children, Early Child Education
Div. of Social Studies Education(M 15/1)
History, Geography, Jurisprudence and Politics, Sociology, Economics, Philosophy, Teaching of Social Studies
Div. of Science Education(M 24/0)
Physics, Chemistry, Biology, Physical Geography, Teaching of Science
Div. of Technical Education(M 7/0)
Electricity, Mechanics, Technical Education
Graduate School of Engineering(M 308/42)
Div. of Architecture(M 25/3)
Residential Design, Architectural Planning, Interior Design, Building Material, Architectural Design, Architectural History, Methodology of Design
Div. of Architectural Engineering(M 16/1)
Structural Engineering, Structural Design, Disaster Prevention, Productive Process of Architecture
Div. of Electrical Engineering(M 29/2)
Electrical Circuits, Electric Materials and High Voltage Engineering, Electric Machinery, Electrical Power and Illuminating Engineering, Fundamentals of Electrical Engineering, Electrical Power Systems
Div. of Electronic Engineering(M 34/10)
Instrumentation and Measurements, Fundamental Electronics, Electronic Control Engineering, Information Processing and System Science, Applied Information Science, Image Information Engineering, Electrical Communication
Div. of Image Science and Engineering(M 40/6)
Photographic Engineering, Photographic Chemistry and Applied Photography, Applied Image Engineering, Image Instrumentation, Vision and Image Technology, Photographic Technology, Photo-sensitive Material Technology, Image Information Research Division, Remote Sensing Data Processing Research Division, Remote Sensing Data Analysis Research Division, Remote Sensing Data Interpretation and Application Research Division
Div. of Image Science and Technology(M 18/2)
Imaging Engineering, Graphic Engineering, Applied Graphic Engineering, Imaging Materials, Plate-making Technology, Printing Technology, Imaging Systems, Image Technology
Div. of Industrial Chemistry(M 38/0)
Industrial Inorganic Chemistry, Industrial Organic Chemistry, Polymer Chemistry, Chemical Engineering, Organic Material Chemistry, Inorganic Material Chemistry
Div. of Industrial Design(M 32/5)
Philosophy and History of Design, Plastic Arts, Visual Information and Design, Industrial Design, Design Materials, Ergonomics, Display Design and Sculpture, Visual Communication Design and Painting
Div. of Mechanical Engineering(M 36/10)
Metals and Alloys, Machine Elements, Thermodynamics and Heat Engines, Manufacturing Technology, Engineering for Precision Machining, Engineering Mechanics
Div. of Mechanical Engineering II(M 22/3)
Elasticity and Plasticity, Automatic Control, Fluids Engineering, Mechanical Engineering for Production, Machine Design, Engineering of Plasticity
Div. of Synthetic Chemistry(M 18/0)
Industrial Physical Chemistry, Synthetic Organic Chemistry, Synthetic Polymer Chemistry, Synthetic Inorganic Chemistry, Environmental Chemistry, Chemical Measurements
(Interdepartmental) Applied Physics, Analytical Chemistry, Mathematics for Engineering, Information Processing Engineering
Graduate School of Horticulture(M 113/12)
Div. of Agricultural Chemistry(M 27/1)
Horticultural Soil Science, Horticultural Plant Nutrition, Biological Chemistry, Food and Nutrition Chemistry, Food Science and Technology, Applied Microbiology
Div. of Environmental Studies for Open Space(M 27/2)
Planting Design, Plant Pathology, Environmental Biology, Landscaping Botany, Nature Conservation
Div. of Horticultural Economics(M 12/3)
Technical Farm Management, Horticultural Economics, Crop Production and Management, Agricultural Marketing, Agricultural Information Science
Div. of Horticultural Science(M 30/4)
Pomology, Vegetable Science, Floriculture and Ornamental Horticulture, Plant Breeding, Horticultural Engineering, Horticultural Machinery and Equipment, Agricultural Meteorology

Div. of Landscape Architecture(M 17/2)
Landscape Architecture Theories and Landscape Planning, Town and Country Planning, Landscape Engineering, Landscape Planning and Space Structure, Garden Art
Graduate School of Human Sciences(M 41/10)
Div. of Behavioral Sciences(M 10/2)
Philosophy, Psychology, Sociology
Div. of Historical Science(M 12/1)
History
Div. of Japanese Literature(M 10/6)
Japanese Linguistics and Literature
Div. of Euro-American Languages and Cultures(M 9/1)
Linguistics and Literary Theory, English and American Literature, German Literature, French Literature
Graduate School of Medicine(D 82/6)
Div. of Internal Medicine(D 5/0)
Internal Medicine, Internal Medicine (Institute of Pulmonary Cancer Research), Neurology, Radiology, Psychiatry, Pediatrics, Dermatology
Div. of Pathological Science(D 13/2)
Pathology, Pathology (Institute of Pulmonary Cancer Research), Microbiology, Parasitology, Experimental Cytopathology, Experimental Chemotherapy, Immunology, Medical Micology
Div. of Prysiological Science(D 11/4)
Anatomy, Physiology, Biochemistry, Pharmacology, Applied Pharmacology, Neuropharmacology, Laboratory Medicine
Div. of Social Medicine(D 1/0)
Hygiene, Public Health, Rural Medicine, Legal Medicine
Div. of Surgery(D 52/0)
Surgery, Neurological Surgery, Surgery (Institute of Pulmonary Cancer Research), Orthopaedic Surgery, Obstertrics and Gynecology, Opthalmology, Otorhinolaryngology, Urology, Oral Surgery, Anesthesiology, Pediatric Surgery
Graduate School of Nursing(M 28/0)
Div. of Nursing(M 28/0)
Biophysics and Biochemistry, Pathobiology, Basic Health Science, Fundamentals of Nursing, Community Health Nursing, Medical-Surgical Nursing, Psychiatric Nursing, Child Nursing, Maternity Nursing, Nursing Education
Graduate School of Pharmaceutical Sciences (D 115/11)
Div. of Pharmaceutical Sciences(D 115/11)
Human Environmental Chemistry, Medicinal Materials, Drug Evaluation and Toxicological Sciences, Pharmaceutics
Graduate School of Science(M 88/7)
Div. of Biology(M 17/0)
Morphology, Physiology, Ecology, Phylogeny
Div. of Chemistry(M 18/1)
Physical Chemistry, Inorganic & Analytical Chemistry, Organic Chemistry, Biochemistry
Div. of Earth Sciences(M 27/2)
Geology, Mineralogy, Applied Earth Sciences, Geophysics
Div. of Mathematics(M 10/4)
Algebra, Geometry, Mathematical Analysis, Applied Mathematics, Statistics
Div. of Physics(M 16/0)
Theoretical Physics, Atomic Physics, Solid State Physics, Experimental Physics
Graduate School of Science and Technology (D 181/43)
Div. of Environmental Science(D 63/13)
Fundamental Sciences of Environment, Environmental Processes, Industrial Design, Living Environmental Planning, Environmental Planning and Landscape Technology
Div. of Mathematics and Physical Sciences (D 50/8)
Mathematics, Physics, Chemistry and Biology, Materials Science, Imaging Science
Div. of Production Science and Technology (D 68/22)
Production Engineering, Systems Engineering, Measurement and Information Science, Environmental Sciences of Bioproduction, Biotechnology, Production and Management of Bio-resources
Graduate School of Social Sciences(M 21/6)
Div. of Economics(M 12/3)
Theoretical Economics, Quantitative Economics Analysis, Applied Economics, International Comparison, Business Administration
Div. of Law(M 9/3)
Theoretical Jurisprudence, Public Law, Private Law, Political Science

---

総合研究大学院大学
(Sôgô Kenkyû Daigakuin Daigaku)

The Graduate University for Advanced Studies

4259 Nagatsuta, Midori-ku, Yokohama-shi, Kanagawa 227
☎ 045-922-1661 FAX 045-922-2338

Founded 1988
Professors 91
Associate Professors 108
Research Assistants 94
Graduate Students/Foreign Students 83/5
Library 389, 352 volumes
Contact: Section of Student Affairs, Secretariat, The Graduate University for Advanced Studies, 4259 Nagatsuta, Midori-ku, Yokohama-shi, Kanagawa, 227
☎ 045-922-1661 FAX 045-922-2338
School of Cultural Studies;
Dept. of Regional Studies
Dept. of Comparative Studies
Kokuritsu Minzokugaku Hakubutsukan (National Museum of Ethnology), 10-1 Senri Expo Park, Suita, Osaka, 565
☎ 06-876-2151 FAX 06-875-0401
School of Mathematical and Physical Science;
Dept. of Statistical Science
Tokei Sûri Kenkyujyo(The Institute of Statistical Mathematics), 4-6-7 Minami-Azabu, Minato-ku, Tokyo, 106

☎ 03-3446-1501 FAX 03-3443-3552
Dept. of Accelerator Science
Dept. of Synchrotron Radiation Science
Ko-enerugii Buturigaku Kenkyusyo (National Laboratory for High Energy Physics), 1-1 Oho, Tsukuba-shi, Ibaraki 305
☎ 0298-64-1171 FAX 0298-64-4602
Dept. of Structural Molecular Science
Dept. of Functional Molecular Science
Bunshi Kagaku Kenkyusho (Institute for Molecular Science), 38 Nishigonaka, Myodaiji, Okazaki, Aichi 444
☎ 0564-54-1111 FAX 0564-54-2254
School of Life Science;
Dept. of Genetics
Kokuritsu Idengaku Kenkyusho (National Institute of Genetics), 1111 Yata, Mishima-shi, Shizuoka 411
☎ 0559-75-0771 FAX 0559-71-3651
Dept. of Molecular Biomechanics
Kiso Seibutsugaku Kenkyusho (National Institute for Basic Biology), 38 Nishigonaka, Myodaiji, Okazaki, Aichi 444
☎ 0564-54-1111 FAX 0564-53-7400
Dept. of Physiological Sciences
Seirigaku Kenkyusho (National Institute for Physiological Sciences), 38 Nishigonaka, Myodaiji, Okazaki, Aichi 444
☎ 0564-54-1111 FAX 0564-52-7913

The Graduate University for Advanced Studies was founded on October 1, 1988 as the first national graduate university in Japan. It provides a ph. D. course of three-year duration only. The University aims at cultivating young scientists of rich originality backed with wide vision and international sense through development of a new postgraduate system. Its characteristic features may be summarized as follows:

1. Research and education are carried out in close cooperation with seven of the Inter-university Research Institutes (referred to as the Parent Institutes, videinfra), by means of the full use of their facilities and equipment. The Inter-university Research Institutes were founded to provide Japanese and foreign scientists with opportunities to perform high-grade joint research in various branches of science; they are equipped with large-scale research facilities and high-quality apparatuses and function as centers for advanced studies.

The academic staff of the University consists of professors and associate professors of the Parent Institutes. Deep expertise in specialized fields is cultivated by education and research guidance tightly consolidated with the high-level research performed at the Parent Institutes.

2. Inter-departmental functions of the University, such as joint seminars and lecture courses, provide the students with opportunities to broaden their scientific interest and international awareness through contacts with faculty members and students of other Schools and/or Departments of the University as well as with those of other universities in Japan and abroad.

3. In order to actively establish new scientific desciplines and to cultivate young able scientists devoting to their development, the University is promoting cooperative researches among two or more Parent Institutes and also with other organizations. The students are encouraged to participate in these programs.

Graduate Programs

School of Cultural Studies(D 9/1)

Dept. of Regional Studies(D 4/1)

Asian Studies, European and African Studies, American and Oceanic Studies

Dept. of Comparative Studies(D 5/0)

Studies of Society and Religion, Studies of Material Culture, Studies of Language and Art

School of Mathematical and Physical Science (D 43/2)

Dept. of Statistical Science(D 5/1)

Fundamental Statistical Theory, Statistical Methodology, Prediction and Control, Interdisciplinary Statistics

Dept. of Accelerator Science(D 11/0)

Accelerator Physics, Accelerator Engineering

Dept. of Synchrotron Radiation Science(D 5/0)

Synchrotron Radiation Source, Synchrotron Radiation Instrumentation, Synchrotron Radiation Application

Dept. of Structural Molecular Science(D 8/1)

Electronic Structure, Material Chemistry

Dept. of Functional Molecular Science(D 14/0)

Molecular Dynamics, Excited State Dynamics

School of Life Science(D 31/2)

Dept. of Genetics(D 13/1)

Molecular Genetics, Cell Genetics, Ontogenetics, Population Genetics, Applied Genetics

Dept. of Molecular Biomechanics(D 12/0)

Molecular Cell Biology, Developmental Gene Expression and Regulation, Regulation Biology

Dept. of Physiological Sciences(D 6/1)

Molecular Physiology, Cell Physiology, Information Physiology, Biological Control System

群馬大学
(Gunma Daigaku)
Gunma University

4-2 Aramaki-machi, Maebashi-Shi, Gunma 371
☎ 0272-32-1611 FAX 0272-34-2406

Founded 1949
Professors 198
Associate Professors 168
Assistant Professors (Tenured) 72
Assistant Professors (Non-tenured) 864
Research Assistants 209
Undergraduate Students/Foreign Students 4, 173/27
Graduate Students/Foreign Students 394/26
Library 545, 977 volumes
Contact: Student Affairs Office

Undergraduate Programs

Faculty of Education(1, 268/0)
- **Dept. of Art**(87/0)
- **Dept. of Domestic Science**(84/0)
- **Dept. of Education and Phychology**(132/0)
- **Dept. of English Language and English/American Literature**(59/0)
- **Dept. of Japanese Language and Literature**(113/0)
- **Dept. of Mathematics**(143/0)
- **Dept. of Music**(82/0)
- **Dept. of Physical Education**(122/0)
- **Dept. of Science**(251/0)
- **Dept. of Social Science**(157/0)
- **Dept. of Technical Education**(38/0)

Faculty of Engineering(1, 532/14)
- **Dept. of Applied Chemistry**(140/0)
- **Dept. of Chemical Engineering**(138/1)
- **Dept. of Civil Engineering**(143/3)
- **Dept. of Computer Science**(141/2)
- **Dept. of Electrical Engineering**(135/2)
- **Dept. of Electronic Engineering**(138/2)
- **Dept. of Mechanical Engineering Ⅰ**(140/3)
- **Dept. of Mechanical Engineering Ⅱ**(136/0)
- **Dept. of Polymer and Textile**(137/0)
- **Dept. of Polymer Chemistry**(144/0)
- **Dept. of Synthetic Chemistry**(140/1)

Faculty of Engineering(620/11)
- **Dept. of Biological and Chemical Engineering**(112/0)
- **Dept. of Chemistry**(166/2)
- **Dept. of Civil Engineering**(50/0)
- **Dept. of Computer Science**(66/3)
- **Dept. of Electronic Engineering**(112/2)
- **Dept. of Mechanical Engineering**(114/4)

Faculty of Medicine(611/0)
- **Dept. of Medicine**(611/0)

Graduate Programs

Graduate School of Education(M 32/0)

Div. of Education of Each Subject

Japanese, Social Science, Mahtmatics, Science, Music, Art, Physical Education, Tecnical Education, Domestic Science

Div. of School Education Science

School Education Science, Education of the Handicapped

Graduate School of Engineering(M 268/13, D 27/4)

Div. of Materials Science(M 10/0, D 0/0)

Div. of Biological & Chemical Engineering(M 31/0)

Div. of Mechanical Engineering(M 37/6)

Div. of Polymer and Textile(M 18/0)

Materials, Thermodynamics, Chemical, Physics, Applied physical, Physical Chemistry, Statistical Mechanics, Biophysics, Polimer and Textile Science, Polimer Processing, Polimer Chemistry

Div. of Applied Chemistry(M 41/0)

Analytical Chemistry, Geochemistry, Inorganics Chemistry, Crystail Chemistry, Solid State Chemistry, Organics Chemistry, Reaction Mechanism, Organometalic Chemistry, Organosilcon Chemistry, Bio Chemistry, Bioorganic Chemistry, Physical Organic Chemistry

Div. of Polymer Chemistry(M 11/0)

Physical Chemistry, Photochemistry, Physical Chemistry of Polymer, Polymer Reactions, Structure and Properties of Polymer, Dyeing Chemistry, Textile Chemistry, Synthetic Inoroganic Materials, Crystal Growth, Ceramic Chemistry

Div. of Synthetic Chemistry(M 8/0)

Organic Chemistry, Synthetic Organic Chemistry, Reactin Mechanism, Colloid Chemistry, Organosilicon Chemistry, Inorganic Materials, Synthetic Inorganic Materials, Carbon Materials, Carbonization Engineering

Div. of Chemical Engineering(M 10/0)

Transport Phenomena, Mass Transfer Operation, Reaction Engineering, Reactor Designing, Fluidization Engineering, Combustion Process, Separation Process with Electlicity, Solid-Liquid Separation Process, Catalytic Chemistry

Div. of Mechanical Engineering Ⅰ(M 16/2)

Strength of Materials, Thery of Elasticity, Dynamics of Machieary, Vibration, Thermal Power Engineering, Fluid Dynamics, Plasma Physics, Metal Machining, Laser Machining, Internal Combustion Engine

Div. of Mechanical Engineering Ⅱ(M 11/0)

Plastic Working, Material Processing, Instrument and Control Engineering, Heat and Mass Transfer, Spray and Combustion System, Strngth and Structure of Metals and Alloys, Diffusion in Metals

Div. of Electrical Engineering(M 11/0)

Electromagnetic· Theory, Electric Machinery, Electroacoustics, Electronic Measurement, Intrument Electronics, Control Engineering, Gaseous Discharge, Energy Conversion, Electric Power Engineering, Wave Propagation

Div. of Electronic Engineering(M 24/2)
Solid State Physics, Semiconductor Engineering, Electric and Magnetic Materials, Thin Film Physics, Electron Devices, Electronic Circuits, Plasma Physics Engineering, Communication Systems, Antennas and Microwave Transmission

Div. of Computer Science(M 23/2)
Information Theory, Numerical Analysis, Computer Systems, Computer Architecture, Mathematical Programming, Decision Thery, Graph Theory, Programming Languages, Computer Algorithms, Compiler Design Theory, Image Processing

Div. of Civil Engineering(M 17/1)
Bridge Engineering, Geotechnical Engineering, Soil Mechanics Hydraulics, Hydrology, Sanitary Engineering, Environmental Engineering, Concrete Engineering

Div. of Chemistry Division(D 9/2)
Molecular Science, Materials Science

Div. of Production Engineering Division(D 12/0)
Biological and Production Engineering, Process System Engineering

Div. of Computer and Communication Division(D 6/2)
Electronic System Engineering, Computer Science

Graduate School of Medical(D 67/9)

Div. of Physiological Medical Sciences(D 17/6)
Anatomy, Morphology, Physiology, Biochemistry, Physiology, Behaivior and Physiology, Behaivior Analysis, Comparative Endocrinology, Physical Biochemistry, Protein Chemistry, Hormone Assay

Div. of Pathological Medical Sciences(D 12/0)
Pathology, Microbiology, Pharmacology, Pharmceutical Chemistry, Clinical Pathology

Div. of Social Medicine(D 6/1)
Hygiene, Public Health, Parasitology, Legal Medicine

Div. of Clinical Medicine, Non-Surgical(D 10/2)
Internal Medicine, Neurology and Rehabilitation, Neuropsychiatry, Pediatrics, Dermatology, Radiology, Nuclear Medicine

Div. of Clinical Medicine, Surgical(D 22/0)
Surgery, Oral Surgery, Orthopedic Surgery, Neurosurgery, Urology, Ophthalmology, Otorhinolaryngology, Obstetrics and Gynecology, Anesthesia and Resucitation

---

一橋大学

(Hitotsubashi Daigaku)

Hitotsubashi University

2-1 Naka, Kunitachi-shi, Tokyo 186
☎ 0425-72-1101 FAX 0425-75-4055, 4336

Founded 1875
Professors 164
Associate Professors 52
Assistant Professors(Tenured) 21
Assistant Professors(Non-tenured) 172
Research Assistants 86
Undergraduate Students/Foreign Students 4, 674/50
Graduate Students/Foreign Students 356/98
Library 1, 325, 936 volumes
Contact: Admission Office ☎ext. 323

Educational philosophy Hitotsubashi University dates back to the shoho koshujo (Institute of Business Training) privately established in 1875. The main purpose of the Institute was to train young men in international trade. At present, we aim at high-level teaching and studying in various fields of social sciences.

Foreign students Basically, we treat foreign students on an equal level with the Japanese student. At the same time, we provide assistance anytime with pleasure in case foreign students are need.

Environment Our university has two campuses. One is in Kunitachi City (with a population of 65, 000) which is located 18 miles west of central Tokyo, and the other is in Kodaira City (with a population of 160, 000) which is located 3 miles north of Kunitachi City. Both campuses are located in quiet and verdant environments.

Facilities University Library, Center for Historical Social Science Literature, Kanematsu Auditorium, The Institute of Economic Research, Information and Documantation Center for Japanese Economic Statistics, Institute of Business Research, Language Laboratory, Gymnasium, Swimming Pool, Computer Center

Student activities There is a wide variety of extra curricular club activities including drama, orchestra, traditional flower arrangement, management study, baseball, football, karate, etc. The school festival is one of the most popular events on campus.

Academic programs for foreign students We have some programs specially designed for foreign students, including Japanese language classes, basic social science seminars, plant visitings, etc. We also have a tutoring system.

Services for foreign students We provide services as follows; medical services, counseling, housing information, part-time job information, scholarship information, cultural exchange programs, etc.

Undergraduate Programs

Faculty of Commerce(1, 222/28)
Dept. of Business Management(325/4)
Dept. of Commerce(281/12)
Faculty of Economics(1, 235/19)
Basic Course(326/0)
Applied Course(291/8)
Faculty of Law(1, 126/3)
Public Law(150/0)
Private Law(273/0)
International Relations(188/0)
Faculty of Social Studies(1, 091/0)
Course in Social Theory(103/0)
Course in Studies of Social Problems and Social Policies(361/0)
Course in Studies of Civilizations and Social His-

tory(106/0)

Graduate Programs

Graduate School of Commerce(M 21/8, D 21/5)

Div. of Specialized Course of Business Management and Accounting(M 14/3, D 16/4)

Forms of Business Enterprise, Corporation Management, Management of Public Enterprise, Management of Public Utilities, Business Organization, S.P. of Business Management, S.P. of History of Business Management Theories, S.P. of Personnel Management, S.P. of Financial Management, S.P. of Business History, S.P. of Management Science, S.P. of Management Statistic S.P. of Management Mathematics, Corporation Accounting, Public Utility Accounting, Tax Accounting, Accounting Systems, S.P. of Accounting, History of Accounting Theories, S.P. of Cost Accounting, S.P. of Management Accounting, S.P. of Auditing, S.P. of Information Management

Graduate School of Commerce(M 21/8, D 21/5)

Div. of Specialized Course of Commerce(M 7/5, D 5/1)

S.P. of Foreign Trade Theory, Foreign Trade Practices, S.P. of Marketing, S.P. of Securities Market, Investment Management, S.P. of History of Commerce, Foreign Trade Commodities, S.P. of Chemical Commodities, S.P. of Energy Commodities, Monetary Economics, Prices and Inflation, S.P. of Money and Banking, International Finance, S.P. of Banking System, Economics of Insurance, S.P. of Marine Insurance, General Average, S.P. of Non-Life Insurance, S.P. of Life Insurance, S.P. of Social Insurance, Management of Land Transportation, Management of Shipping

Graduate School of Economics(M 38/10, D 63/12)

Div. of Theoretical Economics and Statistics(M 21/2, D 33/2)

S.P. in Theoretical Economics, S.P. in Mathematical Economics, S.P. in Economic Planning, S.P. in Public Economics, S.P. in Econometrics, Theory if Economic Development, National Accounting, S.P. in Financial Economics, S.P. in International Economics, S.P. in Economics of Socialism, S.P. in History of Economic Doctrines, Historical and Social Science Literature, S.P. in History of Economic Idea, International Statistics, Problems on Time Series Analysis, S.P. in Statistics, S.P. in Economic Statistics, Statistical Data of Japanese Economy, S.P. in Mathematics for Economics, S.P. in Computer Science, Information Processing. Note: S.P. is an abbereviation of Special Problems

Div. of Economic History and Economic Policy(M 17/8, D 30/10)

Basic Principles of Economic History, S.P. in Economic History of Europe, S.P. in Economic History of Asia, S.P. in Economic History of Japan, Quantitative Economic History, S.P. in Japanese Economy, S.P. in Chinese Economy, S.P. in Southeast Asian Economy, S.P. in Russian Economy, S.P. in American Economy, S.P. in Economic Thought (Gt. Britain and the U.S.A.), S.P. in Economic Thought (German), S.P. in Economic Thought (France), S.P. in Economic Thought (China), S.P. in Economic Geography, S.P. in Economic Location, S.P. in Environmental Economics, S.P. in Economic Policy, S.P. in Foreign Trade Policy, S.P. in Industrial Policy, S.P. in Agricultural Policy, S.P. in Development Economics, Labor Economics, S.P. in Public Finance, S.P. in Taxation Theory, S.P. in Local Finance, S.P. in Public Economics. Note: S.P. is an abbreviation of Special Problems

Graduate School of Law(M 33/13, D 36/11)

Div. of Specialized Course in Economic and Private Law(M 14/6, D 7/4)

Legal History, Philosophy of Law, Foreign Law, Comparative Legal Institutions, Constitutional Law, Comparative Constitutional Law, Administrative Law, Tax of Law, International Law, International Politics, International Organizations, Diplomatic History, Civil Law, Civil Procedure, Conflict of Laws, Commercial Law, Public Control of Business, Labor Law, Criminal Law, Criminal Procedure, Criminology

Div. of Specialized Course in Public Law and International Relations(M 19/7, D 29/7)

Legal History, Philosophy of Law, Foreign Law, Comparative Legal Institutions, Constitutional Law, Comparative Constitutional Law, Administrative Law, Tax of Law, International Law, International Politics, International Organizations, Diplomatic History, Civil Law, Civil Procedure, Conflict of Laws, Commercial Law, Public Control of Business, Labor Law, Criminal Law, Criminal Procedure, Criminology

Graduate School of Research Course in Social Studies(M 49/18, D 95/21)

Div. of Specialized Course in Sociology(M 18/3, D 39/4)

Social Thought, Sociology, Social Psychology, Politics, Educational Sociology, Social Policy, Social History, Social Geography/Social Anthropology

Div. of Specialized Course in Social Problems and Social Policies(M 19/12, D 20/7)

Social Thought, Sociology, Social Psychology, Politics, Educational Sociology, Social Policy, Social History, Social Geography/Social Anthropology

Div. of Specialized Course in Socio-Cultural Area Studies(M 12/3, D 36/10)

Social Thought, Sociology, Social Psychology, Politics, Educational Sociology, Social Policy, Social History, Social Geography/Social Anthropology

---

茨城大学

(Ibaraki Daigaku)

Ibaraki University

2-1-1 Bunkyo, Mito-shi, Ibaraki 310
☎ 0292-26-1621

Founded 1949
Professors 222
Associate Professors 184

Assistant Professors(Tenured) 36
Assistant Professors(Non-tenured) 357
Research Assistants 64
Undergraduate Students/Foreign Students 6, 360/118
Graduate Students/Foreign Students 337/27
Library 663, 593 volumes
Contact: Admission Office

Educational philosophy We believe that at least the undergraduate students should be trained in basic disciplines rather than in advanced specialized subjects. We also believe that students' personal contacts with teachers are important in higher education as well.
Foreign students In a very homogeneous society as ours, it is of particular importance for younger generations to get to know their foreign counterparts with totally different cultural backgrounds.
Environment The University is situated in the Kanto Plains, enjoying rural environment and consists of three campuses: Mito, Hiatachi and Ami. All campuses are located 50–150㎞ north of Tokyo. Mito city (population of 234, 000) where the main campus is located is a castle town with rich cultural heritage.
Facilities University Library, Information Processing Center, Institute of Regional Studies, Izura Institute of Arts and Culture, Center for Educational Technology, Hydrobiological Station, Experimental Farm, Swimming Pool, Gymnasium, Athletic Fields.
Student activities University festival, Freshman welcome party; extra curricular activities, including choral groups, marching bands, student newpaper, cinema fan, baseball, football, soccer, skiing and mountain climbing clubs, etc.
Academic programs for foreign students Classes of the Japanese language, and Japanese social/political/cultural conditions; tutoring system.
Services for foreign students International House for foreign students and researchers; health clinic in Health Center; cultural exchange programs (incl. parties, home visits, home stay); scholarships, exemption from school fees; part-time job information.

Undergraduate Programs

Faculty of Agriculture(542/4)
Dept. of Agricultural Production(328/3)
Dept. of Resource Biology(214/1)
Faculty of Education(1, 747/13)
Dept. of Course in Information and Culture(119/0)
Dept. of Elementary School Teachers Training Course(949/8)
Dept. of Junior High School Teachers Training Course(411/2)
Dept. of Training Course for School Nurse Teachers(181/1)
Dept. of Training Course for Teachers of Mentally Handicapped Children(87/2)
Faculty of Engineering(1, 728/47)
Dept. of Electrical and Electronic Engineering(387/14)
Dept. of Information Science(203/15)
Dept. of Materials Science(371/5)
Dept. of Mechanical Engineering(394/4)
Dept. of Systems Engineering(191/2)
Dept. of Urban and Civil Engineering(182/7)
Faculty of Humanities(1, 676/50)
Dept. of Humanities(565/16)
Dept. of Social Science(1, 109/34)
Faculty of Science(776/2)
Dept. of Biology(139/0)
Dept. of Chemistry(164/1)
Dept. of Earth Sciences(140/1)
Dept. of Mathematics(169/0)
Dept. of Physics(164/0)

Graduate Programs

Graduate School of Agriculture(M 58/4)
Major of Agricultural Chemistry(M 24/0)
Science of Soil and Manure, Biochemistry, Chemistry of Agricultural Products, Applied Microbiology, Chemistry of Agricultural Chemicals
Major of Agricultural Engineering(M 10/0)
Engineering for Land Development and Conservation, Agricultural Hydrotechnics, Agricultural Construction Engineering, Agricultural Machinery
Major of Agriculture(M 9/2)
Crop Science, Plant Breeding, Horticultural Science, Plant Pathology and Applied Entomology, Agricultural Economics, Farm Management
Major of Animal Husbandry(M 15/2)
Animal Breeding and Reproduction, Animal Hygiene, Animal Nutrition and Feeding, Feedstuffs, Chemistry and Technology of Animal Products
Graduate School of Education(M 74/4)
Major of School Education(M 19/1)
School Education
Major of Education for the Handicapped(M 7/0)
Education for the Handicapped
Major of School Subject Education(M 48/3)
Japanese Language Teaching, Social Studies Education, Science Education, Art Education, Health and Physical Education, Home Economics Education, English Language Teaching
Graduate School of Engineering(M 152/15)
Major of Mechanical Engineering(M 8/1)
Mechanical Technology, Industrial Engineering, Heat Engine, Fluid Dynamics
Major of Mechanical Engineering Ⅱ(M 19/1)
Dynamics of Machines, Machine Design, Thermal Engineering, Manufacturing Technology
Major of Electrical Engineering(M 27/3)
Fundamental Theores of Electrical Engineering, Electrical Materials, Electric Power and Electrical Measurements, Electric Machines and Instruments
Major of Metallurgy(M 18/2)
Physical Metallurgy, Extractive Metallurgy, Process Metallurgy, Metallic Materials
Major of Industrial Chemistry(M 18/2)

Analytical Chemistry, Inorganic Chemistry, Organic Chemistry, Physical Chemistry

Major of Precision Engineering(M 16/2)
Foundation and Design of Precision Engineering, Machining Processes and Materials, Precision Instruments and Instrumentation, System and Controls

Major of Electronic Engineering(M 16/1)
Basic Electronics, Electromagnetic Systems, Electronic Circuits, Applied Electronics

Major of Information Science(M 21/3)
Foundation of Information Science, Software, Hardware, System Engineering

Major of Construction Engineering(M 9/0)
Structural Engineering, Hydraulics, Soil and Material, Traffic Engineering

Graduate School of Science(M 80/5)

Major of Mathematics(M 9/0)
Algebra, Geometry, Analysis, Applied Mathematics

Major of Physics(M 17/0)
Theoretical High Energy Physics, Astrophysics, Solid-State Physics, Atomic Physics

Major of Chemistry(M 25/3)
Analytical Chemistry, Structural Chemistry, Synthetic Chemistry, Quantum Chemistry, Coordination Chemistry

Major of Biology(M 15/0)
Systematics, Physiology, Cell Biology, Ecology

Major of Earth Sciences(M 14/2)
Geochemistry, Geology, Earth and Planetary Physics, Petrology and Mineralogy

One-Year Graduate Programs

Humanity Course
Humanities Majors

Special Course for Teachers of Handicapped Children
Education for Handicapped Children Majors

お茶の水女子大学
(Ochanomizu Joshi Daigaku)

Ochanomizu University

2-1-1 Otsuka, Bunkyo-ku, Tokyo 112
☎ 03-3943-3151 FAX 03-3947-4822

Founded 1874
Professors 82
Associate Professors 65
Assistant Professors(Tenured) 19
Assistant Professors(Non-tenured) 223
Research Assistants 34
Undergraduate Students/foreign Students 2, 095/9
Graduate Students/Foreign Students 481/68
Library 483, 151 volumes
Contact: Academic Affairs Division ☎ ext. 253

Educational philosophy Our university aims to develop the students' intellectual, moral, and applicational abilities as well as to help them acquire knowledge in various fields and pursue research in their chosen areas of study. We think it is our duty to educate women who will hold leading positions and devote themselves to cultural development in the new age.

Foreign students You will have many valuable experiences which will help you understand other cultures and ways of thinking and thereby promote mutual understanding. We believe that you will be able to develop friendship with Japanese and foreign students on the campus.

Environment Bunkyo-ku, where the university is located, is in the center of Tokyo. However, the university is in a quiet residential area. There are many schools around the university. Ikebukuro, one of the busiest shopping areas in Tokyo, is only a five-minute ride on the subway from the university.

Facilities University Library, Information Processing Center, University Gymnasium, Swimming Pool, Health Care Center, Student Hall, Student Club House, Dining Hall

Student activities Events: university's festival, foreign students social gathering, excursion, athletic meet Circles: flower arrangement, tea ceremony, chorus groups, orchestra, art, photography/tennis, kendo, archery, basketball, japanese dancing

Academic programs for foreign students Supplementary Japanese language classes, Tutoring system

Services for foreign students Health clinic, personal/psychological counseling

Undergraduate Programs

Faculty of Home Economics(630/4)
Dept. of Child Study(175/3)
Dept.of Food and Nutrition(150/0)
Dept. of Home Life Administration(142/1)
Dept. of Textiles and Clothing(163/0)

Faculty of Letters and Education(990/5)
Dept. of Dance and Music Education (Dancing) (75/0)
Dept. of Dance and Music Education (Music) (59/0)
Dept. of Education (Education) (101/2)
Dept. of Education (Psychology) (79/2)
Dept. of Foreign Literature (Chinese) (54/0)
Dept. of Foreign Literature (English) (142/0)
Dept. of Foreign Literature (French) (43/0)
Dept. of Geography(91/0)
Dept. of History(99/0)
Dept. of Japanese Literature(141/1)
Dept. of Philosophy(106/0)

Faculty of Science(475/0)
Dept. of Biology(113/0)
Dept. of Chemistry(107/0)
Dept. of Information Sciences(41/0)
Dept. of Mathematics(104/0)
Dept. of Physics(110/0)

Graduate Programs

Graduate-School of Home Economics(M 73/7)
Div. of Child Study(M 17/0)
Div. of Food and Nutrition(M 27/1)
Div. of Home Life Administration(M 73/2)
Div. of Textiles and Clothing(M 15/4)
Graduate-School of Humanities(M 197/35)
Div. of Chinese Literature(M 9/0)
Div. of Dance and Music Education(M 40/2)
Div. of Education (including Psychology) (M 43/12)
Div. of English Literature(M 20/0)
Div. of Geography(M 8/0)
Div. of History(M 21/4)
Div. of Japanese Literature(M 35/14)
Div. of Philosophy(M 21/3)
Graduate School of Science(M 67/2)
Div. of Biology(M 25/1)
Div. of Chemistry(M 19/0)
Div. of Mathematics(M 7/0)
Div. of Physics(M 16/1)
Graduate-School of Human Culture(D 144/24)
Div. of Comparative Culture(D 101/16)
Div. of Human Development(D 31/5)
Div. of Human Environment(D 12/2)

埼玉大学
(Saitama Daigaku)
Saitama University

255 Shimo-Okubo, Urawa-Shi, Saitama 338
☎ 048-852-2111 FAX 048-855-0626

Founded 1949
Professors 203
Associate Professors 173
Assistant Professors(Tenured) 20
Assistant Professors(Non-tenured) 530
Research Assistants 49
Undergraduate Students/Foreign Students 6, 359/38
Graduate Students/Foreign Students 495/81
Library 556, 234 volumes
Contact: Admissions Office

Educational philosophy We promote creative research works and education to cultivate men of talent through many excellent staffs and the distinctive organization of the faculties. In particular, our graduate schools are taken notice of, having extraordinary characteristics.
Foreign students We provide various programs, both in theory and practice, to bring up foreign students having enough knowledge promptly adaptable to further development of their home countries.
Environment Urawa City, developing as one of satellite cities around Tokyo, is well known as a pleasant cultural city. Though being distant only 30 kilometers to the north from Tokyo, there still remains much beautiful nature in the nice and quiet circumstance.
Facilities Institute for Policy Science, Chemical Analysis Center, Information Processing Center, University Library, University Hall, Health Service Center, Gymnasium, Swimming pool, etc..
Student activities Annual University festival, Foreign Students Welcome Party and many kinds of extra curricular activities; Judo, Karate, Japanese Fencing, Baseball, Gymnastics, Track and Field Athletics, Chorus, Flower Arrangement, Tea Ceremony, Wind Music, etc..
Academic programs for foreign students Additional courses in Japanese Language and Japanese Students are offered for undergraduate students from abroad. Tutoring system.
Services for foreign students Health clinic, International House, housing information, part-time job information.

Undergraduate Programs

Faculty of Economics(913/10)
Dept. of Economics(167/0)
Dept. of Business(301/6)
Faculty of Education(2, 274/6)
Dept. of Training Course for Primary School Teachers(1, 326/1)
Dept. of Training Course for Junior High School Teachers(582/1)
Dept. of Training Course for Teachers of Schools for the Handicapped (especially for the mentally handicapped) (86/1)
Dept. of Training Course for Kindergarten Teachers(122/1)
Dept. of Adult Education Course(158/2)
Faculty of Engineering(1, 706/24)
Dept. of Applied Chemistry(391/4)
Dept. of Construction Engineering(202/4)
Dept. of Electrical Engineering(191/4)
Dept. of Electronic Engineering(190/2)
Dept. of Environmental Chemistry(391/4)
Dept. of Foundation Engineering(203/1)
Dept. of Information and Computer Sciences (119/3)
Dept. of Mechanical Engineering(410/6)
Faculty of Liberal Arts(624/3)
Dept. of Liberal Arts(624/3)
Faculty of Science(842/1)
Dept. of Biochemistry(147/1)
Dept. of Chemistry(186/0)
Dept. of Mathematics(188/0)
Dept. of Physics(184/0)
Dept. of Regulation Biology(137/0)

Graduate Programs

Graduate School of Cultural Science(M 39/14)
Div. of Course in the Science of Linguistic Culture(M 21/8)

Linguistics, Comparative Literature, American Literature, British Literature, German Literature, French Literature

Div. of Course in the Science of Social Culture (M 18/6)

Theory of Man, History of Cultural Exchange, History of Ancient Japan, Theory of Mass Media, International Law

Graduate School of Education(M 53/3)

Div. of School Education Course(M 20/1)

Philosophy of Education, History of Education, Sociology of Methodology, Educational Administraton, Educational Psychology, Developmental Psychology, Education for the Handicapped, Early Childhood Education

Div. of School Subject Education Culture(M 33/2)

Japanese Language Education, Social Studies Education, Mathematics Education, Science Education, Music Education, Fine Arts Education, Physical Education, English Language Education

Graduate School of Policy Science(M 72/33)

Div. of Policy Science(M 72/33)

Introduction to Policy Science, Political Science, Economics, Infromation/Mathematical Science, Agricultural Policy, Industrial and Trade Policy, Fiscal and Monetary Policy, National Land Development Policy, Labor Policy, Local Pubilc Administraton Policy, Modern Science and Technoloty, Science and Technology Policy, Mathematical Statistics, Stochastic Processes, International Politics and Foreign Affairs, Decision-making Processes, Macroeconomics, Regional Economics, Administrative Sciences

Graduate School of Science and Engineering (M 245/20, D 0/0)

Div. of Applied Chemistry Course(M 31/2)

Advanced Engineering Physical Chemistry, Advanced Industrial Organic Chemistry, Advanced Industrial Inorganic Chemistry, Advanced Synthetic Organic Chemistry

Div. of Construction Engineering Course(M 11/0)

Advanced Seismology, Advanced Lectures on Construction Materials, Advanced Course in Transportation Engineering, Earthquake Engineering

Div. of Course in Biochemistry(M 17/0)

Advanced Cell Biochemistry, Advanced Bioenergetics and Enzymology, Advanced Biochemistry of Biological Substances, Advanced Molecular Biology, Photosynthesis

Div. of Course in Chemistry(M 19/1)

Advanced Quantum Chemistry, Advanced Physical Chemistry, Advanced Coordination Chemistry, Advanced Organic Chemistry, Advanced Chemistry of Natural Products

Div. of Course in Mathematics(M 14/0)

Advanced Analysis, Advanced Geometry, Advanced Algebra

Div. of Course in Physics(M 13/0)

Theory of Gravitational Field, Theory of Elementary Particles, Experimental Nuclear Physics, Advanced Solid State Physics

Div. of Course in Regulation Biology(M 14/0)

Advanced Plant Morphogenesis, Advanced Genetics, Advanced Developmental Biology, Advanced Endocrinology

Div. of Electoronic Engineering Course(M 23/5)

Advanced Magnetic Engineering, Advanced Optoelectronics, Advanced Electronic Circuits, Advanced Principle on Non-Linear Circuits

Div. of Electrical Engineering Course(M 32/4)

Advanced Plasma Physics, Advanced Power System Engineering, Advanced Theory of Electric Machine, Advanced Space and Radio Engineering

Div. of Environmental Chemistry Course(M 21/3)

Environmental Biopysics, Advanced Environmental Analytical Chemistry, Advanced Lecture on the Chemistry and Engineering of Environmental Purification, Advanced Environmental Chemical Process

Div. of Foundation Engineering Course(M 9/0)

Advanced Soil Mechanics, Advanced Hydraulics, Advanced Rock Mechanics, Advanced Structural Engineering

Graduate School of Science and Engineering(D 81/11)

Div. of Course in Biological and Environmental Sciences(D 23/3)

Bioorganic Molecular Functions, Regulation of Biological Informations, Environmental Science

Div. of Course in Material Sciences(D 29/4)

Mathematics and Theoretical Physics, Solid-State Physics and Chemistry, Molecular Functions

Div. of Course in Production and Information Sciences
(D 29/4)

Electronics and Communications, Designing and Evaluation, Science of Production Systems, Science of Production Foundation

---

東京学芸大学

(Tokyo Gakugei Daigaku)

Tokyo Gakugei University

4-1-1 ,Nukui-Kitamachi, Koganei-shi, Tokyo 184
☎ 0423-25-2111 FAX 0423-24-6509

Founded 1949
Professors 146
Associate Professors 158
Assistant Professors(Tenured) 32
Assistant Professors(Non-tenured) 253
Research Assistants 32
Undergraduate Students/Foreign Students 5, 331/10
Graduate Students/Foreign Students 403/114
Library 768, 519 volumes
Contact: Foreign Students Section, Students Affairs Division
☎ ext. 2260

Educational philosophy We aim at giving the students the necessary academic background and training to become competent teachers equipped with highly specialized knowledge and ability.

Foreign students We believe that foreign students can enjoy a rewarding experience in our school, and can contribute a great deal to promoting mutual understanding and the development of friendly relations, especially in education spheres.

Environment Tokyo Gakugei University is located in Koganei-city in Tokyo. It takes about 50 minutes from downtown Tokyo by the Chuo Line (Higashi Nihon Railway Company) and local bus. Located almost in the middle of Japan. Tokyo's climate is mild and warm throughout the year.

Facilities Library, Health Service Center for Education of Children Overseas, Center for Educaton Technology, Research Institute for Education of Exceptional Children, Field Students Institute, Athletic Field, Swimming Pool, Gymnasium

Student activities There are a lot of big events in our university. For example, freshmen welcome picnic, Koganei festival, ski school, etc.

And club activities are very popular in our university, so many students enjoy many kinds of sports and can develop their interests.

Academic programs for foreign students Tutoring system, Supplemental Japanese language course.

Services for foreign students Health clinic, personal/psychological counseling, Housing information, part-time job information, Home stay, Home visit

Undergraduate Programs

Faculty of Education(5, 331/10)

Dept. of Applied Social Sciences(147/1)
Dept. of Art Education(246/1)
Dept. of Asian Studies(61/0)
Dept. of Calligraphy(35/0)
Dept. of Cultural Asset Sciences(66/0)
Dept. of Educational Informatics(120/1)
Dept. of Education of Handicapped Children (205/0)
Dept. of Engineering Education(58/0)
Dept. of English Education(92/0)
Dept. of Environmental Sciences(123/0)
Dept. of European and American Studies(60/1)
Dept. of Fine Arts(62/0)
Dept. of Health and Physical Education(406/0)
Dept. of Home Economics Education(131/0)
Dept. of International Education Studies(50/0)
Dept. of Japan Studies(111/1)
Dept. of Japanese Education(626/0)
Dept. of Kindergarten Education(101/2)
Dept. of Lifelong Education(81/1)
Dept. of Lifelong Sports(137/2)
Dept. of Mathematics Education(591/0)
Dept. of Music(58/0)
Dept. of Music Education(234/0)
Dept. of Remedial Application of Psychology (92/0)
Dept. of School Education(224/0)
Dept. of Science Education(604/0)
Dept. of Social Studies Education(514/0)
Dept. of Special Subjects Education (Calligraphy) (96/0)

Graduate Programs

Graduate School of Education(M 403/114)

Div. of School Education(M 65/24)
Pedagogy, Educational Methods, History of Education, School Administration, Social Education, Educational Psychology, Developmental Psychology, Clinical Psychology, Moral Education, Childhood Education

Div. of Mathematics Education(M 18/1)
Analysis and Applied Mathematics, Algebra and Geometry, Teaching of Mathematics

Div. of Science Education(M 37/10)
Physics, Chemistry, Biology, Astronomy and Earth Science, Teaching of Science

Div. of English Education(M 20/4)
English, English and American Literature, Teaching of English

Div. of Japanese Education(M 47/23)
Japanese Language, Japanese Literature, Chinese Classics, Teaching of Japanese

Div. of Social Studies Education(M 55/15)
History, Geography, Law and Political Science, Economics, Sociology, Philosophy and Ethics, Teaching of Social Studies

Div. of Music Education(M 37/1)
Instrumental Music, Singing, Composition and Conducting, Musicology, Teaching of Music

Div. of Art Education(M 33/7)
Drawing and Painting, Sculpture, Design, Craft, Formative Arts and Drama, Teaching of Art, Calligraphy

Div. of Health and Physical Education(M 42/16)
Physical Education, Methods of Physical Activity, School Health Education, Teaching of Health and Physical Education

Div. of Home Economics Education(M 9/3)
Food and Nutrition, Clothing and Textile, Child Development and Childcare, Home Economics and Dwelling, Teaching of Home Economics

Div. of Engineering Education(M 12/6)
Electricity, Machine, Teaching of Engineering

Div. of Education of Handicapped Children(M 28/4)
Education of Handicapped Children, Physiology and Physiology of Handicapped Children, Development of Handicapped Children, Clinical Studies of Handicapped Children, Teaching Methods of Handicapped Children

One-Year Graduate Programs

Special Education Course
Education of the mentally retarded Major

東京工業大学
(Tokyo Kôgyô Daigaku)
Tokyo Institute of Technology

2-12-1 Ookayama, Meguro-ku, Tokyo 152
☎ 03-3726-1111 Fax 03-3727-2007

Founded 1881
Professors 278
Associate Professors 262
Assistant Professors(Tenured) 14
Assistant Professors(Non-tenured) 242
Research Assistants 416
Undergraduate Students/Foreign Students 4, 927/47
Graduate Students/Foreign Students 2, 415/291
Library 646, 099 volumes
Contact: Foreign Student Affairs Section

Educational philosophy Tokyo Institute of Technology is the leading institution of higher education in the fields of science and engineering in Japan. With the aim of educating the whole person, the Institute emphasizes both technical and liberal arts in order to prepare its students to be educators, researchers, engineers, and leaders.
Foreign students The Institute welcomes applications from all qualified international students. Currently, nearly 500 international students from 36 different countries are enrolled in undergraduate and graduate courses, and other study programs.
Environment The main campus at Ookayama, located just outside of central Tokyo, offers both spaciousness and close proximity to Tokyo's many activities and cultural facilities. A second campus in Nagatsuta, Yokohama is situated among green, wooded hills, yet is still within access of downtown areas.
Facilities Institute Library, Computer Center including CDC supercomputer, Education Center for Foreign Students, Health Service Center, sports training center, auditorium, and numerous research and experiment centers.
Student activities Annual events include the university fair, and international student sightseeing trip. Extra-curricular clubs are available to meet nearly every interest, including popular and classical music, visual and performing arts, language, science, hobbies, and numerous sports activities.
Academic programs for foreign students Supplemental Japanese language classes, classes on Japanese society and culture, tutoring for new students.
Services for foreign students Personal counseling, health clinic, university dormitories, housing information, cultural exchange programs, and so forth.

Undergraduate Programs

Faculty of Science(/5)
Dept. of Applied Physics(/0)
Dept. of Biological Sciences(/0)
Dept. of Chemistry(/1)
Dept. of Information Sciences(/2)
Dept. of Life Science(/2)
Dept. of Physics(/0)
Dept. of Mathematics(/0)
Faculty of Engineering(/42)
Dept. of Architecture and Building(/1)
Dept. of Bioengineering(/3)
Dept. of Biomolecular Engineering(/0)
Dept. of Chemical Engineering(/5)
Dept. of Civil Engineering(/0)
Dept. of Computer Science(/6)
Dept. of Control Engineering(/5)
Dept. of Electrical and Electronic Engineering(/12)
Dept. of Industrical Engineering and Management(/7)
Dept. of Inorganic Materials(/0)
Dept. of Mechanical Engineering(/0)
Dept. of Mechanical Engineering for Production(/0)
Dept. of Mechanical Engineering Science(/0)
Dept. of Metallurgical Engineering(/0)
Dept. of Organic and Polymeric Materials(/0)
Dept. of Physical Electronics(/2)
Dept. of Polymer Chemistry(/0)
Dept. of Social Engineering(/1)

Graduate Programs

Interdisciplinarly Graduate School of Science and Engineering(M 1230/93, D 374/123)
Div. of Applied Physics(M 46/2, D 13/1)
Advanced Course of Radiation Chemistry, Advanced Experiments on Applied Physics, Advanced Probability Theory, Applied Nuclear Physics, Applied Probability Theory, Applied Solid State Physics, Applied Spectroscopy, Colloquium in Applied Physics, Electric and Magnetic Properties of Solids, Exercises in Applied Physics, Fluctuation Phenomena, Functional Analysis, Geophysics, Geochemistry, Low Temperature Physics, Modern Problems in Optics, Nonequilibrium Statistical Physics, Nuclear Spectroscopy, Optical Properties of Matter, Physical Properties of Semiconductors, Physics of High Temperature and High Pressure, Planetary Physics, Principles of Direct Energy Conversion, Radiation Effects on Matter, Seismology, Seminar in Applied Physics, Special Lecture on Applied Physics, Theory of Brownian Motion, Theory of Geomagnetism and Geoelectricity, Theory of Stochastic Processes
Div. of Architecture and Building Engineering(M 69/8, D 8/5)
Architectural Design, Architectural Drawing, Architectural Planning, Building Engineering Laboratory, Building Environmental Engineering Laboratory, Building Equipment, Building Materials, City Planning, Colloquium in

Architecture and Buildng Engineering, Dynamic Analysis on Structures, Environmental Pollution Control Engineering, Exercise in Architecural Planning, Exercise in City Planning, Fire Resisting Structures, Foundation Engineering, Geotechnical Engineering, History of Architecture, Landscape Architecture, Man Environment System Engineering, Manufactured Buildings, Reinforced Concrete Structures, Seminar in Architecutire and Building Engineering, Special Lecture in Architecture and Building Engineering, Steel Structures, Visual Design in Architecture

Div. of Bioengineering(M 30/3, D 0/0)
Biochemical Engineering, Biochemical Process Engineering, Biophysical Chemistry, Biophysics, Biopolymer Chemistry, Chemical Engineering and Industrial Chemistry Laboratory, Cytoengineering, Enzyme Engineering, Exercise on Information Processing, Fundamentals of Bioengineering, Genetic Engineering, Microbial Engineering, Molecular Biology, Organic Chemistry, Physical Chemistry

Div. of Chemical Engineering(M 100/7, D 45/7)
Advanced Bioengineering, Advanced Chemical Engineering Analysis, Advanced Chemical Engineering Planning, Advanced Chemical Equipment Design, Advanced Chemical Reaction Engineering, Advanced Chemical Reactor Design, Advanced Chemical Thermodynamics, Advanced Course of Ceramics, Advanced Course of Mining Industry, Advanced Hear Transfer Operations, Advanced Industrial Chemistry, Organic, Advanced Inorganic Chemistry, Advanced Industrial Chemistry, Advanced Mass Transfer Operations, Advanced Mechanical Separation and Mixing, Advanced Physical Chemistry of Polymers, Advanced Polymer Chemistry, Advanced Process Engineering, Advanced Separation Processes, Advanced Surface Chemistry, Advanced Synthetic Chemistry, Organic, Advanced Transport Phenomena, Biochemical Engineering, Biochemical Reaction Engineering, Biochemical Process, Chemical Kinetics

Div. of Chemical Engineering(M 100/7, D 45/7)
Colloquium in Chemical Engineering, Electronics for Engineering Materials, Fine Chemical Syntheses, Inorganic Reaction Mechanisms, Introduction to Bioengineering, Introduction to Magnetic Resonance, Petroleum Chemistry, Physical Organic Chemistry, Reactivity of Solids, Rheology, Seminar in Chemical Engineering, Special Experiments of Inorganic Materials, Chemical Engineering, and Polymer Science, Special Lecture on Chemical Engineering, Special Lecture on Engineering Inorganic Materials, Solid State Reaction, Structural Inorganic Chemistry, Theory of Catalysis, Topics in Polymer Science

Div. of Chemistry(M 89/1, D 34/2)
Advanced Analytical Chemistry, Advanced Biological Chemistry, Advanced Course of Biophysics, Advanced Course of Developmental Biochemistry, Advanced Course of Radiation Chemistry, Advanced Geochemistry, Advanced Inorganic Chemistry, Advanced Molecular Spectroscopy, Advanced Organic Chemistry, Advanced Physical Chemistry, Colloquium in Chemistry, Directed Laboratory Work in Chemistry, Laboratory Work in Inorganic and Analytical Chemistry, Laboratory Work in Organic and Analytical Chemistry, Laboratory Work in Organic Chemistry, Laboratory Work in Physical Chemistry, Recent Progresses in Chemistry, Seminar in Chemistry

Div. of Civil Engineering(M 37/2, D 6/2)
Advanced Concrete Technology, Advanced Course Landscape Enginnering, Advanced Course of Regional Planning, Advanced River Engineering, Advanced Reinforced Concrete Engineering, Advanced Structural Mechanics, Advanced Theory of Soil Mechanics, Advanced Transportation Planning, Anti-Seismic Design of Structures, Civil Engineering Analysis, Durability and Maintenance of Structure, Earthquake Engineering, Financial Analysis for Infrastructure Planning, Finite Element Method, Investment for Pubilc Facility, Marine Geotechnology, National Infrastructure Planning, Probabilistic Concepts in Engineering Design, Rock Mechanics, Theory and Design of Steel Structures, Water Disaster Prevention, Water Pollution Control, Water Resources Planning, Wave Hydrodynamics, Wind and Atmospheric Engineering

Div. of Computer Science(M 49/7, D 24/11)
Advanced Coding Theory, Advanced Communication System Engineering, Advanced Educational Technology, Advanced Electric Power Engineering, Advanced Electrical Properties of Matter, Advanced Electromagnetic Engineering, Advanced Electron Devices, Advanced High Speed Electron Devices, Advanced High-Voltage Engineering, Advanced Microwave Circuits, Advanced Software Engineering, Applied Graph Theory, Analytical Theory of Image Processing, Colloquium on Computer Science, Colloquium on Electrical and Electronic Engineering, Colloquium on Physical Electronics, Computer Systems Evaluation, Crystal Physics and its Application, Design Theory of Electron Devices, Fault-Tolerant Systems, Fundamentals of Signal Analysis, Foundations of Computing Environments, Information Transmission Theory, Laser Engineering, Light Waveguides, Lightwave Semiconductor Devices, Logic and Software Machine Intelligence, Methods and Techniques in Pattern Recognition, Modern Circuit Theory, Muitl-Dimensional Signal Processing, Natural Language Processing, Optical and Quantum Electronics, Optical Communications, Plasma Engineering Power Electronics, Precision Time and Frequency Engineering, Processor Systems, Seminar on Computer Science, Seminar on Electrical and Electronic Engineering, Seminar on Physical Electronics, Sensing Devices. Signal Noise in Electron Devices, Special Experiments on Computer Science, Special Experiments on Electrical and Electronic Engineering, Special Experiments on Physical Electronics, Special Lecture on Computer Science, Special Lecture on Electrical and Electronic Engineering, Special Lecture on Physical Electronics, Structure of Programming Languages, Surface Acoustic Wave Engineering, Theory of Asynchronous Concurrent Systems, Theory of Electronic Circuits, Theory of Software Structures, Ultrasonic Engineering, Ultrasonic Instrumentaion, Visual Communication Engineering

Div. of Control Engineering(M 39/3, D 9/7)
Advanced Experiments in Industrial Engineering and Management, Advanced Managerial Mathematics Advanced Managerial Operations Research, Advanced Planned Financial Management, Advanced Process Management, Advanced Production Control, Advanced Quality Control, Advanced Separation Process, Colloquium in Industrial Engineering and Management, Information System in Organization, Mathematical Bio-engineering, Methodology in System Engineering, Organization Engineering, Seminar in Industrial Engineering and Management, Special Lecture on Industrial Engineering and Management, System Theory, Topics in System Optimization

Div. of Electrical and Electronic Engineering(M 110/17, D 34/10)
Advanced Coding Theory, Advanced Communication System Engineering, Advanced Educational Technology, Advanced Electric Power Engineering, Advanced Electrical Properties of Matter, Advanced Electromagnetic Engineering, Advanced Electron Devices, Advanced High Speed Electron Devices, Advanced High-Voltage Engineering, Advanced Microwave Circuits, Advanced Software Engineering, Applied Graph Theory, Analytical Theory of Image Processing, Colloquium on Computer Science, Colloquium on Electrical and Electronic Engineering, Colloquium on Physical Electronics, Computer Systems Evaluation, Crystal Physics and its Application, Design Theory of Electron Devices, Fault-Tolerant Systems, Fundamentals of Signal Analysis, Foundations of Computing Environments, Information Transmission Theory, Laser Engineering, Light Waveguides, Lightwave Semiconductor Devices, Logic and Software Machine Intelligence, Methods and Techniques in Pattern Recognition, Modern Circuit Theory, Multi-Dimensional Signal Processing, Natural Language Processing, Optical and Quantum Electronics, Optical Communications, Plasma Engineering, Power Electronics, Precision Time and Frequency Engineering, Processor Systems, Seminar on Computer Science, Seminar on Electrical and Electronic Engineering, Seminar on Physical Electronics, Sensing Devices, Signal Noise in Electron Devices, Special Experiments on Computer Science, Special Experiments on Electrical and Electronic Engineering, Special Experiments on Physical Electronics, Special Lecture on Computer Science, Special Lecture on Electrical and Electronic Engineering, Special Lecture on Physical Electronics, Structure of Programming Languages, Surface Acoustic Wave Engineering, Theory of Asynchronous Concurrent Systems, Theory of Electronic Circuits, Theory of Software Structures, Ultrasonic Engineering, Ultrasonic Instrumentation, Visual Communication Engineering

Div. of Industrial Engineering and Management (M 34/0, D 10/7)
Advanced Experiments in Industrial Engineering and Management, Advanced Managerial Mathematics, Advanced Managerial Operations Research, Advanced Planned Financial Management, Advanced Process Management, Advanced Production Control, Advanced Quality Control, Advanced Separation Process, Colloquium in Industrial Engineering and Management, Information System in Organization, Mathematical Bio-engineering, Methodology in System Engineering, Organization Engineering, Seminar in Industrial Engineering and Management, Special Lecture on Industrial Engineering and Management, System Theory, Topics in System Optimization

Div. of Information Science(M 36/1, D 13/1)
Advanced Course of Game Theory, Advanced Couse on Mathematical Statistics, Advanced Exercises in Information Science, Advanced Experiments on Information Science, Advanced Lectures on Combinatorial Theory, Advanced Lectures on Computational Processes, Advanced Lectures on Information Mathematics, Advanced Lectures on Mathematical Programming, Advanced Theory of Information Science, Applied Game Theory, Applied Probability, Colloquium in Information Science, Foundations of Software, Human Factors in software Development, Mathematical Methods in Operations Research, Special Lectures on Information Science, Time Series Analysis, Topics in Formal Language Studies, Theory of Knowledge Representation, User Interfaces of Computer Systems

Div. of Inorganic Materials(M 36/0, D 15/6)
Advanced Bioengineering, Advanced Chemical Engineering Analysis, Advanced Chemical Engineering Planning, Advanced Chemical Equipment Design, Advanced Chemical Reaction Engineering, Advanced Chemical Reactor Design, Advanced Chemical Thermodynamics, Advanced Course of Ceramics, Advanced Course of Mining Industry, Advanced Hear Transfer Operations, Advanced Industrial Chemistry, Organic, Advanced Inorganic Chemistry, Advanced Industrial Chemistry, Advanced Mass Transfer Operations, Advanced Mechanical Separation and Mixing, Advanced Physical Chemistry of Polymers, Advanced Polymer Chemistry, Advanced Process Engineering, Advanced Separation Processes, Advanced Surface Chemistry, Advanced Synthetic Chemistry, Organic, Advanced Transport Phenomena, Biochemical Engineering, Biochemical Reaction Engineering, Biochemical Process, Chemical Kinetics, Colloquium in Chemical Engineering, Electronics for Engineering Materials, Fine Chemical Syntheses, Inorganic Reaction Mechanisms, Introduction to Bioengineering, Introduction to Magnetic Resonance, Petroleum Chemistry, Physical Organic Chemistry, Reactivity of Solids, Rheology, Seminar in Chemical Engineering, Special Experiments of Inorganic Materials, Chemical Engineering, and Polymer Science, Special Lecture on Chemical Engineering, Special Lecture on Engineering Inorganic Materials, Solid State Reaction, Structural Inorganic Chemistry, Theory of Catalysis, Topics in Polymer Science

Div. of Life Science(M 32/1)
Bioorganic Chemistry, Biophysical Chemistry, Cellular and Molecular Biology, Chemistry of Biomolecules, Enzyme Chemistry, Exercise in Bioorganic Chemistry, Exercise in Biophysical Chemistry, Experimental Methods in Life Science, General Biochemistry, General Life Sci-

ence, Hormonal Biology, Human Life Science, Microbial Physiology, Molecular Developmental Biology, Modlecular Genetics, Molecular Physiology, Life Science Laboratory Courses

Div. of Mathematics(M 22/0, D 12/0)
Advanced Algebra, Advanced Probability and Statistics, Algebraic Functions, Algebraic Topology, Analytic Theory of Differential Equations, Colloquium in Mathematics, Differentiable Manifolds, Differential Geometry, Functional Analysis, Functions of Complex Variables, Seminars in Mathematics, Special Lectures in Geometry, Special Lectures in Analysis, Special Lectures on Applied Mathematics, Special Lectures on Mathematics, Special Lectures on Statistics, Theory of Lie Groups, Theory of Numbers

Div. of Mechanical Engineering(M 78/6, D 17/13)
Advanced Course of Combustion Science, Advanced Course of Continuum Mechanics, Advanced Course of Dynamics of Machinery, Advanced Course of Elasticity, Advanced Course of Engineering Mechanics, Advanced Course of Fluid Mechanics, Advanced Course of Manufacturing Processes, Advanced Course of Mechanical Technology, Advanced Course of Mechanics of Plastic Solids, Advanced Course of Processing, Advanced Course of Strength Design, Advanced Course of Strength of Materials, Advanced Course of Theory of Mechanical Systems, Advanced course of Thermal Engineering, Advanced Course of Vibrations, Advanced Engineering Analysis, Advanced Fracture Mechanics, Advanced Kinematics of Machinery, Advanced Thermo–Fluid Mechanics, Colloquium in Mechanical Engineering, Controlled Nuclear Fusion Engineering, Energy Conversion Engineering, Finite Element Analysis, Fluid Control Systems, Seminar in Mechanical Engineering, Special Drawing of Machine Design, Special Experiments of Mechanical Engineering, Special Lecture on Fundamental Mechanical Engineering, Special Lecture on Mechanical Engineering, Theory of Mechanical Information Design

Div. of Mechanical Engineering Science(M 46/1, D 9/5)
Advanced Colloquium in Mechanical Engineering Science, Advanced Course in Dynamics of Machinery, Advanced Course in Elasticity, Advanced Course in Mechanics of Plastic Solids, Advanced Course of Combustion Science, Advanced Course of Continuum Mechanics, Advanced Course of Engineering Mechanics, Advanced Course of Manufacturing Processes, Advanced Course of Mechanical Engineering Science, Advanced Course of Mechanical Information and Systems, Advanced Course of Mechanics of Processing, Advanced Course of Strength Design, Advanced Course of Theory of Mechanical System, Advanced Course of Vibration, Advanced Design and Illustration of Mechanical Engineering Science, Advanced Engineering Analysis, Advanced Fluid Mechanics, Advanced Fracture Mechanics, Advanced Kinematics of Machinery, Advanced Lecture on Mechanical Engineering Science, Advanced Mechanical Engineering Science Laboratory, Advanced Thermal Engineering, Advanced Thermofluid Mechanics, Colloquium in Mechanical Engineering Science, Controlled Nuclear Fusion Engineering, Energy Conversion Engineering, Finite Element Analysis, Fluid Control Systems, Seminar in Mechanical Engineering Science, Special Lecture on Fundamental Mechanical Engineering

Div. of Mechanical Engineering for Production(M 36/5, D 4/3)
Advanced Course of Engineering Materical Science, Advanced Course of Lubrication Engineering, Advanced Course of Machine Tool, Advanced Course of Medical Engineering, Advanced Course of Precision Machinery, Advanced Course of Strength and Mechanical Behavior of Materials, Advanced Course of Strength of Materials, Advanced Course of Tribology, Advanced Heat Transfer, Binding and Transmission, Colloquium in Mechanical Engineering for Production, Precision Instrumentation, Precision Mechanical Working Systems, Seminar in Mechanical Engineering for Producition, Special Experiments of Mechanical Engineering for Production, Special Lecture on Mechanical Engineering for Production, Theoly of Machine Design Automata, Ultimate Technology

Div. of Metallurgical Engineering(M 37/2, D 17/5)
Advanced Laboratory Work in Metallurgy, Colloquium in Metallurgical Engineering, Corrosion and Passivity of Metals, Crystal Technology, Diffraction Crystallography, Electrosolidification, Fracture in Solids, Functional Coatings, Lattice Imperfections in Solids, Materials Design, Materials for Special Use, Phase Stability in Metals and Alloys, Phase Transformations in Metals and Alloys, Physical Chemistry of Oxides at High Temperature and Electronic Materials, Physical Metallurgy, Seminar in Metallurgical Engineerring, Solidification of Metals and Alloys, Special Lecture on Metallurgical Engineerring, Strength of Materials and Crystal Defects, Structure and Properties of Non–Ferrous Materials, Structure and Properties of Steels and Superallys

Div. of Nuclear Engineering(M 57/4, D 15/3)
Accelerator Physics, Advanced Course of Isotope Separation, Advanced Course of Nuclear Reactor Theory, Colloquium in Nuclear Engineering, Energy Systems, Fracture of Nuclear Materials, Materials for Nuclear Reactors, Neutron Physics, Nuclear Chemical Engineering, Nuclear Chemistry, Nuclear Engineering Laboratory, Nuclear Fuels, Nuclear Fluid Mechanics, Nuclear Radiation, Generation and Detection, Nuclear Reactor Design, Nuclear Reactor Kinetics and Control, Nuclear Reactor Theory, Nuclear Safety Engineering, Plasma Engineering, Radiation Physics, Radiation Protection, Radio–and Radiation–Chemistry, Reactor Heat Engineering, Regulations on Atomic Energy, Seminar in Nuclear Engineering, Special Lecture on Nuclear Engineering

Div. of Organic and Polymeric Materials(M 39/0, D 19/9)
Advanced Course in Chemistry of Textile and Polymeric Materials, Advanced Course in Physics of Textile and Polymeric Matericals, Advanced Course in Processing for Polymeric Materials, Advanced Course of Functional

Materials, Advanced Course of High Modules Fiber and Composites, Advanced Course of Machinery for Textile and Polymers, Advanced Experiments of Organic and Polymeric Materials, Fiber Reinforced Materials, Textile Physical Chemistry, Textile and Polymer Industries

Div. of Physical Electronics(M 48/5, D 16/7)
Advanced Coding Theory, Advanced Communication System Engineering, Advanced Educational Technology, Advanced Electric Power Engineering, Advanced Electrical Properties of Matter, Advanced Electromagnetic Engineering, Advanced Electron Devices, Advanced High Speed Electron Devices, Advanced High-voltage Engineering, Advanced Microwave Circuits, Advanced Software Engineering, Applied Graph Theory, Analytical Theory of Image Processing, Colloquium on Computer Science, Colloquium on Electrical and Electronic Engineering, Colloquium on Physical Electronics, Computer Systems Evaluation, Crystal Physics and its Application, Design Theory of Electron Devices, Fault-Tolerant Systems, Fundamentals of Signal Analysis, Foundations of Computing Environments, Information Transmission Theory, Laser Engineering, Light Waveguides, Lightwave Semiconductor Devices, Logic and Software Machine Intelligence, Methods and Techniques in Pattern Recognition, Modern Circuit Theory, Multi-Dimensional Signal Processing, Natural Language Processing, Optical and Quantum Electronics, Optical Communications, Plasma Engineering, Power Electronics, Precision Time and Frequency Engineering, Processor Systems, Seminar on Computer Science, Seminar on Electrical and Electronic Engineering, Seminar on Physical Electronics, Sensing Devices, Signal Noise in Electron Devices, Special Experiments on Computer Science, Special Experiments on Electrical and Electronic Engineering, Special Experiments on Physical Electronics, Special Lecture on Computer Science, Special Lecture on Electrical and Electronic Engineering, Special Lecture on Physical Electronics, Structure of Programming Languages,Surface Acoustic Wave Engineering, Theory of Asynchronous Concurrent Systems, Theory of Electronic Circuits, Theory of Software Structures, Ultrasonic Engineering, Ultrasonic Instrumentation, Visual Communication Engineering

Div. of Physics(M 58/3, D 21/1)
Advanced Quantum Mechanics, Advanced Statistical Physics, Colloquium in Physics, Crystal Physics, Electron Theory of Solids, Exercise in Solid State Physics, Chemical Physics and Statistical Mechanics, Exercise in Nuclear Physics and Elementary Particle Physics, Field Theory. High Energy Physics, Laboratory Work in Nuclear Physics and Elementary Particle Physics, Laboratory Work in Solid State Physics, Low Temperature Physics, Many Electron Physics,
Nuclear Physics: Nuclear Structure, Nuclear Reaction
Nuclear Spectroscopy, Physics of Dielectrics, Physics of Magnetism and Magnetic Materials, Seminar in Physics, Surface Structures

Div. of Polymer Chemistry(M 47/0, D 16/4)
Advanced Bioengineering, Advanced Chemical Engineering Analysis, Advanced Chemical Engineering Planning, Advanced Chemical Equipment Design, Advanced Chemical Reaction Engineering, Advanced Chemical Reactor Design, Advanced Chemical Thermodynamics, Advanced Course of Ceramics, Advanced Course of Mining Industry, Advanced Hear Transfer Operations, Advanced Industrial Chemistry, Organic, Advanced Inorganic Chemistry, Advanced Industrial Chemistry, Advanced Mass Transfer Operations, Advanced Mechanical Separation and Mixing, Advanced Physical Chemistry of Polymers, Advanced Polymer Chemistry, Advanced Process Engineering, Advanced Separtaion Processes, Advanced Surface Chemistry, Advanced Synthetic Chemistry Organic, Advanced Transport Phenomena, Biochemical Engineering, Biochemical Reaction Engineering, Biochemical Process, Chemical Kinetics, Colloquium in Chemical Engineering, Electronics for Engineering Materials, Fine Chemical Syntheses, Inorganic Reaction Mechanisms, Introduction to Bioengineering, Introduction to Magnetic Resonance, Petroleum Chemistry, Physical Organic Chemistry, Reactivity of Solids, Rheology, Seminar in Chemical Engineering, Special Experiments of Inorganic Materials, Chemical Engineering and Polymer Science, Special Lecture on Chemical Engineering, Special Lecture on Engineering Inorganic Materials, Solid State Reaction, Structural Inorganic Chemistry, Theory of Catalysis, Topics in Polymer Science

Div. of Social Engineering(M 55/15, D 17/4)
Advanced Course of Administration, Advanced Course of Human Resource Planning,Advanced Course of Landscape Engineering, Advanced Course of Reginal Planning, Advanced Course of Social Problems, Advanced Planning Theory

Interdisciplinary Graduate School of Science and Engineering(M 610/20, D 201/55)

Div. of Applied Electronics(M 44/1, D 14/2)
Advanced High Speed Electron Devices, Advanced Sensing Systems, Basic Neurophysiology, Colloquium in Applied Electronics, Design Theory of Electron Devices, Digital Signal Processing, Digital Systems, Fault-Tolerant Systems, Image Information Processing, Laboratory Work in Applied Electronics, Laser Engineering, Method and Techniques in Pattern Recognition, Optical Communications, Precision Time and Frequency Engineering, Quantum Electronics, Random Signal Analysis, Signal and Noise in Electron Devices, Seminar in Applied Electronics, Surface Acoustic Wave Engineering, Theory of Electronic Circuits, Theory of Pattern Information, Ultrasonic Engineering, Ultrasonic Instrumentation

Div. of Electronic Chemistry(M 76/0, D 32/5)
Advanced Catalytic Chemistry, Advanced Polymer Chemistry, Bio-electrochemistry, Chemistry of Metal Finishing, Colloquium in Electronic Chemistry, Electrochemical Energy Conversion, Electrolytic Chemistry of Metals, Electron Transfer Reactions at Electrodes, Fundamentals of Electronic Chemistry, Imaging Materials, Instrumental Analysis, Molecular Design of Functional Polymer, Organic Elcetrochemistry, Organometallic Chemistry, Physical Chemistry of a Liq-

uid State, Quantum Chemistry, Recent Topics of Electronic Chemistry, Seminar in Electronic Chemistry, Solid State Physics and Chemistry, Solution Chemistry of Electrolytes, Special Experiments of Electronic Chemistry, Special Lecture on Electronic Chemistry

Div. of Energy Scinces(M 47/1, D 6/3)
Advanced Electric Power Engineering, Advanced Experiments and Exercises on Energy Engineering, Advanced Experiments and Exercises on Energy Sciences, Advanced Thermo-Fluid Mechanics, Applied Exectiscoty, Applied Nuclear Physics, Colloquium in Energy Sciences, Controlled Nuclear Fusion Engineering, Energy Conversion Engineering, Fundamentals for Energy Science, Introduction to Energy Sciences, Isotope Experiments, Materials Sciences in Energy Technology, Neutron Physics, Nuclear Chemical Engineering,Nuclear Reactor Physics, Physics of Active Phenomena, Plasma Engineering, Power Electronics, Radiation Physics, Ratio and Radiation Chemistry, Reactor Heat Engineering, Solid State Energy Conversion, Special Lecture on Energy Science

Div. of Environmental Chemistry and Engineering (M 49/0, D 27/10)
Advanced Lecture on Environmental Chemistry and Engineering, Analysis of Chemical-Eco Systems, Biochemical Process, Chemical Process for Inorganic Resourecs Utilization, Chemical Reaction Design, Chemical Resources, Chemistry and Environment, Colloquium in Environmental Chemistry and Engineering, Environmental and Chemical Process Control, Environmental and Chemical Process Design, Environmental Chemical Reaction Engineering, Environmental Chemistry and Kinetics, Environmental Microorganisms, Fundamentals of Chemical Energy, Fundamentals of Environmental Process Plant, Laws and Regulations for Projection of Environment, Principles of Chemical Engieeering, Recycling Process of Resources, Special Experiments in Environmental Chemistry and Engineering, Special Lecture on Environmentral Chemistry and Engineering

Div. of Environmental Engineering(M 64/3, D 9/6)
Advanced Course of Landscape Engineering, Appraisal of Regional Infrastracture Project, Building Environment and Services, Building Equipment, City and Rural Planning, Colloqulum in Environmental Engineering, Construction Materials, Earthquake Engineering, Earthquake-resistant Design of Structure, Environmental Engineering Laboratory, Foundation Engineering, Man Environment System Engineering, Marine Geotechnology, Office Environment, Probabilistic Concepts in Engineering Design, Project Management, Quaternary Environmental Changes, Regional Environmental Information, Reinforced Concrete Seminar in Environmental Engineering, Special Seminar in Environmental Engineering, Theory of Urban Space, Thermal Environmental Engineering

Div. of Information Processing(M 86/7, D 34/11)
Advanced Topics in Imaging Technology, Basic Mathematics for Informartion Processing, Colloquium in Information Processing, Computer Image Processing, Digital Signal Processing, Fault-Tolerant Systems, Fine Image Recording, Fundamentals of Information Theory, Fundamentals of Signal Analysis, Fundamentals on Wave Propagation, Image Information Processing, Imaging Systems, Imaging Materials, Imaging Science and Engineering, Information Transmission Theory, Laser Engineering, Light Waveguides, Methods and Techniques in Pattern Recognition, Multi-Dimensional Signal Processing, Optical Communications, Optical Information Processing, Optical Memory Systems, Optical Properties of Semiconductors, Photochemical Processes, Principle of Microoptics, Processor Systems, Quantum Electronics, Random Signal Analysis, Seminar in Information Processing, Special Experiments of Information processing

Div. of Information Processing(M 86/7, D 34/11)
Special Lectures on Information Processing, Solid State Electronic Chemistry, Solid State Physics and Chemistry, Three-dimensional Imaging Technology, Visual Information Processing

Div. of Life Chemistry(M 43/0, D 28/1)
Advanced Chemistry and Biochemistry of Nucleic Acids, Advanced Course of Biophysics, Advanced Course of Developmental Biochemistry, Advanced Course of Molecular Biology, Basic Biochemistry, Basic Organic Chemistry, Biocatalysis, Bio-organic Chemistry, Biophysical Chemistry, Chemistry and Biochemistry of Carbohydrates, Chemistry of Metabolism, Colloquium in Life Chemistry, Directed Laboratory Works in Life Chemistry, Environmental Microorganism, Instrumental Analysis, Isotope Experiments, Medical Chemistry, Microbial Chemistry, Molecular Genetics, Molecular Neurobiology, Recent Progress in Life Chemistry, Seminar in Life Chemistry, Special Experiments of Life Chemistry, Structures of Biological Molecules

Div. of Materials Science and Engineering(M 85/6, D 23/5)
Advanced Course of Mining Industry, Advanced Course of Surface Chemistry of Solids, Advanced Instrumental Analysis, Advanced Quantum Mechanics, Advanced Structural Inorganic Chemistry, Advanced Theory of Crystal Structure Determination, Colloquium in Materials Science and Engineering, Composite Materials, Corrosion and Passivity of Metals, Crystal Growth, Directed Laboratory Work in Materials Science and Engineering, Electron Microscope and Diffraction, Electronics for Engineering Materials, Fracture in Solids, High Pressure Science for Materials, High Temperature Fracture, Laboratory Work in Materials Science and Engineering, Lattice Imperfections in Solids, Materials Design, Materials Properties at High Temperatures, Mechanical Metallurgy, Non-ferrous Metal and Alloys, Phase Stability in Metals and Alloys, Properties of Fused Matters, Properties of Non-crystalline Materials, Solid State Physics(Structure of Solids, Electron Theory of Solids, Solid State Reaction at High Temperatures)

Div. of Precision Machinery Systems(M 49/0, D 11/7)
Advanced Course of Strength Design, Advanced Sensing Systems, Binding and Transmission, Colloquium in

Precision Machinery Systems, Fine Mechanics, Fluid Control Systems, Fundamentals of Control Theory and Signal Analysis, Image Information Processing, Laboratory Work in Precision Machinery Systems Optimization Technique, Precision Instrumentation, Precision Mechanical Working Systems, Random Signal Analysis, Reliability of Mechanical Systems, Seminar in Precision Machinery Systems, Special Group Work on Practice of Precision Machinery Systems, Special Lecture on Fundamentals of Precision Machinery Systems, Special Lecture on Precision Machinery Systems, Technique for Numerical Analysis, Theory of Automated Machine Design

Div. of Systems Science(M 67/7, D 17/5)
Advanced Course of Bioengineering, Advanced Course of Medical Engineering, Advanced Course of Tribology, Advanced Educational Technology, Cognitive Decision Theory, Colloquium in Systems Science and Engineering, Educational Systems Technology, Foundations of Systems Science, Fundamentals of Mathematics for Systems Science, Fuzzy Measure Theory, Fuzzy Theory, General Systems Theory, Information System in Organization, Human Intelligent Behavior, Laboratory Work in Systems Science and Engineering, Learning System, Logic and Reasoning, Mathematical Programming, Seminar in Systems Science and Engineering, Special Lecture on Systems Science and Engineering, System Information, System Planning and Design Systems Sociology, System Statistical Analysis System Theory, Theory of Large Scale Systems, Ultimate Technology

---

東京芸術大学
(Tokyo Geijutsu Daigaku)

Tokyo National University of Fine Arts and Music

12-8 Ueno Koen, Taito-ku, Tokyo 110
☎ 03-3828-6111 FAX 03-3822-3336

Founded 1949
Professors 82
Associate Professors 70
Assistant Professors(Tenured) 10
Assistant Professors(Non-tenured) 617
Research Assistants 30
Undergraduate Students/Foreign Students 2, 001/0
Graduate Students/Foreign Students 689/72
Library 417, 492 volumes
Contact: Overseas Students Centre

Educational philosophy Developing artists of the highest level in traditional as well as contemporary sense. Graduates contributed/will contribute to raise people's interest in arts and music to a large extent.
Foreign students Any overseas student, so long as he or she reached the level we require, is welcome in very course of the dept. Now we have over 100 students from all over the world.
Environment Located at western fringe of Ueno Park, Taioto-ku, Tokyo. Ca. 7 min. walk from JR Ueno Sta. across a beautiful park. The park is well known for its history as well as many cultural institutions (halls, museums, zoo, etc.) in it.
Facilities Central Library, Art Museum, 6 Halls for Music, Nasu Highland Training Institution, Nara Institute of Ancient Researches, Dormitory, Student Hall with a Cafeteria, Gymnasium, etc.
Student activities Wide range of extra curricular activities including sports and arts, Geisai School Festival (Sept.), Welcome & Sayonara Party, Study Tour, etc. for overseas students.
Academic programs for foreign students Japanese language & Japanese society and culture introduction class, Tutoring system.
Services for foreign students Advisory services of Overseas Students Centre: Health clinic, housing information, scholarship information and matters for benefit of students from overseas.

Undergraduate Programs

Faculty of Fine Arts(961/0)
Dept. of Painting(Japanese, Oil, Printing and Wall) (351/0)
Dept. of Sculpture(Wood, Metal, Stone, etc.)(89/0)
Dept. of Crafts(Met. Carving, Met. Hammering, Met. Casting, Lacquer Work, Ceramics and Weaving & Dyeing)(147/0)
Dept. of Design(Visual, Industrial, Formative, Structural and Environmental)(209/0)
Dept. of Architecture(Design and Theory)(80/0)
Dept. of Arts(Aesthetics, Art History—Japanese, Oriental, Occidental and Arts & Crafts—, Conservation & Restoration, Art Anatomy and Fine Arts Education) (85/0)
Faculty of Music(1, 040/0)
Dept. of Composition(84/0)
Dept. of Vocal Music(252/0)
Dept. of Instruments(Piano, Organ, Harp, Strings, Brass & Wood Winds and Percussion)(453/0)
Dept. of Conducting(7/0)
Dept. of Musicology(Aesthetics, Theory, History–Occidental and Oriental–, Solfege and Music Education)(113/0)
Dept. of Japanese Music(Koto, Shakuhachi, Shamisen, Noh, Nagauta and Noh Hayashi)(131/0)

Graduate Programs

Graduate School of Fine Arts(M 337/30, D 72/15)
Japanese Painting, Oil Painting, Printing (wood, litho and copper), Wall Painting, Oil Painting Technique & Material, Sculpture, Metal Carving, Metal Hammering, Metal Casting, Laquer Work, Ceramics, Weaving & Dyeing, Design (Visual, Industrial, Formarive, Structural,

Environmental & Architechtural), Theory of Architecture, Aesthetics, Arts History (Japanese, Oriental, Occidental and Arts & Crafts), Conservation and Restoration Techniques, Conservation Science, Art Anatomy and Fine Arts Education

Graduate School of Music(M 253/25, D 27/2)
Compostion, Vocal Music, Opera, Piano, Organ, Violin, Viola, Cello, Contrabass, Harp, Flute, Oboe, Clarinet, Faggot, Saxophone, Trumpet, Horn, Trombone, Tuba, Percussion Instrument, Conducting, Aesthetics of Music, Theory of Music, History of Music (Occidental and Oriental), Solfege, Music Education, Koto, Shakuhachi, Shamisen, Noh, Nagauta Hayashi and Noh Hayashi

---

東京水産大学
(Tokyo Suisan Daigaku)

Tokyo University of Fisheries

4-5-7 Konan, Minato-ku, Tokyo, 108
☎ 03-3471-1251 FAX 03-3450-4279

Founded 1889
Professors 58
Associate Professors 47
Assistant Professors(Tenured) 13
Assistant Professors(Non-tenured) 77
Research Assistants 38
Undergraduate Students/Foreign Students 1, 333/6
Graduate Students/Foreign Students 216/81
Library 228, 871 volumes
Contact: The Dean, Office of Student Affairs

Educational philosophy Tokyo University of Fisheries provides education and research on studies and scientific techniques related to fisheries and oceanography. Since a specialized university of this kind is unique, its ultimate aim is to offer its contribution to society.

Foreign students We welcome the students from abroad for the future of marine science in the world. We hope that we will contribute to the understanding and cross-cultural relations.

Environment The main campus of the University is located in the south of the urban center of Tokyo, facing the Tokyo waterfront. The campus is within walking distance of the nearest railway station, JR Shinagawa Station, which is one of the main junctions for intercity and suburban trains.

Facilities Circulating Flow Channel, Hydraulics Laboratory, Radioisotope Laboratory, Museum, University Library, Gymnasium for martial arts, Gymnasium

Student activities Annual inter-collegiate match in May and the University Festival in November. A wide variety of extra-curricular activities.—the cultural—Orchestra, Chorus, Computer, Art, Marine Biology, Astronomy, Biology of Botany etc., —the athletic—Rugby, Soccer, Baseball, Tennis, Japanese Archery, Swimming, Diving, Cycling, Skiing, Fishing, etc.

Academic programs for foreign students Supplemental Japanese language class, Tutoring system, Possible to transfer units.

Services for foreign students Personal psychological counseling, vocational guidance. International House and Student dormitory.

Undergraduate Programs

Faculty of Fisheries(1, 333/6)

Dept. of Aquatic Biosciences(324/2)
Aquatic Biology Major, Sea-farming Biology Major, Aquaculture Major

Dept. of Fisheries Resource Management(130/2)
Fisheries Resource Management System Major, Ecology and Economics of Fisheries Resources Major

Dept. of Food Science and Technology(359/2)
Food Chemistry Major, Food Safety and Preservation Major, Food Processing Preservation, Food Engineering Major

Dept. of Marine Science and Technology(449/0)
Marine Environmental Science Major, Fishery Oceanography Major, Fishing Technology and Engineering Major, Fishing Science and Technology Major

Graduate Programs

Graduate School of Fisheries(M 140/39, D 76/42)

Div. of Marine Science and Technology(M 45/17, D 24/11)
Marine Environmental Science, Fisheries Oceanography, Fishing Science and Technology, Fishing Technology and Engineering

Div. of Food Science and Technology(M 41/11, D 17/12)
Food Chemistry, Food Safety and Preservation, Food Processing and Preservation, Food Engineering

Div. of Aquatic Biosciences(M 54/11, D 35/19)
Aquatic Biology, Sea-farming Biology, Aquaculture

One-Year Graduate Programs

Advanced Course of Apprentices for Seamanship
Fishing Boat Operation and Management

Apprentices for Seamanship Course
Fishing Boat Operation and Management Major

東京外国語大学
(Tokyo Gaikokugo Daigaku)

Tokyo University of Foreign Studies

4-51-21 Nishigahara, Kita-ku, Tokyo 114
☎ 03-3917-6111

Founded 1899
Professors 84
Associate Professors 29
Assistant Professors(Tenured) 268
Research Assistants 22
Undergraduate Students/Foreign Students 3089/223
Graduate Students/Foreign Studetns 137/19
Library 228, 201 volumes
Contact: Administration General Affairs Section

Educational philosophy Tokyo University of Foreign Studies is designed to provide comprehensive study and practical and theoretical in foreign languages and culture in order to enable students to gain broad and well-balance understanding of the areas of their specialization being necessary for international activities.
Foreign students Our University widely opens to the foreign students and staff in charge of foreign students and encourage them to develop themselves in their own study. One of our university's distinctive features is a course designed for foreign students in the Dept. of Japanese studies.
Enviroment The University is located in a quiet and verdurous place of Nishigahara, Kita-ku, northern part of Tokyo with such historical remains as Asukayama Park, Rikugien Garden, ex-Furukawateien Garden and Somei Cemetery in a short distance. It is reached by Toden, the one and only available surface car in Tokyo, from Otsuka Station.
Facilities Library, Japanese Language School, Center for the Development of Education Materials is for foreign students, Helth Administration Center, International Hall, Audio Visual Center, Institute for the Study of Languages and Cultures of Asia and Africa, Gymnasium, Student Dinning Hall and Co-op.
Student activities Popular campus events: Homecoming, school festival, international goodwillparty, observation tours for foreign students, etc. Various kinds of extra curricular activities including ESS, dance study group, orchestra group, choral groups, student news paper, drama, rowing club, football club, baseball club, etc.
Academic programs for foreign students Japanese language class for research students, tutoring system, special lectures on Japanese Cultures
Services for foreign students Health clinic, personal/psychological counseling, International Hall, Housing information, part-time job information, Home stay, Home visit, cultural exchange program.

Undergraduate Programs

Faculty of Foreign Studies(3, 089/223)
Dept. of Anglo-American Studies(319/0)
Dept. of Arabic Studies(92/0)
Dept. of Chinese Studies(281/0)
Dept. of French Studies(276/0)
Dept. of German Studies(271/0)
Dept. of Indochinese Studies(189/0)
Dept. of Indonesian Studies(149/0)
Dept. of Indo-Pakistani Studies(157/0)
Dept. of Italian Studies(146/0)
Dept. of Japanese Studies(194/129)
Dept. of Korean Studies(80/0)
Dept. of Mongolian Studies(82/0)
Dept. of Persian Studies(85/0)
Dept. of Portuguese-Brazilian Studies(155/0)
Dept. of Russian Studies(283/0)
Dept. of Spanish Studies(330/0)

Graduate Programs

Graduate School of Language Studies (Master's Program) (M 95/19)
Div. of Asian Languages Ⅰ (M 9/0)
Chinese Language, Chinese Literature, Korean Language and Literature, Mongolian Language and Literature
Div. of Asian Languages Ⅱ (M 8/0)
Urdu Language and Literature, Hindi Language and Literature, Arabic Language and Literature, Persian Language, Persian Literature
Div. of Asian Languages Ⅲ (M 4/0)
Indonesian Language and Literature, Malaysian Language and Literature, Dutch Language and Literature, Thai Language and Literature, Vietnamese Language and Literature, Burmese Language and Literature
Div. of Germanic Language(M 18/0)
English and American Language, English Literature, American Literature, German Language, German Literature
Div. of Japanese Language(M 32/9)
Japanese, Linguistics, Japanese Culture, Japanese Affairs, Phonetics, Literature
Div. of Romance Language(M 18/0)
French Language, French Literature, Italian Language, Italian Literature, Spanish Language, Spanish Literature, Portuguese Language and Literature
Div. of Slavic Languages(M 6/1)
Russian Language, Russian Literature

東京商船大学
(Tokyo Shôsen Daigaku)
Tokyo University of Mercantile Marine

2-1-6 Etchujima, Koto-ku, Tokyo 135
☎ 03-3641-1171 FAX 03-3820-8407

Founded 1875
Professors 41
Associate Professors 40
Assistant Professors(Tenured) 7
Assistant Professors(Non-tenured) 23
Research Assistants 21
Undergraduate Students/Foreign Students 801/0
Graduate Students/Foreign Students 43/20
Library 158, 326 volumes
Contact: Instruction Section-Entrance Exam Unit

Educational philosophy Our aim is to assist students in cultivating their knowledge about transportation science including shipping and shiphandling, information science logistics and mechanical engineering.
Foreign students We earnestly hope that the students from abroad will grasp the kernel of the studies here which promote the welfare of their nations through transportation science.
Environment The town of Etchujima, koto-ku, with a population of 7, 800, is located in the southeast of Tokyo's city area, about one mile east of Tokyo Station. The Sumida River, which runs along Etchujima, is one of the most well-known rivers in Japan. This area is the traditional part of Tokyo.
Facilities University Library, Seaside Training Institute, Training ship " Shioji-maru ". Health Administration Center, Training ship Operation Center, Electronic Computer Center, Sports training Center, Swimming pool, etc.
Student activities Popular campus events include freshmen orientation, school festival, there is wide variety of extracurricular activities, including judo, boating, baseball, rugby, music, photography, tea ceremony, etc.
Academic programs for foreign students Supplementary Japanese classes, Tutoring system.
Services for foreign students Health clinic, Field trip, Year-end party

Undergraduate Programs

Faculty of Mercantile Marine Science(801/0)
Dept. of Electronic and Mechanical Engineering (41/0)
Dept. of Information Engineering and Logistics (46/0)
Dept. of Marine System Engineering(112/0)

Graduate Programs

Graduate School of Science of Mercantile Marine (M 43/20)
Div. of Control Engineering(M 10/6)
Control System Engineering, Plants Engineering, Electrical Engineering, Electronic Engineering
Div. of Engineering(M 14/8)
Marine Steam Plant Engineering, Marine Diesel Engineering, Nuclear Ship Engineering, Marine Auxiliary Machinery, Machine Design, Engineering Materials, Applied Mechanics, Thermo and Fluid Dynamics
Div. of Navigation(M 11/4)
Positioning and Sailing, Marine Traffic Routing, Navigational Measurement, Environmental Science of Navigation, Electronics and Communication Engineering, Ship Maneuvering, Navigation Law, Naval Architecture
Div. of Transportation Engineering(M 8/2)
Engineering of Transportation Management, Engineering of Transportation Facilities, Accident Prevention Engineering, Information and Systems Engineering

Related Subjects
Applied Mathematics, Applied Physics, Maritime Law, Shipping Economics, Marine Policy

東京大学
(Tokyo Daigaku)
The University of Tokyo

7-3-1 Hongo, Bunkyo-ku, Tokyo 113
☎ 03-3812-2111 FAX 03-5684-4957

Founded 1877
Professors 902
Associate Professors 795
Assistant Professors(Tenured) 201
Assistant Professors(Non-tenured) 1, 577
Research Assistants 1, 690
Undergraduate Students/Foreign Students 15, 258/93
Graduate Students/Foreign Students 5, 536/958
Library 6, 290, 748 volumes
Contact: Student Exchange Division

Educational philosophy The University aims to provide its students with opportunities for intellectual development as well as for the acquisition of professional knowledge and skills.
Foreign students We believe that foreign students can enjoy a rewarding experience in our University, and can contribute a great deal to promoting mutual understanding and the development of friendly relations.
Environment The campus is centrally located at Hongo in Tokyo and occupies about 56 hectares of a former estate belonging to feudal lords. Parts of the landscaping of the original estate have been preserved

and provide greenery and open space much needed in an otherwise crowded campus.

Facilities University Museum, Cryogenic Center, Radioisotope Center, Educational Computer Center, Environmental Science Center, Molecular Genetics Research Laboratory, International Center, Health Service Center

Student activities The University of Tokyo has an Athletics Union, which is an organization made up of various sports clubs. The Union consists of 40 clubs, including the Judo (Japanese martial art) Club. As a part of its annual activities, the Union offers instruction courses in golf, sailing, horseback riding, skiing and dancing.

Academic programs for foreign students Japanese language supplementary classes are available at the University. Tutoring system.

Services for foreign students International Lodge: Shared Facilities (Lobby, Conference Room, Library, Japanese Style Room), Accommodation (108 apartments for families, couples and sigle people)

Undergraduate Programs

Faculty of Agriculture(563/0)
- **Dept. of Agricultural Chemistry**(156/0)
- **Dept. of Agricultural Economics**(61/0)
- **Dept. of Agricultural Engineering**(35/0)
- **Dept. of Agrobiology**(79/0)
- **Dept. of Fisheries**(34/0)
- **Dept. of Forest Products**(39/0)
- **Dept. of Forestry**(51/0)
- **Dept. of Veterinary Medical Science**(108/0)

College of Arts and Sciences(388/0)
- **Dept. of Liberal Arts**(255/0)
- **Dept. of Pure and Applied Sciences**(133/0)

Faculty of Economics(865/4)
- **Dept. of Business Administration**(122/2)
- **Dept. of Economics**(743/2)

Faculty of Education(201/0)
- **Dept. of Educational Administration**(47/0)
- **Dept. of Educational Psychology**(37/0)
- **Dept. of Foundations of Education**(55/0)
- **Dept. of Physical and Health Education**(29/0)
- **Dept. of School Education**(33/0)

Faculty of Engineering(2, 007/15)
- **Dept. of Aeronautics**(116/0)
- **Dept. of Applied Physics**(111/1)
- **Dept. of Architecture**(139/1)
- **Dept. of Chemical Engineering**(85/1)
- **Dept. of Civil Engineering**(112/0)
- **Dept. of Electrical Engineering**(110/1)
- **Dept. of Electronic Engineering**(106, 7)
- **Dept. of Industrial Chemistry**(90/0)
- **Dept. of Marine Engineering**(98/2)
- **Dept. of Materials Science**(72/0)
- **Dept. of Mathematical Engineering and Information Physics**(123/1)
- **Dept. of Mechanical Engineering**(107/1)
- **Dept. of Mechanical Engineering for Production**(95/0)
- **Dept. of Metallurgy**(64/0)
- **Dept. of Mineral Development Engineering**(44/0)
- **Dept. of Naval Architecture and Ocean Engineering**(100/0)
- **Dept. of Nuclear Engineering**(83/0)
- **Dept. of Precision Machinery Engineering**(124/0)
- **Dept. of Reaction Chemistry**(33/0)
- **Dept. of Synthetic Chemistry**(80/0)
- **Dept. of Urban Engineering**(115/0)

Faculty of Law(1, 777/0)
- **Dept. of Private Law**(822/0)
- **Dept. of Public Law**(806/0)
- **Dept. of Political Science**(149/0)

Faculty of Letters(814/2)
- **Dept. of History**(215/0)
- **Dept. of Language and Literature**(277/1)
- **Dept. of Philosophy**(133/0)
- **Dept. of Psychology and Sociology**(189/1)

Faculty of Medicine(515/1)
- **School of Medicine**(423/1)
- **School of Health Science**(92/0)

Faculty of Pharmaceutical Science(137/0)
- **Dept. of Pharmaceutical Science**
- **Dept. of Pharmaceutical Techonchemistry**

Faculty of Science(659/2)
- **Dept. of Astronomy**(24/0)
- **Dept. of Biology**(63/0)
- **Dept. of Biophysics and Biochemistry**(48/0)
- **Dept. of Chemistry**(88/0)
- **Dept. of Information Science**(63/2)
- **Dept. of Geology**(52/0)
- **Dept. of Mathematics**(108/0)
- **Dept. of Physics**(154/0)
- **Dept. of Geophysical Institure**(59/0)

Graduate Programs

Graduate School of Agricultural Sciences(M 319/43, D 321/114)

Div. of Agrobiology(M 47/1, D 32/12)
Crop Science, Plant Ecology and Morphogenesis, Horticultural Science, Landscape Architecture and Science, Plant Pathology, Sericultural Science, Plant Breeding and Genetics, Biometrics, Applied Entomology, Radiation Genetics and Chemical Mutagenesis

Div. of Agricultural Chemistry(M 109/8, D 105/30)
Plant Nutrition and Fertilizers, Biochemistry, Organic Chemistry, Food Chemistry, Bioorganic Chemistry, Chemistry and Technology of Animal Products, Soil Science, Applied Microbiology, Analytical Chemistry, Pesticide Chemistry, Microbiology, Food Engineering, Nutritional Biochemistry and Animal Nutrition, Antibiotics, Microbial Genetics and Breeding, Microbial Taxonomy, Physiology, Enzyme Research, Biophysics

Div. of Forestry(M 30/5, D 13/4)
Forest Management, Silviculture, Forest Policy, Forest Hydrology and Erosion Control, Forest Utilization, Forest Botany, Forest Zoology, Forest Landscape Design

Div. of Fisheries(M 27/4, D 39/20)
Fisheries Biology, Aquaculture Biology, Marine Products Technology, Fish Physiology, Fisheries Oceanography, Marine Biochemistry, Marine Planktology, Marine Microbiology, Population Dynamics of Marine Organisms, Biology of Fisheries Resources, Deep-sea and Coastal Fisheries Oceanography, Fisheries Ecology

Div. of Agricultural Economics(M 19/12, D 26/18)
Farm Economics and Accounting, General Agricultural Economics, Agricultural Finance, Agricultural Policy, Agricultural History, International Agricultural Development

Div. of Agricultural Engineering(M 20/3, D 14/7)
Land Reclamation, Conservation and Rural Engineering, Agricultural Water Engineering, Soil Physics and Soil Hydrology, Environmental Engineering, Agricultural Power, Energy and Machinery, Agricultural Process Engineering and Processing Machinery

Div. of Forest Products(M 28/5, D 17/3)
Wood Physics, Wood-based Materials and Timber Engineering, Forest Chemistry, Wood Chemistry, Chemistry of Polymeric Materials, Pulp and Paper Science

Div. of Biotechnology(M 39/5, D 17/5)
Molecular and Cellular Breeding, Bioinformation Engineering, Enzymology, Microbiology and Fermentation, Radiation Microbiology

Div. of Veterinary Medical Science(D 58/15)
Animal Breeding, Veterinary Anatomy, Veterinary Physiology, Comparative Pathophysiology, Veterinary Pharmacology, Veterinary Microbiology, Veterinary Pathology, Veterinary Medicine and Parasitology, Veterinary Surgery and Obstetrics, Biomedical Science, Veterinary Public Health, Veterinary Clinical Phathobiology, Cellular Biochemistry, Veterinary Animal Ethology, Developmental Biology, Laboratory Animal Science

Graduate School of Economics(M 45/12, D 87/17)

Div. of Economic Theory and Economic History (M 21/2, D 54/8)
Economic Theory, Statistics, Economic History, Econimic Policy, Public Finance and Monetary Economics

Div. of Applied Economics(M 20/8, D 25/6)
Industrial Labor, Economic Policy, International Ecnomics, Public Finance and Monetary Economics

Div. of Business Administration(M 4/2, D 8/3)
Business Administration, Business Policy, Accounting

Graduate School of Education(M 85/7, D 116/11)

Div. of Educational Administration(M 9/4, D 12/2)
Educational Administration, Adult Education and Youth Service, Library Science

Div. of Educational Psychology(M 16/1, D 28/2)
Educational Psychology, Educational Information Science

Div. of School Education(M 19/1, D 21/3)
Curricuium, Methods of Education, Comparative Education

Div. of Foundations of Education(M 17/0, D 35/4)
Science of Education, History of Education Sociology of Education

Div. of Physical Education(M 24/1, D 20/0)
Physical Education, Sports Science, Health Education

Graduate School of Engineering(M 1121/136, D 697/281)

Div. of Civil Engineering(M 77/24, D 66/57)
Applied Mechanics Laboratory, Bridge and Steel Structure, Concrete Engineering, Hydraulic Engineering, Coastal Engineering Laboratory, Traffic Engineering, Geotechnical Engineering, Surveying and Regional Planning, Infrastructure Engineering

Div. of Architecture(M 92/31, D 92/33)
Structural Engineering, Architectural Planning and Design, History of Architecture, Welding Engineering, Building Materials Engineering

Div. of Urban Engineering(M 43/6, D 44/21)
Urban Planning, Sanitary Engineering

Div. of Mechanical Engineering(M 48/4, D 21/12)
Applied Mechanics, Mechanical Engineering, General Mechanical Engineering

Div. of Mechanical Engineering for Production(M 35/1, D 9/4)
Mechanical Engineering for Production

Div. of Marine Engineering(M 41/2, D 17/4)
Marine Engineering

Div. of Precision Machinery Engineering(M 49/4, D 36/22)
Precision Machinery Engineering, Medical Precision Engineering

Div. of Naval Architecture and Ocean Engineering(M 38/3, D 17/11)
Applied Dynamics, Naval Architecture: Global Transportation Design, Hydrodynamics, Structural System Engineering, Design Technology, Production System Engineering, Ocean Engineering: Marine Hydrodynamics, Offshore Machinery Engineering, Marine Space Utilization

Div. of Aeronautics(M 66/0, D 46/10)
Flight mechanics: Control Engineering; Helicopter, High Temperature Gas Dynamics, Structural Mechanics: Composite Materials, Viscous Fluid Dynamics: High Speed Gas Dynamics, Aircraft Design, Electric Propulsion: Ionized Gas, Combustion: Aerospace Propulsion, Fluid Machinery: Aerodynamic Acoustics: Gas Turbine, Fluid Dynamics: Fluid Machine: Gas Turbine, Control Engineering: Space Engineering, Aerospace Materials: Strength of Materials

Div. of Electrical Engineering(M 51/9, D 30/13)
Electrical Engineering, Applied Electrical Engineering, Electrical Communication Engineering, Materials for Electrical Engineering, Electrical Energy Generation Engineering

Div. of Electronic Engineering(M 70/16, D 60/24)
Electronic Engineering

Div. of Applied Physics(M 63/0, D 43/5)
Theoretical Physic, Applied Physics, Experimental Physics

Div. of Mathematical Engineering and Information Physics(M 37/2, D 12/3)

Mathematical Engineering and Information Physics, Fundamentals of Mathematical Engineering, Computational Engineering, Information Engineering, Statistical Engineering, Chair V: Language Engineering, Fundamentals of Measurement and Control, Instrumentation Technology, Computational Neuro Science, Control Engineering, Laboratory for Measurement Science

Div. of Nuclear Engineering(M 60/4, D 34/8)
Nuclear Reactor Design, Nuclear Reactor Materials, Nuclear Radiation Measurement, Applied Radiation and Reactor Chemistry, Nuclear Fusion Engineering, Nuclear Fuels and Metallurgy, Nuclear Reactor Heat Transfer, Nuclear Propulsion and Structural Engineering, Nuclear Chemical Engineering

Div. of Mineral Development Engineering(M 12/1, D 4/3)
Applied Geology, Reservoir Engineering, Exploration Geophysics, Rock Engineering, Development Engineering, Petroleum Drilling and Production Engineering, Mining and Tunnelling Machinery, Mineral Procession, Mineral Process Engineering

Div. of Metallurgy(M 34/2, D 16/9)
Iron and Steelmaking, Chemistry of Materials Processing, Surface Technology, Solidification Processing, Mechanical Metallurgy & Technology of Elastoplasticity, Plasma Materials Engineering

Div. of Materials Science(M 37/2, D 21/10)
Applied Solid State Physics, Structure of Metals, Strength of Materials, Nonferrous Metals and Alloys, Ceramic Materials, Glass Science and Engineering

Div. of Industrial Chemistry(M 49/3, D 26/9)
Industrial Chemistry, Industrial Analytical Chemistry

Div. of Synthetic Chemistry(M 45/8, D 29/8)
Synthetic Chemistry, Industrial Synthetic Materials

Div. of Reaction Chemistry(M 23/3, D 10/1)
Reaction Chemistry

Div. of Chemical Engineering(M 36/2, D 20/6)
Materials Science and Engineering, Membrane Engineering, Separation & Purification Engineering, Chemical Reaction Engineering, Protein Engineering

Div. of Information Engineering(M 52/6, D 23/4)
Information Processing Laboratory, Information Devices Laboratory, Information System Laboratory, Urban Planning, Mechanical Engineering, Electronic Engineering, Mathematical Engineering and Information, Computational Engineering

Div. of Chemical Energy Engineering(M 44/3, D 21/4)
Chemical Energy Process Engineering, Materials for Energy, Energy Development Technology, Synthetic Chemistry, Industrial Synthetic Materials, Reaction Chemistry

Div. of Superconductivity Engineering(M 19/0)
Advanced Superconductivity, Superconducting Materials, Superconductor Electronics, Applied Physics of Superconductors, Process Engineering of Superconductors, Material Analysis of Superconductors

Graduate School of Humanities (M 271/19, D 299/20)

Div. of Japanese Language and Literature(M 27/0, D 30/2)
Japanese Language, Japanese Literature

Div. of Chinese Language and Literature(M 6/1, D 11/1)
Chinese Language, Chinese Literature

Div. of Classical Philology(M 5/0, D 6/0)
Hellenistic and Early Christian Literature, Classical Languages and Literature, History and Philosophy of Science, History of Classical Studies, Ancient History, Greek Philology

Div. of English Languges and Literature(M 30/0, D 32/0)
English Literature, English Lingustics, English and General Literature, English and Comparative Literature, English Philology, American Languages and Literature, American Literature

Div. of German Languages and Literature(M 15/0, D 18/0)
German Languages, German Literature, German Philology

Div. of French Languages and Literature

French Languages and Literature(M 20/0, D 29/0)
French Languages, French Literature

Italian Languages and Literature(M 5/0, D 1/0)
Italian Languages, Italian Literature

Div. of Russian Languages and Literature(M 10/0, D 13/2)
Russian Languages, Russian Literature, Slavic Languages and Literature

Div. of Linguistics(M 12/1, D 7/0)
Acoustic Phonetics, Speech Physiology, Semantics and General Linguistics, Austronesian Linguistics, Accentology and Dialectology, Indo–European Linguistics

Div. of Japanese History(M 20/2, D 19/2)
Ancient History, Medieval History, Early Modern History, Modern History

Div. of Oriental History(M 12/3, D 19/5)
Chinese History, South Asian History, West Asian History, Korean History

Div. of Occidental History(M 13/0, D 13/0)
Ancient History, Medieval History, Modern History, Contemporary History

Div. of Archaeology(M 7/2, D 7/0)
Methods of Archaeology, Japanese Archaeology, East Asian Archaeology, American Archaeology

Div. of Philosophy(M 9/0, D 9/0)
Modern Occidental Philosophy

Div. of Chinese Philosophy(M 6/1, D 15/4)
Chinese Philosophy, Chinese Antiquities, Confucianism in Japan

Div. of Indian Philosophy and Literature(M 16/6, D 13/3)
Indian Buddhism, Chinese Buddhism, Japanese Buddhism, Indian Philosophy, Sanskrit Languages and Literature

Div. of Ethics(M 11/0, D 12/0)
History of Social Thoughts, Japanese Ethical Thoughts

Div. of Science and History of Religion

Science and History of Religion(M 18/1, D 19/1)
Hellenistic and Early Christian Literature, History of Ancient Near Eastern Religions, Philosophy of Religion, Religious Ethics, History of Japanese Religion, Modern Christian Thought, Sociology of Religion, New Religious Movements

Islamic Studies(M 2/0, D 2/0)
Modern Near Eastern History, History of Islamic Thought, Modern Near Eastern and Central Asian History

Div. of Aesthetics(M 5/2, D 6/0)
Aesthetics

Div. of History of Art(M 17/0, D 8/0)
History of Western Art, History of Chinese Art, History of Japanese Art

Div. of Psychology(M 5/0, D 10/0)
Experimental Psychology, Neuro Psychology, Mathematical Psychology, Physiological Psychology

Graduate School of International and Interdisciplinary Studies(M 138/35, D 145/53)

Div. of Comparative Literature and Culture(22/6, D 26/8)
Comparative Literature and Culture

Div. of Culture and Representation(M 10/3)
Theories of Art, Linguistic Culture

Div. of Area Studies(M 41/11, D 38/12)
English Studies, German Studies, French Studies, American Studies, Latin American Studies, Asian Studies, West Asian Studies, Thoughts of the World

Div. of International Relations(M 17/6, D 32/17)
International Relations, Comparative Modern Politics

Div. of Social Relations(M 17/7, D 18/8)
Social Relations, Modern Society Analyses

Div. of Cultural Anthropology(M 11/0, D 21/6)
Cultural Anthropology, Pan-Asian Studies, South Asian Studies

Div. of General Systems Studies(M 20/2, D 10/2)
Mathematical System Sciences, Information Science, Systems Theory, Biological Systems, Physical Systems, Environmental Planning, Energy Planning, Ecological System Planning, Global System Planning, Society and Technology Relations

Graduate School of Law and Politics(M 33/8, D 52/7)

Div. of Public Law(M 6/2, D 11/1)
Constitutional Law, Administrative Law, International Law

Div. of Civil and Criminal Law(M 10/4, D 13/4)
Civil Law, Commercial Law, Civil Procedure Law, Criminal Law, Labor Law, Industrial Law, Conflict of Law

Div. of Basic Science of Law(M 1/0, D 7/0)
Philosophy of Law, Principles of Comparative Law, Japanese Legal History, Oriental Legal History, Roman Law, Occidental Legal Law, Anglo-American Law, French Law, German Law, Soviet Law, Chinese Law, Sociology of Law

Div. of Political Science(M 16/2, D 21/2)
Political Science, Science of Public Administration, History of Political Theory, History of Oriental Political Theory, International Politics, Japanese Political and Diplomatic History, Political History, Diplomatic History, American Political and Diplomatic History, Oriental Political and Diplomatic History

Graduate School of Medical Sciences(M 55/16, D 236/51)

Div. of First Basic Medicine(D 30/2)
Anatomy, Physiology

Div. of Second Basic Medicine(D 37/6)
Biochemistry, Molecular Biology, Pharmacology, Radiation Biophysics

Div. of Third Basic Medicine(D 56/12)
Pathology, Bacteriology, Serology, Virology

Div. of Social Medicine(D 12/2)
Preventive Medicine, Public Health, Forensic Medicine, Radiological Health

Div. of First Clinical Medicine(D 38/9)
Internal Medicine, Clinical Research, Advanced Course of Geriatrics, Physical Therapy, Clinical Test

Div. of Second Clinical Medicine(D 3/0)
Pediatrics, Psychiatry, Dermatology, Radiology

Div. of Third Clinical Medicine(D 17/6)
Surgery, Neurosurgery, Thoracic Surgery, Pediatric Surgery, Orthopedics, Anesthesiology, Plastic Surgery, Rehabilitation

Div. of Fourth Clinical Medicine(D 6/4)
Obstetrics and Gynecology, Urology, Ophthalmology, Oto-rhino-laryngology, Oral Surgery

Div. of Health Sciences(M 55/16, D 37/10)
Human Ecology, Epidemiology, Health Administration, Nursing, Health Sociology, Adult Health, Mental Health, Public Health Nutrition, Health Informatics, Radiological Health

Graduate School of Pharmaceutical Sciences(M 129/12, D 102/19)

Div. of Pharmaceutical Sciences(M 42/1, D 39/14)
Pharmaceutical Chemistry, Pharmacognosy and Phytochemistry, Physiological Chemistry, Pharmaceutical Analytical Chemistry, Pharmaceutics Chemical Pharmacology, Organic Natural Product Chemistry, Organic Photo Chemistry

Div. of Pharmaceutical Technochemistry(M 29/1, D 15/0)
Pharmaceutical Technochemistry, Physico-chemical Technology, Physical Chemistry, Pharmaceutical Synthetic Chemistry, Physico-Chemical Analysis

Div. of Pharmaceutical Life-Science(M 58/0, D 48/5)
Toxicology and Pharmacology, Chemical Toxicology and Immunochemistry, Bio-organic Chemistry and Medicinal Chemistry, Hygienic and Forensic Chemistry, Microbial Chemistry, Biochemistry, Cell Biology, Cancer Chemotherapy, Molecular and Cellular Biology Molecular Genetics, Dispensing Pharmacy, Hospital Pharmacy, Administration Cellular Biochemistry, Cellular and Molecular Biology

Graduate School of Science(M 591/26, D 605/65)

Div. of Mathematics(M 55/0, D 52/0)
Number Theory, Algebraic Topology, Partial Differential

Equations, Functional Analysis, Numerical Analysis, Differential Equations, Algebra, Probability Theory, Topology, Axiomatioc Set Theory, Differential Geometry, Algebraic Analysis, Theory of Unitary Representations, Lie Groups, Probability and Dynamical System

Div. of Information Science(M 26/2, D 22/10)
Josephson Computer, Operating System, Computer Architecture, Micro Programing, Computer Graphics and Programing Languages, Graphics, Data Management and System Architecture, System Software, Theory of Autorama, Formal Languages and Kanji Processing, Discrete Mathematics and Programming Languages

Div. of Physics(M 147/6, D 153/7)
Theory of Elementary Particles, Experimental Solid–State Physics, Theory of Solid State Physics, Nuclear and Particle Physics, Biophysics, Plasmaphysics, Theoretical Nuclear Physics, Surface Physics, Solid State Spectroscopy (Synchrotoron Radiation), Nuclear Physics, Quantum Liquids and Solids, Solid–State and Statistical Physics, Experimental Particle Physics and Astrophysics, Experimental Astrophysics, Low Temperature Physics, Quantum Optics, Particle Accelerator, High Pressure Physics, Semiconductors, High Energy Nuclear Physics, Muon Science, Cosmic Ray Physics, High Energy Physics, Solid State Physics, Ultra–Low Temperature Physics, Astrophysics, Experimental Elementary Particle Physics, Theoretical Solid State Physics, Planetary Physics, Molecular Spectroscopy and Quantum Electronics, Statistical Physics, Biophysics and Molecular Biology,Experimental Particle Physics, Neutron Scattering, Intermediate and High Energy Physics, NMR in Condensed Matters, Fluid Dynamics

Div. of Astronomy(M 27/1, D 27/3)
Solar Physics, Celestical Mechanics, Gelactic Astrophysics, Radio Astronomy, Stellar and Galactic Astrophysics, High Energy Astrophysics, Stellar Dynamics, Astrophysics, Infrared Astronomy, Theoretical Astrophysics, Neutrino Physics Experiments

Div. of Geophysics(M 48/2, D 74/14)
Meteoronogy, Physical Volcanology, Cristal Dynamics, Marine Tectonics, Magnetospheric Physics, Solid Earth Geophysics, Seismology, Meteorology, Seismology and Rock Mechanics, Physical Oceanography, Space Plasma Physics, Planetology and Cosmochemistry, Marine Geophysics, Geodynamics, Geochemistry, Geomagnetism

Div. of Chemistry(M 88/4, D 57/7)
Chemical Kinetics, Surface Chemistry, Inorganic Chemistry, Analytical Chemistry, Physical Organic Chemistry, Physical Chemistry, Organic Solid State Chemistry, Solid State Chemistry, Radiochemistry, Atmospheric Chemistry, Geochemistry, Surface Physics and Chemistry, Organic Chemistry, Synthetic Organic Chemistry, Chemical Crystallography, Surface Chemistry and Catalysis, Structural Chemistry, Molecular Spectroscopy, Inorganic and Radiochemistry, Geochemistry (Atmospheric Chemistry), Physical Chemistry of High Polymers

Div. of Biophysics and Biochemistry(M 46/2, D 48/3)
Molecular Immunology, Neurochemistry, Biophysics and Developmental Genetics, Molecular Biology, Biochemistry, Supramolecular Biology, Biochemistry of Photosynthesis, Immunochemistry, Cellular Biochemistry, Tumor Biology & Radiation Oncology, Oncology, Biophysics and Biopolymers, Biophysics

Div. of Zoology(M 26/2, D 25/4)
Physiology, Radiation Biology, Physiological Chemistry, Endocrinology, Molecular Embryology, Comparative Endocrinology, Reproduction Biology, Behavioral Biology, Marine Ecology, Animal Ecology

Div. of Botany(M 21/0, D 31/5)
Cellular Biochemistry, Plant Morphology, Plant Biochemistry, Plant Taxonomy, Plant Physiology, Microbial Ecology, Cytology, Cell Biology, Plant Cell Biology, Genetics

Div. of Anthropology(M 8/0, D 7/1)
Physical Anthropology, Biomechanics, Human Genetics, Prehistoric Archeology, Population Biology, Molecular Biology

Div. of Geology(M 17/4, D 27/7)
Volcanology, Petrology, Palaeontology, Sedimentary Petrology, Ocean Floor Geotectonics, Structural Geology, Mineral Deposits and Chemical Geology, Marine Geology

Div. of Mineralogy(M 9/1, D 8/0)
Diffraction Crystallography, Mineralogy of Planetary Materials, Physics of Planetary Materals, X–ray Crystallography, Structure Mineralogy, Modurated Structure of Minerals

Div. of Geography(M 10/1, D 14/1)
Physical Geography, Human Geography

Div. of Coordinated Sciences(M 50/1, D 41/1)
Statistical Mechanics, Theory of Solid State Physics, Nuclear Solid State Physics, Computer Application to Physics, Surface Physics, Plant Biochemistry, Biophysical Chemistry, Superfluid, Condensed Matter Physics and Biophysics, Solid State Physics, Partial Differential Equations, Plant Physiology, Molecular Biology, Numerical Analysis, Endcrinology and Ethology, Computer Science, Biochemistry and Reproductive Biology, Cell Biology, Radiation Chemistry, Quantum Chemistry and Spectroscopy, Functional Analysis, Quantum Electronics and Spectorscopy, Physical Chemistry, Probability and Dynamical System, Probability, Molecular Biophysics, Information Science, Biochemistry

Div. of History and Philosophy of Science(M 13/0, D 18/2)
Philosophy of Science, History of Ancient and Medieval Science, Early Modern Science and Philosophy of Science, History of Modern Science and Philosophy of Science, Sociology of Science and Technology, History of Chemistry, History of East Asian Science

Div. of Sociology(M 34/4, D 46/6)

Sociology(M 18/1, D 27/1)
Rural and Urban Communities, Social Consciousness, Social Theories, Social Structure and Social Change, Social Change and Economic Sociology, Method of Social Research and Mathematical Sociology

Journalism and Communication Studies(M 10/2, D 8/4)
Economics of Communication Media, Communication Science, Social Information Analysis, Information Behav-

ior, Mass Media Law, Communication Theory, International Communication

Social Psychology(M 6/1, D 11/1)
Interpersonal Relations, Social Psychology of Politics and Economics, Mass Communication, Collective Behavior, Social Cognition

---

東京医科歯科大学
(Tokyo Ikashika Daigaku)

Tokyo Medical and Dental University

1-5-45 Yushima, Bunkyo-ku, Tokyo 113
☎ 03-3813-6111 FAX 03-3818-1575

Founded 1946
Professors 104
Associate Professors 96
Assistant Professors(Tenured) 81
Assistant Professors(Non-tenured) 192
Research Assistants 359
Undergraduate Students/Foreign Students 1147/3
Graduate Students/Foreign Students 222/30
Library 262, 619 volumes
Contact: Undergraduate Admission; Student Division ☎ ext. 2253
Graduate Admission; Department of Medical Office ☎ ext. 3106, Department of Dental Office ☎ ext. 5514

Educational philosophy We deem it both our goal and duty to teach and study the theories and applications of medicine and dentistry, and at the same time contributing to the formation of a well-balanced student character.

Foreign students We welcome warm-hearted students who are willing to study highly advanced subjects of medicine and dentistry as well as the Japanese.

Enviroment The university is located in Bunkyo Ward, near the center of Tokyo, which is the capital city of Japan. There are a number of shrines and historic monuments in the vicinity. It is very conveniently served by the public transportation network.

Facilities University Library, Institute for Medical and Dental Engineering, Medical Research Institute, Health Service Center, Gymnasium, Animal Research Center, Institute of Stomatognathic Science.

Student activities Annual events include an orientation camp for freshmen and two university festivals for sport and art. There are extra-curricular circle activities that include orchestra, chorus, tea ceremony, drama, rowing, Judo, Kendo, soccer, rugby, football and skiing.

Academic programs for foreign students Tutoring system. Courses on Japanese and Japanese affairs.

Services of foreign students personal/psychological counseling.

Undergraduate Programs

Faculty of Dentistry(485/0)
Dept. of Dentistry(485/0)
Faculty of Medicine(662/3)
Dept. of Allied Health Sciences(164/0)
Dept. of Medicine(498/3)

Graduate Programs

Graduate School of Dentistry(D 150/19)
Div. of Dental Basic Science(D 39/6)
Oral Anatomy, Oral Pathology, Oral Microbiology, Oral Physiology, Biochemistry, Dental Pharmacology, Dental Technology
Div. of Dental Clinics(D 111/13)
Oral Surgery, Conservative Dentistry, Prosthodontics, Orthodontics, Preventive Dentist and Public Health, Pedodontics, Dental Radiology, Dental Anesthesiology, Clinic for Disabled Patients, Geriatric Dentistry
Graduate School of Medicine(D 72/11)
Div. of Morphology(D 9/2)
Anatomy, Pathology, Microbiology
Div. of Physiology(D 13/2)
Physiology, Biochemistry, Pharmacology
Div. of Social Medicine(D 7/2)
Hygiene, Public Health, Medical Zoology, Forensic Medicine
Div. of Internal Medicine(D 39/3)
Internal Medicine, Neurology, Neuropsychiatry, Pediatrics, Dermatology, Radiology, Laboratory Medicine
Div. of Surgery(D 4/2)
Surgery, Neuro-Surgery, Thoracic-Surgery, Orthopedic Surgery, Urology, Ophthalmology, Otorhinolaryngology, Obstetrics and Gynecology, Anesthesiology and Critical Care Medicine

---

東京農工大学
(Tokyo Nokō Daigaku)

Tokyo University of Agriculture and Technology

3-8-1 Harumi-cho, Fuchu-shi, Tokyo 183
☎ 0423-64-3311 FAX 0423-60-7376

Founded 1949
Professors 164
Associate Professors 150
Assistant Professors(Tenured) 3
Assistant Professors(Non-tenured) 303
Research Assistants 104
Undergraduate Students/Foreign Students 4, 059/77
Graduate Students/Foreign Students 806/124
Library 390, 770 volumes

Educational philosophy According to social and

state mission of university, our university have a purpose to educate and research the special study of agriculture and technology. And more, we have another purpose to cultivate good educated talent who loves truth and peace.

Foreign students We believe that foreign students can enjoy a rewarding experience in our university, and also can contribute a great deal to promoting mutual understanding and the development of friendly relations.

Environment The Faculty of Agriculture is situated in Fuchu city and the Faculty of Technology in Koganei, Both areas are in westem suburbs of Tokyo called Musasino and now recognized as high-class bedroom towns. Both campuses are apporoximately 40 minutes from the Shinjuku station and 5 kilometers apart from each other.

Facilities Health Service Center, University Library, Fiber and Textile Museum, Sports Athletic Ground, Gymnasium, Tennis Court, Judo & Kendo Hall, Swimming Pool, Welfare Facilities, International House, University Veterinary Clinic, University Farm, University Forests, Pollution Control Center, Computer Center

Student activities Popular campus events include Homecoming, school festival, freshmen welcome party. There are a wide variety of extra curricular activities, including orchestra, chorus, drama, photography, art, go, hiking, baseball, volleyball, tennis, soccer, mountain climbing, judo,etc.

Academic programs for foreign students Supplemental Japanese class, Japanese society class in General Education course and Introduction to fundamental knowledge in each specialized course, Tutoring system.

Services for foreign students Personal/psychological counseling, College housing, Housing information, Part-time job information, Home visit, Overnight observation tour as orientation, Celebration of graduation.

Undergraduate Programs

Faculty of Agriculture(1, 562/14)
- **Dept. of Agricultural Production**(290/2)
- **Dept. of Applied Biological Science**(505/6)
- **Dept. of Environmental Science and Resources** (536/6)
- **Dept. of Veterinary Medicine**(231/0)

Faculty of Technology(2, 497/63)
- **Dept. of Chemical and Biological Science and Technology**(940/10)
- **Dept. of Biotechnology**
- **Dept. of Applied Chemistry**
- **Dept. of Material Systems Engineering**
- **Dept. of Chemical Engineering**
- **Dept. of Mechanical Systems Engineering**(663/19)
- **Dept. of Fundamental Mechanical Engineering**
- **Dept. of Applied Mechanical Engineering**
- **Dept. of Electoronic and Information Engineering** (894/34)
- **Dept. of Applied Physics**
- **Dept. of Electrical and Electronic Engineering**
- **Dept. of Computer Science**

Graduate Programs

Graduate School of Agriculture(M 197/18)

Div. of Agriculture(M 34/4)

Crop Science, Horticultural Science, Agricultural Economics, Zoo-technical Science, Soil Science, Plant Nutrition and Fertilizer Science, Economics of Agricultural Production System, Agricultural Production Technology

Div. of Forestry(M 8/0)

Silviculture, Forest Management, Forest Engineering and Forest Machinery, Forest Hydrology and Erosion Control, Forest Landscape Science

Div. of Agricultural Chemistry(M 44/5)

Bio-organic Chemistry, Biological Chemistry, Microbial Chemistry, Applied Microbiology, Food and Nutrition Chemistry, Animal Products Technology

Div. of Agricultural Engineering(M 22/4)

Farm Machines and Agricultural Processing, Farm Tractor and Farm Power, Irrigation and Drainage, Agricultural Land Engineering, Agricultural Construction Engineering

Div. of Sericulture(M 15/2)

Silkworm Physiology, Silkworm Genetics and Embryology, Biochemistry of Silkworm and Mulberry, Physiology and Fertilizer Science, Economics of Agricultural Production, Ecology of Mulberry Plant, Sericultural Management

Div. of Plant Protection(M 26/1)

Plant Pathology, Applied Entomology, Biological Control, Pesticide Chemistry

Div. of Forest Products(M 26/0)

Wood and Wood based Materials, Wood Processing, Technology of Wood Improvement and Polymeric Materials, Wood Chemical Technology, Forest Products Chemistry

Div. of Environmental Science and Conservation (M 21/2)

Science of Terrestrial Environment, Science of Soil and Aquatic Environment, Science of Pollution Environment, Nature Conservation, Vegetation Management

Graduate School of Technology(M 440/52, D 76/22)

Div. of Chemical and Biological Science and Technology(M 173/12, D 35/14)

Master's course: Biotechnology, Applied Chemistry, Material Systems Engineering, Chemical Engineering

Doctor's course: Molecular Biotechnology, Applied Molecular Chemistry, Functional Material Systems Engineering, Chemical Engineering

Div. of Mechanical Systems Engineering(M 109/18, D 17/2)

Master's course: Fundamental Mechanical Engineering, Applied Mechanical Engineering

Doctor's course: Mechanical Physics, Systems Design Engineering

Div. of Electronic and Information Engineering(M 158/22, D 24/6)

Master's and Doctor's course: Applied Physics, Electrical and Electronic Engineering, Computer Science

Doctoral Course in Agricultural Science, The United Graduate School(D 93/32)

Div. of Science of Plant and Animal Production (D 54/17)

Plant Production, Plant Protection, Animal Production, Management and Economics of Agriculture and Forestry, Agricultural Engineering

Div. of Biochemistry and Biotechnology(D 17/7)

Applied Biological Chemistry, Utilization of Biological Resources

Div. of Science of Resources and Environment(D 22/8)

Forest and Wood Science, Environmental Science

図書館情報大学
(Toshokan Jôhô Daigaku)

University of Library and Information Science

1-2 Kasuga, Tsukuba-shi, Ibaraki 305
☎ 0298-52-0511 FAX 0298-52-0384

Founded 1979
Professors 24
Associate Professors 15
Assistant Professors(Tenured) 6
Assistant Professors(Non-tenured) 33
Research Assistants 12
Undergraduate Students/Foreign Students 636/7
Graduate Students/Foreign Students 27/10
Library 116, 252 volumes
Contact: Division of General Affairs

Educational philosophy The University was founded as the only national institution specially dedicated to the study of library and information science. As the world enters an age of highly developed and diversified information activities, we recognize and accept this challenge, are trying to contribute to the advancement of the field.

Foreign students We hope foreign students acquire well-balanced knowledge and specialized technology, and contribute to the promotion of mutual understanding and the development of international relations.

Environment The campus is located near the center of Tsukuba Science City with a population of about 160, 000, roughly 60 km northeast from the center of Tokyo. The city is situated on a flat terrain at the foot of Mt. Tsukuba (876m), a great number of research institutions, both of national government and private sectors, are established.

Facilities Library with research and development facilities, Foreign language center, Sport and Health science center, Auditorium, Gymnasium, Swimming pool, Atheletics fiejd with all-weather tennis courts

Student activities Regular events cover students' festival, sports festival and freshmen welcome parties. Here is also a wide variety of extra-curricular activities: music and hobby groups, study teams, indoor and outdoor sports clubs, etc.

Academic programs for foreign students Supplementary Japanese language and culture classes, Tutoring system

Services for foreign studetns Personal and psychological counseling, Health care, Cultural exchange program, Visiting trips, Foreign students residence (16 single rooms etc.).

Undergraduate Programs

Faculty of Library and Information Science(636/7)

Dept. of Library and Information Science(636/7)

Graduate Programs

Graduate School of Library and Information Science(M 27/10)

Div. of Library and Information Science(M 27/10)

Principles of Library and Information Science, Society and Information, Information Sources and Materials, Organization of Information, Library and Information Systems

---

電気通信大学
(Denki-tsûshin Daigaku)

The University of Electro-Communications

1-5-1 Chofugaoka, Chofu-shi, Tokyo 182
☎ 0424-83-2161 FAX 0424-81-3224

Founded 1949
Professors 103
Associate Professors 84
Assistant Professors(Tenured) 23
Assistant Professors(Non-tenured) 151
Research Assistants 58
Undergraduate Students/Foreign Students 4, 028/26
Graduate Students/Foreign Students 391/75
Library 299, 647 volumes
Contact: Foreign Students Section, Instruction Division

Educational philosophy We foster and extend the student's abilities to prepare for a professional or academic career in a paticular specialization in science and engineering. Our research activities and educational programs put an emphasis on " Computer, Communication, Control and Materials ".

Foreign students Any student with ambition and diligence is welcome to the University.
Environment The University is located in Chofu City, about 15 km to the west of downtown Tokyo. Chofu City is a residential area of Metropolitan Tokyo, and provides the students with a comfortable environment for his or her campus life.
Facilities Library, Computer Center, Cryogenics Center, Electron Microscope, Space Radio Observatory, Institute of Laser Science, Sports Training Center, Swimming pool, Gymnasium, Auditorium
Student activities Popular campus events includes school festival, freshmen welcome party. There is a wide variety of extra curricular activities, including choral groups, drama, baseball, football, soccer, etc.
Academic programs for foreign students Regular Japanese language class (Japanese language and Studies in Japanese affairs), Supplemental Japanese language class, special class in Physics, Mathematics and Computer, Tutoring system, Information processing seminar for foreign students
Services for foreign students Corner Foreign students' welfare, Health clinic, Personal counseling, College Housing, Information for housing and health insurance and scholarship etc., Home stay, Home visit, Cultural exchange program

Undergraduate Programs

Faculty of Electro-Communications(3, 002/20)
Dept. of Electronic Engineering(685/7)
Dept. of Communications and Systems(671/3)
Dept. of Computer Science and Information Mathematics(678/4)
Dept. of Mechanical and Control Engineering (489/4)
Dept. of Applied Physics and Chemistry(479/2)

Graduate Programs

Graduate School of Electro-Communications(M 317/42, D 71/32)
Div. of Electronic Engineering(M 71/4, D 21/9)
Electron Devices, Optoelectronics and Wave Engineering, Electronic Measurements and Control Engineering, Information and Wave Transmission
Div. of Communications and Systems(M 74/21, D 13/9)
Communication Engineering, Information Systems, Industrial Systems Engineering, Electronics Systems
Div. of Computer Science and Information Mathematics(M 50/7, D 16/9)
Computer Science, Software Engineering, Information Mathematics, Computer Application
Div. of Mechanical and Control Engineering(M 69/8, D 10/2)
Engineering Analysis, Design and Manufacturing System Engineering, Robotic Engineering
Div. of Applied Physics and Chemistry(M 53/2, D 11/3)
Atomic Physics and Its Applications, Condensed Matter Physics and Its Applications, Molecular Science

---

筑波大学
(Tsukuba Daigaku)
University of Tsukuba

1-1-1 Tennodai, Tsukuba-shi, Ibaraki 305
☎ 0298-53-2111 FAX 0298-53-6019

Founded 1973
Professors 515
Associate Professors 442
Assistant Professors(Tenured) 413
Assistant Professors(Non-tenured) 340
Research Assistants 133
Undergraduate Students/Foreign Students 8, 888/109
Graduate Students/Foreign Students 3, 054/649
Library 1, 647, 907 volumes

Educational philosophy The university's aim is to establish free, deep and close exchange in basic and applied sciences with education and research organizations and academic communities in Japan and overseas, and reap the fruits of academic cooperation with them. While developing these relationships, we intend to continue our pursuit of education and research, and through these endeavors to develop men and women with creative intelligence and rich human qualities.
Foreign students We believe that foreign students can enjoy a rewarding experience in our university, and can develop friendly relations in the circumstance of the new science city Tsukuba.
Environment The university campus is located in the center of Tsukuba Science City, 60km northeast of Tokyo and is 60 minutes by highway bus from Tokyo Station. The Tsukuba Mountains lie to the north and Kasumigaura to the southeast. The university is blessed with beautiful natural and cultural surroundings.
Facilities Libraries, various centers (tandem accelerator center, plasma research center, gene experiment center, sport and physical education center, etc).
Student activities Annual campus events include fresh-persons welcoming festival, intramural sports games, school festival, and a welcome party for foreign students and the staff. There are over a hundred student groups of extracurricular activities for culture, art, music and sports.
Academic programs for foreign students Supplemental Japanese language class, Tutoring system
Services for foreign students health clinic, personal/psychological counseling, college housing, housing information, part-time job information, vocational guidance, home stay and home visit information, cultural exchange program

Undergraduate Programs

First Cluster of Colleges(2, 062/9)
College of Humanities(533/3)
College of Natural Sciences(956/1)
College of Social Sciences(573/5)
Second Cluster of Colleges(2, 320/45)
College of Agriculture and Forestry(680/2)
College of Biological Sciences(381/2)
College of Comparative Culture(385/4)
College of Human Sciences(525/1)
College of Japanese Language and Culture(349/36)
Third Cluster of Colleges(2, 372/45)
College of Engineering Sciences(868/8)
College of Information Sciences(536/10)
College of International Relations(408/19)
College of Socio-Economic Planning(560/8)
School of Medicine(629/1)
School of Health and Physical Education(1, 039/3)
School of Art and Design(466/6)

Graduate Programs

Graduate School of Area Studies(MD 125/49)
Graduate School of Art and Design(MD 108/42)
Graduate School of Education(MD 324/32)
Graduate School of Environmental Sciences(MD 215/16)
Graduate School of Health and Physical Education(MD 204/35)
Graduate School of Management Sciences and Public Policy Studies(MD 332/66)
Graduate School of Medical Sciences(MD 64/4)
Graduate School of Sciences and Engineering(MD 347/33)
Graduate School of Agricultural Sciences(MD 135/44)
Graduate School of Art and Design(MD 32/9)
Graduate School of Biological Sciences(MD 81/7)
Graduate School of Chemistry(MD 40/6)
Graduate School of Education(MD 67/14)
Graduate School of Engineering(MD165/50)
Graduate School of Geoscience(MD 56/19)
Graduate School of Health and Sport Sciences(MD 54/19)
Graduate School of History and Anthropology(MD 91/24)
Graduate School of Literature and Linguistics(MD 154/66)
Graduate School of Mathematics(MD 38/4)
Graduate School of Medical Sciences(MD 116/20)
Graduate School of Philosophy(MD 50/19)
Graduate School of Physics(MD 71/4)
Graduate School of Psychology(MD 50/8)
Graduate School of Social Sciences(MD 47/20)
Graduate School of Socio-Economic Planning(MD 57/36)
Graduate School of Special Education(MD 31/3)

宇都宮大学

(Utsunomiya Daigaku)

Utsunomiya University

350 Mine-machi, Utsunomiya-shi, Tochigi 321
☎ 0286-36-1515 FAX 0286-35-5166 0286-37-8466

Founded 1949
Professors 146
Associate Professors 124
Assistant Professors(Tenured) 23
Assistant Professors(Non-Tenured) 287
Research Assistants 46
Undergraduate Students/Foreign Students 4,352/38
Graduate Students/Foreign Students 300/15
Library 415, 807 volumes
Contact: Administration Office

Educational philosophy Established on three faculties with different history, our university has recently restructured itself to meet the needs of rapidly changing modern world. The teaching staff are making every effort to conduct lively education using fresh results of their research.

Foreign students For the foreign students who wish to fulfill themselves through academic activities, we believe our university is a good place to study at and live in with helpful staff and friendly students.

Environment The City of Utsunomiya, the capital of Tochigi Prefecture with a population of 420,000, is located 100 km north of Tokyo, within an hour's reach by Tohoku Sinkansen. The largest city in the northern Kanto area, it is full of amenity with famous resorts like Nikko quite near.

Facilities University Library, Health Service Center, Information Processing Center, Cooperative Research Center, Educational Research Center, Nature Training Institute, University Farm, University Forests, etc.

Student activities Popular university events include the university festival and participation in the Kanto-Koshin'etsu District Universities Athletic Meet. There is a wide choice of clubs, for example, horseriding, gliding, judo, karate, football, birdwatching, orchestra, tea-ceremony, etc.

Academic programs for foreign students Japanese classes, things Japanese classes, Credit-substitute system, Tutoring system.

Services for foreign students Medical examination, Counselling, University housing, Housing information, Part-time job information, Homestay, Cultural exchange parties, Excursion, Skiing tour.

Undergraduate Programs

Faculty of Education(1,401/19)
Comprehensive Education Division(70/2)
Elementary School Teachers Training Division

(908/3)
Junior High School Teachers Training Division (328/13)
Mentally Retarded Children's Teachers Training Division(95/1)
Faculty of Engineering(1,816/9)
Dept. of Applied Chemistry(445/1)
Dept. of Architecture and Civil Engineering(371/2)
Dept. of Electrical and Electronic Engineering (378/5)
Dept. of Information Science(264/0)
Dept. of Mechanical Systems Engineering(358/1)
Faculty of Agriculture(1,135/10)
Dept. of Agricultural Chemistry(177/1)
Dept. of Agricultural Economics(214/6)
Dept. of Agricultural Engineering(193/2)
Dept. of Agriculture(204/0)
Dept. of Animal science(147/0)
Dept. of Forestry(200/1)

Graduate Programs

Graduate School of Education(M 66/2)
School Education Science Division(M 11/2)
Educational Science, Educational Psychology, Education of Mentally and Physically Handicapped
Education in Specific Subjects Division(M 55/0)
Japanese Language and Literature Education, Japanese Language, Japanese Literature, Social Science Education, History and Geography, Ethics and Social Science, Science Education, Physical and Chemical Science, Life and Earth Science, Music Education, Methodology of Playing Music, Composition and Musicology, Art Education, Painting, Carving, Design, Craft, Health and Physical Education, Science of Physical Education, Biomechanics, School Health, Industry and Technology Education, Science of Industrial Arts, English Education, English Language, English and American Literature
Graduate School of Engineering(M 156/6)
Div. of Mechanical Engineering(M 26/2)
Thermal Engineering, Material Engineering, Fluid Engineering, Mechanical Technology
Div. of Precision Engineering(M 23/0)
Instrumentation and Control, Precision Processing, Precision Machine Elements, Mechanical Metallurgy and Plastic Forming
Div. of Electrical Engineering(M 10/1)
Fundamental Electrical Engineering, Electric Power Engineering, Electric and Electronic Instrumentation, Communication Engineering
Div. of Electronic Engineering(M 13/1)
Electro-Physics, Electronic Circuits, Plasma Science, Electronic Control
Div. of Industrial Chemistry(M 18/0)
Inorganic Industrial Chemistry, Organic Industrial Chemistry, Chemical Engineering
Div. of Environmental Chemistry(M 16/0)
Chemistry of Water Quality, Environmental Analytical Chemistry, Organic Reactions, Pollution Control
Div. of Architecture(M 20/0)
Architectural Planning, Planning and Design, Architectural Facilities Engineering, Building Structural Engineering
Div. of Civil Engineering(M 7/1)
Structural Engineering and Civil Engineering Materials, Hydraulics Engineering, Regional Facilities, Regional Planning
Div. of Information Science(M 23/1)
Theory of Computation and Information, Information Processing Machinery, Information Processing, Computing Devices and their Applications
Graduate School of Agriculture(M 78/7)
Div. of Agriculture(M 22/2)
Crop Cultivation, Plant Breeding, Horticultural Science, Plant Pathology, Applied Entomology Sericultural Science, Comparative Agriculture
Div. of Forestry(M 7/1)
Silviculture and Erosion Control, Forest Management, Forest Policy, Forest Engineering, Chemical Technology of Forest Products, Improvement of Wood Materials
Div. of Agricultural Economics(M 6/1)
Farm Management, Agricultural Policy, Agricultural Economics, Agricultural History and Agricultural Location, Agricultural Statistics, Farm Records and Accounting
Div. of Animal Science(M 12/1)
Animal Breeding and Reproduction, Animal Nutrition, Science of Animal Products, Animal Diseases
Div. of Agricultural Engineering(M 9/1)
Agricultural Land Engineering, Agricultural Hydrotechnics, Agricultural Structure Designing, Farm Machinery, Farm Power, Farm Management Technology, Farm Facilities
Div. of Agricultural Chemistry(M 22/1)
Plant Nutrition and Fertilizers, Soil Sciense, Biochemistry, Science of Agricultural Products, Food Chemistry, Applied Microbiology

---

横浜国立大学
(Yokohama Kokuritsu Daigaku)
Yokohama National University

156 Tokiwadai, Hodogaya-ku, Yokohama-shi, Kanagawa 240
☎ 045-335-1451 FAX 045-341-2582

Founded 1949
Professors 229
Associate Professors 176
Assistant Professors(Tenured) 33
Assistant Professors(Non-tenured) 479
Research Assistants 94
Undergraduate Students/Foreign Students 8,321/84
Graduate Students/Foreign Students 945/184
Library 898, 503 volumes
Contact: International Affairs Office, General Affairs Depart-

ment, Administration Bureau

Educational philosophy Our university points at giving students highly sophisticated education to cultivate their intellectual abilities. Also, we are going forward to next century to deepen international and cultural exchange with all over the world through research and education.

Foreign students More than 440 students from overseas are studying at YNU. The number is increasing. We are ready to receive more students from various countries.

Environment The industries with high technology and the research laboratories on high technologies which back up the functions of the Tokyo area are gathered in Yokohama district. The population of this district is more than 3.17 millions.

Facilities Institute of Environmental Science and Technology, Health Service Center, Library, Information Processing Center, Radio Isotope Center, University Hall, Foreign Student House, Gymnasium, Swimming Pool, Cafeteria, Student Activities Facilities, etc.

Student activities There are two groups of circles run by students, physical and cultural activity circles. To enjoy campus life, all students from overseas are invited to join any of the circles free of charges.

Academic programs for foreign students There are supplemental Japanese language class, mother language. Also there are classes for " Topics in Japanese Culture " which is one of the liberal arts subjects and " Japanese Language ". " Japanese Language " may be substituted for any required languages(except for English and one's mother language).

Services for foreign students Tutoring system, health clinic, personal/psychological counseling, Foreign student house, Housing information, Part-time job information, Cultural Exchange program, etc.

Undergraduate Programs

Faculty of Education(2,309/16)
- **Course of Elementary School Teachers**(1,181/5)
- **Course of Junior High School Teachers**(521/28)
- **Course of Teachers of Handicapped Children**(89/1)
- **Course of Humanities and Social Sciences**(152/1)
- **Course of Natural Science**(142/0)
- **Course of Lifelong Integrated Education**(186/1)
- **Course of Integrated Art**(38/0)

Faculty of Economics(1,133/14)
- **Dept. of Economics**(300/3)
- **Dept. of International Economics**(666/11)
- **Dept. of Law and Economics**(167/0)

Faculty of Business Administration(1,096/32)
- **Dept. of Business Administration**(497/28)
- **Dept. of Accounting**(292/1)
- **Dept. of Management Science**(307/3)

Faculty of Engineering(2,939/22)
- **Dept. of Mechanical Engineering and Materials Science**(717/4)
- **Dept. of Materials Science and Chemical Engineering**(832/2)
- **Dept. of Civil Engineering, Architecture and Marine Technology**(726/6)
- **Dept. of Electrical and Computer Engineering**(664/10)

Graduate Programs

Graduate School of Education(M 213/16)

Div. of School Education(M 37/0)
Education, Educational History, Educational Systems, Educational Sociology, Educational Psychology, Developmental Psychology, Social Education

Div. of Social Studies Education(M 34/4)
History, Geography, Law, Politics, Sociology, Economics, Philosophy, Ethics, Asian Cultures, Teaching of Social Studies

Div. of Mathematics Education(M 12/1)
Algebra and Geometry, Analytical and Applied Mathematics, Computer Science, Mathematical Education

Div. of Science Education(M 30/1)
Physics, Chemistry, Biology, Earth Science, Geology, Science Education

Div. of Art Education(M 12/3)
Painting, Sculpture, Construction, Theory of Art, Teaching of Fine Arts

Div. of Teaching of English as a Foreign Language(M 17/2)
English Linguistics, English and American Literature, European and American Studies, Teaching of English

Div. of Special Education(M 9/0)
Education of Handicapped Children, Psychology of Handicapped Children, Pathology of Handicapped Children

Div. of Music Education(M 14/0)
Vocal Music, Instrumental Music, Composition, Conducting of Music, Musicology, Teaching of Music

Div. of Teaching of Japanese Language and Literature(M 19/3)
Japanese Language, Japanese Literature, Chinese Classics, Calligraphy, Teaching of Japanese, Teaching of Japanese as a Foreign Language

Div. of Health and Physical Education(M 12/0)
Physical Education, Kinematics, Physiology and Hygiene, School Health, Teaching of Physical Education

Div. of Home Economics Education(M 10/0)
Food Chemistry, Clothing, Management of Family Life, Nursing, Living Science, Teaching of Home Economics

Div. of Technical Education(M 7/2)
Wood Working and Carpentry, Electricity, Mechanics, Cultivation, Teaching of Technology

Graduate School of Economics(M 22/15)

Div. of Economics(M 10/5)
Economics, History of Economics, Economic Statistics, Economic Policy, Economic History, Public Finance, Money and Banking, Social and Public Policy, Econometrics, Basic Law, Environmental and Public Law, Jap-

anese Economic Law, Internatioal Economic Law

Div. of International Economics(M 12/10)
International Economics, International Relations, International Trade Business, International Finance, Export Industry, History of World Economy, World Economy

Graduate School of Business Administration(M 41/19)

Div. of Business Administration(M 41/19)
Business Administration, Personnel Management, Principles of Marketing, Insurance, Science of Commodities, Business Behavior, Principles of Accounting, Bookkeeping, Management Accounting, Ecological Accounting, Management Science, Human Science, Mathematics of Business, Business Information, Environmental Management, Cost Accounting

Graduate School of Engineering(M 509/58, D 96/61)

Div. of Mechanical Engineering and Materials Science(M 128/11, D 26/18)
Materials Science, Materials Processing, Thermodynamics and Fluid Mechanics, Mechanical Design and Systems, Engineering Intelligent Mechanical Systems

Div. of Materials Science and Chemical Engineering(M 188/19, D 22/10)
Physical Chemistry, Synthetic Chemistry, Materials Chemistry, Chemical Process Engineering, Safety Engineering, Energy Engineering, Chemistry and Design of Organic Compounds having Bioactive

Div. of Civil Engineering, Architecture and Marine Technology(M 85/12, D 22/18)
Civil Engineering, Architecture and Building Science, Regional, Urban and Environmental Planning, Naval Architecture and Ocean Engineering

Div. of Electrical and Computer Engineering (M 108/16, D 26/15)
Electrical Systems, Electronic Engineering, Information Systems,

Graduate School of International and Business Law (M 64/15)

Div. of Economic Relations Law(M 50/15)
Government and Business, Economic Activities and Law

Div. of International Relations Law(M 14/0)
Nation and Economy, International Community and Law

One-Year Graduate Programs

Special Education Course
Education of the Mentally Handicapped Major, Education of the Multihandicapped Major

Local Public Universities

群馬県立女子大学
(Gunma Kenritsu Joshi Daigaku)

Gunma Prefectural Women's College

1395–1 Kaminote, Tamamura–machi, Sawa–gun, Gunma 370–11
☎ 0270–65–8511 FAX 0270–65–9538

Founded 1980
Professors 20
Associate Professors 22
Assistant Professors(Tenured) 2
Assistant Professors(Non–tenured) 33
Research Assistants 6
Undergraduate Students/Foreign Students 587/0
Library 93, 867 volumes
Contact: Instruction Section

Educational philosophy This college was founded to give female students a higher education which will enrich their lives and broaden their cultural horizons. It is our aim that with their enhanced awareness of global issues they will eventually contribute to the betterment of their local communities as well as to that of their own family life.

Foreign students Our college is prepared to accept foreign female students and will provide applicants with further information upon request.

Environment The town of Tamamura is located in northwest of the Kanto Plain. It's a very pleasant place to study, surrounded by countryside and with beautiful views of rivers and mountains. Our neighboring town, Maebashi, is the prefectual capital of Gunma. It has excellent cultural facilities and is convenient for shopping. Tokyo is an hour away by train.

Facilities Our school was relocated in 1982, and most of the present buildings were constructed then; class rooms, teachers' studies and reference rooms, auditorium, library, gymnasium, students' hall, clubroom building and office block. In addition to these, our fine art block was completed in 1990.

Student activities There are 21 cultural clubs and 13 sports clubs; tea ceremony, flower arrangement, drama, Kyudo(Japanese archery), Kendo and so on. A lot of students are active members.

Undergraduate Programs

Faculty of Letters(587/0)
Dept. of Aesthetics and Art History(143/0)
Dept. of English Literature(207/0)
Dept. of Japanese Literature(237/0)

高崎経済大学
(Takasaki Keizai Daigaku)

Takasaki City University of Economics

1300 Kaminamie-machi, Takasaki-shi, Gunma 370
☎ 0273-43-5417 FAX 0273-43-4830

Founded 1957
Professors 34
Associate Professors 11
Assistant Professors (Tenured) 6
Assistant Professors (Non-tenured) 77
Undergraduate Students/Foreign Students 2, 028/17
Library 120, 113 volumes
Contact: Admission Office

Educational philosophy We aim at teaching and studying up-to-date high-level social science: Economics and Business Administration to develop intellectual and applied abilities so students may contribute much to cultural betterment and social improvement.
Foreign students Students from non-Japanese speaking countries who admission to our University must demonstrate proficiency in Japan, since all lectures are given in that language.
Environment Takasaki City has been an important transportation center in central Japan and has grown as a commercial and industrial city. The New Jyoetsu National Railway Line, one of the super rapid transits in the world, was established in 1985 and provides express service from Takasaki Station to Ueno Station in only fifty minutes.
Facilities Library, Gymnasium, Auditorium, and the Institute for Research of Regionla Economy. Sports facilities includes an athletic field and baseball ground.
Student activities Popular campus events includes School Festival, freshmen welcome party. The student has a wide variety of extra curricular activities, including football, soccer, baseball, marching band, hiking club, etc.
Academic programs for foreign students Japanese Language class.
Services for foreign students Health clinic, personal/psychological counselling, housing information, part-time job information, cultural exchange program.

Undergraduate Programs

Faculty of Economics (2, 028/17)
Dept. of Economics (775/6)
Dept. of Business Management (750/9)

東京都立科学技術大学
(Tokyo Toritsu Kagaku Gijutsu Daigaku)

Tokyo Metropolitan Institute of Technology

6-6 Asahigaoka, Hino-shi, Tokyo 191
☎ 0425-83-5111 FAX 0425-83-5119

Founded 1986
Professors 29
Associate Professors 19
Assistant Professors (Tenured) 3
Assistant Professors (Non-tenured) 32
Research Assistants 17
Undergraduate Students/Foreign Students 755/7
Graduate Students/Foreign Students 38/1
Library 58, 854 volumes
Contact: Students' Affairs Unit

Educational philosophy Our Institute was inaugurated in 1986 to meet the needs of the Tokyo Metropolitan Community for higher education and research in these times of rapid industrial growth. It is the mission of the Institute to cultivate frontier sciences and develop new technologies.
Foreign students Foreign students can study high-level and new technologies concerned with mechanical, electronic, aerospace and management system engineerings. They can ejnoy new experiences in friendly atmosphere.
Environment Hino City, with a population of 160, 000, is located in west of Kanto Plains, 27 miles from the center of Tokyo. There are many high technological industries.
Facilities Library, Mechanical, Aeronautical and Electronic Research Laboratories, Gymnasium, Students' Hall.
Student activities Popular campus event includes freshmen welcome party and school festival. There is a wide variety of extra curricular activities including enginepring groups, astronomical group, music, baseball, soccer, tennis, ski, etc.
Services for foreign students Personal/psychological counseling, Housing information, Part-time job information, etc.

Undergraduate Programs

Faculty of Engineering (755/7)
Dept. of Mechanical Systems Engineering (191/1)
Dept. of Electronic Systems Engineering (193/4)
Dept. of Aerospace Engineering (190/1)
Dept. of Management Systems Engineering (181/1)

Graduate Programs

Graduate school of Engineering(M 38/1)
Div. of Applied Engineering Sciences(M 23/1)
Solid Mechanics, Applied Fluid Systems, Energy System Engineering, Mechatronics, Flight Systems Engineering, Space Systems Engineering
Div. of Electronic and Information Sciences(M 15/0)
Electronic Materials Engineering, Power Electronics, System Controll Engineering, Intelligent Information Processing, Production System Engineering, Management Systems Engineering

---

東京都立大学
(Tokyo Toritsu Daigaku)
Tokyo Metropolitan University

1-1 Minami-ohsawa, Hachiohji-shi, Tokyo 192-03
☎ 0426-77-1111 FAX 03-3718-4661

Founded 1949
Professors 166
Associate Professors 163
Assistant Professors(Tenured) 10
Assistant Professors(Non-tenured) 268
Research Assistants 232
Undergraduate Students/Foreign Students 3, 859/10
Graduate Students/Foreign Students 752/80
Library 949, 590 volumes
Contact: Secretariat, General Affairs Section

Educational philosophy As a central institution of higher learning in the metropolis, Tokyo Metropolitan University shall disseminate knowledge, conduct research and instruction in advanced fields of academic enquiry, and promote intellectual, moral, and practical abilities, thereby conrtibuting to the life and culture of the citizens of Tokyo.
Foreign students We believe that foreign students can enjoy a rewarding experience in our school, and can contribute a great deal to promoting mutual understanding and the development of friendly relations.
Environment Tokyo Metropolitan University is located in the south-west part of Tokyo, about 20 minutes from Shibuya-Station by train-car on the Tokyu Toyoko Line and about 10 minutes from Toritsudaigaku-Station on foot. The admistrative building of the university is located on a hill named " Yakumo-ga-oka " with a view of Mt. Fuji to the west.
Facilities Center for Urban Studies, University Library, Computer Center, Makino Herbarium, TMU Tajima Lodge, Auditorium, Gymnasium, Students Activities Room, University Hall
Student activities Popular campus events includes Matriculation Ceremony, Annual Athletics between Tokyo Metropolitan University and University of Osaka Prefecture, University Festival and Commencement. There are some organizations of Students Activities including Student Self-ruling Association, Student News Organization, Athletic Association, Student Cultural Association, and Circle Association
Academic programs for foreign students Guidance of teaching staff-system
Services for foreign students Tutor-system, Orientation, Field trip, Social gathering with teaching staff

Undergraduate Programs

Faculty of Economics(641/5)
Dept. of Economics(641/5)
Faculty of Law(702/0)
Dept. of Law
Dept. of Politics
Faculty of Science(743/1)
Dept. of Biology(114/0)
Dept. of Chemistry(200/1)
Dept. of Geography(80/0)
Dept. of Mathematics(151/0)
Dept. of Physics(198/0)
Faculty of Social Sciences and Humanities(597/0)
Dept. of Languages and Literature (Japanese Language and Literature/Chinese Language and Literature/English Language and Literature/German Language and Literature/French Language and Literature)
Dept. of Social Sciences and Humanities (Sociology/Philosophy/Pedagogy/Psychology/History/Social Welfare)
Faculty of Technology(1, 176/4)
Dept. of Architecture and Building Science(213/2)
Dept. of Civil Engineering(197/0)
Dept. of Electrical Engineering(236/2)
Dept. of Industrial Engineering(207/0)
Dept. of Mechanical Engineering(323/0)

Graduate Programs

Graduate School of Humanities(M 93/10, D 147/22)
Div. of Chinese Language and Literature(M 9/1, D 13/3)
Phonetics and Grammer, Modern Literature and Folk Narrative
Div. of English Language and Literature(M 9/0, D 16/0)
almost all periods and genres of English and American literature, English philology and historical and theoretical linguistics
Div. of French Language and Literature(M 6/0, D 10/0)
French Literature of almost all periods and genres, and stylistics, to the history of ideas from the 17th century to the present
Div. of German Language and Literature(M 4/0,

D 12/1)
German literature of different periods and gernes, German philology, and linguistics

Div. of History(M 20/2, D 26/2)
Japanese, Asian, and European History from ancient through modern and/or contemporary periods

Div. of Japanese Language and Literature(M 16/7, D 23/10)
historical changes, regional dialects, grammatical and other aspects of the Japanese language; literary works, writers, and currents of literary thought from ancient, medieval, modern, through contemporary scenes of Japanese literature

Div. of Pedagogy(M 11/0, D 18/5)
History of Education, Fundamentals of Educational Practice, Institutional Aspects of Education, Education for the Handicapped, Adult Education and Youth Service, Discrimination and Education

Div. of Philosophy(M 8/0, D 10/0)
ancient Greek to contemporary German, French, and Anglo-American philosophy

Div. of Psychology(M 10/0, D 19/1)
Psychology, Experimental Psychology, Applied Psychology

Graduate School of Science(M 120/4, D 96/3)

Div. of Biology(M 26/0, D 25/2)
Cytology, Biochemistry, Neurobiology, Genetics, Developmental Biology, Animal Ecology, Metabolic Physiology, Microbial Ecology, Systematic Botany, Systematic Zoology

Div. of Chemistry(M 39/0, D 18/1)
Inorganic Chemistry, Geochemistry, Radiochemistry and Nuclear Chemistry, Organic Chemistry, Biochemistry, Physical Chemistry, Chemical Kinetics and Reaction Dynamics

Div. of Geography(M 12/3, D 8/0)
Geomorphology and Quaternary Geology; Climatology; Environmental Studies incliding Environmental Geomorphology and Natural Hazards, and Mathematical Modeling and Geographical Information Processing; Urban, Socio-economic and Quantitative Geography

Div. of Mathematics(M 10/0, D 17/0)
Number Theory, Group Theory, Ring Theory, Reprentation Theory, Algebraic Geometry, Complex Manifolds, Different Geometry, Topology, Different Equations, Operator Algebras, Function Theory, Ergodic Theory, Dynamical Systems, Probability Theory, and others

Div. of Physics(M 33/1, D 28/0)
Fluid Mechanics, Nuclear Physics, Astrophysics, High Energy Physics, Solid State Physics, Material Science, Magnetism, Metal Physics, Chemical Physics, Optical Properties of Condensed Matter, Statistical Physics

Graduate School of Social Sciences(M 42/14, D 55/5)

Div. of Economics(M 7/4, D 5/1)
Economic Theory, Economic Policy, Economic History, Business Administration

Div. of Law(M 7/5, D 16/0)
Constitutional Law, Administrative Law, Civil Law, Commercial Law, Criminal Law, Code of Criminal Procedure, Code of Civil Procedure, Labor Law, Social Security Law, International Law, International Private Law, Legal History, Sociology of Law, Philosophy of Law, Medical Law, Environmental Law, Educational Law

Div. of Political Science(M 4/0, D 6/1)
Political Science, History of Political Thought, Political History, International Politics, Public Administration, Urban Government

Div. of Social Anthropology(M 10/1, D 12/2)
Ethnography of East Africa, East Asia, Oceania and Southeast Asia; Social Organization, Kinship, Cosmology, Sociocultural Change, History of Anthropological Theories

Div. of Sociology(M 14/4, D 16/1)
Sociological Theories, Urban Sociology, Social Welfare

Graduate School of Technology(M 181/18, D 18/4)

Div. of Architecture and Building Science(M 38/4, D 6/1)
Architectural History and Theory, Architectural Design and Planning, Building Economics, City Planning, Environmental Engineering, Building Materials and Construction, Structural Analysis and Engineering, Earthquake Engineering

Div. of Civil Engineering(M 22/1, D 1/1)
Traffic Engineering and City Planning, Hydraulics and Hydrology, Sanitary Engineering, Structural Engineering, Applied Mechanics, Engineering Materials, Disaster Prevention Engineering, Soil Engineering

Div. of Electrical Engineering(M 34/5, D 1/0)
Electromagnetic Theory, Network Theory, Power System Engineering, Electric Machinery, Electrical Engineering Application, Electronics, Communication Engineering, Emergency-Oriented Information Engineering

Div. of Industrial Chemistry(M 47/3, D 6/1)
Inorganic Chemistry, Organic Chemistry, Polymer Chemistry, Chemical Engineering, Materials Chemistry, Analytical Chemistry

Div. of Mechanical Engineering(M 40/5, D 4/1)
Material Engineering, Fluid-Thermal Engineering, Precision Engineering, System Dynamics and Control

---

横浜市立大学

(Yokohama Shiritsu Daigaku)

Yokohama City University

22-2 Seto Kanazawa-ku, Yokohama-shi, Kanagawa 236
☎ 045-787-2311 FAX 045-787-2316

Founded 1928
Professors 106
Associate Professors 94
Assistant Professors(Tenured) 44
Assistant Professors(Non-tenured) 517
Research Assistants 119
Undergraduate Students/Foreign Students 3, 336/54
Graduate Students/Foreign Students 158/18
Library 422, 865 volumes
Contact: Student Affairs Section 045-787-2035

Educational philosophy The international port town of Yokohama has created the university as a center for the pursuit of truth, the teaching of culture and science at the highest level, the nurturing of people as moral, intellectual, and practical beings, so that they can contribute to international peace and the welfare of mankind, and to the elevation of the continuous improvement in the lives and culture of the people of Yokohama.

Foreign students We should like to welcome you to our university with its unique history and traditions. We hope that you will soon get accustomed to the system and the atmosphere and become part of the student body at the university.

Environment Seto campus and Fukuura campus consist in Kanazawa ward, and Urafune campus is in Minami ward. These wards are located in the south of Yokohama, the second largest city in Japan, with a population of 3, 200, 000. In the neighborhood, there are temples and sites from the 12 th century (the Kanazawa period).

Facilities A university hospital; A gymnasium with a heated indoors swimming pool; a club activities building; library; university center (both of which will be rebuilt in the near future); social & cultural research building; general research building; science research building; information technology center.

Student activities Freshers' excursion, university festival, overseas student' speech contest & orientation, graduation excursion, 57 societies in a variety of culture–related subjects: social, Japanese culture, languages, arts, music; & 30 sports–related societies.(applied to faculty students only)

Academic programs for foreign students Overseas students have special tutors who instruct them in matters related to their studies as well as in other matters of interest. As a rule, self–paying students receive tuition in Japanese within one year of their enrollment. (applied to faculty students only)

Services for foreign students Reductions and exemptions in tuition, financial support for overseas students, counseling by the administration, hostel(9 rooms), possible lodging in company hostels, overseas student' common room.(applied to faculty students only)

Undergraduate Programs

Faculty of Economics and Business Administration(1, 494/36)

Dept. of Economics Course(762/9)

Dept. of Business Administration Course(732/27)

Faculty of Liberal Arts and Science(1, 279/18)

Dept. of Liberal Arts Course(785/15)

Dept. of Science Course(494/3)

Faculty of School of Medicine(136/0)

Dept. of Medical Science Course(136/0)

Graduate Programs

Graduate School of Economics(M 24/5)

Mathematical Economics, Economic Statistics, Economic History, Social Philosophy, Economic Policy, Public Finance, Monetary Theory, International Economics, Social Policy, History of the Japanese Economy, History of Western Economics, etc.

Graduate School of Business Administration(M 27/12)

Business Administration, Management of Organisations, Market Research, Managerial Engineering, Topic in Business Administration, Topics in Management Control, Special Topics in the History of Management, History of Commerce, Monetary Theory, Banking, The Securities Market

Graduate School of Integrated Science(M 53/1)

Div. of System Element(M20/0)

Div. of System Function(M 33/1)

Introduction to Integrated Science, General Mathematical Science, General Material Science, General Biological Science, Advanced Enzymology, Advanced Microbiology, Advanced Crystal Growth Theory, Advanced Dispersive Structure Theory, Advanced Biological System, Advanced Biotechnology, Advanced Solid State Physics, Advanced Solution Chemistry, Advanced Molecular Design, Defect Control in Crystals, Science of Thin Solid Film, Advanced Colloid and Interface Science

Graduate School of Medical Science(D 80/0)

Div. of Physiology Anatomy, Physiology, Biochemistry, Pharmacology

Div. of Pathology Pathology, Medical Parasirology, Bacteriology

Div. of Social Dedicine Hygiene, Public Health, Legal Mediology

Div. of Internal Medicine Internal Medicine, Pediatrics, Radiology, Psychiatry, Dermatology

Div. of Surgery Surgery, Orthopedics, Neurological Surgery, Otorhino laryngology Obstertrics and Gynecology, Urology Ophhalmology, Oral Surgery, Anaesthesiology

Private Universities

青山学院大学
(Aoyama Gakuin Daigaku)

Aoyama Gakuin University

4-4-25 Shibuya, Shibuya-ku, Tokyo 150
☎ 03-3409-8111 FAX 03-3409-0927

Founded 1874
Professors 267
Associate Professors 76
Assistant Professors(Tenured) 25
Assistant Professors(Non-tenured) 720
Research Assistants 49
Undergraduate Students/Foreign Students 19,381/62
Graduate Students/Foreign Students 462/9
Library 890, 445 volumes
Contact: International Exchange Center ☎ 03-3409-7923

Educational philosophy Aoyama Gakuin has as its aim education based upon the Christian faith and as its purpose the building up of persons who live in sincerity before God, who seek for truth with humility, and who actively take responsibility for all people and for society in a spirit of love and service.

Foreign students To enable foreign students at Aoyama Gakuin University to adjust to their environment and to pursue their studies effectively, some support systems have been established.

Environment Aoyama Gakuin University is located in the central part of Tokyo, not far from Shibuya station, and faces National Highway Route 246, commonly known as Aoyama Dori(Aoyama Boulevard).

Facilities Libraries, Majima Memorial Archives, Wesley Hall, Reserch Institutes Information Science Research Center, Foreign Language Laboratory The Tsunashima Facility, Memorial Hall, Swimming Pool, Yatsugatake Lodge

Student activities Worship, Celebration of Advent, School Festival, Welcome Party, Farewell party. There is a wide variety of extra curricular activities athletic clubs and hobby clubs, including student news paper, baseball, football, soccer, music club, Japanese culture club, academic study club, etc.

Academic programs for foreign students Japanese language class, Japanology, Tutoring system, Adviser system

Services for foreign students Student Health Center, Student Counseling Center, College housing, Housing information, Part-time job information, Vocational guidance, Homestay, Home visit, Cultural exchange program

Undergraduate Programs

School of Business Administration(2497/20)
Dept. of Business Administration(2497/20)
College of Economics(2466/10)
Dept. of Economics(2466/10)
School of International Politics, Economics and Business(1259/0)
Dept. of International Business(419/0)
Dept. of International Economics(424/0)
Dept. of International Politics(416/0)
College of Law(2216/1)
Dept. of Private Law
Dept. of Public Law
College of Literature(4278/29)
Dept. of Education(901/13)
Dept. of English(1487/2)
Dept. of French(637/1)
Dept. of History(633/9)
Dept. of Japanese(620/4)
College of Science and Engineering(2541/2)
Dept. of Chemistry(446/0)
Dept. of Electronics and Electrical Engineering (521/2)
Dept. of Industrial and Systems Engineering (561/0)
Dept. of Mechanical Engineering(535/0)
Dept. of Physics(478/0)

Graduate Programs

Graduate School of Literature(M 118/0, D 70/3)
Div. of Education(M 22/0, D 9/0)
Education, History of Education
Div. of Psychology(M 5/0, D 4/0)
Theoretical Psychology, Experimental Psychology, Educational Psychology, Developmental Psychology, Psychological Experiment, Psychology of Learning, Clinical Psychology, Social Psychology, Psychotherapy, Educational Measurement
Div. of English and American Literature(M 35/0, D 13/0)
English Literature, American Literature, English Linguistics, History of English Language, Comparative Literature, Thesis Writing, Children's Literature
Div. of French Literature and Language(M 11/0, D 6/0)
Medieval French Language and Literature, 16th Century French Literature and Language, 17 th Century French Literature and Language, 18 th Century French Literature and Language, 19th Century French Literature and Language, 20 th Century French Literature and Language, French Language, French Poetry, French Novel
Div. of Japanese Literature and Language(M 15/0, D 14/0)
Ancient Japanese Literature, Medieval Japanese Literature, Middle Ages Japanese Literatue, Modern Times Japanese Literature, Japanese Poetry, Modern Japanese Literature, History of Japanese Language
Div. of History(M 30/0, D 24/0)
History of Japan, History of Japanese Culture, Japanese Archaeology, History of Orient, History of Oriental Culture, Paleolithic Cultures in South and East Asia, History

of Europe, History of European Culture, European Social History

Graduate School of Economics(M 13/0, D 2/0)

Div. of Economics(M 13/0, D 2/0)

History of Economics, Microeconomics, Macroeconomics, The Theory of Economic Planning, Economic Dynamics, Economic History of Europe, Economic History of America, Economic History of Japan, Economic Policy, Social Policy, Labor Economics, Public Finance, Taxation, Financial Policy, Mathematical Statistics, Economic Statistics, Economic Location Theory and Policy, World Economics

Graduate School of Law(M 14/0, D 1/0)

Div. of Private Law(M 7/0, D 1/0)

Civil Law, Private International Law, Civil Procedure, Foreign Laws(Anglo-American Law), Foreign Laws (French Law), Labor Law, Economic Law, Legal Philosophy, Sociology of Law, European Legal History, Commercial Law

Div. of Public Law(M 7/0)

Constitutional Law, Comparative Study of Constitutional Law, Administrative Law, Criminal Law, Criminal Procedure, International Law, Communication Law, Politics, Political History, Theory of Political Process, Labor Law, International Relations, Foreign Laws(Anglo-American Law), Foreign Laws(French Law), Economic Law, Legal Philosophy, Sociology of Law, European Legal History, Educational Law

Graduate School of Business Administration(M 20/2, D 6/1)

Div. of Business Administration(M 20/2, D 6/1)

Management Information Systems, System Analysis, Organizational Psychology, Personnel Management, Business Mathematics, Business Statistics, Theory of Enterprise, Socialistic Enterprise, Management Theory, Business Strategy, Top Management, History of Business, International Accounting, History of Accounting, Computerized Accounting, Financial Accounting, Tax Accounting, Managerial Accounting, Auditing, International Business Communication, Insurance Institution, Insurance Enterprise, International Trade Policy, Japanese Foreign Trade Policy, Terminal Economics, Port Economics, Advertising Communication, Marketing Environment, Marketing Managenment, Marketing Systems, Marketing Channels, Cost Management, Business Budgeting,

Graduate School of International Politics, Economics and Business(M 35/0, D 33/1)

Div. of International Politics(M 0/0, D 18/0)

Political Science, Economic Theory, Principles of Management, Quantitative Analysis, Statistical Analysis, Systems Science, American Studies, Southeast Asian Studies, Middle East and African Studies, European Studies, Soviet Studies, Chinese Studies, International Politics, International Relations, Political and Diplomatic History, International Law, International Organizations, National Security

Div. of International Economics(M 0/0, D 10/1)

Political Science, Economic Theory, Principles of Management, Quantitative Analysis, Statistical Analysis, Systems Science, American Studies, Southeast Asian Studies, Middle East and African Studies, European Studies Soviet Studies, Chinese Studies, International Economics, International Economic History, Internatioanl Economic Policy, International Finance, Economic Development, Public Finance

Div. of International Business(M 0/0, D 5/0)

Political Science, Economic Theory, Principles of Management, Quantitative Analysis, Statistical Analysis, Systems Science, American Studies, Southeast Asian Studies, Middle East and African Studies, European Studies, Soviet Studies, Chinese Studies, General Management, International Business, Corporate Economics, International Business History, Business Systems, Multinational Enterprise, Business Administration, Strategic Management, Theory of Business Organization, International Business Finance International Labour Relations, Princilpes of Marketing, International Marketing, International Physical Distribution, Financing Practices, Industrial Engineering, Valuation of the Firm, Management Acoounting, International Accounting,

Div. of International Business (Evening Division) (M 35/0, D 0/0)

Mathematics in Economics and Business, Statistical Analysis, Quantative Methods, Selected Topics in Quntitative Analysis, Analysis of World's Economic Markets, General Management, Business Systems, Business Administration, Strategic management, Theory of Business Organaization, Finance and Portfolio Theory, International Business, International Marketing, International Personnel Management, International Business Finance, Selected Topics in Management, Systems and Decision Science, Management System and Informatics, Selected Topics in Management Sciecne, Financial Accounting, Management Accounting, International Accounting, Selected Topics in Accounting, Selected Topics in International Management, Economic Theory, Modern Econmics, International Finance, International Trade International Development Policies, Selected Topics in Modern Economics, Seminar in International Economics, Modern Political Science, International Relations, National Security, International Economic Law, Current Issues in International Economic Law, Selected Topics in Political Science, Seminar in Internationl Politics, Business History English

Graduate School of Science and Engineering (M 136/2, D 13/0)

Div. of Physics(M 26/0, D 7/0)

Advanced Quantum Medranics and Exercise, Elementary Particle Physics, Advanced High Energy Physics, Solid State Physics, Advanced Applied Physics, Advanced Data Analysis, Advanced Statistical Mechanics, General Relativity, Advanced Nuclear Physics, Applied Nuclear Physics, X-ray and Neutron crystallography, Advanced General Physics, Physics Colloquium for Graduate Course, Advanced Theoretical Physics Seminar, Advanced Laboratory Works in Physics, Advanced Laboratory Works in Applied Physics

Div. of Chemistry(M 37/0, 4/0)

Advanced Physical Chemistry, Advanced Inorganic Chemistry, Advanced Organic Chemistry, Advanced Bio

Chemistry, Advanced Analytical Chemistry, Advanced Lecture on Chemical Topics, Colloquium on Chemical Topics, Modern Laboratory Practice

Div. of Mechanical Engineering(M 32/1, D 1/0)
Advanced Fluid Dynamics, Thermo Reaction Engineering, Advanced Course of Machine-Tool Engineering, Strength of Materials Specially Course, Advanced Theroy of Machine Elements, Mechanical Kinematics Specially Course, Advanced Gas Dynamics, Advanced Lecture on Materials Scinece, Advanced Fluid Engineering, Advanced Lecture on Applied Thesmodynamics, Advanced Lecture on Non-metalic Materials, Special Topics in Mechanical Engineering, Advanced Engineering Design, Advanced Control Engineering, Special Topics in Mechanical Engineering, Mechanical Engineering Lecturing Specially Course, Mechanical Engineering Laboratory Specially Course, Advanced Heat Transfer

Div. of Electronics and Electrical Engineering(M 22/0, D 1/0)
Advanced Electronic Measurements, Advanced Acoustic Engineering, Synthesis of Optimal Control System, Information Engineering, Advanced Electronic Communications, Material Science for Electronics, Magnetics, Semiconductor Devices Theory, Signal Processing, Switching Circuit Theory, Advanced Electronic Circuit, Quantum Electronics, Advanced Electronics, Bio-electronics, Electronic Materials, Power Electronics, Advanced Seminar, Special Graduate Seminar, Directed Research

Div. of Industrial and Systems Engineering(M 19/1, D 0/0)
Advanced Studies in Computer Science, Advanced Studies in Design of Business System, Advanced Mathematical Programming, Advanced Production Management, Advanced Graph Theory, Advanced Numerical Analysis, Advanced Production and Design of Logistic Systems, Readings in Industrial Engineering, Simulation Studies in Industrial Engineering, Advanced Decision Analysis, Advanced Management Planning, Advanced Reliability Engineering,

---

足利工業大学
(Ashikaga Kôgyô Daigaku)

Ashikaga Institute of Technology

268-1 Omae, Ashikaga-shi, Tochigi 326
☎ 0284-62-0605 FAX 0284-62-5009

Founded 1967
Professors 54
Associate Professors 32
Assistant Professors(Tenured) 36
Assistant Professors(Non-tenured) 56
Research Assistants 4
Undergraduate Students/Foreign Students 2, 445/1
Graduate Students/Foreign Students 10/0
Library 91, 324 volumes

Contact: Admissions Office

Educational Philosophy AIT aims at providing opportunities for everyone on the campus to endeaor in an effort to enhance the institution's resources for research and education. This, we believe, will bring up humanity-oriented engineers who can value the harmony with Nature.

Foreign students Foreign student enrollments have been relatively small so far. We do hope, however, that we will be able to accept as many students as possible from overseas, thus promoting friendship and understading with the rest of the world.

Environment Ashikaga, with a population in 170,000, is about 80 kilometers north of Tokyo. The city is famous as the site of Ashikaga Gakko, Japan's oldest school. AIT's campus, located in the western suburb of the city, provides an ideal learning environment rich in natural beauty.

Facilities Library, Computer center, Language Laboratory, Gymnasium, Baseball ground, Soccer ground, Sports ground, Cafeteria, Tennis court, Auditorium

Student activities Main campus events: school festival, ball game tournament, atheletic meething, marathon race, etc. Extra curricular activities: baseball club, tennis club, automobile club, kendo club, cheering squad, American football club, travel club, etc.

Services for foreign students Health clinic, Housing information, Part-time job information,etc.

Undergraduate Programs

Faculty of Architecture(510/0)
Dept. of Civil Engineering(478/0)
Dept. of Electrical Enginering(480/0)
Dept. of Mechanical Engineering(494/1)
Dept. of Industrial and Systems Engineering (483/0)

Gradute Programs

Graduate School of Engineering(M 10/0)
Div. of Civil Engineering(M 2/0)
Concrete Engineering, Hydraulics, Sanitary Engineering, Soil Mechanics, Steel Structures, Structural Mechanics, Surveying, Concrete Structures, Construction Materials,

Div. of Electrical Engineering(M 2/0)
Power Electronics, Energy Conversion, Electronics Materials, Information Engineering, Communication Engineering

Div. of Mechanical Engineering(M 6/0)
Control Engineering, Energy Conversion, Fluid Mechanics, Material Science, Precision Engineering, Strength of Materials, Thermodynamics

亜細亜大学
(Ajia Daigaku)

Asia University

5-24-10 Sakai, Musashino-shi, Tokyo 180
☎ 0422-54-3111 Fax 0422-55-8232

Founded 1941
Progessors 94
Associate Professors 40
Assistant Professors(Tenured) 20
Assistant Profssors(Non-Tenured) 264
Research Assistants 3
Undergraduaduate Students/Foreign Students 6, 625/363
Graduate Students/Foreign Students 129/44
Library 376, 000 volumes
Contact: Undergraduate Admissions–
Office for International Affairs
–Graduate Admissions–
Academic Affairs & Registration

Educational Philosophy The Educational Phiolosophy of Asia University is to foster the virtues of self-help and cooperation in its students, to assist students in maximizing their potential, and to help students find fulfillment through cooperative efforts and mutual understanding.

Foreign students We welcome international students and endeavor to provide them with a quality education and rewarding student life which will allow them a broad range of opportunities following their expense at Asia University.

Environment Musashino, with a population of approximately 140, 000 is a quiet, yet conveniently located city in Western Tokyo. The Asia University campus is within 30 minutes of Kichijoji and Shinjuku on the Chuo Line.

Facilities Library, computing facilities, Laboratory, English Speaker's Lounge, Gymnasium, Auditorium, track and field, baseball grounds, tennis courts, golf driving range.

Student activities Annual events include the Freshman Retreat, Athletic Festival and Cultural Festival. There is also a wide variety of extracurricular sports, academic and recreation activities for students to participate in.

Academic programs for foreign students The Special Course for Foreign Students is a one-year intensive Japanese language course for international students. Supplemental Japanese language classes are also offered for regular matriculated students.

Services for foreign students General advising, health srevices, personal counseling, housing/housing information, part-time job information, vocational advising, cultural experience/exchange opportunities.

Undergraduate Programs

Faculty of Business Administration(2, 226/200)
Dept. of Business Administration(2, 226/200)
Faculty of Economics(2, 007/98)
Dept. of Economics(2, 007/98)
Faculty of International Relations(242/18)
Dept. of International Relations(242/18)
Faculty of Law(2, 150/47)
Dept. of Law(2, 150/47)

Graduate Programs

Graduate school of Business Administration(M 42/24)

Div. of Business Administration(M 42/24)

Business & Society, Industrial System, Business Management, Business Finance, Business Labor Relations, Managerial Marketing, Business History, Business Psychology, International Management, Principles of Marketing, Principles of Business Administration, Research on Business Strategy, Top Management, Organization, Small Business, Management in Socialist Countries, Business Engineering, Computer, Industrial Marketing, Advertising, Research on Distribution Systems, Principles of Accounting, Business Budgeting, Auditing, Financial Analysis, Principles of Book-keeping, Management Accounting, Financial Accounting, Cost Accounting, Tax Management, Reading Business Literature in English, Reading Accounting Literature in English, Reading Business and/or Accounting Literature in German, Reading Business and/or Accounting Literature in French, Reading Business and/or Accounting Literature in English

Graduate school of Economics(M 21/12. D 6/1)

Div. of Economics(M 21/12. D 6/1)

Theoretical Economics, Macro Economics, Micro Economics, Economics Growth, Public Economics, Western Economic History, Oriental Economic History, Economic History in Japan, History of Economic Doctrines, History of Economic Thoughts, History of Social Thoughts, Policies of Economic Policy, Agricultural Policy, Industrial Policy, Transportation Policy, Population Policy, Economic Studies of Japan, Public Enterprise Economics, Principles of Public Finance, Taxation Theories, Monetary Economics, Monetary Policy, Economic Theories of Money and Currencies, Labor Economics, Industrial Relations, Principles of Statistics, Economic Statistics, International Economics, International Monetary Economics, Economics and Development, International Trade, Principles of International Relations, Principles of International, Economic Development and Political System, Economic Development and Social Structure, Economic Development and Culture Change, Comparative Economic Systems, Economic Development and International Cooperations, Special Studies, Studies on English Books, Studies on German Books, Studies on French Books, Studies on Indonesian Books, Studies on Spanish Books

Graduate school of Law(M 52/4. D 8/3)

Div. of Law(M 52/4. D 8/3)

Constitutional Law, Administrative Law, International Law, Political Science, Political Thought Advanced Historical Survey, Internationsl Politics, Diplomaric History,

Administrative Science, Tax Law, Criminal Law, Criminal Procedure, Criminal Policy, Criminology, Civil Law, Commercial Law, International Private Law, Civil Procedure, Labor Law, Anglo-American Law, German Law, French Law, Legal History, Study of the Original Text (English)

跡見学園女子大学

(Atomi Gakuen Joshi Daigaku)

Atomi Gakuen Women's College

1-9-6 Nakano, Niiza-shi, Saitama 352
☎ 0484-78-3333

Founded 1965

Undergraduate Programs

Faculty of Literature
Dept. of Aesthetics and Art History
Dept. of Culture Studies
Dept. of English Literature
Dept. of Japanese Literature

麻布大学

(Azabu Daigaku)

Azabu University

1-17-71 Fuchinobe, Sagamihara-shi, Kanagawa 229
☎ 0427-54-7111 FAX 0427-54-7661

Founded 1890
Professors 52
Associate Professors 46
Assistant Professors (Tenured) 28
Assistant Professors (Non-tenured) 45
Research Assistants 9
Undergraduate Students/Foreign Students 1,820/2
Graduate Students/Foreign Students 9/1
Library 102, 005 volumes
Contact: Liaison Bureau, International Exchange Comittee

Educational philosophy The University celebrated its centenary in 1990. It is the idea of Azabu University to give instructions and conduct research in the fields of Veterinary Medicine, Animal Sciences and Production, Environmental Sciences and Medical Technology, to contribute to the progress of science and public health (in this country, and at the same time), to encourage the students to become good citizens.

Foreign students The University is expanding its program of specialists who have advanced academic backgrounds, increased knowledge of Veterinary Medicine, Animal Sciences and Production, Environmental Sciences and Medical Technology. Applicants are required to go through the general admission program in Japanese.

Environment The University is located in the place of great natural beauty at Sagamihara city of a half million population in Kanagawa Prefecture, and shortly to the central part of Tokyo and Yokohama, the nearest station is Yabe of Yokohama JR Line. The Sagami River made this area as the plains of Sagami.

Facilities The library keeps over 102,005 bound books. Research Institute of Biosciences are to function as a research center and cooperative studies in Japan and overseas. The Science Information Center is equipped with a versatile computer, and connected to The Univetrsity of Tokyo.

Student activities The office for international affair hold a social meeting with teaching staff and students from abroad in spring and autumn. Every students from abroad will participate the festival of university in November, and take exercise in the many clubs as for the athletic, riding, field and track, and others as same as Japanease students.

Academic programs for foreign students The University has not the supplementary lessons, consultation by tutor, and the educational system for substitute of the curriculum for students from abroad, but The office for International Exchange will support everything.

Services for foreign students The University will support health clinic, personal and psychological counseling, and also serve housing information, part-time job information, vocational guidance and others, as same as Japanease student.

Undergraduate Programs

School of Veterinary Medicine (1,196/1)
Dept. of Veterinary Medicine Program Course (873/1)
Dept. of Animal Environment and Production Program Course (323/0)
College of Environmental Health (615/1)
Dept. of Environmental Health (310/0)
Dept. of Higienic Technology (305/1)

Graduate Programs

Graduate School of Veterinary Science (D 9/1)
Div. of Veterinary Science (D 9/1)
Veterinary Anatomy, Veterinary Physiology
Veterinary Biochemistry, Veterinary Phamacology
Veterinary Pathology, Veterinary Microbiology
Veterinary Parasitology, Veterinary Surgery
Veterinary Radiology, Veterinary Internal Medicine
Veterinary Public Health, Laboratory Animal Science
Animal Health, Animal Nutrition, Infectious Diseases
Animal Breeding, Molecular Biology, Theriogenology

文化女子大学
(Bunka Joshi Daigaku)
Bunka Women's University

3-22-1 Yoyogi, Shibuya-ku, Tokyo 151
☎ 03-3299-2311 FAX 03-3370-6202

Founded 1964
Professors 37
Associate 23
Assistant Professors(Tenured) 20
Assistant Professors(Non-tenured) 41
Research Assistants 7
Undergraduate Students/Foreign Students 1,935/136
Graduate Students/Foreign Students 33/20
Library 147, 356 volumes
Contact: Admission Office

Educational philosophy Having both the fashion department and the living arts department within itself, Bunka Women's Unversity attempts to help its students grow and challenge the creation of new beauty with their new knowledge and techniques. There will be a literature department newly established in 1991.
Foreign students There are a great number of foreign students at the university, mainly from the republic of China, the republic of Korea, and the people's republic of China. Since all classes are instructed in Japanese, foreign students are asked to have enough Japanese knowledge and fluency.
Environment The university is located near Shinjuku Station and approximately 7 minutes on foot from the south exit of the station. Adjacent to the Shinjuku business district, the transportation to and from the campus is convenient.
Facilities Along with the unique costume museum and the library, there are various newest equipments installed on campus.
Student activities Participating " the freshman Camp ", to start with, students are expected to attend various school events such as " the college festival " and " the ball games days ".
Academic programs for foreign students There are special subjects provided for foreign students to learn and understand more about Japanese Culture.
Services for foreign students The students counselling office provides necessary advice and services to foreign students. All foreign students are invited to a sightseeing trip, a Kabuki performance, and so on.

Undergraduate Programs

Faculty of Home Economics(1935/136)
Dept. of Fashion(965/67)
Dept. of Living Arts(970/69)

Graduate Programs

Graduate School of Home Economics(M 29/18, D 4/2)
Div. of Clothing Science(M 29/18)
Div. of Clothing Environmental Science(D 4/2)

文教大学
(Bunkyô Daigaku)
Bunkyo University

Koshigaya campus: 3337 Minami Ogishima, Koshigaya-shi, Saitama 343
Shonan campus: 1100 Namegaya, Chigasaki-shi, Kanagawa 253
☎ 0489-74-8811 FAX 0489-74-9439

Founded 1966
Professors 109
Associate Professors 56
Assistant Professors(Tenured) 18
Assistant Professors(Non-tenured) 319
Research Assistants 15
Library 216, 656(Koshigaya)volumes 180, 693 Volumes(shonan)
Contact: Koshigaya campus Admission

Educational philosophy In keeping with the nation's fundamental statuses on education, which declare the love of truth and justice to be the central pillar of postwar Japanese education, Bunkyo University has compassion and concern for other human beings as the watch-word of its educational policy.
Foreign students Faculty of Information and Communication, Faculty of International Studies in Chigasaki city, Kanagawa Pref, and Faculty of Language and Literature in Koshigaya city, Saitama Pref. are very positive to receive foreign students who are eager to study Japanese culture, economics, history, literature as well as Japanese language. Bunkyo University has a unique Institute of Language and Culture in the Koshigaya Campus in which Japanese language teachers pay particular attention to foreign students.
Environment The Koshigaya Campus is situated in a new-developed residential area north-east of Tokyo. The transportation system with fast commuter trains has developted. The Campus is within six minutes' walk from Koshigaya station on Tobu line. The atmosphere of the area is very favourable.
The Shonan Campus is situated south-west of Tokyo on the outskirts of Chigassaki city. The bus is available from Chigasaki station and several other stations. The Campus on the hill commands a fine view of Mt. Fuji.
Facilities The Koshigaya Campus in which 3075 Japanese students and 20 foreign students are enrolled has the following facilities. Institute of Clinical Counseling, Institute of Domestic Science, Institute of Language

and Culture, Library, Bunkyo University Computer Center, Health and Counseling Center, Gymnasium and Swimming pool.

The Shonan Campus in which Japanese students and 16 foreign students are enrolled has Library, Health and Counseling Center, Gymnasium and Swimming pool.

Student activities Campus events include freshmen welcome party in April, athletic meeting in May, school festival in the fall and homecoming. Some students belong to their favourite sports clubs, such as football, baseball, soccer, tennis, swimming, dacing, volleyball, etc. Some students belong to other clubs, such as painting, drama, choral groups, symphony, volunteer work, English speaking society, etc.

Academic programs for foreign students Tutoring system in each faculty which receives foreign students helps them to study in pleasant circumstances. It leads to not only mutual understanding but also making foreign student more active to learn things Japanese.

Services for foreign students Foreign students can always pick up some information on accomodation and a part-time job and other work. They have an opportunity to visit Japanese families in the area who are familiar with foreign custom.

Undergraduate Programs

Faculty of Education(1292/0)
- **Dept. of Elementary School Teacher's Course** (1148/0)
- **Dept. of Junior High School Teachers' Course** (144/0)

Faculty of Human Science(712/0)
- **Dept. of Human Science**(712/0)

Faculty of Information & Communication(1436/2)
- **Dept. of Mass Communication**(304/0)
- **Dept. of Management and Information Science** (578/1)
- **Dept. of Information Systems**(554/1)

Faculty of Language and Literature(1380/20)
- **Dept. of Japanese Language and Literature Course**(463/20)
- **Dept. of British and American Language and Literature Course**(458/0)
- **Dept. of Chinese Language and Literature Course**(459/0)

Faculty of International Studies(243/14)
- **Dept. of International Studies**(243/14)

千葉工業大学
(Chiba Kôgyô Daigaku)
Chiba Institute of Technology

2-17-1 Tsudanuma, Narashino-shi, Chiba 275
☎ 0474-75-2111

Founded 1942

Undergraduate Programs

Faculty of Engineering
- **Dept. of Architecture**
- **Dept. of Civil Engineering**
- **Dept. of Computer Sciences**
- **Dept. of Electrical Engineering**
- **Dept. of Electronics**
- **Dept. of Industrial Chemistry**
- **Dept. of Industrial Design**
- **Dept. of Industrial Management**
- **Dept. of Mechanical Engineering**
- **Dept. of Metallurgical Engineering**
- **Dept. of Precision Engineering**

Graduate Programs

Graduate School of Engineering
- **Div. of Civil Engineering**
- **Div. of Industrial Chemistry**
- **Div. of Metallurgical Engineering**

千葉経済大学
(Chiba Keizai Daigaku)
Chiba Keizai University

3-59-5 Todoroki-cho, Chiba-shi Chiba 260
☎ 0472-53-9111 FAX 0472-54-6600

Founded 1988
Professors 19
Associate Professors 6
Assistant Professors(Tenured) 6
Assistant Professors(Non-tenured) 31
Research Assistants 1
Undergraduate Students/Foreign Students 730/0
Library 84, 600 volumes
Contact: Admission Office

Educational philosophy With the motto of cultivating persons of sound judgement and creativity, the college offers a unique curriculum to enable the students to be good economists for an international society armed with sound and sufficient knowledge and ability in language and information processing.

Foreign students The College offers sellective small–class seminars for comparative and on–the–spot studies of economic policies and developments of various countries in order to facilitate mutual understanding among the students.

Environment In Chiba City (Population: 827,000) with various public educational and cultural institutions are located nearby. The City of Tokyo is accessible within an hour by public transportation facilities. The College is locatd in a favorable educational environment in 12 minutes on foot from Nishi–Chiba Station of Japan Railway.

Facilities Small–class seminar rooms on every floor, library, gymnasium, language laboratory room, computer training room, study material display hall, cafeteria, student lounge.

Student activities Annual campus events are freshmen welcome party, school festival, camp training activities of various sporting and cultural clubs such as baseball, tennis, football, skiing, table tennis, golf, tea ceremony, flower arrangement, historical research, computer science, shohgi–chess clubs, etc.

Services for foreign students Personal counseling, housing information, part–time job information. Attendance to community college lectures held at our College.

Undergraduate Programs

Faculty of Economics (730/0)

千葉商科大学
(Chiba Shôka Daigaku)
Chiba University of Commerce

1–3–1 Konodai, Ichikawa–shi, Chiba 272
☎ 0472–72–4111 FAX 0473–71–6881

Founded 1928
Professor 76
Associate Professors 16
Assistant Professors (Tenured) 9
Assistant Professors (Non–tenured) 122
Research Assistants 0
Undergraduate Students/Foreign Students 7,230/0
Graduate Students/Foreign Students 33/0
Library 359, 996 volumes
Contact: Public Relations Office

Educational philosophy Taking the founding spirit into consideration, the faculty aims to teach theory and practice of commerce, economics, and other related fields. We provide students with basic and essential knowledge which, in due course, leads them to a comprehensive study of the fields discussed.

Foreign students We regret to say that we can not accept foreign students into our University, since we are not ready to accept them.

Environment Ichikawa is in the western part of Chiba Prefecture, and is a suburban residential city, with a population of 428,000. It is only 20 minutes by train from Tokyo station. The neighborhood of the University is well known for its rich history: many famous monuments and temples are within walking distance.

Facilities Library, Research Building, Institute of Economics, Computer Room, Gymnasium, Swimming Pool, Tennis Court, Playing Grounds, Student's Hall, Tateyama Seminar House

Student activities Under the automous students union, there are some 60 clubs and groups that belong to the Cultural Association and the Athletic Association. Every year the University celebrates the Athletic Festival, the Cultural Festival, and the other events.

Undergraduate Programs

Faculty of Commerce and Economics (7,230/0)
  Dept. of Commerce (2,607/0)
  Dept. of Economics (2,253/0)
  Dept. of Business Management (2,370/0)

Graduate Programs

Graduate School of Commerce (M 17/0)
  Div. of Commerce (M 17/0)
Survey of Commerce, Theory of Marketing,
Insurance Industry, International Finance,
Theory of Stock Exchange,
Products and Merchandise,
Commercial Policy for Small Business,
Theory of Small Business,
Principles of the Studies of Management,
Historical Studies of Management
Managerial Organizations,
Financial Management,
Personnel Management, Management Planning,
Principles of Bookkeeping,
Principles of Accounting, Financial Charts,
Cost Accounting Theory,
Accounting Management, Management Analysis,
Reading Management Studies from Abroad,
Management and Business Administration Research,
Information Management Research

Graduate School of Economics (M 16/0)
  Div. of Economics (M 16/0)
Principles of Economics
International Economics,
History of Japanese Economy,
History of European Economy,
History of Economic Thought in Japan,
Theory of Chinese Economy,
Industrial Structures, Industrial Policy,
Industrial Economics,
Transportation Industry and Economics,
Economic Geography, Public Finance,

Studies of Finance,
International Finance,
Studies of Statistics,
Economic Statistics,
Social Policy,
History of Social Thought,
Reading Economical Studies from Abroad

中央学院大学
(Chûôgakuin Daigaku)
Chuogakuin University

451 Kujike, Abiko-shi, Chiba 270-11
☎ 0471-83-6516 FAX 0471-83-6532

Founded 1966
Professor 52
Associate Professors 28
Assistant Professors(Tenured) 19
Assistant Professors(Non-tenured) 48
Research Assistants 0
Undergraduate Students/Foreign Students 2,869/41
Library 163, 539 volumes
Contact: Admission Office

Educational philosophy The aim of education of Chuogakuin University is to nurture and establish fair social and ethical views. Its goal is to create persons of business with capability and creativity through small-class education.
Foreign students It is hoped that foreign students pursuit learning and deepen their understand of Japanese cultures and civilizations, thus serving to promote future international exchanges between their home countries and Japan.
Environment The City of Abiko where the campus is located is Tokyo's bedroom town with a population of 120,000, easily accessible to the center of Tokyo within 50 minutes of train ride. The area, full of cultual atomosphere, rich in historical associations, still maintains its beautiful natural scenery.
Facilities Library; gymnasium; a host computer and 150 personal computers. Reseach institutions include Local Public Entities Study Organization, Comprehensive Research Institute, Comparative Culture Center and Information Science Research Center.
Student activities Popular campus events include: sports festival, school festival, etc. Every year Chuogakuin sponsors ekiden marathon race which many runners from nearby schools and other institutions join. Extra curricular activities include arts and sports of various kind such as calligraphy, pictures, athletics, aikido, baseball, etc.
Academic programs for foreign students alternative course system.
Services for foreign students Counseling; help to find housing and part-time jobs.

Undergraduate Programs

Faculty of Commerce(1839/39)
Dept. of Commerce(1839/39)
Faculty of Law(1030/2)
Dept. of Law(1030/2)

中央大学
(Chûô Daigaku)
Chuo University

Tama Campus(Faculties of Law, Economics, Commerce and Literature) 742-1 Higashinakano, Hachioji-shi, Tokyo 192-03
Korakuen Campus(Faculty of Science and Engineering)1-3-27 Kasuga, Bunkyo-ku, Tokyo 112
☎ 0426-74-2212 FAX 0426-74-2214

Founded 1885
Professors 417
Associate Professors 84
Assistant Professors(Tenured) 55
Assistant Professors(Non-tenured) 961
Research Assistants 3
Undergraduate Students/Foreign Students 29,733/116
Graduate Students/Foreign Students 578/60
Library 1,100,100 volumes
Contact: International Center(Tama Campus)

Educational philosophy The academic spirit upon which Chou University was founded is based on the founders' desire to provide practical education and opportunities for personal maturity and intellectual growth to all qualified and willing students.
Foreign students We welcome all students who are interested in studying Japanese and learning about Japan and on our part, by associating with those students, our Japanese students will learn about the world.
Environment The Tama Capmus, located in the Tama Hills Natural Park in the western suburbs of Tokyo, is equipped with all available products of modern technology amidst the greenery. The Korakuen Campus on high ground overlooking a famous Japanese garden, Korakuen, is located conveniently in the center of Tokyo.
Facilities Central Library, Science & Engineering Library, Computer Center, Audio-Visual Laboratory, International Center, Gymnasiums, Swimming pools, Several athletic fields, Horse riding ground and stables.
Student activities University Festival, Freshmen Welcome Festival, Homecoming Day. Activities designed by Foreign Student Association. 200 organized athlete/social clubs and more than 100 informal circles for a wide variety of interests ranging from puppet play to Judo.
Academic programs for foreign students Japanese language courses, Special seminars in Japanese

studies.

Services for foreign students Orientation for freshmen, Housing and scholarship aarangements, Summer seminar with Japanese students, Friendly get-togethers with faculty and administrative members, Follow-up communication with graduates.

Undergraduate Programs

Faculty of Commerce(6,212/44)
Dept. of Accounting(2,133/1)
Dept. of Business Administration(2,059/14)
Dept. of Marketing and Trade(2,020/29)
Faculty of Economics(5,765/39)
Dept. of Economics(2,423/6)
Dept. of Industrial Economics(1,489/12)
Dept. of International Economics(1,853/21)
Faculty of Literature(4,842/13)
Dept. of Education (Education major/Psychology Major)(113/3)
Dept. of History (Japanese History Major/Oriental History Major/Western History Major)(942/1)
Dept. of Literature (Japanese Literature Major/ English and American Literature Major/German Literature Major/French Literature Major)(2,670/3)
Dept. of Philosophy(939/6)
Dept. of Sociology(Sociology Major/Social Studies of Information and communication Major/Subcourses of Information and communication/Subcourses of Library and Information Science)(178/0)
Faculty of Science and Engineering(5,232/15)
Dept. of Applied Chemistry(828/0)
Dept. Civil Engineering(1,042/1)
Dept. of Electrical and Electronic Engineering (963/7)
Dept. of Industrial and Systems Engineering (730/0)
Dept. of Mathematics(301/0)
Dept. of Physics(471/1)
Dept. of Precision Mechanical Engineering(897/6)

Graduate Programs

Graduate School of Commerce(M 26/7, D 16/2)
Div. of Commerce(M 26/7, D 16/2)
Principles of Business Administration, History of Management Theories, Business Management, Financial Management, Production Management, Marketing Management, Labor and Industrial Relations, Industrial Sociology, Business History, Principles of Accounting, History of Accounting Theories, Financial Accounting, Management Accounting, Cost Accounting, Auditing, Tax Accounting, Financial Statement Analysis, Principles of Commerce, Management in Retailing, Marketing Theory and Systems, International Marketing, History of Commerce, International Trade Theory, International Trade Policy, The World Economy, Economic Affairs in China, Economic Affairs in Europe and the U.S.A., Theory of Transportation and Communication, Public Utilities, Money and Banking, International Finance, Securities Market, Insurance, Marine Insurance, Management Information Systems, Mathematical Analysis for Management Decisions, Principles of Economics, History of Economic Theories, Economic Growth, Methodological Issues in Economics, Business Cycles, Economic History, Econometrics.
Graduate School of Economics(M 36/11, D 20/4)
Div. of Economics(M 36/11, D 20/4)
Theory of Economics, Econometrics, Statistics, History of Economics, History of Social Thought, Occidental Economic History, Japanese Economic History, Theory of Economic Policy, Public Finance, Fiscal and Monetary Policy, Theory of Money and Banking, Social Accounting, International Economics, Economic Affairs in Europe and the U.S.A., Economic Affairs in Asia, Economic Affairs in Japan, Industrial Economics, Agricultural Economics, Economic Theory of Transportation, Industrial Economics, Economic Geography, Social Policy, Labor Economics, Demography
Graduate School of Law(M 54/6, D 51/3)
Div. of Public Law(M 4/0, D 7/1)
Constitutional Law, Administrative Law, Public International Law, Anglo-American Public Law
Div. of Private Law(M 21/6, D 14/1)
Civil Law, Commercial Law, Civil Procedure, Labor Law, Private International Law, Anglo-American Law
Div. of Criminal Law(M 14/0, D 17/0)
Criminal Law, Criminal Procedure, Criminal Policy, Criminology, History of Legal Institutions
Div. of Anglo-American Law(M 1/0)
Sources of Law, Anglo-American Constitutional Law, Anglo-American Contract Law, Anglo-American Tort Law, Anglo-American Property Law
Div. of Political Science(M 14/0, D 13/1)
Political Theory, History of Political Thought, Political History, Public Administration, Regional Politics, International Politics, International Political History, Political Sociology, Comparative Politics, History of Social Thought
Graduate School of Literature(M 93/10, D 77/13)
Div. of Japanese Literature(M 14/4, D 22/12)
Ancient Japanese Literature, Japanese Literature in the Heian Period, Japanese Literature in the Middle Ages, Japanese Literature in the Edo Period, Modern Japanese Literature, Contemporary Japanese Literature, Japanese Linguistics, History of Japanese Language, Japanese Literature Written in Chinese Style
Div. of English and American Literature(M 17/0, D 10/0)
Modern English Literature, American Literature, English Expression, History of English Linguistics, English Drama, English Novel, Modern English Poetry, American Novel
Div. of German Literature(M 4/0, D 5/0)
German Literature, German Linguistics
Div. of French Literature(M 6/0, D 4/0)
Medieval and Renaissance French Literature, French Literature in the Seventeenth and Eighteenth Centuries, Modern French Literature, Contemporary French Literature, French Linguistics, French Drama
Div. of Japanese History(M 8/0, D 15/0)

Ancient Japanese History, Japanese History in the Middle Ages, Japanese History in the Edo Period, Modern Japanese History, Political History of Japan, Japanese Paleography, Classics of Historiography and Historical Records

Div. of Asian History(M 9/2, D 6/0)
Ancient Chinese History, Chinese History in the Middle Ages, Chinese History in the Early Modern Ages, Modern Chinese History, North and Central Asian History, west Asian History

Div. of Western History(M 6/0)
History of Ancient Orient and Classical Antiquity, European History in the Middle Ages, European History in the Early Modern Ages, Modern European History, Contemporary History in Europe and the U.S.A.

Div. of Philosophy(M 17/1, D 8/0)
Ancient and Medieval Philosophy, European Philosophy in the Early Modern Ages, Modern European Philosophy, Contemporary European Philosophy, Chinese Philosophy, History of Moral Philosophy in Japan

Div. of Sociology(M 12/3, D 7/1)
General Theory of Sociology, Social Pathology, Social Psychology. Comparative Sociology, Industrial Psychology, Family Sociology, General Theory of Modern Sociology, Regional Sociology, Sociology of Groups and Organizations, Industrial Sociology, Sociology of Work, Social Research, Political Sociology

Graduate School of Science and Engineering(M 201/3, D 4/1)

Div. of Physics(M 25/0)
Mathematical Physics, Fluid Mechanics, Statistical Physics, Quantum Physics, Materials Science, Solid State Physics, Polymer Physics, Polymer Science, Applied Crystal Physics, Algebra, Applied Mathematics, Radio-frequency Spectroscopy, Quantum Optics, Physics of Energies, Magnetism of Matter, Elementary Particle Physics, Nuclear Physics

Div. of Civil Engineering(M 26/3, D 3/1)
Surveying, Construction Materials, Hydraulics, Fluid Dynamics, Fluvial Hydraulics, Soil Engineering, Sanitary Engineering, Steel Structures, Highway Engineering, Applied Mechanics, Transportation Planning, Coastal Engineering, Applied Mathematics, Compipsite Materials, Numerical Analysis in Civil Engineering, Engineering Geology, Foundation Engineering, Paving Method

Div. of Precision Mechanical Engineering(M 67/0, D 1/0)
Vibration Engineering, Control Engineering, Precision Machining, Precision Instruments, Precision Measurements, Engineering Instrumentation, Optical Engineering, Fluid Mechanics, Plasticity Technology, Structural Mechanincs, Applied Mathematics, Composite Materials, Advanced Metrology, Vibration Engineering, Applied Elesticity, Applied Mechanism, Applied Engineering Dynamics, Control Engineering

Div. of Electrical Engineering(M 54/0)
Electrical Machines, Semiconductor Devices, Applied Electronics, Microwave Engineering, Network Theory, Acoustical Engineering, Electronic Measurements, Active Circuits, Electrical Materials, Discharge Phenomena, Network Engineering, Control Engineering, Computer Control Engineering, Communication Systems, Applied Mathematics, Compisite Materials, Information Engineering, Information Processing, Information Theory, Systems Engineering, Computer Aided Design, Applied Discrete Mathematics, Reliance Engineering

Div. of Industrial Chemistry(M 29/0, D 0/0)
High Polymer Chemistry, Synthetic Polymers, Industrial Inorganic Chemistry, Analytical Chemistry, Environmental Engineering, Powder Technology, Chemical Engineering, Organic Synthesis, Chemistry of Fats and Oils, Applied Electrochemistry, Quantum Chemistry, Organic Reactions, Reaction Rate, Inorganic Materials, Instrumental Alalysis, Life Sciences

---

大東文化大学

(Daitô Bunka Daigaku)

Daito Bunka University

1-9-1 Takashimadaira, Itabashi-ku, Tokyo 175
☎ 03-3395-1111 FAX 03-3932-6902

Founded 1923
Professors 202
Associate Professors 64
Assistant Professors(Tenured) 37
Assistant Professors(Non-tenured) 363
Research Assistants 4
Undergraduate Students/Foreign Students 12,979/285
Graduate Students/Foreign Students 111/21
Library 661, 994 volumes
Contact: International Division

Educational philosophy We aim at synthesizing and developing two basic ways of life, mamely the Oriental thoughts and cultures and the Western thoughts and coutures.

Foreign students We are convinced that we can give you something very precious because it has been our university that has strivod to synthesize the opposing forces in man, namely spiritualism and materialism.

Environment Our main campus is located at Itabashi-ku, Tokyo. In 1967, another campus was opened in Higashi-Matsuyama City, Saitama Prefecture. The general culture course for freshman and sophomores is carried out there.

Facilities Institutes of Legal Studies, Business Research, Foreign Language Education, Japanese Economy, Humane Studies and Centers of the following fields: Calligraphy Culture, Data Processing, Sports.

Student activities Popular campus events include two-nights trip to our countrysides in every autumn and our school festival in November.

Academic programs for foreign students We have a special program for overseas students. This is the Japanese Language Program Which is a one-year course opened to those students who wish to enter the University (undergraduate program, graduate schools

and postgraduate courses.)
Services for foreign students Health clinic, personal counseling, housing infromation and various kinds of scholarship.

Undergraduate Programs

Faculty of Economics(5,134/134)
Dept. of Economics(3,026/87)
Dept. of Business Administration(2,108/47)
Faculty of Foreign Languages(2,037/42)
Dept. of Chinese Language(846/17)
Dept. of English Language(1191/25)
Faculty of International Relations(893/50)
Dept. of International Cultures(464/12)
Dept. of International Relations(429/38)
Faculty of Law(1761/7)
Dept. of Law(1586/7)
Dept. of Political Science(175/0)
Faculty of Literature(3154/52)
Dept. of Chinese Literature(713/8)
Dept. of Education(573/21)
Dept. of English and American Literature(595/5)
Dept. of Japanese Literature(1273/18)

Graduate Programs

Graduate School of Economics(M 25/5, D 5/4)
Div. of Economics(M 25/5, D 5/4)
Theoretical Economics, History of Economic Thoughts, History of Japanese Economy, History of Western Economy, Economic Policy, Public Finance, Social Policy, Management Accounting
Graduate School of Jurisprudence(M 25/0)
Div. of Law(M25/0,D25/0)
Constitution Law, International Law, Administrative Law, Political Science, History of Diplomatic Relations, Criminal Law, Criminal Procedure Act, Civil Law, Civil Proceedings Act, Commercial Code, Labour Laws, British • American • German • French Laws, Annals of Legistlation, British Original Textbooks.
Graduate School of Literature(M 36/3, D 20/9)
Div. of Chinese Literature(M 13/3, D 9/0)
Chinese Philosophy, Chinese Literature, Sound System of Chinese Language, English Language
Div. of English and American Literature(M 7/0)
English Literature, English Language, American Literature.
Div. of Japanese Literature(M 17/0, D 14/0)
Japanese Literatures in the following period: ancient, medieval, modern and recent times. Chinese Language and Literature, English Language.

獨協大学
(**Dokkyô Daigaku**)
Dokkyo University

1-1 Gakuen-cho, Soka-shi, Saitama 340
☎ 0489-42-1111 FAX 0489-41-6621

Founded 1964
Professors 141
Associate Professors 37
Assistant Professors(Tenured) 21
Assistant Professors(Non-tenured) 293
Undergraduate Students/Foreign Students 8,291/65
Graduate Students/Foreign Students 59/1
Library 501, 458 volumes
Contact: International Center

Educational philosophy We aim at fostering healthy, creative, practical and emotionally mature individuals; competent in foreign languages who can make significant contributions to the international community, thus enhancing peaceful and friendly relations between Japan and all nations.
Foreign students We welcome overseas applicants whose ability to understand and express themselves in both written and spoken Japanese is sufficiently high to enable them to derive full benefit from the scheme of study for which they are applying.
Environment Dokkyo University is in Soka-shi, located in the southeast of Saitama-ken next to Tokyo. It has over 200,000 people, and its size is 27.55 km^2. It takes about one hour by subway from Soka-shi to central Tokyo.
Facilities University Library, Research Institute of Foreign Language Teaching, Center for Data Processing and Computer Science, International Center
Student activities We have a students' association which forms an integral part of a student's total education with cultural and sports clubs as well as a large number of circles. Annual University Festival is in November.
Academic programs for foreign students Japanese language class as the first foreign language
Services for foreign students Health Center, Personal/Psychological Counseling, Dormitory(for the limited number), Housing Information, Part-time Job Information, Scholarship Information

Undergraduate Programs

Faculty of Foreign Languages(3,065/6)
Dept. of German(736/1)
Dept. of English(1,830/2)
Dept. of French(499/3)
Faculty of Economics(3,468/57)
Dept. of Economics(1,714/11)
Dept. of Management Science(1,754/46)
Faculty of Law(1,758/2)

Dept. of Law(1,758/2)

Graduate Programs

Graduate School of Foreign Languages(M 19/0, D 3/0)
Div. of German(M 5/0, D 1/0)
Div. of English(M 12/0, D 2/0)
Div. of French(M 2/0)
Graduate School of Economics(M 17/1)
Div. of Economics(M 17/1)
Graduate School of Law(M 18/0, D 2/0)
Div. of Law(M 18/0, D 2/0)

獨協医科大学
(Dokkyô Ika Daigaku)
Dokkyo University School of Medicine

880 Kitakobayashi, Mibu-machi, Shimotsuga-gun, Tochigi 321-02
☎ 0282-86-1111 FAX 0282-86-5678

Founded 1972
Professors 69
Associate Professors 57
Assistant Professors(Tenured) 142
Assistant Professors(Non-tenured) 186
Research Assistants 341
Undergraduate Students/Foreign Students 718/5
Graduate Students/Foreign Students 87/0
Library 160,000 volumes
Contact:Instruction Office ☎ 0282-87-2108

Educational philosophy Our university aims at educating students to be humanitarian doctors or scholars in medicine, cultivating the individual student's competency, fulfilling the mission of the community health center, and promoting the study of medical science through international exchange programs.
Foreign students Foreign students will enjoy the campus life with their counterparts, receiving a good education and training to be doctors through comprehensive course programs offered by the excellent teaching staff.
Environment Mibu-machi is located about 100 km north of Tokyo, and 35 km south of Nikko, an internationally famous sightseeing place. It is a comparatively small town, with 40,000 people living, full of greenery and fresh air. It makes an ideal environment for the study of medicine.
Facilities Library offers CD-ROM on-line and medical library net-work and other services;two hospitals, Information Education Center, Multi-Research Laboratory, DNA Research Laboratory, Language Laboratory, Gymnasium.
Student activities Extra curricular activities are highly valued. The Students' Society has 26 sports clubs and 16 cultural clubs. Every student is supposed to belong to one of them. Freshmen Welcome Party. Thunder Fest in spring by cultural clubs. School Festival in fall by all clubs. Sports Day.
Services for foreign students To ensure a healthy student life, the staff of Student Counselling Department including two doctors and a health nurse provide personal/psychological counselling, health clinic, housing information, etc.

Undergraduate Programs

Faculty of Medicine(718/5)

Graduate Programs

Graduate School of Medicine(D 87/0)
Divisions: Internal Medicine, Morphology, Physiology, Social Medicine, Surgery

---

江戸川大学
(Edogawa Daigaku)
Edogawa University

1-474 Komaki, Nagareyama-shi, Chiba 270-01
☎ 0471-52-0661 FAX 0471-54-2490

Founded 1990
Professors 16
Associate Professors 5
Assistant Professors(Tenured) 8
Assistant Professors(Non-tenured) 3
Research Assistants 3
Undergraduate Students/Foreign Students 277/0
Library 19738 volumes
Contact:Instruction department

Educational philosophy We aim at teaching and studying up-to-date high-level applied sociology and mass communication so students may contribute much to the field of mass communication and social research. We place great importance on computer and English education.
Environment Nagareyama city, with population of 130,000, is located in the Kanto plain, 19 miles north of Tokyo. It takes only 30 minutes from the heart of Tokyo by train.
Facilities Library, Arena, Computer Center, T. V. studio,
Student activities Popular campus events includes, freshmen welcome sports festival, freshman camp, school festival. There is a wide variety of extra curricular activities, including drama, brass band, soccer, rugby, etc.

Undergraduate Programs

Faculty of Sociology(277/0)
Dept of Applied Sociology(131/0)
Dept of Mass Communication(146/0)

フエリス女学院大学
(Fuerisu Jogakuin Daigaku)
Ferris University

37 Yamate-cho, Naka-ku, Yokohama-shi, Kanagawa 231
☎ 045-662-4521 FAX 045-662-6102

Founded 1965
Professors 36
Associate Professors 23
Assistant Professors(Tenured) 7
Assistant Professors(Non-tenured) 143
Research Assistants 10
Undergraduate Students/Foreign Students 1,754/7
Library 170,000 volumes
Contact: Entrance Examination Section

Educational philosophy Ferris Girl's School, the first school for women in Japan, was founded in 1870 by Miss Mary E. Kidder, a missionary of the Reformed Church in America. Ferris is a Protestant Christian school dedicated to teaching young women to live responsibly in today's world. The school's motto is: " Let each of you look not only to her own interests, but also to the interests of others "
Environment The campus is located in the Bluff area of Yokohama, Japan's second largest city, and its largest port. In 1988 the 2nd campus was opened in a new suburb Yokohama. It takes about 45 minutes by train between two campus.
Facilities Ferris University has two campuses. Each campus has the library that has a great selection of books, students' hall, cafeteria and school store. Ferris University has two music training institutes in Paris and Wien, a seminarhouse in Hakone.
Student activities We wish them to experience natural Japanese campus life, culture and many other activities in Japan.
Academic programs for foreign students Introduction to Japanese Affairs is a required course for foreign students. This course's credit is included at Humanities in General Education Courses.

Undergraduate Programs

College of Music(121/0)
Dept. of Vocal Music(49/0)
Dept. of Instrumental Music(49/0)
Dept. of Musicology(23/0)
Faculty of Letters(1633/0)
Dept. of English Literature(669/0)
Dept. of Japanese Literature(668/0)
Dept. of Asian and European Studies(296/7)

学習院大学
(Gakushûin Daigaku)
Gakushuin University

1-5-1 Mejiro, Toshima-ku, Tokyo 171
☎ 03-3986-0221 FAX 03-5992-1005

Founded 1949
Professors 136
Associate Professors 34
Assistant Professors(Tenured) 10
Assistant Professors(Non-tenured) 407
Research Assistants 37
Undergraduate Students/Foreign Students 7,705/4
Graduate Students/Foreign Students 336/7
Library 881, 008 volumes
Contact:Admission Section

Educational philosophy We aim at fostering students with broad vision, vigorous creativity and plentiful sensitivities who can eventually prove themselves benefitial to the society, contributing to creation, preservation, and further development of culture as well as to the welfare of human beings, through pursuing profound theories of Arts and Sciences and their application.
Foreign students We are currently promoting various plans for accepting foreign students, particularly in the studies of Japanese culture and history.
Environment Mejiro-machi, with a population of 11,962, is located in the northeastern part of the great metropolis, Tokyo. The 20 ha. campus enjoys a quiet atmosphere with beautiful trees.
Facilities University Library, The Computer Center, Reseach Institute for Oriental Cultures, Archives, Radio Carbon Laboratory, Center for International Exchange, Swimming pool, Gymnasium, Auditorium
Student activities Popular campus events includes freshmen welcome party, freshmen camp, the four university athletic meet, the competitive athletic meeting with University, 42 athletic sports clubs and 81 cultural work circle clubs.
Services for foreign students Health clinic, personal/psychological counseling, Housing information, part-time job information, home stay, Cultural exchange program.

Undergraduate Programs

Faculty of Law(2,217/0)
Dept. of Law(1,156/0)
Dept. of Political Studies(1,061/0)
Faculty of Economics(2,102/0)
Dept. of Economics(1,025/0)
Dept. of Management(1,077/0)
Faculty of Letters(2718/4)
Dept. of English and American Language and Literature(558/0)

Dept. of French Language and Literature(391/0)
Dept. of German Language and Literature(194/0)
Dept. of History(355/0)
Dept. of Japanese Language and Literature(452/4)
Dept. of Philosophy(462/0)
Dept. of Psychology(306/0)
Faculty of Sciences(668/0)
Dept. of Chemistry(181/0)
Dept. of Mathematics(283/0)
Dept. of Physics(204/0)

Graduate Programs

Graduate School of Law(M 15/0, D 4/0)
Div. of Law(M 15/0, D 4/0)
Graduate School of Political Studies(M 5/1, D 9/0)
Div. of Politics(M 5/1, D 9/0)
Graduate School of Economics(M 3/0, D 1/0)
Div. of Economics(M 3/0, D 1/0)
Graduate School of Managemetn(M 8/0, D 6/1)
Div. of Management(M 8/0, D 6/1)
Graduate School of Humanities(M 149/3, D 82/2)
Div. of Philosophy(M 31/1, D 14/0)
Div. of History(M 28/1, D 1/0)
Div. of Japanese Language and Literature(M 36/1, D 13/2)
Div. of English Language and Literature(M 18/0, D 10/0)
Div. of German Language and Literature(M 15/0, D 8/0)
Div. of French Language and Literature(M 9/0, D 8/0)
Div. of Psychology(M 12/0, D 10/0)
Graduate School of Sciences(M 45/0, D 9/0)
Div. of Physics(M 17/0, D 4/0)
Div. of Chemistry(M 21/0, D 2/0)
Div. of Mathematics(M 7/0, D 3/0)

白鷗大学
(Hakuô Daigaku)
Hakuoh University

1117 Daigyoji, Oyama-shi, Tochigi 323
☎ 0285-22-1111 FAX 0285-22-8989

Founded 1986
Professors 19
Associate Professors 14
Assistant Professors(Tenured) 6
Assistant Professors(Non-tenured) 51
Research Assistants 2
Undergraduate Students/Foreign Students 1,226/11
Library 30,000 volumes
Contact:Admission Office

Educational philosophy We aim at teaching and producing students specializing in computer science to meet the demands of present and future business conditions and students capable of managing small and medium-sized industries. We also aim at developing broad-minded business elites who can cooperate with other nations.

Foreign students All foreign students would be able to enjoy a rewarding experience in our school and to contribute a great deal to promoting mutual understanding among fellow classmates and to gain longlasting and cherishable friendships.

Environment Hakuoh University, located in Oyama City, north of Tokyo, is famous for its silk cloth. Oyama, with a population of 130,000 and growing, is just over one hour by train from Nikko, a city famous for its magnificient shrines and temples of the Tokugawa Shogunate.

Facilities Library, Computer Center, Gynasium, Restaurants, Research Institutes

Student activities Popular campus events includes school festivals, X'mas dance parties, symposium. There is a wide variety of extra curricular activities, including choral groups, dance, baseball, football tennis, etc.

Academic programs for foreign students Japanese language lessons and learning about the Japanese various conditions.

Services for foreign students Health clinic, housing information, part-time job information, cultural exchange program.

Undergraduate Programs

Faculty of Business Management(1226/11)
Dept. of Business Management(1226/11)

法政大学
(Hôsei Daigaku)
Hosei University

2-17-1 Fujimi, Chiyoda-ku, Tokyo 102
☎ 03-3264-9315 FAX 03-3238-9873

Founded 1880
Professors 377
Associate Professors 82
Assistant Professors(Tenured) 15
Assistant Professors(Non-tenured) 1, 321
Research Assistants 63
Undergraduate Students/Foreign Students 27, 501/316
Graduate Students/Foreign Students 477/23
Library 1, 200, 762 volumes
Contact: International Center

Educational philosophy Established in 1880 with the motto " Liberty and Progress ", Hosei University has grown to be one of Japan's leading institutions of higher education. Hosei's public role may be defined as providing an educated citizenry with excellent problem solving abilities.

Foreign students Welcomed since 1904, many Hosei graduates have assumed leading roles in their own countries. Convinced of the future importance of these students, we are resolved to continue promoting overseas student study.

Environment Hosei has three campuses : Ichigaya, close to the heart of Japanese politics, economics and arts, makes full use of its city location. Tama, surrounded by sprawling, picturesque grounds, is just over an hour thence. Koganei is located precisely between these two.

Facilities 3 libraries,10 research institutes,3 sports centers, 2 training centers, 2 swimming pools, all sports equipment, Hakuba Mountain Villa, Ishioka Athletic Grounds, Fuji Seminar House, computer room.

Student activities Starting with its Orientation Festival in April, Hosei hosts a large number of events including sports, college, music and film festivals. Three hundred student cultural, sports and academic clubs, provide wide scope for extra–curricular activities.

Academic Programs for foreign students Japanese is treated as a regular foreign language. Courses such as " Outlines in Japanese Culture " and " Modern Japanese Technology " are available depending on the faculty and adviser and tutor systems are available to all students.

Services for foreign students Medical health clinics, housing information, part–time job information, graduate employment information, financial aid to the foreign student association, company tours, speech contests and parties.

Undergraduate Programs

Faculty of Business Administration(4, 057/132)
  Dept. of Business Administration(4, 057/132)
Faculty of Ecomics(5, 819/36)
  Dept. of Commerce(587/1)
  Dept. of Economics(5, 232/35)
Faculty of Engineering(3, 916/26)
  Dept. of Architecture(600/4)
  Dept. of Civil Engineering(548/0)
  Dept. of Electrical Engineering(1 287/11)
  Dept. of Industrial and Systems Engineering (690/6)
  Dept. of Mechanical Engineering(791/1)
Faculty of Law(5, 526/26)
  Dept. of Law(3, 991/11)
  Dept. of Political Science(1, 535/15)
Faculty of Letters(4, 433/52)
  Dept. of Education(390/1)
  Dept. of English(1, 287/15)
  Dept. of Geography(423/1)
  Dept. of History(432/2)
  Dept. of Japanese(1, 420/30)
  Dept. of Philosophy(481/3)
Faculty of Social Sciences(3, 750/44)
  Dept. of Applied Economics(2, 080/21)
  Dept. of Sociology(1, 670/23)

Graduate Programs

Graduate School Engineering(M 169/8, D 15/1)
  Div. of Construction Engineering(M 48/1, D 2/1)
Structural Mechanics, Structural Analysis, Matrix Structural Analysis, Theory of Elasticity & Plasticity, Vibration Analysis, Plane Structure, Shell Structure, Reinforced Concrete Structures, Steel Structure, Tension Structure, Construction Materials, Soil Mechanics, Land Planning, Remote Sensing, Disaster Prevention Engineering, City Planning, Regional Planning, Hydraulics, Hydrology, Structural Mechanics in Architectural Engineering, Methodology of Architectural Planning, Architectural Design, Space Composition, Building Economics, Engineering Information System, Environmental Vibration, History of Construction Engineering, History of Architecture, Urban History, Urban Design, Community Planning, History of Architecture in Culture, Architectural Design, Construction Engineering Laboratory, Mathematical Logic, Applied Physics, Stochastic Processes, Optimal Control, Knowledge Information System, Computer Architecture, Bio–Informatics, Artificial Intelligence, Recognition and Understanding, Fuzzy Systems, Security of Systems, Ergonomics, Engineering Statistics, Urban Structural System, Systems Engineering Research, Systems Engineering Laboratory, Advanced Studies of Structural Analysis, Advanced Studies of Structural Engineering, Advanced Studies of Composite Materials, Advanced Studies for Regional & Urban Planning, Advanced Studies of Applied Hydrology, Advanced Studies of Architectural Planning, Advanced Studies of Environmental Engineering, Advanced Studeis of History of Architecture, Composite Materials Environmental Engineering, Construction Engineering, System Modeling, Production Control

  Div of Electrical Engineering(M 49/3, D 3/0)
Numerical Analysis, Circuit Engineering, Semiconductor Devices Engineering, Materials Engineering, Beam Technology, Quantum Electronics Engineering, Electromagnetic Wave Engineering, Power Electronics, Telecommunication Engineering, Computer Engineering, Applied Mathematics, Electromagnetic Theory, Information Science, Control System Engineering, Electric(Power)Energy Engineering, Power Electronics, High Voltage Engineering, Information Processing, Measuring System Engineering, Sensor Engineering, Operations Research, Industrial Process Systems, Applied Physics, Electrical Engineering Research, Advanced Circuit Engineering, Advanced Electronic Devices Engineering, Advanced Semicondutor Technology, Advanced Materials Engineering, Advanced Beam Technology, Advanced Electromagnetic Wave Engineering, Advanced Computer Engineering Research

  Div. of Mechanical Engineeing(M 40/0, D 3/0)
Theory of Elasticity, Applied Plasticity, Strength of Materials, Rheology, Stress Analysis, Metallic Materials, High Temperature Materials, Non–Metallic Materials, Mechanical Vibration, Control Engineering, Tribology, Fluid Me-

chanics, Heat Power, Combustion Science & Technology, Heat Transfer, Applied Thermodynamics, Mass Transfer, Powder Technology, Chemical Process Systems, Thermodynamic Properties in Chemical Engineering, Applied Interfacial Chemistry, Environmental Engineering, Applied Mathematics, Numerical Analysis, Mechanical Engineering, Advanced Solid Mechanics, Advanced Materials Science, Advanced Machine Elements, Advanced Fluid Mechanics, Advanced Thermal Engineering, Advanced Chemical Process Engineering

Div. of Systems Engineering(M 32/4, D 7/0)
Mathematical Logic, Applied Physics, Stochastic Processes, Optimal Control, System Modelling, Production Control, Measuring Electronics, Knowledge Information System, Computer Architecture, Bio–Informatics, Artificial Intelligence, Intelligent Robotics, Information Recognition, Fuzzy Systems, Safety Engineering of Systems, Biocybernetics, Ergonomics, Mathematical Programming, Urban Structural System, Industrial Process Systems, Operations Research, Remote Sensing, Systems Engineering Research, Advanced Seminar on Logico–Mathematical Science, Advanced Seminar on Control Systems, Advanced Seminar on Information Systems, Advanced Seminar on Applied Systems Engineering, Advanced Seminar on Human System

Graduate School of Humanities(M 125/1, D 54/2)

Div. of English Literature(M 17/0, D 5/0)
Trends in English Literature, Trends in American Literature, English Literature, American Literature, English Linguistics, Teaching English as a Second Language, Essay Writing

Div. of Geography(M 26/0, D 8/0)
Geography, Applied Geography, Topography, Geographical Fieldwork, Cartography, Physical Geography, Regional Geography, Human Geography

Div. of Japanese History(M 28/0, D 18/0)
Japanese History, Readings in Japanese History, Oriental History, Occidental History, Historical Research Methodology, Japanese Palaeography, Japanese Archeology, Ancient Japanese History, Pre–modern Japnese History, Modern Japanese History

Div. of Japanese Literature(M 27/0, D 13/2)
Japanese Literary Art, History of Japanese Literary Criticism, Readings in Ancient Japanese Literary Arts, Seminar on Ancient Japanese Literary Arts, Readings in Medieval Japanese Literary Arts, Seminar on Medieval Japanese Literary Arts, Readings in Pre–modern Japanese Literary Arts, Seminar on Pre–modern Japanese Literary Arts, Readings in Modern Japanese Literary Arts, Seminar on Modern Japanese Literary Arts, History of Japanese Linguistics, History of Okinawan Literary Art, Chinese Literature, Japanese Literature, Modern Literature, Noh Theater, Japanese Linguistics

Div. of Philosohy(M 27/1, D 10/0)
Theory of Epistemology, Metaphysics, History of Philosophy, Logic, Seminar on Philosophy, Readings in Philosophy

Graduate School of Social Sciences(M 72/8, D 40/3)

Div. of Economics(M 25/6, D 13/1)
Economics, Readings in Economics, History of Economics, Economic Policy, Finance, Readings in Finance, Economic History, Money and Banking, Statistics, Mathematics for Statistics, Stochastics, Business Administration, Readings in Business Administration, Accounting, Readings in Accounting

Div. of Politics(M 8/1, D 6/2)
Political Theory, Political History, History of Political Thought, Political Systems, Political Processes, Administrative Processes, Municipal Policy, Comparative Politics, Socialism, International Politics, International Political History, International Relations, Political Science, Administrative Processes International Political Science

Div. of Private Law(M 11/1, D 3/0)
Civil Law, Commercial Law, Civil Procedure, Bankruptcy Law, Readings in Jurisprudence, Labor Law, Constitutional Law, Criminal Law, International Private Law, Philosophy of Law, History of Japanese Public Law, Administrative Law, Topics in Anglo–American Law, Comparative Law, Criminal Procedure, Public Law, Court Procedure, Social Security Law, Educational Law, International Law

Div. of Sociology(M 28/0, D 18/0)
Foundations of Sociology, Sociology, Social Research, Social Psychology, Basic Theory of Social Problems, Social Law, Social Thought, Comparative Studies in International Society, International Society, Economic Society, Labor Problems, Basic Theory of Economics, Economics, Basic Theory of Social Environment, Readings in Sociology, Basic Research in Sociology, Legal Sciology, Political Sociology

---

星薬科大学

(Hoshi Yakka Daigaku)

Hoshi University

Ebara 2–4–41, Shinagawa–ku Tokyo 142
☎ 03–3786–1011 FAX 03–3787–0036

Founded 1911
Professors 18
Associate Professors 15
Assistant Professors(Tenured) 9
Assistant Professors(Non–tenured) 27
Research Assistants 37
Undergraduate Students/Foreign students 1, 222/0
Graduate Students/Foreign Students 90/10
Library 79, 000 volumes
Contact: Registrar Section

Educational philosophy The founder of this school, Hajime Hoshi who was the first in Japan to succeed commercially in production of important alkaloids such as morphine and so on, envisioned to establish a place of learning pharmaceutical sciences to nurture men and women talented enough to serve the world.

Foreign students It is belief of this school that humanity and harmony are precious. Through pharmaceutical science,this school aims to nurture students to become talented people who will serve mankind all over the world.

Enviroment The 36, 000 m² campus, located in the southern part of Tokyo, is tranquil and blessed with an abundant of greenery. Gotanda or Meguro Station is a transfer point for the JR Line. Togoshi-Ginza or Musashi-Koyama area, near the university, is convenient for shopping.

Facilities Garden with medicinal plants, Gymnasium, Hall(designed by a well known American architect, Antonin Raymond), Institute of Medicinal Chemistry, Library(four-storey), MS, NMR, Radio-isotope, Swimming Pool,Tennis Courts

Student activities April : Entrance ceremony, Freshmen Orientation;October or November : Hoshi University Festival;March : Graduation Ceremony. There are 38 clubs ranging from sports(ski, volleyball, judo and so on)to literature(sadou, chorus etc.)and academics (micro-computer etc.).

Undergraduate Programs

Faculty of Pharmaceutical Sciences(1, 222/0)
- **Dept. of Pharmaceutical Sciences**(606/0)
- **Dept. of Hygienic Pharmaceutical Sciences**(616/0)

Graduate Programs

Graduate School of Pharmaceutical Sciences(M 77/9, D 13/1)

Analytical Chemistry, Applied Pharmacology, Biochemistry, Bioactivities, Biopharmaceutical Chemistry, Clinical Chemistry, Drug Manufacturing Chemistry, Hygienic Chemistry, Instrumental Analysis, Microbiology, Organic Chemistry, Pharmaceutics, Pharmacognosy, Pharmacology, Physical Chemistry, Synthetic Organic Chemisry

茨城キリスト教大学

(Ibaraki Kirisuto-kyô Daigaku)

Ibaraki Christian College

6-11-1 Omika-cho, Hitachi-shi, Ibaraki 319-12
☎ 0294-52-3215

Founded 1967

Undergraduate Programs

Faculty of Literature
- **Dept. of Bible**
- **Dept. of English**
- **Dept. of Petagogy**

国際武道大学

(Kokusai Budô Daigaku)

International Budo University

841 Shinkan, Katsuura-shi, Chiba 299-52
☎ 0470-73-4111 FAX 0470-73-4148

Founded 1984
Professors 24
Associate Professors 18
Assistant Professors(Tenured) 15
Assistant Professors(Non-tenured) 35
Research Assistants 14
Undergraduate Students/Foreign Students 2, 030/1
Library 44, 000 volumes

Educational Philosophy We aim at not only developing budo skills but also at cultivating highly qualified international budo and sports leaders with both strong backgrounds in academic subjects and thorough training in the philosophy and spirit of budo and physical education.

Foreign students We have been accepting only athletic trainees whose aims are the mastery of judo and kendo skills. We are not yet prepared to accept undergraduate students, exchange students.

Environment The university is located in the city of Katsuura, in Chiba Prefecture, just 110 kilometers southeast of Tokyo. A growing seaside resort and an important fising port, Katsuura, polulation more than 25, 700, combines city comfort with a smalltown atmosphere.

Facilities library, 2 budo halls(judo, kendo, tamokuteki), 2 gymnasiums, official indoor swimming pool, official track and field ground, tennis courts, soccer groud, archery courts, Budo Science Academy

Student activities The popular campus event is university festival. There is a wide variety of extra curricular activities : athletic clubs include more than 27 budo and sport clubs, and cultural clubs include 9 clubs.

Undergraduate Programs

Faculty of Physical Education(2030/0)
- **Dept. of Budo**(891/0)
- **Dept. of Physical Education**(1139/1)

国際基督教大学
(Kokusai Kirisutokyo Daigaku)

International Christian University

3-10-2 Osawa, Mitaka-shi Tokyo 181
☎ 0422-33-3131 FAX 0422-33-9887

Founded 1949
Professors 73
Associate Professors 39
Assistant Professors(Tenured) 29
Assistant Professors(Non-tenured) 87
Research Assistants 9
Undergraduate Students/Foreign Students 2070/179
Graduate Students/Foreign Students 208/15
Library 389, 934 volumes
Contact: Admission Office ☎ 0422-33-3058-59

Educational philosphy ICU is a community in which people from different cultures live, study and work together. The international dimension has been built into its faculty,administration and student body to the greatest extent possible in Japan, so that the contributions of various educational philosophies will be reflected in its academic program.
Foreign students Being situated in Japan, ICU sees itself as a bridge leading both into and out of Japan. ICU may serve the particular purposes of offering to Japanese a view of the outside world and to non-Japanese an introduction into the Japanese culture.
Environment ICU is located in Mitaka City,a suburban community adjacent to the district comprising Tokyo proper. Mt. Fuji towers beyond and can be seen from the campus when not shrouded by clouds. The trip from Tokyo Station to Mitaka Station by express of semi-express,takes 30 to 40 minutes by the East Japan Railway's Chuo Line.
Facilities The campus is a spacious wooded area of 156 acres,one of the largest in Japan. Facilities include University Hall,Library,Physical Education Center, Integrated Learning Center, Science Hall, Education and Research Building,dorms,etc.
Student activities Extracurricular activities are centered in clubs and informal circles in the sports arts, academic or social fields, which are organized on student initiative. Various activities are planned and carried out by members. Membership is open. Other events include Christianitity Week,ICU Festival, Christmas programs and others.
Academic programs for foreign students About 30% of the total of 700 courses are taught in English. Besides, intensive and semi-intensive Japanese language courses in various levels are offered. Japan Studies programs provides a comprehensive understanding of Japan in the world today.
Student for foreign students Student Affairs Office is in charge of on- and off-campus housing,scholarships and financial aid,introduction of part-time jobs and cultural exchange programs. English speaking counsellor is available to give professional guidance/psychotherapy.

Undergraduate Programs

College of Liberal Arts(2060/179)
Div. of Education(230/6)
Div. of Humanities(349/18)
Div. of Languages(556/90)
Div. of Natural Sciences(272/4)
Div. of Social Sciences(653/60)
Div. of International Studies

Graduate Programs

Graduate School of Comparative Culture(M 35/5, D 18/2)
Div. of Comparative Culture (**Master's**)
History and Intellectual History of the East,Religion and Philosophy of the West, Value Concepts, Patterns of Thought, Modernization, Symbol and Expression, Religion and Philosophy of the East, Art and Literature of the West, History and Intellectual History of the West, Style, Cultural Transformation, Christianity and Culture, Understanding of Man, Comparative Cuture, Images of the World, Community Studies, Art of the East, Literature of the East, History of the East, Intellectual History of the East, Religion of the West, Philosophy of the West, Art of the West, Literature of the West, Cultural Communication and Transformation
Div. of Comparative Culture (**Doctoral**)
Christianity and Culture(West, East), Asian Culture;(Aspects of Japanese Culture,Cultural Interchange in Asia,) European Culture:(Ancient, Medieval & Modern)American Culture, Cultural Interchange and Acculturation
Graduate School of Education(M 51/0, D 20/2)
Div. of Philosophy of Education (**Master's**)
Educational Psychology, Guidance and Counseling, A-V Education, Advanced Educational Sociology, Philosophy of Education,History of Western Educational Thought, Comparative Educaton
Div. of Educational Psychology (**Master's**)
Philosophy of Education, A-V Education, Comparative Education, Advanced Educational Sociology, Educational Psychology, Guidance and Counseling,
Div. of Audio-Visual Education (**Master's**)
Philosophy of Education,Educational Psychology, Guidance and Counseling, Comparative Education, Advanced Educational Sociology, A-V Educaton.
Div. of English Teaching (**Master's**)
Philosophy of Education, Educational Psychology, Guidance and Counseling, A-V Education, Comparative Education, Advanced Educational Socilogy, General Lingusistics, English Linguistics, Old English, Methods of English Teaching, Language Acquisition, Language, Linguistics, English Language, Middle English.
Div. of Principles of Education (**Doctoral**)

Philosophy of Education : Problems of Philosophy of Education, Studies in History of Educational Thought, Studies in Comparative Education, Educational Psychology : Learning,Behavior and Evaluati on, Personality, Development and Culture, Inter-personal Relation, mental health & Clinical Psychology

Div. of Methodology of Education (**Doctoral**)

Audio-Visual Education : Studies in A-V education, Mass Communication, Educational Technology, English Teaching: Studies in Linguistics, Studies in English Language, Studies in English Teaching

Graduate School of Natural Sciences(M 13/0)

Div. of Natural Science

Mathematical Science, Physical Structure of Matter, Biological Science,History and Philosophy of Science, Chemical Structure of Matter, Genetic Information, Biological Regulation, Science Teaching, Biologica l Science, Integrated Basic Science, Physical Structure of Matter,

Graduate School of Public Administration(M 48/4, D 23/2)

Div. of Public Administration (**Master's**)

Political Theory, International Relations, Communication in the Organization, International Relations & Mass Media, Public Administration, Social Stratification, Public Law, International Law, Economic Theory,Statistical Analysis, International Economy, Modern Theory of Business, Economic Anthropology, Economic Policy, Comparative Politics and Government, Public Policy Theroy, Economic Cooperation, Sociology of Development, Social Change, Legal Anchropology, Comparative Organization, Political & Administrative Systems, Administrative Organization, Development Policy, Industrial Relations, Multi-National Business, International Organization, Money and Bangking, Foreign Trade, Economic History, Politics & Culture, Public Management, Management of International Conference, National Income Analyasis, Welfare Economics, Distribution Economy, Political Thought, Political & Diplomatic History, International Polictics,

Div. of Public Administration (**Doctoral**)

Political Process, Polictics and Culture, Political Theory, Histroy of Political Thought, International Relations, International Law, Political & Diplomatic History, Public Administration, Public Law, Industrial Relations, Economic Theory(Econometrics), Economic Policy, International Economy, Money & Banking, Distribution Economy, Business Decision-making, Corporation Finance & Accounting

日本社会事業大学

(Nihon Shakaijigyô Daigaku)

Japan College of Social Work

3-1-30 Takeoka, Kiyose-shi, Tokyo 204
☎ 0424-92-6111 FAX 0424-92-6816

Founded 1946
Professors 16
Associate Professors 7
Assistant Professors(Tenured) 4
Assistant Professors(Non-tenured) 40
Research Assistants 4
Undergraduate Students/Foreign Students 621/6
Graduate Students/Foreign Students 26/0
Library 100, 085 volumes
Contact: General Affairs Division

Educational plilosophy In accordance with existing socioeconomic conditions and national welfare policies, Japan College of Social Work seeks to be a training center for leaders in the field of social welfare. Training will include practical instruction given in social welfare institutions, and theoretical study and research done on campus.

Foreign students We hope that foreign students have a rewarding experience in our campus life, and can respond to new international society and contribute to world social welfare in the 21st century.

Environment Kiyose city is located in the northwestern part of Tokyo. The city is rich in green and has good facilities for transportation, the Seibu line, the JR line and the Kan'etsu expressway. There is various welfare and medical facilities, so it is the best place to study social welfare.

Facilities Social work library, Social work research institute, Center for mentally retarded children(Clinical training facility) Swimming pool, Gymnasium,

Student activites [Program for unique activities] orientation camp(for all entering students), integration camp (for the 2・3 year students), [Popular campus events] College festival, Freshmen welcome festival, [Circle activities]Many circles of social welfare relation including volunteer work, Drama, Baseball, etc.

Academic programs for foreign students Supplemental Japanese language class. Substitutions curriculum system.

Services for foreign student Health clinic, personal/psychological, Student dormitory, Housing information, Part-time job information, Cultural exchange program,

Undergraduate Programs

Faculty of Social Welfare(621/6)

Dept. of Child Welfare(390/2)

Dept. of Social Work(231/4)

Graduate Programs

Graduate School of Social Services(M 26/0)
Social Welfare Theory, Social Problems, Comparative Study of Overseas Social Welfare, History of Social Welfare, Welfare Administration, Community Welfare, Familly Welfare, Welfare for the Handicapped, Welfare for the Elderly, Specific Studies for Welfare Planning, Specific Studies for Welfare practice

日本赤十字看護大学
(Nihon Sekijûji Kango Daigaku)

The Japanese Red Cross College of Nursing

4-1-3 Hirro, Shibuya-ku, Tokyo 150
☎ 03-3409-0875 FAX 03-3409-0589

Founded 1986
Professors 15
Associate Professors 4
Assistant Professors(Tenured) 7
Assistant Professors(Non-tenured) 48
Research Assistants 9
Undergraduate Students/Foreign Students 238/0
Library 29, 665 volumes
Contact: Office

Educational philosophy Our aim is to educate those who can put The Red Cross doctrine in practice, those who can pursue a post graduate course after leaving this college, and those who can develop themselves as nurses after leaving this college.
Policies about recieving foreign students We do not admit foreign students.
Environment The college is in Shibuya Ward, Tokyo. Shibuya is near the center of Tokyo, and has some big chopping areas. But the college is located in a quiet residential area. There are several universities and high schools around the college.
Facilities Library, Swimming pool, Gymnasium, Auditorium, Language Laboratory
Student activities Campus events: college festival, freshman camp, caroling, Extra curricular activities: volunteer work, volleyball, tennis, choral group, etc.

Undergraduate Programs

Faculty of Nursing(238/0)
Dept. of Nursing(238/0)

日本ルーテル神学大学
(Nihon Rûteru Shingaku Daigaku)

Japan Lutheran Theological College

3-10-20 Osawa, Mitaka-shi, Tokyo 181
☎ 0422-31-4611

Founded 1964

Undergraduate Programs

Faculty of Literature
Dept. of Social Welfare
Dept. of Theology

日本女子体育大学
(Nihon Joshi Taiiku Daigaku)

Japan Women's College of Physical Education

8-9-1 Kita-karasuyama, Setagaya-ku, Tokyo 157
☎ 03-3300-2251 FAX 03-3300-0174

Founded 1922
Professors 28
Associate Professors 9
Assistant Professors(Tenured) 3
Assistant Professors(Non-tenured) 28
Research Assistants 12
Undergraduate Students/Foreign Students 1, 460/2
Library 81, 022 volumes
Contact: Admission Office

Educational philosophy Our College and Junior College have served educational and developmental needs in Physical Education in Japan since 1922, under the strong conviction that health and physical fitness is one of the important factors of human well-being.
Foreign students We are confident to urge you to consider an investiment of your time as part of realizing your potential in our new programs which provides Sports Science, Physical Education, Health and Physical Fitness Major.
Environment The campus is located not far from Shinjuku(20 minutes distant westward from Shinjuku by Keio Line)and surrounded by some of the remaining natural beauties of the old Musashino Plain,making students' life comfortable.
Facilities Library including Tokuyo Memorial Hall, Laboratory for Exercise Physiology, Laboratory for Information Processing,Gymnasiums, Swimming Pool, Track and Field, etc.

Student activities Popular campus events includes Anniversary of College's Founding, College Festival, College-Exhibition of Performances. Students enjoy a wide variety of extra-curricular activities, including Judo, Japanese Archery,Modern Dance, Flower Arrangement, etc.

Undergraduate Programs

Faculty of Physical Education(1, 460/2)

日本女子大学
(Nihon Joshi Daigaku)

Japan Women's University

Mejiro Campus: 2-8-1 Mejirodai, Bunkyo-ku, Tokyo 112
Nishiikuta Campus: 1-1-1 Nishiikuta, Tama-ku, Kawasaki-shi, Kanagawa 214
☎ Mejiro: 03-3943-3131 FAX Mejiro: 03-3942-6518
☎ Nishiikuta: 044-966-2121
FAX Nishiikuta: 044-952-6819

Founded 1901
Professors 108
Associate Professors 48
Assistant Professors(Tenured) 23
Assistant Professors(Non-tenured) 420
Research Assistants 61
Undergraduate Students/Foreign Students 5434/32
Graduate Students/Foreign Students 148/7
Library 420, 000 volumes
Contact: Admission Office, Mejiro Campus ☎ 03-3942-6504
FAX: 03-942-6502

Educational philosophy Ever since the foundation by Rev. Jinzo Naruse, we have endeavored to give each student a deep consciousness of great responsibility as a person, as a woman, and as a member of a nation, and also have respected three principles of education: " True Conviction, " " Creativity, " and " Cooperation and Service. "

Foreign students We have welcomed foreign students since the early stage after the foundation. We have made every effort to help foreign students to study comfortably here and hoped all students to have international understandings.

Environment Mejiro Campus, which is located in a quiet neighborhood in Bunkyo-Ward, the educational and cultural center of Tokyo, has been the main campus since 1901. Nishiikuta Campus is situated in the green belt of Tama Area, but convenient from Shinjuku, the new center of Tokyo Metropolitan Government.

Facilities Libraries, Naruse Memorial Auditorium, Naruse Memorial Hall(museum), Student Health Centers, Counseling Centers, Student Dormitories, Students' Centers, Seminar House, Language Laboratories, Computer Laboratories

Student activities Festival in autumn(Mejiro-sai) and freshmen welcome parties are popular events for students. We have a wide variety of extra curricular activities including societies for the study of Kabuki, Noh, and Sumo, English Speaking Society, golf, tennis, horse-riding, tea ceremony, flower arrangement, chorus, ceramic art, etc.

Academic programs for foreign students Japanese Language I & II and Japan Studies A & B are special subjects for foreign students and these credits may be considered as the ones of the specified subjects in the general education. Totoring system.

Services for foreign Students We give the same services for foreign and Japanese native students : health clinic, counseling, dormitories(foreign students have the priority), part-time job information, vocational guidance, housing information

Undergraduate Programs

Faculty of Home Economics(2623/18)
- **Dept. of Child Studies**(403/5)
- **Dept. of Clothing**(323/5)
- **Dept. of Food and Nutrition Food Science Major Nutrition Major**(367/2)
- **Dept. of Household Economics**(348/2)
- **Department of Housing**(361/4)
- **Dept. of Sciences for Home Economics, Section I: Chemistry Major, Mathematics Major, physics Major, Section II: Biology and Agricultural Science**(821/0)

Faculty of Humanities(2165/12)
- **Dept. of Education**(329/3)
- **Dept. of English**(584/3)
- **Dept. of History**(343/0)
- **Dept. of Japanese**(563/5)
- **Dept. of Social Welfare**(346/1)

Faculty of Integrated Arts and Social Sciences (646/2)
- **Dept. of Contemporary Sociology**(134/0)
- **Dept. of Education**(173/1)
- **Dept. of Humanities and Cultures**(127/0)
- **Dept. of Psychology**(90/1)
- **Dept. of Social Welfare**(122/0)

Graduate Programs

Graduate School of Home Economics(M 59/3)
- **Div. of Child Studies**(M 19/1)
- **Div. of Clothing**(M 10/0)
- **Div. of Food and Nutrition**(M 20/1)
- **Div. of Housing**(M 10/1)

Graduate School of Humanities(M 62/1, D 27/3)
- **Div. of Education**(M 20/0, D 10/0)
- **Div. of English Language and Literature**(M 9/0, D 8/0)
- **Div. of Japanese Language and Literature**(M 18/1, D 6/1)
- **Div. of Social Welfare**(M 15/0, D 3/2)

自治医科大学
(Jichi Ika Daigaku)
Jichi Medical School

3311-1 Yakushiji, Minamikawachi-machi, Kawachi-gun, Tochigi 329-04
☎ 0285-44-2111

Founded 1972

Undergraduate Programs

Faculty of Medicine
Dept. of Medicine

Graduate Programs

Graduate School of Medicine
Div. of Community Medicine
Div. of Environmental Health
Div. of Human Biology

東京慈恵会医科大学
(Tokyo Jikei Kai Ika Daigaku)
The Jikei University School of Medicine

3-25-8 Nishi-Shinbashi, Minato-ku, Tokyo 105
☎ 03-3433-1111 FAX 03-3435-1922

Founded 1881
Professors 75
Associate Professors 69
Assistant Professors(Tenured) 189
Assistant Professors(Non-Tenured) 185
Research Assistants 606
Undergraduate Students/Foreign Students 708/0
Graduate Students/Foreign Students 49/0
Contact: Section of Education Affairs

Educational philosophy Patient-centered medical care
Environment Premedical course(2 yrs.)at Kokuryo Campus, 10 min. walk from Kokuryo Station of Keio Line(train). Medical course(4 yrs.)at Shinbashi(School and Main Hospiatal) Campus, 15 min. walk from Shinbashi Station(JR train)or 5 min. walk from Onarimon Station(Metropolitan Mita Line).
Facilities Kokuryo Campus : Premedical Library and Sports Facilities. Shinbashi Campus: Medical Library, Medical Museum, Biomedical Research Institute, Radioisotope Laboratory, Laboratory Animal Research Center, medical Informatics Laboratory, etc.
Student activities Kokuryo Festival for students attending premedical course in November and Atago Festival medical students in October are popular campus events. As students extracurriculum activities, there are 15 cultural and 27 sports clubs.

Undergraduate Programs

Faculty of Medicine(707/0)

Graduate Programs

Graduate School of Medicine(D 48/0)
Div. of Basic Medical science, Social Medical Science Clinical Medical Science.(D 48/0)
Basic. medical science : Anatomy, Physiology, Biochemistry, Notrition, Pharmacology, Pathology, Bacter; ology(Microbiology), Parasitology, Laboratory Medicine. Social Medical Science : Hygiene, Public Health, Legal medicine, Clinical medical Science : Internal Medicine, Pediatrics, Neuropsychiatry, Radiology, Dermatology, Sorgery, Orthopedic Surgery, Neurosurgery, Plastic and Reconstructive Surgery, Cardiac Surgery, Obstetricsand Gynecology, Otorhinolaryngology, Urology, Ophthalmology, Anesthessilogy.

実践女子大学
(Jissen Joshi Daigaku)
Jissen Women's University

4-1-1 Osakaue, Hino-shi,Tokyo 191
☎ 0425-85-0311 FAX 0425-85-0327

Founded 1899
Professors 55
Associate Professors 23
Assistant Professors(Tenured) 2
Assistant Professors(Non-tenured) 132
Research Assistants 4
Undergraduate Students/Foreign Students 3282/0
Graduate Students/Foreign Students 45/7
Library 235, 560 volumes
Contact: Admission office

Educational philosophy Our ultimate aim is cultivating the intellectual, moral and practical abilities of our students, with emphasis on the development of their sound characters. So our students are expected to become women who will contribute much to cultural betterment and social improvement.
Foreign students Being small in size, our school has the advantage of keeping friendly relationships between teachers and students. So we believe that foreign students can enjoy their lives and obtain their expected results.
Environment Our University is located in the city of Hino(population 162, 894), in the western part of Tokyo. The City has retained much of its natural beauty and quietness. This makes for an enjoyable learning

environment. Though located in a rural area, Hino is convenient to the urban area.

Facilities Library, 3 Seminar houses(Hakone, Karuizawa, Tsumagoi), dormitory, Gymnasium, Outdoor swimming pool, all-weather tennis courts, Athletic field.

Student activities There is a wide variety of extra curricular activities and events, such as club activities (69 clubs), freshmen welcome party, school festival, athletics days and so on. The purpose of these students activities is to promote friendship among the students and to enrich their lives.

Services for foreign students Health clinic, personal counseling, college housing, housing information, part-time job information, vocational guidance. Foreign students can get the same services as the Japanes students.

Undergraduate Programs

Faculty of Home Economics(1, 370/0)
Dept. of Clothing Science(549/0)
Dept. of Food Science (Food Studies Course/ Register's Dietician Course) (821/0)
Faculty of Literature(1, 912/0)
Dept. of Aesthetics and Art History(501/0)
Dept. of English Literature(718/0)
Dept. of Japanese Literature(693/0)

Graduate Programs

Graduate School of Home Economics(M 18/0)
Div. of Clothing science(M 9/0)
Clothing Ecology, Clothing Materical Science, Clothing Environmental Design, Colthing Environmental Culture, Living Information Science, Experimental Psychology.
Div. of Food Science and Nutrition(M 9/0)
Nutrition, Sitology, Cooking science, Food Hygiene, Public Hygiene, Polymer Chemistry, Dietetics.
Graduate School of Literature(M 17/3, D 10/4)
Div. of English Literature(M 9/0)
Current of Modern English Literary Thoughts, Special Studies on English literature, Seminars in English Literature, English Linguistics, Greek, Latin, Advanced German, Advanced French.
Div. of Japanese Literature(M 8/3, D 10/4)
Japanese Literature, Japanese Linguistics, Chinese Classics, Chinese Thought,

上武大学

(Jôbu Daigaku)

Jobu University

634 Toyatuka-machi, Isesaki-shi,Gunma 372
☎ 0270-32-1010 FAX 0270-32-1021

Founded 1968
Professors 28
Associate Professors 16
Assistant Professors(Tenured) 13
Assistant Professors(Non-tenured) 57
Undergraduate Students/Foreign Students 2, 245/30
Library 57, 564 volumes

Educational philosophy Being small in size, the students acquainted with their professors and the university has advantage of keeping friendly relationships between students and professors.

Foreign students Our university is open for foreign youths willing to contribute to international relationship through better understanding.

Environment The university has two campuses : Department of Comercial Science is in Isesaki city and Department of management and Information Science is in Shimmachi, both of which are about 55miles north of Tokyo.

Facilities Library, Computer center, Gymnasium, etc.

Student activities School Festival, Welcome Sports For Freshmen, baseball, jubo, tennis, basketball, athletics, etc.

Undergraduate Programs

Faculty of Commercial Science(1, 113/21)
Dept. of Commercial Science(1, 113/21)
Faculty of Management and Information Science (1, 132/9)
Dept. of Management and Information Science (1, 132/9)
Business Management Theory, Business Administration, Information Science, Programing Language Computers, Seminars, Constitution, Commercial Law, Labor Law, Industrial Sociology, Information Sociology, Social Psychology, Industrial Psychology, Reading in Foreign Languages, Marketing, Accounting, Insurance, International Economy, Operating System, etc. Accunting, Marketing, Economics of Commerce, Statistics, Insurance Commercial Law, Bookkeeping Financial Management, Civil Law, Business Administration Tax Law, Reading in Foreign Languages, Business English Economics, International Economics History of Economic Doctrines, An Introduction to Information Science, Programing Language, Programing Training, Computer Training, etc.

城西大学

(Jôsai Daigaku)

Josai University

1-1 Keyakidai, Sakado-shi, Saitama
☎ 0492-86-2233 FAX 0492-85-7167

Founded 1965
Professors 68
Associate Professors 53
Assistant Professors(Tenured) 28
Assistaant Professors(Non-tenured) 172

Research Assistants 30
Undergraduate Students/Foreign Students 7514/127
Graduate Students/Foreign Students 54/2
Library 340, 000 volumes

Educational philosophy The former Chancellor, Mikio Mizuta, fouded on the principle that " the pursuit of studies is not for sake of studies in themselves but as a means towards of virtues. " Consequently, the whole University is dedicated to educating young minds so that they can do for the world.

Foreign students Foreign students who entered into Josai University can master Japanese language and other studies. Various experiences in school will be useful after homecoming in each conutry and promote mutual undertanding.

Environment The town Sakado, with a population of 94, 000, is located in the west of Saitama Prefecture, northwest of Tokyo. Its environments is far from the hustle and bustle of the city, and is of irreplaceable value where studies and sports prevail.

Facilities Center for Inter-Cultural Studies & Education,Life Science Research Center, Information Science Research Center, Isotope Center, Library, Art Gallery of Ukiyoe, Gymnasium with swimming pool.

Student activities Josai students participate in a wide spectrum of extra-carricular clubs and activities, ranging from Western-derived sports like American football to traditional Japanese arts like tea ceremony. In addition, the university holds its own special festivals like week-long Koma Festival.

Academic programs for foreign students Supplementary Japanese language class.

Services for foreign students Health Clinic, House information, Part-time Job information, home visit, cultural exchange program.

Undergraduate Programs

Faculty of Economics(5547/127)
  Dept. of Economics(2842/42)
  Dept. of Business Administration(2705/85)
Faculty of Science(883/0)
  Dept. of Mathematics(505/0)
  Dept. of Chemistry(378/0)
Faculty of Pharmacology(1084/0)
  Dept. of Pharmacy(586/0)
  Dept. of Pharmaceutics(498/0)

Graduate Programs

Graduate School of Economics(M 12/2)
Finance, Statistics, Social Policy.

Graduate School of Pharmacology(M 39/0, D 3, 0)
Analytical Chemistry, Microbiology, Organic Chemistry, Physiological Chemistry, Pharmaceutics, Photochemistry, Synthetic Organic Chemistry.

女子栄養大学
(Joshi Eiyô Daigaku)

Kagawa Nutrition College

3-9-21 Chiyoda, Sakado-shi, Saitama 350-02
☎ 0492-83-2133 FAX 0492-82-3720

Founded 1961
Professors 34
Associate Professors 17
Assistant Professors(Tenured) 2
Assistant Professors(Non-tenured) 92
Research Assistants 29
Undergraduate Students/Foreign Students 1338/4
Graduate Students/Foreign Students 14/0
Library 63, 290 volumes
Contact: Admission Office

Educational philosophy The eating habits of human being is an important factor in maintaining good health, and is a culture too. We have always aimed at exhorting research and education on a double theme-the people's nutrition and dietary life of the human body.

Foreign students The school consists of the nutrition faculty, and is a very unique college in Japan. Study and campus life in this college is a strict affair but can also be quite pleasant.

Environment The campus is located in Sakado city, a city of 60, 000 people, 33 km West of Tokyo. Though located in a rural area,it takes only 45 minutes to the urban area(Ikebukuro in Tokyo Metropolitan City)by Tobu line express.

Facilities Library, Audio-visual room, Metabolic House, Computer room, Farm, Gymnasium, Training room, Ground, Tennis court, Dormitory, Dining hall, Students hall, Shopping service, Club house.

Student activities When one is a freshman, the whole school and faculty members go on a two day excursion together, combining study and making friends. In June there is the campus fete, and the following are the extracurricular activities: Japanese fencing, tea ceremony, dietary life research, etc.

Academic programs for foreign students At the beginning of the academic year and/or semester, an orientation program is scheduled for foreign students which covers registrations, academic programmes, health insurance, housing, etc.

Services for foreign students Committee members of the Foreign Affairs are in charge of personal counceling for foreign students. Other personal services are available through the Office of Student Affairs.

Undergraduate Programs

Faculty of Nutrition(1338/4)
  Dept. of Health and Nutrition(468/0)
  Dept. of Nutrition Sciences(865/4)

Graduate Programs

Graduate School of Nutrition Sciences(M 9/0, D 5/0)

Div. of Nutrition Sciences(M 9/0, D 5/0)

Nutritional Physiology, Nutritional Biochemistry, Clinical Chemistry, Clinical Nutrition, Maternal and Child Nutrition, Food Science, Food Hygiene, Applied Nutrition, Cookery, Health Care Administration, Methods of Experiment in Nutrition, Methods of research in Nutrition

---

順天堂大学

(Juntendô Daigaku)

Juntendo University

2-1-1 Hongo, Bunkyo-ku, Tokyo 113
☎ 03-3813-3111 FAX 03-3814-9100

Founded 1951
Professors 83
Associate Professors 76
Assistant Professors(Tenured) 144
Assistant Professors(Non-tenured) 317
Research Assistants 346
Undergraduate Students/Foreign Students 1, 493/0
Graduate Students/Foreign Students 105/1
Library 211, 909 volumes
Contact: Admission Office

Educational philosophy With the school of Medicine and the Faculty of Health and Physical Education, Juntendo University is a unique comprehensive health university. The School of Medicine is committed to training understanding and able doctors. The Faculty of Heath and Physical Education trains health and physical education leaders who are famililar with health science. We foster the total growth of students, not only the intellectual but also the emotional and social.

Foreign students Almost all classes are conducted in Japanese. So all applicants are required to submit the certificate from the JLPT. All applicants for admission to both the undergraduate schools of Juntendo University are also required to pass the entrance examination of the respective school within the university.

Environment The School of Medicine is a cityscape in the heart of Tokyo and is easy to reach. There are many hospitals and universities in its neighborhood. The Faculty of Health and Physical Education can be reached in about twenty minutes from Narita International Airport. It is located in a quiet rural district in the central part of Chiba Prefecture. But it is just about 25 miles away from the center of Tokyo.

Facilities The School of Medicine has four thoroughly equipped educational hospitals. The Faculty of Health and Physical Education has newly built sports facilities such as gymnasiums, a swimming pool, grounds for field and track events and ball games, etc.

Student activites All the undergraduate freshmen are required to stay at the residence hall on the campus of the Faculty of Health and Physical Education for one year. We want you to enjoy close relationships with other students of diverse backgrounds and outlooks, and to grow personally as well as intellectually. The students are encouraged to join some of the various campus clubs that round out student life.

Academic programs for foreign students We receive only foreign students who are or will be graduates of four-year colleges or universities at the time of application. You will be admitted as regular graduate students, or auditors or special students or internatioal students of the undergraduate schools. We have no special programs for foreign sutdents.

Services for foreign students It is almost impossible for foreign sutdents to do part-time jobs during the team. You are requested to concentrate on classes and campus activities. We do not offer special services for foreign students. However, we are always ready to serve you in any matter you need help for.

Undergraduate Programs

Faculty of Health and Physcial Education(925/0)

Dept. of Health(268/0)

Dept. of Physical Education(657/0)

Faculty of Medicine(568/0)

Graduate Programs

Graduate School of Physical Education(24/0)

Div. of Physical Education(M 2/0)

Theory of Physical Education, Psychology in Physical Education and Sports (Seminar, Lab. work), Sociology in Physical Education (Lecture, Seminar), Administration in Physical Education (Seminar), Nutrition (Lecture), Introduction to Information Proccesion

Div. of Science of Physical Fitness(M 8/0)

Science of Physical Fitness (Lecture, Seminar), Theory of Physical Training(Lab. work), Measurement of Physical Fitness (Lab. work), Physiology of Exercise (Lecture, Lab. work)

Div. of Science of Coaching(M 6/0)

Science of Coaching (Lecture, Seminar, Lab. work), Kinesiology (Lecture, Lab. work)

Div. of Sports Medicine(M 6/0)

Sports Medicine (Lecture, Seminar), Physical Disorder in sports (Internal Medicine Orthopedic), Theory of Rehabilitation (Lecuture), Rehabilitation (Lab. work)

Div. of Health Care Administraion(M 2/0)

Theories in Health Care Administration (Lecture), Health Care Administration in Communities (Seminar), Human Ecology (Lecture), Health Sociology (Lecture), Health Disorder and Epidemiology (Lecture), Mass Health Examination (Lab. work)

Div. of School Health(M 0/0)

School Health (Lecture, Seminar), Healthful Living (Lecture), Mental Health (Lecture), Educational Materials in Health Education (Lab. work), Organized Activities in Health (Lecture)

Div. of Environmental Health(M 0 /0)

Environmental Health (Lecture, Seminar, Lab. work), Labor Health (Lecture), Problems of Environmental Pollution (Seminar), Pathological Microbiology (Lecture)

Graduate School of Medicine(D 81/1)

Div. of Physiology(D 3/1)

Anatomy, Physiology, Biochemistry, Pharmacology

Div. of Pathology(D 9/0)

Pathology, Bacteriology, Parasitorogy, Immunology

Div. of Sociomedical(D 1/0)

Hygine, Pubulic Health, Forensic Medicine

Div. of Medicine(D 39/0)

Internal Medicine, Psychiatry, Neurology, Pediatrics, Dermatology, Radiology, Clinical Pathorogy, Medical Ultrasonic

Div. of Surgery(D 29/0)

Surgery, Thoracic Surgery, Pediatric Surgery, Neurosurgery, Orthopedic Surgery, Urology, Ophthalmology, Oto-rhinolaryngology, Gynecology, Anesthesiology

---

鎌倉女子大学

(Kamakura Joshi Daigaku)

Kamakura Women's College

1420 Iwase, Kamakura-shi, Kanagawa 247
☎ 0467-44-2111

Founded 1959

Undergraduate Programs

Faculty of Home Economics

Dept. of Child Study

Child Culture and Nursery Nurses Training Program
Kindergarten Teachers Training Program
Primary School Teachers Training Program

Dept. of Domestic Science

Administrators of Ordinary Dietichians Training Program
Domestic Science Teachers Training Program

神奈川歯科大学

(Kanagawa Shika Daigaku)

Kanagawa Dental College

82 Inaoka-cho, Yokosuka-shi, Kanagawa 238
☎ 0468-25-1500 FAX 0468-23-0118

Founded 1964
Professors 33
Associate Professors 23
Assistant Professors(Tenured) 39
Assistant Professors(Non-tenured) 104
Research Assistants 137
Undergraduate Students/Foreign Students 921/1
Graduate Students/Foreign Students 58/0
Library 108, 053 volumes
Contact: Administrative Office, Faculty of Dentistry Admission Office

Educational philosophy Founded on the spirit of the Fundamental Law of Education, we will rear students into fine personality and extended knowledge, studying and teaching advanced academic theories and techniques of dentistry, and producing able dentists,to add to cultural improvement and social welfare promoting.

Foreign students We welcome foreign students to our College, encouraged by the fact that foreign students and we have exerted positive influence on each other, judging from achivements in education.

Environment Our College is in the heart of Yokosuka of some 400, 000 population, close to Kamakura, a historic city, favored by mountains and oceans. Our College can be easily reached from Tokyo in an hour, and from Yokohama, an international harbor, in just 25 minutes. Our environments are best fit for education.

Facilities Library, Gymnasium, College Hospital, etc.

Student activities We have club activities, including American football, baseball, golf, Rugby football, music, and " Go ". Several of the sport clubs are always ranked among the topmosts in the Sports Festival for All Dental Students. Also, we have such cultural events as a Garden Party and a College Festival.

Undergraduate Programs

Faculty of Dentistry(921/1)

Graduate Programs

Graduate School of Dentistry(D 58/0)

Oral Anatomy, Oral Physiology, Oral Biochemistry, Oral Bacteriology, Oral Pathology, Dental Pharmacology, Dental Technology, Public Health and Dental Health, Conservative Dentistry, Prosthetic Dentistry, Oral and Maxillofacial Surgery, Orthodontics, Pediatric Dentistry, Oral Radiology.

神奈川工科大学

(Kanagawa Kôka Daigaku)

Kanagawa Institute of Technology

1030 Shimo-ogino, Atsugi-shi, Kanagawa 243-02
☎ 0462-41-1211 FAX 0462-42-3737

Founded 1975
Professors 64
Associate Professors 38

Assistant Professors(Tenured) 7
Assistant Professors(Non-tenured) 86
Research Assistants 31
Undergraduate Students/Foreign Students 3, 670/0
Graduate Students/Foreign Students 39/1
Library 124, 453 volumes
Contact: Amissions Section

Educational philosophy We aim at cultivating scientific engineers full of creativity and humanity.
Foreign students We have no special system for foreign students in the entrance examinations, but we give them our consideration as much as possible. We believe that the foreign students matriculated in our university can enjoy kind and careful instructions.
Environment Atsugi-City is located in the center of Kanagawa Prefecture, 50 minutes from Shinjuku Station and 40 minutes from Yokohama Station. It boasts four universities, four junior colleges and many technological institutes of famous frontier companies, which makes it " Academic Research City ".
Facilities Library housing 120, 000 books, Electronic Computer Center, First Research Laboratory, Second Research Laboratory, Third Research Laboratory, First Gymnasium, Second Gymnasium, Student Hall, etc.
Student activities Popular campus events include freshmen welcome party, sports festival, campus festival. There is a side variety of extra curricular activities, including light music, student news paper, baseball, soccer, tennis, etc.

Undergraduate Programs

Faculty of Engineering(3670/0)
Dept. of Chemical Technology(824/0)
Dept. of Computer Science & Engineering(532/0)
Dept. of Electronic & Electrical Engineering(884/0)
Dept. of Mechanical Engineering(887/0)
Dept. of Mechanical Systems Engineering(543/0)

Graduate Programs

Graduate School of Technology(M 39/1)
Div. of Chemical Technology(M 13/0)
Inorganic Industrial Chemistry, Industrial Organic Chemistry, Industrial Physical Chemistry, Inorganic Materials Chemistry, Chemical Engineering
Div. of Electronic & Electrical Engineering(M 8/0)
Power and Control Engineering, Acoustics and Image Engineering, Physical Electronics, Electronic Circuit Engineering
Div. of Mechanical Engineering(M 15/1)
Strength of Materials and Structure, Thermal Engineering, Fluids Engineering, Production Engineering
Div. of Mechanical Systems Engineering(M 3/0)
Comutational Mechanics, Thermal and Fluid Systems, Mechanical Systems Dynamics and Control, Production Systems Engineering

神奈川大学
(Kanagawa Daigaku)
Kanagawa University

3-27-1 Rokkakubashi, Kanagawa-ku Yokohama, 221
☎ 045-481-5661 FAX 045-491-7915

Founded 1928
Professors 220
Associate Professors 104
Assistant Professors(Tenured) 20
Assistant Professors(Non-tenured) 418
Research Assistants 49
Undergraduate Students/Foreign Students 13, 108/17
Graduate Students/Foreign Students 110/7
Livrary 532, 000 volumes
Contact: Public Relations Department

Educational philosophy To contribute society by striving to preserve and enhance inherited culture, and to cultivate talents of creativity and international outlook. We hope and expect our students develop a strong sense of individuality, love for truth and courage in their convictions.
Foreign students We give warm welcome to students from all the corners of the earth, and can contribute a great deal to promoting mutual understanding and the development of friendly relations.
Environment Located only 2 km north of central Yokohama, Japan's second largest city looking out on Tokyo bay and developing into one of a center of culture, economy and technology in the metropolitan area. Besides, Hiratsuka Campus is central part of Kanagawa Prefecture.
Facilities On the site of 110, 000m^2 stand faculties buildings, laboratories,library, gymnasium, University Hall and other facilities. Also seminar houses in the rural area, and similar facilities in Hiratsuka Campus.
Student activities Like all good educational institutions, we aim at developing all the potentialities of our students, intellectual, physical and social, 130 recognized sports and cultural clubs and 180 informal ones form the center of students' social life
Services for foreign students Health clinic, personal/psychological counseling, housing information, part-time job information, vocational guidance,study jaunt,social meeting

Undergraduate Programs

Faculty of Economics(4661/0)
Dept. of Economics(3443/0)
Dept. of International Trade(1218/0)
Faculty of Law(2315/2)
Dept. of Law(2315/2)

Faculty of Business Administration(487/11)
Dept. of International Business and Management(487/11)
Faculty of Foreign Language(1263/3)
Dept. of Chinese(174/0)
Dept. of English(721/3)
Dept. of Spanish(368/0)
Faculty of Science(351/0)
Dept. of Biological Sciences(108/0)
Dept. of Information Sciences(124/0)
Dept. of Materials Science(119/0)
Faculty of Engineering(4031/1)
Dept. of Applied Chemistry(693/0)
Dept. of Architecture(565/0)
Dept. of Electrical Engineering(1053/0)
Dept. of Industrial Engineering and Management(695/1)
Dept. of Mechanical Engineering(1025/0)

Graduate Programs

Graduate School of Economics(M 12/2, D 9/2)
Economic Theories with their Histrical Background, Economic History of Europe and Japan, Economic Policies International Economy and Trade, Public Finance and Monetary Economics, Management and Accounting
Graduate School of Engineering(M 77/0, D 2/0)
Div. of Applied Chemistry(M 25/0, D 2/0)
Molecular and Material Science and Engineering, Energy Conversion Science and Engineering, Polymer Science and Engineering, Biomolecular Science and Engineering, Inorganic Materials and Analytical Chemistry
Div. of Architecture and Building Engineering(M 15/0, D 0/0)
Building Structural Engineering, Architectural Planning
Div. of Electrical Engineering(M 23/0, D 0/0)
Electromagnetic Waves and Circuits, Ultrasonics Engineering, Electronic Devices Engineering, Functional Materials Engineering, Applied Measurements Engineering, Image Processing and Information Theory
Div. of Mechanical Engineering(M 14/0, D 0/0)
Engineering Materials, Engineering Manifacture, Heat and Flow Engineering, Mechanical Systems Engineering
Graduate School of Law(M 8/2, D 2/1)
Civil Law, Public Law including Political Science, General Subjects

---

神田外語大学
(Kanda Gaigo Daigaku)

Kanda University of International Studies

1-4-1 Wakaba, Chiba-shi, Chiba 260
☎ 0472-73-1233 FAX 0472-72-1777

Founded 1987
Professors 28
Associate Professors 8
Assistant Professors(Tenured) 15
Assistant Professors(Non-tenured) 75
Undergraduate Students/Foreign Students 1, 333/0
Library 34, 747 volumes
Contact: general affairs department

Educational Philosophy Kanda Gaigo Daigaku (Kanda University of International Studies)is a small private university dedicated to the pursuit of excellence in international studies, particularly in the study of foreign languages. At present these include English, Chinese, Spanish and Korean.
Environment Centre of Tokyo. The campus is adjacent to the Makuhari Messe, which includes an international convention centre, and stadium and hotels, and near the Makuhari beach and yacht harbour.
Facilities The library(including the Rexroth collection), gymnasium and sports facilities, audio-visual laboratory and recording studio, computer centre, Language Research Institute, Inter-cultural Communication Institute, English Language Institute.
Student activities There are forty-five students clubs in operation, 22 of which are culture-oriented and 23 sporting. The annual univesity festival, held in autumn, features a variety of academic and cultural activities including symposia, speech contents, drama, and Spanish and Korean dancing.

Undergraduate Programs

Faculty of Foreign Languages(1, 333/0)
Dept. of Chinese language(237/0)
Dept. of English and American language(902/0)
Dept. of Korean laguage(95/0)
Dept. of Spanish language(99/0)

関東学園大学
(Kantô Gakuen Daigaku)

Kanto Gakuen University

200 Fujiagu, Ohta-shi Gunma 375
☎ 0276-31-2711 FAX 0276-31-2708

Founded 1976
Professors 48
Associate Professors 14
Assistant Professors(Tenured) 12
Assistant Professors(Non-tenured) 15
Research Assistants 1
Undergraduate Students/Foreign Students 2, 537/3
Graduate Students/Foreign Students 23/0
Library 120, 257 volumes

Educational philosophy The University spirit aims at developing a healthy mind and creativity.
Foreign students We hope that foreign students

can enjoy the campus life and can contribute to improving international understanding.
Environment The city of Ohta with a population of 140, 000, is located about 100 kilometer's distance from Tokyo and it is surrounded by beautiful mountain and provides an excellent environment for education.
Facilities Computer Center, Sports Training Center, Library, Gymnasium
Student activities School festival, A wide variety of extra curricular activities including baseball, American football, football
Academic programs for foreign students Housing information and arrangement

Undergraduate Programs

Faculty of Law(269/0)
Dept. of Law
Faculty of Economics(2, 268/0)
Dept. of Economics(1, 143/0)
Dept. of Business Management(1, 125/3)

Graduate Programs

Graduate School of Economics(M 23/0)
Theoretical Economics, History of Economic Thought, Finance, International Finance, Public Finance, Agricultural Economics, Economic Policy, Statistics, Economic History, Tax Law, International Economics, Economics of Population, Accounting

関東学院大学

(Kantô Gakuin Daigaku)

Kanto Gakuin University

4834 Mutsuura-cho, Kanazawa-ku, Yokohama-shi, Kanagawa 236
☎ 045-781-2001 FAX 045-786-7038

Founded 1884
Professors 114
Associate Professors 63
Assistant Professors(Tenured) 20
Assistant Professors(Non-tenured) 397
Undergraduate Students/Foreign Students 9, 278/24
Graduate Students/Foreign Students 83/10
Library 443, 918 volumes
Contact: International Center ☎ 045-786-7015 FAX : 045-786-7044

Educational Philosophy We aim at building up character based upon the Christian spirit and teaching and studying academic theories and applications. The school motto is " Be a man, serve the world. "
Foreign students We welcome foreign students. For, in globalization, true teaching and studying do not exist without learning cross-culturally. We believe that mutual understanding encourages real peace in the world.
Environment The University is located in Yokohama, with a polulation of 3, 227, 000. Its environs are such famous historical scenic points as "Kamakura" and " Kanazawa Bunko ". It is also surrounded by greenery and the ocean.
Facilities Library, Christian Education Center, Computer Center, International Center, Counseling Center, Hayama Seminar House, Gymnasium, etc.
Student activities Popular campus events include the school festival, freshmen welcome party and homecoming. There is a wide variety of extra-curricular activities, including rugby, baseball, Shakespeare drama, marching band, Judo, Kendo, basketball, volleyball,etc.
Academic programs for foreign students Japanese Studies(counted as courses in General Education) Japanese Language(counted as first foreign language)
Services for foreign students Health clinic, Counseling, Housing information, part-time information, Special Orienration about study and campus life.

Undergraduate Programs

Faculty of Economics(2, 855/18)
Dept. of Business Administration(1, 370/14)
Dept. of Economics(1, 485/4)
Faculty of Engineering(2, 743/6)
Dept. of Architectural Environmental Engineering (430/0)
Dept. of Architecture(511/2)
Dept. of Civil Engineering(407/0)
Dept. of Electrical Engineering(495/1)
Faculty of Engineering(2,743/6)
Dept. of Industrial Chemistry(361/0)
Dept. of Mechanical Engineering(539/3)
Faculty of Humanities(1, 536/0)
Dept. of English and American Literature(770/0)
Dept. of Sociology(766/0)

Graduate Programs

Graduate School of Economics(M 3/2, D 5/1)
Div. of Economics(M 3/0, D 2/0)
Economy, History of Economics, Theories of World-Economy, Economic Policy, History of Social Thought, American Economy, Asian Economy, Population Problems, Transportation Economy, Business Economics, Labour Problems Mathematical Economics, Theory of Finance, Public Finance, European Economy, Theory of Industry, Theory of Banking System
Div. of History of Economics/History of Social Economics(D 5/1)
Economy, History of Economics, Socio-Economic History, Economic Policy, Theory of Industry, Theories of World Economy, Economic History, Mathematical Economics, Theory of Banking System, Theories of Transportation Economy
Graduate School of Engineering(M 68/5, D 7/2)
Div. of Architecture(M 18/1, D 1/0)

History of Architecture, Architectural Planning, Structural Engineering for Building, Building Equipment Engineering, Architectural Environmental Engineering, Architectural Planning, History of Modern Architecture, Installation Process of Building Equipments, Illuminating, City Planning, Building Struction Planning, Vibration Theory of Structure, Structural Mechanics, Building Materials and Construction, Building Equipment Autocontrol, Air Conditioning Planning, Architectural Environmental Engineering Planning, Building Sanitary Engineering Planning

Graduate School of Engineering (M 68/5, D 7/2)

Div. of Civil Engineering (M 3/1)

Bridge Engineering, Transportation Engineering, Concreate Engineering, River and Sea Engineering, Sanitary Engineering, Structural Mechanics, Tunnel Engineering, Construction Planning and Methods, Harbour Engineering, Steel Structure, Mechanics of Fluid, Engineering Geology, Sanitary Engineeing, Soil Mechanics, Prestressed Concrete Structures

Div. of Electrical Engineering (M 3/0)

Theory and Applications of Electromagnetism, Electronics and its Applications, Electric Power Engineering, Illuminating Engineering, Control Engineering, Solid State Physics, Theory of Electric Circuits, Electromagnetic Fields, Electric and Magnetic Materials, Theory of Electronic Circuits, Electronic Measurements, Applied Measurements, Electron Devices, High Frequency Techniqes, Micro Wave Techniques, Semiconductor Engineering, High Voltage Engineering, Physics of Electric Discharge, Power Transimission System, Theory of Electrical Machinery Control Engineering, Industrial Application of Electric Power, Electro-Acoustics, Electronic Computer and Data Processing, Applied Mathematics, Automatic Control, Reliability Engineering

Div. of Industrial Chemistry (M 15/0)

Organic Industial Chemitry, Theoretical and Industrial Electrochemistry, Inorganic Industrial Chemistry, Synthetic Chemistry, Chemical Engineeing and Reaction Kinetics, Metal Finishing, Physical Chemistry of Industry, Theory of Reaction Engineering, Plan and Chemical Engineering, Battery Chemistry, Theory of Organic Reaction, Polymer Chemistry, Chemical Metallurgy, Catalytic Chemistry, Radiation Chemistry, Quantum Chemistry, Theory of Organic Structure

Div. of Mechanical Engineering (M 29/3, D 6/2)

Method of Measurement for Mechanical Engineering, Hydraulics, Fluid Mechanics, Internal Combustion Engines, Machine Working, Metal and Its Treatment, Pneumatic Engineering, Strength of Material, Engineering Problems on Vibratation, Boundary Layer, Cavitation Phenomena, Thermo-Aerodynamic, Welding, Crankless Piston Engine, Surface Treatment of Metals, Metallurgy, Non-Destructive Testing, Electric Measurements, Manufacturing Process and Equipment, Photo-Elasticity, Theory of Plasticity, Optimum Design, Theory of Combustion, Machinery Dynamics, Theory of Gass Turbine, Theory of Elasticity

川村学園女子大学

(Kawámura Gakuen Joshi Daigaku)

Kawamura Gakuen Woman's University

1133 Sageto, Abiko-shi, Chiba 270-11
☎ 0471-83-0111 FAX 0471-83-0115

Founded 1988
Professors 20
Associate Professors 12
Assistant Professors (Tenured) 10
Assistant Professors (Non-tenured) 26
Research Assistants 7
Undergraduate Students/Foreign Students 710/0
Library 30, 880 volumes
Contact: Masato Kimura, Head of Division, Education Division, Education Affairs Department, Kawamura Gakuen Woman's University

Educational philosophy We aim at providing a well rounded, fully international education for women, firmly based on the guiding principles of Kawamura Gakuen's founder Fumiko Kawamura.

Foreign students Social courses for foreign students and returnees have been established and preparations made for the reception of these in the university curriculum and organization.

Environment The Abiko Campus located some 40 minutes from the center of Tokyo is a peaceful and attractive learning environment. Abiko has a long cultural history, and the beauty of its natural surroundings has attracted numerous artists and writers.

Facilities The library contains some 30, 000 volumes. Moreover, the various types of documentation and academic information required for educational and research purposes are made available to both teaching staff and students. The gymnasium occupies a surface area of about 1, 300 square metres and is equipped with locker and shower facilities.

Student activities The students have their own autonomous organization, " Gakuyukai ", and extra-curricular student club and circle activities are energetically pursued. There is a variety of events forming part of the annual college calendar, including an orientation camp for new students, a Sports Festival, general College Festival, etc.

Academic programs for foreign students Special courses provided in particular for foreign students and returnees include Japanese Affairs I and II, Japanese Language I, II, III and IV. These courses constitute together a comprehensive presentation of Japanese culture,society and the Japanese language.

Services for foreign students At present, these remain inadequate for the time being because of the recent date of University Foundation.

Undergraduate Programs

Faculty of Liberal Arts(710/0)
Dept. of English Language and Literature(320/0)
Dept. of Psychology(176/0)
Dept. of History(214/0)

敬愛大学
(Keiai Daigaku)
Keiai University

1-5-21 Anagawa, Chiba-shi, Chiba 260
☎ 0472-51-6363 FAX 0472-51-6407

Founded 1966
Professors 20
Associate Professors 7
Assistant Professors(Tenured) 4
Assistant Professors(Non-tenured) 42
Research Assistants 1
Undergraduate Students/Foreign Students 1, 047/0
Library 97, 748 volumes

Educational philosophy We aim at teaching and studying deepening for leaning to develop intellectual and moral through the medium of personal contact and applied required seminar for all and a small number of students. This is based on " KEITEN AIJIN ", 'Respect the heaven and the earth, love a mankind'.

Foreign students We are preparing to remote for receiving and selection foreign students. We believe that foreign students can contribute to promoting mutual understanding and the development of friendly relations and also a great deal to connect with an activation of our campus.

Environment The city of Chiba, with a population of 780, 000, is located in Boso peninsula, 25 miles south east of Tokyo. Though located in a very quiet rural area, with construction of Nippon Convention Center (Makuhari Messe)Chiba is becoming the stage for several international conferences and events.

Facilities Economic and Culture Center, Library, Audio-visual education booth, Data processing Center, Gym, Martial-arts Gym, Auditorium, Training Room, etc.

Student activities Popular campus events include study and training outside the campus for freshmen (April). Physical training festival(May). School festival (October). Study and training for leaders(February). Gymnastic circle.....11 Literary circle.....10 etc.

Undergraduate Programs

Faculty of Economics(1047/0)
Dept. of Economics(1047/0)

慶應義塾大学
Keiô Gijuku Daigaku
Keio University

2-15-45 Mita, Minato-Ku, Tokyo 108
☎ 03-3453-4511 FAX 03-3769-2047

Founded 1858
Professors 510
Associate Professors 260
Assistant Professors (Tenured) 223
Assistant Professors (Non-tenured) 1, 125
Research Assistants 427
Undergraduate Students/Foreign Students 24, 623/143
Graduate Students/Foreign Student 2, 043/252
Library 2, 482, 647 volumes
Contact: International Center

Educational philosophy As the oldest institute of higher learning in Japan founded in 1858 by Yukichi Fukuzawa, a highly recognized intellectual leader modern Japanese history, Keio, from its initial years, has adhered to the principle of fostering independence and self-respect along with academic excellence.

Foreign students From its initial years, Keio has promoted interchanges with institutions abroad, receiving international students. Keio welcomes highly qualified applicants who wish to pursue their academic endeavors.

Environment Keio has altogether five campuses: two in metropolitan Tokyo(one in Mita as the main campus and the other for the School of Medicine), two (one for General Education and the other for Faculty of Science & Technology)in the Hiyoshi area of Yokohama, and a new campus in Fujisawa(named Shonan Fujisawa Campus), each of which plays different role.

Facilities Keio boasts facilites related to its academic activities such as the very modern New Library administered under the American Library Science system, as well as the hi-tech equipped New Wing at its University Hospital.

Student activities Highlights of students activities at Keio are annual the Mita-Festival in autumn and semi-annual baseball games against Waseda University, a rival private university. Many students enjoy both cultural and sports activities by both autonomous and university recognized clubs.

Academic programs for foreign students Keio has an independent Japanese Language Program (Bekka)at the Center for Japanese Studies, for those international students who wish to prepare to acquire or supplement Japanese language proficiency.

Services for foreign students The Office of the International Center serves international students at Keio. Its staff answer questions unique of international students. Counselling by a professionally trained counsellor can be also arranged upon request.

Undergraduate Programs

Faculty of Business and Commerce(4, 212/34)
Faculty of Economics(5, 150/10)
Faculty of Environmental Information(587/0)
Faculty of Law(5, 284/32)
Dept. of Law(2, 676/14)
Dept. of Political Science(2, 608/18)
Faculty of Letters(3, 840/47)
Dept. of History(421/2)
Dept. of Library and Information Science(150/6)
Dept. of Literature(983/5)
Dept. of Philosophy(280/2)
Dept. of Sociology, Psychology, Education and Human Sciences(1, 034/15)
Dept. of Others(972/17)
Faculty of Medicine(620/0)
Dept. of Others(213(Freshman and sophomore)/0)
Dept. of Medicine(407/0)
Faculty of Policy Management(565/1)
Faculty of Science and Technology(3, 255/19)
Dept. of Administration Engineering(420/3)
Dept. of Applied Chemistry(493/3)
Dept. of Chemistry(131/0)
Dept. of Electrical Engineering(592/7)
Dept. of Instrumentation Engineering(384/0)
Dept. of Mathematics(200/0)
Dept. of Mechanical Engineering(884/3)
Dept. of Physics(151/0)
Dept. of Others(1, 110(Freshman)/0)

Graduate Programs

Graduate School of Business Administration (M 166/11)
Master: Accounting, Information Processing System, Managerial Economics, Human Behavior in Organizaion, Human Resource Management, Production Policy, Finance, Marketing, Business Environment, International Business, Business Policy, Economic Analysis for Man agement Decisions, Management Control System, Management Information System, Organization Design, International Production Policy, Financial Theory, Investment Analysis and Management, Market Strategy, Consumer Behavior, Industrial Policy and Business, Business History, Management of Small Enterprises, Management in Service Industries, Statistical Analysis of Data in Behavioral Science Areas, Japanese Management, Organization Strategy, Management of Finacial Instituions, Theory of Disribution Policy, Management of Technology, Business Environment and Administrative Policy
Graduate School of Business and Commerce(M 35/29, D 65/29)
Div. of Commerce(M 35/12, D 65/17)
Master: Advanced Study of Introduction to Marketing, Advance Study of Marketing Management, Seminar in Introduction to Marketing, Seminar in Marketing Management, Seminar in Finance, Advanced Study of International Finance, Advanced Study of Insurance, Advanced Study of Management of Insurance, Seminar in Transportation Economics, Advanced Study of Industrial Organization, Advanced Study of Econometrics, Advanced Study of Statistics, Advanced Study of International Economics, Advanced Study of International Economic Policy, Seminar in History of Industry, Practice in Business History, Doctoral: Special Study : Marketing System, International Economics, Transportation Economics, Finance, Insurance, Econometrics, Statistics, History of Industry, Seminar in Marketing Management, Advanced Study of Money and Banking
Div. of Management and Accounting (M 17/5, D 36/8)
Master: Advanced Study: Science of Business Administration, Management Administration, Introduction to Production Management, Personnel Management, Accounting, Cost Accounting, Management Accounting, Theory of Industrial Relations, Labor Economics, Social Law, Seminar in Industrial Relation, Japanese Management, Manegement Accounting, Doctoral: Special Study: Science of Business Administration, Accounting, Theory of Industrial Relations, Seminar in Special Study of Science of Business Administration
Graduate School of Economics(M 36/11, D 65/12)
Div. of Economic History(M 4/1)
Master: History of Western Economy, Advanced Study of Western Economic Histroy, Japanese Economic History, Seminar in Advanced Study of Economic History of the West, History of Japanese Economy, Seminar in Advanced Study of Economic History of Japan, The Reading of Historical Documents, History of Economic Thoughts
Div. of Economic Policy(M 16/7)
Master: Economic Policy, Seminar in Economic Policy, Agricultural Economics, Seminar in Agricutural Economics, Industrial Economics, Seminar in Industrial Economics, Japanese Economy, Seminar in Japanese Economy, Labor Economics, Social Policy, Structure of Economic Life, Study of History of Labor Movement, Seminar in Labor Economic Theory, International Economics, Seminar in International Economics, International Political Economy, Economic Geography, Seminar in Economic Geography, Urban Economy, Seminar in Urban Economics
Div. of Economic Theory(M 16/3)
Master: Theoretical Economics, Advances Study of Theoretical Economics, Seminar in Theoretical Economics, Econometrics, Special Study of Econometrics, Seminar in Econometrics Statistics, Special Study of Statistics, Seminar in Statistics, Public Finance, Seminar in Public Finance. Money and Banking, Seminar in Money and Banking, social Thoughts, Seminar in Social Thoughts, History of Economic Thoughts, Seminar in History of Economic Thoughts,
Div. of Economics(D 65/12)
Doctoral: Theoretical Economics, Econometrics, Statistics, Public Finance, Money and Banking, Social Thoughts, History of Economic Thoughts, Economic Thoughts, History of Western Economy, Seminar in Ad-

vanced Study of Economic History of the West, History of Japanese Economy, Seminar in Advanced Study of Economic History of Japan, Economic Policy, Agricultural Policy, Industrial Policy, Labor Economics, International Economics, Economic Geography,

Graduate School of Human Relations(M 71/10, D 51/4)

Div. of Education(M 14/5, D 10/0)

Master: Advanced Study of Pedagogy, Seminar in Pedagogy, Advanced Study of Histroy of Education, Advanced Study of Educational Psychology, Practice in Educational Psychology, Seminar in Educational Administration, Advanced Study of Educational Philosophy, Advanced Study of Educational Sociology, Comparative Pedagogy, Doctoral: Special Study of Pedagogy, Special Study of Histroy of Education, Special Study of Educational Psychology, Special Study of Educational Administration, Special Study of Pedagogy Current Problem

Div. of Psycology(M 4/0, D 10/2)

Master: Advanced Study of Psychology, Advanced Studies in Behaviormetrics, Advanced Studies in Behavior, Human Engineering & Erogonomics, Advanced Psychological Practice, Seminar in Psychology of Perception, Seminar in Developmental Psychology, Seminar in Behavior Analysis, Seminar in Cognitive Psychology, Seminar in Biopsychology, Doctoral: Advanced Experimental Psychology, Sepcial Studies in Human Engineering and Ergonomics, Special Studies in Behavior, Advanced Seminar in Psychology of Perception, Advanced Seimar in Developmental Psychology, Advanced Seminar in Behavior Analysis, Advanced Seminar in Cognitive Psychology, Advanced Seminar in Biopsychology, Special Studies in Behaviormetrics

Div. of Sociology(M 71/10, D 51/4)

Master: Scientific Methodology, Research Methods & Methodology, Advanced Studies in Histroy of Society, Seminar in History of Sociology, Advanced Studies in Sociological Theories, Advanced Studies of Sociology, Advanced Studies in Anthropological Theories, Advanced Studies in Cultural Anthropology, Advanced Studies in Folklore, Advanced Studies in Historical Folklore, Advanced Studies in Communication, Advanced Studies in Mass Communication, Seminar in Behavioral Science, Advanced Studies in Social Psychology, Advanced Studies in Personality Assessment, Advanced Studies in Clinical Psychology, Advanced Studies in Psychopathology, Doctoral: Special Studies of Sociology, Seminar in Special Study of Social Phychology, Special Studies in Communication, Special Studies in Cultural Anthropology, Special Studies in Histrical Folklore, Advanced Seminar in Behavioral Science, Special Studies in Personality Assesment, Special Studies in Clinical Psychology

Graduate School of Law(M 76/24, D 82/16)

Div. of Civil Law(M 33/3, D 21/7)

Master: Foreign Laws(English-American, German, French), Advanced Lecture of Legal Philosophy, Law in Japan, Judicial System, Advanced Lecture of Civil Law, Advanced Lecture of Commercial Law, Advanced Lecture of Civil Procedure Code, Social Law, Histroy of Law, Doctoral: Advanced Study of English & American Law, Advanced Study of Civil Law, Special Study of Commercial Law, Advanced Study of Procedure Code, Joint Seminar in Civil Procedure Code, Special Study of Social Law, Joint Seminar in Social Law, Special Study Limited of Law, Joint Seminar in Histroy of Law, Special Study of Legal Philosophy

Div. of Public Law(M 13/2, D 14/0)

Master: Foreign Laws(English-American, German, French), Law in Japan, Advanced Lecture of Legal Philosophy, Judicial System, Special Lecture of Constitutional Law, Special Lecture of Administrative Law, Special Lecture of International Law, Special Lecture of Criminal Law, Special Lecture of Criminal Procedure Code, Special Lecuture of Penology, Joint Seminar in Penal Law, Joint Seminar in Civil Procedure Code, Special Lecture of Social Law, Advanced Lecture of History of Law, Medico Legal Study, Doctoral: Advanced Study of English & American Law, Special Study of Constitutional Law, Special Study of Administrative Law, Taxation Seminar in International Tax Issues-Advanced, Joint Seminar in International Law, Special Study of Criminal Law, Special Study of Criminal Procedure Code, Joint Seminar in Penal Law, Joint Seminar in Civil Procedure Code, Special Study of Social Law, Special Study Limited of Law, History of Law

Div. of Political Science(M 30/19, D 47/9)

Master: Advanced Study on Political Thoughts, Advanced Study on Politics & Society, Advanced Courses on Japanese Studies, Advanced Courses on Area Studies, Special Studies on International Relations, Special Lecture of Constitutional Law, Special Lecture of Administrative law, Special Study of International Law, Advanced Lecture of Histroy of Law, Doctoral: Advanced Study on Political Thoughts, Advanced Study on Politics & Society, Advanced Course on Japanese Studies, Advanced Course of Area Studies, Special Study of International Relations, Special Study of Constitutional Law, Special Study of Administrative Law, Taxation Seminar in International Tax Issues-Advanced, Special Study of International Law, Special Study Limited of Law, Joint Seminar in History of Law

Graduate School of Letters(M 124/10, D 92/6)

Div. of Chinese Literature(M 3/1, D 8/3)

Master: Chinese Literature, Seminar in Chinese Literature, Chinese Linguistics, Seminar in Chinese Linguistics, Comparative Study of Japanese and Chinese Literature, History of Rituals and Performing Arts, History of Literary Criticism, History of Drama, Asian History, Archaeology and Ethnology, Doctoral: Ancient Chinese Literature, Medieval Chinese Literature, Pre-Modern Chinese Literature, Seminar in Pre-Modern Chinese Literature, Modern Chinese Literature, Comparative Study of Japanese and Chinese Literature, Chinese Linguistics

Div. of English and American Literature(M 16/0, D 11/0)

Master: Medieval English Literature, Seminar in Medieval English Literature, Modern English and American Literature, Seminar in Modern English and American Literature, Contemporary English and American Literature, Seminar in Contemporary English and American Literature, Seminar in History of English Language, English Linguistics, Seminar in English Linguistics, American Literature, Doctoral: Medieval English Literature, Seminar in Medieval English Literature, Pre-Modern English Literature, Seminar in Pre-Modern English Literature, Contemporary English Literature, Seminar in Contemporary English literature, American literature, Seminar in American Literature, English Linguistics, Linguistics

Div. of French Literature(M 27/0, D 12/0)
Master: Medieval French and French Literature, Seminar in French and French Literature, Pre-Modern French and French Literature, Seminar in Pre-Modern Frech and French Literature, Contemporary French Literature, Seminar in Contemporary French Literature, Seminar in French Linguistics, History of French Language, Comparative European Literature, History of Literary Criticism, Lingusitics, History of Drama, Classical Literature, Doctoral: Medieval French Literature, Pre-Modern French Literature, Seminar in Pre-Modern French Literatrue, Contemporary French Literature, Seminar in Contemporary French Literature, French Linguistics

Div. of German Literature(M 4/0, D 7/0)
Master: Medieval German Language and Literature, Seminar in Medieval German Language and Literature, Pre-Modern German Language and Literature, Seminar in Pre-Modern German Language and Literature, Contemporay German Literature, Seminar in Contemporary Literature, Seminar in German Linguistics, History of German Language, Comparative European Literaure, History of Literary Criticism, Linguistics, History of Drama, Seminar in English Linguistics, Classical Literature, Doctoral: Medival German Literature, Pre-Modern German Literature, Seminar in Pre-Modern German Literature, Contemporary German Literature, Seminar in Contemporary German Literature, Geraman Linguistics

Div. of History(M 30/1, D 19/0)
Master: Japanese History, Seminar in Japanese History, Asian History, Seminar in Asian History, Western History, Seminar in Western History, Archaeology and Ethnology, Linguistics, Geography, Paleography, Economic History, Political History, History of Law, Doctoral: Japanese History, Seminar in Japanese History Asian History, Seminar in Asian History, Western History, Seminar in Western History, Archaeology and Ethnology, Seminar in Archaeology and Ethnology

Div. of Japanese Literature(M 12/4, D 7/1)
Master: Ancient Japanese Literature(Pre-Heian Period), Seminar in Ancient Japanese Literature(Pre-Heian Period), Ancient Japanese Literature(Heian Period), Seminar in Ancient Japanese Literature(Heian Period), Medieval Japanese Lirterature, Seminar in Medieval Japanese Literatire, Pre-Modern Japanese Literature(Edo Preiod), Seminar in Pre-Modern Japanese Literature(Edo Period), Modern Japanese Literature, Seminar in Modern Japanese Literature, Japanese Literature, Japanese Linguistics, History of Rituals and Performing Arts, Lecture on Buddhism, Lecture on Chinese Writing by the Japanese, History of Literary Criticism, History of Drama, Lecture of Shido Bunko, Japanese History, Archaeology and Ethnology, Parleography, Doctoral(Japanese Lireratur): Ancient Japanese Literature(Pre-Heian Period), Seminar in Ancient Japanese Literature(Heian Period), Ancient Japanese Literature(Heian Period), Seminar in Ancitent Japanese Literature(Heian Period), Medieval Japanese Literatrue, Seminar in Medieval Japanese Literature, Per-Modern Japanese Literature(Edo Period), Seminar in Pre-Modern Japanese Literature (Edo Period), Modern Japanese Literature, Seminar in Modern Japanese Literature, Japanese Literature, Japanese Linguistics, Comparative Study of Japanese and Chinese Literature, Seminar in Compartive Study of Japanese and Chinese Literature

Div. of Library and Information Science(M 7/2, D 6/2)
Master: Information Science, Information Media, Seminar in Information Media, Information Storage and Retrievals, Seminar in Information Storage and Retrievals, Information System, Seminar in Information system, Research Methods, Information Analysis, Mechanical to Information Processing, Doctoral: Infomation Media, Seminar in Information media, Information Hadling, Seminar in Information Handling, Information Systems, Seminar in Information Systems

Div. of Philosophy(M 25/2, D 22/0)
Master: Philosophy, Seminar in Philosophy, Text Reading(Philosophy), Ethics, Seminar in Ethics, Text Reading(Ethics), Aesthetics, Seminar in Aesthetics, Art History, Seminar in Art History, Aesthetics and Science of Arts, Doctoral: Philosophy, Seminar in Philosophy, Ethics, Seminar in Ethics, Aesthetics, Seminar in Aesthetics

Graduate School of Medicine(D 69/3)

Div. of Internal Medicine(D 45/2)
Doctoral: Advanced Internal Medicine, Advanced Internal Medicine : Seminar, Advanced Internal Medicine : Practice, Diagnostics And Treatment, Advanced Dietology, Advanced Radiology : Practice, Advanced Pediatrics, Advanced Pediatrics : Seminar, Advanced Pediatrics : Practice, Advanced Pediatrics, Advanced Pediatrics : Seminar, Advanced Pediatrics : Practice, Advanced Psychiatry, Advanced Psychiatry : Seminar, Advanced Psychatry : Practice, Advanced Mental Health, Advanced Mental Health, Advanced Mental Health : Seminar, advanced Mental Health : Practice, Advanced Neurology, Advanced Neurology : Seminar, Advanced Neurology : Practice, Neuroanatomy, Advanced Neurological Surgery, Advanced Dermatology, Advanced Dermatology : Seminar, Advanced Dermatology : Practice, Advanced Dermatopathology, Advanced Dermatopathology : Practice, Advanced Dermatopathology : Seminar, Advanced Dermatoetiology, Advanced Dermatoetiology : Seminar, Advanced Dermatoetiology : Practice, Advanced Radiology, Advanced Radiophysics, Advanced Health Bhysics, Advanced Image-Diagnostics, Advanced Image-Diagnostics : Seminar, Advanced Image-Diagnostics : Seminar, Advanced Radiation Oncology, Advanced Radiation Oncology : Pracice, Advanced Nuclear Medicine, Ad-

vanced Nuclear Medicine: Seminar, Advanced Nuclear Medicine: Practice, Advanced Internal Medicine: Practice, Advanced Surgery : Practice, Advanced Obstertrics and Gynecology: Practice

Div. of Pathology(D 6/0)

Doctoral: Advanced Pathology, Practice, Seminar, Advanced Parasitology, Practice, Advanced Legal Medicine, Advanced Surgery, Advanced Legal Medicine : Practice, Advanced Heliminthology : Seminar, Advanced Protozoology : Seminar, Practice, Advanced Basic Legal Medicine, Practice, Seminar, Advanced Applied Legal Medicine, Seminar, Practice

Div. of Physiology(D 3/1)

Doctoral: Advanced Anatomy: Seminar, Advanced Histology: Seminar, Advanced Embryology: Seminar, Practice, Neuroanatomy: Seminar, Practice, Physiology of Embryo, Advanced Physiology, Physiology : Practice, Advanced Pathology: Practice, Advanced Physiology, Physiology : Seminar, Practice, Neurophysiology: Practice, Advanced Chemical Physiology, Functional Biochemistry : Practice, Clinical Physiology, General Physiology, Advanced Endocrinology, Advanced Medical Chemistry, Medical Chemistry: Practice, Medical Chemistry: Seminar, Advanced Enzyme Chemistry, Advanced Enzyme Chemistry : Seminar, Advanced Internal Medicine: Seminar, Advanced Molecular Biology, Practice: Advanced Cell Genetics, Advanced Pharmacology, Advanced Toxicology, Advanced Clinical Pharmacology

Div. of Preventive Medicine(D 7/0)

Doctoral: Advanced Enviornmental Health: Seminar: Practice, Advanced Public Health: Seminar, Practice, Advanced Biostatistics: Practice, Advanced Hospital Administration: Practice, Advanced Medical Care, Advanced Microbiology: Seminar, Practice, Advanced Virology: Seminar, Practice, Advanced Immunology: Seminar, Practice

Div. of Surgery(D 8/0)

Doctoral: Advanced Surgery: Seminar, Practice, Surgical Operation: Practice, Advanced Neurophysiology, Clinical Oncology, Advanced Radiology : Practice, Advanced Orthopedics: Seminar, Practice, Orthopedic Operation: Practice, Rehabilitation Medicine: Practice, Advanced Ophthalmology: Seminar, Practice, Ophthalmic Therapeutics, Advanced Otorhinolaryngology: Seminar, Advanced Bronchoesophagology: Practice, Advanced Logopedics and Phoniatrics, Advanced Urology: Seminar, Advanced Urological Operation, Advanced Radiology : Seminar, Advanced Obstetrics: Seminar, Practice, Advanced Gynecology: Seminar, practice, Advanced Gynocological Endocrinology, Advanced Gynecological Surgery, Advanced Family Planning, Advanced Obstetrics and Gynecology, Advanced Clinical Anesthesiology: Seminar, Pracrice, Advanced Anesthetic Pharmacology, Practice, Advanced Anesthetic Physiology, Practice, Advanced Plastic Surgery: Seminar, Practice, Plastic Surgical Therapeutics, Practice, Advanced Tissue Transplantation, Practice, Advanced Plastic Oral Surgery, Practice, Medical Special Lecture

Graduate School of Science and Technology (M 913/86, D 193/30)

Div. of Administration Engineering (M 92/26, D 27/9)

Industrial Engineering, Applied Statistics, Operations Research, Special Study on Administration Engineering, Selected Topics in Administration Engineering, Administration Engineering, Analysis of Management Decisions, Management, Computer Science, Economy Engineering, Topics in Econometrics, Psychometrics, Optimization, Systems Engineering, Information Science, Numerical Mathematics, Mathematical Economics, Mathematical Statistics A, Linear Algebra, Statistics, Human Engineering, Planning and Control for Profit

Div. of Applied Chemistry(M 108/6, D 13/0)

Applied Surface Chemistry, Advanced Laboratory Experiments in Applied Chemistry, Special Studies on Applied Chemistry, Special Topics in Applied Chemistry, Seminar on Applied Chemistry, Applied Electrochemistry, Applied Quantum Chemistry, Chemistry of Surfactants, Advanced Course of Chemical Engineering, Topics in Industrial Chemistry, A History of Chemistry, Environmental Chemistry Advanced Course, Advanced Instrumental Analysis, Advanced Inorganic Chemistry, Topics in Organics Synthetic Chemistry, Topics in Organic Reaction Mechanisms, High Temperature Synthetic Chemistry, Advanced Polymer Sicence, Engineering Chemistry of Polymers, Solid State Processes, Chemistry of Materials, Bioorganic Chemistry, Advanced Course of Electrochemistry, Coordination Steraochemistry, Advaned Course of Chemical Reaction Engineering, Science of Amorphous Materials, Powder Science, Design of Material Properties, Solid State Physics, Advanced Course of Physical Chemistry, Fundamental Principles in Physics, Advanced Industrial Organic Chemistry, Advanced Course of Organic Chemistry, Physical Organic Chemistry, Chemistry of Fasts and Fatty Oils, Advanced Course on Quantum Mechanics

Div. of Biomedical Engineering(M 41/5, D 5/1)

Genetic Information, Introduction to Medical Image Processing, Biomaterials, Biomedical Information Engineering, Aspects of Molecular Recognition, Environmental and Industrial Health, Advanced Course of Environmental Science, Visual Information, Neural Information Processings, Human Injury and Its Protection, Mechanics of Human Motion, Cognitive Engineering, Special Study on Biomedical Engineering, Topics in Biomedical Engineering, Biomedical Engineering, Biofunctional Polymers, Biofunctional Materials, Applied Biomedical Instrumentation, Structure of Human Body, Biosystems, Modeling and Control in Biomedical Systems, Chemistry of Bioactive Substance, Physical Properties of Biological Menbranes, Biological Transport Phenomena, Biotechnology, Natural Products Chemistry, Dynamic Natural Products Chemistry, Human Reliability, Congnitive Science, Aspects of Biosensor, Biomechanics, Microbial Transformation, Molecular Biology

Div. of Chemistry(M 42/0, D 11/1)

Subjects, Topics in Surface Chemistry, Interfacial Electrochemistry, Topics in Industrial Chemistry, A History of Chemistry, Graduate Research in Chemistry, Chemistry

Research, Structural Chemistry, Quantum Mechanics of Atoms and Molecular, Topics in Molecular Physics, Methodology in Sorganic Synthesis, Synthetic Organic Chemistry, Seminar on Symthetic Organic Chemistry, Electron Transfer and Photocatalysis, Chemistry of Bioactive Substance, Chemistry of Natural Product, Bioorganic Chemistry, Natural Products Chemistry, Seminar on Natural Products Chemistry, Structural Chemistry of Natural Products, Topics in Interface Science, Microbial Transformation, Topics in Corrosion Science, Infrared and Ramar Spectroscopy, Topics in Physical Chemistry, Fundamental Principles in Physic, Basic Principle of Molecular, Spectroscopy, Inorganic Chemistry by Magnetic Resonance, Topics in Organic Chemistry, Organometallic Chemistry, Topics in Solution Chemistry

Div. of Computer Science(M 76/4, 15/3)
Topics in Computer Operating Systems, Scientific Computing, Image Science and Technology, Memory Systems, Symbol Manipulation, Computer Architectures, Special Study on Computer Science, Special Study on Computer Science, Topics in Computer Science, Advanced Topics in Computer Science, Computer Systems, Computer Networks, Theory of Computing, Representation and Semantics of Computations, Computer Graphics, Systems Engineering, Systems Optimization, Systems Simulation, Natural Language Processing, Signal Processing, Data Structures and Information Retrieval, Computational Logic, Artificial Intelligence Systems, Artificial Intelligence, Advanced Mathematical Statistics, Human Engineering, Cognitive Science, Pattern Information Processing, Distributed Systems, Compiler Construction, Programming Languages, Programming Mehtodologies, Theory of Programming, Discrete Mathematics

Div. of Electrical Engineering(M 178/20, D 47/9)
Biomedical Information Engineering, Electronic Process in Liquids, Topics in Computer Operating System, Applied Mathematical Analysis, Applied Nuclear Physics, Applied Electron Physics, A History of Chemistry, Image Science and Technology, Computer System, Representation and Semantics of Computation, Topics on Atomic Energy, Modern Network Theory, Advanced High Voltage Engineering, Advanced High–Voltage, Computer Graphics, Communication Systems, Signal Processing, Advnced Infromation Technology, Artifical Intelligence, Statistical Inference, Topics in Mathematical Analysis A, Topics in Mathematical Analysis B, Linear System Theory, Fundamental Principles in Physics, Prasma Electronics, Software Engineering, Introduction to Elementary Particle Physics, Electromechanical Energy Conversion, Special Study on Electrical Engineering, Topics in Electrical Engineering, Analysis of Electromagnetic Field, Finite Element and Boundary Element Methods for Electric and Magnetic Fields, Electromagnetic Engineering, Advanced Power Engineering, Thin Film Electronics, Wave electronics, Seminoconductor Device, Seminconductor Physics, Opto Electronics, Optical Communication, Non–Liner Circuit Theory, Theory of Nonlinear Oscillation, Feedback Control Theory, Advanced Course in Solid State Physics, Solid State Physics, Topics in Mechanics, Laser Engineering, Robotics

Div. of Instrumentation Engineering(M 75/2, D 7/1)
Space Communication, Introduction to Energy Conversion Technology, Applied Mathematical Analysis, Applied Nuclear Physics, Advanced Applied Physics, Circuit Theory, A History of Chemistry, Advanced Course in Computer Technology, Special Study on Instrumentation Engineering, Special Topics in Instrumentation Engineering, Recitation in Instrumentation Engineering, Transmission Theory on Measurement, Pattern Recognition, Optical Properties of Solids, Theory of Nonlinear Oscillations, Advanced Course in Solid State Physics, Solid State Physics, Fundamental Principles in Physics, Topics on Atomic Energy, Industrial Instruments, Electrical Properties of Polymers, System Optimization, Database Systems, Statistic Inference, Advanced Course in Control Engineering, Bioengineering, Biophysics, Topics in Modern Measurement, Science and Technology of Sensing, Introduction to Elementary Particle Physics, Electronic Circuits for Metrology, Introduction to Electron Transport, Therory of Electron Transport, Advanced Course in Propagation of Electromagnetic Waves, Semiconductor Physics, Topics on Analysis by Physical Method, Topics on Plasma Physics, Progress in Dielectrics, Topics on Mechanics, Quantum Optics, Advanced Course on Quantum Mechanics

Div. of Material Science(M 56/1, D 1/0)
Optodevice Technology, Functional Polymers, Functional Ceramics, Advanced Composite Materials, Physics of Crystals, Molecular Design of Polymers, Electrical Properties of Polymers, Physical Properties of High Polymers, Continuum Mechanics Approach to Strength and Fracture of Materials, VSLI Technology, Magnetic Properties of Solids, Biofunctional Polymers, Bio–Organic Materials, Superconductor, Theory of Electron Transport, Advanced Course of Statistical Physics, Physics of Thin Films and Solid Surfaces, Semiconductor Devices, Semiconductor Physics, Optical Properties of Solids, Topics on Surface Analysis, Special Study of Material Science, Topics in Material Science, Design of Material Properties, Advanced Solid State Physics, Materials Processing, Progress in Dielectrics, Quantum Optics, Avanced Course on Quantum Mechanics

Div. of Mathematics(M 39/2, D 27/0)
Topics in Topology, Applied Probability Theory, Topics in Applied Mathematics, Applied Statistics, Operations Research, Topics in Probability Theory, Topics in Functional Analysis, Topics in Functional Equaions, Special Course in Mathematics, Topics in Geometry, Topics in Computer Mathematics, Optimization, Topics in Time Series Anaysis, Topics in Information Theory, Topics in Mathematical Analysis, Topics in Mathematical Theory, Mathematical Seminar, Special Course in Mathematics, Mathematical Statistics: Advanced Course, Linear Algebra, Topics in Algebra, Statistics

Div. of Mechanical Engineering(M 196/19, D 27/5)
Applied Mathematical Analysis, Applied Nuclear Physics, Stochastic Systems Control, Advanced Course in Ma-

chining Processes, Special Study on Mechanical Engineering, Topics in Mechanical Engineering, Advanced Course in Strength of Materials, Advanced Course in Dynamics of Machines, Physical Metallurgy, Topics on Atomic Energy, Transient Vibrations of Mechanical Systems, Human Injury and Its Protection, Mechanics of Human Motion, Computer Aided Design and Manufacturing, Biological Transport Phenomena, Research and Development for new Products, Advanced Course of Precision Measurement, Design Theory, Materials Processing and Joining, Advanced Course in Mechanics of Metal Processing, Advanced Lecture on Turbomachinery, Advanced Lecture on Elasticity, Advanced Course of Tribology, Advanced Course of Heat Transfer, Engineering Thermophysics, Advanced Course on Internal Combustion Engine, Advanced Machine Tools, Materails Science of High Polymers, Continuum Mechanics of Solid, Continuum Mechanics Approach to the Strength and Fracture of Materials, Advanced Course of Strength of Materials, General Remarks on Strength of Materials, System Control Theory, Digital Control, Advanced Thermodynamics, Thermo Aerodynamics, Advanced Combustion Science and Technology, Analytical Mechanics on Gear, Theory of Nonlinear Oscillations, Metal Surface and Surface Treatment, Random Vibration, Solid State Physics, Molecular Thermodynamics, Oil Hydraulics, Fusion Working Technology, Characteristics of Airtoils and Wings, Transport Phenomena in Tarbulent Flows, Topics on Mechanics, Fluid Solid Interactions, ·Measurements and Experimental Analysis in Fluid Mechanics, Fluid Physics, Advanced Lecture on Fluid Dynamics

Div. of Physics(M 42/1, D 13/1)
Applied Mathematical Analysis, Advanced Applied Physics, A History of Chemistry, Topics in Computer Mathematics A, Computational Physics, Quantum Mechanics of Atoms and Molecules, Special Topics in Nuclear Physics, Topics on Atomic Energy, Nuclear Reactor Physics, Continuum Mechanics of Solids, Advanced Experimental Physics, Advanced Mathematical Physics, Topics in Modern Measurement, Topics in Physics, Fundamental Principles in Physics, Advanced Course of Statistical Physics, Semiconductor Physics, Field Theory, Opto-Electronics, Optical Properties of Solids, Theory of Nonlinear Oscillations, Topics in Interface Science, Advenced Solid State Physics, Graduate Researchin Physics, Physics Seminar, Topics in Spectroscopy, Plasma Electronics, Topics on Plasma Physics, Laser Physics

---

恵泉女学園大学
(Keisen Jogakuen Daigaku)
Keisen Jogakuen College

2-10-1 Minamino, Tama-shi, Tokyo 206
☎ 0423-76-8215 FAX 0423-76-8218

Founded 1988
Professors 21
Associate Professors 5
Assistant Professors(Tenured) 8
Assistant Professors(Non-tenured) 42
Undergraduate Students/Foreign Students 628/9
Library 72, 202 volumes

Educational philosophy The spirit of Christianity has provided a firm foundation for the school's many educational programs. Founder Michiko Kawai's call for schools which educate women to think globally and independently is further fulfilled by Keisen Jogakuen College's programs.

Foreign students To help students attain a cosmopolitan outlook the college also continues the Keisen tradition of accepting both foreign students and student returnees from abroad.

Environment The College began classes in April 1988, and locate itself at Tama City, which has been developed as a " New Town " of Tokyo Metropolis. The campus is beautifully surrounded by the forest and park, and the traveling time from Tokyo urban center is less than 1 hour.

Facilities Library 72, 000 volumes, Aerobics dance studio, Tennis courts(all-weather), Multipurpose play ground 5, 000m^2.

Student activities Freshman fellowship, School festival, Christmas candle service, Thai work camp. Hand-bell choir, Frauen choir, Musical society, Braille and Talk with hands circle, etc. Tennis, Ski, Lacrosse, Golf clubs.

Academic programs for foreign students Japanese Language Courses; Introductory, Intermediate, Advanced Japanese State of Affairs, Adviser system, All courses in the Dept. of Japanese Studies.

Services for foreign students Health clinic, personal/psychological counseling. We can provide all kinds of efforts for foreign students as the case may be.

Undergraduate Programs

Faculty of Humanities(628/0)
Dept. of British and American Studies(348/0)
Dept. of Japanese Studies(280/0)

北里大学
(Kitasato Daigaku)
Kitasato University

5-9-1 Shirokane, Minato-ku, Tokyo 108
☎ 03-3444-6161 FAX 03-3444-2530

Founded 1962
Professors 171
Associate Professors 134
Assistant Professors(Tenured) 312
Assistant Professors(Non-tenured) 338
Research Assistants 709

Undergraduate Students/Foreign Students 6, 696/0
Graduate Students/Foreign Students 182/15
Library 420, 135 volumes
Contact: Administrative Office of the University

Educational philosophy We are teaching students under four educational philosophy which Dr. Shimasaburo Kitasato, a world-famous bacteriologist, embodied through all his life. The four philosophy are " pioneering spirit, repayment of kindness, wisdom and practice, and indomitable spirit "

Foreign students It is desirable for foreing students to study on either Japanese government scholarships or scholarships of their own countries.

Environment We have four campuses and six faculties. The campuses are located in Shirokane(Tokyo), Sagamihara(Kanagawa), Towada(Aomori)and Sanriku (Iwate). Six faculties are set up in suitable locations where respective faculty can make use of its characteristic. Thus we serve for the need of the area.

Facilities Two university hospitals(Sagamihara), high grade computer systems, library and gymnasium (each campus), seminar houses(Yakumo, Sanriku, Oshika, Tadami), stock farms(Yakumo, Oshika)

Student activities Annual events include school festival, baseball tournament, etc. students can also join clubs of extra curricular activities such as symphony orchestra, chorus group, volunteer work, bow gun, table tennis, japanese archery, horseback riding, kendo, karate, etc.

Academic programs for foreign students Graduate school has introduced a system to teach students in a small group.

Services for foreign students We also provides counseling service to foreign students. Some campuses have accommodations for foreign students.

Undergraduate Programs

Faculty of Fisheries Sciences(802/0)
- **Dept. of Aquacultural Sciences**(401/0)
- **Dept. of Marine Food Chemistry**(401/0)

Faculty of Hygionic Sciences(1, 611/0)
- **Dept. of Biosciences**(190/0)
- **Dept. of Chemistry**(497/0)
- **Dept. of Hygienic Technology**(517/0)
- **Dept. of Industrial Hygiene**(407/0)

Faculty of Medicine(794/0)
- **Dept. of Medicine**

Faculty of Nursing(425/0)
- **Dept. of Nursing**

Faculty of Pharmaceutical Sciences(1, 273/0)
- **Dept. of Phamaceutical Sciences**(645/0)
- **Dept. of Phrmaceutical Technology**(628/0)

Faculty of Veterinary Medicine and Animal Sciences(1, 791/0)
- **Dept. of Animal Sciences**(500/0)
- **Dept. of Engineering for Animal Husbandry**(442/0)
- **Dept. of Veterinary Medicine**(849/0)

Graduate Programs

Graduate School of Fisheries Sciences(M 12/3, D 4/1)

Div. of Fisheries Sciences(M 12/3, D 4/1)
Physilolgy of Aquatic Organisms, Marine Environmental Sciences, Aquaculture, Primary production, Marine Biological Chemistry, Marine Food Chemistry, Marine Biotechnology, Marine Resources Chemistry

Graduate School of Hygienic Sciences(M 34/3)

Div. of Hygienic Sciences(M 34/3)
Analytical Chemistry, Analytical Morphology, Applied Organic Chemistry, Bio-organic chemistry, Biophysical Chemistry, Cell Biology, Chemistry of Biologically Active Substances, Clinical Chemistry, Food Sanitary, Hematology, Hemogenetics, Immunology, Industrial Health Administration Mental Health, Microbiology, Molecular Biology, Organic Chemistry, Pathology Physiology, Public Health, Radiation Science, Water and Wastewater Treatment Engineering

Div. of Health Sciences(D 0/0)
Cell Mophology, Chemistry of Biologically Active Substances, Clinical Chemistry, Community Health, Environmental Chemistry, Environmental Health, Health Administration, Hematology, Immunology, Microbiology, Physiology, Radiation hygiene, Sanitary Engineering

Graduate School of Medicine(D 49/3)

Div. of Clinical Medicine(D 29/1)
Clinical Pathology, Dermatology, Internal Medicine, Pediatrics, Psychiatry, Radiology

Div. of Pathological Sciences(D 3/0)
Microbiology, Pathology, Parasitology

Div. of Physiological Sciences(D 4/1)
Anatomy, Biochemistry, Molecular Biology, Pharmacology, Physiology

Div. of Socio-medical Sciences(D 2/0)
Legal Medicine, Hygiene and Community Medicine, Medical Chemistry

Div. of Surgical Medicine(D 11/1)
Anesthesiology, Emergency Medicine, Neurosurgery, Orthopedics, Ophthalmology, Obstetrics and Gynecology, Otorhinolaryngology, Plastic Surgery, Surgery, Thoracic Surgery, Urology

Graduate School of Nursing(M 10/0)

Div. of Nursing(M 10/0)
Nursing Fundamentals, Health Nursing, Psychiatric Mental Health Nursing, Oncology Nursing, Infection control Nursing

Graduate School of Pharmaceutical Sciences(M 47/2, D 8/2)

Div. of Pharmaceutical Sciences(M 47/2, D 8/2)
Analytical Chemistry, Biochemistry, Biopharmaceutics, Clinical Pharmacology, Clinical Pharmacy, Hygienic Chemistry, Immunolgy and Virology, Medicinal Chemistry, Microbiology, Microbial Chemistry, Organic Synthesis, Pharmaceutical Chemistry, Pharmaceutical Technology, Pharmacology, Pharmacognosy and Phytochemistry, Physical Chemistry, Physical Pharmacy, Public Health

Graduate School of Veteinary Medicine and Animal Sciences(M 15/1, D 3/0)

Div. of Animal Sciences(M 8/1, D 1/0)

Animal Breeding and Reproduction, Animal Feeding and Management, Animal Nurtition, Animal Sciences, Environmental Science, Grassland Science, Science of Animal Products, Structure and Envronmental Engineering

Div. of Engineering for Animal Husbandry(M 7/0)

Agricultural Machinery, Farmland Reclamation, Grassland Science, Structure and Environmental engineering, Water Utilization for Animal Husbandry

Div. of Veterinary Medicine(D 2/0)

Compartive Oncolgy, Laboratory Animal Science, Poultry Diseases, Small Animal Medicine Toxicology, Veterinary Anatomy, Veterinary Hygiene, Veterinary Infectious Diseases, Veterinary Internal Medicine, Veterinary Medicine, Veterinary Microbiology, Veterinary Parasitology, Veterinary Pathology, Veterinary Pharmacology, Veterinary Pharmacotherapeutitcs, Veterinary Physiological Chemistry, Veterinary Physiology, Veterinary Protozoiasis, Veterinary Public Health, Veterinary Radiology and Radiation Biology, Veterinary Reproduction, Veterinary Surgery

工学院大学

(Kôgakuin Daigaku)

Kogakuin University

1-24-2 Nishi-Shinjuku, Shinjuku-ku, Tokyo 163
☎ 03-3342-1211

Founded 1949

Undergraduate Programs

Faculty of Engineering
Dept. of Architecture
Dept. of Chemical Engineering
Dept. of Electrical Engineering
Dept. of Electronic Engineering
Dept. of Industrial Chemistry
Dept. of Mechanical Engineering
Dept. of Production Planning and Management System Engineering

Graduate Programs

Graduate School of Engineering
Div. of Architecture
Div. of Electrical Engineering
Div. of Industrial Chemistry
Div. of Mechanical Engineering

國學院大學

(Kokugakuin Daigaku)

Kokugakuin University

4-10-28 Higashi, Shibuya-ku, Tokyo 150
☎ 03-3409-0111 FAX 03-5485-0154

Founded 1882
Professors 132
Associate Professors 56
Assistant Professors(Tenured) 15
Assistant Professors(Non-tenured) 459
Research Assistants 4
Undergraduate Students/Foreign Students 7,635/1
Graduate Students/Foreign Students 138/3
Library 800,000 volumes
Contact: International Exchange Affairs

Educational philosophy The purpose of education in the University is to teach Japanese Classics, inquire into Shinto, and promote extensively studies in various fields of humanities. Ultimately the University aims at character-building of capable youth who may contribute to the progress of Human Culture.

Foreign students We believe foreign students can enjoy a rewarding experience in our school, and contribute to intercultural understanding and world peace by working towards great international exchange and by studying the cultures of countries throughout the world.

Environment There are two campuses, which are thirty minutes apart by subway. The Shibuya campus is located in Shibuya Ward in the middle of Tokyo, while the Shin-ishikawa campus is surrounded by the leafy greenery of suburban Midori Ward in Yokohama, Kanagawa Prefecture.

Facilities The Institute for Japanese Culture and Classics, Library, Archaeology Museum, Shinto Museum, Gymnasium, Auditorium, etc.

Student activities Studying alone does not make up the whole of college life. Students need to participate in various extra-curricular activities to enrich their students such life. There are two kinds of such activities. One is the athletic clubs which aim at intermural competitions. The other one is hobby clubs.

Academic programs for foreign students Japanese Language as a foreign language, Japanese Studies as general education for foreign student.

Services for foreign students Health clinic, personal/Psycological counceling, Housing information, part-time job information, vocational guidance

Undergraduate Programs

Faculty of Economics(2202/1)
Dept. of Economics(2202/1)
Faculty of Law(2137/0)
Dept. of Law(2137/0)

Faculty of Letters(3296/0)
Dept. of History(750/0)
Dept. of Literature(1898/0)
Dept. of Philosophy(304/0)
Dept. of Shinto(344/0)

Graduate Programs

Graduate School of Economics(M 4/0, D 6/0)
Div. of Economics(M 4/0, D 6/0)
Theoretical Economics, History of Economic Theory, Money and Banking, Science of Public Finance, Economic Policy, International Economy, Social Policy, Statistics, History of Japanese Economy, History of Western Economy, Econometrics, Economic Fluctuation, History of Oriental Economy, Developmental History of Japanese Capitalism, History of Japanese Banking, Science of Economic History, Data of Japanese Economy, Business Management, Accountancy, History of Business Management
Graduate School of Law(M 8/2, D 1/0)
Div. of Law(M 8/2, D 1/0)
Constitutional Law, Comparative Constitutional Law, International Law, Criminal Law, Political Theory, Civil Law, Commercial Law, Japanese Legal History, Anglo-American Law, Administrative Law, History of International Politics, Philosophy of Law, International Private Law, Western Legal History, Oriental Legal Law, Chinese Legal History, Labor Law, Law of Criminal Procedure, Theory of Public Administration, Economic Law, Political History, History of Political Thoughts
Graduate School of Letters(M 91/1, D 47/0)
Div. of Japanese History(M 39/0, D 14/0)
Theory of Historical Science, Research of Individual Era in Japanise History, Research of History on Special Subjects, Philology, Mythology, Theory of History on Foreign Countries Related to Japan, Archaeology, Introduction to Archaeology
Div. of Japanese Literature(M 38/1, D 29/0)
Theory of the Japanese Literature, History of the Japanese Literature, Research on Works and Writers, Research of the Japanese Literature, History of the Chinese Literature written by Japanese, Japanese Phonology, Japanese Phraseology, Japanese Phonological History, History of the Japanese Language, History of the Japanese Linguistics, Related Foreign Literature, Related Foreign Linguistics
Div. of Shinto(M 14/0, D 4/0)
Theory of Shinto, Shinto Theology, History of Shinto Schools, History of Shinto, Shinto Classics, Liturgical Practices, Religious Celebration, Study of Religion, History of Religion, Religious Philosophy

One-Year Graduate Programs

Shinto Course
Shinto Major

国士舘大学
(Kokushikan Daigaku)
Kokushikan University

4-28-1 Setagaya, Setagaya-ku, Tokyo 154
☎ 03-3422-5341 FAX 03-3413-7420

Founded 1917
Professors 150
Associate Professors 87
Assistant Professors(Tenured) 43
Assistant Professors(Non-tenured) 410
Research Assistants 3
Undergraduate Students/Foreign Students 12, 272/162
Graduate Students/Foreign Students 71/1
Livrary 432, 429 volumes

Educational philosophy The main purpose of our educational policy is to develop people who, while having an awareness and pride in being Japanese, at the same time seek additional knowledge from abroad in order to be able to function on an international scale.
Foreign students We hare been active in promoting international, academic and cultural exchange and education for researches and contributing to mutual understanding and coorperation with other countries.
Environment The Setagaya campus is located in a very quiet and pleasant environment, with an abundance of greenery, in one of Tokyo's redidential areas. Shrines and temples, some dedicated to famous personages in Japanese history such as Yoshida Shoin and Ii Naosuke, are located near the school.
Facilities Center for information science, Cultural studies of politics, Studies of relationship between religion and civilization, University library, Shibata Hall multi pourpose hall
Student activities Popular campus events includes school festival, freshmen welcome party, orientation, field trips, farewell party, home-stay, sports and festival.
Academic programs for foreign students Special lectures for foreign students: Japanese language, Things Japanese(1~3)
Services for foreign students Health clinic, personal counseling, housing information, part-time job information, vocational guidance, cultural exchange program, domitory services.

Undergraduate Programs

Faculty of Political Science and Economics(3, 709/117)
Dept. of Political Science(851/9)
Dept. of Economics(1, 649/16)
Dept. of Business Administration(1, 209/92)
Faculty of Physical Educartion(1, 130/5)
Dept. of Physical Education
Faculty of Engineering(1, 238/18)

Dept. of Mechanical Engineering(304/6)
Dept. of Electrical Engineering(295/6)
Dept. of Civil Engineering(305/6)
Dept. of Architecture(334/4)
Faculty of Law(1, 562/8)
Dept. of Law(1, 562/8)
Faculty of Literature(2, 305/11)
Dept. of Education (**Education/Ethics/Elementary Education**) (834/5)
Dept. of History and Geography (**Japnese Histary/Oriental History/Geography**) (929/0)
Dept. of Literature (**Chinese Literature/Japanese Language and Literature**) (542/6)

Graduate Programs

Graduate School of Economics(M 51/0)
Div. of Economics(M 50/1)
Economics, Finance, History of Economics, International Economics
Graduate School of Political Science(M 18/0, D 2/0)
Div. of Political Science(M 18/0, D 2/0)
Administration Science, International Politics, International Relations, Political History and Thought

---

駒澤大学
(Komazawa Daigaku)
Komazawa University

1-23-1 Komazawa, Setagaya-ku, Tokyo 154
☎ 03-3418-9562 FAX 03-3418-9017

Founded 1882
Professors 225
Associate Professors 56
Assistant Professors(Tenured) 25
Assistant Professors(Non-tenured) 510
Research Assistants 5
Undergraduate Students/Foreign Students 14, 251/87
Graduate Students/Foreign Students 149/6
Library 963842 volumes
Contact: Komazawa University International Center

Educational philosophy We endeavors to provide students with a solid education grounded in the spirit of Zen Buddhism by which it is hoped that they will be able to make positivie contributions to world peace and the well-being of mankind and to seek truth through academic fields of East and West.
Foreign students We convince that foreign students can learn Japanese cultures especially influenced by Buddhism as well as modern academic fields and they can enjoy impressive experiences through our students' interchange.
Environment It is located next to Tokyo Olympic Memorial Park in one of 23 words of Central Tokyo in scenic northwest of Kanto Plains. It is 4 miles south of Shibuya convenient to the center of Tokyo but quiet and peaceful surrounded with greens and colorful floras.
Facilities Buddhist Library, Zen Buddhist Institute, 2 Gymnasiums, Student Hall, Audio-visual Rooms, Auditoriums, Computer Room, International Center, Institutes of Judicial Research, Population Research, Accounting
Student activities 40 sports and 25 culture extra curricular activity Clubs, more than 100 each sports and culture voluntary clubs, School Festival, Freshmen Welcome Party, Senior Farewell Party, University-wide Athletic Meeting, Zen Meditation Session, Field Trips, Seminars' Get together
Academic programs for foreign students Supplemental Japanese language classes, Supplemental Japanese Culture lectures
Services for foreign students Personal counseling, Housing information, Part-time Job information Cultural exchange program, Health clinic

Undergraduate Programs

Faculty of Literature(3, 000/26)
Dept. of English and American Literature(650/1)
Dept. of Geography(563/0)
Dept. of History(640/1)
Dept. of Japanese Literature(596/6)
Dept. of Social Science(551/18)
Faculty of Buddhism(874/5)
Dept. of Buddhism(531/5)
Dept. of Zen Buddhism(343/0)
Faculty of Business Administration(1, 754/20)
Dept. of Business Administration(1, 754/20)
Faculty of Economic Science Economics(2, 731/50)
Dept. of Commerce(1, 099/15)
Dept. of Economics(1, 632/15)
Faculty of Law(2, 681/6)
Dept. of Law(1, 626/4)
Dept. of Political Science(1, 055/2)

Graduate Programs

Graduate School of Business Administration(M 3/0, D 1/0)
Div. of Business Administration(M 3/0, D 1/0)
Business Management, Theory of Commercial Business Management, History of Japanese Business Management, Theory of Public Enterprise, Theory of Control-Technique, Theory of Business Management Control, Theory of Financial Management, Theory of Labor-Control, Theory of Financial Policy, Management Mathematics, Accounting, Theory of Control-Accounting, Theory of Accounting Supervision, Theory of Cost Accounting, Management Engineering, Theory of Money Market, Theory of International Economy, Finance, Statistics, Theory of Distribution, Theory of Insurance, His-

tory of Japanese Economy, Theory of Economic Policy, Science of Information, Economics, Business Management History, Theory of Management, Theory of Marketing, Theory of Enterprise Form, Foreign Documentary Records in English; German; France; Russian; Chinese, Trade Business Management, Trade Theory, Insurance Control

Graduate School of Commerce(M 7/0)

Div. of Commerce(M 7/0)

Commerce, Theory of Security Market, Theory of Trade, Theory of Transportation, Theory of Insurance, Commercial History, Theory of Commercial Policy, Management, Theory of Labor Control, Accounting, Theory of Cost Accounting, Theory of Accounting Supervision, Theory of Accounting for Taxation, Theory of Control Accounting, Theoretical Economics, Business Management, Business Management Control, Book-keeping Theory

Graduate School of Economics(M 9/0, D 2/0)

Div. of Economics(M 9/0, D 2/0)

Theoretical Economics, History of Economic Doctrine, Theory of Economic Change, Economic History, Theory of Economic Policy, Theory of Agricultural Policy, Theory of Industrial Policy, Theory of Commercial Policy, Economic Geography, Theory of Money Market, Theory of International Money Market, Finance Special Lecture on Statistics, Theory of Labor Economics, Theory of Population, Theory of Trade, Theory of Insurance, Accounting, Management, Theory of Transport Economy

Graduate School of Humanities(M 72/3, D 41/3)

Div. of Buddhism(M 24/0, D 16/2)

Zen Buddhism, Buddhism, Indian Buddhism, Indian Philosophy, Japanese Buddhism, Religious Anthropology, Chinese Classics, Chinese Buddhism, Tibetan Buddhism, Japanese Buddhism History, Buddhism Doctrine, Indian Buddhism History, Chinese Buddhism History, History of Chineses Zen Buddhism, History of Japanese Zen Buddhism, Buddhist Art, Religion, Religious Philosophy, Fundamental Problems of Studies on Buddhism Doctrine, History of Buddhist Arts, Special Problems of Religious Sciences, Special Study of Religions

Div. of English Literature(M 9/0, D 4/0)

English Literature, English Language, Thought of English Literature, Comparative Literature

Div. of Geography(M 2/0, D 2/0)

Topography, Physical Geography, Human Geography, Cartological History, Cartology, Practice of Field Works for Cartology, Topography, Geography, Regional Geography

Div. of Japanese History(M 11/0, D 6/0)

Japanese History(Ancient Times), Japanese History (Middle Ages), Japanese History(Modern Ages Ⅰ), Japanese history(Modern Ages Ⅱ), Oriental History, Occidental History, Chinese Classics, Archaeology

Div. of Japanese Literature(M 8/2, D 3/0)

Ancient Japanese Literature, Middle Japanese Literature, Modern Japanese Literature, History of Japanese Language, Japanese Linguistics, Chinese Classics, Japanese Linguistics, Comparative Literature

Div. of Psychology(M 9/0, D 6/1)

Psychology, Clinical Psychology, Zen Psychology, Mental Development, Adjacent Province of Psychlogy

Div. of Social Science(M 9/1, D 4/0)

Theoretical Sociology, Theoretical Sociology, Family Sociology, Religious Sociology, Agricultural Sociology, Industrial Sociology, Urban Sociology, Social Welfare, Sociological Law, Sociological Psychology, Mass Communication, Religious Ethnology, Religious Folk Lore

Graduate School of Law(M 12/0, D 2/0)

Div. of Private Law(M 7/0, D 1/0)

Civil Law, Commercial Law, Code of Civil Procedure, Law of Bankruptcy, Compulsory Execution, Labor Law, Law of Industrial Property, History of Law, Foreign Law, Taxation Law

Div. of Public Law(M 5/0, D 1/0)

Constitution, Administrative Law, Criminal Law, Criminal Procedure, Criminal Policy, Law of Industrial Property, Japanese Constitution, International Public Law

---

国立音楽大学

(Kunitachi Ongaku Daigaku)

Kunitachi College of Music

5-5-1 Kashiwa-cho, Tachikawa-shi, Tokyo 190
☎ 0425-36-0321

Founded 1950

Undergraduate Programs

Faculty of Music
- **Dept. of Composition**
- **Dept. of Instrumental Music**
- **Dept. of Music Education**
- **Dept. of Musicology**
- **Dept. of Vocal Music**

Graduate Programs

Graduate School of Music
- **Div. of Composition**
- **Div. of Instrumental Music**
- **Div. of Music Education**
- **Div. of Musicology**
- **Div. of Vocal Music**

杏林大学
(Kyôrin Daigaku)
Kyorin University

Mitaka Campus: 6-20-2 Shinkawa, Mitaka-shi, Tokyo 181
Hachioji Campus: 476 Miyashita-cho, Hachioji-shi, Tokyo 192
☎ 0422-47-5511 FAX 0422-46-7474

Founded 1966
Professors 117
Associate Professors 51
Assistant Professors(Tenured) 66
Assistant Professors(Non-tenured) 190
Research Assistants 187
Undergraduate Students/Foreign Students 3,384/47
Graduate Students/Foreign Students 59/0
Library 305, 200 volumes
Contact: Kohoshitsu

Educational philosophy We aim to educate students with lofty ideals according to our motto, " Pursuit of Truth, Goodness and Beauty ", established by the founder of our university.
Foreign students Our policy is to warmly welcome foreign students wishing to study in Japan.
Environment Traffic-Mitaka Campus: 20 minutes by bus from Mitaka Station on Chuo Line, Hachioji Campus: 30～40 minutes by bus from Hachioji Station on Chuo Line
Facilities School of Medicine Affiliated Hospital. Study Hall with Videotape Recorders. Kyorin University has three libraries, one for medical science on the Mitaka campus, one for hygienics and one for cultural and social science, both on the Hachioji campus.
Academic programs for foreign students Special Japanese Training Course : This is an intensive course for one year for the foreign students who wish to enter the undergraduate schools or who wish to attain proficiency in Japanese equal to the Japanese undergraduate students.
Services for foreign students Foreign students and returnees can consult casually about their various problems in learning and adapting to Japanese life with a special adviser who is an expert on domestic and foreign conditions.

Undergraduate Programs

School of Medicine(644/1)
Dept. of Medicine
School of Health Sciences(517/1)
Dept. of Medical Technology(287/1)
Dept. of Health Sciences(230/0)
Faculty of Social Sciences(1421/4)
Dept. of Social Sciences
Faculty of Foreign Languages(802/16)
Dept. of English(423/5)
Dept. of Chinese(185/2)
Dept. of Japanese(194/34)

Graduate Programs

Graduate School of Medicine(D 40/0)
Div. of Internal Medicine(D 24/0)
Internal Medicine, Geriatric Medicine, Pediatrics, Neuropsychiatry, Dermatology, Radiology, Clinical Pathology
Div. of Surgery(D 15/0)
Surgery, Orthopedics, Neurosurgery, Obstetrics and Gynecology, Ophthalmology, Otorhinolaryngology, Urology, Anesthesiology, Emergency Medicine, Chest Surgery
Div. of Physiological Sciences(D 1/0)
Anatomy, Physiology, Biochemistry, Pharmacology
Div. of Pathological Sciences(D 0/0)
Pathology, Microbiology, Parasitology
Div. of Social Medicine(D 0/0)
Hygiene, Public Health, Forensic Medicine, Hospital Administration,
Graduate School of Health Sciences(M 16/0, D 2/0)
Div. of Health Sciences(M 16/0, D 2/0)

共立薬科大学
(Kyôritsu Yakka Daigaku)
Kyoritsu College of Pharmacy

1-5-30 Shibakoen, Minato-ku, Tokyo 105
☎ 03-3434-6241 FAX 03-3434-5343

Founded 1930
Professors 16
Associate Professors 16
Assistant Professors(Tenured) 10
Assistant Professors(Non-tenured) 38
Research Assistants 22
Undergraduate Students/Foreign Students 857/0
Graduate Students/Foreign Students 30/0
Library 46, 470 volumes
Contact: Administrative Office ☎ ext. 231

Educational philosophy We aim at teaching pharmaceutical sciences as a branch of life sciences based mainly on chemistry and biology. Our goal of teachings is to bring forth and develop the powers of the mind as a pharmacist and also a contribution in cultural improvement of human beings.
Foreign students We are very glad to receive foreign students in the college, and the mutual communication between foreign and Japanese students will give good results in learning sciences for both.
Environment The main campus is in the heart of the metropolitan Tokyo, Shibakoen, which is a park area with a lot of greens and historical interests. The second campus is in Urawa, Saitama, and has facilities

for physical education and a herb garden.

Facilities Many instrumental analytical apparatus, sports training center, swimming pool, gymnasium, auditorium, herb garden, cottage in mountainous resort, and so on.

Student activities Campus events includes; freshman orientation travelling to northern resort, athletic meeting, college festival and many other student programs. Extra curricular activities are also polular, and cooperative activities with other universities are also common.

Academic programs for foreign students Although not for only foreign students, we have a lot of supplemental exercising classes for students with poor understanding of the classes.

Services for foreign students The services are available, such as health clinic, psychological counseling, college housing for women, house information, part-time job information and others.

Undergraduate Programs

Faculty of Pharmaceutical Sciences(857/0)
Dept. of Biological Pharmacy(347/0)
Dept. of Pharmaceutical Sciences(512/0)

Graduate Programs

Graduate School of Pharmaceutical Sciences(M 29/0, D 1/0)
Div. of Pharmaceutical Sciences(M 29/0, D 1/0)
Analytical Chemistry, Biochemistry, Hygienic Chemistry, Medicinal Chemistry, Microbial Chemistry, Organic Chemistry, Pharmaceutics, Pharmacognosy, Pharmacology, Physical Chemistry

---

共立女子大学
(Kyôritsu Joshi Daigaku)
Kyoritsu Women's University

2-2-1 Hitotsubashi, Chiyoda-ku, Tokyo 101
☎ 03-3237-2433

Founded 1949

Undergraduate Programs

Faculty of Arts and Letters
Dept. of Arts
Dept. of Literature
Faculty of Home Economics
Dept. of Art for Home Life
Dept. of Clothing
Dept. of Foods
Faculty of International Culture
Dept. of International Culture

Graduate Programs

Graduate School of Arts and Letters
Div. of Dramatic Arts
Div. of English Literature
Div. of Japanese Literature
Graduate School of Home Economics
Div. of Clothing
Div. of Foods

明治薬科大学
(Meiji Yakka Daigaku)
Meiji College of Pharmacy

1-35-23 Nozawa, Setagaya-ku, Tokyo 154
☎ 03-3424-1001 FAX 03-3424-3040

Founded 1902
Professors 33
Associate Professors 12
Assistant Professors(Tenured) 16
Assistant Professors(Non-tenured) 39
Research Assistants 60
Undergraduate Students/Foreign Students 1756/0
Graduate Students/Foreign Students 37/0
Library 133, 300 volumes
Contact: Entrance Examination Section, Administrative Office, ☎ ext. 612

Educational philosophy The college was established for separating pharmacy practice from the medical profession, educating pharmacists, and thus contributing to the health of the people.

Foreign students We would like to encourage foreign students to apply to the collge.

Environment The collge has two campuses in Tokyo The Setagaya campus is located in the central part, 15 minutes by Subway from Shibuya. The Tanashi Campus is conveniently located in the western suburbs, 30 minutes by train from Shinjuku or Ikebukuro. There are the rich variety of cultural facilities in both campus areas.

Facilities Libraly, instrumental and analysis center, medicinal botanical garden, dormitory for male students at Setagaya, seminar house in the countryside, small museum of pharmaceutical science and industry, gymasiums, sports grounds.

Student activities The students of the College are most eager to participate in the extra curricular activities. About 30 clubs and 10 circles covering reserch, cultural and athletic fields give students opportunities to build their characters and promote their mutual understanding.

Services for foreign students The capacity of housing is not yet large enough to accommodate of foreign students. Those who are not able to find in our Student Dormitory will have to live in private boarding houses and apartments. Health clinic, College housing

Undergraduate Programs

Faculty of Pharmacy(1756/0)
Department of Pharmaceutical Science(586/0)
Department of Pharmaceutical Chemisty(588/0)
Department of Biopharmacy(582/0)

Graduate Programs

Graduate School of Pharmacy(M 34/0, D 3/0)
Div. of Pharmaceutical Science
Pharmaceutical Chemistry, Analytical Chemistry, Pharmacognosy, Biochemistry, Pharmacology, Pharmacy, Physical Chemistry, Microbiology, Chemistry of Hygiene, Medicinal Organic Chemisty

---

明治学院大学
(Meiji Gakuin Daigaku)
Meiji Gakuin University

1-2-37 Shirokanedai, Minato-ku, Tokyo 108
☎ 03-3448-5152 FAX 03-3449-0102

Founded 1877
Professors 158
Associate Professors 75
Assistant Professors(Tenured) 26
Assistant Professors(Non-tenured) 532
Research Assistants 27
Undergraduate Students/Foreign Students 12, 458/21
Graduate Students/Foreign Students 114/2
Library 579, 100 volumes
Contact: Center for Interantional Cooperation in Education (CICE)

Educational philosophy We search for the truth boldly and yet with humility by : continuing to seek meaning for human existence; working for the weak; regarding everyone as precious, without respect to national boundaries; loving freedom; and honoring human rights, while also contributing to world peace,all of these being in response to the Christian principles of our founders.
Foreign students We are endeavoring to realize its plans for international exchanges by further developing historically deep relationships with related churches and universities, as well as by building exchange relationships with educational institutions in Asia, America and Europe.
Environment There are two campuses. The Shirokane campus encompasses 40, 000m^2,which is located in the heart of Tokyo. The Yokohama campus occupies 200, 000 m^2, on a hill in natural surroundings on the eastern edge of Totsuka-ward in Yokohama, an hour from the Shirokane campus.
Facilities We are proud of the modern and well-equipped facilities of Foreign Language Education Institute, Education Technology Center, Information Processing Center, libraries, and gymnasium.
Student activities Popular campus events include homecoming, school festival, freshmen orientation and welcoming party.There is also a wide range of athletic, study, and other extracurricular interest groups.
Academic programs for foreign students For the benefits of foreign students, up to 12 credit units for Things Japanese A, B, and C and be transferred as part of 36 credit units of General Education coureses.
Services for foreign students Health clinic, personal/psychological counseling, housing information, part-time job information, vocational guidance, cultural exchange program

Undergraduate Programs

Faculty of Literature(2, 546/2)
Dept. of Art Studeis(79/0)
Dept. of English Literature(1, 701/2)
Dept. of French Literature(688/0)
Dept. of Psychology(78/0)
Faculty of Economics(3, 492/9)
Dept. of Economics(1, 727/2)
Dept. of Commerce(1, 765/7)
Faculty of Sociology and Social Work(2, 319/4)
Dept. of Sociology(1, 390/1)
Dept. of Social Work(929/3)
Faculty of Law(3,141/0)
Dept. of Law(3, 024/0)
Dept. of Political Science(117/0)
Faculty of International Studies(960/6)
Dept. of International Studies(960/6)

Graduate Programs

Graduate School of Literature(M 27/0, D 7/0)
Div. of English Literature(M 27/0, D 7/0)
Old and Middle English Literature, Old and Middle English Literature Seminar, Modern English Literature, Modern English Literature Seminar, American Literature, American Literature Seminar, English Linguistics, English Linguistics Seminar, Advanced Lectures in American and English Literature, Old and Middle English, Advanced Lectures in English Linguistics
Graduate School of Economics(M 27/1)
Div. of Economics(M 13/0)
Economic Theory, Economic Theory Seminar, Mathematics for Economics Major, Mathematics for Economics Major Seminar, Statistics for Economics Majors, History of Economics, History of Economics Seminar, History of Social Thought, History of Social Thought Seminar, Economic History of Western Europe, World Economics, World Economics Seminar, The Japanese Economy, The Japanese Economy Seminar, Money and Banking, Money and Banking Seminar, Public Finance, Public Finance Seminar, Economic Policy, Economic

Policy Seminar, Agricultural Policy, Agricultural Policy Seminar, Industrial Policy, Industrial Policy Seminar, Commercail Policy, Labor Economics Theory, Labor Economics Theory Seminar, Social Policy

Graduate School of Economics(M 27/1)

Div. of Commerce(M 14/1)

Commerce, Commerce Seminar, Foreign Trade, Commercial Policy, Commercial Policy Seminar, History of Commerce, Maritime Insurance, Maritime Insurance Seminar, Maritime Law, Commodities, Money and Banking, Business Planning, Business Planning Seminar, Business Organizations, Business Organizations Seminar, Business Finance, Business Finance Seminar, Industrial Labor Management, International Business Administration, International Business Administration Seminar, History of Accounting, History of Accounting Seminar, Accounting Methods, Accounting Methods Seminar, Finance Accounting, Cost Accounting, Auditing, Auditing Seminar, Tax Accounting

Graduate School of Sociology and Social Work(M 31/1, D 8/0)

Div. of Sociology(M 15/0)

Sociology, Sociology Seminar, Social Psychology, Social Psychology Seminar, Family Sociology, Family Sociology Seminar, Industrial Sociology, Industrial Sociology Seminar, Public Relations Theory, Public Relations Theory Seminar, Urban Sociology, Urban Sociology Seminar, Rural Sociology, Rural Sociology Seminar, Social Pathology, Social Pathology Seminar, Criminal Sociology, Criminal Sociology Seminar, Social Education, Social Education Seminar, Educational Sociology, Educational Sociology Seminar, Labor Sociology, Labor Sociology Seminar, Individuals, Communication and Society, Individuals, Communication and Society Seminar, Cultural Sociology, Cultural Sociology Seminar, Social Research Field Work, Advanced Lectures in Sociology, Research Seminar

Graduate School of Sociology and Social Work(M 31/1, D 8/0)

Div. of Social Work(M 16/1)

Principles of Social Work, Principles of Social Work Seminar, Social Work Methods, Social Work Methods Seminar, Clinical Practice in Social Work, Advanced Lectures in Social Welfare, Advanced Lectures in Social Welfare Seminar, Mental Health, Clinical Psychology, Field Work in Social Research, Social Research

Graduate School of Sociology and Social Work(M 31/1, D 8/0)

Div. of Sociology and Social Work(D 8/0)

Research Seminar

Graduate School of Law(M 5/0, D 3/0)

Div. of Law(M 5/0, D 3/0)

Theories of Law, Theories of Law Seminar, Constitutional Law, Constitutional Law Seminar, Administrative Law, Administrative Law Seminar, Tax Law, Tax Law Seminar, International Law, International Law Seminar, Civil Law, Civil Law Seminar, Commercial Law, Commercial Law Seminar, Civil Procedure, Civil Procedure Seminar, Criminal Law, Criminal Law Seminar, Labor Law, Labor Law Seminar, Foreign Law, Foreign Law Seminar, Politics, Politics Seminar, Economic Law, Economic Law Seminar, Public Law, Advanced Lectures in Theories of Law, Theories of Law Seminar, Constitutional Law, Constitutional Law Seminar, Administrative Law, Administrative Law Seminar, International Law, International Law Seminar, Civil Law, Civil Law Seminar, Commercial Law, Civil Procedure, Civil Procedure Seminar, Criminal Law, Criminal Law Seminar, Labor Law, Labor Law Seminar, Foreign Law, Foreign Law Seminar, Politics, Politics Seimnar

Graduate School of International Studies(M 6/0)

Div. of International Studies(M 6/0)

Basic Theories of Area Studies, The Japanese Language and Culture, The Theory of the State, The Structure of Thoughts, Life Techniques and Culture, Theoreis of Growth and Distribution, Basic Theory of the World Society, Theory of the World Order, The Study of States and Nations, Theory of Global Resources and Environment, Theory of Non-Govermental Organizations, Transnational·Enterprises, Theory of Capital and Technology Flow, Basic Theory of Peace and Conflicts, Peace Thoughts, Religions and Peace, Conflict Studies, Disarmament Studies, Inequality Studies, The Study of Resource Problems

---

明治大学

(Meiji Daigaku)

Meiji University

1-1 Kanda Surugadai, Chiyoda-ku, Tokyo 101
☎ 03-3296-4545 FAX 03-3296-4266

Founded 1881
Professors 437
Associate Professors 114
Assistant Professors(Tenured) 56
Assistant Professors(Non-tenured) 974
Research Assistants 49
Undergraduate Students/Foreign students 34, 065/235
Graduate Students/Foreign students 786/59
Library 1, 322, 766 volumes
Contact: Office of International Programs ☎ 03-296-4140, 4141

Educational philosophy The principles of Meiji University are " Independence with Self-Government " and " Invincible Rights of Freedom ". Our main educational policies are the followings : to foster students with global vision and train them to evaluate themselves accurately so that they can respond to various problems of the changing society.

Foreign students Meiji University welcomes qualified students from abroad. We hope students study hard and enjoy a rewarding experience on our campus, and contribute a lot to understanding mutual cultures between ours.

Environment Meiji University has three campuses.

The main campus is located near the administrative and business center of Tokyo. One of the two branch campuses, Izumi campus is 30 minutes by train from the main campus and situated on an open expanse of lawn. Ikuta campus, another branch campus is in the southern suburbs of Tokyo.

Facilities Library, Institutes of Humanities, Social Sciences, Science & Technology, Center for International Programs, Information Science Center, three museums(Commodity, Criminological, Archaeological), Gymnasium, Audio-Visual Center

Student activities Popular campus events include campus festival, homecoming and freshman welcome activities. We have over 500 cultural and athletic clubs. Students are invited to join them. The intercollegiate sports clubs are the most outstanding in Japan and won many national championships in rugby football, skiing, baseball and judo, etc.

Academic programs for foreign students Regular and extra Japanese language class. Tutoring system necessary for selected students(not for all).

Services for foreign students Health clinic, Personal counseling, Scholarship information, Housing information, Part-time job information, Homestay, Cultural exchange program.

Undergraduate Programs

School of Agriculture(2558/27)
Dept. of Agriculture(1030/1)
Dept. of Agricultural Chemistry(698/5)
Dept. of Agricultural Economics(830/21)
School of Arts and Letters(4916/16)
Dept. of Literature(2995/10)
Dept. of History and Geograpy(1921/6)
School of Business Administration(3438/73)
Dept. of Business Administration(3438/73)
School of Commerce(6681/60)
Dept. of Commerce(4996/43)
Dept of Industrial Administration(1685/17)
School of Law(5274/11)
Dept. of Law(5274/11)
School of Political Science and Economics (6519/33)
Dept. of Economics(4622/26)
Dept. of Political Science(1897/7)
School of Science and Technology(4679/15)
Dept. of Architecture(878/3)
Dept. of Computer Science(213/4)
Dept. of Electrical Engineering(650/2)
Dept. of Electronics and Communication(647/4)
Dept. of Industrial Chemistry(557/1)
Dept. of Mathematics(121/0)
Dept. of Mechanical Engineering(771/0)
Dept. of Physics(111/0)
Dept. of Precision Engineering(731/1)

Graduate Programs

Graduate School of Agriculture(M 52/1, D 3/0)

Div. of Agriculture(M 21/1)
Agricultural Land Improvement, Hydraulic & Structural Engineering, Agricultural Machinery, Landscape Architecture, Green Conservation, Structural Engineering, Landscape Engineering, Crop Science, Plant Protection, Horticulture, Processing & Storage of Agricultural Products, Plant Breeding, Advanced Animal Physiology & Anatomy, Reproduction in Domestic Animals, Laboratory Animal Science, Animal Feeding, Soil Fertilizer Chemistry, Utilization of agricultural Chemicals, Vegetable Horticulture, Floriculture, Nutrition of Domestic Animals, Animal Breeding

Div. of Agricultural Chemistry(M 24/0, D 1/0)
Utilization of Microorganisms, Utilization of Livestock Products, Nutritional Chemistry, Biochemisry, Analytical Chemistry, Solid Clay Chemistry, Plant Nutrition & Fertilizer Science, Agricultural Chemistry, Food Chemistry, The Utilization of Agricultural Products, Advanced Organic Chemistry, Enzyme Chemistry, Chemical Engineering, Radiation Biology

Div. of Agricultural Economics(M 7/0, D 2/0)
Agricultural, Political & Administrative Science, Agricultural Economics, Rural Sociology, Agricultural Administrative Science, Economic Analysis of Agricultural Marketing, Agricultural Labor Science, Agricultural Finace Theory, Farm Accounting, Rural Planning, Comparative Agriculture, Agricultural Marketing, Agricultural Social Accounting, Planning of Land Utilization

Graduate School of Arts and Letters (M 92/10, D 57/10)

Div. of Drama(M 9/0, D 7/0)
Theory of Drama, Theory of Japanese Drama, History of Western Drama, Philosophy of Art, Comparative Literature

Div. of English and American Literature(M 15/0, D 3/0)
English Literature, American Literature, English Linguistics, Philosophy of Art, Compartive Literature, English and Canadian Literature

Div. of French Literature(M 5/0, D 8/0)
Early Modern French Literature, Modern French Literature, Philosophy of Art, Comparative Literature, Contemporary French Literature, French Linguistics

Div. of Geography(M 5/0, D 3/0)
Physical Geograhpy, Human Geography, Regional Geography

Div. of German Literature(M 2/0, D 5/0)
Early Modern German Literature, Modern German Literature, Contemporary German Literature, History of German Literary Thought, German Lyrical Poems, Philosophy of Art, Compartive Literature

Div. of History(M 43/3, D 22/0)
Japanese History, Asian History, European History, Archaeology, Intellectual History, Cultural History, Mediaval Japanese History, Modern Japanese History, Modern Japanese Religious History, North-Eastern Asian History

Div. of Japanese Literature(M 15/3, D 14/4)
Ancient Japanese Literature, Medieval Japanese Literature, Early Modern Japanese Literature, Modern Japanese Literature, Japanese Philology, History of Japanese

Literature Thought, Chinese Literature, Japanese Drama, Philosophy of Art, Comparative Literature

Graduate School of Business Administration(M 38/9, D 23/2)

Div. of Business Administration(M 38/9, D 23/2)
International Business, Business Administration, Hisotry of Management Theory in America, Business Management(UK, USA, Germany), Economic Management in Socialist Countries, Economics of Public Utilities and Public Enterprise, Theory of Capital Centralization, Small Business Management, Marketing and Consumer Behavior, Production Management, Personnel Administration, Industrial Relations, Organizational Psychology, Sociology of Management, Business History, Japanese Business History, Management of Information Statistics, Modern Organization Theory, Linear Programming(LP), Dynamic, Management and Organization, Business Management Metamorphosis, Organization Theory Business Corporation Finance, Business History, Financial Accounting Theory, Accounting Theory, Accounting Principles, Auditing, Information Systems in Accounting, Informational Accouting, Cost Accounting, Business Budgeting, Business Analysis, French Business Administration, Theory of contemporary capitalism, Business Information Systems, Management Engineering, English Business History, Comparative Business History, Management Accounting

Graduate School of Commerce(M 31/8, D 14/5)

Div. of Commerce(M 31/8, D 14/5)
Economics Theory, Public Finance, Economic Policy, European Economic History, Commercial History in Japan, Commercial Theory, Marketing Decision Support Systems, Cooperatives and Distributive Trades, Wholesale and Retail Management, Principles of Business Administration, Production Management, Industrial Management, Labor Management, The Historical Development of Accounting, Auditing, Principles of Cost Accounting, Cost Accounting, Management Accounting, Business Analysis, Financial Statement Analysis, Modern Monetray Theory and Policy, Financial Institutions Business and Industrial Finance, Business Finance, The Securities Market, Risk and Insurance Theory, Social Insurance, Transport Theory, Land Transport, Ocean Transport and Shipping, Trade Theory, Global Economics, International Finance, International Marketing, Foreign Trade Practices

Graduate School of Engineering(M 293/2, D 8/0)

Div. of Electrical Engineering(M 89/1, D 39/0)
Physical Electronics, Optical Electronics, Electronic Instrumentation and Measurement, Electrical Materials, Magnetism and Magnetic Materials, Magnetics, High Voltage Physics, Dielectric Physics, Electromagnetic Field Analysis, Circuit Synthesis, Electromechanical Dynamics, Electric Power System, Light. Application Engineering, Statistical Thermodynamics, Electromechanical Energy Conversion, Power Electronics, Electronic Computers, Logical Mathematics, Computer Science, Analog Operational Engineering, Digital Operation Engineering, Information Processing Engineering, Electromagnetic Wave Theory, Electronic Communication, Acoustical Engineering, Algebra, Network Analysis, Electric Cincuit Synthesis, Control Engineering, Electronic Instrumentation and Measurement Systems Theory, Fault Tolerant Systems, VLSI design Methodology, Cybernetics, Physics, Chemical Physics, Mathematical Theory of Computers via Digital Expression, Quantam Mechanics, Mathematical Programming, System Engineering, Analytics

Div. of Architecture(M 57/1, D 3/0)
Architectural Design, History of Japanese Architecture, History of Modern Architecture, Protection and Conservation of Cultural Properties, History of Architecture/Architectural Design, Architectural Planning, Building Design and Architectural Design, Building Systems, Architectural Economics, Land Use Theory, Regional Planning, Architectural Design and Regional and City Planning, Structural Design in Architectures, Architectural Materials, Structural Analysis, Aseismic Design and Structures, Architectural Environment Engineering, Water Supply and Drainage, Air-conditioning Equipment, Acoustic Design and Planning, Assessment of the Architectural Environment, Equipment Planning, History of Science and Technology

Div. of Industrial Chemistry(M 44/0, D 44/0)
Chemical Equilibrium, Advanced Organic Chemistry, Organic Industrial Chemistry, Advanced Quantum Chemistry, Inorganic Chemistry, Inorganic Industrial Chemistry, Chemical Engineering, Industrial Analytical Chemistry, Applied Mathematics, Solid-state Physics, Chemical Physics, Environmental Industrial Chemistry, Material Science

Div. of Mechanical Engineering(M 103/0, D 2/0)
Strength of Materials, Vibration of Continuous Systems, Elastic Mechanics, Machine Design Engineering, Design Engineering, Mechanical Dynamics, Fluid Engineering, Thermodynamics, Thermal Engineering, Applied Thermotics, Materials Science and Engineering, Machine Manufacturing Processes, Plasticity Technology, Instrumentation Engineering, Control Engineering, Management Control Engineering, Production System Engineering, Engineering Analysis, Applied Physics, Solid-state Physics

Graduate School of Law(M 51/4, D 43/6)

Div. of Civil Law(M 24/1, D 13/2)
Property Law, Family Law, Commercial Law, Economic Law, Civil Procedure, Sociology of Law, Japanese Legal History, Oriental Legal History, European Legal History, Company Law, Japanese Ancient Legal History, Chinese Ancient Legal History

Div. of Public Law(M 27/3, D 30/4)
Constitutional Law, Administrative Law, Criminal Law, Criminal Procedure Law, Criminal Policy, Labor Law, International Law, Legal Philosophy, Anglo-American Law, German Law, Public Law, Constitutional Law, Constitutional Theory, Modern European Legal Thought

Graduate School of Political Science and Economics(M 49/8, D 32/4)

Div. of Economics(M 30/5, D 10/1)
Theoretical Economics, Macro Economics, Price Theory, Econometrics, Monetary Economics, History of Economic Theories, Ideologies and Economics, Public Finance,

History of Public Finance, Statistics, Population Theory, Contemporary Theories of Economics, General Theory of Economics, Agricultural Economics, Theory of Industrial Policy, Seminar on Tertiary Economics, Theory of Economic Cooperatives, Social Policy Development, History of Western Economic Thought, History of Japanese Economies, Economic Geography, Public Finance and Taxation, Social Welfare Policy, History of European Economics, Economic Mathematics, Socialist Economies

Div. of Political Science(M 19/3, D 22/3)
Political Science, Comparative Politics, Political Systems, Political Process, Public Administration, Local Politics and Administration, Urban Politics and Public Policy, General Theories of States, Political Thought, Political History of Europe, Diplomatic History, Japanese Political Thought, Political History of Japan, Journalism, International Relations, Constitutional Law, General Theory of Sociology, Social Anthropology, Social Psychology, Sociological Study of Families, Cultural Sociology, General Theory of Sociology

---

明海大学
(Meikai Daigaku)
Meikai University

Urayasu Campus: 8 Akemi, Urayasu-shi, Chiba 279
☎ 0473-55-5111 FAX 0473-55-5420
Sakado Campus: 1-1 Keyakidai, Sakado-shi, Saitama 350-02
☎ 0492-85-5511 FAX 0492-71-0612

Founded 1970
Professors 78
Associate Professors 42
Assistant Professors(Tenured) 57
Assistant Professors(Non-tenured) 201
Research Assistants 73
Undergraduate Students/Foreign Students 3, 608/48
Graduate Students/Foreign Students 41/0
Library 148, 918 volumes
Contact: Admission Office ☎ 0473-55-5116

Educational philosophy We want to awaken the minds of the students to a more international feeling towards the prosperity of mankind.

Foreign students We expect you to study hard. We also hope you make the most of such occasions as social meetings and field trips to promote your relations with the staff and faculty and to deepen your understanding of Japanese culture.

Environment The Urayasu Campus with the faculties of laguages and economics is located in Urayasu, Chiba Prefecture. Nearby is Tokyo Disneyland. Dental studies, both under- and post-graduate, are offered on the Sakado Campus, Sakado, Saitama Prefecture. Both cities are adjacent to Tokyo.

Facilities The International Exchange Center, Library, Postdoctoral Dental Institute, Computer rooms, AV rooms, Gymnasium, Playing fields, Tennis courts, etc.

Student activities The school festival is held every fall. There is a wide variety of extracurricular activities including a Marching Band, Literary Arts, Drama, and Soccer.

Undergraduate Programs

Faculty of Dentistry(944/4)
  Dept. of Dentistry(944/4)
Faculty of Economics(1, 383/34)
  Dept. of Economics(1, 383/34)
Faulty of Languages and Cultures(1, 281/10)
  Dept. of Chinese(260/1)
  Dept. of English(731/3)
  Dept. of Japanese(290/6)

Graduate Programs

Graduate School of Dentistry(D 41/0)
Oral Anatomy, Oral Anatomy, Oral Phisiolosy, Oral Biochemistry, Oral Microbiology, Oral Pathology, Dental Pharmacology, Dental Microbiology, Operative Dentistry, Endodontics, Periodontology, Prosthetic dentistry, Prosthetic dentistry, Oral Surgery, Oral Surgery, Orthodontics, Dental Radiology, Pedodontics, Dental Health, Oral Diagnosis

---

明星大学
(Meisei Daigaku)
Meisei University

2-1-1 Hodokubo, Hino-shi, Tokyo 191
☎ 0425-91-5111 FAX 0425-91-8181

Founded 1964
Professors 137
Associate Professors 13
Assistant Professors(Tenured) 15
Assistant Professors(Non-tenured) 110
Research Assistants 16
Undergraduate Students/Foreign Students 6,868/5
Graduate Students/Foreign Students 92/8
Library 477, 328 volumes
Contact: Admission Office

Educational philosophy The principles guiding the Meisei Educational Institute since 1923 are the harmonious oneness of matter and mind, respecting one's own self equally with others, and following the idea of the ceaseless creative development of the universe; education is, in the true sense of the word, developing sincerity of mind by using everything in the universe as educational materials, and the nurturing of individual personalities, to develop natural talents and abilities, leads to individuals who can contribute to the civilization and peace of the world.

Foreign students Respect for individuality. By thoroughly developing the natural gifts of individuals, we nurture human beings who will contribute to culture and to the peace of mankind.

Environment Meisei University is located in Hino City in the western suburbs of Tokyo, with a fine view of Mount Fuji to the west over the Tama Hills. To the east it overlooks the beautiful Tama River and the vast expanse of the Musashino Plain.

Facilities High Resolution Analytical Electron Microscopy Research Center, Information Science Research Center, Post-War Educational History Research Center, Shakespeare Research Center for Shakespeariana Taro Cosmic Ray Laboratory, Tokyo Lincoln Center for Lincolniana

Student activites The University provides not only facilities indispensable for students, such as campus shop, cafeteria, clubrooms, student counseling center, etc., but also individual lockers upon request for laboratory experiments.

Academic programs for foreign students Undergraduate: Foreign Language Subjects, 1. The 1st and 2nd year course for credit(required): Japanese Language, 2. The 3rd and 4th year course not for credit (required): Japanese Language

Graduate: 1. Master's Program The 1st and 2nd year course not for credit(required): Japanese Language Seminar, 2. Doctor's Program The 1st, 2nd and 3rd year course not for cred it(required): Japanese Language Seminar

Services for foreign students Entrance Examination Section, Admission Division, Instruction Office

Undergraduate Programs

College of Humanites(3, 591/5)
- **Dept. of Economics**(1, 141/4)
- **Dept. of English Language and English and American Literature**(522/1)
- **Dept. of Psychology and Pedagogy**
- (**Pedagogy Course**) (586/0)
- (**Psychology Course**) (646/0)
- **Dept. of Sociology**(696/0)

College of Science and Engineering(3, 277/0)
- **Dept. of Chemistry**(499/0)
- **Dept. of Civil Engineering**(761/0)
- **Dept. of Electrical Engineering**(821/0)
- **Dept. of Mechanical Engineering**(773/0)
- **Dept. of Physics**(423/0)

Graduate Programs

Graduate School of Humanities(M 33/3, D 12/0)

Div. of Engilish and American Literature(M 4/0,D 5/0)

English Literature, American Literature, Comparative Literature, Classical Literature, English Linguistics, French Literature, German Literature

Div. of Pedagogy(M 12/2, D 3/0)

Pedagogy, History of Education, Educational Psychology, Educational Sociology, Educational History

Div. of Psychology(M 14/0, D 4/0)

Lecture & Seminar: Experimental Psychology & Comparative Psychology(Cognitive Behavior in Animals and Men), Clinical Psychology(Assessment), Experimental Psychology & Environmental Psychology(Psychology of Perception & Environmental Psychology), Educational Psychology (Educational Technology, Educational Evaluation & Educational Counseling), Developmental Psychology(Social Development), Educational Psychology(ATI. & Teacher-Student Relationship), Behavior Analysis, Applied Behavior Analysis, Psychological Measurement of Evaluation, Special Studies, Psychology of Personality, Abnormal & Social Psychology

Div. of Sociology(M 3/1, D 0/0)

Theoretical Sociology, Sociology, Applied Sociology, Rural Sciology, Political Sociology, History of Sociology

Graduate School of Science and Engineering(M 42/1, D 5/4)

Div. of Chemistry(M 14/0, D 2/2)

General Lectures, Special Lectures and Special Experiments: Inorganic Chemistry, Organic Chemistry, Physical Chemistry, Analytical Chemistry, Special Studies, Exercises and Experiments: Inorganic Chemistry, Organic Chemistry, Physical Chemistry, Analytical Chemistry

Div. of Civil Engineering(M 4/0, D 0/0)

Special Lectures and Special Experiments and Seminar: Sanitary Engineering, Hydraulics, Special Study and Special Experiments and Seminars: Bridge Engineering, Concrete and Reinforced Concrete Engineering, Applied Mechanics, Sanitary Engineering, Habor Engineering, River Engineering, Railway Engineering, Regional and City Planning, Execution of Civil Engineering, Structural Engineering, Soil Engineering, Water Engineering, City Planning, Applied Mathematics,

Div. of Electrical Engineering(M 5/1, D 1/1)

Solid-State Electronics, Semiconductor Physics, Physic of Properties of Matters, Properties of Dielectrics, Electronic Appliances, Thoory and Application of Charged Particles, Picture Processing, Communication Engineering, Opto-Quantum Electronics, Electrical Measurements, Automatic Control Systems, Data Communications, Electronic Intelligence, Applied Electronics, Power Apparatus and Systems, Electric Machinery,

Div. of Mechanical Enginerring(M 4/0, D 0/0)

Advanced Dynamics of Machinery, Practics and Exercise on Dynamics of Machinery, Manufacturing Technology, Strength of Materials, Heat Engineering, Fluid Dynamics, Industrial Materials, Machine Design, Energy Engineering, Internal Combustion Engine, Refrigerating Machine, Production Engineering, Automatic Control, Surface Engineering, Applied Mathematics, Dynamics of Machinery, Manufacturing Technology Steam Power Plant Engineering

Div. of Physics(M 15/0, D 2/1)

Quantum Mechanics, Mathematical Physics, MathemStatistical Mechanics, Elementary-Particle Theory, Theory of Solid-State Physics, Chemical Physics,

Nuclear Physics, Health Physics, Nuclear Radiation Physics, Nuclear Instruments and Measurement, Cosmic Rays, Physical Optics, Atomic and Molecular Physics, Solid Molecular Physics

武蔵工業大学
(Musashi Kôgyo Daigaku)

Musashi Institute of Technology

1-28-1 Tamazutsumi, Setagaya-ku, Tokyo 158
☎ 03-3703-3111

Founded 1949

Undergraduate Programs

Faculty of Engineering
- **Dept. of Architecture**
- **Dept. of Civil Engineering**
- **Dept. of Electrical and Electronic Engineering**
- **Dept. of Electronics and Communication Engineering**
- **Dept. of Industrial Engineering**
- **Dept. of Mechanical Engineering**

Graduate Programs

Graduate School of Engineering
- **Div. of Architecture**
- **Div. of Civil Engineering**
- **Div. of Electrical Engineering**
- **Div. of Industrial Engineering**
- **Div. of Manuracturing Engineering**
- **Div. of Mechanical Engineering**
- **Div. of Nuclear Engineering**

武蔵野音楽大学
(Musashino Ongaku Daigaku)

Musashino Academia Musicae

1-13-1 Hazawa, Nerima-ku, Tokyo 176
☎ 03-3992-1121

Founded 1929

Professors 79
Associate Professors 79
Assistant Professors(Tenured) 88
Assistant Professors(Non-tenured) 211

Undergraduate Programs

Faculty of Music
- **Dept. of Composition**
- **Dept. of Instrumental Music**
- **Dept. of Music Education**
- **Dept. of Musicology**
- **Dept. of Voice**

Graduate Programs

Graduate School of Music
- **Div. of Composition**
- **Div. of Instrumental Music**
- **Div. of Music Education**
- **Div. of Musicology**
- **Div. of Voice**

武蔵野美術大学
(Musashino Bijutsu Daigaku)

Musashino Art University

1-736 Ogawa-cho, Kodaira-shi, Tokyo 187
☎ 0423-41-5011 FAX 0423-45-1404

Founded 1929
Professors 74
Associate Professors 8
Assistant Professors(Non-tenured) 234
Research Assistants 31
Undergraduate Students/Foreign Students 2286/44
Graduate Students/Foreign Students 109/24
Library 154, 644 volumes
Contact: Section for Instruction

Educational philosophy Our school aims at the total education in the field of art and design, and we endeavor to train students for fresh and creative artists and designers and have them go out into the world with aesthetic culture. To realize such aim, our education is characterized by strict training in formative art so that there is accurate expression of objects, as well as a close relationship between teachers and pupils.
Foreign students We expect that foreign students enjoy our professional education and contribute international mutual understanding and the development of friendly relations. There may be many difficulties in the way of accomplishing your studies far away from home. We do, however, believe that you can overcome such difficulties and will make your experience in our school rewarding.
Environment Our Takanodai campus is in Kodaira city, which is located on the western outskirts of Tokyo. Change at Kokubunji on the JR Chuo Line for the Seibu Bus for Ogawakami juku(Bidai mae). You can admire the natural beauty of the Musashino, the southwest region of the Kanto plain.
Facilities Museum-Library, Gymnasium, Takanodai Hall A(Cafeteria, coffee house and stationery shop), Takanodai Hall B(Rooms for student circles and an exhibition room).
Student activities Fifty or more circles are active under the control of Extra Curricular Activities Council.

Their activities reach the climax during the annual school festival called Geijutsusai(Art Festival). Various exhibitions are held all the year round.

Academic programs for foreign students Supplemental Japanese language class, Study of Japanese culture.

Services for foreign students Health clinic, personal/psychological counseling, Housing information, part-time job information, etc.

Undergraduate Programs

College of Art and Design(2286/44)
Dept. of Japanese Painting(105/4)
Dept. of Painting(452/6)
Dept. of Sculpture(124/2)
Dept. of Visual Communication Design(331/4)
Dept. of Industrial, Interior and Craft Design(360/3)
Dept. of Scenography, Display and Fashion Design(354/11)
Dept. of Architecture(322/7)
Dept. of Science of Design(178/4)
Dept. of Imaging Arts and Sciences(60/3)

Graduate Programs

Graduate School of Art and Design(M 109/24)
Div. of Fine Arts(M 62/6)
Japanese Painting, Painting, Printmaking, Sculpture, Science of Art and Design
Div. of Design(M 47/18)
Visual Communication Design, Industrial, Interior and Craft Design, Scenography, Display and Fashion Design Architecture, Science of Design

---

武蔵野女子大学
(Musashino Joshi Daigaku)

Musashino Women's College

1-1-20 Shin-machi, Hoya-shi, Tokyo 202
☎ 0424-68-3111 FAX 0424-68-3154

Founded 1924
Professors 21
Associate Professors 7
Assistant Professors(Tenured) 6
Assistant Professors(Non-tenured) 147
Research Assistants 4
Undergraduate Students/Foreign Students 1, 149/31
Library 155, 449 volumes
Contact: Language Education and Research Center ☎ 0424-68-3207 Undergraduate Affairs Division ☎ 0424-68-3200 Fax 0424-68-3347

Educational philosophy Our aim is to nurture academic knowledge, refinement and gentility in young women, and also to deepen our studies to contribute to the development of Japanese culture, in the spirit of Buddhism.

Foreign students We feel it is important to receive foreign students actively and promote an increase in foreigners who are knowledgable about Japan so that Japanese may acquire an international way of thinking and also to promote mutual understanding.

Environment Located in the suburbs of Tokyo, M.W.C. has a 100, 000m^2 campus which has many trees and flowers even though it is convenienty near the city. The students can quietly study literature and question the true nature of human life.

Facilities A library with 150, 000 volumes, Institute of Buddhist Culture Research, Noh Research Center, Language Education and Research Center, Cross-Culture Center, a Computer Room, and recreational facilities which include a pool and tennis courts.

Student activities First Semester: April-September(Summer Vacation: July-August), Second Semester: October-January(Christmas and New Years Vacation), Spring Vacation : Februaty-March. Club activities : tea ceremony, flower arrangement, Noh drama, tennis, calligraphy, Japanese Koto, mandolin club, and others.

Academic programs for foreign students Students can take Japanese language and general Japanese studies instead or English, French, and German. Supplemental Japanese language classes will be given at Language Education and Research Center.

Services for foreign students In our L.E.R.C. we counsel foreign students on college life and personal life. Students can take part in extra curricular activities, social gatherings, film showings, and others for the purpose of promoting understanding of Japanese culture.

Undergraduate Programs

Faculty of Literature(1549/31)
Dept. of English and American Literature(795/25)
Dept. of Japanese Literature(754/6)

武蔵大学
(Musashi Daigaku)

Musashi University

1-26-1 Toyotama-kami, Nerima-ku, Tokyo 176
☎ 03-3991-1191 FAX 03-3994-2146

Founede 1921
Professors 87
Associate Professors 25
Assistant Professors(Tenured) 6
Assistant Professors(Non-tenured) 250
Research Assistants 1
Undergraduate Students(Foreign)Students 3, 661/0
Graduate Students(Foreign)Students 27/0
Library 430, 000 volumes
Contact: Undergraduate; Admissions Office, ☎ ext.115

Graduate Admission Administrative Ofiice of each School
☎ ext. 193(Economics), 203(Humanities)

Educational philosophy Musashi university strives to continue the traditions of small scale education established by the old Musashi High School while seeking to avoid, whithin the limits of a Private institution, the pitfalls of mass education. This aim is achieved by means of a vigorous seminar system that extends over a student's four years. The advisor system also provides the student with individual guidance on both a personal and academic level.

Foreign students At present there is no special entrance examination for foreign students. Such students would be required to take the regular entrance examination given yearly in the middle of February.

Environment Musashi Univeristy is situated in a quiet residential district in Nerima Ward, Tokyo. While close to the center of city, the campus, with its trees and flowing brook, is a relaxing environment where traces of the Musashi Plain still remain.

Facilities Research Information Center (libraly, economic date facilities, humanities general research facilities, language laboratory); Science Information Center (computer room, audio visual room, natural science laboratory and research facilities); General Research Facilities; Asaka Grounds; Gymnasium;Pool; Dormitories for overnight trips, etc.

Student activities Freshman Seminar Camps(Economics Department); Seminar Meeting within the university; Seminar Meetings with other universities; Intramural Athletic Meets; Athletic Meets among the four universities; Shirakijisai(School Festival); Ski Trips; in addition, numerous events sponsored by cultural and athletic clubs.

Academic programs for foreign students At the graduate school, the tutors were set up occasionally for the foreign research students sent by the financial aid of the Japan Foundation.

Undergraduate Program

Faculty of Economice(1, 932/0)
  Dept. of Business Administration(940/0)
  Dept. of Economics(992/0)
Faculty of Humanities(1, 729/0)
  Dept. of Jananese Culture(529/0)
  Dept. of Sociology(528/0)
  Dept. of Western Culture(672/0)

Graduate Programs

Graduate School of Eonomics(M 2/0, D 3/0)
  Div. of Economics(M 2/0, D 3/0)
Economic Theory and History, Economic Policy, Finance and Banking, Business Administration and Accounting
Graduate School of Humanities(M 22/0)
  Div. of English Language and British & American Literature(M 4/0)
  Div. of French Language and Literature(M 4/0)
  Div. of German Language and Literature(M 2/0)
  Div. of Japanese Language and Literature(M 12/0)
Anglo-American, German, French, and Japanese literature, clutural histories, and lingustics, and comparative literature

---

日本文化大学
(Nippon Bunka Daigaku)
Nippon Bunka University

977 Katakura-cho, Hachioji, Tokyo 192
☎ 0426-36-5211

Founded 1978

Undergraduate Programs

Faculty of Law
  Dept. of Law

日本大学
(Nihon Daigaku)
Nihon University

4-8-24 Kudan-Minami, Chiyoda-ku, Tokyo 102
☎ 03-3262-2271 FAX 03-3265-8968

Founded 1889
Professors 977
Associate Professors 483
Assistant Professors(Tenured) 612
Assistant Professors(Non-tenured) 2, 390
Research Assistants 635
Undergraduate Students/Foreign Students 67, 891/553
Graduate Students/Foreign Students 1, 609/95
Library 4, 416, 652 volumes
Contact: Office of International Division

Foreign students We have been undertaken the special entrance examination for the students from abroad since 1978.

Environment With 14 colleges and 81 departments, it is the largest university in Japan. Each of its colleges has its own campus. The campuses are located in Tokyo, Chiba, Kanagawa, Saitama, Shizuoka, and Fukushima.

Facilities All of the colleges are fully equipped with a library and all other requisite research and athletic facilities.

Student activities One of the most exciting events in our campus life is the Campus Festival in Fall. Nihon University has many academic, cultural, and athletic clubs. Some of them including 34 athletic teams represent Nihon University in intercollegiate competition.

Academic programs for foreign students Most of the colleges provide Japanese language and its related subject such as " Society of Japan " as required subjects in the curriculum.

Services for foreign students Orientation for freshman, Year end party, Recreation program, Health check, Introduction to the attached hospitals, Personal/psychological counseling, Housing information, Information on scholarship programs offered by external institutions, etc.

Undergraduate Programs

Faculty of Agriculture and Veterinary Medicine(7,346/66)
- **Dept. of Agricultural Chemistry**(633/6)
- **Dept. of Agricultural Engineering**(672/1)
- **Dept. of Agriculture**(630/7)
- **Dept. of Animal Science**(649/2)
- **Dept. of Applied Biological Science**(429/2)
- **Dept. of Fisheries**(654/3)
- **Dept. of Food Economics**(712/25)
- **Dept. of Food Technology**(681/8)
- **Dept. of Forestry**(660/1)
- **Dept. of Land Development**(743/11)
- **Dept. of Veterfinary Medicine**(883/0)

Faculty of Art(3, 688/105)
- **Dept. of Broadcasting**(555/22)
- **Dept. of Cinema**(510/16)
- **Dept. of Drama**(536/16)
- **Dept. of Fine Arts**(582/25)
- **Dept. of Literary Arts**(518/3)
- **Dept. of Music**(478/1)
- **Dept. of Photography**(509/22)

Faculty of Commerce(5, 231/81)
- **Dept. of Accounting**(1, 075/5)
- **Dept. of Business Administration**(1, 578/42)
- **Dept. of Commerce**(2, 578/34)

Faculty of Dentistry(945/0)
- **Dept. of Dentistry**(945/0)

Faculty of Dentistry at Matsudo(939/0)
- **Dept. of Dentistry**(939/0)

Faculty of Economics(5, 538/121)
- **Dept. of Economics**(3, 283/54)
- **Dept. of Industrial Management**(2, 255/67)

Faculty of Engineering(4, 852/10)
- **Dept. of Architecture**(1, 051/1)
- **Dept. of Civil Engineering**(1, 001/0)
- **Dept. of Electrical Engineering**(1, 097/4)
- **Dept. of Industrial Chemistry**(697/1)
- **Dept. of Mechanical Engineering**(1, 006/4)

Faculty of Humanities and Sciences(8, 765/60)
- **Dept. of Applied Earth Science**(293/0)
- **Dept. of Applied Mathematics**(312/0)
- **Dept. of Applied Physics**(223/0)
- **Dept. of Chemistry**(409/0)
- **Dept. of Chinese Literature**(498/4)
- **Dept. of Education**(522/6)
- **Dept. of English Literature**(648/6)
- **Dept. of Geography**(402/0)
- **Dept. of German Literature**(398/1)
- **Dept. of History**(626/4)
- **Dept. of Japanese Literatuire**(616/4)
- **Dept. of Mathematics**(285/0)
- **Dept. of Philosophy**(457/1)
- **Dept. of Physical Education**(1, 123/2)
- **Dept. of Physics**(253/0)
- **Dept. of Psychology**(601/13)
- **Dept. of Sociology**(1, 099/19)

Faculty of Industrial Technology(6, 232/17)
- **Dept. of Architectural Engineering**(1, 041/1)
- **Dept. of Civil Engineering**(954/0)
- **Dept. of Electorical Engineering**(988/8)
- **Dept. of Industrial Chemistry**(871/2)
- **Detp. of Industrial Engineering and Management**(876/2)
- **Dept. of Mathematical Engineering**(484/2)
- **Dept. of Mechanical Engineering**(1, 018/2)

Faculty of International Relations(1, 413/15)
- **Dept. of Intercultural Relations**(693/0)
- **Dept. of International Relations**(720/15)

Faculty of Law(7, 264/44)
- **Dept. of Business Law**(1, 003/4)
- **Dept. of Journalism**(558/20)
- **Dept. of Law**(2, 505/2)
- **Dept. of Management and Public Administration**(941/7)
- **Dept. of Political Science and Economics**(2, 257/11)

Faculty of Medicine(748/0)
- **Dept. of Medicine**(748/0)

Faculty of Pharmacy(679/3)
- **Dept. of Biopharmacy**
- **Dept. of Pharmacy**

Faculty of Science and Technology(10, 251/31)
- **Dept. of Aerospace Engineering**(632/6)
- **Dept. of Architecture**(1, 338/4)
- **Dept. of Civil Engineering**(1, 349/0)
- **Dept. of Electrical Engineering**(868/5)
- **Dept. of Electronic Engineering**(644/6)
- **Dept. of Industrial Chemistry**(1, 013/3)
- **Dept. of Mathematics**(571/0)
- **Dept. of Mechanical Engineering**(876/3)
- **Dept. of Oceanic Architecture and Engineering**(679/1)
- **Dept. of Pharmacy**(251/1)
- **Dept. of Physics**(664/0)
- **Dept. of Precision Mechanical Engineering**(703/2)
- **Dept. of Transport Civil Engineering**(663/0)

Graduate Programs

Graduate School of Agriculture(M 77/3, D 8/1)
- **Div. of Agriculture**(M 4/0, D 1/0)

Agrobiology, Applied Entomology, Biochemistry, Biometry, Crop Science, Floriculture, Horticulture, Landscape Architecture, Landscape Planning, Measurement in

Micrometeorological Factors, Plant Breeding, Plant Pathology, Pomology, Regional Planning, Vegerable Crop Science

Div. of Agricultural Chemistry(M 23/0, D 0/0)
Biochemistry, Enzyme Chemistry, Fermentation Chemistry, Fertilizers, Food Chemistry, General Microbiology, Nutritional Chemistry, Soil Science, Utilization of Agricultural Products

Div. of Agricultural Economics(M 7/1, D 1/0)
Agricultural Accounting, Agricultural Cooperation, Agricultural Economics, Agricultural Finance, Agricultural Marketing, Agricultural Politics, Agricultural Politics, Agricultural Problems and Issues on Developing Countries, Farm Management, International Agricultural Theory, Rural Sociology

Div. of Agricultural Engineering (M 5/1)

Agricultural Building, Agricultural Structures Engineering, Agriculture Hydrotechnics, Farm Consolidation Engineering, Farm Machinery, Postharvest Technology, Regional Conservation Engineering, Regional Planning, Rural Planning Engineering

Div. of Animal Science(M 14/1, D 2/0)
Animal Breeding, Animal Industry, Animal Morphology and Physiology, Animal Nutrition, Animal Products Science, Biochemistry, Economics of Animal Industry, Feed Science, Forage Crop Science, Grassland Science, Physiology and Endocrinology of Reproduction, Reproductive Physiology and Endocrinology

Div. of Fisheries(M 16/0, D 1/1)
Aquaculture and Fish Propagation, Fisheres Resources and Environment, Fisheries Science, Live Diet for Aquaculture, Marine Biochemistry, Marine Biology, Physiology of Aquatic Animal, Sea and Fishing Condition, Utilization of Marine Products

Div. of Food Technology(M 8/0, D 0/0)
Cold Chain System, Food Additives, Food Analysis, Food Chemical Engineering, Food Hygiene, Food Manufacturing, Food Packaging, Food Preservation, Food Refrigeration, Food Science and Chemistry, Microanalysis, Nutiritional Biochemistry, Nutritional Chemistry of Food, Physicochemical, Properties of Food, Raw Materials of Food

Graduate School of Art(M 14/1)

Div. of Literaty Arts(M 14/1)
Chinese literature, English & American Literature, French Literature, German Literature, History of Literature, Japanese Literature, Literature, Mass Communication, Philosophy, Psychology of Art, Science of Art, Sociology of Art,

Graduate School of Business Administration(M 22/8, D 10/0)

Div. of Accounting(M 10/1, D 4/0)
Accounting, Accounting Management, Auditing, Book–Keeping, Cost Accounting, Financial Statements, History of Accounting, Tax Accounting

Div. of Business Administration(M 2/2, D 4/0)
Business Administration, Business Organization, Business Planning, Financial Economics, Financial Management, History of Economics Theories, History of Management, Information Management, Management, Management Economy, Organization Enterprise, Personnel Management, Production Control, Sales Management, Theoretical Economics

Div. of Commerce(M 10/5, D 2/0)
Business Cycle, Business Finance, Business History, Co–operation, Commerce, Commercial Policy, Consumer Behavior, Financial Institutions, Foreign Trade, Harbor Management, Insurance, International Finance, Industrial Policy, Marine Insurance, Marketing, Products Planning, Public Finance, Securities Market, Social Security, Theoretical Economics, Transportation

Graduate School of Dentistry(D 103/0)

Div. of Basic Dentistry(D 23/0)
Anatomy, Biochemistry, Dental Legal Medicine, Dental Metal Materials, Dental Non–Metal Materials, Dental Pharmacology, Hygiene, Immunology, Legal Medicine, Microbiology, Oral Anatomy, Oral Biochemistry, Oral Histology, Oral Hygiene, Oral Microbiology, Oral Pathology, Oral Pysiology, Pathology, Pharmacology

Div. of Clinical Dentistry(D 80/0)
Oral Surgery, Conservative Dentistry, Prosthodontics, Orthodontics, Dental Radiology, Pedodontics

Graduate School of Dentistry at Matsudo(D 47/0)

Div. of Dentistry(D 47/0)
Conservative Dentistry, Dental Anesthesiology, Dental Materials, Dental Orthodontics, Oral Anatomy, Oral Biochemistry, Oral Diagnostics, Oral Microbiology, Oral Pathology, Oral Pharmacology, Oral Physiology, Oral Public Health, Oral Radiology, Oral Sugrery, Pedodontics

Graduate School of Economics(M 29/7, D 5/1)

Div. of Economics(M 29/7, D 5/1)
Accounting, Accounting Theory, Auditing, Banking, Business Cycles, Business Finance, Business Management, Cost Accounting, Economic Policy, Exchanges, Finance, Finance of Small Enterprises, Financial Economics, Financial Policy, Financial Statement, Fisheries Economics, Foreign Literature of Economics, Foreign Trade, History of Economic Thought, History of Financial Systems

Graduate School of Engineering(M 90/2, D 3/1)

Div. of Architecture(M 25/2, D 3/1)
Applied Analysis, Architectural Chemistry, Architectural Planning, Building Materials, City Planning, Environmental Engineering, Ergonomics, History of Architecture, Interior Planning, Mathematical Statistics, Prevention and Protection Engineering for Buliding Disaster, Regional Planning, Special Functions, Stuructural Engineering

Div. of Civil Engineering(M 11/0, D 0/0)
Applied Analysis, Applied Mathematical Analysis, Civil Environmental Engineering, Coastal and Harbor Engineering, Construction Materials, Execution Works for Civil Engineering, Highway Engineering, Mathermatical Statistics, River Hydaulics, Sanitary Engineering, Soil Engineering, Special Functions, Stuructural Engineering

Div. of Electrical Engineering(M 10/0, D 0/0)
Applied Analysis, Communication Systems, Computer Science, Conversion Engineering, Electoronic Measurements, Electric Power Application, Electrical Machines,

Electromagnetic Wave Engineering, Electromagnetic Wave Transmission Engineering, Electron Theory of Solids, Electronic Materials and Devices, Electronical Mateials Technology, Fundamentals of Materials Science, Lighting and Visual Environment Engineenring, Mathematical Analysis, Mathematical Statistics, Plasma Technology, Power Conversion Engineering, Quantum Mechanics, Semiconductor Engineering, Signal Analysis, Special Functions, Systems Engineering, Thin Films and Surfaces of Solids, Ultrasonics

Div. of Industrial Chemistry(M 19/0, D 0/0)
Analyitical Chemistry, Applied Analysis, Aromatic Compound Chemistry, Chemical Engineering, Chemical Physics, Electrochemistry, Environmental Science, Industrial Organic Chemistry, Inorganic Industrial Chemistry, Inorganic Mateial, Instrumental Analysis, Mathematical Statistics, Natural Products Chemistry, Organic Industrial Chemisty, Organic Materials, Organic Photochemistry, Organic Synthetic Chemistry, Physical Chemistry, Special Functions

Div. of Mechanical Engineering(M 25/0, D 0/0)
Applied Analysis, Applied Energy Engineering, Applied Heat Engineering, Boundary–Layer Theory, Design of Hydraulic Machineries, Elasticity and Plasticity, Engineering Materials, Fatigue Strength of Materials, Flow and Fracture of Solids, Fluid Engineering, Fracture Mechanics, Gas Turbine, Hydraulics & Pneumatics, Machine Element Design, Materials Processing, Mathematical Statistics, Mechanical Properties of Solids, Non–Destructive Inspection, Powder Technology, Special Functions, System Engineering, Thermal Engineering, Tribology, Vibrations in Rotating Machinery, Vortex Flows, Welded Materials Technology

Graduate School of Industrial Technology (M 148/16, D 10/5)

Div. of Architecture and Architectural Engineering(M 31/5, D 0/0)
Applied Mathematics, Applied Physics, Architectural Planning, Building Materials, Building Structures, Disaster–Proof Engineering, Environmental Engineering of Architecture, History of Industrial Technology, Structural Mechanics

Div. of Civil Engineering(M 10/0, D 3/1)
Applied Mathematics, Applied Physics, City Planning, Concrete Engineering and Reinforced Concrete Engineering, Construction System Engineering, Hydraulic Engineering, Sanitary Engineering, Soil Engineering, Structural Engineering, Surveying, Traffic Engineering

Div. of Electrical Engineering(M 29/3, D 2/1)
Applied Mathematics, Applied Physics, Communication Engineering, Computer Science and Electronics, Control Systems and Equipments, Electric Materials, Electric Measurement, Electrical Network, Electro–Acoustics, Electromagnetic Theory, Energy Conversion, High Voltage Engineering, Illuminating Engineering, Magnetics Technology, Opto–Electronics, Semiconductor Engineering, Solid State Physics for Electronics Engineers, Ultrasonics

Div. of Industrial Chemistry(M 18/0, 0/0)
Analytical Chemistry, Applied Mathematics, Applied Physics, Chemical Engineering, Chemical Plant Engineering, Environmental Technology, Experimantal Design, Inorganic Industrial Chemistry, Material Science, Microbial Chemistry, Organic Industrial Chemistry, Physical Chemistry, Polymer Engineering

Div. of Management Engineering(M 21/7, D 0/0)
Applied Mathematics, Applied Physics, Computer Programming, Development Planning, Ergonomics, Industrial Social Psychology, Management, Managerial Accounting, Personnel Management and Labor Relations, Plant Engineering, Production Control Systems and Physical Distribution Systems, Production Management, Science of Labor, Small Business Administraion, Systems Engineering, Work Study, Worker Psychlogy and Working Condition

Div. of Mathematical Engineering(M 12/0, D 2/0)
Advanced Numerical Analysis, Applied Mathematics, Applied Physics, Contrl Engineering, Fluid Mechanics, Mathematical Planning, Nuclear Engineering, Numerical Analysis, Numerical Methods, Radiation Detction and Measurement, Theory of Elasticity and Plasticity, Vibration Engineering

Div. of Mechanical Engineering(M 27/1, D 3/3)
Applied Mathematics, Applied Physics, Automatic Control Systems, Detction and Measurement on Applied Physics, Engineering Materials, Fluid Engineering, Foudry Engineering, Mechanics of Machines, Surface Engineering, Technology of Machining, Technology of Plasticity, Theory of Design, Theory of Elasticity, Themodynamics and Heat Transfer, Welding Engineering

Graduate School of International Relations(M 20/6)

Div. of International Relations(M 20/6)
Agricultural Economics, American History, American Literature, American Politics, Asian Law, Asisan Politics, Classical Japanese Literature, Conparative Literature (Japanese and European), Eastern Culutre, Economic Development, European Law, French Literature, German Literature, Internatinal Marketing, International Economics, International Finance, International Management, International Relations, International Taxation, Japanese History, Labor Economics, Marine Resources, Modern Japanese History, Modern Japanese Litearture, Political System, Private Law, Security System, Western Culture

Graduate School of Law(M 95/2, D 29/3)

Div. of Political Science(M 20/2, D 10/3)
Constitutional Law, Economic Policy, History of Political Thought, International Law, International Politics, International Relations, Occidental History of Politics, Oriental History of Politics, Politics, Political Philosophy, Public Administration, Public Finance, Social Policy, Japanese History of Politics

Div. of Private Law(M 28/0, D 4/0)
American Law, Civil Law, Civil Procedure, Commercial Law, Economic Law, Foreign Private Law, French Law, German Law, Incorporeal Property, Judicial Law, Labor Law, Legal History of Private Law, Philosophy of Law, Private International Law, Sociology of Law

Div. of Public Law(M 47/0, D 15/0)

Administrative Law, Constitutional Law, Criminal Law, Criminal Policy, Criminal Procedure, Economic Law, International Law, International Organization, Judicial Law, Labor Law, Legal History of Public Law, Philosophy of Law, Social Security, Sociology of Law, Tax Law

Graduate School of Literature and Social Sciences (M 154/12, D 56/5)

Div. of Chinese Literature(M 8/5, D 4/1)
Chinese Language, Chinese Literature, Chinese Thought, Ethics, History of Chinese Language, History of Chinese Literature, History of Chinese Thought, Japanese Language, Oriental History(Ancient and Medieval)

Div. of Education(M 14/0, D 6/2)
Education, Education Literature, Educational History, History of Education, Physical Education, Physical Education Literature

Div. of English Literature(M 25/1, D 6/0)
English Grammar, English Linguistics, English Literature, English Literature of the Renaissance, English Phonetics, English Poetry, English Romanticists, Greek, Latin, Old and Middle English, Sanscrit

Div. of German Literture(M 6/0, D 4/0)
German Language, German Literature, Medieval German Literature, Science of German Literature

Div. of History-Japanese History-Oriental History(M 17/0, D 9/0)
Ancient and Medieval History, Ancient History of Japan, Archaeology of East Asia, European and American Bibliography, History of Asia, History of Europe and America, History of Japan, Japanese Bibliography, Medieval History of Japan, Methodology of History of Japan, Modern History of Asia, Modern History of Japan

Div. of Japanese Literature(M 17/3, D 7/2)
Ancient Japanese Literture, Chinese History, Chinese Literture, Contemporary Japanese Literature, Japanese Literary Arts, Japanese Philosophy, Medieval Japanese Literature, Modern Japanese Literture

Div. of Philosophy(M 25/1, D 4/0)
Classics, Ethics, History of Ethics, History of Japanese, History of Philosophy, History of Religions, Philosophy

Div. of Psychology(M 33/1, D 9/0)
Animal Experiment, Applied Psychology, Cerebral Injury, Clinical Psychology, Clinical Psychology of Maladjusted Children, Criminal Psychology, Educational and Vocational Guidance, Educational Psychology, Electro-Physiological Experiment, Experimental Psychology, Foreign Language, General Psychology, Mentally Retarded, Personnel Management, Psychological Statistics, Psychological Testing, Psychology of Economy, Psychology of Physical Education, Psychosis

Div. of Sociology(M 9/1, D 3/0)
Cultural Sociology, General Sociology, History of Sociology, Industrial Sociology, Labor Problems, Science of Journalism, Social Planning, Social Psychology, Social Research, Social Work, Sociology of Education, Statistics

Graduate School of Medicine(D 77/77)

Div. of Internal Medicine(D 23/0)
Clinical Biochemistry, Clinical Hematology, Clinical Histopathology, Clinical Microbiology, Clinical Serology, Dermatology, Internal Medicine, Neurology, Pediatrics, Psychiatry, Radiology

Div. of Pathology(D 4/0)
Immunology, Microbiology, Pathology

Div. of Physiology(D 5/0)
Anatomy, Biochemistry Pharmacology, Physiology

Div. of Social Medicine(D 3/0)
Forensic Medicine, Hospital Administration, Hygiene, Public Health

Div. of Surgery(D 42/0)
Anesthesiology, Audiology Bronchoesophagology, Gynecology, Neurosurgery, Obstetrics, Ophthalmology, Orthopedics, Otorhinolaryngology, Surgery, Urology, Venereology

Graduate School of Science and Technology(M 550/13, D 56/8)

Div. of Aerospace Engineering(M 23/0, D 1/0)
Aerodynamics Experimental Method, Aeronautical and Cosmical Equipments, Aeronautical Engineering, Aerospace Engineering, Aerospace Engineering, Applied Mathematics, Computational Aerodynamics, Finite Element Method, Fluid Mechanics, High-Speed Aeromechanics, Instrumentation, Instumentation and Control Engineering, Instrumentation and Control Measurement, Jet Engines, Mechanics of Aircraft, Technology of Aircraft, Thermodynamics, Vibration Engineering

Div. of Architecture(M 91/5, D 5/0)
Analysis of Framed Structure, Architectural Design, Architectural Environment Engineering, Architectural Planning, Architectural Structure, Architecture, Building Foundation Engineering, Building Materials, City Planning, Disaster Prevention Engineering, History of Design Architecture, History of Modern Architecture, Matrix Structural Analysis, Plastic Analysis of Structure, Real Estate Economics, Real Estate Finance & Taxation, Real Estate Law, Real Property Evaluation, Real Property Management, Reinforced Concrete Engineering, Seismological Engineering, Structural Dynamics

Div. of Civil Engineering(M 18/3, D 0/2)
Civil Engineering, Civil Engineering Planning, Civil Engineering Structure, Construction Materials, Hygienic Engineering, River-Sea Engineering, Soil Mechanics

Div. of Electrical Engineering(M 41/1, D 2/0)
Applied Optical Electronics, Automata, Control Engineering, Electric Discharge Engineering, Electric Machinery and Tools, Electric-Power Engineering, Electrical Circuit, Electrical Engineering, Electrical Materials, Electromagnetic Wave Engineering, Electronic Device, Energy Engineering, Fundamentals of Information Engineering, Fundamentals of Systems Engineering, Integrated Circuit, Laser Engineering, Measurement Engineering, Medical Electronics Engineering, Microwave Engineering, Optical Environment Engineering, Quantum Electronics, Semiconductor Engineering, Sound Wave Engineering, Super-Conduction and Magnetic, Vibration Engineering

Div. of Electronic Engineering(M 75/1, D 5/2)
Automata, Communication Method, Electrical Circuit, Electromagnetic Wave Engineering, Electromagnetism and Plasma, Electronic Device, Electronic Engineering,

Electronic Measurement Engineering, Electronics Computer, Electronics Solid State Engineering, Image Processing Engineering, Information Engineering, Information Network, Information Transmission Engineering, Integrated Circuit, Magnetic Engineering, Magnetism Solid State Engineering, Medical Electronics Engineering, Microwave Circuit, Microwave Device, Optical Engineering, Quantum Electronics, Reliability Engineering, Semiconductor Engineering, Sound Wave Engineering, Systems Engineering, Theory of Fundamental Control

Div. of Geography(M 8/0, D 8/2)
Applied Geography, Earth Science, Economic Geography, Geography, Geology, Land and Water Science, Physical Region Theory, Social Geography, Survey, Topology, Water Pollution

Div. of Industrial Chemistry(M 63/0, D 5/0)
Analytical Chemistry, Catalyst Chemistry, Ceramics Solid State, Chemical Engineering, Electrochemistry, Energy Resources, Environmental Engineering, Inorganic Industrial Chemistry, Organic Industrial Chemistry, Organic Synthetic Chemistry, Physical Chemistry, Polymer Engineering, Polymer Solid State, Polymer Solid State Engineering, Polymer Synthetic Chemistry, Safety Engineering, Surface Chemistry

Div. of Mathematics(M 15/0, D 4/0)
Algebra, Applied Analysis, Applied Mathematics, Applied Statistics, Computational Mathematics, Geometry, Mathematical Analysis, Mathematics, Probability and Statistics

Div. of Mechanical Engineering(M 54/0, D 2/0)
Antidust Engineering, Applied Elasticity, Applied Mathematics, Automotive Engineering, Control Engineering, Elasticity and Plasticity, Engineering Mechanics, Fluid Engineering, Heat Engineering, Heat Engines, Machine Materials, Mechanical Engineering, Mechanical Technology, Mechanics of Plasticity, Plasticity in Engineering

Div. of Oceanic Architecture and Engineering(M 51/1, D 6/2)
History of Ocean Construction Technology, Aquaculture Engineering, Basic Oceanography, Wave Dynamics, Oceanographic Observation, Ocean Environmental Planning, Osean Environmental Engineering, Oceanic Facility Planning, Oceanic Architectural Designing, Osean Steel Structural Engineering, Ocean Concrete Structural Engineering, Floating Structure Studies, Ocean Structure Studies, Fluid Mechanics, Ocean Structural Materials Engineering, Applied Elasticity, Plasticity, Ocean Construction Project Studies, Sea-Bed Engineering, Earthquake-proof Oceanic Engineering

Div. of Physics(M 55/0, D 11/0)
Applied Accelarator Physics, Crystal Dislocation and Lattice Defects, Crystallography, High-Energy Physics, History of Science, Linear Accelerator, Low Temperature Physics, Low Temperature Physics Laboratory, Magnetic Materials, Many Body Problems, Nuclear Engineering, Nuclear Physics, Nuclear Reaction, Physics, Plasma Physics, Plasma Physics Laboratory, Quantum Mechanics, Radiation Measure, Solid State Electron Theory, Solid State Physics, Statistical Mechanics, Statistical Physics, Theory of Electromagnetism, Theory of Elementary Particles, Theory of Ionization Gas, Theory of Plasma Measurement, Theory of Relativity

Div. of Precision Mechanical Engineering(M 31/2, D 0/0)
Acoustic Engineering, Applied Electronic Engineering, Applied Mathematics, Control Engineering, Electricity-Applying Measurement, Engineering Mechanics, Finite Element Method, Fluid Engineering, Heat Engineering, Human Engineering, Information Device, Information Engineering, Machine Elements, Material Engineering, Mechanical Engineering, Mechanics of Thin-Plate Structure, Optical-Applying Measurement, Plasticity in Engineering, Precision Mechanical Engineering, System Engineering

Div. of Transport Civil Engineering(M 25/0, D 3/0)
Applied Mechanics, Civil Engineering Planning, Concrete Engineering, Soil Engineering, Soil Mechanics, Structural Engineering, Traffic Environmental Engineering, Traffic Institution Engineering, Traffic System Engineering, Transportation Engineering, Transportation Planning

Graduate School of Veterinary Medicine(M 3/0, D 3/0)

Div. of Veterinary Medicine(M 3/0, D 3/0)
Applied Veterinary Science, Basic Veterinary Science, Biomedical Science, Fish Pathology, Medical Zoology, Veterinary Anatomy, Veterinary Clinical Pathology, Veterinary Clinics, Veterinary Hygiene, Veterinary Infectious Diseases, Veterinary Internal Medicine, Veterinary Microbiology, Veterinary Obsterics and Gynecology, Veterinary Pathology, Veterinary Pharmacology, Veterinary Physiological Chemistry, Veterinary Physiology, Veterinary Public Health, Veterinary Radiology, Veterinary Surgery, Veterinary Virology

---

日本体育大学

(Nippon Taiiku Daigaku)

Nippon College of Physical Education

7-1-1 Fukasawa, Setagaya-ku, Tokyo 158
☎ 03-5706-0903 FAX 03-5706-0912

Founded 1893
Professors 56
Associate Professors 30
Assistant Professors(Tenured) 12
Assistant Professors(Non-tenured) 118
Research Assistants 49
Undergraduate Students/Foreign Students 5, 797/2
Graduate Students/Foreign Students 67/10
Library 190, 000 volumes
Contact: Student Affairs

Educational philosophy The aim of our college was to enlighten the people about their physical condition and take the leadership in popularizing P. E. Now we contribute to human health and happiness by teaching the importance of sports in human lives.

Foreign students Foreign students are welcomed to take our subjects and join to club activities. Basic knowledge of Japanese should be necessary, as we have all lectures and activities in Japanese.

Environment We have two campuses; Fukasawa in Setagaya and Yokohama. Fukasawa campus is convenient for the urban area. Yokohama campus has many field for specific sports and good circumstance.

Facilities Library, Research Laboratory, Sports Training Center, Health Control Center, Gymnasium, Swimming Pool

Student activities Orientation for freshmen, Health check up Sport test, Teaching and nursing practice, Camping, Swimming, P. E. performance and demostration, Skiing, Skating

Services for foreign students Counseling

Undergraduate Programs

Faculty of Physical Education(5797/2)
Dept. of Health Education(4054/0)
Dept. of Martial Arts(641/0)
Dept. of Physical Education(441/2)
Dept. of Physical Recreation(661/0)
Graduate School of Physical Education(M 67/10)

One-Year Graduate Programs

Physical Education Course
Physical Education Major

日本歯科大学
(Nippon Shika Daigaku)
The Nippon Dental University

1-9-20 Fujimi, Chiyoda-ku, Tokyo 102
☎ 03-3261-8311 FAX 03-3264-8399

Founded 1907
Professors 63
Associate Professors 66
Assistant Professors(Tenured) 108
Assistant Professors(Non-tenured) 286
Research Assistants 235
Undergraduate Students/Foreign Students 1, 580/0
Graduate Students/Foreign Students 130/0
Library 53, 382 volumes
Contact: Department of Instructive Affairs

Educational philosophy The University's philosophy of education is " Balance among learning, technology and character ". It sets value on confidence between instructors and students. The University's education increases the ability of dentists-to-be who are required to accept responsibility.

Environment Fujimi in Chiyoda-ku, where the School at Tokyo is located, is at the very center of Tokyo and has a long tradition as a educational district. The School at Niigata is located by the coast in Niigata city, the biggest city on Japan Sea side with a population of 490, 000.

Facilities Libraries, Dental Research Institutes, Museum of Medical Science, Computer center, Seminar house, Dental hospitals, Medical hospital, Gymnasiums, athletic fields, Holiday lodge,

Student activities Fujimi Festival in November and Hamaura Festival in May are the main campus events. Besides, there are many avtivities including tournaments of basketball, volleyball and dodgeball, and ski training. Others; volunteer works, various cultural and sports circles.

Undergraduate Programs

Faculty of Dentistry at Tokyo(922/0)
Dept. of Dentistry(922/0)
Faculty of Dentistry at Niigata(658/0)
Dept. of Dentistry(658/0)

Graduate Programs

Graduate School of Dentistry, Tokyo(D 112/0)
Div. of Basic Dentistry(D 28/0)
Anatomy, Histology, Physiology, Biochemistry, Pathology, Microbiology, Pharmacology, Preventive and Comunity Dentistry, Dental Material Science
Div. of Clinical Dentistry(D 84/0)
Endodontics, Operative Dentistry, Periodontlogy, Partial and Complete Denture, Crown and Bridge, Oral and Maxillofacial Surgery, Anesthesiology, Orthodontics, Pedodontics, Radiology
Graduate School of Dentistry, Niigata(D 18/0)
Div. of Dentistry(D 18/0)
Anatomy, Histology, Physiology, Biochemistry, Pathology, Microbiology, Pharmacology, Preventive and Comunity Dentistry, Dental Material Science, Endodontics, Operative Dentistry, Periodontology, Partial and Complete Denture, Crown Bridge, Oral and Maxillofacial Surgery, Anesthesiology, Orthodontics, Pedodontics, Radiology

---

日本工業大学
(Nippon Kôgyô Daigaku)
Nippon Institute of Technology

4-1 Gakuendai, Miyashiro-machi, Minamisaitama-gun, Saitama 345
☎ 0480-34-4111 FAX 0480-34-2941

Founeded 1967
Professors 46
Associate Professors 29
Assistant Professors(Tenured) 39
Assistant Professors(Non-tenured) 104
Research Assistants 1
Undergraduate Students/Foreign Students 3, 544/10
Graduate Students/Foreign Students 77/2
Library 144, 693 volumes
Contact: Admission Office

Educational philosophy The educational principle of our Institute is to provide advanced education for those who have scholastic abilities and capabilities equivalent to those of graduates of technical high schools. We aim at producing engineers throughly grounded in technical aspects of engineering.
Foreign students To further mutual understandings with both cultural and technical aspects, we positively accept students from other countries, who want to advance their technological knowledge and contribute to industrial world in their native countries.
Environment The campus of NIT is located in the northwest of the Kanto Plains, and you can reach NIT easily from the center of Tokyo. It takes 40 minutes from Ueno to Tobu Dobutsu Koen, from which about 13 minutes walk will introduce our expansive campus.
Facilities Machining and Processing Center, Materials Testing Center, Information Technology Center, Electrical Laboratories Center, Ultra High Voltage Laboratory, Building Engineering Center, Musem of Industrial Technology, Health and Physical Education Center.
Student activities Following the motto, " Your college life from your activities ", 28 sports clubs and 17 culture circles play an important role in students' lives on campus. Sports meetings, music festival, ski lessons and other events are scheduled every year for students.
Academic programs for foreign students Supplemental Japanese language class
Services for foreign students Health clinic, Personal counseling, Housing information, Part-time Job information, Vocational guidance.

Undergraduate Programs

Faculty of Enigneering(3544/10)
Dept. of Mechanical Engineering(1006/0)
Dept. of Electrical and Electronics Engineering (1025/1)
Dept. of Architecute(957/3)
Dept. of Systems Engineering(552/6)

Graduate Programs

Graduate School of Engineering(M 71/1, D 6/1)
Div. of Mechanical Engineering(M 16/1, D 3/1)
〈Mechanical Engineering〉, Special lecture on Machine element design; Plastic working; Control engineering; Automobile engineering; Fluid power system; Metal surface technology, etc. 〈Electrical Engineeing〉, Special lecture on Electric engineering;Transmission lines; Image engineering; Electron devices; Electric materials; Plasma engineering; Electric circuit, etc. 〈Architecture〉 Special lecture on Architectural planning; Regional planning; Building construction; Structural Materials; Steel structure; History of architecture, etc.
Div. of Electrical Engineering(M 41/1, D 2/0)
Div. of Architecture(M 14/0, D 1/0)

日本医科大学
(Nippon Ika Daigaku)
Nippon Medical School

1-1-5 Sendagi-cho, Bunkyo-ku, Tokyo 113
☎ 03-3822-2131

Founded 1952

Undergraduate Programs

Faculty of Medicine
Dept. of Medicine

Graduate Programs

Graduate School of Medicine
Div. of Anatomy
Div. of Anesthesiology
Div. of Biochemistry
Div. of Clinical Pathology
Div. of Dermatology
Div. of Emergency and Critical Care
Div. of Hygiene and Public Health
Div. of Internal Medicine
Div. of Legal Medicine
Div. of Microbiology and Immunology
Div. of Neuropsychiatry
Div. of Neurosurgery
Div. of Obstetrics and Gynecology
Div. of Ophthalmology
Div. of Orthopedics
Div. of Otorhinolaryngology
Div. of Pathology
Div. of Pediatrics
Div. of Pharmacology
Div. of Physiology
Div. of Radiology
Div. of Surgery
Div. of Urology

日本獣医畜産大学

(Nihon Jûi Chikusan Daigaku)

Nippon Veterinary and Animal Science University

1-7-1 Kyonan-cho, Musashino-shi, Tokyo 180
☎ 0422-31-4151 FAX 0422-33-2094

Founeded 1881
Professors 31
Associate Professors 22
Assistant Professors(Tenured) 27
Assistant Professors(Non-tenured) 56
Research Assistants 15
Undergraduate Students/Foreign Students 1, 174/0
Graduate Students/Foreign Students 15/1
Library 75, 000 volumes
Contact: Division of Academic Affarirs(ext. 221, 222)

Educational philosophy The mission of the University is to enhance human welfare and culture. This institution aims at producing well-rounded personalities throught the physical as well as intellectual education of its students. It also provides students with basic education and professional skills to enrich the knowledge and experties of the larger community.

Foreign students Our school welcomes foreign students from all over the world, regardless of race or nationality, who intend to acquire knowledge of veterinary and animal science, especially in the graduate course, and back home, to contribute to the development of their own country.

Environment Our campus is conveniently located in the western sector of the Tokyo metropolitan area within a half-hour train ride from downtown Tokyo. The environment is pleasant for studying and favorable for keeping large variety of animals. In addition, our campus is advantageously located near leading public resarch organisations in central Japan.

Facilities Library, Veterinary Medical Teaching Hospital, Experimental Farm, Laboratory of Molecular Oncology, Computer room, Kennel for Quarantined Animals, etc.

Student activities We have many clubs. Learing society of the agricultural problem, chorus, football, baseball, judo, fishing and so on.

Undergraduate Programs

Faculty of Veterinary and Animal Science(1, 174/0)

Dept. of Animal Science(233/0)
Dept. of Food Science and Technology(319/0)
Dept. of Veterinary Science(622/0)

Graduate Programs

Graduate School of Veterinary Science(D 15/1)
Veterinary Anatomy, Veterinary Physiology, Veterinary Biochemistry, Veterinary Parmacology, Veterinary Pathology, Veterinary Microbiology, Veterinary Parasitology, Veterinary Internal Medicine, Veterinary Surgery, Veterinary Radiology, Veterinary Reproduction, Veterinary Clinical Pathology, Veterinary Hygiene, Veterinary Public Health, Laboratory Animals, Fish Deseases, Wild Animal Medicine

二松學舎大学

(Nishôgakusha Daigaku)

Nishogakusha University

6 Sanban-cho, Chiyoda-ku, Tokyo 102
☎ 03-3261-7406 FAX 03-3263-6987

Founded 1877
Professors 41
Associate Professors 18
Assistant Professors(Tenured) 16
Assistant Professors(Non-tenured) 45
Research Assistants 2
Undergraduate Students/Foreign Students 1885/1
Graduate Students/Foreign Students 45/8
Library 1400, 000 volumes
Contact: The instructions department

Educational Philosophy Our university was founded in 1877 by Chushu Mishima, a famous schollar of Orientalism in Meiji era. He wanted to set the spirit of Orientalism which had been the basis of Japanese spirit for hundreds of years in the country on the education of students.

Foreign students We welcome students from the foreign countries all over the world who want to study with us and research the essence of Japanese and Chinese literature.

Environment We have two campuses. One is located in Shonan in Chiba Prefecture and the other is located in Chiyoda-ku in Tokyo. The former, for 1st and 2nd year is surrounded with the natural ambiences and the latter, for 3rd and 4th is in Tokyo, the most active city in the world.

Facilities Two libraries with all kinds of books and materials for study and research. A wide field for various kinds of sports. Gymnasium, a dormitory for girls' students, a facility in the mountain resort.

Student activities In the spring, one day tour for visiting the historic and literary sites for freshmen. In the fall, athletic meeting and university fair and exhibitions for club activities. Open lectures for adults including students in the summer.

Undergraduate Programs

Faculty of Lterature(1885/1)
Dept. of Chinese Literature(602/0)

Dept. of Japanese Literature(1206/1)

Graduate Programs

Graduate School of Literature(M 24/2, D 21/6)
Div. of Chinese literature and philosophy(M 12/2, D 10/0)
Chinese philosophy, Chinese literature
Div. of Japanese Literature(M 12/0, D 11/6)
Literature of ancient age(Nara era), Literature of Former middle age(Heian era), Literature of later middle age (Kamakura, Muromachi era), Literature of Recent age (Edo era), Literature of modern age(after Meiji era), Study of national language

---

桜美林大学
(Ôbirin Daigaku)
Obirin University

3758 Tokiwa-machi, Machida-shi, Tokyo 194-02
☎ 0427-97-2661 FAX 0427-97-1887

Founded 1966
Professors 57
Associate Professors 27
Assistant Professors(Tenured) 24
Assistant Professors(Non-tenured) 129
Research Assistants 4
Undergraduate Students/Foreign Students 3, 484/32
Library 275, 000 volumes
Contact: Center for International Studies

Educational philosophy We are a liberal arts oriented university with a strong teaching commitment. We have a large foreign faculty and have strong junior year abroad programs that promote global citizen awarness in our students.
Foreign students Foreign students may enter as regular 4 year students. We also welcome Junior Year Abroad students from other contries and support them through the Center for International Studies.
Environment The city of Machida, with its population of 400, 000, is located in the suburbs of Tokyo. The location is very convenient to Shinjku and other "Central parts " of Tokyo. Meseums, parks and public libraries are in the city.
Facilities Language Laboratories, Sports Center, Gymnasium, Computer Center, Auditorium, Club Houses, Seminar Houses in Several Areas in Japan.
Student activities School festivals, welcome parties and various cultural activities are planned on campus. Obirin has many extra curricular activities which include football, soccer, flower arranging, archery, Karate and such.
Academic programs for foreign students The Reconnaissance Japan program provides Japanese language classes at different levels and courses about Japan in English.
Services for foreign students Health clinic, personal/psychological counseling, homestay, dormitory, cultural information, vocational guidance, international programs

Undergraduate Programs

School of Economics(1816/0)
Dept. of Commerce(921/0)
Dept. of Economics(895/0)
School of International Studies(534/32)
Comparative Culture Major
International Relations Major
American Studies Major
Japanese Studies Major
Asian Studies Major
School of Literature(1133/0)
Dept. of Chinese(433/0)
Dept. of English(701/0)

大妻女子大学
(Ôtsuma Joshi Daigaku)
Otsuma Women's University

12 Sanban-cho, Chiyoda-ku, Tokyo 102
☎ 03-5275-6000 FAX 03-3261-8119

Founded 1949
Professors 54
Associate Professors 16
Assistant Professors(Tenured) 7
Assistant Professors(Non-tenured) 161
Research Assistants 27
Undergraduate Students/Foreign Students 2, 505/0
Graduate Students/Foreign Students 49/3
Library 260, 000 volumes
Contact: Section of Educational Affairs

Educational philosophy As an institute of higher education for women originally aiming at fostering impeccable ladies as housewives and mothers, our university seeks to equip its students with the knowledge and skills necessary to play the fullest possible role in society. Otsuma also emphasizes the value of extracurricular activities and dormitory life in the development of character.
Environment Otsuma is located in a quiet area of central Tokyo, immediately to the west of the Imperial Palace and close to Chidorigafuchi Park and the British and Vatican embassies. Convenient public transport provides direct access to such areas as Shibuya, Shinjuku and the Ginza.
Facilities Library, Institute of Human Living Sciences, Center for Information Processing and Audio-Visual Education, Gym, Health Center, Dormitory
Student activities Campus events : freshmen welcome party, medical examination, school festival, etc Club activities : flower arrangement, chorus, cook-

ing, tea ceremony, photograph, musical, drama, folk song, mandolin, tennis, golf, ski, ping-pong, hiking, badminton, volleyball, basketball, fencing, etc.

Undergraduate Programs

Faculty of Domestic Science(1, 523/0)
Dept. of Clothing Science(496/0)
Dept. of Food Science
(Food Science Coure/Dietician's Course)(488/0)
Dept. of Pedology
(Pedology Course/Child Education Conrse)(539/0)
Faculty of Language & Literaure(982/0)
Dept. of Japanese Literature(497/0)
Dept. of English Literature(485/0)

Graduate Programs

Graduate School of Domestic Science(M 32/1, D 4/2)
Div. of Clothing Environment(M 10/1, D 4/2)
Div. of Food Science(M 10/0)
Div. of Pedology(M 12/0)
Graduate School of Language & Literature(M 13/0)
Div. of Japanese Literature(M 11/0)
Div. of English Literature(M 2/0)

麗澤大学
(Reitaku Daigaku)
Reitaku University

2-1-1 Hikariogaoka, Kashiwa-shi, Chiba 277
☎ 0471-73-3601 FAX 0471-73-1100

Founded 1959
Professors 41
Associate Professors 21
Associate Professors(Tenured) 17
Associate Professors(Non-tenured) 56
Research Assistants 3
Undergraduate Students/Foreign Students 67/0
Library 220, 000 volumes
Contact: Foreign Students Office ☎ 0471-73-3690

Educational philosophy Since its establishment, Reitaku has aimed, fist of all, at producing persons of moral excellence and reliability; it has also aimed at producing international-minded of society—people with skills and knowledge of foreign languages as well as international viewpoints, who can freely work and exchange opinions with people of the world, where distances, physical and psychological, are rapidly diminishing.
Foreign students Reitaku has a long history and experiences of accepting students from abroad. We are confident, therefore, that our students will find our unique programmes of Japanese studies both satisfactory and rewarding.
Environment The city of Kashiwa is located thirty kilometers to the northeast of Tokyo. Kashiwa became a city in 1954, and ever since that time it has been attracting attention and developing rapidly into a thriving residential center located nearby the capital of Tokyo.
Facilities International students can stay in campus dormitories with Japanese students, in order to give them ample opportunity to communicate with native students. A relaxed atmosphere is provided by the 100-acre campus set in wooded, rolling hills with lots of sports facilities, a student store, and a cafeteria.
Student activities Students can enjoy various types of extra curricular activities such as baseball, martial arts, golf, drama, English Speaking Society, etc. Freshman welcome party, Universty festival and dormitory festival are popular events among students.
Academic programs for foreign students Foreign students in English, German, and Chinese Departments can take up to 20 credits of Japanese language and culture, which can be counted as part of the 136 credits required for graduation. In Japanese Department, 8 credits can be counted as such.
Services for foreign students During the summer vacation, we offer a Home-stay program to all foreign students. Also we introduce students to the local community through cross-cultural meetings.

Undergraduate Programs

Faculty of Foreign Language(764/67)
Dept. of English(230/4)
Dept. of German(143/1)
Dept. of Chinese(241/0)
Dept. of Japanese(150/62)

立教大学
(Rikkyô Daigaku)
Rikkyo University

3-34-1 Nishi, Ikebukuro, Toshima-ku, Tokyo 171
☎ (03)3985-2204 FAX (03)3986-8784

Founded 1874
Professors 235
Associate Professors 68
Assistant Professors(Tenured) 25 330
Assistant Professors(Non-tenured) 556
Research Assistants 17
Undergraduate Students/Foreign Students 12015/54
Graduate Students/Foreign Students 388/28
Library 980, 000 volumes

Educational philosophy Rikkyo was founded in 1874 as St. Paul's School by a Christian Missionary dedicated to "providing education based on Christianity". Rikkyo has grown to 13, 000 students and we endeavor to provide our students with broader and more refined technical skills but we try to provide an extra dimension: education of the spirit.

Foreign students International students are admitted with one of these statuses: Regular student(degree candidate who has passed the entrance exam), Special International student(non-degree candidate), Graduate Research Student, Auditing Student(non-degree).

Environment Two campuses: the original campus built in 1911 near to Ikebukuro Station in Northwest Tokyo. The old brick buildings contrast with the modern, lively city center surrounding. The new campus at Niiza: twenty kilometers to the west on the Tobu train. New and spacious buildings in a quieter, more suburban setting.

Facilities At Niiza: Large Gymnasium complex, AV library and classrooms, computer center, language labs, 600 seat auditorium, new repository library, Swimming pool, athletic grounds. Ikekuro: library, gymnasium, chapels, Main Computer Center, International residence hall(graduate students), clinic, Women's Dormitory, Science labs.

Student activities The University encourages a wide variety of Cultural and Athletic extracurricular activities. There are 79 societies and clubs forming the Cultural Association and 49 athletic clubs in the Athletic Association. There are several Christian Volunteer-Service organizations cooperating with the Chapel. Rush. is held for all groups in spring and fall.

Academic programs for foreign students The Center for International Studies coordinates programs that include Japanese language courses, Japanology, and a Tutoring ystem.

Services for foreign students Advising and guidance on life and study, scholarships, housing, and part-time jobs, visa regulations, home visits, cultural exchange with Japanese people and assistance by volunteer groups.

Undergraduate Programs

Faculty of Arts(3221/29)
- **Dept. of Education**(317/4)
- **Dept. of English and American Literature**(801/0)
- **Dept. of French Literature**(267/0)
- **Dept. of German Literature**(241/0)

Faculty of Arts(3221/29)
- **Dept. of History**(575/9)
- **Dept. of Japanese Literature**(577/13)
- **Dept. of Phychology**(259/3)
- **Dept. of Teology**(184/0)

Faculty of Economic(3791/12)
- **Dept. of Business Administration**(1874/5)
- **Dept. of Economics**(1915/7)

Faculty of Science(639/2)
- **Dept. of Chemistry**(262/0)
- **Dept. of Methematics**(142/2)
- **Dept. of Physics**(253/0)

Faculty of Social Relations(2164/11)
- **Dept. of Industrial Relations**(1026/2)
- **Dept. of Social Relations**(551/3)
- **Dept. of Tourism**(587/6)

Faculty of Law and Politics(2199/44)
- **Dept. of International and Comparative Law**(329/4)
- **Dept. of Law and Politics**(1870/0)

Graduate Programs

Graduare School of Arts(M 138/17, D 76/2)

Div. of Education(M 17/3, D 4/0)

Philosophy of Education, History of Japanese Education, Foreign Educational Thought, Sociology of Education, Educationl Psychology and Communication, Methods of Education, Adult Education, Pedagogy, Logic of Education, Human Relations in Education, Master's Thesis, Methodology of Education, Moral Education, Vocational Education, Adult Education for Farm People, Educational Theory of Social Studies, History of Modern Education, Cultural Environment for Children, Music Education, Parental Relations, Educational Surveys, History of Library Science and Collection Development, Counseling Psychology, Home Education, History of Japanese Education, Doctoral Thesis

Div. of English and American Literature(M 15/1, D 6/0)

Methodology, English and American Literature, English Philology and Linguistics, Master's Thesis, English Poetry, American Literature and Comparative Literature, English and American Religious Literature, Contemporary American Novel, Irish Literature, English Drama Contemporary English and American Novel, Contemporary American Novel and Theory of the Novel, Medieval English Literature, American Black Literature, English and American Poetry, American Literature, Conetmporary English Literature, English Prose Literature and Juvienile Literature, English Novel and Prose, Art, American Drama, Doctoral Thesis, Art, German Literature

Div. of French Literature(M 12/0, D 2/0)

French Literature, French Language, Master's Thesis 17 th and 20th Century, 20th Century, 18th Century Medieval and 16th Century, 19th and 20th Century, 19th Cenrury, French Lixixology, 18th Century French Literature, French Drama, 16th Century, Doctoral Thesis

Div. of German Literature(M 4/0, D 9/0)

German Literture, German Language, German Language and Literature, Master's Thesis, Medieval German Literature, Modern German Literature, Contemporary German Literature, German Drama, Science of Literature, German Philology and Linguistics, German Literature and Philology, Doctoral Thesis, Art

Div. of Geography(M 10/1, D 11/0)

Agricultural System and Pastoralism in Africa, Rural Differentation in Southeast Asia, Comparative Analysis on Villege-level Folk, Culture in Japan and Europe, Life and Village of Mountain Dwellers, Family, Kinship and Cosmology in the Philippines, Survey of Natural Environments, Field Study in Selected Areas, African Culture, Southeast Asian Agriculture, Culture in Oceania, South Asian Studies, Master's Thesis, Oceania: Cultural

Anthropology, Paleontology, Environmental Science, Teaching Methods for Science, Human Adaptation and Biological Basis of Culture, South Asia : Ethnology and Archaeology, Southeast Asia : Human Geography, Africa : Human Geography, North : Ethno-Archaeology, Doctoral Thesis

Div. of History(M 28/5, D 17/0)

Japanese History, Historiography, Asian History, Western History, Master's Thesis, Ancient Japanese History, Medieval Japanese History, Early Modern Japanese History, Mordern Japanese History, Ancient Chinese History, Vietnamese History, History of Southeast Asia, Modern Chinese History, History of Japan-China Relations, History of Inter-Asian Relations, Ancient Roman History, Modern British History, Modern History, Modern German History, American History, Chinese Social History, Doctoral Thesis

Div. of Japanese Literature(M 25/4, D 15/2)

Japanese Literature in the Nara Period, Japanese Language, Japanese Literature, Bibliography, Chinese Literature, Master's Thesis, History of Waka Poetry in the 8 th through 16th Centuries, Modern Japanese Literature, Ancient and Modern Japanese Literature, The 9 th through 11th Centuries, The 17th through 19th Centuries, The 12th through 16th Centuries, Japanese Philology, Modern Japanese Literature and Contemporary Japanese Literature, Doctoral Thesis, Art

Div. of Psychology(M 9/1, D 3/0)

Psychology of Perception, Developmental Psychology, Social Psychology, Psychology of Personality, Industial Psychology, Mathematical Psychology, Animal Psychology, Clinical Psychology, Master's Thesis, Physiological Psychology, Psycology of Learning, Psychology of Perception, Experimental Social Psychology, Group Dynamics, Experimental Psychology, Human Engineering, Environmental Psychology, Cognitive Psychology, Child Psychology, Psychology of Personality, Doctoral Thesis

Div. of Theology(M 18/2, D 9/0)

Systematic Theology, Christian Ethics, Christian, Education, Christian Art, Philosophy, Bibical Studies, Textual Criticism of the Bible, Bible(Old, New Testament), Church History, History of Christian Doctrines, Christian Doctrines, Theological Texts in German, Master's Thesis, Patrology, History of Religious Music, Medieval Western Philosophy, Systematic Theology and Contemporary Theology, History of Christianity and Religions in Japan, Contemporary British Theology, Art, The Old Testament and Oriental Studies, Modern Philosophy, Philosophy of Religion, Sociology of Religion, Doctoral Thesis

Graduate School of Economics(M 40/13, D 12/2)

Div. of Economics

Methodology of Economics, History of Economic Doctrines, Modern Economics and Econometrics, Theory of Reproduction, Theory of Value, Theory of Trade Cycle, Theory of National Accounts, Public Finance, Local Government Finance, Money and Banking, Theory of Money, International Finance, Statistics, European Economic History, American Ecomomic History, English Economic History, German Economic History, Japanese Economic History, History of Social Thought, Economic Policies, Industrial Policies, Agricultural Policies, Theory of Cooperative Association, Social Policies, International Economics, Economics of Socialism, Foreign Trade, Principles of Management, Business Organization, Production Control, Corporate Finance, Personnel Administration, Business Analysis, Business History, Accounting, History of Accounting, Management Accounting, Financial Accounting, Cost Accounting, Marketing and Distribution, Transportation, Master's Thesis, Money and Credit, Methods of Study of Economic History, History of the Development of Capitalism in Japan,Industrial Relations, Methodology of Business Administration, Business History, Public Enterprise, Study of Commercial Economics, Doctoral Thesis

Graduate School of Science(M 41/2, D 14/1)

Div. of Atomic Physics(M 17/0, D 8/1)

Nuclear Physics, Quantum Mechanics, Quantum Electrodynamics, Interaction of Elementary Particles, Applied Mathematics The Theory of Matter, Theory of Relativity, Electronics, Nuclear Radiation Detection, Experimental Nuclear Physics, Radiation Physics. Cosmic-Rays, Nuclear Astrophysics, Molecular Genetics, Biological Macromolecules, Living Systems, Radiation Genetics, Biology, Biochemistry, General Biology, Atomic Physics, Advanced Course in Physical Experiments

Div. of Chemistry(M 18/2, D 4/0)

Analytical Chemistry, Inorganic Chemistry, Radiochemistry, Applied Radiochemistry, Geochemistry, Organic Chemistry, High Polymers, Biochemistry, Protein Chemistry, Molecular Genetics, Chemical Kinetics, Physical Chemistry, Structural Chemistry, Quantum Chemistry, X-ray Crystallography, General Biology, Spectrachemistry, Radiochemistry, Micro-manipulation of Organic-Compounds, Instrumental Analysis,

Div. of Mathematics(M 6/0, D 2/0)

Mathematics, Mathematical Analysis, Modern Mathematical Analysis, Algebra, Foundations of Mathematics, Applied Mathematics, Geometry, Topology, Theory of Number, Statistics, Electronic Computers, The History of Mathematics, Probability Theory

Graduate School of Social Relations(M 27/2, D 9/4)

Div. of Applied Sociology/Sociology(M 27/12, D 9/4)

Applied Sociology, Behavioral Science, Economics-Special Study, Organization Theory, Urban Sociology, Comparative Industrial Theory,Tourism Theory, Methodology of the Social Sciences, Sociology, Theoretical Sociology, History of Sociology, Community Studies, Social class and Stratification, Study of Professionalism, Industrial Sociology, Comparative Organizational Studies, Life Culture, Study of Urban Sociology, Public Relations, Ethics and Regulations for Mass Communicaion, Mass Communication Studies, News Analysis, Polular Journalism, History of Mass Communication, Family Therapy, Social Welfare, Organizational Theories, Managerial Sociology, Comparative Industrial Relations, Human Resource Management, Industrial Relations, Labor Relations, Business Administration, Management Studies, Study of Behavioral Science, Multivariate Analysis,

Model Construction, Mathematical Statistics, Business Data Processing, Accounting, Modern Economics, Methodology of Social Sciences, Modern Economics, International Finance, Tourism Industry Studies, Tourism Development, Psychology of Tourism, Service Science, Sociology of Leisure, Tourism Culture Studies, Economic Study of Tourism, Data Processing, Hotel Industry, Tourism Studies, Hospitality Management Studies

Graduate School of Law(M 24/5, D 7/2)

Div. of Comparative Law/Civil and Criminal Law

Theory of Comparative Law, Anglo-American Law, French Law, German Law, Comparative Public Law, Copmparative Private Law, Comparative Labor Law, Comparative Criminal Law, Legal Thought, International Trade Law, International Law, Case Studies, Civil Law, Commercial Law, Civil Procedure, Labor Law, Conflict of Laws, Criminal Law, Criminal Procedure, Public Law, Criminology, Economic Law, Criminology, Constitutional Law, Comparative Constitutional Law, Philosophy of Law, History of Legal Theories, Conflict of Laws, Comparative Constitutional Law, Administrative Law, Analysis of Political Process, Political History of Japan, Diplomatic History of Postwar Japan, Political Sociology, Public Administration, Theories of Comparative Politics, Comparative History of Political Thoughts, History of European Political Thought

---

立正大学

(Risshô Daigaku)

Rissho University

4-2-16 Osaki, Shinagawa-ku, Tokyo 141

☎ 03-3492-6649 FAX 03-5487-3347

Founded 1872
Professors 145
Associate Professors 20
Assistant Professors(Tenured) 9
Assistant Professors(Non-tenured) 383
Research Assistants 9
Undergraduate Students/Foreign Students 9, 435/43
Graduate Students/Foreign Students 169/20
Library 560, 216 volumes
Contact: Amission Office

Educational philosophy Rissho University's educational principles are derived from St. Nichiren's teachings. Its essense is to make a positive contribution to world peace and the well-being of mankind. So, we aim at cultivating a well-balanced personality which can think independently and fulfill the roles of leadership in international society.

Foreign students Rissho University keeps its eyes and heart open to the world. As reflection of this, it actively promotes programs to aceept students from abroad. Our university opens its doors wide to any student with a serious goal to learn and contribute to society.

Environment Rissho University has two campuses at Osaki in Tokyo, and at Kumagaya in Saitama prefecture. At present, a large portion of the Osaki-campus structure is under reconstruction. The Kumagaya-campus has an area of 356, 000 square meters and is covered in woods. It is located in Kumagaya city, a one hour train-ride from Tokyo.

Facilities Libraies, Museum, Center for Information Technology, Dormitories, Guest House, Gymnasiums, Rugby Field, Soccer Field, Baseball Field, Tennis Courts, Marshal Arts Gymnasuiums, Japanese Archery Range, Student Hall, Dining Hall, Lodges, Swimming Pool, Laboratories.

Student activities There is a wide variety of extra-curricuar activities, including sports, literary activities, art, music and scholarship. The number of currently chartered clubs is about 130 and in addition, there are about 70 interest associations. Popular campus events include orientation camp for freshmen, RU festiva, athletic meet, homecoming and so on.

Academic programs for foreign students RU offers special programs for foreign students, in order to develop their ability in Japanese and to braden their perspective on the social issues on Japan. It also provides a Adviser System, Tutorial System and other systems to aid in thier campus-life.

Services for foreign students Health clinic, Personal/psychological counseling, University housing, Housing information, Part-time job information, Vocational guidance, Academic and cultural exchanges programs, Intensive summer English program, Home visit, Visting businesses, etc.

Undergraduate Programs

Faculty of Buddhist Studies(939/6)
Dept. of Nichiren Buddhism(541/0)
Dept. of Buddhism(398/6)
Faculty of Business and Management(1, 302/5)
Dept. of Business and Management
Faculty of Economics(2, 211/13)
Dept. of Economics
Faculty of Law(1, 197/0)
Dept. of Law
Faculty of Letters(3, 786/19)
Dept. of English and American Literature(630/1)
Dept. of Geography(685/5)
Dept. of History(679/1)
Dept. of Japanese Literature(605/5)
Dept. of Philosophy(478/2)
Dept. of Sociology(709/5)

Graduate Programs

Graduate School of Economics(M 18/9)

Div. of Economics

Marxist Economic Theory, Economic Theory, European Economic History, Japanese Economic History, Socio-Economic History, Public Finance Theory, Financial Theory, International Economics, Theory of Economic Policy, Agricultural Economics, Labor Economics, Statistical Theory, Welfare Economics, Public Economics, Regional Economics, Environmental Economics, Environmental Affairs, Industrial Location Theory

Graduate School of Literature(M 118/9, D 33/2)

Div. of Buddhist Studies(M 37/1, D 11/0)

Nichiren Buddhism, History of Nichiren Sect, Buddhist Studies, History of Buddhism, Oriental Philosophy, Religious Studies, Buddhist Archaeology

Div. of English and American Literature(M 9/0, D 4/0)

Method of Studying English Literature, English Linguistics Buddhism, English Literature, American Literature, Exercise of English Linguistics, Study of Shakespeare, Modern English Literature, Occidental Classic Literature, English Writing, Latin, Greek

Div. of Geography(M 9/0, D 6/2)

Methods in Regional Geography, Methods in Human Geography, Methods in Physical Geography, Regional Geography Seminar, Human Geography Seminar, Physical Geography Seminar, Regional Georaphy Special Lecture, Human Geography Special Lecture, Physical Geography Special Lecture, Field Study

Div. of History(M 20/0, D 7/0)

Japanese History Old Japanese Documents, Archaeology, Ancient Documents, History of Fine Art, Asian History, Old Asian Documents, European & American History, European & American History, Documents and Articles of European and American History, Modern History

Div. of Japanese Literature(M 19/8)

Japanese Literature, Japanese Linguistics

Div. of Philosophy(M 11/0)

Western Philosophy, Oriental Philosophy, Logic, Phychology

Div. of Sociology(M 13/0, D 5/0)

Theoretical Sociology, Religious Sociology, Cultural Sociology, Urban Sociology, Social Welfare, Methodology of Social Welfare, Group Sociology, Social Psychology

---

流通経済大学

(Ryûtsû Keizai Daigaku)

Ryutsu Keizai University

120 Hirahata, Ryugasaki-shi, Ibaraki 301
☎ 0297-64-0001 FAX 0297-64-0011

Founded 1965
Professors 50
Associate Professors 21
Assitant Professors(Tenured) 14
Assitant Professors(Non-tenured) 83
Undergraduate Students/Foreign Students 3, 732/80
Graduate Students/Foreign Students 20/10
Library 131, 672 volumes
Contact: Admission Office

Educational philosophy We are dedicated to the development of talented students who will actively contribute to the physical distribution industry and society as a whole through their specialization in the fields of economics, business administration, and sociology.

Foreign students We welcome students worldwide with the conviction that their study here will broaden their international horizons and contribute to the development of mutual friendship and cooperation between our nations.

Environment The campus is located in the quiet agricultural bedroom community of Ryugasaki, population 52, 000. It is in the center of a triangle formed by Narita Airport 40 minutes to the East, Tsukuba Science City 30 minutes to the North, and Central Tokyo 50 minutes to the West.

Facilities Graduate School and Library, Two Research Centers, Library(Japanese and foreign books), Computer Center, Job Center, Gymnasium, Training Center, Three Athletic Fields, Judo and Kendo Dojos, Tennins Courts

Student activities Annual events begin with Freshman Orientation and include the Tsukubane Festival and Seminar Softball Tournament. Major activities include martial arts such as Judo, Kendo, Karate, and Shorinji Kempo as well as baseball, rugby, soccer, American football, Tennis, and cultural clubs.

Academic programs for foreign students Supplemental Japanese language and culture classes and seminars.

Services for foreign students Health Clinic, Guidance Counseling, Job Counseling, International Friendship House(foreign student dormitory), Language study abroad, homestay, exchange student program, European and U. S. study tours.

Undergraduate Programs

Faculty of Economics(3036/70)

Dept. of Economics(1881/26)

Dept. of Business administration(1155/44)

Faculty of Sociology(696/10)

Dept. of Sociology

Graduate Programs

Graduate School of Economics(M 20/10)

Div. of Economics

Economics, Econometrics, History of Economics, Economic Growth, Japanese Economic History, Western Economic History, Commerce and Business History, Economic Policy, World Economy, Agricultural Economics, Transportation Economics, Marketing, Physical Distribution Economics, Physical Distribution Management, Economic Geography, Small and Medium Businesses of the world, Logistics System, Monetary Economics, Public Finance, Statistics, Social Policy, Social Security

One-Year Graduate Programs

Advanced Economic Studies Course

Advanced Economic Studies Major

相模女子大学
(Sagami Joshi Daigaku)
Sagami Women's University

2-1-1 Bunkyo, Sagamihara-shi, Kanagawa 228
☎ 0427-42-1411 FAX 0427-42-1732

Founded 1990
Professors 35
Associate Professors 8
Assistant Professors(Tenured) 3
Assistant Pofessors(Non-tenured) 111
Research Assistants 12
Undergraduate Students/Foreign 1, 681/0
Library 187, 000 volumes
Contact: Admission Office

Educational philosophy Our school has been thinking about the life style of women, and has promoted the idea of " education for independent women " since as far back the Meiji Era. We can boast of a long tradition and achievement, and it might be said that the history of our school is the history of women's education in Japan.
Foreign students We don't have a special entrance examination for non-Japanese students now. So they have to take the same exmination as Japanese students.
Environment Our school is located in Sagamihara City in Kanagawa Prefecture. Our campus contains 170, 000m^2, with cherry blossoms, hydrangea and other gorgeous flowers throuth the year. We have parks, libraries, theaters and medical centers in the surrounding.
Facilities The construction of the new library will start before long as a commemorative enterprise celebrating our ninety years' anniversary.
Student activities We have a sport festival in May for all college students, and the Minazukisai('June festival')wherein student clubs demonstrate their activities and the annual November Aioisai('Sagami students festival')for all students form kindergarden to the university. A special course of skiing is open in winter.

Undergraduate Programs

Faculty of Liberal Arts(1, 676/0)
- **Dept. of Japanese Literature**(614/0)
- **Dept. of English and American Literature**(597/0)
- **Dept. of Nutrition**(238/0)
- **Dept. of Nutrition Administrator Training**(227/0)

埼玉工業大学
(Saitama Kôgyo Daigaku)
Saitama Institute of Technology

1690 Fusaiji, Okabe-machi, Osato-gun, Saitama 369-02
☎ 0485-85-2521 FAX 0485-85-2523

Founded 1976
Professors 25
Associate Professors 12
Assistant Professors(Tenured) 13
Assistant Professors(Non-tenured) 34
Undergraduate Students/Foreign Students 1, 381/19
Library 53, 344 volumes

Educational philosophy Our institute is a bachelor-of-engineering degree granting institution acquainting students not only with fundamentals of engineering but also with state-of-the-art technology through Buddhistic educational philosophy.
Foreign students Foreign students have been warmly received. Both professors and officials are making every effort to make foreign students' life on campus meaningful and fruitful.
Environment Situated at Okabe, a town(pop. 18, 500)in the northwestern part of the Kanto Plain, boasting its rural serenity surrounded by vegetable fields with a scenic view of distant mountain ranges. The climate is moderate for most of the year. About 11/2-hour train ride from Tokyo.
Facilities Library, Machine Shop, Center for Environmental Measurement and Research, Center for Information Sciences and Education, Gymnasium-cum-Auditorium,etc.
Student activities Among annual main events are the freshmen orientation tour, the campus festival, Mt. Fuji climbing, a skiing clinic, etc. Varsity sports are ping-pong, football, martial arts, etc. Intramural sports include rugby and cycling. There are a light music club, a ham club, etc.
Academic programs for foreign students Courses on Japanese language, culture and economy designed to help foreign students get used to life in Japan sooner are provided in the curriculum.
Services for foreign students Medical care, counseling, scholarship recommendation, awards to distinguished foreign students, etc. A lounge is available to foreign students for their meeting, relaxation, etc.

Undergraduate Programs

Faculty of Engineering(1, 381/19)
- **Dept. of Mechanical Engineering**(445/4)
- **Dept. of Environmental Engineering**(458/4)
- **Dept. of Electronic Engineering**(478/11)

埼玉医科大学
(Saitama Ika Daigaku)
Saitama Medical School

38 Morohongou, Moroyama-cho, Iruma-gun, Saitama 350-04
☎ 0492-95-1111 FAX 0492-95-0784

Founded 1972
Professors 72
Associate Professors 45
Assistant Professors(Tenured) 104
Assistant Professors(Non-tenured) 122
Research Asistants 394
Undergraduate Students/Foreign Students 722/0
Graduate Students/Foreign Students 61/0
Library 157, 512 volumes
Contact: Student Affairs Section

Educational philosophy We aim to educate medical students to be good practional medical doctors who are thoughtfull, have deep affection on life, and are able to sacrify themselves to their patients. We have tutor system to realize close relationship between students and professors.
Foreign students All of lectures and practice are given in Japanese therefore foreign students must be well-trained in Japanese language until the 2nd year when special medical caliculum start.
Environment Moroyama-cho has population of about 40, 000, locates in a rural area 70km north west of central Tokyo, and takes about 1 hour by train from Ikebukuro via Tojo-sen to Sakado, transfer to Ogosesen for Higashimoro and additional 15 minutes' walk to our school.
Facilities Premedical school for 1st year, Hospital (1, 483 beds), Central Library, Center for Psyconeurological Dieseases, Center for Cardiac Diseases, Junior College(Departments of Nursing, Medical Technology and Physical Therapy).
Student activities Extra-curricular activities of sport such as football, American football, soccer, baseball, tennis, judo, shorinjikenpo, volleyball, basket ball, ice hockey, ski, and also some cultural activities.

Undergraduate Programs

Faculty of Medicine(722/0)

Graduate Programs

Saitama Medical School Graduate School(D 61/0)
Anatomy, Physiology, Biochemistry, Pharmacology, Pathology, Bacteriology, Hygiene, Public Health, Parasitology, Forensic Medicine, Internal Medicine, Psychiatry, Pediatrics, Surgery, Neurosurgery, Orthopedics, Dermatology, Urology, Opthalmology, Otorhinolaryngology, Obstetrics & Gynecology, Radiology, Anesthesiology

作新学院大学
(Sakushin Gakuin Daigaku)
Sakushin Gakuin University

908 Takeshita-machi, Utsunomiya-shi, Tochigi 321-32
☎ 0286-67-7111 FAX 0286-67-7110

Founded 1989
Professors 13
Associate Professors 8
Assistant Professors(Tenured) 15
Assistant Professors(Non-tenured) 24
Research Assistants 3
Undergraduate Students/Foreign Students 611/4
Library 28, 443 volumes

Educational philosophy Our target is how to develop international-minded business administrators capable of responding to the changing currents of society, so that highly intergrated trainings ranging from business management to computer science to foreign languages are being practiced.
Foreign students With rather small-sized and family-like atmosphere, foreign students can enjoy campus life, easily establishing friendly relations with teaching and administration staff as well as with Japanese students.
Environment With only a 46-minute ride from Tokyo by Tohoku shinkansen Bullet Train, Utsunomiya City is evolving into one of the busiest satellite cities of Tokyo in terms of business and finance. Our campus is in the suburb of the city, so one can enjoy both rural and urban life.
Facilities A variety of useful facilities: Computer Training Room of the basis of one computer for every one of students, Library with bountiful academic as well as cultural books, Multi-purpose Gymnasium, etc.
Student activities We have such popular campus events as school festival, sporting day, company inspection tour, etc. We also have a wide variety of extra curricular activities including baseball, volleyball, football, tennis, golf, skiing, soccer, various track and field sports, etc.
Academic programs for foreign students Supplemental Japanese language class is being practiced in order to make foreign students possible to keep up with every sophisticated and high level lecture given in Japanese in class.
Services for foreign students Reqular medical cheque, personal/psychological counseling, housing information, cultural exchange information, vocational information & guidance, part-time job information, academic consulatation, etc.

Undergraduate Programs

Faculty of Business management(611/4)
Dept. of Business management

産能大学
(Sannô Daigaku)
Sanno College

1573 Kamikasuya, Isehara-shi, Kanagawa 259-11
☎ 0463-92-2211 FAX 0463-93-0554

Founded 1979
Professors 24
Associate Professors 14
Assistant Professors(Tenured) 14
Assistant Professors(Non-tenured) 37
Research Assistants 2
Undergraduate Students/Foreign Students 1, 971/39
Library 100, 000 volumes and 1, 330 titles of academic journals
Contact: College Operations Section FAX: 0463-92-6671

Educational philosophy The mission of the School of Management and Informatics of the SANNO College is to educate students to be able to meet changing needs of the business society by acquiring practical management knowledge and skills to use computers, and developing their think-and-do competence and refining their inherent abilities.
Foreign students Non-Japanese students from any country are always welcome by SANNO College. We expect them to mingle themselves with Japanese students by establishing a common understanding and friendship, thereby enriching campus activities.
Environment Isehara-shi (population 89, 000) enbracing the campus is in Kanagawa-ken, some 50 km west of Shinjuku, Tokyo, and 30 km east of the Fuji-Hakone National Park, with Mt. Oyama to the north and Sagami Bay to the south. Historically, the campus site is known as the old castle of a warlord Uesugi Sadamasa in the 15th Century.
Facilities Gymnasium, Library, Students' dining hall, Computer practice facility, Institute of International Management Studies, Institute of Inoformation Science, Institute of Cross-cultural Studies, etc.
Student activities Faculty reception party for freshmen, participation to various inter-college/community sports tournaments and games, summer tennis school, visits to industrial firms/plants, theaters and museums, campus visits by foreign students, annual campus festival, winter skiing school, faculty farewell party for graduates, etc.
Academic programs for foreign students Supplemental Japanese language class, Study of Japanese management and related terminology, Comparative analysis of business and industry(America, Asia, Europe, etc.), and other Special lectures on Japanese management and social systems
Services for foreign students Foreign students' counselling service includes helping students find dormitories or home-stay families, working opportunities, etc. through the Corporate Friendship Network for Foreign Students.

Undergraduate Programs

Faculty of Management & Informatics(1, 791/39)
Dept. of Management Sciences(729/26)
Dept. of Information Science(1, 062/13)

東京理科大学
(Tokyo Rika Daigaku)
Science University of Tokyo

1-3 Kagurazaka, Shinjuku-ku, Tokyo 162
☎ 03-3260-4271 FAX 03-3260-4294

Founded 1881
Professor 310
Associate Professors 106
Assistant Professors(Tenured) 117
Assistant Professors(Not-Tenured) 501
Reserch Assstants 169
Undergraduate Students/Foreign Students 18, 118/19
Graduate Students/Foreign Students 1, 101/13
Library 546, 400 volumes
Contact: Adimission Office

Educational philosophy The history of the Science University of Tokyo date back to 1881. when the founders opened Tokyo Butsurigaku-Koshusho, the Predecessor of the present University. The founders set a firm goal development of the nation should be based on the spread of scientific knowledge.
Foreign students Over 27 students from abroad are attending University classes with number rising each year.
Enviroment The Science University of Tokyo has three Campuses-at Kagurazaka in the heart of Tokyo, at Noda east of Tokyo in Chiba Prefecture and at Oshamanbe in Hokkaido, Japan's northernmost island.
Facilities The Data Processing Center has five Computer systems including the IBM 3090-180 and 3081-GX4. These computers are installed on four campuses and linked to form an intramural network.
Student activities Extra curricular activities are as important a part of student life as study and research. More than 100 clubs on the University Campuses currently provide opportunities for students to pursue their individual interests.
Academic programs for foreign students University offers lectures on “ Japanese Language ” and “ about Japan ”
Services for foreign students The University does not have a student dormitory but there are houses, rooms and apartments for rent in the vicinity of the University.

Undergraduate Programs

Faculty of Engineering Division 1(2, 477/3)
Dept. of Architecture(482/1)
Dept. of Electrical Engineering(556/1)
Dept. of Industrial Chemistry(482/0)
Dept. of Management Science(489/1)
Dept. of Mechanical Engineering(468/0)
Faculty of Pharmaceutical Sciences(878/2)
Dept. of Pharmaceutical Sciences(445/0)
Dept. of Pharmaceutical Technochemistry(433/2)
Faculty of Science Division(3, 421/3)
Dept. of Applied Chemistry(546/0)
Dept. of Applied Mathematics(626/0)
Dept. of Applied Physics(544/1)
Dept of Chemistry(551/0)
Dept. of Mathematics(566/1)
Dept. of Physics(588/1)
Faculty of Science and Technology(5, 658/11)
Dept. of Applied Biological Science(462/0)
Dept. of Architecture(624/3)
Dept. of Civil Engineering(467/0)
Dept. of Electrical Engineering(682/3)
Dept. of Industrial and Engineering Chemistry(622/1)
Dept. of Industrial Administration(613/1)
Dept. of Information Sciences(481/3)
Dept. of Mathematics(571/0)
Dept. of Mechanical Engineering(591/0)
Dept. of Physics(545/0)
Faculty of Industrial Science and Technology(1, 117/0)
Dept. of Applied Electronics(384/0)
Dept. of Materials Science and technology(370/0)
Dept. of Biological Science and Technology(363/0)

Graduate Programs

Graduate School of Science
Div of Chemistry
Div. of Mathematics
Div. of Physics
City and District Planning, Electro Chemistry Toxicology and Microbiology of Mycotoxins, Solid-State and low temperatrue theory, Mathematical logic, linguistics, Theoretical nuclear Physics, etc.
Graduate School of Engineering
Graduate School of Pharmacevtical Science
Graduate School of Science and Technology

聖学院大学
(Seigakuin University)

Seigakuin University

1-1 Tozaki, Ageo-shi, Saitama 362
☎ 048-781-0031 FAX 048-726-2962

Founded 1988
Professors 17
Associate Professors 5
Assistant Professors(Tenured) 9
Assistant Professors(Non-tenured) 48
Research Assistants 1
Undergraduate Students/Foreign Students 786/1
Library 99, 247 volumes
Contact: Admission Office

Educational philosophy Seigakuin's Educational Philosophy is based on the spirit of Protestant Christianity, in the tradition of freedom, reverence and search for truth. We endeavor to develop the entire person including maturity in the spiritual dimension, and to form a community that contributes to the development of all the people of the world through the tradition of scholarly research and education.

Foreign students University students in the Comparative Political Science and Economics course study America, Europe, the Soviet Union and East Asia, and are eager to interact with foreign students, learning about the culture and social structure of those countries, and providing mutual stimulation.

Environment The University is located in the cities of Omiya and Ageo in the Saitama Central Urban Development zone.Public transportation is excellent for commuting, with nearby stations of the following lines: Takasaki, Kawagoe/Saikyo, Shin'etsu Shinkan, Tohoku Shinkan, and Keihin Tohoku. The campus itself is blessed with peaceful and abundant natural beauty.

Facilities There is a 100, 000 volume library, a gymnasium, a language laboratory, video projecting equipment, a computer classroom, an athletic field, tennis courts and student halls. Karuizawa Seminar House can be used by groups for retreats and meetings from April through November.

Student activities A two-day freshman orientation program and a weekly Assembly Hour for activities and various educational, religious and cultural activities, and summer retreat, the student Association Leaders' Camp, Christmas, special lectures add to campus life. Clubs include Tennis, American Foobtall, Soccer, Golf, Choir, Handbell Choir, Woodwind Orchestra, English Speaking Society, etc.

Academic programs for foreign students Foreign students and Japanese students returning from overseas can take four courses in Japanese as a foreign language. Seigakuin University Language Institute also offers opportunities to study Japanese, assisting students to master the language and move into the regular course of study.

Services for foreign students At the Religious Center there are Chaplains capable of counselling in English and Japanese. Housing and part time work are handled by the Student Affairs Office. For students who so desire, efforts are made to find homestay families.

Undergraduate Programs

Faculty of Political Economy(786/1)
Dept. of Political Economy

成城大学
(Seijô Daigaku)
Seijo University

6-1-20 Seijo, Setagaya-ku, Tokyo 157
☎ 03-3482-1181 FAX 03-3484-2698

Founded 1950
Professors 108
Associate Professors 31
Assistant Professors(Tenured) 2
Assistant Professors(Non-tenured) 201
Research Assistants 1
Undergraduate Students/Foreign Students 4, 350/0
Graduate Students/Foreign Students 136/4
Library 660, 000 volumes
Contact: Administration Office

Educational philosophy Seijo University has two features we can be proud of. One is that we have a number of first-rate professors whose academic achievents are highly estimated. The other is that we have an adequate number of professors in proportion to the number of students.

Foreign students We welcome foreign students and believe that they can enjoy a rewarding experience in our university.

Environment Seijo University is situated in the south-western part of Tokyo. This part uccd tu be called " Musashino " —a sylvan province with plenty of nature, and despite its rapid Urbanization the area still preserves a great deal of natural beauty rich in verdure.

Facilities Newly opened library, Computer center, The Institute of Economic Studies, The Institute of Folklore Studies, Swimming pool, Gymnasium, Auditorium

Student activities Freshman camp, school festival and an athletic meet are held every year. There is a wide variety of extra curricular activities, including orchestra, chorus, student news paper, drama, baseball, soccer, golf, hockey, etc.

Academic programs for foreign students Tutoring system

Services for foreign students Health clinic, Personal counseling, Housing information

Undergraduate Programs

Faculty of Arts and Literature(1, 690/0)
Dept. of Art Studies(271/0)
Dept. of Cultural History(267/0)
Dept. of English(342/0)
Dept. of European Culture(266/0)
Dept. of Japanese(269/0)
Dept. of Mass-Communication Studies(275/0)
Faculty of Economics(1, 618/0)
Dept. of Business Administration(835/0)
Dept. of Economics(783/0)
Faculty of Law(1, 042/0)
Dept. of Law

Graduate Programs

Graduate School of Economics(M 14/2, D 5/0)
Div. of Business Administration(M 8/2)
Business Administration, Organization Theory, Business History, Japanese Business History, American Industrial History, European Business History, Personal Management, Financial Management, Public Enterprise, Management of Small Business, Auditing, Managerial Accounting, Auditing, Quality Control, Information Management, Marketing, Commercial Law
Div. of Economics(M 6/0, D 5/0)
Economic Theory, International Economics, History of Economic Doctorines, General Economic history, Japanese Economic History, American Economic History, Contemporary Economic History of Japan, European Economic History, Asian Economic History, Public Finance, Economic Policy, Industrial Policy, Monetary Economics, International Monetary Economics, Statistics, Transportation Policy, Social Policy, Theory of Population, Economic Geography, Civil Law, Economic Law
Graduate School of Law(M 14/1)
Div. of Law(M 14/1)
Legal Philosophy/Jurisprudence, Legal History, Constitutional Law, Administrative Law, Administration, Civil Law, Commercial Law, Labor Law, Economic Law, Civil Procedure, Criminal Law and Procedure, International Law, International Economic Law, Private International Law, International Relations, Comparative Law, English Law, American Law, Soviet Law, Latin-American Law
Graduate School of Literature(M 63/1, D 40/0)
Div. of Aesthetics and History of Art(M 23/0, D 8/0)
Aesthetics, (Master's), Art(Master's), History of Japanese Art(Master's), History of Eastern Art(Master's), History of Western Art(Master's), Comparative Study of History of Art
Div. of Communication Studies(M 5/0, D 4/0)
Elementary Social Psychology(Master's), Elementary Communication Studies(Master's), Special Topics in Communication Studies(Master's), Methodology of Communication Studies(Master's), Comparative Communication Studies(Master's), Tutorial in Communica-

tion Studies, Mass–Communication Studies(Master's), Communication(Doctoral), Mass–Communication(Doctoral)

Div. of English Studies(M 5/0, D 8/0)
Middle–Age English Literature, Elizabethan Drama, 18th–Century English Literture, English Novel, English Poetry, Enlish Criticism, English Philology, American Novel, Latin Language and Literature(Master's), Contemporary English(Master's)

Div. of European Culture(M 7/0, D 8/0)
Greek and Roman Philosophy, Western Classics, Comparative philology, German Philology, German Philology and Literature, German History, German Philosophy, French Philology, French Philology and Literature, French History, French Philosophy

Div. of Japanese Folk Culture(M 14/0, D 6/0)
Japanese Folk Culture, Japanese Ethnography, Social Anthropology, History of Folk Religion, Religion Ethnography, History of Japanese Culture, History of Japanese Folk Culture, Pre–Historic Culture, History of Eastern Culture, Religio–Sociology, Folk Entertainment, History of Japanese Philosophy

Div. of Japanese Literture(M 9/1, D 6/0)
Ancient Japanese Literature, Middle–Age Japanese Literature, Modern Japanese Literature, Contemporary Japanese Literature, History of Japanese, Introduction to Japanese Literature(Master's), Japanese Language and Literature(Master's), Japanese Literature and Foreign Literature(Master's)

成蹊大学

(Seikei Daigaku)

Seikei University

3–3–1 Kichijoji–Kitamachi, Musashino–shi, Tokyo 180
☎ 0422–51–5181 FAX 0422–56–0116

Founded 1949
Professors 121
Associate Professors 37
Assistant Professors(Tenured) 10
Assistant Professors(Non–tenured) 430
Research Assistants 45
Undergraduate Students/Foreign Students 7, 035/0
Graduate Students/Foreign Students 116/6
Library 510, 009 volumes
Contact: Office of Academic Affairs

Educational philosophy Seikei's traditional philosophy of education is manifested in its emphasis on character building. By helping students acquire technical knowledge and develop their own personalities, the University aims to produce well–informed future leaders who will contribute to the betterment of society.
Foreign students It is our belief that international students are a valuable asset to the University in that they contribute a great deal to promoting mutual understanding and the internationalization of the campus.
Environment Seikei University lies in a peaceful residential quarter which is not far away from the central part of Tokyo. Its beautiful campus, amid a huge clump of zelkova trees, provides a pleasant environment ideally suited for college education.
Facilities University Library, Center for Asian and Pacific Studies, Information Processing Center, Swimming Pool, Gymnasium
Student activities Popular campus events include Athletic Meet, Annual Seikei Boat Regatta, Keyaki Festival, and Intercollegiate Sports Festival. Extra–curricular life at Seikei is extremely active. More than 200 registered student organizations offer a variety of activities, ranging from drama to football.
Academic programs for foreign students Supplemental Japanese language class, Tutoring System
Services for foreign students Health clinic, personal/psychological counseling, Housing information, part–time job information, vocational guidance, Home visit, excursion

Undergraduate Programs

Faculty of Economics(1, 959/0)
  Dept. of Business(781/0)
  Dept. of Economics(1, 178/0)
Faculty of Engineering(1, 468/0)
  Dept. of Applied Physics(113/0)
  Dept. of Electrical Engineering(335/0)
  Dept. of Industrial Chemistry(328/0)
  Dept. of Industrial Engineering(323/0)
  Dept. of Mechanical Engineering(369/0)
Faculty of Humanities(1, 803/0)
  Dept. of Cultural Sciences(693/0)
  Dept. of English and American Literature(732/0)
  Dept. of Japanese Literature(378/0)
Faculty of Law(1, 805/0)
  Dept. of Law(1, 163/0)
  Dept. of Political Science(642/0)

Graduate Programs

Graduate School of Business(M 6/1, D 2/0)
Business Management, Theory of Business, Financial Management, Industrial Relations, Business History, Management, Marketing, Business Planning, Industrial Business Management, Personnel Management, Advanced Accounting, Financial Accounting, Auditing, Cost Accounting, Managerial Accounting, Business Analysis, Tax Accounting, International Accounting, Corporate Accounting, Accounting of Business Law, Risk Management, Seminar in Business, Seminar in Accounting
Graduate School of Economics(M 1/0, D 2/1)
Macroeconomic Analysis, Microeconomic Analysis, History of Economic Thought, International Economics, Econometrics, Economic Policy, Statistics, Public Finance, Money and Banking, International Finance, Labor Economics, Social Policy, Economic Planning, Industrial Organization, Economic Development, Economic History of Europe, Economic History of Japan, Seminar : Eco-

nomic Theory, Seminar: Applied Economics, Seminar: Economic History

Graduate School of Engineering(M 81/0, D 1/0)

Div. of Electrical Engineering(M 21/0, D 0/0)

Advanced Electrical Circut Theory, Electrical Communication Theory, Electromagnetic Fields and Energy, Advanced Electric Discharge Phenomena, Advanced Electrical Engineering Materials, Electrical Machinery Analysis, Control Systems, Energy Conversion, Electrical EnergyTransmission, Power System Engineering, Systems Engineering, Topics in Electric Power Application, Applied Superconductivity, Numerical Analysis of Electromagnetic Fields, Advanced Electronics, Plasma Engineering, Date Transmission, Input and Output Equipments, Microwave Engineering, Telecommunication Networks Engineering, Semiconductor physics, Topics in Electronic Phenomena, Advanced Applied Physics, Ionic Crystals, Advanced Modern Physics, Introduction to Nuclear Physics, Advanced Applied Mathematics, Advanced Applied physics, Advanced Course in Computer, Formal Language, Computer Logic Circuts, Tmage Processing, etc.

Div. of Industrial Chemistry(M 26/0, D 0/0)Instrumentation in Analytical Chemistry, Advanced Physical Chemistry, Kinetics and Mechanisms of Chemical Relations, Advanced Organic Chemistry, Advanced Ceramics, Modern Synthetic Organic Chemistry, Material Science of Polymers, Polymer Structures, StructuralInorganic Chemistry, Advanced Oil and Fat Chemistry, Advanced Applied Biological Chemistry, Chemistry of Catalysis, Advanced Chemical Engineering, Selected Topics in Chemistry, Nutrition Chemistry, etc.

Div. of Information Sciences(M 21/0, D 0/0)

Advanced Computer Architecture, Formal Language, System Programs, Simulation Systems, Information Management System, Advanced Topics in Operations Research, Mathematical Statistics, Computer Graphics, Advanced Boolean Algebra, Theory of Scheduling, System Analysis, Data Base Management, Advanced Engineering Ecomics, Operations Management, Artificaial Intelligence, Advanced Applied Mathematics, Theory of Management Information System, Pattern Recognition, Advanced Topics in Computer Science, Advanced Programming Exercises, Individual Study, Information Structures, Real-time Systems, Graph Theory, Artificial Intelligence, etc.

Div. of Mechanical Engineering(M 13/0, D 1/0)

Advanced Mechanics of Solids, Advanced Strength of Materials, Advanced Dynamics Machinery, Advanced Theory of Vibration, Advanced Noise Control, Advanced Automobile Engineering, Advanced Mechanics of Material Processing, Advanced Thermoengineering, Advanced Hydrodynamics, Advanced Control Engineering, Advanced Design Engineering, Advanced Elasticity, Advanced Applied Mathematics, Mathematical Statistics, Advanced Experimentation, Analysis of Mechanics of Solids Problems, Analyses of Dynamics of Machinery Problems, Analyses of Machining Problems, Analyses of Thermoengineering Problms, Analyses of Hydrodynamics Problems, Analyses of Control Engineering Problems, Analyses of Design Problems, Advanced Machine Tools, Research on Special Topics, Preparation for Disseratation, etc.

Graduate School of Humanities(M 13/1)

Div. of English and American Literature(M 2/0)

Special Research of English Literature, Seminar(English Literature), Special Research of American Literature, Seminar(American Literature), Special Research of the English Language, Seminar(English Linguistics), Special Research of Methods of English Expression, etc.

Div. of Japanese Literature(M 9/1)

Special Research of Japanese Literature, Seminar(Japanese Literature)Special Research of Japanese Linguistics Seminar(Japanese Linguistics)

Div. of Western Civilization(M 2/0)

Seminar of Western Civilization Seminar(Western Civilization)Comparative Studies of Culture

Graduate School of Law and Political Science(M 4/1, D 6/1)

Div. of Law(M 2/1, D 2/1)

Constitutional Law, Administrative Law, Civil Law, Commercial Law, Criminal Law, Civil Procedure Law, International Law, Labor Law, Philosophy of Law, History of Japanese Law, History of European Law, Foreign Law (Anglo-American Law), Foreign Law(German Law), Foreign Law(French Law), Conflict of Laws, Industrial Law, Criminology, Sociology of Law

Div. of Political Science(M 2/0, D 4/0)

Political Science, History of Political Theory, History of Japanese Political Thought, Political History of Japan, Diplomatic History of America, Public Administration, Constitutional Law, Sociology

---

清泉女子大学

(Seisen Joshi Daigaku)

Seisen Women's College

3-16-21 Higashi Gotanda, Shinagawa-ku, Tokyo 141
☎ 03-3447-5551 FAX 03-3447-5493

Founded 1950
Professors 36
Associate Professors 8
Assistant Professors(Tenured) 6
Assistant Professors(Non-tenured) 104
Undergraduate Students/Foreign Students 1, 646/0
Library 158, 876 volumes
Contact: Admission Office

Educational philosophy The College is dedicated to a philosophy of education which adapts Christian humanism to the needs of Japanese society. It recognizes as the ultimate purpose of study, the attainment of truth, and the development of respect for human dignity.

Environment The College is conveniently located in Central Tokyo and beautifully situated in a quiet,hilly district of the City. The campus is renowned for its beautiful Azalea garden and the original building, a former residence of Lord Shimazu.

Facilities A new College library housing a collection of 160, 000 volumes and over 1, 000 periodical titles. A separate tape library of audio and audio-visual tapes. Gymnasium and tennis courts. Club Activities Center. Auditorium.

Student activities Circles sponsored by each department invite scholars and Critics to lecture and organize social functions. In addition to such study and research activities numerous club activities include choral groups, drama and sports.

Academic programs for foreign students A course in Japanese for foreigners is being planned in conjunction with the newly established course by the Japanese Literature Department in the teaching of Japanese as a foreign language.

Undergraduate Programs

Faculty of Letters(1, 646/0)
- **Dept. of Christian Culture**(376/0)
- **Dept. of English Literature**(495/0)
- **Dept. of Japanese Literature**(465/0)
- **Dept. of Spanish Language & Literature**(310/0)

聖徳大学
(Seitoku Daigaku)
Seitoku University

531 Sagamidai, Matsudo-shi, Chiba 271
☎ 0473-65-1111 FAX 0473-63-1401

Founded 1990
Professors 20
Associate Professors 7
Assistant Professors(Tenured) 6
Assistant Professors(Non-tenured) 26
Research Assistants 1
Undergraduate Students/Foreig Students 500/0
Library 195, 546 volumes
Contact: The Insturction Section

Educational philosophy Seitoku's ultimate objective is to educate women to that they will be able to contribute to building a happy, peaceful society for every one. We hope to help you in your development as an educated woman who is prepared to deal wisely and responsibly with moral issues.

Foreign students The experience of Seitoku encourages an enthusiasm for ideas and a commitment to excellence which enable you to contribute to promoting mutual understanding and the development of friendly relations.

Environment The Campus it self is only half an hour away by train from the ceter of Tokyo. So Seitoku is convenient to the urban area, though located in a rural area on the Edogawa River. Seitoku offers a personal place where one's ideas and questions can be persued in a stimulating environment.

Facilities Music Hall with a pipe organ, Library, Computer Center, Gymnasium, Auditorium, Language Laboratories, Music Laboratories, Dinning Hall, Residence Facilities, etc.

Student activities Extracurricular life at Seitoku offers you many opportunities to develop the strengths and skills that are especially important for women. By becoming active participants in student goverment, clubs, social issues, sports and residence hall life, you can have fun while learning.

Academic programs for foreign students Supplemental Japanese Languae class, Supplemental Japanese History and Culture class, Tutoring system.

Services for foreign students Health Clinic, Personal/Psychological Counseling, College Housing, Housing Information, Vocational Guidance, Home Stay, Home Visit, Cultural Exchange Program, etc.

Undergraduate Programs

Faculty of Humanities(500/0)
- **Dept. of Early Childhood Education**(240/0)
- **Dept. of Japanese Culture**(144/0)
- **Dept. of British and American Culture**(116/0)

専修大学
(Senshû Daigaku)
Senshu University

3-8 Kandajimbo-cho, Chiyoda-ku, Tokyo 101
☎ 03-3265-6211

Founded 1880
Professors 247
Associate Professors 58
Assistant Professors(Tenured) 29
Assistant Professors(Non-tenured) 353
Research Assistants 2
Undergraduate Students/Foreign Students 21, 152/223
Graduate Students/Foreign Students 111/24
Library 850, 000 volumes
Contact: International Academic Affairs Office 2-1-1 Higashimita, Tama-ku, Kawasaki-shi, Kanagawa 214 ☎ 044 (911)1250

Educational philosophy Senshu University has a philosophy based on freedom of reserch with a critical eye towards authoritarianism and social inflexibility and with the aim of training and educating young people to absorb humanitarianism and a peaceful consciousness within a democratic discipline.

Foreign students We always welcome foreign students. Our basic idea is to permit Japanese and students from other nations to opportunities to develop mutual understanding and to develop their international sense through friendly campus relations.

Environment The university has campuses in two places: Kanda in downtown Tokyo and Ikuta in the suburbs. The former location is surrounded by other buildings in the metropolitan center close to the Imperial Palace. The Ikuta campus is located in a green belt area less than 20 Km from the Shinjuku metropolitan subcenter. It lies amid natural surroundings in which scenery changes from season to season.

Facilities Libraries, Language Laboratory, Information Science Center, Health Center,Seminar Houses, Gymnasium, Training room, Swimming pool, etc.

Student activities We have a variety of student events and activities on the campuses including, school festivals a freshmen orientation and party, and other cultural and sports activities. At present, there are over 200 student clubs which are run by student organization.

Academic for foreign students Special curricula for foreign students include Japanese language, Japanese nature and culture, Japanese current affairs, Japanese history, Japanese society and science, Japanese politics and economics.

Services for foreign students Health clinic, Personal/psychlogical counseling, Housing information, Scholarship information, Vocational guidance, Home visits, Cultural exchange program.

Undergraduate Programs

Faculty of Business Administration(3, 796/76)
  Dept. of Business Administration(3, 263/58)
  Dept. of Information Control(533/18)
Faculty of Commerce(4, 311/71)
  Dept. of Accounting(967/7)
  Dept. of Commerce(3, 344/64)
Faculty of Economics(3, 840/39)
  Dept. of Economics(3, 840/39)
Faculty of Law(3, 781/17)
  Dept. of Law(3, 781/17)
Faculty of Literature(2, 566/18)
  Dept. of English and American Literature(693/0)
  Dept. of Humanities(1, 177/8)
  Dept. of Japanese Literature(696/10)

Graduate Programs

Graduate School of Business Administration(M 14/9, D 2/0)
  Div. of Business Administration
Business Administration, Business Management, Business Organization, Corporate Financial Management, Labor Managenent, Managerial Morphology, Quality Control, Marketing, Science Technology, Accounting, Behavior Science, Financial Management, Business Mathematics, Financial Analysis, Business History, Information Science, Information Theory, Information Mathematics, Mathematical Statistics, Operations Research
Graduate School of Commerce(M 23/10, D 2/1)
  Div. of Commerce
Theory of Commerce, Structure of Distribution, History of Commerce, Commercial Policy, Foreign Trade, Insurance, Money & Banking, Transportation, Theroy of Merchandise, Marketing, Business Management, Busiess Administration, Principles of Bookkeeping, Finacial Accounting, Managerial Accounting, Cost Accounting, Auditing, Tax Accournting, International Accounting, Readings in Foreign Books on Commerce
Graduate School of Economics(M 7/1, D 6/0)
  Div. of Economics
Theoritical Economics, History of Economics, Japaese Economic History, Eastern Economic History, Western Economic History, Historical Science, Economic Policy, Agricultural Policy, Social Policy, Pubilic Finance, Statistics, Money & Banking
Graduate School of Law(M 11/0, D 11/0)
  Div. of Private Law(M 5/0)
Principles of Private Law, Civil Law, Commerical Law, Civil Procedure, Labor Law, Anglo-American Law, Constitutional Law, Japanese Legal History, Economic Law, Readings in Foreign Books on Private Law
  Div. of Public Law(M 6/0, D 7/0)
Constitutional Law, Adminstrative Law, Criminal Law, Criminal Procedure, Criminology, International Law, International Political History, Japanese Legal History, Public Administration, Political Science, Anglo-American Law, Local Government, Economic Law, Readings In Foreign Books on Public Law,
  Div. of Civil Law(D 4/0)
Civil Law, Commercial Law, Civil Procedure, Labor Law, Anglo-American Law, Economic Law, Law
Graduate School of Literature(M 16/2, D 19/1)
  Div. of English Literature(M 4/0, D 1/0)
Dramatic Literature of the Elizabethan Era, Modern English Novels, Modern English Poetry & Prose, English Literature, English Linguistics, American Literature, Critical Stylistics, German Literature
  Div. of Japanese Literature(M 8/2, D 12/1)
Japanese Literature in Nara Era, Japanese Literature in the Heian Era, Japanese Literature in the Kamakura Era, Japanese Literature in the Meiji Era, Japanese Linguistics, Japanese Grammar, Chinese Classics
  Div. of Philosophy(M 4/0, D 6/0)
Ancient & Medieval Philosophy, Mondern & Contemporary Philosophy, Philosophical Methodology, Practical Philosophy, Hisotry of Japanese Mentality, Sociology, Pedagogy

---

洗足学園大学
(Senzoku Gakuen Daigaku)
Senzoku Gakuen College

290 Hisamoto, Takatsu-ku, Kawasaki-shi, Kanagawa 213
☎ 044-877-3211 FAX 044-856-2972

Founded 1967
Professors 38
Associate Professors 5
Assistant Professors(Tenured) 2

Assistant Professors(Non-tenured) 331
Research Assistants
Undergraduate Students/Foreign Students 1095/23
Library 103, 886 volumes
Contact: Admission Office

Educational philosophy Our aim is to teach contemporary advanced level art and science to develop humane heart, noble character and the daring spirit so that our students may contribute to cultural enhancement and social improvement.
Foreign students We believe that foreign students will have a rewarding experience in our school, and we hope they can contribute a great deal to promoting mutual understanding and the development of friendly relations.
Environment The campus is located on the south bank of the Tama river, the opposite bank of which belongs to Tokyo. It takes 8 minutes on foot from Mizonokuchi station on both JR and the Tokyu Lines. Students can go to the downtoun of Tokyo in 25 minutes and Yokohama in 50 minutes.
Facilities The Library, Concert hall, Musical practice building, Gymnasium, Indoor swimming-pool, Opera Institute, Conducting Institute, Institute of piano performance, Choral Center, Sound Laboratory, Language Labo.
Student activities Polular campus events includes the school festival, frechmen welcome parties and so on. There is wide variety of extra curricular activities, including photography club, movie study club, tennis, volleyball, basketball teams, swimming, yachting, skiing clubs, etc.
Academic programs for foreign students Supplementary Japanese language classes.
Services for foreign students Individual counseling, Housing information, part-time job information, dinner party with faculty members.

Undergraduate Programs

Faculty of Music(1, 095/23)
Dept. of Music
Musical Composition major
Instrumental Music major
Musical Education major
Vocal Music major(1, 095/23)

One-Year Graduate Programs

Musical composition major
Music course
Musical Composition major
Instrumental Music major
Vocal Music major

芝浦工業大学
(Shibaura Kôgyô Daigaku)
Shibaura Institute of Technology

3-9-14 Shibaura, Minato-ku, Tokyo 108
☎ 03-5476-3127 FAX 03-5476-2949

Founded 1926
Professors 92
Associate Professors 72
Assistant Professors(Tenured) 51
Assistant Professors(Non-tenured) 212
Research Assistants 3
Undergraduate Students/Foreign 5, 618/22
Graduate Students/Foreign Students 262/4
Library 195, 769 volumes
Contact: Center for International Programs

Educational philosophy Engineering with humanity, engineering to contribute to the human life—Technology with love for the mother earth, S. I. T. intends to develop students with wider and deeper knowledge of science and engineering, and to contribute to international societies.
Foreign students S. I. T. welcomes foreign students into our city-located, liberal atmosphere. Through their studies and student activities, foreign students will develop their knowledge and friendship with Japanese and other foreign students.
Environment The main campus is located at Shibaura, Minato-ku, downtown Tokyo. Minato-ku is the center of international politics, economics and culture, where major embassies and related facilities are located. Another campus is situated amid the beautiful surroundings in Ohmiya, on the outskirts of Tokyo.
Facilities Research Laboratory of Engineering, Center of Education and Research, Computer Center, Libraries, Gymnasium, Sports Ground, etc.
Student activities Popular campus events include school festival, freshmen welcome party, sports fair, and tour. There is a wide variety of extra curricular activities including student societies for news paper, tea ceremony, baseball, handball, judo, karate, shooting, scuba diving, etc.
Academic programs for foreign students Japanese grammar class, Japanese language class. Tutors and counselors are available specifically for foreign students to help solve their personal, social, academic, and career problems.
Services for foreign students Health clinic, personal/psychological counseling, housing information, part-time job information, factory tour, bowling tournament, softball games, etc.

Undergraduate Programs

Faculty of Engineering(5, 618/22)
Dept. of Architecture(432/0)
Dept. of Architecture & Building Engineering (444/0)
Dept. of Civil Engineering(390/1)
Dept. of Electrical Communication(411/7)
Dept. of Electrical Engineering(405/4)
Dept. of Electronic Engineering(416/6)
Dept. of Industrial Chemistry(433/0)
Dept. of Industrial Management(401/1)
Dept. of Mechanical Engineering(427/3)
Dept. of Mechanical Engineering II(443/0)
Dept. of Metallurgical Engineering(404/0)

Graduate Programs

Graduate School of Engineering(M 262/4)
Div. of Architecture and Civil Engineering(M 98/3)

Architectural Planning, History of Architecture, City Planning, Planning of Building Equipment and Facilities, Environmental Engineering, Structural Engineering(Architectural), Construction Technology and Management, Traffic Engineering, Structural Engineering (Civil), Grotechnical Engineering, Hydraulics

Div. of Electrical Engineering(M 70/0)

Solid State Physics, Semiconductor and Electronic Materials, Electronic Device and Materials, Optoelectronics Engineering, Electronic Circuit Engineering, Automatic Control Engineering, Energy Conversion and Control Systems Engineering, Information Systems Engineering, Communication Systems Engineering, Spacecraft Dynamics and Control Engineering, Information Structural Engineering, Large-Scaled Integrated Circuit Design

Div. of Industrial Chemistry(M 18/0)

Industrial Physical Chemistry, Macromolecular Materials Engineering, Industrial Organic Chemistry, Organic Physical Chemistry, Industrial Analytical Chemistry

Div. of Mechanical Engineering(M 54/0)

Thermal Engineering, Energy Conversion Engineering, Fluid Engineering, Composite Materials Engineering, Engineering Mechanics, Machining Processes Engineering, Structural Safety Engineering, Man-Machine Systems, Biomedical Engineering

Div. of Metallurgical Engineering(M 22/1)

Ferrous Materials, Physical Metallurgy, Metal Processing, Material Processing, Chemical Metallurgy, Welding Metallurgy, Alloy Materials

---

白百合女子大学
(Shirayuri Joshi Daigaku)

Shirayuri Women's College

1-25 Midorigaoka,Chofu-shi,Tokyo 182
☎ 03-3326-5050 FAX 03-3326-4550

Founded 1965

Professors 34
Associate Professors 16
Assistant Professors(Tenured) 6
Assistant Professors(Non-tenured) 125
Research Assistants 3
Undergraduate Students/Foreign Students 1890/0
Graduate Students/Foreign Students 14/0
Library 140, 000 volumes

Educational philosophy The college aims at a harmonious education for women carried on in a Christian spirit to prepare them for accomplishing their role in a progressive society.

Environment The wooded campus was formerly the site of the Tsumura Juntendo Garden for medicinal herbs. And yet it is only about 25 minutes by train on the Keio Line from Shinjuku.

Undergraduate Programs

Faculty of liberal arts(1890/0)
Dept. of the Child Development and Juvenile Culture(462/0)
Dept. of the English Literature(538/0)
Dept. of The French Literature(448/0)
Dept. of The Japanese Literature(452/0)

Graduate Programs

Graduate School of Letters(M 12/0)
Div. of Developmental Psychology(M 6/0)

Research in Developmental Psychology, Research in Personality Psychology, Research in Clinical Psychology for Children, Seminar in Developmental Psychology, Special Lecture in Developmental Psychology

Div. of Children's Literature(M 6/0)

Children's Literature of the World, Research in Child Welfare, Research in Children's Literature, Research in Dramas for Children, Seminar in Children's Literature of the World, Seminar in Dramas for Children, Special Lecture in Children's Literature

---

湘南工科大学
(Shônan Kôka Daigaku)

Shonan Institute of Technology

1-1-25 Tsujido Nishikaigan, Fujisawa-shi, Kanagawa 251
☎ 0466-34-4111

Founded 1963

Undergraduate Programs

Faculty of Technology
Dept. of Electrical Engineering

Dept. of Information Science
Dept. of Mechanical Engineering

昭和音楽大学
(Shôwa Ongaku Daigaku)

Showa Academia Musicae

808 Sekiguchi,Atsugi-shi,Kanagawa 243
☎ 0462-45-1055 FAX 0462-45-4400

Founded 1983
Professors 25
Associate Professors 14
Assistant Professors(Tenured) 7
Assistant Professors(Non-tenured) 148
Research Assistants 1
Undergraduate Students/Foreign Students 607/0
Library 81, 010 volumes
Contact: Public Relations Office 1-16-1, Manpukuji, Asao-ku, Kawasaki-shi, Kanagawa 215 ☎ 044-9533-1230
FAX 044-953-6580

Educational philosophy We expect students to grow musically and mentally. The lessons are taught by the comitted faculty who themselves are superb performers. Our cooperation with the Japan Opera Foundation enables the students to study in a professional surroundings.
Foreign students Our college offers variety of courses to meet the demand of individual student. Each class is strongly limited in size to ensure the high quality of education.
Environment The city of Atsugi, where the school is located, lies in the middle of Kanagawa prefecture, west of Kanto Plain. The campus is facing the Sagami River and the mountains of Tanzawa. The environment best suited for artistic pursuit.
Facilities Private piano rooms, Lesson rooms, Ensamble rooms, Library, concert hall, studio for orchestra rehearsals, electric music studio, women's dormitory, dining hall, bookstore.
Student activities Annual concerts by students of chorus, brass band, orchestra, Handel's MESSIAH and opera are held. Aside from musical extra curricular activities, there are film making, photograph, Italian language, etc. The biggest event is school festival in Nov.
Services for foreign students Individual and thorough counseling before enrollment, dormitory for women, 30% deduction of tuition, finalcial support.

Undergraduate Programs

Faculty of Music(607/0)
  Dept. of Composition(20/0)
  Dept. of Instrumental Music(214/0)
  Dept. of Vocal Music(373/0)

One-Year Graduate Programs

Music Course
  Instrumental Music Major
  Vocal Music Major

昭和薬科大学
(Shôwa Yakka Daigaku)

Showa College of Pharmaceutical Sciences

5-1-8 Tsurumaki, Setagaya-ku, Tokyo 154
☎ 03-3426-3381

Founded 1949

Undergraduate Programs

Faculty of Pharmaceutical Sciences
  Dept. of Bio-Pharmacy
  Dept. of Pharmacy

Graduate Programs

Graduate School of Pharmaceutical Sciences
  Div. of Pharmaceutical Sciences

昭和大学
(Shôwa Daigaku)

Showa University

1-5-8 Hatanodai, Shinagawa-ku, Tokyo 142
☎ 03-3784-8000 FAX 03-3786-0072

Founded 1928
Professors 116
Associate Professors 123
Assistant Professors(Tenured) 177
Assistant Professors(Non-tenured) 578
Research Assistants 471
Undergraduate Students/Foreign Students 2, 207/0
Graduate Students/Foreign Students 339/33
Library 169, 000 volumes
Contact: Admission Office

Educational philosophy Showa University is comprised of the schools of Medicine, Dentistry and Pharma ceutical Science and two associated Schools of Nursing. Close cooperation among the five faculties has proven fruitful in education and research, and the result place Showa University in a very high position among the private medical schools of Japan.
Facilities Five medical and one dental hospital, Li-

brary, Analysis Center, RI Center, Information processing Center, Medicated botanical garden, Gymnasium, Swimming pool, Sports training Center

Student activites Popular campus events includes school festival, freshmen welcome party. Clubs related to sports offer such activities as skiing, basketball, badminton, hardcourt tennis, judo, karate, rugby, and soccer. Cultural clubs offer activities that serve as hobbies as well as studies, these range from such subjects as music, literature, art and Igo to clinical priventive medicine.

Services for foreign students Health clinic, Visiting fellow house

Undergraduate Programs

Faculty of Medicine(739/0)
  Dept. of Medicine
Faculty of Dentistry(687/0)
  Dept. of Dentistry
Faculty of Pharmaceutical sciences(781/0)
  Dept. of Biopharaceutical sciences(345/0)
  Dept. of Pharmaceutical sciences(436/0)

Graduate Programs

Graduate School of Medicine
Anatomy, Physiology, Biochemistry, Pathology, Pharmacology, Bacteriology, Medical Zoology, Hygine, Public Health, Internal Medicine, Surgery, Obsterics and Gynecology, Ophthalmolgy, Dermatology, Urology, Otorhinolaryngology, Pediatrics, Psychiatry and Neurology, Radiology, Anesthesiology, Clinical Pathology
Graduate School of Dentistry
Oral Anatomy, Oral Physiology, Oral Biochemistry, Oral Microbiology, Oral Pathology, Dental Pharmacology, Dental Techonology, Hygiene and Oral Health, Conservative Dentistry, Proshetic Dentistry, Oral Surgery, Orthodontics, Pedodontics, Dental Radiology, Anesthesice
Graduate School of Pharmaceutical sciences
Biological Chemistry, Hygienic Chemistry, Physiological Chemistry, Toxicology, Microbial Chemistry, Analytical Chemistry, Pharmaceutic Industrial Chemistry, Pharmaceutical Chemistry, Physical Chemistry, Pharmacognosy and Plant Chemistry, Pharmacy, Pharmacology

---

昭和女子大学
(Shôwa Joshi Daigaku)

Showa Women's University

1-7 Taishido, Setagaya-ku, Tokyo 154
☎ 03-3411-5111 FAX 03-3411-5171

Founded 1920
Professors 72
Associate Professors 33
Assistant Professors(Tenured) 31
Assistant Professors(Non-tenured) 82
Research Assistants 14
Undergraduate Students/Foreign Students 2250/29
Graduate Students/Foreign Students 81/8
Library 290,000 volumes
Contact: Admission Office, Administration Office

Educational philosophy We aim at teaching and studying up-to-date high level art and sciences to develop intellectual, moral and applied abilities so students may contribute a great deal to cultural betterment and social improvement keeping in mind our school motto " To be a light to the world "

Foreign students We believe that foreign female students can enjoy a rewarding experience in our school, and contribute a great deal to promoting mutual understanding and the development of friendly relations.

Environment Our campus is conveniently located in the town of Sangenjaya near Shibuya in the southwest area of Tokyo. Showa Women's University campus consists of 570,000 square meters of land and 110,000 square meters of buildings in all.

Facilities Institute of Modern Culture, Institute of Women's Culture, Boston Campus, Dormitories(3), Retreat Facilities(3), Libraries(2), Computer Center, Gymnasium, World-famous Hitomi Memorial Hall, Open College, etc.

Student activities Popular campus events include school festival, freshmen welcome party. There is a wide variety of extra curricular activities including volunteer work, choral groups, student newspaper, drama, tea ceremony, flower arrangement, modern dance, golf, karate, Koto club, etc.

Academic programs for foreign students Supplementary Japanese language class, tutoring system, transfer system of curriculum, etc.

Services for foreign students Dormitories, living education on and off campus, special summer training program, scholarships, homestay, home visits, vocational guidance, cultural exchange program, etc.

Undergraduate Programs

Faculty of Domestic Science(1084/12)
  Dept. of Living Arts(620/7)
  Dept. of Living Science (Course of Food Science/Course of Administrative Dietetics) (464/5)
Faculty of Literature(1166/17)
  Dept. of English and American Literature(588/0)
  Dept. of Japanese Literature(578/17)

Graduate Programs

Graduate School of Domestic Science(M 33/3)
Div. of Living Design(M 18/2)
Housing Products, Housing Environment, High Polymer Materials, Housing Structure and Materials, Technology of Cleaning, Processing of Clothing, House Design, etc.
Div. of Science of Food and Nutrition(M 15/1)

Food Function, Nutrition, Food Chemistry, Food Analysis, Food Preservation, Food Packing, Food Cooking

Graduate School of Science for Living System(D 5/2)

Div. of Living System

Science of Living Philosophy, Comparative Study of Living Science, Historical Science of Living Products, Science of Materials for Living Products, Science of Function of Living Products, Science of Food Function, etc.

Graduate School of Literature(M 31/3, D 12/0)

Div. of English and American Literature(M 0/0, D 6/0)

Special Studies for English and American Literature, Seminar in the English Language, History of English Studies, Seminar in English and American Literature, etc.

Div. of Japanese Literature(M 21/3, D 6/0)

Ancient Literature in Japan, Early Medieval Literature in Japan, Chinese Literature, SpecialJapanese Philology, Japanese Philology, etc.

淑徳大学
(Shukutoku Daigaku)

Shukutoku University

200 Daiganji-cho, Chiba-shi, Chiba 280
☎ 0472-65-7331 FAX 0472-65-8310

Founded 1965
Professors 25
Associate Professors 8
Assistant Professors(Tenured) 4
Assistant Professors(Non-tenured) 43
Undergraduate Students/Foreign Students 2
Graduate Students/Foreign Students 16/5
Library 101, 800 volumes
Contact: Admisson of Information Section

Educational philosophy Feature : The University offers courses in social welfare. It selects a limited number of students annually(400)and provides them with an education consisting of both practical training and research. The primary subject of studay is the relationship between man and society. This is studied from the point of view of both the individual and the group.

Undergraduate Programs

Faculty of Social welfare(1916/2)

Dept. of Social welfare

Graduate Programs

Graduate Programs of Social welfare(M 16/5)

Div. of Social welfare

創価大学
(Sôka Daigaku)

Soka University

1-236 Tangi-cho, Hachioji, Tokyo 192
☎ 0426-91-2206 FAX 0426-91-2039

Founded 1971
Professors 151
Associate Professors 54
Assistant Professors(Tenured) 27
Assistant Professors(Non-tenred) 148 /c.400
Research Assistants 16
Undergraduate Students/Foreign Strdents 5823/53
Grauate Students/Foreigh Students 112/13 c.6000
Library 580, 000 volumes
Contact: International Section

Educational philosophy 1. Be the highest seat of learning for humanistic education 2. Be the cradle of a new culture 3. Be the fortress for the peace of mankind

Foreign students Soka University is opening its doors of learning not only to the people of Japan but to the entire world. We believe that foreign students can enjoy a rewarding experience in our university and can contribute a great deal to promoting mutual understanding and the development of friendly relations.

Environment Soka University is located on a small hill along stretch of the Tama hills in the suburbs of the city of Hachioji, it is situated in an ideal quiet environment away from the bustle of city, free from noise and pollution, and surrounded by clean air and abundant greenery.

Facilities Central Library, Audio-Visual Education Institute, Computer Science Lab., Music Lab., Gymnasium, Swimming Pool, Learning Center Annex, Outdoor Concert Hall, House of Classics, Center for Alumni, Auditorium

Student activities Social life is a significant aspect of the university experience. To form friendship based on mutual inspiration and growth is to acquire the greatest of treasure. Soka University has a rich tradition of academic, cultural and athletic events are a result of the co-operative efforts of the university staff.

Academic programs for foreign students Supplemental Japanese Language class, Tutoring system

Services for foreign students Health clinic, personal/psychological Counseling, Housing Information, Part-time job information, Vocational guidance

Undergraduate Programs

Faculty of Economics(1403/12)

Dept. of Economics

Faculty of Law(1433/3)

Dept. of Law

Faculty of Letters(438/8)

Dept. of English Literature(113/2)

Dept. of Sociology(111/6)
Dept. of Humanity(89/0)
Dept. of Japanese Language and Literature(61/0)
Dept. of Foreign Language(Chinese Major Russian Major)(64/0)
Faculty of Business Administration(976/20)
Dept. of Business Administration(976/20)
Faculty of Education(631/9)
Dept. of Education(293/6)
Dept. of Child Education(338/3)

Graduate Programs

Graduate School of Economics(M /4, D /1)
Div. of Economics
Graduate School of Law(M /0, D /1)
Div. of Law
Graduate School of Letters(M /3, D /1)
Div. of English Literature(M /0, D /0)
Div. of Sociology(M /2, D /1)
Div. of Education(M /1, D /0)

上智大学
(Jôchi Daigaku)
Sophia University

7-1 Kioi-cho, Chiyoda-ku, Tokyo 102
☎ 03-3238-3111 FAX

Founded 1913
Professors 287
Assistant Professors 98
Assistant Professors(Tenured) 93
Assistant Professors(Non-Tenued) 394
Research Assistants 74
Undergraduate Students/Foreign Studetns 10, 616/230
Graduate Students/Foreign Students 801/137
Library 667, 723 volumes
Contact: Admissions Office: ☎ 03-3238-3167

Educational philosophy We hope that all who study here will be able to attain Sophia(higher wisdom), which is founded in the source of all wisdom and goodness, God. We will strive for a deeper understanding of the meaning of human life and the whole universe through the means at our disposal.
Foreign students Departments on Yotsuya campus have special exam procedures in February. Comparative Culture entrance application procedures allow non-residents to be accepted easily. Some departments are very anxious to receive degree students.
Environment The main campus of the University is at Yotsuya. It is situated just inside the outer moat of the old city of Tokyo. The Palace, the Diet, the Diet Library are within a short walking distance, and central Tokyo can be reached in about twenty minutes by public transporation.
Facilities Central Library and Research Institutes, Machine Hall, Krupp Hall, Computer Center, Gymnasium, Swimming pool
Student activities Freshmen Orientation Camp, The annual athletic meet between Sophia and Nanzan University, The Sophia Festival, more than 250 extracurricular activity groups
Academic programs for foreign students Summer session in Asian Studies. Many teachers of Japanese as a foreign language at Comparative Culture, including 4-semester intensive Japanese Language Institute. Courses in Japanese language count towards graduation.
Services for foreign students Few services for applicants; most start at orientation for new students. Scholarships introduced; visa extentions facilitated. Parties arranged with International Students' Club cooperation. Contract-related students get special services; airport meeting, housing arrangements.

Undergraduate Programs

Faculty of Comparative Culture(772/121)
Dept. of Comparative Culture
Dept. of Japanese Language and Studies
Faculty of Economics(1464/50)
Dept. of Economics(733/7)
Dept. of Management(731/43)
Faculty of Foreign Studies(2054/7)
Dept. of English Language and Studies(794/5)
Dept. of French Language and Studies(266/0)
Dept. of German Language and Studies(233/0)
Dept. of Portuguese Language and Luso-Brazilian Studies(243/2)
Dept. of Russian Language and Studies(255/0)
Dept. of Spanish Language and Hispanic Studies(263/0)
Faculty of Humanities(3128/25)
Dept. of Education(266/3)
Dept. of English Literature(456/1)
Dept. of French Literature(238/0)
Dept. of German Literature(250/0)
Dept. of History(306/1)
Dept. of Japanese Literature(226/0)
Dept. of Journalism(296/9)
Dept. of Philosophy(274/3)
Dept. of Psychology(276/0)
Dept. of Social Welfare(278/1)
Dept. of Sociology(262/7)
Faculty of Law(1499/5)
Dept. of International Legal Studies(482/4)
Dept. of Law(1017/1)
Faculty of Science and Technology(1573/6)
Dept. of Chemistry(378/0)
Dept. of Electrical & Electronics Engineering(363/3)
Dept. of Mathematics(209/1)
Dept. of Mechanical Engineering(386/2)
Dept. of Physics(237/)
Faculty of Theology(126/16)

Dept. of Theology

Graduate Programs

Graduate School of Economics(M 20/14, D 4/2)

Div. of Economics/Economic Systems and Organizations

Economic Theory, History of Economics, Economic History of Europe, Economic History of Japan, Economic Policy, Public Economics, Public Finance, Monetary Economics, Studies in Income Distribution, International Economics, Economic Development, Asian Economics, Econometrics, Mathematics for Economists, Statistics, Business Management, Business Organization, Theory of Organization and Leadership, International Business Management, International Management Policy, International Monetary Problems, Finatial Management, Finantial Statement Analysis, Industrial Sociology, Accounting, Marketing

Graduate School of Foreign Studies(M 136/52, D40/1)

Div. of Comparative Culture(M 60/47)

Asian Studies–East Asian History, History of Japanese Thought, Japanese Anthropology, Art,Chinese Art, Asian Art, Japanese Literature, International Business–The Economics of the Firm, Economics of Innovation, International Trade Theroy, The Multinational Corporation, Comparative Personnel Administration, The Japanese Industrial System, Maketing in Japan, Comparative Southeast Asian Economic System International Economics and Development Studies– Development Theory and Policy, Politics and Development, Peace, Human Rights and Development, Development Sociology, Regional Economic Development: Brazil, China, India, Sub–Saharan Afica International Relations–International Relations of the Contemporary Middle East, Japan's International Relations, Seminar in Copmarative Culture

Div. of Interanational Relations(M 26/3, D 16/1)

Area Studies–Russia, Spain, Latin America, China and Southeast Asia, Middle East International Relations, International Politics, Foreign Policy Decision–Making, Theories of International Politics, Peace Research, History of International Politics, History of International Relation, Development Economics, Sociology of International Law, International Cultural Relations, Comparative Political Behavior, Comparative Polictical Sociology

Div. of Linguistics(M 50/2, D 24/0)

Phonetics and Phonemics, Experimental Phonetics, Theory of Grammar, Semantics, Information Science, Sociolingustics, Historical Comparative Linguistics, Comparative Linguistics of Romance Lauguages, Theory and Methodology of Foreign Language Teaching, Language Testing, Psycho–phonetics, Teaching Japanese as a Foreign Language, Japanese Linguistics, English Syntax, German Syntax, French Syntax, Russian Syntax, German Semantica, Russian Semantics, English Stylistics, Germatn Stylistics, Spanish Stylistics, History of English Language, History of the German Language, History of French Language, History of Spanish Language, History of Portuguese Language, Clinical Study of Language Pathology, Aphasia Disorders, Auditory Disorders, Speech Pathology, Neuroanatomical basis of language

Graduate School of Humanities(M 137/25, D 131/20)

Div. of Education(M 33/0, D 26/1)

Educational Philosophy, Educational History, Educational Method, Educational Curriculum, Educational Sociology, Lifelong Education, Educational Psychology

Div. of English & American Literature(M 17/0, D 19/0)

English Literature–Poems, Plays, Novels, American Literature–Poems, Plays, Novels, English Philology

Div. of French Literature(M 8/0, D 10/0)

History of French Thought, Modern French Poetry, Romanticism, Anti– Naturalism, French Revolution and Literature, Contemporary French Literature, Research on Pascal, Research on Baudelaire, Research on Claudel, French Linguistics

Div. of German Literature(M 5/0, D 7/0)

Modern Literature, Classicism, Romanticism,19th Century Literature, Contemporary Literature, German Language, German Literary Arts, German Lyric Poems

Div. of History(M 14/0, D 23/1)

Japanese History–Ancient Period, Early Middle Ages, Middle Ages, Modern Period, Modern Era, Ancient Writings, Oriental History–Middle Times, Western History–Ancient Period, Medieval Period, Medieval Europe, Modern Period, Contemporary Period

Div. of Japanese Literature(M 14/3, D 18/6)

Literature of Nara period, Literature of Heian period, Literature of Kamakura period, Literature of Muromachi period, Literature of Edo period, Literature of Meiji Taisho period, Semantics and Syntax of Japanese Language, Historical Research of Japanese Language, Chinese Classics

Div. of Journalism(M 25/16, D 14/9)

Communication Theory, History of Journalism, Mass Media, Topics in the Press, Topics in Broadcasting, Topics in Advertising, Laws & Ethics of Mass Communications, American Mass Media, Topics in International Communication, Information Science

Div. of Sociology(M 21/6, D 14/3)

Theory of Social Change, Sociology of Religion, Sociology of Family, Social Survey, Comparative Sociology, Social Stratification and Mobility, Sociology of Small Group, Urban Sociology, Industrial Sociology, Social Security, Method of Social Work Practice, Clinical Social Work, Mental Health in Childhood and Adolescence

Graduate School of Law(M 19/3, D 15/3)

Div. of Law

Legal Philosophy,Canon Law, Legal History, Comparative Law, Constitution, Administrative Law, Politics, Public Administration, Civil Law, Commercial Law, Law of Civil Procedure, Criminal Law, Labor Law, Economic Law, European Law, International Law, International Organization Law,Law of International Transactions, International Labor Law, International Civil Procedure, International Politics

Graduate School of Philosophy(M 18/0, D 16/0)

Div. of Philosophy

Ancient Philosophy, Medieval Philosophy, Modern Philosophy, Present–Day Philosophy, Mathematical Logic, Ethics, Bioethics, Philosophy of Evolution, History of Eastern Religions

Graduate School of Science and Technology (M 203/5, D 41/8)

Div. of Applied Chemistry(M 31/0,D 2/0)

Combustion and Explosion, High Polymer Synthesys, Chemistry of Hydrocarbons, Chemical Engineering, Industrial Materials Science, Chemical Reaction Engineering, Chemical Kinetics, Instrumental Analysis, Chemical Reactions in Electrical Discharges, Industrial Physical Chemistry, Synthetic Organic Chemistry, Physical Properties of High Polymers, Petrochemical Technology, Applied Catalytic Researches, Industrial Inorganic Chemistry, Pollution

Division of Biological Science(M 11/0, D 6/0)

Neuroethology, Neurochemistry, Molecular Genetics, Comparative Biochemistry, Physical Anthropology, Developmental Biology, Philosophical Foundations of Life Science, Bioethics

Division of Chemistry(M 37/0, D 2/0)

Structural Chemistry, Chemical Thermodynamics, Electrolyte Solutions, Electrode Kinetics, Physical Chemistry, Structural Inorganic Chemistry, Isotope Chemistry and Radio Chemistry, Mineral Chemistry, Inorganic Chemistry, Instrumental Analysis, Organic Photochemistry, Organometallic Compounds, Organic Radiation Chemistry, Natural Organic Compounds, Metabolic Biochemistry, Molecular Genetics, Applied Microbiology, Food Biochemistry

Div.of Electrical & Electronics Engineering(M 34/0, D 12/4)

Electromagnetic Theory, Quantum Mechanics, Architecture of Medium and Large Computers, Dynamic Continuous System Simulation, Power Electronics Circuits, Electromechanical Energy Conversion, Bio–medical Engineering, Network Synthesis, Communication Systems, Image Processing, Pattern Recognition, Applied Electromagnetic Measurement, Electronic Circuit Theory, Signal Processing, Solid State Electronics, Solid State Device Physics, Integrated Circuit Engineering, CAD, Antenna Engineering, Transmission Theory and Antennas, Radio Wave Engineering, Communication Technology, Electron Tubes, Energy Systems, Optical Transmission Devices, Electric Materials, Industrial Application of Electric Motors

Division of Mathematics(M 13/1, D 7/0)

Algebra–Representation Theory of Finite Algebraic Groups, Graph Theory, The Representations of the General Linear Groups and those of the Symmetry Groups, The Rings of Group Invariants Geometry–Classification of Germs of Holomorphic Mappings and that of Complex Surfaces, The Involutive Automorphisms of Simple Lie Groups and their Fixed Sets, Complex Manifold Theory, Gauge Theory Analysis–The Teichmueller Spaces and Pseudo–conformal Mapping, Linear Partial Differential Equations of Elliptic Type, Control Theory of Systems with Ordinary or Partial Differential Equations Functional Analysis–Topological Vector Spaces, Fourier Series and Fourier Transforms Applied Mathematics–Infinite Dimensional Lie Algebras, Complex WKB Method

Div. of Mechanical Engineering(M 63/5, D 56/2)

Dynamics of Machinery, Mechanical Engineering Design, Noise and Vibration Control, Fluid Dynamics, Hydraulic Machinery, Fluid Power Engineering, Combustion Engineering, Internal, Combustion Engines, Heat Transfer, Cutting Mechanics, Machine Tools, Strength of Materials, Solid Mechanics, Structural Mechanics, Materials Engineering, Structural Materials, Fracture Mechanics, Systems Engineering, Numerical Analysis, Control Engineering, Optimum Control and Planning, Discrete Systems, Information Engineering

Div. of Physics(M 33/3, D 27/2)

Theoretical Physics, Solid State Physics, Atomic Physics, Physics of Matter, Nuclear and Particle Physics, Astrophysics

Graduate School of Theology(M 18/4, D 3/4)

Div. of Theology/Systematic Theology(M 21/4, D 18/1)

Domatic Theology, Scripture, Moral Theology, Liturgical Studies, Practical Theology, Church History

---

聖路加看護大学
(Seiruka Kango Daigaku)
St. Luke's College of Nursing

10–1 Akashi–cho, Chuo–ku, Tokyo 104
☎ 03–3543–6391 FAX 03–5565–1626

Founded 1920
Professors 22
Associate Professors 5
Assistant Professors(Tenured) 13
Assistant Professors(Non–tenured) 52
Research Assistants 10
Undergraduate Students/Foreign Students 244/0
Graduate Students/Foreign Students 36/0
Library 50, 000 volumes
Contact: Admission Office

Educational philosophy Our college was founded based on a Christian philosophy. Its goal is to prepare a nurse who is not only proficient and knowledgeable in the science of nursing practice, but, also is a caring well–rounded individual. Our college prepares nurses who respect others as well as themselves and endeavor at all times to promote mutual understanding and public welfare through active participation in society.

Foreign students We understand that accepting foreign students is a very important problem. However, we have not yet decided any particular policy in this respect. It is still under discussion.

Environment Our college is located near Ginza, Akashi–cho(formerly Tsukiji)near the banks of the Sumida River between Kachidoki Bridge and Tsukuda–

Ohashi bridge. The Tsukiji district was the cradle of modern culture in Japan and today is still rich in historical interest. At the entrance of the college there still exists a stone monument commemorating the beginning of Western studies.

Undergraduate Programs

Faculty of Nursing(244/0)
Dept. of Nursing

Graduate Programs

Graduate School of Nursing(M 29/0, D 7/0)
Div. of Nursing
Nursing

聖マリアンナ医科大学

(Sei Marianna Ika Daigaku)

St. Marianna University School of Medicine

2-16-1 Sugao, Miyamae-ku, Kawasaki-shi, Kanagawa 213
☎ 044-977-8111

Founded 1971

Undergraduate Programs

Faculty of Medicine
Dept. of Medicine

Graduate Programs

Graduate School of Medical Research
Div. of Basic Medicine
Div. of Clinical Basic Mdicine
Div. of Clinical Medicine
Div. of Social Medicine

杉野女子大学

(Sugino Joshi Daigaku)

Sugino Women's College

4-6-19 Kamiosaki, Shinagawa-ku, Tokyo 141
☎ 03-3491-8151

Founded 1964

Undergraduate Programs

Faculty of Home Economics
Dept. of Clothing Science

駿河台大学

(Surugadai Daigaku)

Surugadai University

698 Azu, Hanno-Shi, Saitama 357
☎ 0429-72-1110 FAX 0429-72-1149

Founded 1987
Professors 39
Associate Professors 19
Assistant Professors(Tenured) 21
Assistant Professors(Non-tenured) 34
Undergraduate Students/Foreign Students 1702/2
Library 94, 292 volumes
Contact: Admission Office ☎ 0429-72-1211

Educational philosophy The University is contributing to the development of new forms of education designed to help Japanese students and those from other countries function effectively in an age of increasing internationalization.
Foreign students The university is very eager to welcome foreign students from all over the world and encourge interaction with Japanese students.
Environment The University is located in Hanno City, Saitama Prefecture, about 40 kilometers northwest of central Tokyo. Hanno, with a population of 73, 000, is a quiet, rather traditional city surrounded by beautiful mountains, lakes, forests, and rivers.
Facilities Main library, Audiovisual Center, Computer Center, Gymnasium, Auditoriums, Multipurpose Athletic Field, Tennis Courts, Baseball Diamond, Golf Driving Range, Student Union
Student activities Major annual events include University Festival, Sports Festival and Freshmen Orientation Camp. Extracurricular activity groups include a variety of sports clubs and groups sharing interests in such things as art and music appreciation.
Academic programs for foreign students Japanese as a second language course, individual counseling, tutorial system
Services for foreign students Welcome party, health clinic, personal/psychological counseling, housing information, part-time job information, vocational guidance; homestay, home visit, cultural exchange programs

Undergraduate Programs

Faculty of Law(1382/2)
Dept. of Law
Faculty of Economics(324/0)
Dept. of Economics(156/0)
Dept. of Management and Information Science (168/0)

大正大学
(Taishô Daigaku)
Taisho University

3-20-1 Nishisugamo, Toshima-ku, Tokyo 170
☎ 03-3918-7311 FAX 03-3918-9179

Founded 1925
Professors 57
Associate Professors 21
Assistant Professors(Tenured) 12
Assistant Professors(Non-tenured) 140
Undergraduate Students/Foreign Students 3059/28
Graduate Students/Foreign Students 192/23
Library 255, 093 volumes
Contact: Planning Department Division of Entrance Exam

Educational Philosophy Taisho University was established with Buddhism as its founding spirit and is a center for the education of the whole person. We essential aim through at the teaching and studying students will form their character and thus be able to serve world society.
Foreign students We hope that foreigh students can make a friendly relation ship. Hope you will successfully complete the program of your study.
Environment Taisho University is situated to the northeast of the center of Tokyo with two campuses, (main campus) " Sugamo campus " in the town of Toshima-ku with a population of 249, 900. In 1978, The University opened the Saitama campus to house the general education. The area is very confortable one with nature.
Facilities Library, Chemical Center, Institute of Comprehensive Buddhist Studies, Counselling Institute, Campus Center, Men's/Women's Dormitories, Gymnasium, Tennis Court,
Student activities Popular campus events includes, University festival, Anniversary, Freshman Welcome tour Buddhist Memorial Service, Buddhist study tour for students. There is a wide variety of extra curricular activities, including problems of handicapped children. Tea Ceremony, Public Speaking, Judo, Karate, Kendo.
Academic programs for foreign students Supplemental Japanese Language, Culture, Nature, Society.
Services for foreign students Hostering Tuition, Special guidance, Personal/Psychological Counseling, Housing information, Cultural exchange program, Free talking dinner party.

Undergraduate Programs

Faculty of Buddhist Studies(777/6)
Dept. of Buddhist Studies
Faculty of Letters(2282/22)
Dept. of History(446/1)
Dept. of Literature(Japanese Literature/English Language and Literature)(668/4)
Dept. of Philosophy(452/7)
Dept. of Sociology(333/6)
Dept. of Social Welfare(363/4)

Graduate Programs

Graduate School of Letters(M 154/14, D 38/9)
Div. of Buddhist Studies(M 101/7, D 21/4)
Studies in Buddhism, Buddhist Studies, Buddhist History, Seminar in Buddhist Texts, Exercises in Sanskrit Texts, Indian Philosophy, Buddhist Art History, Advanced Study of " Tendai Buddhisms ", " Shingon Buddhism ", " Judo Buddhism ", Exerciese in " Tendai Buddhism ", " Shingon Buddhism ", " Judo Buddhism ".
Div. of History(M 21/2, D 2/2)
Japanese History, Asian History, Western History, Archeology, Buddhist History, Seminar in Historical Science, Seminar on the Study of Ancient Documents and Chronicles, Theory of Historical Science, Geography.
Div. of Japanese Literature(M 12/3, D 5/2)
Japanese Literature, Japanese Language, Classical Chinese Literature, Classical Chinese(Kanbun)
Graduate School of Letters(M 154/14, D 38/9)
Div. of Religious Studies(M 20/2, D 10/1)
Topics in Religious Studies, Religious Studies, The Philosophy of Religion, The History of Religious Thought, The Psychology of Religions, The Sociology of Religions, The Ethnology of Religions, The Folklore of Religions, Religious Studies, The History of Comparative Thought

高千穂商科大学
(Takachiho Shôka Daigaku)
Takachiho College of Commerce

2-19-1 Omiya, Suginami ku, Tokyo 168
☎ 03-3313-0148 FAX 03-3313-9034

Founded 1903
Professors 33
Associate Professors 13
Assistant Professors(Tenured) 3
Assistant Professors(Non-tenred) 71
Undergraduate Students/Foreign Strdents 2, 235/12
Library 126, 000 volumes
Contact: Admission Office

Educational philosophy Our mission is to educate persons who are able to work for society with their broad culture, deep professional knowledge, and international views. These ideals have been maintained as our philosophy ever since Takachiho College of Commerce came into existence as a University of commerce, management, and economics.
Foreign students Our policy for education is to

develop student's awareness and attitude for researching commerce and business management. We want foreign students to work as professionals in international situation.

Environment Our College is located at Musashiono Valley. It is very convenient to get to populous cities such as shinjuku, Shibuya, and Kichijoji. Takes less half an hour to the central part of Tokyo. Good academic atmosphere to study, next to Omiya Shrine.

Facilities Library, Research Institute, Computer Center, Language Laboratory, Student Center, Gymnasium, Sports Training Center

Student activities (1)Popular campus events–College Festival, Cultural Festival, Sports Festival. (2)Extracurricular Activities–Baseball, Kendo, Tennis, Soccer, Judo, etc.

Academic programs for foreign students Japanese language, Japanese culture and affairs.

Services for foreign students Health Clinic, Personal Counseling, Housing Information, Part–time Job Information, Cultural Exchange Program

Undergraduate Programs

Faculty of Commerce(2, 235/12)
Dept. of Commerce(2, 001/6)
Dept. of Business Management(234/6)

拓殖大学

(Takushoku Daigaku)

Takushoku University

3–4–14 Kohinata, Bunkyo–ku, Tokyo 112
☎ 03–3947–2261 FAX 03–3947–5333

Founded 1900
Professors 130
Associate Professors 50
Assistant Professors(Tenured) 31
Assistant Professors(Non–tenured) 204
Research Assistants 35
Undergraduate Students/Foreign Students 9463/436
Graduate Students/Foreign Students 172/55
Library 277, 220 volumes
Contact: International Dept

Educational philosophy Through a history of 90 years, the object of the university is to train internationally–minded men and women who will follow the pioneer spirit of their predecessors while cooperating with other nations for the maintenance of world peace and welfare.

Foreingn students The environment around the campus is a friendly, hospitable and safe city for foreign students. We would enjoy having you as a student in our university. We are able to respond to your academic needs. We welcome your interest and application.

Environment The main campus of Takushoku University is centrally located in a quiet residential area, and in the beautiful ward of Tokyo which is called the Bunkyo–Ku as an Educational center in Japan. The location in Bunkyo–Ku is a most suitable environment for education. There is a efficient mass transit subway system to get around on.

Facilities Computer center, Sports training center, Swimming pool, Gymnasium, Theater or hall, Library, Baseball field, Tennis court, International guest house, Foreign associate Schools, Institutes, Japanese language teacher training course, Language laboratories

Student activities Popular campus events include campus festival, freshmen welcome party, day trip with Japanese students, bus tour to various districts and farewell party. There are a wide variety of extracurricular activities, including Sumo, Basket ball, Swimming, Soccer, Chinese student society, Korean student society, social gathering, and forum.

Academic programs for foreign students Intensive Japanese Language Course for Foreign Students who wish to enter the regular class at the university, Advisor Group System for Foreign Students, System of Substiturtion Subjects, Supplemental English Language Class, Rosaku Seminar

Services for foreign students Health clinic, College housing for men and women, Housing information, Home stay Part–time job information, Scholarship information, Vocational guidance, Home visit personal/Psychological counseling, Cultural exchange program, etc.

Undergraduate Programs

Faculty of Commerce(3448/349)
Dept. of Business Administration(2633/202)
Dept. of Foreign Trade(815/147)
Faculty of Political Science and Economics(3762/71)
Dept. of Political Science(1246/21)
Dept. of Economics(2516/50)
Faculty of Foreign Languages(1007/6)
Dept. of English and American Language(500/3)
Dept. of Chinese Language(250/2)
Dept. of Spanish Language(257/1)
Faculty of Engineering(1246/10)
Dept. of Mechanical Systems Engineering(325/2)
Dept. of Electronic Engineering(313/4)
Dept. of Information and Data Processing Engineering(318/4)
Dept. of Industrial Design(290/0)

Graduate Programs

Graduate School of Economics(M 63/5, D 8/7)
Div. of International Economy(M 63/5, D 8/7)
Economics, Economic Policy, Economic History, Finance, Social Policy, International Economy, Development Economy, International Trade, International Finance, Public International Laws, International Tax

Laws, International Politics, Economic History in China, Chinese Economy, Economy in the Soviet Russia and Eastern Europe, Economy in the Southeast Asia, Economy in America, Economy in the Middle East, Studies of Foreign Documents

Graduate School of Commerce(M 79/26, D 22/17)

Div. of Commerce(M 79/26, D 22/17)

Commerce, Principle of Commerce, Foreign Trade, Finance, Principle of Business Administration, Transport, Business Management, History of Business Administration, Form of Business Enterprise, International Business, Administration, Business Strategy, Management Information, Industrial Psychology, Financial Accounts, Management Accounts, Financial Audit, Commercial Law, Labor Laws, Tax Laws, Studies of Foreign Documents

---

多摩美術大学

(Tama Bijutsu Daigaku)

Tama Art University

3-15-34 Kaminoge, Setagaya-ku, Tokyo 158
☎ 03-3702-1141 FAX 03-3702-2235

Founded 1935
Professors 56
Associate Professors 27
Assistant Professors(Tenured) 5
Assistant Professors(Non-tenured) 118
Research Assistants 46
Undergraduate Students/Foreign Students 2474/0
Graduate Students/Foreign Students 72/14
Library 86, 000 volumes
Contact: Admission Office, Tama Art University 1723 Yarimizu, Hachioji, Tokyo 192-03

Undergraduate Programs

Faculty of Fine Arts and Design(2474/0)

Dept. of Architecture(316/0)

Dept. of Design(1, 154/0)

Dept. of Painting(668/0)

Dept. of Research of Art and Design(235/0)

Dept. of Sculpture(101/0)

Graduate Programs

Graduate School of Fine Arts and Design(M 72/14)

Div. of Design(M 20/6)

Craft Design, Graphic Design, Industrial Design, Interior Design, Textile Design

Div. of Painting(M 34/7)

Ceramic Art, Japanese Painting, Oil Painting, Print Making

Div. of Sculpture(M 18/1)

Metal, Plaster, Stone, Wood

玉川大学

(Tamagawa Daigaku)

Tamagawa University

6-1-1 Tamagawa Gakuen, Machida-shi, Tokyo 194
☎ 0427-28-3111

Founded 1949

Undergraduate Programs

Faculty of Agriculture

Dept. of Agricultural Chemistry

Dept. of Agriculture

Faculty of Engineering

Dept. of Electronic Engineering

Dept. of Information and Communication Engineering

Dept. of Mangement Engineering

Dept. of Mechanical Engineering

Faculty of Letters

Dept. of Arts

Arts Education for Children Course, Dramatic Arts Course, Fine Arts Course, Music Course

Dept. of Ecucation

Dept. of English and American Literature

Dept. of Foreign Languages

English Course, French Course, German Course

Graduate Programs

Graduate School of Engineering

Div. of Electronic Engineering

Div. of Mechanical Engineering

Div. of Production Development Engineering

Graduate School of Letters

Div. of Education

Div. of English Literature

多摩大学

(Tama Daigaku)

Tama Institute of Management & Information Sciences

1-1-4 Hijirigaoka, Tama-shi, Tokyo 206
☎ 0423-37-7111 FAX 0423-37-7100

Founded 1989
Professors 23
Associate Professors 5
Assistant Professors(Tenured) 2
Assistant Professors(Non-tenured) 8

Research Assistants 1
Undergraduate Students/Foreign Students 445/0
Library 23, 025 volumes
Contact: Office

Educational philosophy " Open Up the 21st Century "—this is the basic idea under which our institute was established. Our goal is to raise students with a broad view of things and a wide range of application through our international, interdisciplinary and practical curriculum.
Foreign students We have no special admission system for foreigners. Foreigners need to sit for the same entrance examination as the Japanese.
Environment Our campus is situated on the hilltop of the so called " Tama New Town " area that commands a distant view of many beautiful mountains and can be reached in about one hour by train from the heart of Tokyo. Tama City is a growing town and its population is expected to be 300, 000 in the near future.
Facilities Audio Visual Room, Library, Computer Aided Instruction Room, Cafeteria, Sports Arena, Language Lab, etc.
Student activities A yearly campus festival and many club activities: tennis, soccer, baseball, volleyball, basketball, American football, dramatic art, personal computer, etc.

Undergraduate Programs

Faculty of Management Information(445/0)
Dept. of Management Information(445/0)

帝京大学
(Teikyô Daigaku)
Teikyo University

359 Otsuka,Hachiouji-shi,Tokyo 192-03
☎ 0426-76-8211 FAX 0426-76-0388

Founded 1966
Professors 268
Associate Professors 178
Associate Professors(Tenured) 192
Associate Professors(Non-tenured) 422
Research Associate 415
Undergraduate Students Foreign Students 17,126/1
Graduate Students Foreign Students 205/6
Library 313, 631 volumes
Kyomuka(ext300~303)Ryugakusei Bekka(ext644)

Educational philosophy To develop a world citizen, who can concentrate on the fun-damentals, acquire a wide range of knowledge without prejudice, and make decisions from an international perspective. International education to link the minds and hearts of the world.

Policies about recieving foreign students In order to internationalize out esucation, Teikyo University has newly established the one-year foreign student's progrem, with the aim of improving the quality of Japanese language education while developing future leaders on an international level.
Environments Schools of Lib. Arts, Law & Economics: Hachioji city, 30 km west of central Tokyo; School of Medicine: Itabashi ward, 12 km north-west of central Tokyo; Pharmaceutical Sciencesr: Lake Sagami, Kanagwa prefecture; Science & Engin.: Utsunimiya city, Tochigi.
Facilities 3 hospitals; 8 research insitutes; ewtensive libraries on every campus; Hachioji has over 340,000 books; new, six-story physical education & cafeteria builking; several computers and audio-visual rooms.
Student activities Popular campus events include the Teikyo Group's concert-style entrance ceremony, freshmen welcome party and school festivals of each campus. Club actvities are also popular, especially rugby, kerate and baseball, which has maintained a good record.
Academic programs for foreign students Teikyo Foreign Student's Program- Japanese Language Course; exchange & study abroad programs through Teikyos British campus and affiliated U.S. campuses (5).
Sereices for foreign students At present, there are no speciel services for foreign students, although advisors are available to counsel. Teikyo will be conducting Japanèse language lessons and private company internships for students form affiliated U.S. campuses, during summer vacation.

Undergraduate Programs

Faculty of Economics(3,724/0)
Dept. of Economics(3,724/0)
Faculty of Literature(6,206/0)
Dept. of Japanese Literature(942/0)
Dept. of English Literature(737/0)
Dept. of Esucation(1,288/0)
Dept. of History(946/0)
Dept. of Sociology(959/0)
Dept. of Psychology(489/0)
Dept. of International Culture(845/0)
Faculty of Economics(4,095/0)
Dept. of Economics(4,095/0)
School of Medicine(913/0)
Dept. of Medicine(913/0)
School of Pharmaceutical Sciences(999/0)
Dept. of Pharmacy(505/0)
Dept. of Biological Pharmacy(494/0)
Faculty of Science and Engineering(1,189/1)
Dept. of Mechanical and Precision SystemDept. of 254/0)
Dept. of Electricity and Electronics System(250/0)
Dept. of Materials Science and Engineering(149/0)
Dept. of Information Sciences(305/1)

Faculty of Science and Engineering
Dept. of Biosciences(231)

Graduate Programs

Graduate School of Economics(M 43/3, D 4/0)
Div. of Economics(M 43/3, D 4/0)
Econometrics, Study of the International Economy, History of Western Economics, History of Eastern Economics, History of the Japanese Economy, Monetary Theory
Graduate School of Law(M 12/0, D 2/0)
Div. of Law(M 12/0, D 2/0)
Constituional Law, Administrative Law, International Public Law (basic and special study courses)
Graduate School of Literature(M 15/1, D 9/1)
Div. of Japanese Literature(M 9/1, D 3/1)
Japenese Linguistics, Japanese Literature–Nara Period, Japanese Literature–Heian Period, related seminars

Div. of English Literature(M 6/0, D 6/0)
English Linguistcs, English Literature, Contemporary English Literature (both lectures and seminars)
Graduate School of Medicine(84/1)
Div. of First Division of Fundamental Medicine(9/1)
Anatomy I & II, Physiology I,II & III, Biochemistry
Graduate School of Medicine(84/0)
Div. of Second Division of Fundamental Medicine(6/0)
Patology I, II & III, Pharmacology, Bacteriology, Parasitology
Graduate School of Medicine(84/1)
Div. of Social Medicine(2/0)
Hygiene, Public Health, Forensic Medicine
Graduate School of Medicine(84/1)
Div. of First Division of Clinical Medicine(40/0)
Internal Medicine I,II,III,IV,V & VI
Graduate School of Medicine(84/1)
Div. of First Division of Clinical Medicine(27/0)
Anesthesiology, Urology, Otorhinolaryngology, Opthamology, Obstetrics & Gynecology, Orthopedics
Graduate School of Pharmaceutical Sciences(M 33/0, D 3/0)
Div. of Pharmaceutical Sciences(M 33/0, D 3/0)
Synthetic Pharmaceutical Chemistry, I Organic Chemistry
Bichemical Pathophysiology
Chemotherapy
Immunology
Pharmacology
Clinical Biochemistry
Pharmaceutics
Spesial Lecture on Incurable Diseases
Hygienic Chemistry
Environmental Hygienics

帝京技術科学大学
(Teikyô Gijutsu Kagaku Daigaku)
Teikyo University of Technology

2289–23 Oyatsu–shi, Uruido, Ichihara, Chiba 290–01
☎ 0436–74–5511 FAX 0436–74–7551

Founded 1987
Professors 36
Associate Professors 24
Assistant Professors(Tenured) 10
Assistant Professors(Non–tenured) 19
Research Assistants 6
Undergraduate Students/Foreign Students 2183/0
Library 48, 000 volumes
Contact: Admission Office

Educational philosophy We aim at teaching wide knowledge and practical ability in informatics, and at educating development and creation in technology and science.
Foreign students We have never accepted foreign student, because our school is very new. We will make a much effort to teach and study informatics for foreign students.
Environment The city of Ichihara, with a population of 260, 000, is located 6 miles south of the city of Chiba, 30 miles southeast of Tokyo. The area is very quiet in the forest.
Facilities Computer center, Library, Learning Laboratory, Electronics Research Laboratory, Sports Training Center, Gymnasium.
Student activities Popular campus events includes school festival, freshman welcome party. There is a wide variety of extra curricular, including light music groups, baseball, football, soccer, etc.

Undergraduate Programs

Faculty of Informatics(2, 183/0)
Dept. of Information Engineering(585/0)
Dept. of Information Systems(583/0)
Dept. of Information Management(1, 015/0)

東邦音楽大学
(Tôhô Ongaku Daigaku)
Toho College of Music

84 Imaizumi, Kawagoe–shi, Saitama 356
☎ 0492–35–2157 FAX 0492–35–1165

Founded 1965
Professors 12
Associate Professors 14

Assistant Professors (Tenured) 4
Assistant Professors (Non-tenured) 52
Undergraduate Students/Foreign Students 617/5
Library 38, 773 volumes
Contact: Admission Office (the educational affairs department)

Educational philosophy "The development of a student into a refined person who appreciates the values of music" is one of the founding goals of this college. The most important purpose in this college is to develop the students' whole personality through musical education. This college gives the students not only techniques and knowledge on music, but also higher liberal arts education.
Foreign students Through the participation in the events of the 750th Anniversary of the Municipalizing in Berlin and the Musical Festival in Europe or the Joint Concerts in Singapore and in Taiwan, we would make efforts to promote the international exchange and to accept the foreign students in the countries in Asia.
Environment The city of Kawagoe in Saitama-Ken with a population of 300, 000 is a kind of castle town and looks just as it did in the old days. It takes about fifty minutes from there to Tokyo by Train. Being free from the din and bustle of a great city, Kawagoe is rich in the nature and a good place to study music.
Facilities Library (21884 volumes related to music), 50 th Anniversary Hall and Conservatore (Tokyo), Practice Rooms (with pianos), Audiovisual Laboratory (for CD, LD, LP, VHS)
Student activities The main campus events consist of Regular Concerts (in spring and in fall), School Festiva (in spring) and Concert Tour. There are twelve club activities; Tennis Club, Opera Society, Light Music Society, etc.
Academic programs for foreign students Japanese language (4 subjects), Japanese affairs (4 subjects). Theories of Composition, Choral Conducting as the lectures for the foreign students. Observation tour in suburbs of Tokyo, the special lecture for Japanese traditional culture (e. g. the handicrafts).
Services for Foreign students Personal and psychological counseling, Health clinic, Housing information

Undergraduate Programs

Faculty of Music (617/5)
Music Course
Composition major,
Instrumental Music major,
Vocal Music major

桐朋学園大学
(Tôhô-Gakuen Daigaku)
Toho-Gakuen College of Music

1-41-1 Wakaba-Cho, Chofu-shi, Tokyo 182
☎ 03-3307-4101 FAX 03-3326-8844

Founded 1961
Professors 51
Associate Professors 27
Assistant Professors (Tenured) 16
Assistant Professors (Non-tenured) 279
Research Assistants 2
Undergraduate Students/Foreign Students 930/0
Library 93, 584 volumes
Contact: Admission Office

Educational philosophy The ultimate aim of education at Toho Gakuen is to let students fulfill themselves, to enable each student to search for and discover for himself the meaning of making music, through private lessons and diversified and extensive studies in classes.
Foreign students Foreign students can enjoy a various kinds of valuable experiences through their lives at Toho Gakuen. Especially, they can study under its superb music teachers and among its talented college students.
Environment Toho Gakuen is located about 5 minutes' walk from Sengawa Station on Keio Line. It takes about half an hour by train from Shinjuku, one of the busiest down towns in Tokyo.
Facilities Library, Gymnasium, Swimming pool
Student activities Popular campus events include music performances (solo, orchestra, chamber music, composition, opera, etc.), held throughout the year, and the school festival in early October.
Academic programs for foreign students We have 'Special Audit Student' course especially for foreign students who want to study at our college at longest for a year and at shortest a month.

Undergraduate Programs

Faculty of Music (930/0)

東邦大学
(Tôhô Daigaku)
Toho University

5-21-16 Omori Nishi, Ota-ku, Tokyo 143
☎ 03-3762-4151 FAX 03-3768-0660

Founded 1925

Professors 120
Associate Professors 97
Assistant Professors(Tenured) 118
Assistant Professors(Non-tenured) 86
Research Assistants 436
Undergraduate Students/Foreign Students 3, 178/0
Graduate Students/Foreign Students 185/8
Library 244, 636 volumes
Contact: Toho University School of Medicine 5-21-16 Omori Nishi, Ota-ku, Tokyo 143 ☎ 03-3762-4151 Toho University School of Pharmaceutical Sciences Toho University School of Faculty of Science 2-2-1 Miyama, Funabashi-shi, Chiba 274 ☎ 0474-72-1141

Educational philosophy Toho University strives to instill its students with " respect for nature, awareness of the dignity of life, and humility of the heart toward man. " Indeed, this is our school motto.
Foreign students Toho University has a history of accepting foreign students, especially from China, Korea, and Taiwan. All prospective students must pass written and oral entrance examinations, conducted in Japanese.
Environment Toho University has two main campuses: Omori and Narashino. The Omori campus is located in an urban setting Ota Ward, while the Narashino campus is situated in Chiba Prefecture, a more suburban area.
Facilities Hospital, research center, library, sports grounds, gymnasium, cafeteria, student center.
Student activities In addition to a variety of sport and other clubs—e. g. kendo, basketball, football, golf, photography, music, etc. —major student activities include the annual Freshman Welcome Party(in April) and the Student Festival(in October).

Undergraduate Programs

School of Medicine(638/0)
Dept. of Medicine(638/0)
School of Pharmaceutical Sciences(955/0)
Faculty of Pharmaceutical Sciences(626/0)
Faculty of Biopharmaceutical Sciences(329/0)
Faculty of Science(1, 585/0)
Dept. of Chemistry(515/0)
Dept. of Biology(400/0)
Dept. of Physics(335/0)
Dept. of Biomolecular Science(188/0)
Dept. of Information Science(147/0)

Graduate Programs

Graduate School of Medicine(D 74/7)
Morphological Intervention, Anatomy, Pathology, Clinical Pathology, Physical Function, Physiology, Biochemistry, Pharmacology, Microbiology, Immunology, Molecular Biology, Social Medicine: Hygiene, Public Health and Hygiene, Legal Medicine, Hospital Management, Non-Surgical Medicine: Internal Medicine, Pediatrics, Neuropsychiatry, Radiology and Radiotherapy, Dermatology, Psychosomatic Medicine, Nephrology, Diabetology, Surgical Medicine: Surgery, Orthopedics, Neurosurgery, Obstetrics and Gynecology, Urology, Otorhinolaryngology, Opthalmology, Anesthesiology
Graduate School of Pharmaceutical(M 53/1, D 1/0)
Courses in Advanced Special Studies in Therapeutic Medicine(M 54/1, D 1/0)
Therapeutic medicine and pharmaceutics.
Graduate School of Science(M 47/0, D 10/0)
Courses in Advanced Special Studies in Chemistry(M 11/0, D 2/0)
Inorganic-Analytical Chemistry, Organic Chemistry, Physical Chemistry
Courses in Advanced Special Studies in Biology(M 17/0, D 4/0)
Plant Physiology, Ecology, Animal Physiology, Physiological Chemistry
Courses in Advanced Special Studies in Physics(M 19/0, D 4/0)
Fundamental Physics, Solid-State Physics, Applied Physics

桐蔭学園横浜大学
(Tôin Gakuen Yokohama Daigaku)

Toin University of Yokohama

1614 Kurogane-cho, Midori-ku, Yokohama-shi, Kanagawa 225
☎ 045-972-5881 FAX 045-972-5972

Founded 1988
Professors 21
Associate Professors 15
Assistant Professors(Tenured) 4
Assistant Professors(Non-tenured) 26
Research Assistants 11
Undergraduate Students/Foreign Students 528/0
Library 18, 953 volumes
Contact: Admission Office ☎ ext 228

Educational philosophy This private university, with its four-point program of " Liberty, Learning, Integrity and Loyalty ", in further pursuit of these principles, aims at training young individuals for the international community of science and engineering in the coming new age.
Environment The University enjoys abundant greenery on its campus on a hill north of the historic Port of Yokohama, well within commuting distance from Yokohama and Tokyo.
Facilities Library, Computer center, Gymnasium, Auditorium(Memorial Hall)
Student activities Popular campus events includes Freshmen camp, Annual marathon race and school festival. There is a wide variety of extra curricular activities, including volunteer work, drama, rugby, tennis, golf and etc.

Undergraduate Programs

Faculty of Engineering(528/0)
  Dept. of Control and Systems Engineering(361/0)
  Dept. of Materials Science and Technology(167/0)

東海大学
(Tôkai Daigaku)
Tokai University

2-28 Tomigaya, Shibuya-ku, Tokyo 151
☎ 03-3467-2211 FAX 03-3469-0196

Founded 1942
Professors 555
Associate Professors 321
Assistant Professors(Tenured) 207
Assistant Professors(Non-tenured) 774
Research Assistants 243
Undergraduate Students/Foreign Students 30255/185
Graduate Students/Foreign Students 764/66
Library 1, 187, 530 volumes
Contact: International Affairs Section 1117 Kitakaname, Hiratsuka, Kanagawa 259-12 ☎ 0463-58-9541 FAX 0463-35-2458

Educational philosophy The founding spirit is directed toward contributing to the cause of world peace and universal well-being by devoting persons capable of creating an age of spiritual and materialistic harmony; persons who are able to act positively and vigorously in devoting themselves to attainiment of a world society based on humanism and mutual respect.
Foreign students Based on the idea of promoting mutual understanding beyond political systems and borders, Tokai University has been accepting ever-increasing foreign students from more than 25 countries including USSR, Germany, China, Korea, Taiwan and USA, to overcome various obstacles caused by cultural differences and to review the roots of our cultural background.
Environment In scenic west in the heart of Sagami Plain, the main campus is located in Hiratsuka-city close to Shonan Coast, with a population of 300, 000 and 70 minutes by train from downtown Tokyo. The area is rich in history and culture, with a splendid view to Mt. Fuji.
Facilities Libraries, Hospitals, University Press, Computer Center, Health Care Center, Marine Science Museum, Human Science Museum, Research & Training Vessels, Research & Information Center, Training Centers, Gymnasiums, Auditorium, Swimming Pools, Overseas Facilities in Denmark, Austria and Hawaii.
Student activities Popular campus events include; Foundation Festival, Freshmen Welcoming, Softball Competition, etc. Extra curricular activities include; Baseball, Judo, Kendo, Karate, Volleyball, Golf, Basketball, Football, Drama, Dance, Music, Newspaper, E. S. S, Art, Marching Band, Cinema, Electronics, Chemistry, Volunteer Work, etc.
Academic programs for foreign students Intensive Japanese Language Program(1 year, pre-college). Foreign Students Course with special curricula. Special Japanese Language Course for Exchange Students. Tutoring System, Advisor System, Scholarship Services.
Services for foreign students Foreign Student Dormitory, Health Care Center, Personal Counselling, Housing Information, Vocational Guidance, Foreign Student Association, Freshmen Welcoming Barbecue Party, Excursions, Technical Visits, Home Visit, Japanese Language Speech Contest, Kabuki-Theatre, Bazaar and Cultural Exchange Programs.

Undergraduate Programs

School of Engineering(11, 686/53)
  Dept. of Aeronautics and Astronautics(428/4)
  Dept. of Applied physics(412/2)
  Dept. of Architecture and Building Engineering(1, 073/2)
  Dept. of Civil Engineering(1, 114/3)
  Dept. of Communications Engineering(1, 075/7)
  Dept. of Control Engineering(412/5)
  Dept. of Electrical Engineering(1, 033/1)
  Dept. of Electronics(1, 086/13)
  Dept. of Electro Photo Optics(405/0)
  Dept. of Industrial Chemistry(781/2)
  Dept. of Management Engineering(826/7)
  Dept. of Metallurgical Engineering(434/0)
  Dept. of Nuclear Engineering(417/1)
  Dept. of Precision Mechanics(431/1)
  Dept. of Prime Mover Engineering(1, 066/0)
  Dept. of Production Engineering(694/5)
School of Humanities and Culture(1, 770/24)
  Dept. of Arts(438/6)
  Dept. of Human Development(887/9)
  Dept. of International Studies(445/9)
School of Law(1, 445/3)
  Dept. of Law(1, 445/3)
School of Letters(4, 704/53)
  Dept. of Civilization (Asian Studies/European Studies) (1, 430/8)
  Dept. of English Literature(532/8)
  Dept. of History (Japanese History/Oriental History/Occidental History/Archaeology) (535/1)
  Dept. of Japanese Literature(538/2)
  Dept. of Mass Communications(1, 120/33)
  Dept. of Nordic Studies(549/1)
School of Marine Science and Technology(3, 325/2)
  Dept. of Fisheries(835/0)
  Dept. of Marine Civil Engineering(586/0)
  Dept. of Marine Mineral Resources(427/2)
  Dept. of Marine Science(409/0)
  Dept. of Nautical Engineering(136/0)

Dept. of Naval Architecture(196/0)
Dept. of Ocean Engineering(736/0)
School of Medicine(690/0)
Dept. of Medicine(690/0)
School of Physical Education(1, 512/0)
Dept. of Judo and Kendo(209/0)
Dept. of Physical Education(848/0)
Dept. of Physical Recreation(455/0)
School of Political Science and Economics (2, 582/49)
Dept. of Business Administration(870/32)
Dept. of Economics(878/14)
Dept. of Political Science(834/3)
School of Science(1, 671/1)
Dept. of Chemistry(414/0)
Dept. of Mathematical Science(425/1)
Dept. of Mathematics(421/0)
Dept. of Physics(411/0)

Graduate Programs

Graduate School of Arts(M 6/0)
Course of Music(M 6/0)
Research in Music, Musicology; History of Japanese Music, Ethnomusicology, History of Western Music, Aesthetics, Music Theory, Pedagogy of Music
Course of Fine Arts and Design(M 0/0)
Research in Fine Arts, Research in Design, Aesthetics, Science of Art, Special Researches of Theoretical Side of Fine Arts, History of Japanese Fine Arts, History of Oriental Fine Arts, History of Western Fine Arts, Arts and Crafts, Design Aesthetics
Graduate School of Economics(M 10/8, D 3/1)
Course of Applied Economics(M 10/8, D 3/1)
Economics, Economic History and Affairs, Economic Policy, Business Management
Graduate School of Engineering(M 357/19, D 20/5)
Course of Aeronautics and Astronautics(M 27/0, D 5/0)
Aeronautical Engineering, Space Engineering, Space Science, Flight And Aerodynamics, High Speed Aerodynamics, Structure Dynamics, Air Trancportation Technology, Aeroengine Engineering, Combustion Engineering, Electric Prepulsion Engineering, Rocket Technology, Modern Control System, Space Flight Dynamics, Space Environment Science, Space And Astrophysics, Space Evolution Theory
Course of Applied Science(M 41/3, D 1/0)
Nuclear Engineering, Applied Physics, System Control Theory, Reactor Physics, Radiation Physics, Radiation Measurements, Nuclear Fuel, Nuclear Fusion Reactor Technology, Reactor Safety, Reactor Heat Engineering, Reactor Engineering Laboratory, Reactor Instrumentation, Applied Functional Analysis, Radiation Environment Engineering, Nuclear Materials, Health Physics, Radiation Chemistry, Nuclear Chemical Engineering, Radiation Chemistry, Strength of Materials, Applied Radio Isotope Engineering, Engineering Physics, Sybernetics Engineering, Statistical Physics, Applied Solid State Engineering, Applied Random Process, Solid State Devics, Solid State Electronics, Fluid Mechanics, Applied Materials Science, Amorphous Semiconductor Engineering
Course of Architecture and Building Engineering (M 20/1, D 0/0)
Architectural Design, Building Equipment, Structural Mechanics, Building Materials And Construction, Architectural History, Architectural Plannig, Building Equipment, Structural Mechanics
Course of Civil Engineering(M 10/2, D 0/0)
Structural Engineering And Mechanics, Soil Mechanics And Foundation Engineering, Hydraulics And Sanitary Engineering, Advanced Surveying, Applied Mechanics, Structrual Mechanics, Structural Engineering, Engineering Materials, Reinforced Concrete, Civil Engineering Planning, Land And Urban Planning, Earthquake Engineering, Soil Mechanics, Soil Mechanical Engineering, Soil Engineering Geology, Hydraulics, River Engineering, Sanitary Engineering, Transportation Engineering, Applied Mathematics, Computer Analyses in Engineering, Water Pollution Control, Concrete Engineering, Highway Engineering
Course of Electrical Engineering(M 51/2, D 3/2)
Electrical Engineering, Communcations Engineering, Applied Mathematics, Numerical Analysis, Stochastic Process, Discrete Mathematics, Engineering Science, Quantum Mechanics, Semiconductor Electronics, Device Electronics, Thin Film Electronics, Thin Film Engineering, Statistical Mechanics, Thermodynamics, Applied Optics, Organic Materials, Plasma Electronics, Bioelectronics, Quantum Biology, Compound Semiconductors, Laser Engineering, Integrated Circuits, Cryogenics, Optimal Control Theory, Control Systems, Stochastic Systems, Applied Control Theory, Fundamental Control Theory, Robotics, Fuzzy Systems, Simulation Technology, Image Processing, Pattern Recognition, Artificial Intelligence, Data Base, Biological Engineering, Computer Systems, Computer Architecture, Software Engineering, Mathematical Logics, Logic Design, Computer Science, Computer Language, System Engineering, Digital Signal Processing, Analog Signal Processing, Network Theory, Electronic Circuits, Communication Theory, Electromagnetic Filed Theory, Electrical Discharge Engineering, Dielectrics, Electronic Materials, Energy Conversion, Power Electronics, Electric Machinery, Linear Moter, Power System Engineering, Power System Analysis, High Voltage Engineering, Fine Electronic Materials, Applied Plasma Physics, Information Networks, Communication Systems, Acoustics, Electromagnetic Wave Engineering, Optical Communications, Electromagnetic Wave Applications, Space Communications, Satellite Communications, Electric Power Engineering, Bionics, Network Synthesis, Active Circuits, Integrated Circuit Technology, Applied Plasma Physics, Solid State Physics, Radio Wave And Optical Communications, Power System Engineering, Image Processing, Dielectrics, Intergrated Circuits, Waveform Transmission, Laser Engineering
Course of Electronics(M 71/4, D 6/2)
Electronics, Control Engintering, Applied Mathamatics, Numerical Analysis, Stochastic Process, Discrete Mathematics, Engineering Science, Quantum Mechanics,

Semiconductor Electronics, Device Electronics, Thin Film Electronics, Thin Film Engineering, Statistical Mechanics, Thermodynamics, Applied Optics, Organic Materials, Plasma Electonics, Bioelectonics, Quantum Biology, Compound Semiconductors, Laser Engineering, Integrated Circuits, Cryogenics, Optiomal Control Theory, Control System, Stochasitc Systems, Applied Control Theory, Fundamental Control Theory, Fundamental Control Theory, Robotics, Fuzzy Systems, Simulation Technology, Image Processing, Pattern Recognition, Artificial Interlligence, Data Base, Biological Engineering, Computer Systems, Computer Architecture, Software Engineering, Mathematical Logic, Logic Design, Computer Science, Computer Language, System Engineering, Digital Signal Processing, Network Theory, Electronic Circuits, Communication Theory, Electromagnetic Field Theroy, Material Science, Applied Solid State Science, Solid State Surfaces, Optoelectronics, Crystal Engineering, Digital Control Theory, Process Control, Industrial Instrumentation, Control Systems And Equipments, Servomechanism and Equipments, Control Engineering, Semiconductor Electronics, Electonic Measurement, Solid State Physics, Automáte And Language, Application of Tensor Analysis, Acoustic Engineeing, Industial Instrumentation, Numerically Controlled Machine Tools, Logical Design, Crystal Engineeirng, Digital Engineering,

Course of Electro Photo Optics(M 19/1, D 1/1)

Research of Optical Science And Engineering, Research of Imaging Science And Engineering, Applied Optics, Non–Linear Optics, Information Processing of Optics, Optical Materials, Materials for Image Information, Imaging Information, Photo Chemistry, Materials for Electro Photo Optics, Energy And Photon, Physiological Optics, Wave Optics, Solid State Physics, Imaging Science, Semi–Conductor Physics, Image Processing, Optical Design, Opto–Electronics, Imaging Information, Photon And Energy, Imaging Materials, Imaging System

Course of Industrial Chemistry(M 12/1, D 0/0)

Industrial Inorganic Chemistry, Analytical Chemistry, Industrial Physical Chemistry, Industrial Organic Chemistry, Synthetic Organic Chemistry, Chemical Engineering, Inorganic Materials Chemistry, Properties of Inorganic Functional Materials, Inorganic Structural Chemistry, Industrial Electrochemistry, Industrial Polymer Chemistry, Physical And Chemical Properties of Polmers, Hydrocarbon Chemistry, Organics Materials Chemistry, Industrial Chemical Engineering, Separation Process Engineering, Computer Aided Plant Design, Environmental Technology, Industrial Analytical Chemistry, Instrumental Analytical Chemistry, Gualitative Analytical Chemistry, Energy And Resources, Catalytic Chemistry, Photo And Radiation Chemistry, Biotechnology

Course of Management Engineering(M 16/2, D 1/0)

System Engineering, Industrial Engineering, Automatic Control Engineering, Marketing Engineering, Office Management Engineering, Quality Control Engineering, Stastical Engineering, Decision Support System, Numerical Control, Robotics, Industrial Engineering, Human Engineering, Management Engineering, Mathematical Engineering, Cost Accounting Engineering, Programming Language, Information System Design, Work Study, Process, Statistical Engineering, Social Engineering, Labor Safety Management, Industrial Psychology, Information Engineering, Learning Engineering, Reliability Engineering

Course of Mechanical Engineering(M 54/1, D 1/0)

Material Engineering, Thermal Engineering, Fluid Engineering, Machining, Mechanical Dynamics, Strength of Materials, Elaticity, Lubrication Engineering, Heat Transfer, Internal Combustion Engine, Internal Combustion Engineering, Car Engineering, Fluiddynamics, Fluid Machinery, Metal Working, Precision Machining, Mechanical Dynamics, Precision Machine Elements, Precision Measurements, Presicion Machinery, Control Engineering, Electric Engineering, Atomic Energy Engineering

Course of Metallurgical Engineering(M 36/2, D 2/0)

Materials Science, Metallurgy Physical Chemistry of Metal, Statistic Thermodynamics, Materials Science, Strength of Materials, Structure And Properties of Steels, Casting, Radiographic Technology of Materials, Physics of Metal, Heat Treatment, Surface Technology of Metals, Powder Metallurgy, Electrical And Electronic Engineering Materials, Welding Engineering, Solidification of Metals, New Materials Science, Functional Materials, Engineering Metal Surface, Metallurgy of Iron And Steel

Graduate School of Law(M 7/0)

Course of Business Law(M 3/0)

Business Administrative Law, Civil Law, Commercial Law, Economic Law, Labor Law, Intangible Property Law, Civil Procedure, Seminar of Business Law, Tax Law, Social Security Law, Medical Law, International Transaction Law, Public Law, International and Comparative Law

Course of International and Comparative Law(M 1/0)

Internatinal Law, International Transaction Law, Anglo–American Law, German Law, French Law, Socialist Law, Asian Law, Chinese Law, Sociology of Law, Seminar of International and Comparative Law, Constitution, Japanese Legal Hitory, Philosophy of Law, Intangible Property of Law, Public Law, Business Law

Course of Public Law(M 3/0)

Constitution, Administrative Law, Tax Law, Criminal Law, Criminal Procedure, Social Security Law, Medical Law, Japanese Legal History, Philosophy of Law, Seminar of Public Law, Economic Law, Labor Law, International Law, Sociology of Law, Business Law, International and Comparative Law

Graduate School of Letters(M 37/11, D 31/12)

Course of Civilization Studies(M 7/0, D 3/0)

Theory of Civilization, Comparative Studies of Civilization, Modern Civilization, Science and Technology, History of Science and Technology, Asian Civilization, European Civilization, Japanese Civilization, Research

Methods of Civilization

Course of English Literature(M 7/2, D 7/1)

Modern English Literature, Contemporary English Literature, Medieval English Literature, American Literature, English Linguistics, Research Methods of English Literature

Course of History(M 7/0, D 3/0)

The Theory of History, Japanese History, The History of Japanese Religion, Japan's Foreign Policy, Diplomatics, Oriental Hitory, Occidental History

Course of Japanese Literature(M 10/6, D 14/9)

Japanese Literature, Japanese Linguistics, Old Japanese Literature, Medieval Japanese Literature, Japanese Edo Literature, Modern Japanese Literature, Chinese Classics, Research Methods of Japanese Literature

Course of Mass Communications(M 6/3, D 4/2)

Communication, Information Society, Mass Media, Research Methods of Mass Communication, Individual and Society

Graduate School of Marine Science and Technology(M 92/1, D 11/1)

Course of Living Marine Resources(M 19/0, D 2/0)

Marine Bilogy, Fisheries Resource Exploitation, Mari-Culture, Fishing Grounds Study, Fisheries Economics, Benthos Ecology, Marine Ecology, Fish Physiology, Systematic Zoology, Planktology, Marine Microbiology, Rearing and Cultivating of Early Marine Animals, Phycology, Benthic Invertebrates, Fish Diseases, Cell Biology, Management Fishery Biology

Course of Marine Engineering(M 47/1, D 3/0)

Ocean Engineering, Ocean Civil Engineering, Ocean System Engineering, Ocean Development Engineering, Marine Measurement Engineering, Marine Electronics, Marine Electronic Measurement, Marine Radio Engineering, Digital Signal Processing, Remoto Sensing Technology for Oceanography, Underwater Acoustic Engineering, Marine Optics, Marine Material Engineering, Coastal Oceanography, Geofluid Dynamics, Ocean Numerical Simulation, Marine Politics, Ocean Data Analysis, Physical Oceanography, Applied Oceanography, Structural Analysis, Steel Structure Engineering, Soil And Foundation Engineering, Management of Engineering, Coastal Engineering, Hydraulics, Ocean Structure, Harbour Engineering, Oceanic Environment Engineering, Plasticity And Plastic Design, Fluid Dynamics, Manned And Unmanned Submersible Technology, Material Mechanics, Structural Design Philosophy, Engineering of Control Systems, Dynamical Engineering of Floating Structures, Systems Analysis for Maritime Industries

Course of Marine Science(M 26/0, D 6/1)

Physical Oceanography, Chemical Oceanography, Solid Earth Science, Descriptive Oceanography, Ocean Wave Theory, Descriptive Oceanography of Coastal Water, Ocean Dynamics, Marine Meteorology, Study of Physical Property of Sea Water, Ocean Currents Relating to Dispersion and Transport, Chemical Oceanography, Sea –Water Chemistry, Organics Chemistry of Sea Water, Radio Chemistry, Chemical Sedimentology, Geophysics, Seabed Mineralogy, Submarine Structural Geology, Marine Remote Sensing, Physics of Earth's Crust, Submarine Geophysics, Submarine Geology, Marine Ecology, Planktology, Estuarine and Coastal Hydrography

Graduate School of Medicine(D 88/4)

Course of Ecological and Environmental Medical Science(D 4/1)

Epidemiology, Community Health, Medical Information, Infectious Diseases and Immunology, Medical Virology, Pathogenesis of Infectious Diesese, Gnotobiology, Parasitic Protozoology, Helminthology, Medioal Entmology, Occupational Medicine, Environmental Health, Principle of Health Care Service, Medical Informatics, Biomedical Instrumentation and Measurements, Systems Approach to Physiology, Forensic Toxicology, Traffic Accident, Forensic Pathology, Experimental Oncology, Medical Information Processing, Medical Electronics, Clinical Gnotobiology, Geriatrics, Clinical Bacteriology, Biochemical Oncology, Cerebral Blood Flow Physiology, Tropical Medicine, Emergency Critical Care Medicine, Membrane Biology, Simulation Technigue of Human Function, Computer System, Hyper and Hypobaric Medicine

Course of Functional Medical Science(D 5/0)

Neurophysiology, Autonomic Function and Sensory Physiology, Research Methods in Neurophysiology, Cardiovascular Physiology, Respiratory Physiology, Methods for the Evaluation of Cardio–Pulmonary Function, Metabolism, Biochemical Pathology, Enzymology, Pharmacokinetics, Pharmacodynamics, Neuropharmacology, Molecular Genetics, Molecular Biology of Viruses, Radiation Biology, Experimental Oncology, Medical Information Processing, Medical Electronics, Clinical Gnotobiology, Geriatrics, Clinical Bacteriology, Biochemical Oncology, Cerebral Blood Flow Physiology, Tropical Medicine, Emergency Critical Care Medicine, Membrane Biology, Simulation Technuque of Human Function, Computer System, Hyper and Hypobaric Medicine, Physiology of Digestion Absorption and Intermediary Metabolism, Physiology of Biomechanical Muscle Function, Applied Physiology, Physical Fitness and Sports Medicine

Course of Medicine(D 43/1)

Clinical Cardiology, Cardiopulmonary function, General Pulmonology, Gastroenterology, Morphological Hepatology, Metabolic Hepatology, Clinical Immunology, Clinical Hematology, Nephrology, Neurology, Pathophysiology of Cerebral Vascular Disorder, Cerevral Metabolism, Pediatric Nutrition, Neonatology, Vaccinology, Child Health, CHild Psychiatry, Psychoanalysis, Psychosomatic Medicine, Medical Psychology, Interpretation of pathophysiology, Laboratory Diagnosis, Clinical Chemistry, Rehabilitation Medicine, Evaluation and Diagnosis in Rehabilitation Medicine, Therapeutics in Rehabilitation Medicine, Photoallergy and Photoimmunology of the Skin, Histopathology of the Skin, Pathochemistry of the Skin, Diagnostic Radiology, Therapeutic Radiology, Radiation Physics, Gastroenterological Endoscopy, Endoscopic Treatment, Gastrointestinal Medicine, Experimental Oncology, Medical Information Processing, Medical Electronics, Clinical Gnotobiology, Geriatrics, Clinical Bacteriology, Biochemical Oncology, Cerebral Blood Flow Physiology, Tropical Medicine, Emergency Critical Care Medicine, Membrane Biology, Simulation Technique of Human Function, Computer System, Hyper and Hypobaric Medicine

Course of Morphological Medical Science(M 9/1, D 0/1)

Ultramicroscopic Morphology, Topographic Anatomy, Histolgy, Applied Anatomy, Transplantation Immunology, Transplantation Surgery, Artificial Organs, Cell Morphology, Cell Biology, Melecular Cell Biology, Cytochemistry, Immunopathology, Tumor Pathlogy, Experimental Pathology, Pathology of Endocrine and Metabolic Diseases, Organ Pathology, Cell Structure and Function in Pathology, Experimental Oncology, Medical Information Processing, Medical Electronics, Clinical Gnotobiology, Geriatrics, Clinical Bacteriology, Biochemical Oncology, Cerebral Blood Flow Physiology, Tropical Medicine, Emergency Critical Care Medicine, Membrane Biology, Simulation Technique of Human Function, Computer System, Hyper and Hypobaric Medicine

Course of Surgery(D 27/1)

Cardiac Surgery, Vascular Surgery, General Thoracic Surgery, General Surgery, Surgical Oncology, Endocrine Surgery, Pediatric Surgery, Urologic Surgery, Urologic Oncology, Urologic Infection, Optics of the Eye, Clinical Exercise on Optics of the Eye, Ophtalmic Surgery, Biochemistry of the Eye, Otorhinoloaryngology, Neuro-Otology, Head and Neck Surgery, Obstetrics and Gyncology, Gynecological Oncology, Obsterical, Gynecological Anesthesiology, Reproduction, Neurosurgery, Neurology, Orthopaedic Diagnosis, Joint Surgery, Traumatology, Experimental Oncology, Medical Information Processing, Medical Electronics, Clinical Gnotobiology, Geriatrics, Clinical Bacteriology, Biochemical Oncology, Cerebral Blood Flow Physiology, Tropical Medicine, Emergency Critical Care Medicine, Membrane Biology, Simulation Technique of Human Function, Computer System, Hyper and Hypobaric Medicine, Clinical Anesthesiology, Intensive Care Unit Practice, Dolorogy, Pain CLinic Clerkship, Physical Fitness and Sports Medicine

Graduate School of Physical Education(M 14/0)

Course of Physical Education(M 14/0)

Principle in Physical Education, Psychology in Physical Education, Sociology in Physical Education, Social Physical Education, Administration of Physical Education, Pedagogies in Physical Education, Research of Physical Fitness, Physiology of Exercise, Test and Measurement of Physical Fitness, Health Administration, Public Health, Methodology of Physical Education, Research of Coaching, Kinesiology, Physical Recreation, Recent Topics in Leisure and Recreation Activities, Research and Practice in Recreation Activities, Administration and Management of Facilities in Physical Recreation, Survey in Physical Recreation

Graduate School of Political Science(M 12/0, D 4/0)

Course of Political Science(M 12/0, D 4/0)

Political Science, Comparative Politics, Japanese Political History, Western Political History, History of Japanese Political Thought, History of Western Political Thought, Internatioal Politics, Public Administration, Local Government, Urban Policy, Social Education Administration, Political Process, Diplomatic History, International Relations, Economic Policy, Research Methodology

Graduate School of Science(M 62/0, D 10/2)

Course of Chemistry(M 20/0, D 3/2)

Physical Chemistry, Inorganic Chemistry, Organic Chemistry, Analytical Chemistry, Educational Chemistry, Natural Science Education, Biochemistry, Polymer Chemistry

Course of Mathematics(M 15/0, D 1/0)

Algebra, Geomentry, Analysis, Mathematical Statistics, Combinatorics and Computers, Applied Mathematics, History of Mathematics, Mathematics for Education, Natural Science Education

Course of Physics(M 27/0, D 6/0)

High Energy Nuclear Physics, Elementary Particle Physics, Plasma Physics, Condensed Matter Physics, Atomic Spectroscopy, Macromolecular Physics, Accelerator Physics, Solid State Geophysics, Thoretical Nulcear Physics, Quantum Mechanics, Quantum Field Theory, Particle Physics, High Energy Physics, Solid State Physics, Statistical Mechanics, Law Temperature Physics, The Accelerator Physics, Relativity, Educational Physics, Natural Science Education

One-Year Graduate Programs

Marine Science & Technology Course
Navigation Major

常磐大学
(Tokiwa Daigaku)
Tokiwa University

1-430-1 Miwa, Mito-shi, Ibaraki 310
☎ 0292-32-2511 FAX 0292-31-6078

Founded 1983
Professors 33
Associate Professors 11
Assistant Professors(Tenured) 11
Assistant Professors(Non-tenured) 70
Undergraduate Students/Foreign Students 1316/10
Graduate Students/Foreign Students 13/1
Library 123, 000 volumes
Contact: Center for International Studies ☎ 0292-32-2663

Educational Philosophy We put emphasis on human-centered science education and practical instruction, inspiring enterprising students to satisfy the requirements of our changing modern times.

Foreign students We cordially welcome foreign students who are willing to make a challenge to improve themselves with zeal and passion, and promote mutual understanding and friendship.

Environment Mito City(Population–233, 000)is the present administrative center of Ibaraki Prefecture. In the Edo period it was the seat of the Mito branch of the Tokugawa Family. There still remain several historical relics and cultural properties of the time such as the Kodokan Institute and Kairakuen Park.
Facilities Center for Media and Information(Library, Computer Center, Audio–Visual Floor), Center for International Studies, Animal Psychological Research Laboratories, Swimming Pool, Gymnasium, etc.
Student activities Polular campus events include sports festival, Tokiwa Festival, freshman welcome and graduation party.
Services for foreign students Personal/psychological counselling, Housing information, Part–time job information, cultural exchange program

Undergraduate Programs

College of Human Science(1316/10)
Dept. of Administration of Human Organization(344/6)
Dept. of Communication(474/2)
Dept. of Human Relations
Sociology major, Psychology major, Education major (498/2)

Graduate Programs

Graduate School of Human Science(M 13/1)
Div. of Human Science(M 13/1)
Evolution and the Adaptaion of Man, Man and the Environment, Man and Organization, Man and Information, Man and Communication

---

東京基督教大学
(Tokyo Kirisutokyô Daigaku)
Tokyo Christian University

3–301–5–1 Uchino, Inzai–machi, Imba–gun, Chiba 270–13
☎ 0476–46–1131 FAX 0476–46–1405

Founded 1990
Professors 9
Associate Professors 4
Assistant Professors(Tenured) 5
Assistant Professors(Non–tenured) 22
Research Assistants 2
Undergraduate Students/Foreign Students 43/4
Library 45, 332 volumes
Contact: Academic Dean's Office

Educational Philosophy Upholding the motto of our university, " Christ is all, and is in all, " (Col. 3: 11)it is our sincere hope that hundreds of internationally–minded people after receiving specialized training here at TCU will go out into the world both to evangelize the world and to work toward the solution of problems, thus promoting peace & stability.
Foreign students TCU is for training Christian Workers for worldwide service and the cross–cultural studies are important in this training. We are now trying to make every possible assistance available to foreign students.
Environment Our campus has a lot of trim lawn space, trees, flowers, ponds and is located in a quiet residential area. This area is a rapidly–growing township of Chiba New Town which is midway between Tokyo and Tokyo New International Airport at Narita. Convenient both to downtown Tokyo and overseas travel from Narita.
Facilities Library, Kyoritsu Christian Institute for Theological Studies and Mission, Chapel, Gymnasium, Student Hall, Computer and Language Laboratory, Piano and Organ Lesson Center and other Instrument practice rooms
Student activities Campus Calendar includes Fellowship Outing, Founder's Day Lecture, Summer Evangelistic Outreach, Summer Overseas Service, Holy Land Study Tour, Fall Retreat, Campus Concert, Autumn Festival, Christmas Concert, Christmas Service & Party, besides various Sports Club Activities.
Academic programs for foreign students Several classes are conducted in English.
Services for foreign students All students are required to live in dormitories on campus. Health clinic and personal counseling are available. Part–time jobs on campus are available.

Undergraduate Programs

Faculty of Theology(43/4)
Dept. of Theological Studies(23/4)
Dept. of International Christian Studies(20/0)

東京音楽大学
(Tokyo Ongaku Daigaku)
Tokyo College of Music

3–4–5 Minami Ikebukuro, Toshimaku, Tokyo 171
☎ 03–3982–3186 FAX 03–3986–4577

Founded 1907
Professors 33
Associate Professors 33
Assistant Professors(Tenured) 43
Assistant Professors(Non–tenured) 145
Research Assistants 19
Undergraduate Students/Foreign Students 1, 221/4
Two–year Advanced Course 64/6
Library 106, 769 volumes
Contact: Admission Office ☎ ext. 210

Educational philosophy 1. To offer instruction designed to prepare students for performance careers.

2. To offer instruction designed to prepare students for carreers in music education.
Foreign students Foreign students are accepted on a one year " special status " basis. Students who present qualifications of equal educational level can be considered. A basic ability in spoken Japanese is preferred for these students, but not required.
Environment Tokyo College of Music is located at Ikebukuro, Tokyo. Ikebukuro is located in northern Tokyo and is one of the major districts of the Tokyo Metropolis. The school is about a ten minute walk from the station and near the Tokyo Metropolitan Art Space Hall where concerts are performed daily by national and international orchestras and performers.
Facilities The music library has more than 30, 000 records, CDs and laser discs; music studio, recording studio, Japanese traditional music research center.
Student activities Popular campus events include school music festival, various concerts, recitals, master classes, and a wide variety of extra curricular activities.
Academic programs for foreign students Supplemental Japanese language classes are available.
Service for foreign students Health clinic, personal counseling, housing information.

Undergraduate Programs

Faculty of Music(1, 221/4)
  Dept. of Instrumental Music(739/0)
  Dept. of Vocal Music(231/0)
  Dept. of Music Education(211/0)
  Dept. of Composition and Cunducting(40/0)

Two-Year Advanced Course

Accompaniment Methods, Compositoion, Conducting, Diction, Keyboard Harmony, Opera Workshop, Orchestra Ensemble, Orchestra Performance, Percussion Methods, Piano Performance, Ruthmique, Score Reading, Solfege, String Methods, Traditional Japanese Instrument, Vocal Techniques, Wind Ensemble, Advanced Musicology, Analysis and Appreciation of Music, Comparative Musicology, Methods of Basic Composition for School Students, Music Appreciation, Music, Therapy, Phonetics Orchestration, Psychological Effect of Music, Ethnomusicology, History of Asian Music, History of Traditional Japanese Music, History of Western Music and etc.

東京薬科大学
(Tokyo Yakka Daigaku)

Tokyo College of Pharmacy

1432-1 Horinouchi, Hachioji-shi, Tokyo 192-03
☎ 0426-76-5111

Founded 1880

Undergraduate Programs

Faculty of Pharmacy
  Dept. of Biopahrmacy
  Dept. of Pharmaceutical Sciences
  Dept. of Pharmaceutical Technology

Graduate Programs

Dept. of Clinical Pharmacy
  Div. of Clinical Pharmacy
Dept. of Pharmaceutical Sciences
  Div. of Biochemistry
  Div. of Dispensing Pharmacy
  Div. of Hygienic Chemistry
  Div. of Pharmaceutical Analytical Chemistry
  Div. of Pharmaceutical Chemistry
  Div. of Pharmaceutics
  Div. of Pharmacognosy
  Div. of Pharmacology

東京電機大学
(Tokyo Denki Daigaku)

Tokyo Denki University

2-2 Kanda-Nisikicho, Chiyoda-ku, Tokyo 101
☎ 03-3294-1551 FAX 03-3295-1590

Founded 1907
Professors 137
Associate Professors 68
Assistant Professors(Tenured) 25
Assistant Professors(Non-tenured) 259
Research Assistants 58
Undergraduate Students/Foreign Students 8, 770/5
Graduate Students/Foreign Students 200/4
Library 234, 484 volumes
Contact: Admission Office

Educational philosophy The founder established our school for the Purpose of cultivating excellent engineers and promoting the spread of engineering, by the belief that development of country depends on the education of engineering. This spirit and philosophy are still alive in our university.
Foreign students We welcome foreign students. In future, foreign students will increase more and more. We hope our university will contribute to the world by science education and study of engineering.
Environment We have 3 campuses: Kanda Campus is located in the heart of Tokyo, over looking the House of Parliament and the Imperial Palace. Hatoyama Campus is located in Hatoyama-machi, Saitama Prefecture, 50 km from Kanda Campus. Chiba New Town Campus is located in Inzai-machi, Chiba Prefecture, 30 km from Kanda Campus.
Facilities Center for Research, Computer Center,

Library, Educational Technology Center–Educational TV System, Language Laboratory, Micro–computer Center, Fukuda Memorial Hall, Sports Training Center, Budo–jo Gymnasium

Student activities Popular campus events includes Homecoming, Athletic meet, School festival, Freshmen welcome party. There are about 100 club activities in our school. judo, kendo, yachting, alpine, guitar, art, Red Cross Volunteers, amateur wireless, computer, etc.

Services for foreign students Foreign students can be given many services as Japanese students. As for health service, personal counseling, part–time job information, recreation houses, cafeteria service, stationery store, etc.

Undergraduate Programs

Faculty of Engineering: First Division(3, 752/2)

Dept. of Applied Science(514/0)

Dept. of Architecture(513/0)

Dept. of Electrical Communication Engineering (581/1)

Dept. of Electrical Engineering(585/0)

Dept. of Electronic Engineering(573/0)

Dept. of Mechanical Engineering(533/0)

Dept. of Precision Machinery Engineering(453/1)

Faculty of Science and Engineering(2, 733/3)

Dept. of Applied Electronic Engineering(412/1)

Dept. of Civil and Structural Engineering(490/0)

Dept. of Industrial Mechanical Engineering(498/1)

Dept. of Information Sciences(407/0)

Dept. of Mathematical Sciences(445/0)

Dept. of Systems and Management Engineering (481/1)

Graduate Programs

Graduate School of Engineering(M 63/1, D 2/0)

Div. of Electrical Engineering(M 48/1, D 2/0)

Advanced Electric Machines, Energy Conversion Engineering Power System Theory, Electrical Power System Theory, Advanced Nuclear Power Engineering, Circuit Theory, Advanced Integrated Circuits, Advanced System Theory, Advanced Control Engineering, Control Computers, Advanced Electronic Measurement, Advanced Power Electronics, Electric and Electrical Materials, Advanced Electric and Electrical Materials, Quantum Electronics, Superconducting Technology, Pattern Recognition, Information Network Engineering, Advanced Communication System, Random Signal Theory, Radio Information System Engineering, Electronic Properties of Materials, Optical Processes in the Material, Electrical Conduction Theory, Advanced Applied Mathematics, Digital Processing of Speech Singals, Electromagnetic Wave Engineering, Semiconductor Physics and Technology, Advanced Electronic Devices Plasma Technology, Gaseous Discharge Engineering, Digital Signal Processing, Biomagnetism

Div. of Electronic Engineering(M 8/0)

Semiconductor Physics and Technology, Advanced Electronic Devices, Amorphous Semiconductor Technology, Plasma Technology, Gaseous Discharge Engineering, Digital Signal Processing, Simulation Engineering, Biomagnetism, Robotics, Neurocomputing, Bioengineering, Advanced Applied Mathematics

Div. of Information and Communication Engineering(M 7/0)

Distributed Information Systems, Man–Machine Interface, Biological Information Systems, Perception and Processing of Acoustical Information, Digital Processing of Speech Signals, Sound Field Control Engineering, Advanced Communication Systems, Transmission Theory of Signal Waveforms, Optoelectronics, Electromagnetic Wave Engineering, Electromagnetic Wave Theory, Advanced Applied Mathematics

Graduate School of Science and Engineering(M129/2, D 6/1)

Div. of Applied Electronic Engineering(M 11/1)

Applied Electronic Device Engineering, Sensor Technology, Integrated Circuit Engineering, Electronic Materials, Applied Electoronic Theory, Quantum Instrumentation, Quantum Physics Statistic Physics, Drive System Engineering, Automation Engineering, Electronic Control Apparatus, Mechatoronics, Biocybernetics, Prosthesis, Biomedical Electronic Instrumentation, Biomedical Information Process, Advanced Applied Solid State Electronics, Advanced Electromagnetics, Advanced Circit Network Theory, Advanced System Control Theory, Seminar in Applied Electronics, Research Work in Applied Electronics.

Div. of Applied Systems Engineering(M 4/0)

Research Work in Applied System Engineering, Advanced Study in Control Engineering, Advanced Study in Information Engineering, Advanced Study in Production System for Machining, Advanced Study in Energy System, Advanced Study in Research & Development System, Advanced Study in Security System Against Disaster, Advanced Study in Civil Engineering System, Advancod Study in Building Engineering System, Advanced Study in Environmental Engineering System, Advanced Study in Applied Electronics

Div. of Civil and Structural Engineering(M 31/0)

Advanced Applied Mechanics, Advanced Topics in Structural Engineering, Advanced Earthquake Engineering, Advanced Concrete Engineering, Advanced Environmental Engineering, Treatise on Planning & Design of Civilworks, Advanced Structural Design, Advanced Structural Engineering, Advance Steel structre, continuum Mechanics, Reliability Analysis in Civil Engineering, Advanced Earthquake engineering, Advanced Soil Mechanics, Advanced Foundation Engineering, Advanced Hydraulics, Advanced Hydrology, Advanced Fluid Mechanics, Advanced Wind Engineering, Advanced Environment Engineering, Advanced Topics in Structual Engineering, Theory and Design of Steel Structures, Advanced Prestressed Concrete, Advanced Topics of Economy in Construction, Design Theory on Building, Structures, Advanced Urban Design, Advanced

Community Planning, Advanced Architectural Design, Advanced Architectural Environmental Engineering, Architectural Design Practice, Architectural Environmental Engineering Laboratory, Advanced Architectural Installation Engineering, Environmental Fluid Mechanics, Environmental Materials Science, Research Work in Civil Engineering

Div. of Information Sciences(M 9/0)
Applied Analysis, Algebra for Information Sciences, Theory of Dynamical Systems, Combinatorial Mathematics, Physics for Information Sciences, Theory of Stochastic Processes, System Theory, Stochastic System Theory, Random Signal Theory, Numerical Processing, Theory of Computation, Automata Theory, Artificial Intelligen– ce, Principles of Programming Languages, Compiler Theory, Database Theory, Information Systems, Information Theory, Information Transmission Theory, Computer Networks, Digital Signal Theory, Seminar in Information Sciences, Research Course in Information Sciences

Div. of Mathematical Sciences(M 16/0, D 2/1)
Advanced Analysis, Topics in Advanced Algebra, Advanced Geometry, Mathematics for Physical Sciences, Linear Systems, Topics in Advanced Analysis, Functional Analysis, Advanced Analysis, Topics in Advanced Algebra, Topics in Advanced Geometry, Applied Partial Differential Equations, Topics in Mathematical Programm– ing, Topics in Applied Mathematics, Time Series Analysis, Topics in Mathematical Physics, Theoretical Physics, Topics in Computer Mathematics, Topics in Automa Theory, Topics in Programming Languages, Theory of Computation, Seminar in Mathematical Sciences, Research Work in Mathematical Sciences, Exercises in Advanced Analysis, Topics in Stochastic Processes, Mathematics for Information Sciences, Exercises in Mathematics for Information Sciences, Linear Systems, Exercises in Mathematical Physics, Topics in Databases, Reseach Work in Mathematical Sciences, Advanced course in Mathematics, Advanced course in Computer Science, Advanced course in Mathematical Sciences, Seminar in Mathematical Sciences

Div. of Mechanical Engineering(M 30/0)
Advanced Strength of Materials, Advanced Dynamics of Machinery, Advanced Materials of Science, Advanced Thermal Engineering, Advanced Hydrodynamics, Advanced Machine Design, Advanced Finite Element Method, Advanced Mechanical Vibration, Advanced Hydraulic Machinery, Advanced Machining Technology, Nontraditional Machining, Applied Control Engineering, Theory of Heat and Mass Transfer, Advanced Instrumentation Technology, Advanced Plastic Working, Advanced Internal Combustion Engine, Advanced Burning Engineering, Research Work in Engineering

Div. of Systems Engineering(M 32/1)
System Reliability Engineering, Advanced Control Engineering, Advanced Information Systems, Advanced Mathematical Statistics, System Design, Human Factors Engineering, Electrical Drive System Engineering, Energy Conversion Engineering, Advanced Knowledge Engineering, Pattern Recognition, Logical Programming, Advanced Automata Theory, System Control Theory, Advanced Data Engineering, Advanced Symbolic Logic, Advanced Computer Theory, Advanced Software Scienc– e, General Lessons in Science, Seminar, Research Work in System Engineering, Theory of Optimal Control, Biological System Theory, Advanced Electronics Engineering, Advanced Sensor Technology

---

東京歯科大学
(Tokyo Shika Daigaku)
Tokyo Dental College

1–2–2 Masago, Chiba–shi, Chiba 260
☎ 0472–79–2222 FAX 0472–79–2052

Founded 1890
Professors 43
Associate Professors 37
Assistant Professors(Tenured) 76
Assistant Professors(Non–tenured) 317
Research Assistants 125
Undergraduate Students/Foreign Students 912/0
Graduate Students/Foreign Students 158/6
Library 139, 397 volumes
Contact: Department of Foreign Affairs

Educational philosophy We aim at teaching and studying up–to–date high–level dental science to develop intellectual, moral and applied abilities so students may contribute much to dental care service.

Foreign students We believe that foreign students can enjoy a rewarding experience in our school, and can contribute a great deal to promoting mutual understanding and the development of friendly relations.

Environment The Chiba City, with a population of 820, 000, is located in the north–west of Chiba Pref. and regarded as a suburb of metropolis, Tokyo. Our campus is located in the well–arranged and calm area surrounded by many residences indicating quite appropriate for education and dental care services.

Facilities The building for both infirmary and educational research facility is most up–to–date facilitated. Abundant storaged library, center for morphological research, center for functional research, molecular research center, computer center, gymnasium, auditorium

Student activities Popular campus event include student festival, freshmen welcome party. There is a wide variety of extra curricular activities including almost all kind of sports and choral group, symphony, tea ceremony, flower arrangement, natural exploration and so on.

Academic programs for foreign students As a part of tutoring system, several home parties are arranged for the students from abroad.

Undergraduate Programs

Faculty of Dentistry(912/0)

Graduate Programs

Graduate School of Dentistry(D 158/6)
Department of Anatomy, Department of Hitology, Department of Physiology, Department of Biochemistry, Department of Oral Pathology, Department of Pathology, Department of Pharmacology, Department of Microbiology, Department of Dental Technology, Department of Hygiene, Department of Preventive & Community Dentistry, Department of Forensic Odontology, Department of Endodontics, Department of Periodontics, Department of Conservative Dentistry, Department of Pedodontics, Department of Oral & Maxillofacial Surgery, Department of Dental Anesthesiology, Department of Complete Denture Prosthodontics, Department of Crown and Bridge Prosthodontics, Department of Removable Partial Prosthodontics, Department of Orthodontics, Department of Dental Radiology, Department of Oral Medicine, Department of Internal Medicine, Department of Surgery

---

東京工科大学
(Tokyo Kôka Daigaku)

Tokyo Engineering University

1404–1 Katakura–cho, Hachioji–shi, Tokyo 192
☎ 0426–37–2111 FAX 0426–37–2118

Founded 1986
Professors 39
Associate Professors 9
Assistant Professors(Tenured) 10
Assistant Professors(Non–tenured) 15
Undergraduate Students/Foreign Students 1, 612/0
Library 24, 000 volumes
Contact: Tokyo Engineering University, ☎ext. 2012

Educational philosophy To meet the great social demand for qualified engineers in the field of advanced technologies specializing in electronics.
Foreign students Even though the university does not have any policy specific to international students, it is open to them as well as to home students.
Environment Our university is located in Hachioji, a suburban city 40 kilometers west of Tokyo. Hachioji, which is often referred to as an academic city, now has 21 universities and colleges, and provides an excellent environment for students. The university provides school bus transportation to and from nearby railway stations.
Facilities The university is proud of its computer systems including more than 300 personal computers and workstations as well as other laboratory facilities, a library and a gymnasium including bowling alleys.
Student activities There are various athletic and cultural circles organized by student groups. Unfortunately, this has yet to be fully developed in our school.
Academic programs for foreign students As for the course for international students, personal tutors and transfer of academic credit are unavailable at present.
Services for foreign students This also applies to counselling, accommodation, home–stay program, cultural exchange program.

Undergraduate Programs

Faculty of Engineering(1, 612/0)
  Dept. of Electronics(539/0)
  Dept. of Information Technology(533/0)
  Dept. of Mechatronics(540/0)

東京工芸大学
(Tokyo Kôgei Daigaku)

Tokyo Institute of Polytechnics

1583 Iiyama, Atsugi–shi, Kanagawa 243–02
☎ 0462–41–0454

Founded 1966

Undergraduate Programs

Faculty of Engineering
  Dept. of Architecture
  Dept. of Electronics
  Dept. of Imaging Engineering
  Dept. of Industrial Chemistry
  Dept. of Photographic Engineering

Graduate Programs

Graduate School of Engineering
  Div. of Imaging Engineering
  Div. of Industrial Chemistry

東京国際大学
(Tokyo Kokusai Daigaku)

Tokyo International University

1–13–1 Matoba–kita Kawagoe–Shi, Saitama 350
☎ 0492–32–1111 FAX 0492–32–1119

Founded 1965
Professors 99
Associate Professors 36
Assistant Professors(Tenured) 25
Assistant Professors(Non-tenured) 95
Research Assistants 1
Undergraduate Students/Foreign Students 5, 360/133
Graduate Students/Foreign Students 119/57
Library 253, 723 volumes
Contact: International Center FAX 0492-34-3824

Educational philosophy We attach special importance to teaching students in practical science and learning, aiming to give education adapted to the demands of the times.

Foreign students We welcome foreign students from any country of the world, and expect that each of the students including those from Japan, who has his or her own unique culture, mix with each other, promote mutual exchange and understanding.

Environment Kawagoe City, with a population of 300, 000, is located 40 kilometers northwest of central Tokyo and as a former castle town, is rich in historic relics. Due to the convenient location of the university, students may either enjoy the fast pace of Tokyo, or the rarefied atmosphere of a large forest park of the Musashino Plain.

Facilities Libraries, Audio-visual libraries, Personal computers training rooms, Audio-visual training and exrecise rooms, Auditoriums and Language Laboratories.

Student activities Popular campus events include Freshmen welcome party, School festival, All-school athletic meeting, Annual English Language Speech Contest for Prizes offered by the president of the university. There is a variety of extra curricular activities, including various sports, amateur clubs for studying movies, travels, railways, micro-computers, etc.

Academic programs for foreign students Foreign students are offered opportunities to study in supplemental Japanese language courses, and those who earned credits in these courses are qualified to transfer these credits as part of the credits in other elective required courses.

Services for foreign students There is " Adviser system, " under which advisers help foreign students quickly adapt themselves to their life in Japan. Condominiums for foreign students, part-time job information, homestay, cultural exchange programs between students and local communities.

Undergraduate Programs

Faculty of School of Business and Commerce(3, 428/98)
  Dept. of Business and Commerce(2, 867/76)
  Dept. of Management Information Systems(561/22)
Faculty of School of Economics(582/14)
  Dept. of Economics(344/2)
  Dept. of International Economics(238/12)
Faculty of School of International Studies and Human Relations(1, 350/21)
  Dept. of International Studies(805/13)
  Dept. of Human Relations(545/8)

Graduate Programs

Graduate School of Business and Commerce(M 50/19, D 4/1)
Courses of Accounting: Accounting-Bookkeeping Theory•Cost Accounting, Management Accounting•Management Analysis•Auditing, International Business Accounting•Tax Laws. Courses of Business Administration: Business Administration•Management Science, International Management•Financial Management, Labor Management•Management Engineering, Information Resource Management. Courses of Business and Commerce: Commerce•Distribution Theory•Marketing Manageme- nt, International Marketing•Marketing Research, etc. Related Subjects: International Economics •Economic Policy, Public Finance•Commercial Law

Graduate School of International Studies(M 42/31)
A) Courses: Political Science•International Politics, International Law•International Institutions, International Economics•International Finance, International Development •International Economic, Geography•International Management. B) Courses: Methodology of Area Studies• Studies on Chinese & Asian Area•Studies on Middle Eastern Area•Studies on European Area•Studies on American Area. C) Courses: Cultural Anthropology•Comparative Religions, Comparative Culture•Studies on Nationalism, World Environments Studies•International Co-operation, Statistical Survey Methods•International Marketing, etc.

Graduate School of Sociology(M 23/6)
General Education: Theoretical Sociology•Methods of Social Research Methodology of Applied Sociology• Study of Social Changes•Study of Social Thought• Study of Small Groups•Advanced Study in Social Psychology, etc. Specialized Subjects (Industrial Sociology): Industrial Sociology•Industrial Psychology• Human Engineering Science of Social•Information• Medical Sociology, etc. Specialized Subjects (Clinical Social Psychology): Clinical Social Psychology•Study of Deviation and Social Problems•Criminal Social Psychology•Study of Human Relations•Social Psychiatry•Study of Group Psychology•Cultural Social Psychology

---

東京家政学院大学
(Tokyo Kasei Gakuin Daigaku)

Tokyo Kasei Gakuin University

2600 Aihara-cho, Machida-shi, Tokyo 194-02
☎ 0427-82-9811

Founded 1963

Undergraduate Programs

Faculty of Home Economics
Dept. of Home Economics
Dept. of Housing and Planning
Faculty of Humanities
Dept. of Cultural Arts Studies
Dept. of Japanese Cultural Studies

東京家政大学
(Tokyo Kasei Daigaku)

Tokyo Kasei University

1-18-1 Kaga, Itabashi-ku, Tokyo 173
☎ 03-3961-5226 FAX 03-3962-7136

Founded 1881
Professors 45
Associate Professors 26
Assistant Professors(Tenured) 16
Assistant Professors(Non-tenured) 71
Research Assistants 8
Undergraduate Students/Foreign Students 3, 450/16
Graduate Students/Foreign Students 20/0
Library 195, 580 volumes
Contact: Admission Office

Educational philosophy We are now facing newly perceived challenges because of the pace of modernization. In the midst of these challenges, our motto is still " affection, diligence, and intelligence, " in keeping with the university's policy of maintaining the best of traditional values.
Foreign students We invite you to join our student body. Study and discuss the changing world in a green and quiet atmosphere.
Environment The school was founded in 1881. Itabashi Campus is located near Ikebukuro, one of Tokyo's busiest centers. But close as it is to the bustle of Ikebukuro, the Itabashi campus is a different world. It is a truly rural setting, abounding in trees, flowers and country lawn. A 45-minute ride from Ikebukuro will bring you to our Sayama Campus, which was completed in 1986. This campus is almost an extension of beautiful Inariyama Park. The area is one solid shade of green, broken only by the changing colors of the trees. Iruma River, a short walk from the campus, borders Sayama on the west.
Facilities The buildings of Itabashi Campus include 2 anniversary halls, 5 main buildings, the Auditorium, the Library, the Dining Hall, and 2 gymnasiums. Each of the buildings is furnished with the latest office and teaching equipment. On Sayama Campus there are 3 main buildings for administration, the Department of Liberal Arts and the Faculty of Humanities. Surrounding these three halls are the Library, the Auditorium-Gymnasium Hall, the Dining Hall, the Health Center, and the Counseling Room. Incorporated into these buildings are such state-of-the-art facilities as the Audio-Visual Hall, the Language Laboratory, the Typing-Data Processing Room, and the Brain Wave Measurement Room.
Student activities The Welcome Party will be given in April, when about 50 clubs are introduced. You can make your campus life more joyful by choosing what you like among clubs. An Annual Festival, called " Ryokuensai ", and Sports Festival will be given in November. And you can also take part in Ski-Class in December.
Academic programs for foreign students Supplemental Japanese Language and Japanese Culture classes are tentatively scheduled in the near future.
Services for foreign students There will be tea party to welcome the foreign students. During your stay you will be given a two-day tour. And a second tea, this one a farewell party, will be given at the end of your stay.

Undergraduate Programs

Faculty of Home Economics(2, 671/15)
Dept. of Juvenile Education (Juvenile Science Major, Juvenile Education Major) (548/2)
Dept. of Food and Nutrition (Food and Nutrition Major, Administrative Dietician Major) (1, 084/2)
Dept. of Clothing Science and Fine Arts (Clothing Major, Fine Arts Major) (1, 039/11)
Faculty of Humanities(779/1)
Dept. of English Language and Literature(464/0)
Dept. of Psychology and Education(315/1)

Graduate Programs

Graduate School of Home Economics(M 20/0)
Div. of Food and Nutrition(M 12/0)
Advanced Food Science, Seminar for Food Science, Experiments in Food Science, Advanced Cookery Science, Seminar for Cookery Science, Experiments in Cookery Science, Advanced Food Hygiene, Seminar for Food Hygiene, Experiments in Food Hygiene, Advanced Public Nutrition, Seminar for Public Nutrition, Experiments in Public Nutrition, Advanced Clinical Nutrition, Seminar for Clinical Nutrition, Experiments in Clinical Nutrition, Advanced Nutritional Biochemistry, Seminar for Nutritional Biochemistry, Experiments in Nutritional Biochemistry, Research on Food and Nutrition
Graduate School of Home Economics(M 20/0)
Div. of Textile and Clothing(M 8/0)
Advanced Course of Textile and Clothing Materials, Seminar for Textile and Clothing Materials, Experiments in Textile and Clothing Materials, Advanced Textile Processing, Seminar for Textile Processing, Experiments in Textile Processing, Advanced Care of Clothing, Seminar for Care of Clothing, Experiments in Care of Clothing, Advanced Clothing Construcion, Seminar for Clothing

Construcion, Advanced Course of Physical and Hygienic Function of Clothing, Advanced Hand Craft, Practice in Hand Craft Textile Design. Metalwork. Embroidary, Advanced Costume Design, Advanced Course of History of Costume, Advanced Color Scheme, Research on Textile and Clothing

東京経済大学
(Tokyo Keizai Daigaku)
Tokyo Keizai University

1-7 Minami-cho, Kokubunji-shi, Tokyo 185
☎ 0423-21-1941 FAX 0423-24-1354

Founded 1900
Professors 72
Associate Professors 26
Assistant Professors(Tenured) 8
Assistant Professors(Non-tenured) 218
Undergraduate Students/Foreign Students 7,462/1
Graduate Students/Foreign Students 31/19
Library 407,655 volumes
Contact: Admission Office

Educational philosophy The chief aim of education at the foundation of the school in 1900 was to bring up able businessman who could play an active part in international trade. Today we aim at instructing and researching up-to-date theories of sciences as well as their applications to the business world.
Foreign students We have student exchange programs with some universities in China, Germany and the U.S., though accepting no special application for general foreign students as yet. However, we are very keen to promote global thinking.
Environment The City of Kokubunji, with the population of 98,000, is situated 13 miles (30 minutes by train) west of Shinjuku, the new hub Tokyo. It is a quiet residential area on the north of Kokubunji Cliff line with a lot of beautiful gardens as well as the ruins of Musashi-Kokubunji, Chief temple of 8th century.
Facilities James Maitland 8th Earlof Lauderdale Library, A.V center, Computer Center, Training Center, Swimming pool, Gymnasium, etc.
Student activities Popular campus events includes school festival, cultural events, etc. There is a wide variety of extra curricular activities, including Choral group, mandoline club, student news paper, baseball, football, soccer, boats, etc.
Services for foreign students Health clinic, personal/Psychological counseling, Housing information, Part-time job information, Cultural exchange program.

Undergraduate Programs

Faculty of Business Administration(3,715/1)
 Dept. of Business Administration(3,715/1)
Faculty of Economics(3,747/0)
 Dept. of Economics(3,747/0)

Graduate Programs

Graduate School of Business Administration(M 12/7, D 2/1)
Principles of Business Administration (Special Thesis of Business Management, History of Business Administration Theories, Business and Environment), Business History (Japanese Business History, European Business History, History of Industrial Technology), Economics of Business (Small and Medium Enterprises, Retail & Whole-sale Management, Industrial and Science-technology Policy), Business Management (Business Management, Business Financial Management, International Management, Marketing, Business Organization, Industrial Psychology), Industrial Engineering (Industrial Engineering, Statistics of Business, Management Information System), Accounting (Bookkeeping, Accounting, Financial Statements, Managed Accounting, Tax Accounting, Auditing), Commercial Science (Advertising, Foreign Trade, International Finance, Principle of Transportation, Insurance)
Graduate School of Economics(M 10/7, D 7/4)
Economic Theory (Economic Theory, History of Economic Theories, History of Sicial Thought, Theory of Business Cycle), Economic History (Economic History of Europe, Economic History of Japan), Economic Policies (Economic Policies, International Economics, Japanese Economy), Public Finance, Manetary Economics (Public Finance, Manetary Economics), Theory of Social Policy (Theory of Social Policy)

東京医科大学
(Tokyo Ika Daigaku)
Tokyo Medical College

6-1-1 Shinjuku, Shinjuku-ku, Tokyo 160
☎ 03-3351-6141

Founded 1952

Undergraduate Programs

Faculty of Medicine
 Dept. of Medicine

Graduate Programs

Graduate School of Medicine
 Div. of Internal Medicine
 Div. of Morphological Medicine
 Div. of Physiological Medicine
 Div. of Social Medicine
 Div. of Surgical Medicine

東京神学大学
(Tokyo Shingaku Daigaku)
Tokyo Union Theological Seminary

3-10-30 Osawa, Mitaka-shi, Tokyo 181
☎ 0422-32-4185 FAX 0422-33-0667

Founded 1949
Professors 12
Associate Professors 1
Assistant Professors(Tenured) 2
Assistant Professors(Non-tenured) 31
Undergraduate Students/Foreign Students 93/8
Graduate Students/Foreign Students 66/5
Library 82, 788 volumes
Contact: Admission Office

Educational philosophy Training to be Ministers Based on protestant liberal Belief.
Foreign students Founded by KYODAN(United Church of Christ in Japan). But every candidetes other than KYODAN is received.
Environment The campus is located in Mitaka, about twelve miles west of downtown Tokyo. The four-acre campus is adjacent to the International Christian University, with which a Meaningful cooperative relationship is maintained.
Facilities Library; As of May 1990 the Library has on its shelves some 83, 000 volumes, the largest collection of theological books of any library in Japan. Missiology Institute; (Japan & Asian)
Student activities An athletic meeting, Morning service, Christmas service, Prayer meeting & Practical church training in summer.
Services for foreign students Dormitory is availabele for foreign students living with Japanese students.

Undergraduate Programs

Faculty of Theology(93/8)

Graduate Programs

Graduate School of Theology(M 54/4, D 12/1)
Div. of Biblical Theology(M 18/1, D 6/0)
Old Testament Hebrew Readings, Biblical Archaeology, Old Testament Exegesis, O.T.Theology Special Lecture - s, O.T.Theology Seminar, O.T.Studies Seminar, O.T. Studies Special Research, O.T.Thesis Seminar, Aramaic, Syriac, New Testament Exegesis, N.T.Special Lectures, N.T.Special Studies, N.T.Studies Seminar, N.T.Thesis Seminar Systematic Theology Special Lectures, S.T. Studies Seminar, S.T.Special Studies, S.T.Collegisl Seminar, S.T.Thesis Seminar, Church History Special Lectures, History of Doctrine Seminar, Pastoral Psychology, Christian Education Special Lectures, Church Music, Seminar in Asian Mission, Seminar in Japan Mission, Clinical Pastoral Education, Christian Education Special Studies, Homiletice Seminar, Integrative Lectures, Pastoral Theology Seminar, Worship
Graduate School of Theology(M 54/4, D 12/1)
Div. of Systematic Theology(M 36/3, D 6/1)
Old Testament Hebrew Readings, Biblical Archarology, Old Testament Exegesis, O.T.Theology Special Lecture - s, O.T.Theology Seminar, O.T.Studies Seminar, O.T. Studies Special Research, O.T.Thesis Seminar, Aramaic, Syriac, New Testament Exegesis, N.T.Special Lectures, N.T.Special Studies, N.T.Studies Seminar, N.T.Thesis Seminar Systematic Theology Special Lectures, S.T. Studies Seminar, S.T.Special Studies, S.T.Collegisl Seminar, S.T.Thesis Seminar, Church History Special Lectures, History of Doctrine Seminar, Pastoral Psychology, Christian Education Special Lectures, Church Music, Seminar in Asian Mission, Seminar in Japan Mission, Clinical Pastoral Education, Christian Education Special Studies, Homiletice Seminar, Integrative Lectures, Pastoral Theology Seminar, Worship

東京農業大学
(Tokyo Nôgyô Daigaku)
Tokyo University of Agriculture

1-1-1 Sakuragaoka, Setagaya-ku, Tokyo 156
☎ 03-3420-2131 FAX 03-3706-8851
Faculty of Bioindustry:
196 Aza Yasaka, Abashiri-shi, Hokkaido 093
☎ 0152-48-2116 FAX 0152-48-2940

Founded 1891
Professors 143
Associate Professors 77
Assistant Professors(Tenured) 105
Assistant Professors(Non tenured) 193
Research Assistants 54
Undergraduate Students/Foreign Students 7, 193/68
Graduate Students/Foreign Students 159/35
Library 441, 655 volumes
Contact: NODAI Center for International Programs: ☎ 03-3706-2323(direct), 03-3420-2131 ext.601-603 FAX 03-5477-4561

Educational philosophy The university's principle in education is the practical application of science and technology in agriculture, based on fundamental science. Emphasis is placed on experiments and practice of theories and techniques in the laboratory and in field training.
Foreign students Active international exchange is one of our institutional goals, and we encourage foreign students to learn through our educational systems and with assistance in daily life as well as in academic endeavors.

Environment Setagaya Ward is a residential area located in the southwest portion of the Tokyo metropolitan area. It has ample public transportation, parks and shopping facilities. The university is located in quiet, pleasant surroundings, with the Equestrian Park directly in front of it.

Facilities University farms, NODAI Research Institute, NODAI Bioresources Institute, Computer Center, Food Processing Center, Institution for Utilization of Scientific Techniques, Research and Education, Gymnasium, Auditorium, etc.

Student activities In addition to the school culture festival and games day, there is a wide variety of special-interest clubs, sports and other activities open to all students. At the culture festival, groups of foreign students sometimes present their native dances and foods to the public.

Academic programs for foreign students A separate entrance examination from the Japanese applicants is given to foreign applicants and returnees.

Services for foreign students Housing information, part-time job information, home visits, cultural exchange programs, homestays, annual foreign student party, field trips for foreign students.

Undergraduate Programs

Faculty of Agriculture(6, 559/68)
- **Dept. of Agriculture**(860/16)
- **Dept. of Agricultural Chemistry**(548/2)
- **Dept. of Agricultural Economics**(733/7)
- **Dept. of Agricultural Engineering**(553/5)
- **Dept. of Grewing and Fermentation**(562/5)
- **Dept. of Forestry**(630/3)
- **Dept. of International Agricultural Development** (657/6)
- **Dept. of Landscape Architecture**(631/11)
- **Dept. of Nutrition (Major in Nutrition)** (771/8)
- **Dept. of Zootechnical Science**(614/5)

Faculty of Bioindustry(634/0)
- **Dept. of Bioproduction**(150/0)
- **Dept. of Business Science**(329/0)
- **Dept. of Food Science and Technology**(155/0)

Graduate Programs

Graduate School of Agriculture(M 128/24, D 31/11)

Div. of Agricultural Chemistry(M 32/3, D 9/3)
Soil Science, Plant Nutrition and Fertilizer Science, Biological Chemistry, Applied Microbiology, Food Processing, Nutritional Food Chemistry, Environmental Science, Pesticide Chemistry, Microbiological Genetics and Breeding, Instrumental Analytical Chemistry

Div. of Agricultural Economics(M 13/7, D 4/2)
Agricultural Economics, Farm Management, Agricultural History, Agricultural Geography, Labor Science, International Economics and Agricultural Development, Agricultural Education, Agricultural Law, Agricultural Policy

Div. of Agricultural Engineering(M 3/0)
Water Development and Conservation Engineering, Land Development and Conservation Engineering, Structural Engineering, Agricultural Production Systems Engineering, Systems Control Engineering, Overseas Agricultural Development

Div. of Agricultural Science(M 26/8, D 9/5)
Crop Science, Horticultural Science, Plant Pathology, Applied Entomology, Genetics Breeding, Physiology and Ecology of Plants, Cytogenetics, Landscape Architecture, Environmental Control in Biology, Grassland Science, Biometry, Aquatic Biology, Molecular Biology.

Div. of Bioregulation Studies(D 3/1)
Gene Regulation, Regulation in Biofunction, Environmental Control in Bioproduction, Ecochemical Regulation, Bioresources Development and Management, Bioactive Natural Products, Gene Resources

Div. of Brewing and Fermentation(M 6/0)
Alcoholic Beverages Production, Seasonings Processing. Food Chemistry, Applied Microbiology, Fermentation Materials, Enzyme Chemistry, Molecular Biology, Biochemical Engineering, Environmental Science, Microbial Ecology, Food Economics

Div. of Food and Nutritional Science(M 12/1)
Nutritional Biochemistry, Food Chemistry, Applied Food Technology, Nutritional Physiology, Human Nutrition, Clinical Nutrition, Public Health Nutrition, Science of Food Quality, Food Technology, Science of Cookery, Applied Microbiology, Molecular Biology, Cell Technology for Food, Nutritional Ecology, Nutritional Toxicology, Biochemistry

Div. of Forestry(M 12/1, D 5/0)
Silviculture, Soil and Water Conservation, Forest Management and Policy, Wood Science and Technology, Forest Products Chemistry, Forest Engineering, Forest Ecology, Forest Influences, Forest Products Economics, Wood Adhesives, Wood Chemistry

Div. of International Agricultural Development(M 4/0)
Agro-biological Resources Development, Environment of Agro-biological Production, Agricultural Development Economics, Farm Management and Extension for Agricultural Development, Tropical Crop Science, Horticultural Crop Propagation in Tropics, Post Harvest Technology, Pest and Disease Control, Conservation of Natural Environment, Agricultural Development Policy, International Agricultural Cooperation, International Economics, Education and Training for Agricultural Developme- nt, Regional Agricultural Development

Div. of Landscape Architecture(M 8/1)
Landscape Planning, Landscape Design, Landscape Architectural Engineering, Botany for Landscape Architecture, Topics of Landscape Architectural History, Topics of Landscape Design Theory, Topics of Landscape Materials, Landscape Planting, Lawns and Groundcovers

Div. of Zootechnical Science(M 12/3, D 1/0)
Animal Reproduction, Animal Breeding, Animal Physiology, Animal Nutrition, Animal Health, Biochemistry and Technology of Animal Foods, Livestock Farm Management, Laboratory Animal Science, Animal Immunology, Animal Management and Behavior, Biometrics in Ani-

mals, Animal Cytogenetics, Animal Embryonic Technology, Comparative Endocrinology, Functional Anatomy of Animals, Physiology of Useful Microorganism, Technology of Animal Food Preservation, Macromolecular Biochemistry

東京造形大学
(Tokyo Zôkei Daigaku)
Tokyo University of Art and Design

2707 Motohachioji-machi, Hachioji-shi, Tokyo 193
☎ 0426-61-4401 FAX 0426-63-2484

Founded 1966
Professors 32
Associate Professors 24
Assistant Professors(Tenured) 5
Assistant Professors(Non-tenured) 84
Undergraduate Students/Foreign Students 1, 323/0
Library 38, 627 volumes
Contact: Admission Office ☎ 0426-65-5067

Educational philosophy The fundamental ideas of the university in the programs of study are (1) to respect students' individuality and (2) to meet the social and industrial needs of the time.
Foreign students There are two admission procedures. Either a student has to pass the entrance examination, or has to be accepted after an interview, following the recommendation of a designated recommender. For further information, ask to Admission Office.
Environment Our university is located in Hachioji-city, on the western edge of Tokyo, and established by Yoko Kuwasawa with 135 students in 1966, as the only advanced educational center of the Bauhaus movement in Japan. Student intake at the present time is still limited to 300.
Facilities Our university have more remarkable facilities. Therefore. 1) Library: Library is adopting "Open Systems "and collecting on fine Arts and Design materials. 2) Technical Center: Many equipments and instruments are concentrated this center. All students make use of this center.
Student activities We have many number (38) of extra curricular activities, managed by students. Most important events is school festival. It is open October.

Undergraduate Programs

Faculty of Art(1, 323/0)
  Dept. of Design(917/0)
  Dept. of Fine Art(406/0)

東京情報大学
(Tokyo Jôhô Daigaku)
Tokyo University of Information Sciences

1200-2 Yatoh-cho, Chiba-shi, Chiba 280-01
☎ 0472-36-1101 FAX 0472-36-2215

Founded 1988
Professors 21
Associate Professors 9
Assistant Professors(Tenured) 18
Assistant Professors(Non-tenured) 23
Research Assistants 3
Undergraduate Students/Foreign Students 1, 259/14
Library 32, 080 volumes
Contact: School Affairs Division ☎ ext.214 2, 0472-36-14 08(Direct)

Educational philosophy Our intention with regard to education is to foster the advancement of information science and technology while at the same time striving to deepen state-of-the-art computer knowledge.
Foreign students Most of the foreign students from South East Asian countries are extremely interested in computer sciences. We, however, aim to give these students a complete education in all facets of computer technology.
Environment Onaridai, home site of the university, is located 5 miles east of downtown Chiba, and is a quiet and ideal area for study and research. Though located in a newly developing area, Onaridai has an easy access to major cities of Chiba-ken within half an hour or so by train.
Facilities Audio-Visual Studio, Computer Center, Computer training room open to students, Gymnasium, Library and other learning Center, Physical training room.
Student activities There are more than 40 different types of extra-curricular activities which range from cultural circles to sports; most of which are given direct financial support from the university.
Academic programs for foreign students We are scheduling special programs especially geared to foreign students with the object of enhancing their ability in spoken and written Japanese.
Services for foreign students The department of student affairs take special pains to find accommodation and part-time employment for all foreign students, as well as providing excursions to nearby areas.

Undergraduate Programs

Faculty of Business Administration and Information Science(1, 259/14)
  Dept. of Business and Management Information

(727/6)
Dept. of Information System(532/8)

東京女子大学
(Tokyo Joshi Daigaku)

Tokyo Woman's Christian University

2-6-1 Zempukuji, Suginami-ku, Tokyo 167
☎ 03-3395-1211 FAX 03-3399-3123

Founded 1918
Professors 88
Associate Professors 22
Assistant Professors(Tenured) 9
Assistant Professors(Non-tenured) 264
Research Assistants 29
Undergraduate Students/Foreign Students 3, 592/4
Graduate Students/Foreign Students 46/3
Library 456, 000 volumes
Contact: Graduate School and College of Arts and Sciences: Registrar's Office,
College of Culture and Communication: Registrar's Office, College of Culture and Communication 4-3-1 Mure, Mitaka-shi, Tokyo 181

Educational philosophy Tokyo Woman's Christian University aims at education based on Christianity with an emphasis on liberal arts. It encourages students to develop international understanding. There are 7 departments in the College of Arts and Sciences, and 3 departments in the College of Culture and Communication.

Foreign students We welcome applications from qualified foreign students who have sufficient knowledge of Japanese to pursue academic studies in Japanese. Classes, especially seminars, are very small, enabling teachers and students to get to know each other very well.

Environment We have two campuses in a quiet residential area in the northwestern part of Tokyo. Both of the beautiful campuses provide students with an ideal environment for academic pursuits.

Facilities Chapel, Auditorium, Library, Institute for Comparative Studies of Culture, Center for Woman's Studies, Center for Information Science, Language Laboratory, Audiovisual Room.

Student activities Annual events on both campuses: Spring/Freshman Orientation Camp, Play Day, the Alumnae Reunion Party; Summer/various camps; Fall/Students Cultural Festivals; Winter/Christmas (Christmas Service, Performance of the Messiah) Extra curricular activities students enjoy through the year are Choir, Shakespear Performance group, Noh study group, Aikidoh, tennis, field hockey, tea ceremony, etc.

Academic programs for foreign students Japanese Language (as a second language) and Japanese Studies (as a general education course) for foreign students

Services for foreign students Personal/psychological counseling, academic counseling and general campus information, dormitory, housing information, part-time job information

Undergraduate Programs

Faculty of Arts and Sciences(2, 711/4)
  Dept. of English(698/0)
  Dept. of History(442/0)
  Dept. of Japanese Literature(447/0)
  Dept. of Mathematics(247/0)
Faculty of Philosophy(105/0)
  Dept. of Psychology(273/3)
  Dept. of Sociology and Economics(499/1)
Faculty of Culture and Communication(881/0)
  Dept. of Communication(277/0)
  Dept. of Cross-cultural Studies(332/0)
  Dept. of Languages(272/0)

Graduate Programs

Graduate School of Humanities(M 38/3)
  Div. of English(M 11/0)
English Philology and Linguistics, English Literature, American Literature
  Div. of History(M 10/2)
Japanese History, Oriental History, Occidental History
  Div. of Japanese Literature(M 13/1)
Japanese Philology and Linguistics, Classical Japanese Literature, Modern Japanese Literature
  Div. of Philosophy(M 4/0)
Philosophy, Christian Theology
Graduate School of Science(M 8/0)
  Div. of Mathematics(M 8/0)
Algebra, Geometry, Analysis, Applied Mathematics

東京女子体育大学
(Tokyo Joshi Taiiku Daigaku)

Tokyo Women's College of Physical Education

620 Aoyagi, Yagawaue, Kunitachi-shi, Tokyo 186
☎ 0425-72-4131 FAX 0425-76-2397

Founded 1962
Professors 15
Associate Professors 16
Assistant Professors(Tenured) 5
Assistant Professors(Non-tenured) 30
Research Assistants 2
Undergraduate Students/Foreign Students 1, 457/0
Library 96, 190 volumes
Contact: Admission Office

Educational philosophy The founder emphasized

sincerity, friendliness and perseverance as her phylosophy of education in training women teachers of physical education; to be concrete, they should be simple in life, aspired in learning and courteous in manners. The college aims at producing proficient physical educators of 21 century.

Foreign students Requirments and methods of selection are the same as with Japanese applicants.

Environment The college locates at Kunitachi City, College town, with excellent educational circumstances. Near by the colleges is Tachikawa City, center of Tama District of Tokyo. With dozens of colleges and high schools scattered around the school besides beautiful nature retaind and cultural environments.

Facilities A track and field stadium, Tennis court, 5 Professional Gymnasium, Indoor swimming pool, Sports training Center, Computer center, Piano lesson room, Golf training yard, and so on.

Student activities There is a wide variety of professional club activities. Sports clubs are Gymnastics, Volleyball, Basketball, Athletic sports, Tennis, Swimming, Skiing, and so on(total 20). Recreation and Culture clubs are Camera, Golf, Aquadiving, Folk dance and so on(total 14). School festival will be held on every autumn.

Undergraduate Programs

Faculty of Physical Education

東京女子医科大学
(Tokyo Joshi Ika Daigaku)

Tokyo Women's Medical College

8-1 Kawada-cho, Shinjuku-ku, Tokyo 162
☎ 03-3353-8111 FAX 03-3353-6793

Founded 1900
Professors 90
Associate Professors 84
Assistant Professors(Tenured) 111
Assistant Professors(Non-tenured) 197
Research Assistants 507
Undergraduate Students/Foreign Students 617/0
Graduate Students/Foreign Students 72/1
Library 30, 900 volumes
Contact: Student Office ext. 22113～4

Educational philosophy Yayoi Yoshioka Founder of the College was a doctor and was convinced that medicine was a noble profession for which women were ideally suited.

Foreign students We belive that the foreign medical students in our college can deepen their knowledge and techinique that have acquired in their countries, and staying in Tokyo will be a rewarding experience in their lives.

Environment Tokyo women's Medical College is located in the town of Kawada-cho, in the west of Shinjuku ward, a very convenient place. Shinjuku is famous for the' tall and modern scrapers sky. From the top of these buildings, you can have a very beautiful view of the city and on clear days you can also see Mt. Fuji. We have a post office, bank, medical books shop, beauty parlour and barber and small restaurants in the neighborhood.

Facilities College Hospital, Diabetes Center, Institute of Biomedical Engineering, Institute of Clinical Endocrinolog, Institute of Gastroenterology, Institute of Geriatrics, Institute of Laboratory Animals, Institute of Rheumatology, Kindney Center, Maternal and Perinatal Center, Medical Research Institute, Neurological Institute, The Heart Institute of Japan, Library, Cafeteria, Division of Information Science, Museum, etc.

Student activities A great variety of Student club exist for extracunicular activities. In the area of cultural activities, there are Ikebana club, Art club, Koto club Medical English Study Society, etc. In the area of sports, there are tennis, Swimming club, Badminton club, Skiing club, Basketball club, housemanship club, etc.

Undergraduate Programs

Faculty of Medicine(617/0)

Graduate Programs

Graduate School of Medicine(D 72/1)
Anatomy, Pathology, Microbiology, Physiology Biochemistry, Pharmacology, Hygiene and Public Health, Legal Medicine, Parasitology, Medicine Hemotology, Medicine, Cardiology, Gastroenterology, Neurology, Psychiatry, Pediatrics, Pediatric Cardiology, Dermatology, Radiology, Surgery, Gastroenterological Surgery, Orthopedic Surgery Ophthalmology, Otolaryngology, Obstetrics and Gynecology, Anestheriology, Urology, Cardiovascular Surgery, Pediatric Cardiovascular Surgery, Plastic and Reconstructive Surgery

---

東洋英和女学院大学
(Tôyô Eiwa Jogakuin Daigaku)

Toyo Eiwa Women's University

32-1 Miho-cho, Midori-ku, Yokohama-shi, Kanagawa 226
☎ 045-922-5511 FAX 045-922-5517

Founded 1989
Professors 18
Associate Professors 11
Assistant Professors(Tenured) 8
Assistant Professors(Non-tenured) 29
Undergraduate Students/Foreign Students 495/1

Library 103, 767 volumes
Contact: International Academic Exchange Committee: Exchange Students

Educational philosophy We aim at providing students with broad and interdisciplinary perspectives and helping them adapt to a variety of situations in this changing society. Emphasis is placed on a foreign language education and the broadening of the students' international perspectives so that they can play major roles both in Japanese society and in the international community.

Foreign students Foreign students are considered to be important in promoting mutual understanding between Japan and the rest of the world. They are welcome at our University and they are admitted in September. Courses in the Japanese language at the appropriate levels are offered for these students. Moreover, courses taught in English are also available.

Environment The University is located in a scenic northwest of the center of the city of Yokohama and has a wide campus of about 165, 000m² in a hilly area which is adjacent to " the Miho Forest of Yokohama Citizen ". Though located in a rural area, the campus is convenient to reach either the center of Yokohama or of the capital city, Tokyo.

Facilities Library, Computer Lecture Room, Audio Visual Language Laboratory, Audio Visual Lecture Room, Psychological Laboratory, Gymnasium, Assembly Hall, Tennis Courts, etc.

Student activities Popular campus events include freshmen orientation camp and university festival. There is a wide variety of extracurricular activities, including drama, choral group, English newspaper, golf, tennis, lacrosse, volleyball, field hockey, etc.

Academic programs for foreign students Japanese language courses, Japanology and Advisor system.

Services for foreign students Health service, personal/psychological counseling, housing information and part-time job information.

Undergraduate Programs

Faculty of Humanities(495/1)
Dept. of Human Sciences(211/0)
Dept. of Social Sciences(284/1)

東洋大学
(Tôyô Daigaku)
Toyo University

5-28-20 Hakusan, Bunkyo-ku, Tokyo 112
☎ 03-3945-7559 FAX 03-3945-7221

Founded 1887
Professors 253
Associate Professors 94
Assistant Professors (Tenured) 67
Assistant Professors (Non-tenured) 536
Research Assistants 13
Undergraduate Students/Foreign Students 16, 284/219
Graduate Students/Foreign Students 242/16
Library 774, 895 volumes
Contact: International Programs Office

Educational philosophy Following the spirit of its founder, Toyo University aims to encourage students in seeking out the truth and determining their principles for themselves, with its guiding emphasis on facts and demonstration rather than-a mere conceptual and deductive philosophy.

Foreign students Adding to its substantial curriculam, Toyo University with its helping and friendly Japanese students offers students from overseas a very warm atmosphere and ample opportunities for learning things Japanese.

Environment Bunkyo-ku where there is our main campus is indeed rich in scenic beauty with many surrounding old shrines, temples, parks, gardens and famous schools for medium to higher education, and presents an excellent studying circumstance unattainable in the other towns in central Tokyo.

Facilities Totaling 3 libraries comprising of more than 750, 000 volumes of books, 4 seminar houses, athletic facilities including gymnasia, playing fields, tennis courts, a baseball ground and an officially approved stadium, etc.

Student activities Anniversary of the Founder's Death on June 6, Day for the Four Sages in November, Sports Festival in May and University Festival in November. We have within our campuses no less than 600 student circle activities ranging from academy and research oriented to art and sport related.

Academic programs for foreign students Intensive Japanese language courses for students from overseas are about to be introduced, while provisions of special supplementary courses and tutorial systems are still under consideration.

Services for foreign students Health clinic, Personal counseling, Housing information, Part-time job information, Vocational guidance, Homestay information, Cultural exchange activities, etc.

Undergraduate Programs

Faculty of Business Administration(2, 546/59)
Dept. of Business Administration
Dept. of Commerce
Faculty of Economics(2, 414/37)
Dept. of Economics
Faculty of Engineering(3, 694/16)
Dept. of Architecture
Dept. of Applied Chemistry
Dept. of Civil Engineering
Dept. of Electrical Engineering
Dept. of Information and Computer Science

Dept. of Mechanical Engineering
Faculty of Law(2, 762/15)
Dept. of Law
Dept. of Management Law
Faculty of Literature(2, 734/39)
Dept. of Chinese Philosophy and Literature
Dept. of Education
Dept. of English and American Literature
Dept. of History
Dept. of Indian Philosophy
Dept. of Japanese Literature
Dept. of Philosophy
Faculty of Sociology(2, 134/53)
Dept. of Sociology
Dept. of Applied Sociology (Mass Communications/Social Welfare/Social Psychology/Library Science)

Graduate Programs

Graduate School of Business Administration(M 9/1)
Div. of Business Administration(M 9/1)
Graduate School of Economics(M 13/0, D 4/0)
Div. of Economics(M 13/0, D 4/0)
Graduate School of Engineering(M 70/1, D 1/0)
Div. of Applied Chemistry(M 14/0, D 0/0)
Div. of Architecture(M 11/0, D 1/0)
Div. of Civil Engineering(M 8/0, D 0/0)
Div. of Electrical Engineering(M 21/0, D 0/0)
Div. of Mechanical Engineering(M 16/0, D 0/0)
Graduate School of Law(M 16/3, D 0/0)
Div. of Private Law(M 3/0, D 0/0)
Div. of Public Law(M 13/0, D 0/0)
Graduate School of Literature(M 57/2, D 26/0)
Div. of Buddhism(M 8/0, D 2/0)
Div. of Chinese Philosophy(M 6/0, D 0/0)
Div. of English and American Literature(M 12/0, D 2/0)
Div. of Japanese History(M 11/0, D 0/0)
Div. of Japanese Literature(M 13/0, D 13/0)
Div. of Philosophy(M 7/0, D 9/0)
Graduate School of Sociology(M 31/12, D 15/0)
Div. of Sociology(M 18/0, D 6/0)
Div. of Social Welfare(M 13/0, D 9/0)

津田塾大学
(Tsuda Juku Daigaku)

Tsuda College

2-1-1 Tusda-machi, Kodaira-shi, Tokyo 187
☎ 0423-42-5111 FAX 0423-41-2444

Founded 1900
Professors 48
Associate Professors 28
Assistant Professors(Tenured) 4
Assistant Professors(Non-tenured) 195
Research Assistants 3
Undergraduate Students/Foreign Students 2,559/0
Graduate Students/Foreign Students 75/0
Library 193, 187 volumes

Educational philosophy Our college, by tradition, takes pride in the smallness in size, believing that it maintains the superb academic standard and high-quality education. The students are encouraged to participate in decision-making in nearly every area of campus life.

Foreign students We warmly receive foreign students annually from our partner colleges overseas, including Bryn Mawr College, Univ. of Massachusetts at Amherst, Western Washington Univ., the Australian National Univ. in Canberra, and Ehwa Women's College in Seoul.

Environment The 24-acre campus in a lovely woodsy setting in the western suburbs of Tokyo. A big public park is nearby and a path along the stream is our girls' favorite promenade.

Facilities Three dormitories accommodation 300 students, a chapel, a library, a co-op store, a Memorial Hall housing a student union, a gym and a cafeteria. 60 personal computers and a SUN/4 research computing system.

Student activities Orientation for Freshmen in April, Play Day in May, College Festival in November, Christmas Worship Service. Athletic, culture and music clubs total eighty. A seminar house in Gumma Prefecture, and a cottage in Nagano Prefecture, both are convenient to moutaineering and skiing.

Academic programs for foreign students Intensive Japanese, Introduction to Japanese Studies, Translation and Linguistics and International Relations are offered. Students can consult their academic advisors in selecting courses.

Services for foreign students A room in the dormitory is provided and a Big Sister helps each foreign student. During vacations, she has the opportunity to travel around the country with our students or live with Japanese families. Counseling services are provided.

Undergraduate Programs

Faculty of Liberal Arts(2, 553/10)
Dept. of English Language and Literature(1, 007/1)
Dept. of International and Cultural Studies(1,104/9)
Dept. of Mathematics(442/0)

Graduate Programs

Graduate School of International Studies(M 6/1, D 15/0)
Div. of International and Cultural Studies(M 6/1, D 15/0)
Comprehensive Studies of International Relations: History

Comprehensive Studies of International Relations: Methology
International Politics, International Institutions, International Economics, Comprehensive Culture, Social Structure, Nationalism and Ethnicity, American Studies, Asian Studies, European Studies, Russian Studies, African Studies, Tutorial
Graduate School of Literary Studies(M 17/0, D 19/0)
Div. of English Language and Literature(M 17/0, D 19/0)
Special Studies in English Literatue, English Poetry, Study of English Drama, English Novels, American Literature, English Philology and Linguistics, Research Guidance
Graduate School of Mathematics(M 11/0, D 7/0)
Div. of Mathematics(M 11/0, D 7/0)
Topics in Analysis, Topics in Algebra, Topics, in Geometry, Topics in Computer Mathematics, Special Lecture on Mathematics, Special Course of Algebra, Seminar

---

鶴見大学
(Tsurumi Digaku)
Tsurumi University

2-1-3 Tsurumi,Tsurumi-ku, Yokohama-shi,Kanagawa 230
☎ 045-581-1001 FAX 045-572-8009

Founded 1963
Professors 56
Associate Profrssors 27
Assistant Professors(Tenured) 43
Assistant Professors(Non-tenured) 182
Research Assistants 134
Undergraduate Students/Foreign Students 2, 335/1
Graduate Students/Foreign Students 77/2
Library 400, 000 volumes
Contact:Admission Office

Educational philosophy Tsurumi University's founding Spirit is based firmly on the teaching of Keizan who emphasized " Awakening and Advancemnt of Humanities. "
Foreign students Student and Faculty Exchanges Committee has been set up for vistors from abroad.
Environment Tsurumi University is located in the east part of the international city of Yokohama and is favored by a cosmopolitan environment that is bright clean and healthy.
Facilities University Library, covering a total floor space of 7, 363 square meters, has a vast collection —some 400, 000 books and 8, 766 magazinens.
Student activities April=Matriculation ceremony, Freshmen orientation, Reglar health checks. July=Start of summer vacation. November=Campus festival. March=Commencement ceremony.
Services for foreign students Health checks, health consultations, and counseling service.

Undergraduate Programs

Faculty of Dental Medicine(891/1)
Dept. of Dental Medicine(891/1)
Faculty of Literature(1, 444/0)
Dept. of English and American Literature(712/0)
Dept. of Japanese Literature(732/0)

Graduate Programs

Graduate School of Dental Medicine(D 60/2)

Oral anatomy, oral histology, oral physiology, oral biochemistry, oral pathology, oral microbiology, dental pharmacology, dental engineering, preventive dentistry, operative dentistry, periodontology, endodontics, prosthodontics (crown and bridge, partial denture and complete denture), oral and maxillofacial surgery, orthodontics, pedodontics, dental radiology and dental anesthesiology.
Graduate School of Literature(M 17/0)
Div. of English and American Literature(M 8/0)
Required subjects
English literature (medieval, modern, contemporary), American literature (19 th century), (20 th century), English linguistics, seminar on English literature, seminar on American literature, seminar on English linguistics.
Elective subjects
Special lecture on linguistics, special lecture on comparative literature, seminar on English expressions, theory of literary criticism, history of Western literary thought.
Div. of Japanese literature(M 8/0)
Required subjects
Japanese literature (Nara Period, Heian Period, Kamakura and Muromachi periods, Edo Period, modern), Japanese philology, Japanese poetry literature, narrative literature, haiku poetry literature, Edo Period literature, modern fiction, classical bibliography, modern biblioraphy
Elective subjects
history of Japanese Buddhism, Buddhist literature, Japanese historic materials, Sino-Japanese comparative literature, classical Chinese poetry.

上野学園大学
(Ueno Gakuen Daigaku)
Ueno Gakuen College

4-24-12 Higashi Ueno, Taito-ku, Tokyo 110
☎ 03-3842-1021 FAX 03-3843-7548

Founded 1958
Professors 18
Associate Professors 8
Assistant Professors(Tenured) 7
Assistant Professors(Non-tenured) 71

Research Assistants 2
Undergraduate Students/Foreign Students 445/0
Library 117, 000 volumes
Contact: Gakumubu

Undergraduate Programs

Educational philosophy The aim of education at Ueno Gakuen is to enable students to cultivate qualities of intellect, together with the spirit of " Awareness of Self " so dear ro the founder Zogoro Ishibashi, through their study of music, including hard training, and other academic pursuits.

Foreign students Though the students' specialty is music, they need to have enough ability to read, write and understand Japanese.

Environment The College is located in Ueno which still retains much of its old downtown tradition in Asakusa area where Asakusa Temple stands. Tokyo National Univ. of Fine Arts & Music, Tokyo National Museum, and Western Art Gallery enhance its historical and cultural features.

Facilities Research Archives for Japanese Music, Inst. for the Study of Musical Instruments, Centre for the Performance of Early Music, Centre for Lang. Studies, International Inst. for the Study of Compar. Culture, Ueno Gakuen College Library.

Student activities Freshman welcome concert & hiking; college festival. Extra curricular activities (clubs and study groups) include: chorus, Gregorian chant, medieval Renaissance & baroque music, contemporary music, brass ensemble, jazz, tennis, swimming, flower arrangement, English.

Services for foreign students personal counseling

Faculty of Music(445/0)
Dept. of Musicology(28/0)
Dept. of Instrumental Music(356/0)
Dept. of Vocal Music(61/0)

聖心女子大学
(Seisin Joshi Daigaku)
University of the Sacred Heart

4-3-1 Hiroo, Shibuya-ku, Tokyo 150
☎ 03-3407-5811 FAX 03-5485-3884

Founded 1948
Professors 44
Associate Professors 17
Assistant Professors(Tenured) 9
Assistant Professors(Non-tenured) 245
Research Assistants 0
Undergraduate Students/Foreign Students 2,706/3
Graduate Students/Foreign Students 35/1
Library 270, 138 volumes
Contact:Admission Office

Educational philosophy The University of the Sacred Heart, dedicated to the education of women, with the motto, " Where there is love, there God is " is a center of education and scholarship based on the ideals of Christian humanism.

Foreign students The University of the Sacred Heart welcomes foreign students and wants to promote internatonal understanding among students of different nationalities.

Environment The University is conveniently located a mere five minute walk from the Hiroo subway station (Hibiya Line), and fifteen minutes from JR Shibuya station by bus. The campus of nearly 70, 000m^2 is located in an extensive residential area of Tokyo.

Facilities Library, Academic Buildings No.1, No.2, Marian Hall Auditorium, Chapel, Computer Rooms, Language Laboratory, Gymnasium, Tennis Courts, Dining Hall, Students Residences, The Christian Culture Research Institute.

Student activites Orientation for Freshmen, Special lecture by guest speakers, Masses for students. Madeleine Sophie Social Service Group, Yearbook Editorial Committee, Sacred Heart Festival Executive Committee, E.S.S., English and Japanese Dramatic clubs, Orchestra and Glee clubs, Tennis and Ski clubs, and many others.

Academic programs for foreign students Japanese Language Classes, Seminars on Japanese Culture. Regular classes are open to foreign students according to their language ability.

Services for foreign students Student Housing on campus, Health Insurance, Scholarship (partial), Home Stay, Part-time job information, Counseling, Welcoming Parties.

Undergraduate Programs

Faculty. of Liberal Arts(2, 076/3)
General Cultural Subjects Program for all the Freshmen(482/0)
Dept. of Foreign Language & Literature (English Language & Literature) (534/0)
Dept. of Japanese Language & Literature (Japanese Language & Literature(212/0)
Dept. of History & Social Sciences (History, Human Relations(398/3)
Faculty. of Liveral Arts(2, 076/3)
Dept. of Philosophy(107/0)
Dept. of Education (Education, Elementary Education, Psychology(341/0)

Graduate Programs

Graduate School of Literary Studies(M 35/1)
Div. of English Literature(M 13/0)
Milton, Suprasegmental in English, Contemporary British Fiction, Study of 19th Century British Fiction, Medieval

English Literature: A Special Study, Study of American Drama, Shakespeare: Selected Tragedies, English Romanticism

Graduate School of Literary Studies(M 35/1)
Div. of History(M 11/0)

Study of Medieval Japanese History, Study of Modern Japanese History, Study of Ancient Japanese History, Studies of Medieval Japanese History, Studies of Modern Japanese History, Seminar in Modern Japanese History, Seminar in History of Japanese Culture, History of Chinese Fine Arts, Readings in Chinese History, Seminar in India & West-Asian Cultural History, Modern Indian History, Oriental Archaeology, Studies of Ancient Europe, Study of Medieval European History, Seminar in Modern European History, History of Modern Europe

Graduate School of Literary Studies(M 35/1)
Div. of Japanese Literature(M 11/1)

Study of Ancient Japanese Literature, Study of Medieval Japanese Literature, Study of KINSEI Literature (CHIKAMATSU), Study of Modern Japanese Literature, Study of Japanese Philology

和光大学
(Wakô Daigaku)

Wako University

2160 Kanai-cho, Machida-shi, Tokyo 194-01
☎ 044-988-1431 Fax 044-989-2241

Founded 1966
Professors 68
Associate Professors 13
Assistant Professors(Tenured) 4
Assistant Professors(Non-tenured) 156
Research Assistants 2
Undergraduate Students/Foreign Students 3,505/39
Library 192, 663 volumes
Contact: Office of Registration and Instruction, ☎ ext. 277

Educational philosophy Wako University was found in 1966 and on the principles " Small class education ", " Synthesis of broad culture and specialties ", " Interdisciplinary research among five Departments ". It has a great regard for freedom of study and education and believes in humanism.

Foreign students Wako University is seeking students who foster international visions and rich intelligence for the modern society and who are ready to accept the educational ideals our University offers.

Environment The camups of our University is located in the center of Tama heights in the southern suburbs of Tokyo and in 45 minutes from Shinjuku on the Odakyu Line. It is conveniently near the City of Machida and the City of Yokohama. There are many historic relics of ancient Tama at the area.

Facilities Lectures are given here in the 2 Schools: Humanities and Economics. The campus is composed of 8 school buildings, a library, 2 gymnasium, an auditorium, a swimming pool, a computer room, a lunguage laboratory and a dictation room for handicapped students.

Student activites Our University develops both intellectual and extracurricular life. Extracurricular acttivities: the student clubs; volunteer activieies, choral groups, marching band, kendo, Amerian football, baseball, soccer and football, etc.

Academic programs for foreign students Supplemmental Japanese language class for foreign student. Tutoring system.

Services for foreign students Housing services, part-time job informations, counseling services, health clinic, a welcome party.

Undergraduate Programs

Faculty. of Ecomonics(1, 681/15)
Dept. of Business economics(391/4)
Dept. of Economics(1, 290/11)
Faculty. of Humanities(1, 824/24)
Dept. of Art(428/19)
Dept. of Human Science(765/3)
Dept. of Literature(631/2)

早稲田大学
(Waseda Daigaku)

Waseda University

1-6-1 Nishiwaseda, Shinjuku-ku, Tokyo 169
☎ 03-3203-4141 FAX 03-3202-8583

Founded 1882
Professors 794
Associate Professors 138
Assistant Professors(Tenured) 55
Assistant Professors(Non-tenured) 1, 984
Research Assistants 150
Undergraduate Students/Foreign Students 44, 038/369
Graduate Students/Foreign Students 3, 144/486
Library 3, 666, 300 volumes
Contact: International Center

Educational philosophy Waseda university aims to uphold the independence of learning, to promote the practical utilization of knowledge, and to create good citizeniship.

Foreign students " Harmony between the Cultures of East and West " is one of the concepts on which Waseda University was founded, and Waseda today continues that tradition unbroken.

Environment Waseda University has three campuses in Tokyo, located a few kilometers from Shinjuku, a rapidly growing business and commercial center, covering a total land area of 388, 000 m^2. The new Tokorozawa campus, Saitama, was added as the fourth campus of the University in 1987.

Facilities Main Library, Tsubouchi Memorial Theatre Museum, Center for Japanese Language, Center for Informatics, University Clinic, Student Counseling Center, Okuma Auditorium, Gymnasium

Student activities Welocome Party for Freshmen, One day Excurtion (twice a year), Summer Camp, University Festival, Ski-school for foreign students/about 500 intramural student organizations such as sport, language, art and music, literature, press, natural science and engineering

Academic programs for foreign students Tutorial System, Supplementary study of Japanese, Special subjects for foreign students

Services for foreign students Tuition assistance, Subsidy for study trip, Subsidy for key money ,Counseling room, Foreign students'association, Extracurricular activities for foreign students, Common room for foreign students

Undergraduate Programs

School of Commerce(5, 644/60)

School of Education(5, 279/18)

Dept. of Education(1, 060/9)

Dept. of English Language and Literature(764/4)

Dept. of Japanese Language and Literature(835/1)

Dept. of Science(1, 021/3)

School of Human Sciences(2, 344/38)

Dept. of Basic Human Sciences(521/17)

Dept. of Human Health Sciences(777/15)

Dept. of Sports Sciences(1, 046/6)

School of Law(6, 014/12)

School of Literature(5, 406/59)

School of Political Science and Ecnomics(5, 734/40)

Dept. of Ecnomics(3, 778/32)

Dept. of Political Science(1, 956/8)

School of Science and Engineering(7, 454/137)

Dept. of Applied Chemistry(586/10)

Dept. of Applied Physics(391/5)

Dept. of Architecture(884/9)

Dept. of Chemistry(142/2)

Dept. of Civil Engineering(473/1)

Dept. of Electrical Engineering(997/23)

Dept. of Electronics and Communication Engineering(537/13)

Dept. of Industrial Engineering and Management(680/13)

Dept. of Materials Science and Engineering(455/8)

Dept. of Mathematics(322/3)

Dept. of Machanical Engineering(1, 527/37)

Dept. of Mineral Resources Engineering(304/10)

Dept. of Physics(156/3)

School of Social Sciences(3, 627/3)

Graduate Programs

Graduate School of Economics(M 52/6, D 24/2)

Div. of Applied Economics(M 19/5, D 7/1)

Economic Analysis and Public Policy, International Economy, Money and Banking, Social Policies, Public Finance

Div. of Theoretical Economics and Economic History(M 33/1, D 17/1)

Theoretical Economics, History of Economic Theories, Statistics, Japanese Economic History, European Economic History

Graduate School of Education(M 63/0, D 0/0)

Div. of Educational Sciences(M 17/0)

Pedagogy, Developmental Psychology, Science of School Management, Curriculum and Instruction, Moral Education, Comparative Education, Adult and Social Education, Life-long Education

Div. of English Language Education(M 12/0)

Teaching English as a Foreign Language, Endlish Linguistics, English Literature, American Literature

Div. of Japanese Language and Literature Education(M 21/0)

Methods of Teaching Japanese, Japanese Linguistics, Japanese Literature

Div. of Social Studies Education(M 13/0)

Methods of Teaching Social Studies, History, Geography, Political Science, Economics, Sociology

Graduate School of Commerce(M 158/68, D 49/11)

Business Administration, Labor Management Relations, Accounting, Theory of International Trade, Management of International Trade, International Marketing, Marketing, Commodity Science, Advertising, Monetary Economics, Investment Management, Transportation Economics, Life Insurance, Economics of Insurance, Economics, Public Finance, Social Insurance, Theory of Labor Economics, Economic Statistics, Economic History, Economic and Business History

Graduate School of Law(M 197/22, D 78/11)

Div. of Civil Law(M 110/11, D 33/7)

Civil Law, Commercial Law, Civil Procedure, Bankruptcy, Insolvency Laws and Corporate Reorganization, Labor Law, International Private Law, Economic Law

Div. of Fundamental Legal Studies(M 15/0)

Phylosophy of Law, Japanese Legal History, Chinese Legal History, Roman Law, Anglo-American Law, French Law, Socialist Nation's Law

Div. of Public Law(M 72/11, D 45/4)

Constitutional Law, Administrative Law, Criminal Law, Criminal Procedure, Criminology and Criminal Policy, Internatiopnal Law, International Treaty Relations

Graduate School of Literature(M 415/40, D 306/10)

Div. of Art(M 54/3, D 40/0)

Dramatic Arts, Motion Pictures, History of Arts

Div. of Chinese(M 10/0, D 6/0)

Chinese Literature, Chinese Linguistics

Div. of English(M 43/0, D 13/0)

English and American Literature, English Linguistics

Div. of French(M 32/0, D 14/0)

French Literature, French Linguistics

Div. of German(M 12/0, D 9/0)

German Literature, German Linguistics

Div. of History(M 64/1, D 82/5)

Japanese History, Oriental History, Western History, Archaeology

Div. of Japanese(M 83/21, D 33/3)
Japanese Literature, Japanese Linguistics

Div. of Japanese Language and Culture(M 10/8, D 1/0)
Japanese Language, Japanese Culture

Div. of Oriental Philosophy(M 16/2, D 23/1)
Oriental Philosophy, Special Problems in Oriental Philosophy

Div. of Pedagogy(M 16/3, D 13/1)
Pedagogy

Div. of Psychology(M 26/0, D 18/0)
Psychopathology, Psychology, Newrophysiology

Div. of Philosophy(M 23/0, D 24/0)
Basic Problems in Philosophy, Special Problems in Philosophy, History of Philosophy, Philosophy

Div. of Russian(M 13/0, D 10/0)
Russian Literature, Russian Linguistics

Div. of Sociology(M 13/2, D 20/0)
Sociology

Graduate School of Political Science(M 62/8, D 46/1)
Political Science, International Politics, A General Theory of Public Administration, Local Government, History of Japanese Politics, History of Occidental Politics, Political Thoughts, Constitutional Law, Administrative Law, Mass Communication

Graduate School of Scinece and Engineering (M 1, 474/78, D 220/29)

Div. of Applied Chemistry(M 176/6, D 24/2)
Inorganic Meterial Chemistry, Inorganic Synthetic Chemistry, Polymer Chemistry, Fuel Chemistry, Applied Biochemistry, Electronic Material Chemistry, Quantum Chemistry, Chemical Engineering, Synthetic Organic Chemistry, Organic Reaction Mechanism, Organic Shytesis

Div. of Architecture and Civil Engineering(M 230/15, D 34/8)
History of Architecture, Architectural Design, City Planning, Building Structure, Building Services Engineering, Architectural Environment, Urban Environment, Building Materials and Construction, Structural Design, Structural Analysis Concrete Engineering, City Planning, Soil Engineering and Construction, Soil Mechanics, Hydraulics Engineering/Water Polution Control Engineering

Div. of Chemistry(M 21/0, D 3/0)
Quantum Condensed Matter Chemistry, Electronic State of Molecul, Structural Chemistry of Excited Moleculels, Structural Chemistry of Solid Surfaces and Interfaces, Catalyfic Reaction, Function Organi Chemistry, Structural Organic Chemistry, Inorganic Solution Chemistry

Div. of Electrical Engineering(M 288/15, D 31/5)
Stochastic Systems, Information Systems, Digital Computer Technology, Computer Control, Calculators, Caluclators Software, Control Engineering, Semiconductor Engineering, Electric Machines and Apparatus, Power Systems Engineering, Dielectric Materials, Electric Insulation, Circuit Theory, Circuit Engineering, Telematics, Networks and Systems, Engineering of Information System, Telecommunication Sciences, Computer Architecture, Informatics, Light, Electromagnetic Waves and Radio Engineering, Electronics, Acoustics and Audio Engineering

Div. of Mathematics(M 79/7, D 37/0)
Foundations of Mathematics, Computer Sciences, Algebraic Geometry, Algebraic Analysis, Number Theory, Algebra, Automorphic Functions, Topology, Geometry, Theory of Differential Manifolds, Theory of Lie Groups, Algebraic Analysis, Functional Analysis, Theory of Evolution Equations Analysis on Manifolds, Partial Differential Equations, Theory of Ordinary Differential Equations, Theory of Non–linear Partial Differential, Equations, Theory of Functions, Mathematical Statistics, Numerical Mathematics, Numerial Analysis

Div. of Mechanical Engineering(M 307/18, D25/6)
Engineering Mathematics, Fluid Engineering,Internal Combustion Engine, Heat Engineering, Structural Dynamics, Design Engineering, Mechanics of Materials, Machine Design, Mechanical Design Science, Computer Aided Design, Precision Machining, Applied Maerial Engineering, Material Design, Bio–control Engineering, Process Control Engineering, Control Engineering, Instrumentation and Control Engineering, Materials Handling, Plasticity and Metal Technology, Business Management, Production Management, Plant Engineering, Operations Research, Inforamation System Engineering, Human Factors Engineering, Environment Engineering

Div. of Mineral Industry and Materials Engineering(M 173/11, D 22/4)
Earth and Mineral Sciences, Exploration and Exploitation Engineering, Mining and Environment Control Technology, Applied Mechanics, Mineral Processing, Petroleum Engineering, Safety Engineering, Structural Geology, Palaeontology, Ferrous Metallurgy, Nonferrous Metallurgy, Electrochemistry for Metals High Temperature Chemistry of Materials Processing Ferrous Materials, Corrosion–Resistant Materials, Solic State Physics for Materials, Surface Engineering, Foundry Engineering, Solidification Processing, Powder Metallurgy, Thin Film Materials, Ceramic Materials Engineering, Materials for Electronics

Div. of Pure and Applied Physics(M 200/44, D 44/4)
Mathematical Physics, Experimental Astrophysics, Cosmology, Theory of Elementary Particle, Theoretical Nuclear Physics, Experimental Nuclear Physics, Nucleonics, Atomic Collision in Solid and Cosmic Ray Physics, Statistical Physics, Theoretical Solic State Physics, Corpuscular Beam Physics in Solids, Surface Science, Optical Properties of Matters, Physics of Magnetism, Theoretical Biology, Physics of Magnetism, Theoretical Biology, Experimental Biophysics, Molecular Biophysics, Developmental Biology, Animal Physiology, Endocrinology, Genetics, Plant Physiology, Ecology, Physiological Ecology, Regulatory Biology, Macromolecular Physics, Radiation Effects of Organic Molecules, Crystal Physics, Applied Optics, Optical Physics, Information Technology, Transducer Technology, Electronics for Information Processing, Control Engineering

和洋女子大学
(Wayô Joshi Daigaku)
Wayo Women's University

2-3-1 Kohnodai, Ichikawa-shi, Chiba 272
☎ 0473-71-1111 FAX 0473-71-1125

Founded 1949
Professors 38
Associate Professors 16
Assistant Professors(Tenured) 6
Assistant Professors(Non-tenured) 69
Research Assistants 2
Undergraduate Students/Foreign Students 1561/18
Library 178, 029 volumes
Contact: Administration Office

Educational philosophy Our basic philosophy toward the education of the students is to foster sound and harmonious character, to bestow profound knowledge and to offer the opportunities to study specialized arts and sciences, so that they may become highty-cultivated women.

Foreign students We are confident that foreign students together with Japanese students, can gain plentiful knowledge and develop their abilities in many fields through the specialized studies and campus life.

Environment Our campus is located in Ichikawa-City, Chiba Prefecture. The City is adjacent to the Tokyo city area with the famous Edo River running between, so the students can enjoy their urban life. The campus is surrounded by many historically famous places and scenic spots.

Facilities On the campus, Auditorium, Gymnasium, Indoor Swimming Pool, Library, Computer Center, Tea Ceremony House and other facilities are available.

Student activities There are about 30 kinds of extracurricular activities, including calligraphy, drama, chorus, braille, English speaking, fine arts, youth hostel, skiing, golf, volleyball, tennis, table tennis and others.

Academic programs for foreign students Supplemental Japanese language class

Services for foreign students Same as for Japanese students, such services as health clinic, counselling, housing information, dormitory, part-time job information are available.

Undergraduate Programs

Faculty of Literature and Home Science(1561/18)
- **Dept. of Clothing**(313/13)
- **Dept. of English and American Literature**(452/1)
- **Dept. of Food and Nutrition Administrator Training**(322/1)
- **Dept. of Japanese Literature**(474/3)

女子美術大学
(Joshi Bijutsu Daigaku)
Women's College of Fine Arts

1900 Asamizodai, Sagamihara-shi, Kanagawa 228
☎ 0427-78-6111 FAX 0427-78-6636

Founded 1900
Professors 39
Associate Professors 18
Assistant Professors(Tenured) 8
Assistant Professors(Non-tenured) 106
Research Assistants 31
Undergraduate Students/Foreign Students 1, 290/0
Library 72, 896 volumes
Contact: Educational Affarirs Section

Educational philosophy Founded in 1990 to teach woman special techniques of Arts and also to improve their social status. We now aim at teaching and studying high-level theories and techniques of Arts, with the purpose of raising women with higher culture and aesthetic creativity.

Foreign stuents We will welcome foreign students. But regrettably, we have no special admission system for foreign students. Foreign applicants must take the same entrance examination as Japanese applicants in February each year.

Environment Our college is located in Sagamihara-shi, Kanagawa Prefecture, about 37 kilometers south-west from the heart of Tokyo. We are blessed with rich natural environment, surrounded by public parks. The city authorities are planning various cltural facilities in the area.

Facilities Studios, Library, Art Museum, Gymnasium, Athletic ground.

Student activities Campus events include frechmen welcome party, athletic meeting, swimming and skiing school, " Art Festival ". There are many extra-curricular activities, in photograph, art class for children, comics, advertisement, drama, chorus, folksong, hiking, basketball, tennis, skiing, modern dance, etc.

Undergraduate Programs

Faculty of Arts(1, 290/0)
- **Dept. of Painting (Oil Painting Course, Japanese Painting Course)** (539/0)
- **Dept. of Design (Graphic, Product and Interior Design Course, Environment Design Cours)**(399/0)
- **Dept. of Crafts**(140/0)
- **Dept. of Science of Arts**(212/0)

八千代国際大学
(Yachiyo Kokusai Daigaku)
Yachiyo International University

1-1 Daigaku-cho, Yachiyo-shi, Chiba 276
☎ 0474-88-2111 FAX 0474-88-8290

Founded 1988
Professors 33
Associate Profrssors 10
Assistant Professors(Tenured) 11
Assistant Professors(Non-tenured) 28
Research Assistants 1
Undergraduate Students/Foreign Students 878/0
Library 43, 079 volumes
Contact: Admisson Office

Educational philosophy We aim to foster the people who can judge and create independently having international knowledge and view of things. They will communicate and coexist in the global society.

Foreign students We have accepted foreign student individually on the basis of their academic standard and Japanese proficiency. To promote the mutual understanding of different cultures, we are now arranging special exchange programs.

Environment The University is located in Yachiyo-shi, midway between Tokyo, the capital of Japan. and Narita, the Narita International Airport. The campus is in the abandant greenery environment with international urban atomosphere.

Facilities Library, Computer Laboratory. Audio-Vidual Room, Gymnasium. Training Gymnasium, Ground

Student activities The main campus events include Freshmen Orientation Camp, Seminar Trip, School Festival, etc. There are various extracurricular activities such as Rugby, Baseball, Soccer, Tennis as well as the cultural activities like Drama, Publishing and ESS.

Undergraduate Programs

Faculty of Political Economics(878/0)
Dept. of Political Economics

横浜商科大学
(Yokohama Shôka Daigaku)
Yokohama College of Commerce

4-11-1 Higashi Terao, Tsurumi-ku, Yokohama-shi, Kanagawa 230
☎ 045-571-3901

Founded 1968

Undergraduate Programs

Faculty of Commerce
Dept. of Commerce
Dept. of Foreign Trade and Tourism
Dept. of Management Information

CHUBU

NIIGATA
ISHIKAWA
TOYAMA
FUKUI
NAGANO
GIFU
YAMANASHI
AICHI
SHIZUOKA

CHUBU REGION CLIMATE

- Inland District
  Low precipitation year-round, with broad summer-winter temperature gap.
- Tokai District (Pacific Ocean Side)
  Heavy rainfall in summer, while winter is generally clear, with low rainfall and mild temperatures.
- Hokuriku District (Japan Sea Side)
  Winter snowfall fairly heavy, summer temperatures quite mild.

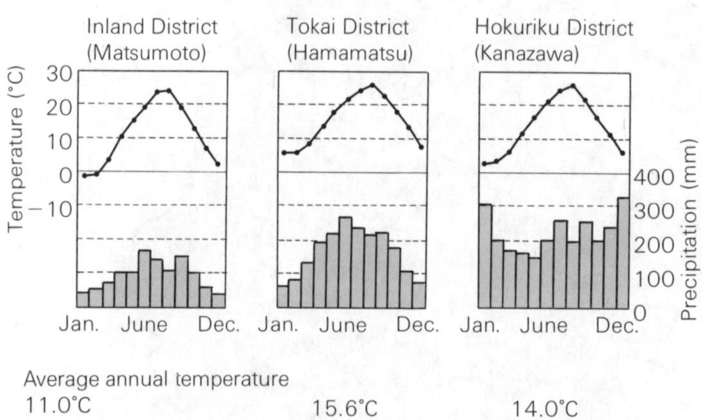

	Inland District (Matsumoto)	Tokai District (Hamamatsu)	Hokuriku District (Kanazawa)
Average annual temperature	11.0°C	15.6°C	14.0°C
Annual precipitation	1,067mm	1,928mm	2,645mm

National Universities

愛知教育大学
(Aichi Kyôiku Daigaku)

Aichi University of Education

1 Hirosawa Igaya-cho, Kariya-shi, Aichi 448
☎ 0566-36-3111 FAX 0566-36-1751

Founded 1873
Professors 139
Associate Professors 124
Assistant Professors(Tenured) 5
Assistant Professors(Non-tenured) 290
Research Assistants 19
Undergraduate Students/Foreign Students 4, 259/3
Graduate Students/Foreign Students 135/18
Library 527, 371 volumes
Contact: Admission Section

Educational philosophy The university aims to conduct academic and creative research, prepare students for teaching, and contribute to the progress of culture and the good of the society. Six departments of integrated arts and sciences were newly set up, to prepare students for a wide variety of professional fields.

Foreign students Since its establishment, the university maintains its tradition in the education of teachers. Foreign students can broadly conduct research in the field of education and allied studies. We welcome those students with a clear sense of purpose.

Environment The university is located in the suburbs of the City of Kariya, which is adjacent to Nagoya, the key city of the economic area in Central Japan, and the City of Toyota, whose automobile industry is world-famous. Surroundings of the spacious campus include a lake, woods, and natural iris fields carefully protected for its literary significance.

Facilities Library, Center for Educational Technology, Lounge and Assembly Hall, Auditorium, Gymnasiums, Martial Arts Gymnasium, Swimming pool, Student Center, Cafeteria, Botanical Garden and Farm, etc.

Student activities University festival, sports festival, and a variety of extracurricular activities: orchestra, brass band, chorus, drama, movie, fine arts, calligraphy, tea ceremony, photography, track and field, swimming, baseball, tennis, basketball, volleyball, soccer, judo, Japanese fencing, Japanese archery, horseback riding, etc.

Academic programs for foreign students Supplementary Japanese language classes, lectures in the various fields to further students' intellectual understanding and appreciation of the different aspects of Japan and its culture, tutorial program, and field trips.

Services for foreign students Counseling, and housing information including dormitories for full-time students.

Undergraduate Programs

Faculty of Education(4, 258/3)
Dept. of Primary School Teachers(1, 830/0)
Dept. of Junior High School Teachers(551/0)
Dept. of Teacher Training Course of Mentally Retarded Children(61/0)
Dept. of Teacher Training Course of Physically Handicapped Children(60/1)
Dept. of Kindergarten Teachers(94/2)
Dept. of Health Science Teachers(210/0)
Dept. of Senior High School Teachers(176/0)
Dept. of Integrated Arts and Sciences(1, 276/0)

Graduate Programs

Graduate School of Research Division of Education(M 135/18)

Div. of School Education(M 23/3)
Pedagogy, History of Education, Educational Sociology, Adult Education, Group Activity Education, Career Guidance, Educational Psychology, Developmental Psychology, Education in Early Childhood, Psychology in Early Childhood, Study of Curriculum and Teaching Method for Early Childhood Education, Educational System

Div. of Japanese(M 9/2)
Japanese Language, Japanese Literature, Teaching of Japanese, Chinese Philosophy and Literature, Calligraphy

Div. of English(M 5/0)
English Language, English and American Literature, English Teaching Methodology

Div. of Social Sciences(M 12/5)
Philosophy, Ethics, History, Geography, Law, Politics, Sociology, Economics, Social Studies Education

Div. of Handicapped Children(M 16/3)
Education of Handicapped Children, Psychology of Handicapped Children, Pathology of Handicapped Children, Health of Handicapped Children, Education of Physically Handicapped Children

Div. of Mathematics(M 8/1)
Algebra, Geometry, Topology, Analysis, Applied Mathematics, Mathematics Education

Div. of Natural Sciences(M 13/1)
Fundamental Physics, Applied Physics, Inorganic and Physical Chemistry, Organic Chemistry, Taxonomy and Morphology, Physiology and Ecology, Astronomy • Geophysics Geology • Mineralogy

Div. of Arts(M 28/1)
Vocal Music, Instrumental Music, Compositision Conducting, Musicology, Music Education, Painting, Sculpture, Design, Science of Art, Arts Education

Div. of Health and Physical Education(M 14/1)
Science of Physical Education, Biomechanics, Physiology and Hygienic, School Health, Teaching Methodology of H & P.E.

Div. of Home Economics(M 6/0)

Food and Nutrition, Textiles and Clothing, Home Management, Child Development and Care, Home Economics Education

Div. of Engineering(M 1/0)

Wood Work, Metal Work, Electricity, Machine, Cultivation, Education of Industrial Arts

One-Year Graduate Programs

Education Course

Natural Science Major

Special Education Course

Education of Mentally Retarded Children Major

福井医科大学
(Fukui Ika Daigaku)

Fukui Medical School

23-3 Shimoaizuki, Matsuoka-cho, Yoshida-gun, Fukui 910-11

☎ 0776-61-3111

Founded 1978
Professors 36
Associate Profrssors 34
Assistant Professors(Tenured) 28
Assistant Professors(Non-tenured) 59
Research Assistants 130
Undergraduate Students/Foreign Students 620/0
Graduate Students/Foreign Students 70/3
Library 78,457 volumes
Contact: Student Division ☎ ext. 2143

Educational philosophy The aim of the education in Fukui Medical School is to produce clinical doctors and medical researchers who, on the basis of character development, have acquired both medical ethics, emphasizing the respect of life, and highly advanced medical knowledge.

Foreign students Foreign students intending to be successful students or researchers in this school are requested to understand Japan and get accustomed to Japanese customs as early as possible.

Environment The campus is situated to the east of Fukui City, which is flanked by the Sea of Japan, and is not far from Eiheiji Temple, a mecca for Zen Buddhism. The Kuzuryu River flowing nearby provides rich green fields and quiet and idyllic surroundings where students may spend a pleasant campus life.

Facilities Library, Gymnasium, Martial Arts Gym, Archery Range, Central Reasearch Laboratories, Laboratory Animal Center, and Radioisotope Research Institute.

Student activities A feature of the enriched school life here is School Festival in which all students from the different clubs are involved and present medical exhibits every year.

Academic programs for foreign students Tutoring system

Services for foreign students Housing information, Cultural exchange program

Undergraduate Programs

Faculty of Medicine(620/0)

Dept. of Medicine(620/0)

Granduate Programs

Postgraduate Course of Medical Sciences(D 70/3)

Div. of Morphology(D 11/1)

Anatomy, Anesthesiology, Biochemistry, Dentistry and Oral Surgery, Dermatology, Environmental Health, Experimental Radiology and Health Physics, Immunology, Internal Medicine, Legal Medicine, Microbiology, Neurosurgery, Obstetrics and Cynecology, Ophthalmology, Orthopedic Surgery, Otorhinolaryngology, Parasitology, Pathology, Pediatrics, Pharmacology, Physiology, Psychiatry, Radiology, Surgery, Urology

Div. of Physiology(D 22/0)

Div. of Biochemistry(D 34/2)

Div. of Ecology(D 3/0)

福井大学
(Fukui Daigaku)

Fukui University

3-9-1 Bunkyo, Fukui-shi, Fukui 910

☎ 0776-23-0500 FAX 0776-27-8518

Founded 1949
Professors 106
Associate Professors 120
Assistant Professors(Tenured) 14
Assistant professors(Non-tenured) 111
Research Assistants 26
Undergraduate Students/Foreign Students 3,238/36
Graduate Students/Foreign Students 228/9
Library 362,198 volumes
Contact: Student Personnel Service Bureau

Educational philosophy The University has adapted to meet the advancement of science and the needs of the local community, and now is planning to offer a Doctor's degree in the faculty of Engineering, and a Master's degree in the faculty of Education, in the near future.

Foreign students Students from abroad are welcome to our university, whose campus as well as surroundings is quiet without the din and bustle of big cities. They can enjoy stimulating and comfortable college life.

Environment Fukui City, with a population of 240,000, is located in the nearly center of Japanese Archipelago and within easy access of major cities, Tokyo/Kyoto. Fukui is blessed with a beautiful natural environment. In the midst of this beauty is a distinct cultural heritage, and a number of ancient artfacts.

Facilities University Library, Health Service Center, Research and Guidance Center of Teaching Practice, Information Prosessing Center, Experimental Facility for Low Temperature Physics, Gymnasium, Swimming Pool.

Student activities University Festival. There is a wide variety of extra curricular activities, including choral groups, brass band, volunteer circle, International Exchange Club, tea ceremony, American football, tennis, soccer, golf, ping-pong, etc.

Academic programs for foreign students Supplemental Japanese Language class, Tutoring system.

Services for foreign students Foreign Students House.

Undergraduate Programs

Faculty of Education(846/8)
- **Dept. of Education**(73/0)
- **Dept. of English**(48/0)
- **Dept. of Fine Arts**(24/1)
- **Dept. of Health and Physical Education**(34/0)
- **Dept. of Home Economics**(25/0)
- **Dept. of Japanese**(116/1)
- **Dept. of Mathematics**(92/0)
- **Dept. of Music**(31/1)
- **Dept. of Natural Science**(94/2)
- **Dept. of Social Science**(83/1)
- **Dept. of Technological Studies**(23/0)
- **Course for Information and Socio-cultural Studies**(118/2)
- **Course for Teachers of Schools of the Mentally Retarded**(85/0)

Faculty of Engineering(2, 392/28)
- **Dept. of Applied Chemistry and Biotechnology** (121/0)
- **Dept. of Applied Physics**(119/1)
- **Dept. of Architecture and Civil Engineering** (163/3)
- **Dept. of Electrical and Electronics Engineering** (200/6)
- **Dept. of Information Science**(272/8)
- **Dept. of Materials Science and Engineering** (181/1)
- **Dept. of Mechanical Engineering**(299/2)

Graduate Programs

Graduate School of Engineering(M 228/9)

Div. of Applied Chemistry(M 34/1)
Organic Chemical Reactans, Functional Polymer Chemistry, Colloid and Surface Chemistry, Biochemistry and Biochemical Processing

Div. of Applied Physics(M 20/0)
Quantum Physics, Solid State Physics, Instrumntation Engineering, Physics of Materials

Div. of Architecture(M 19/2)
Building Construction, Structural Analysis, Planning of Architecture, Theory of Architecture, Environmental Engineering

Div. of Electrical Engineering(M 30/1)
Electrical Fundamentals, Electrical Machinery, Electrical Power System, Electrical Communication, Systems Control

Div. of Electronics(M 24/0)
Quantum Electronics, Information Transmission and Processing, Solid State Electronics, Digital Image and Signal Processing

Div. of General Construction Engineering(M 17/1)
Geotechnics, Disaster Prevention Engineering, Regional and Urban Planning, Structural Engineering, Environmental Planning

Div. of Industrial Chemistry(M 18/0)
Inorganic Industril Chemistry, Polymer Chemistry, Synthetic Organic Chemistry, Chemical Engineering, Polymer Materials

Div. of Information Science(M 17/1)
Information Science Fundamentals, Computer Hardware, Information Processing, Information Devices

Div. of Mechanical and Industrial Engineering(M 18/2)
Strength of Materials, Instrumntation, Machine Design, Thermofluid Mechanics

Div. of Mechanical Engineering(M 14/1)
Materials Enginering, Manufacturing Processes, Thermal Engineering, Fluid Engineering, Mechanical Dynamics

Div. of Polymer Engineering(M 17/0)
Polymer Materials, Polymer Physics, Polymer Processing, Material Design, Composite Material

---

岐阜大学
(Gifu Daigaku)
Gifu University

1-1 Yanagido, Gifu-shi, Gifu 501-11
☎ 0582-30-1111 FAX 0582-30-1410

Founded 1949
Professors 209
Associate Professors 180
Assistant Professors(Tenured) 63
Assistant Professors(Non-tenured) 505
Research Assistants 194
Undergraduate Students/Foreign Students 4, 937/23
Graduate Students/Foreign Students 414/47
Library 693, 018 volumes
Contact: Student Office

Educational philosophy We aim at developing the intellectual, moral and practical abilities of the students under the spirit of the Fundamental Law of Education and providing the society with young people who can contribute to it in future.

Foreign students We believe that foreign students can enjoy a worthly experience in our university, and can contribute to promote our mutual understanding and the development of friendly relation.

Environment The town of Gifu, with a population of 410, 000, is located in the northern part of Nobi Plain and has developed in the heart of the Gifu Castle towered on Mt. Kinka. The cormorant fishing which is held on Nagara River flows through Gifu has history for 1, 200 years.

Facilities University Library, Center for Cooperative Research, Computing Center, Center of Instrumentation, Radioisotope Laboratory, Gymnasium, Hall of Military arts, Swimming pool, Health administration center, etc.

Student activities [campus events] school festival, field trip, skiing school, welcome party, etc. [club activities] orchestra, circle for international exchange, society for the study of education for handicapped children, society for study of biochemistry, art, yacht, volleyball, soccer, baseball, swimming, track and field, etc.

Academic programs for foreign students Supplementary Japanese Language Class, Tutoring system, Credit exchange programme.

Services for foreign students Health clinic, Personal/psychological counceling, College housing, Housing information, Part-time job information, Lending services: daily necessaries, bicycle, etc. Vocational guidance, Home stay/visit program, Cultural exchange program

Undergraduate Programs

Faculty of Agriculture(1, 066/1)
- **Dept. of Agricultural Chemistry**(61/0)
- **Dept. of Agricultural Engineering**(49/0)
- **Dept. of Agricultural Science**(35/0)
- **Dept. of Forestry**(33/0)
- **Dept. of Poultry and Animal Science**(34/1)
- **Dept. of Biological Production System**(224/0)
- **Dept. of Biological Resources and Production**(218/0)
- **Dept. of Utilization of Biological Resources**(230/0)
- **Dept. of Veterinary Medicine**(182/0)

Faculty of Education(1, 421/0)
- **Training Course for Junior High School Teachers**(313/0)
- **Training Course for Primary School Teachers**(936/0)
- **Training Course for Teachers for Special Subjects (Science)** (106/0)
- **Training Course for Teachers of School for the Handicapped**(66/0)

Faculty of Engineering(1, 931/16)
- **Dept. of Chemistry**(451/1)
- **Dept. of Industrial Chemistry**(9/0)
- **Dept. of Synthetic Chemistry**(10/0)
- **Dept. of Civil Engineering**(431/3)
- **Dept. of Construction Engineering**(9/0)
- **Dept. of Electronics and Computer Engineering**(540/8)
- **Dept. of Electrical Engineering**(4/0)
- **Dept. of Electronic Engineering**(3/0)
- **Dept. of Mechanical Engineering**(463/4)
- **Dept. of Precision Engineering**(10/0)
- **Dept. of Textile Engineering**(1/0)

School of Medicine(519/6)
- **Dept. of Medicine**(519/6)

Graduate Programs

Graduate School of Agriculture(M 94/13)

Div. of Agricultural Chemistry(M 37/3)
Science of Soil and Manure, Biological Chemistry, Nutritional and Food Chemistry, Applied Microbiology, Utilization of Agricultural Products, Chemistry of Plant Products

Div. of Agricultural Engineering(M 8/0)
Irrigation and Drainage Engineering, Agricultural Hydraulic Engineering, Land Reclamation Engineering, Agricultural Structural Engineering, Farm Power Machinery, Agricultural Equipment and Machinery

Div. of Agricultural Science(M 15/1)
Crop Science, Horticultural Science, Plant Disease Science, Entomology, Genetics and Plant Breeding, Agricultural Economics, Physical Distribution of Agricultural Products

Div. of Forestry(M 15/1)
Forest Management, Forest Production, Tree Biochemistry, Wood Technology, Wood Chemistry

Div. of Poultry and Animal Science(M 19/8)
Poultry Genetics, Poultry Management, Animal Nutrition and Feeding, Biochemistry of Domestic Animal, Dairy and Meat Technology, Management of Animal and Poultry Farm

Graduate School of Engineering(M 223/20)

Div. of Civil Engineering(M 15/1)
Structural Mechanics, Hydraulic Engineering, Concrete Engineering, Geotechnical Engineering

Div. of Construction Engineering(M 18/2)
Transport Engineering, Water Resources Engineering, Environmental Engineering, Disaster Prevention Engineering

Div. of Electrical Engineering(M 41/4)
Fundamental Electrical Engineering, Applied Electronics Engineering, Electric Power Engineering, Electrical Machinery and Apparatus

Div. of Electronic Engineering(M 25/6)
Fundamentals of Electronic Engineering, Solid State Electronics, Communication Systems, Instrumentation and Information Processing

Div. of Industrial Chemistry(M 31/0)
Applied Inorganic Chemistry

Div. of Mechanical Engineering(M 32/2)
Strength of Materials, Thermal Engineering, Fluid Mechanics and Machine, Power Engineering, Materials and Mechanical Processing

Div. of Precision Engineering(M 26/3)
Precision Machining, Instrumentation and Control, Applied Mechanics, Deformation Process Engineering

Div. of Synthetic Chemistry(M 25/1)
Physical Chemistry, Synthetic Inorganic Chemistry, Syn-

thetic Organic Chemistry

Div. of Textile Engineering(M 10/1)

Spinning Technology, Weaving Technology, Physics of Fiber Assemblies, Fiber Materials

Graduate School of Medicine(D 80/13)

Div. of Internal Medicine(M 31/3)

Internal Medicine, Dermatology, Neurology and Psychiatry, Pediatrics, Radiology, Laboratory Medicine

Div. of Morphology(M 11/5)

Anatomy, Pathology, Bacteriology

Div. of Physiological Science(D 9/1)

Physiology, Biochemistry, Pharmacology

Div. of Social Medicine(D 6/2)

Hygiene, Public Health, Forensic Medicine, Parasitology

Div. of Surgery(D 23/2)

Surgery, Gynecology and Obstetrics, Orthopedic Surbery, Neurosurgery, Ophthalmology, Oto–Rhino–Laryngology, Urology, Anesthesiology, Oral Surgery

The United Graduate School of Veterinary Medicine(D 17/1)

Div. of Veterinary Medicine(D 17/1)

Basic Veterinary Science, Pathogenetic Veterinary Science, Applied Veterinary Science, Clinical Veterinary Medicine

One–Year Graduate Programs

Education course

Education Major

浜松医科大学
(Hamamatsu Ika Daigaku)

Hamamatsu University School of Medicine

3, 600 Handa–cho, Hamamatsu–shi, Shizuoka 431–31
☎ 053–435–2111 FAX 053–433–7290

Founded 1974
Professors 37
Associate Professors 31
Assistant Professors(Tenured) 30
Assistant Professors(Non–tenured) 148
Research Assistants 140
Undergraduate Students/Foreign Students 637/6
Graduate Students/Foreign Students 86/7
Library 84, 823 volumes
Contact: Division for Student Affairs

Educational philosophy Hamamatsu University School of Medicine was founded with an aim at teaching and studying high level medical sciences and their application. The goal of this program is the training of clinicians and basic researchers having highly developed medical knowledge and techniques, so as to contribute to the health and welfare of the society.

Foreign students Qualified foreign students are willingly admitted to our university, and their number has been increasing in recent years. We hope that they will, in the future, contribute to the development of medical sciences in their home countries.

Environment Hamamatsu is located between Tokyo and Osaka, and is a commercial and industrial city with a population of 530, 000. Due to a mild climate, it is a comfortable city to live. It has a convenient transportation system and is surrounded by scenic places.

Facilities Several kinds of facilities are available for research and study on medical sciences. They are Institute for Experimental Animals, Equipment Center, Hospital, Health Administration Center, etc..

Student activities There are 51 varieties of extra–curricular club activities. A student can participate in several activities.

Academic programs for foreign students Each foreign student has his own tutor who may give an advice concerning the problems of the study as well as of campus life.

Services for foreign students Students are advised, with our supervision, to find private apartments near the campus because of unavailability of the university dormitory for foreign students. Cultural exchange programs are often sponsored by local public and volunteer groups.

Undergraduate Programs

Faculty of Medicine(637/6)

Graduate Programs

Graduate School of Medical Science(D 86/7)

Morphology, Physiology, Biochemistry, Ecology

上越教育大学
(Jôetsu Kyôiku Daigaku)

Joetsu University of Education

1 Yamayashiki–machi, Joetsu–shi, Niigata 943
☎ 0255–22–2411 FAX 0255–22–4050

Founded 1978
Professors 59
Associate Professors 71
Assistant Professors(Tenured) 22
Assistant Professors(Non–tenured) 30
Research Assistants 22
Undergraduate Students/Foreign Students 828/0
Graduate Students/Foreign Students 427/7
Library 129, 079 volumes
Contact: Research Cooperation Office, School Affairs Section

Educational philosophy It is the aim of the institution to educatonal research and instruction in both theory and practice. This is necessary not only to produce teachers who are highly qualified and competent professionals, but also to meet the needs of society now and in the future.

Foreign students We will make foreign students feel at home here and help them in their studies. We hope the students will feel their stay here has been rewarding and the school will do everything possible to create a friendly and academically positive atmosphere.

Environment Joetsu University of Education is located on a gentle, wooded hillside above Joetsu City. The city has a population of 130, 000 and is both historically important and scenically attractive. Intracity and intercity transportation systems are excellent.

Facilities The university library, the Center for Educational Research and Development, the Center for Research and Training in Educational Information, the center for skills training, the Research Center for the Handicapped, the swimming pool, auditorium, and gymnasium are all located on or within easy reach of the main campus.

Student activities There are over forty of extracurricular activities offered on the campus. These include such things as classes in tea ceremony, calligraphy, drama, brass band, and Japanese music. Sports include tennis, volleyball, baseball, ping-pong, kendo, and skiing, among others.

Academic programs for foreign students Tutoring system

Services for foreign students Services for foreign students include: a health center, student dormitories, a housing information center, a spacious cafeteria, home stay programs, and an exchange with elementary and high schools in the area

Undergraduate Programs

Faculty of School Education(828/0)

Graduate Programs

Graduate School of Education(M 427/7)

Division of Languages, Division of Social Studies, Division of Fine Arts and Music, Division of Physical Education, Home Economics and Industrial Arts, Division of Early Childhood Education, Division of Educational Basics, Division of Educational Organization and Administration, Division of Educational Methods, Division of Student Guidance, Division of Education for the Handicapped

金沢大学

(Kanazawa Daigaku)

Kanazawa University

920, 1-1, Marunouchi, Kanazawa, Ishikawa
☎ 0762-62-4281 FAX 0762-23-7835

Founded 1949
Professors 327
Associate Profrssors 259
Assistant Professors(Tenured) 96
Assistant Professors(Non-tenured) 484
Research Assistants 275
Undergraduate Students/Foreign Students 8, 087/15
Graduate Students/Foreign Students 962/55
Library 1, 250, 000 volumes
Contact: Student Affairs Bureau

Educational philosophy Aiming to stand in the forefront of the intellectual and academic development in the world today, we are preparing for the integrated doctoral programs covering a wide range of interdiciplinary areas among the Faculties.

Foreign students We believe it is our reaponsibility to contribute to improve the culture of the world and the welfare of mankind by receiving as many foreign students as we can.

Environment Our campuses are all located in Kanazawa, one of the largest cities on the coast of the Sea of Japan. Kanazawa was called " Library of the Nation " as a major center of learning during the Edo period. Today, it has developed into a modern city with an elegant atmosphere.

Facilities The University has begun to move to the new campus, where a functional library, a computer center and research facilities have been built. New gymnasiums, playgrounds, tennis courts and pools will be constructed.

Student activities Foreign students are welcome to join in a wide range of sports and cultural clubs as their extracurricular activities. Various events for foreign students such as a field trip, a skiing class and a party are held every year.

Academic programs for foreign students We offer extracurricular supplementary classes of Japanese language and culture. And the College of Liberal Arts provides regular undergranduate students with courses of Japanese language and culture.

Services for foreign students Our Foreign Students Center offers professional counselor's health care advice and information on dormitories, housing and part-time jobs. Many opportunities for exchange with citizens of Kanazawa are provided.

Undergraduate Programs

Faculty of Economics(848/6)
Dept. of Economics(848/6)

Faculty of Education(1, 243/1)
Dept. of Training Course for Elementary School Teachers(525/0)
Dept. of Course for Integrated Science(79/0)
Dept. of Training Course for Junior High School Teachers(234/1)
Dept. of Training Course for Senior High School Teachers(78/0)
Dept. of Training Course for Special School Teachers for the Deaf(55/0)
Dept. of Training Course for Special School Teachers for the Mentally Retarded(63/0)
Dept. of Training Course for Special School Teachers for the Speechhandicapped(79/0)
Dept. of Course for Sports Science(65/0)
Faculty of Law(799/1)
Dept. of Law(799/1)
Faculty of Letters(649/0)
Dept. of Behavioral Sciences(212/0)
Dept. of History(182/0)
Dept. of Literature(245/0)
Faculty of School of Medicine(688/0)
Dept. of Medicine(688/0)
Faculty of Pharmaceutical Sciences(333/0)
Dept. of Pharmaceutical Sciences(172/0)
Dept. of Pharmaceutical Technochemistry(161/0)
Faculty of Science(694/0)
Dept. of Biology(112/0)
Dept. of Chemistry(165/0)
Dept. of Earth Sciences(121/0)
Dept. of Mathematics(145/0)
Dept. of Physics(149/0)
Faculty of Technology(2, 198/7)
Dept. of Chemistry and Chemical Engineering (519/1)
Dept. of Civil Engineering(475/1)
Dept. of Electrical and Computer Engineering (491/3)
Dept. of Mechanical Systems Engineering(713/2)

Graduate Programs

Graduate School of Economics(M 15/6)
Div. of Economis(M 15/6)
Economic Theory, Contemporary Capitalism, Modern Economics, Econometrics, Statistics, Economic History of Europe, History of Japanese Economy, Agrarian History of Modern Japan, Modern Chinese Economic History, History of Political Economy, History of Social Thought, Public Finance, Local Government Finance, Monetary Economics, Banking and Financial Systems, International Economics, World Economy, Social Security, Labor Economics, Principles of Economic Policy, Modern Economic Policy, Economics of Regional Development, Regional Economics, Economic Planning, Industrial Engineering, Accouting Theory, Management Accounting, Information Science, Business Management, Comparative Study of Economic System

Graduate School of Education(M 92/4)
Div. of Domestic Science Education(M 9/2)
Home Economics Education, Food Science, Dwellings, General Family and Household
Div. of Education for the Handicapped(M 5/0)
Pedagogy of Handicapped Children, Psychology of Handicapped Children, Clinical and Medical Study of Handicapped Children
Div. of English Education(M 5/0)
Teaching of English as a foreign Language, English Lingusitics, Britsh and American Literature
Div. of Fine Art Education(M 2/0)
Education through Art, Painting, Sculpture, Formative Design, Theory of Formative Arts
Div. of Health and Physical Education(M 13/0)
Health and Physical Education, Physical Education, Kinematics, School Health Science
Div. of Japanese Language Education(M 11/1)
Japanese Language Education, Japanese Philology, Japanese Literature, Chinese Literature, Calligraphy
Div. of Mathematics Education(M 4/0)
Mathematical Education, Algebra, Geometry, Analysis, Mathematics Education
Div. of School Education(M 17/0)
Approaches to Education, Social Psychology, Learning Psychology, Developmental Psychology
Div. of Science Education(M 7/0)
Science Education, Physics, Chemistry, Biology, Earth Sciences
Div. of Social Studies Education(M 10/1)
Social Education, History, Geography, Jurisprudence, Political Science, Economics, Sociology, Philosophy, Art
Div. of Technology Education(M 9/0)
Technical Education, Electrical and Electronics Engineering, Mechanical Engineering, Plant Culture
Graduate School of Law(M 15/1)
Div. of Law(M 15/1)
Public Law, Civil Law, Basis of Jurisprudence, Politics and International Relations
Graduate School of Letters(M 43/4)
Div. of American and English Literature(M 4/0)
(Common Lectures for Divisions of American and English Literature, German Literature and Japanese Literature) Japanese Philology, Japanese Literature, Chinese Language and Literature, English Literature, English and American Literature, American Literature, English Philology, German Literature, German Linguistics, French Literature and Linguistics, Special Linguistics
Div. of German Literature(M 6/0)
(Common Lectures for Divisions of American and English Literature, German Literature and Japanese Literature), Japanese Philology, Japanese Literature, Chinese Language and Literature, English Literature, English and American Literature, American Literature, English Philology, German Literature, German Linguistics, French Literature and Linguistics, Special Linguistics
Div. of Japanese Literature(M 10/3)
(Common Lectures for divisions of American and English Literature, German Literature and Japanese Literature), Japanese Philology, Japanese Literature, Chinese

Language and Literature, English Literature, English and American Literature, American Literature, English Philology, German Literature, German Linguistics, French Literature and Linguistics, Special Linguistics

Div. of History(M 10/0)

Japanese History, Asian History, Western History, Geography, Archaeology

Div. of Philosophy(M 13/1)

Western Philosophy, Indian Philosophy, Chinese Philosophy, History of Religion, Sociology, Cultural Anthropology, Psychology

Graduate School of Medicine(D 257/7)

Div. of Internal Medicine(D 105/1)

Internal Medicine, Neurology, Neuropsychiatry, Pediatrics, Radiology, Nuclear Medicine, Dermatology, Laboratory Medicine

Div. of Pathology(D 14/3)

Pathology, Microbiology, Parasitology, Virology, Pathophysiology, Immunogiology

Div. of Physiology(D 6/0)

Anatomy, Physiology, Biochemistry, Pharmacology, Neurophysiology, Biophysics, Molecular Biology, Molecular Immunology, Experimental Therapeutics

Div. of Social Medicine(D 10/0)

Hygiene, Public Health, Legal Medicine

Div. of Surgery(D 122/3)

Surgery, Orthopaedic Surgery, Neurosurgery, Urology, Ophthalmology, Otorhinolaryngology, Obstetrics and Gynecoiogy, Anesthesiology, Oral Surgery

Graduate School of Natural Science and Technology(D 94/21)

Div. of Life Sciences(D 26/5)

Bioactive and Related Substances Chemistry, Physical and Chemical Biodynamics, Molecular Physiology, Molecular and Cellular Biology, Environmental Biology and Health Science

Div. of Physical Sciences(D 34/5)

Mathematical Science, Science for Structure of Matter, Materials Science and Engineering, Chemical Science, Science for Natural Environment

Div. of System Science and Technology(D 34/11)

Mathematical Foundation of System Science, Electronics and Computer Science, Electro–mechanical System, Engineering for Design and Production, Energy System, Civil Engineering

Graduate School of Pharmaceutical Sciences(M 50/0)

Div. of Pharmaceutical Sciences(M 26/0)

Chemistry, Analytical Chemistry, Biochemistry, Pharmacognosy and Natural Products Chemistry, Pharmacology, Microbiology, Hygienic Chemistry

Div. of Pharmaceutical Technochemistry(M 24/0)

Pharmaceutical Chemistry, Pharmaceutics, Physical Chemistry, Synthetic Organic Chemistry, Biology, Radiation Biology

Graduate School of Science(M 117/3)

Div. of Biology(M 23/2)

Systematic Botany, Phytogeography, Field Work of Systematic Botany and Plant Ecology, Field Work of Plant Sociology, Plant Physiology, Plant Biochemistry, Animal Biochemistry, Developmental Biology, Ecology, Animal Physiology, Physiology of Fertilization

Div. of Chemistry(M 27/1, D 27/0)

Theoretical Chemistry, Structural Analysis, Organic Chemistry, Synthetic Organic Chemistry, Inorganic Chemistry, Analytical Chemistry, Geochemistry, Biochemistry, Biological Oxidation, Radiochemistry, Nuclear Geochemistry, Coordination Chemistry

Div. of Earth Science(M 16/0)

Mineralogy and Crystallography, Petrology and Geochemistry, Geology, Paleontology, Crustal Structure and Geotectonics, Sedimentation and Tectonics, Geotectonics and Geophysics

Div. of Mathematics(M 10/0)

Mathematical Analysis, Complex Analysis, Algebra, Geometry, Applied Mathematics, Differential Equations

Div. of Physics(M 41/0)

Solid State Physics, Plasma Physics, Biophysics, Molecular Physics, Basic Theory of Matter, Theory of Matter, Quantum Field Theory, Particle Physics, Nuclear Physics, Mathematical Physics

Graduate School of Technology(M 279/9)

Div. of Chemistry and Chemical Engineering(M 63/0)

Physical and Analytical Chemistry, Chemical Engineering Fundamentals, Synthesis of Materials, Separation and Mixing Processes, Chemistry of Functional Materials, Energy and Environment, Material Sciences

Div. of Civil Engineering(M 35/2)

Structural Engineering, Water Engineering, Geotechnical Engineering, Urban and Regional Facility Planning, Environmental Health Engineering

Div. of Electrical and Computer Engineering(M 84/5)

Electronic Materials, Electron Devices, Electronic Circuit, Instrument and Control, Energy Conversion and Power Systems, Computer Engineering, Information and Communication Engineering, Electrical Energy Conversion Laboratory

Div. of Mechanical System Engineering(M 97/2)

Solid Mechanics and Dynamics, Engineering Materials, Strength and Mechanism in Design, Automatic Mechanics, Production Engineering, Production System, Electro –Mechanical Network, Energy Conversion, Machinery for Energy Conversion, Material Sciences

---

三重大学

(Mie Daigaku)

Mie University

1515 Kamihama–cho, Tsu–shi, Mie 514

☎ 0592–32–1211 FAX 0592–32–5028

Founded 1949
Professors 266
Associate Professors 239

Assistant Professors(Tenured) 56
Assistant Professors(Non-tenured) 588
Research Assistants 181
Undergraduate Students/Foreign Students 5, 944/18
Graduate Students(Foreign) 517/28
Library 661, 044 volumes
Contact: Student Affairs Division, Foreign Section

Educational philosophy The educational philosophy of Mie University is to educate young people to be good citizens and leaders in the future development of society through study and research of the external environment (Bioresources and Engineering), human physical well-being (Medicine) and inner human spirit (Humanities and social sciences, and Education).
Foreign students We intend to encourage students from abroad to apply for academic and cultural programs at Mie University to enhance their knowledge, expand their cultural awareness of Japan and help to develop a sense of international cooperation both here and abroad.
Environment The campus is located in the northeastern part of Tsu with a population of about 150, 000, the capital of Mie Prefecture. It faces Ise Bay to the east and to the west, the peaks of the Suzuka Mountains can be seen from the campus. The climate in Mie Prefecture is mild throughout the year. The campus is ten to fifteen minutes' walk from Edobashi Station.
Facilities Students' Hall, University Library, Facility for Fisheries Experimentation, Facility for Gene Experimentation, Facility for Animal Experimentation, Gyms (2), Track and Field, Swimming Pool, Information Processing Center
Student activities Popular campus events includes university festival, freshmen welcome party. There is a wide variety of extracurricular activities: Brass Band, Puppet Play Troupe, Baseball Club, Yacht Club, Soccer Club, Tennis Club, etc.
Academic programs for foreign students Classes for State of Affairs in Japan, Japanese Conversation, Reading in Japanese; Extracurricular Guidance
Services for foreign students Health Administration Center, Foregn Students' House, Homestay, Home Visit, Cultural Exchange Programs

Undergraduate Programs

Faculty of Humanities and Social Sciences(1, 204/6)
Dept. of Humanities(423/1)
Dept. of Social Sciences(781/5)
Faculty of Education(1, 347/0)
Training Course for Teachers of Elementary Schools(745/0)
Training Course for Teachers of Junior High Schools(349/0)
Training Course for Teachers of Schools for Handicapped Children(80/0)
Training Course for Kindergarten Teachers(112/0)
Dept. of Information Science Education(61/0)
Faculty of Medicine(597/0)
Dept. of Medicine(597/0)
Faculty of Engineering(1, 519/12)
Dept. of Mechanical Engineering(202/2)
Dept. of Mechanical Engineering and Material Science(203/3)
Dept. of Electrical Engineering(216/2)
Dept. of Electronic Engineering(217/2)
Dept. of Molecular Materials Engineering(404/0)
Dept. of Architecture(197/3)
Dept. of Information Engineering(80/0)
Faculty of Bioresources(914/0)
Dept. of Bioresources(914/0)

Graduate Programs

Graduate School of Education(M 58/1)
Div. of School Education(M 8/0)
Pedagogy, Pedagogical Psychology, Early Childhood Education
Div. of Education for the Handicapped(M 5/0)
Pedagogy for the Handicapped
Div. of Education in Subject(M 45/1)
Japanese, Social Science, Geography, History, Philosophy-Ethics, Mathematics, Physics, Chemistry, Biology, Earth Science, Art, Health and Physical Education, Technology Education
Graduate School of Medicine(D 154/8)
Div. of Morphological Medicine(D 14/3)
Anatomy, Pathology, Microbiology
Div. of physiological Medicine(D 7/0)
Physiology, Biochemistry, Pharmacology
Div. of Social Medicine(D 2/0)
Hygiene, Public Health, Medical Zoology, Forensic Medicine
Div. of Internal Medicine(D 60/3)
Internal Medicine, Psycho-Neurology, Pediatrics, Dermatology, Radiology, Laboratory Medicine
Div. of Surgery(D 71/2)
Surgery, Thoracic Surgery, Oral Surgery, Orthopedic Surgery, Urology, Ophthalmology, Otorhinolaryngology, Obstetrics and Gynecology, Anesthesiology, Neurosurgery
Graduate School of Engineering(M 171/9)
Div. of Mechanical Engineering(M 24/1)
Machinery Dynamics, Fluid Engineering, Machineshop Technology, Thermal Engineering
Div. of Mechanical and Materials Engineering(M 25/1)
Materials Dynamics, Machinery and Materials, Production Design, Material Prosessing
Div. of Electrical Engineering(M 20/2)
Fundamentals of Electrical Engineering, Electric Power Engineering, Communications Engineering, Electronic Physics
Div. of Electronic Engineering(M 26/2, D 26/0)
Electronic Materials, Electronic Devices, Information Processing, Measurements and System Control, Field Common in Electricity

Div. of Industrial Chemistry(M 30/1)
Inorganic Industrial Chemistry, Organic Industrial Chemistry, Inorganic Material Chemistry, Organic Material Chemistry

Div. of Chemistry of Resources(M 23/1)
Physical Chemistry for Resources, Analytical Chemistry for Resources, Reaction Mechanism Chemistry, Molecular Design Chemistry

Div. of Architecture(M 23/1)
Regional Environmental Science, Architectural Design and Planning, Building Environment and Equipment, Structural Mechanics and Deign

Geaduate School of Bioresources(M 134/10)

Div. of Sciences for Agricultural Production (M 24/4)
Sciences for Agricultural Production, Economics of Bioresources

Div. of Forest Resources(M 14/0)
Forest Resources, Exploitation of Forest Resources

Div. of Fisheries Science and Marine Biological Production(M 21/2)
Cultivation of Fishery Resources, Exploitation of Fishery Resources, Aquatic Environment, Economics of Bioresources

Div. of Bioproduction Engineering(M 27/3)
Agricultural Civil Engineering, Bioproduction and Machinery

Div. of Exploitation of Bioresources(M 48/1)
Agricultural Chemistry, Chemistry for Fishery Resources, Bioscience

One-Year Graduate Programs

Special Education Course

Education of the mentally handicapped children Major

長岡技術科学大学
(Nagaoka Gijutsu Kagaku Daigaku)

Nagaoka University of Technology

1603–1 Kamitomioka–machi, Nagaoka–shi, Niigata 940–21
☎ 0258–46–6000 FAX 0258–46–6085

Founded 1976
Professors 66
Associate Professors 61
Assistant Professors(Tenured) 6
Assistant Professors(Non–tenured) 90
Research Assistants 37
Undergraduate Students/Foreign Students 1, 037/27
Graduate Students/Foreign Students 624/46
Library 79, 090 volumes
Contact: Admission section, educational affairs Department

Educational philosophy To broaden students' understanding of the ever–advancing science and technology primarily through graduate programs of study and, thereby, to train them to take the lead in research activities useful for the further advancement of technology.

Foreign students Readily accepted are foreign students and researchers who have specific interest in our undergraduate and graduate programs.

Environment Located in the center of Niigata Prefecture, Nagaoka affords the advantages of life in a small city and the country. Population: 185, 000. Location: 250km northwest of Tokyo.

Facilities University Library, Language Center, Physical Education and Medical Center, Analysis and Instrumentation Center, Technological Development Center, Central Machine Shop, Information Procesing Center, Radioisotope Center, Sound and Vivration Engineering Laboratory, Laboratory of Beam Technology, Department of Sciences and Mathematics

Student activities Several students activities such as homecoming, athletic meets such as ball games, a long distance relay, a swimming contest as well as 18 cultural clubs and 34 sports clubs are organized.

Academic programs for foreign students Some courses of Japanese language and cluture can be replaced, after their completion, with foreign languages and liberal arts courses. Foreign student tutorial system is available regarding research and learning as well as daily life.

Services for foreign students Counselors help foreign students with their health care. International House provides accomodation for foreign students and researchers. They are assisted on request for services such as looking for part–time jobs and Japanese families to host them. They are frequently invited to international events in the community.

Undergraduate Programs

Faculty of Engineering(1, 037/27)
Dept. of Bio engineering(66/0)
Dept. of Civil engineering(144/7)
Dept. of Electrical and electronic systems engineering(142/5)
Dept. of Electronic engineering(139/5)
Dept. of Materials science and technology(135/2)
Dept. of Mechanical systems engineering(161/6)
Dept. of Planning and production engineering (145/2)

Graduate Programs

Graduate School of Engineering(M 552/19 D 72/27)

Div. of Civil engineering(M 82/5)
Planning and environmental engineering, Disaster control engineering, Structural engineering

Div. of Electrical and electronic systems engineering(M 98/5)
Eectrical power systems, Transmission of information,

Computer science and systems

Div. of Electronic engineering(M 90/0)

Fundamental of electricity and electronics, Electronic devices, Radio and optical engineering

Div. of Materials science and technology(M 88/1)

Material analysis engineering, Inorganic materials engineering, Organic materials engineering

Div. of Mechanical systems engineering(M 101/5)

Solid material system engineering, Heat and fluid engineering, Control engineering

Div. of Planning and production engineering(M 93/3)

Machine element and machine design, Production engineering, Materials science and engineering

Div. of Energy and environment science(D 20/8)

Energy and systems engineering, Energy and materials engineering, Environment and systems engineering

Div. of Information science and control engineering(D 24/10)

Intelligent information engineering, Information processing engineering, Precision control engineering

Div. of Materials science(D 28/9)

Structural materials engineering, Functional materials engineering, Materials characterization engineering

---

名古屋工業大学

(Nagoya Kôgyô Daigaku)

Nagoya Institute of Technology

Gokiso-cho, showa-ku, Nagoya 466
☎ 052-732-2111

Founded 1949
Professors 117
Associate Professors 108
Assistant Professors(Tenured) 34
Assistant Professors(Non-tenured) 113
Research Assistants 63
Undergraduate Students/Foreign Students 5, 416/20
Graduate Students/Foreign Students 498/47
Library 365, 714 volumes
Contact: Office

Educational philosophy The Institute aims to cultivate persons who contribute to world peace and welfare through teaching and studying within industry, while still promoting technical development of local industry.

Foreign students We believe that all students can enjoy a rewarding experience in N.I.T. and also serve for the promotion of mutual understanding and friendly relations between own countries.

Environment Nagoya located roughly at the center of Japan, is a city with a population of 2. 15 million. It is the prefectural seat of Aichi prefecture, as well as the site of Nagoya Castle, famous for the golden dolphins on its roof.

Facilities University Library, Instrument and Analysis Center, Center for Cooperative Research, Ceramic Engineering Research Laboratory, Center of Information Processing Education, Health Administration Center, Gymnasiums, University Hall

Student activities Campus events are school festival (KODAI-SAI), welocome party, farewell party and a study tour. Now we have 31 sports clubs and 20 cultural circles. Foreign students are welcome to join in clubs and societies.

Academic programs for foreign students Japanese Language and Culture Courses for undergraduate students who wish to improve their proficiency in Japanese Tutorial System

Services for foreign students Health service and treatment of accidents and illness is given by Heath Administration Center. The counselling service is available to foreign students. The Institute has accommodations for students.

Undergraduate Programs

Faculty of Engineering(4, 349/20)

Dept. of Applied Chemistry(643/4)

Dept. of Materials Science and Engineering(812/1)

Dept. of Mechanical Engineering(690/2)

Dept. of Systems Engineering(514/4)

Dept. of Electrical and Computer Engineering(1, 064/8)

Dept. of Architectuer, Urban Engineering and Civil Engineering(626/1)

Graduate Programs

Graduate School of Engineering(M 415/20, D 83/27)

Div. of Materials Scienco and Engineering(M 136/5, D 27/7)

Pysical and Analytical Chemistry, Chemical Engineering, Inorganic Chemistry, Polymer Chemistry,Oraganic Chemistry and Biochemistry, Material Fundamentals, Material Charactarization, Material Properties, Oraganic Materials Design, Ceramics Synthesis, Metallic Materials Design

Div. of Systems Engineering(M 110/5, D 23/7)

Thermal Energy, Fluid Mechanics, Mechanics, Production Technology, Electoronic-Mechanical Engineering, Physical Instrumentation, Instrumentation System Engineering, Mathematics for System Science, Management Systems Engineering

Div. of Electrical and Computer Engineerig(M 102/5, D 21/8)

Solid State Physics, Electron Devices, Electric Energy, Circuit and Systems, Communication Systems, Information Processing, Computer Science

Div. of Architecture, Urban Engineering and Civil

Engineering(M 67/5, D 12/5)
Infrastructure Planning, Architectural Design and Urban Planning, Structural Engineering and Mechanics, Environmental and Disaster Engineering, Structural Planning and Construction Engineering, Construction Materials and Environmental Management

Div. of Engineering Science
Engineering Mathematics, Material Science, Physical chemistry, Fundamentals of Electrical Engineering, Engineering Mechanic, Analytical Chemistry, Graphic Science for Engineering

名古屋大学
(Nagoya Daigaku)

Nagoya University

Furo-cho, Chikusa-ku, Nagoya-shi, Aichi 464-01
☎ 052-781-5111 FAX 052-781-1754

Founded 1939
Professors 457
Associate Professors 388
Assistant Professors(Tenured) 147
Assistant Professors(Non-tenured) 1, 097
Research Assistants 606
Undergraduate Students/Foreign Students 8, 899/22
Graduate Students/Foreign Students 2, 276/301
Library 2, 171, 690 volumes
Contact: International Afffairs Section

Educational philosophy The name of Nagoya may be better known by the University than by the City because of scientific achievements born out of Nagoya University. Research activities will not be mere continuation of past activities but will involve reformation of organizaton which will enable us to conduct interdisciplinary research and create new fields of research.

Foreign students Nagoya university is considered like a small town in the big Nagoya city. We hope we are good friends and neighbors each other in this town. We wish you to have a happy and healthy stay in our campus and to continue your study successfully.

Environment Nagoya, with population of 2.15 million, is located in the flat area on the central Japan Proper. Nagoya, which has been the castle town of Nagoya Castle, is now the center of the industrial enconomy, administration, culture and transportation of Tokai areas as one of the leading city in Japan.

Facilities University library, Research Center of Health, Physical Fitness and Sports, Center for Linguistic and Cultural Research, Swimming pool, Gymnasium, Auditorium, Computation Center

Student activities Popular campus events includes school, festivals, field trip, visiting factory, party. There is a wide variety of extra curricular activities.

Academic programs for foreign students Supplemental Japanese language class, Tutoring system

Services for foreign students Health clinic, Personal/psychological counseling, International Residence, Foreign Student House, Housing information, Part-time job information, Homestay, Cultural exchange program

Undergraduate Pragrams

Faculty of Agriculture(788/0)
- Dept. of Agricultural Chemistry
- Dept. of Agronomy
- Dept. of Animal Science
- Dept. of Food Science and Technology
- Dept. of Forest Products
- Dept. of Forestry

Faculty of Economics(985/5)
- Dept. of Business Administration
- Dept. of Economics

Faculty of Education(301/0)
- Dept. of Education
- Dept. of Educational Phychology

Faculty of Engineering(3, 490/9)
- Dept. of Aeronautical Engineering
- Dept. of Applied Chemistry
- Dept. of Applied Physics
- Dept. of Architecture
- Dept. of Chemical Engineering
- Dept. of Civil Engineering
- Dept. of Electrical Engineering
- Dept. of Electrical Engineering II
- Dept. of Electronic-Mechanical Engineering
- Dept. of Electronics
- Dept. of Information Engineering
- Dept. of Materials Processing Engineering
- Dept. of Materials Science and Engineering
- Dept. of Mechanical Engineering
- Dept. of Mechanical Engineering II
- Dept. of Nuclear Engineering
- Dept. of Synthetic Chemistry

Faculty of Law(888/0)
- Dept. of Law
- Dept. of Political Science

Faculty of Letters(630/0)
- Dept. of History and Geography
- Dept. of Literature
- Dept. of Philosophy

Faculty of Medicine(612/6)
- Dept. of Medicine

Faculty of Science(1, 025/2)
- Dept. of Biology
- Dept. of Chemistry
- Dept. of Earth Sciences
- Dept. of Mathematics
- Dept. of Molecular Biology
- Dept. of Physics
- Dept. of Physics II

Graduate Programs

Graduate School of Agriculture(M 189/12, D 90/35)

Div. of Agricultural Chemistry
Soil Science, Plant Nutrition and Fertilizer, Biological Chemistry, Nutritional Biochemistry, Microbiology, Pesticides Chemistry

Div. of Agronomy
Theory of agronomy and Plant Breeding, Crop Science, Horticultural Science, Plant Pathology, Applied Entomolgy and Nematology, Sericultural Science, Theory of Farm Management and Agricultural policy, Theory of Landcultivation, Bilological Resourses and Environmental Sciences

Div. of Animal Science
Animal Physiology, Animal Genetics, Animal Reproduction, Animal Nutrition, Functional Anatomy, Chemistry of Animal Products, Fisheries, Animal Management and Environment, Grassland Science

Div. of Biochemical Regulation
Developmental and Genetic Regulation, Metabolic Regulation, Chemical and Cellular Regulation, Nutritional Regulation

Div. of Food Science and Techonolgy
Chemistry and Plant Products, Chemistry of Animal Products, Organic Chemistry, Physical Chemistry, Fermentation Techonology, Bio-reaction Technology

Div. of Forest Products
Chemistry of Forest Products, Wood Technology, Wood Physics, Chemical Techonology of Wood, Wood Industrial Machinery

Div. of Forestry
Silviculture, Forest Managemant, Forest Engineering, Soil and Water Conservation, Forest Protection

Graduate School of Econimics(M 26/12, D21/12)

Div. of Business Adiministration
Business Administration, Production Management, Accounting, Information Management, Financial Management

Div. of Economics
Economic Theory, Economic History, Principles of Economic Policy, Agricultural Policy Industrial Organization and Industrial Policy, Labor Economics, International Economics, History of Economic Thoughts, Statistics and Econometrics, Public Finance, Money and Banking

Graduate School of Education(M 31/4, D 34/2)

Div. of Developmental Clinical Studies
Clinical Studies for Developmental Help, Clinical Studies for Family Development

Div. of Education
Philosophy of Education, History of Education, Curriculum, Methods of Education, Sociology of Education, School Management, Education Administration & System, Adult Education, Technical & Technological Education, Comparative Education, Information Science of Education

Div. of Educational Psychology
Psychology of Development & Learning, Psychology of Personality & Psychological Assessment, Mental Developmental Disorders & Clinical Psychology, Social & Industrial Psychology, Educational Statistics & Survey, Child Psychology

Graduate School of Engineering (M 846/52, D 166/71)

Div. of Aeronautical Engineering
Fluid Mechanics, Engines, Propulsion, Structure, Flight Dynamics, Automatic Control

Div. of Applied Chemistry
Chemistry of Industrial Inorganic Reactions, Applied Chemistry of Oils, Chemistry of Industrial Organic Reactions, Chemistry of Oraganic Materials, Chemistry of Inorganic Materials, Techno-analytical Chemistry, Industrial Oraganic Chemistry

Div. of Applied Physics
Theoretical Solid State Physics, Applied Optics, Industrial Solid State Physics, Engineering of Plasticity, Dielectric & Thermal Properties of Solids, Engineering Mathematics, Dynamics in Engineering Science

Div. of Architecture
Building Construction, Structural Concrete Engineering, Steel Structure, Architectural Design, Architectural Planning, Architectural Environmental Engineering, Disaster Prevention & Safety Engineering

Div. of Chemical Engineering
Fluid Mechanics & Mechanical Unit Operation, Design of Chemical Machinery & Equipment, Combustion & Heart Transmission, Chemical Thermodynamics & Chemical Reaction Engineering, Diffusional Unit Operation, Catalysis Engineering, Transport Phenomena, Process System Engineering & Process Control, Industrial Physical Chemistry

Div. of Civil Engineering
Structural Mechanics, Soil Mechanics, Hydraulics, Civil Engineering Planning, Civil Engineering Design, Civil Engineering Execution, Information Retrieval

Div. of Crystalline Materials Science
Crystal Growth Engineering, Material Coordination Engineering, Device Materials Engineering

Div. of Electrical Engineering
Fundamentals of Electrical Engineering, Electroacoustics, Electric Power Applications, Electric Power Generation Transmission & Distribution Engineering, Electical Machinery & Apparatus, Electromagnetic Waves, General Electrical Engineering

Div. of Electrical Engineering II
Computation and System Engineering, Ionized Gas, Electrical Material Science & Devices, Electronic Control Engineering, Physical Electronics

Div. of Electronic-Mechanical Engineering
Fundamentals of Electonic-Mechanical Engineering, Application and Design of Electronic Machinery, Precision Processing Technology, Sensor and Electric Instrumentation, Integrated Mechanical Engineering

Div. of Electronics
Fundamentals of Electronics, Electron Tubes, Semiconductor Electronics, Electronic Circuit Engineering, High Frequency Engineering, Industrial Electronics

Div. of Geotechnical Engineering
Engineering for Geotechnical Prevention of Disasters

Div. of Information Engineering
Fundamentals of Information Engineering, Computer Language, Information Processing, Knowledge Information, Information System Engineering, Mathematical

Software

Div. of Iron and Steel Engineering

Materials Processing Design Engineering, Materials Reaction Engineering, Phase Transformation and Solidification, Deformation Processing of Materials, Thermal Materials Processing and Joining, Composite Materials Engineering, Materials Processing Analysis and Evaluation

Div. of Mechanical Engineering

Thermodynamics & Heat Engines, Machineshop Technology & Precision Processings, Fluid Mechanics, Dynamics of Machinery & Design, Strength of Materials, Applied Mechanics

Div. of Mechanical Engineering II

Internal-Combustion Engines & Gas Turbines, Materials Science & Machine Design, Control Mechanics & Components, Fluid Machinery, Deformation Processes & Die Engineering

Div. of Metallurgy

Materials Physics, Materials Physical Chemistry, Surface-Interface Engineering, Materials Design Engineering, Strength of Materials, Applied Solid State Physics, Intelligent Material, Techno-Analytical Chemistry

Div. of Nuclear Engineering

Nuclear Instruments, Applied Nuclear Chemistry, Radiation Detector Engineering, Radiation Safety, Nuclear Chemical Engineering, Applied Nuclear Physics, Nuclear Reactor Engineering, Reactor Materials

Div. of Synthetic Chemistry

Petro-chemistry, Chemistry of Polymerization, Applied Physical Chemistry of High Polymers, Catalysis & Catalytic Reaction, Industrial Instrumental Analytical Chemistry, Synthetic Radiation Chemistry

Graduate School of Law

Div. of Political Science and Public Law

Public Law, Political Theory and History, International Politics and Public Administration

Div. of Private and Criminal Law

Civil Code, Commercial Law, Criminal Law and Procedure, Fundamental Sciences in Law

Graduate School of Letters(M 115/17, D 79/12)

Div. of Chinese Literature

Chinese Literature

Div. of English Literature

English Literature, English Linguistics

Div. of French Literature

French Literature

Div. of German Literature

German Literature

Div. of History and Geography

Japanese History, Archaeology, Oriental History, Occidental History, Geography

Div. of Japanese Language and Culture

Japanese Language and Culture

Div. of Japanese Literature

Japanese Literature, Japanese Linguistics

Div. of Oriental Philosophy

History of Chineses Philosophy, History of Indian Philosophy

Div. of Philology

Linguistics

Div. of Philosophy

Philosophy, History of European Philosophy, Aesthetics and Art History

Div. of Sociology

Sociology, Comparative Sociology

Div. of Psychology

Psychology

Graduate School of Medicine(D 234/23)

Div. of Internal Medicine

Internal Medicine, Psychiatry, Pediatrics, Dermatology, Radiology, Geriatrics, Laboratory Medicine, Neurology, Medicine & Immunology

Div. of Pathology

Pathology Bacteriology, Medical Zoology, Immunology, Germfree Life, Virology, Cancer Cell Biology, Medical Mycology, Molecular Pathogenesis

Div. of Physiology

Anatomy, Physiology, Biochemistry, Pharmacology, Clinical Pharmacy, Environmental Medicine

Div. of Social Medicine

Forensic Medicine, Hygiene, Public Health, Preventive Medicine

Div. of Surgery

Surgery, Orthopedic Surgery, Obstetrics and Gynecology, Ophthalmology, Urology, Otorhinolaryngology, Anaesthesiology, Oral Surgery, Neurosurgery, Thoracic Surgery, Hyperbaric Medicine, Plastic and Reconstructive Surgery, Pediatric Surgery

Graduate School of Science(M 184/13, D 196/14)

Div. of Astrophysics

Infrared Astronomy, High Energy Astronomy, Submillimeter Astronomy, Physics of Interstellar Molecules, Solar Emissions, Cosmic Ray Phenomena, Cosmic Ray Origins and Their Intensity, Modulation Mechanism

Div. of Biology

Botany: Cell Fuction • Plant Physiology, Cell Biochemistry, Physiological Genetics • Cell Biology

Zoology: Molecular Genetics • Molecular Evolution, Physiological Zoology, Insect Endocrinology, Comparative Biology

Div. of Chemistry

Analytical Chemistry, Inorganic Chemistry, Organic Chemistry, Physical Chemistry, Quantum Chemistry, Biochemistry, Organic Reaction Chemistry, Isotope Chemistry, Solid State Chemistry, Molecular Physics, Fuction of Molecules

Div. of Earth Sciences

Structural Geology, Petrology and Economic Geology, Geochemistry, Geophysics, Historical Geology, Seismology

Div. of Mathematics

Analytics, Algebra, Geometry, Applied Mathematics, Mathematical Logic, Functional Analysis, Mathematical Statistics, Mathematical Planning, Computer Mathematics, Mathematical Science, Topological Structure

Div. of Molecular Biology

Informational Macromolecules, Genetic Analysis, Cell Motility, Bioenergetics, Cell Regulation, Biological Response, Neuroscience

Div. of Physics

Fundamental Physics: Fundamental Theory of Physics, Atomic Physics, Space Physics, Biophysics,
Nuclear Physics: Theory of Elementary Particles, Nuclear Theory, High Energy Physics, Nuclear Measurement, General Relativity

Div. of Physics II

Statistical Physics: Fundamental Theory of Solid State, Properties of Matter, Polymer and Biophysics,
Solid State Physics: Theory of Solid State, Electromagnetic State, Crystallography, Molecular Structure

Div. of Sciences of Atmosphere and Hydrosphere

Inorganic Geochemistry, Organic Geochemistry, Hydrological Physics, Atomospheric Physics, Chemical Biology, Atmospheric Environment

---

新潟大学
(Niigata Daigaku)
Niigata University

8050 Ikarashi 2-nocho, Niigata-shi, Niigata 950-21
☎ 025-262-6098 FAX 025-262-0699

Founded 1949
Professors 346
Associate Professors 303
Assistant Professors(Tenured) 115
Assistant Professors(Non-tenured) 535
Research Assistants 329
Undergraduate Students/Foreign/ 9, 441/14
Graduate Students/Foreign 761/32
Library 1, 166, 224 volumes
Contact: Student Affaries Section ☎ 025-262-6240

Educational philosophy We aim to educate Promising young people enabling them to understand and comtribute to world cultures and prosperity.

Foreign students We are eager to promote the international exchange programs with the purpose of opening our door to the world. We earnestly hope and expect to accept more foreing studonto who will study and do research in their chosen fields, and become driving forces in world develpment.

Environment Niigata City where the University campuses are located is the biggest city in the prefecture with its 500, 000 population. The areas surrounding the City are famous for their rice-production, which is the highest in Japan. To the east are beautiful mountain ranges, while on the west is the Sea of Japan, which shows what a suitable natural environment we have for research and study.

Facilities University Libararies, Health Administration Center, Brain Research Institute, Research Institute for Hazards in Snowy Areas, Informatin Processing Center, Reserch Laboratory for Gene Experimentaion Gymnasium, Athletic Grounds, Swimming Pool, University Hospitals

Student activites School festival, freshmen welcome party. There is a wide variety of extra curricular activities, choral groups, drama, brass band, orchestra, radio club, baseball, judo, volley ball, rugby football, soccer, basket ball, karate, etc.

Academic programs for foreign students Supplemental Japanese language class, Tutoring system, Japanese studies class

Services for foreign students Health clinic, Personal/Psychological counseling, College housing, Housing Information, Part-time job information, Homestay, Short Bus Trip for Visting Facilities, Exchange party, Farewell party

Undergraduate Programs

Faculty of Agriculture(692/0)
- **Dept. of Agricultural Chemistry**(127/0)
- **Dept. of Agricultural Engineering**(141/0)
- **Dept. of Agronomy**(139/0)
- **Dept. of Animal Husbandry**(132/0)
- **Dept. of Forestry**(153/0)

Faculty of Economics(969/5)
- **Dept. of Economics**(969/5)

Faculty of Education(2, 014/0)
- **Special Trainig Course for Calligraphy Teachers**(64/0)
- **Special Training Course for Music Teachers**(128/0)
- **Training Course for Elementary School Teachers**(1, 140/0)
- **Training Course for Junior High School Teaches**(493/0)
- **Traning Course for Kindergarten Teachers**(111/0)
- **Training Course for Teachers of Retarded Children**(78/0)

Faculty of Engineering(2, 150/7)
- **Dept. of Civil Engineering and Architecture**(421/1)
- **Dept. of Electrical and Electronic Engineering**(425/3)
- **Dept. of Information Engineering**(323/2)
- **Dept. of Material and Chemical Engineering**(486/1)
- **Dept. of Mechanical Engineering**(495/0)

Faculty of Humanities(708/0)
- **Course of Culture and Civilization**(492/0)
- **Course of Phulosophy and Behavioral Science**(216/0)

Faculty of Law(1, 072/1)
- **Dept. of Law**(1, 072/1)

School of Dentistry(431/0)

School of Medicine(710/0)

Faculty of Science(695/1)
- **Dept. of Biology**(125/0)
- **Dept. of Chemistry**(149/0)
- **Dept. of Gelolgy and Mineralogy**(86/0)
- **Dept. of Mathematics**(146/0)
- **Dept. of Physics**(189/1)

Graduate Programs

Graduate School of Agriculture(M 74/2)

Div. of Agronomy(M 14/1)

Crop Science, Horticultural Science, Plant Breeding, Farm Management, Plant Pathology

Div. of Forestry(M 11/0)

Silvics, Forest Management, Forest Mensuration, Erosion Control Engineering and Logging Technology, Wood Technology

Div. of Agricultural Chemistry(M 20/1)

Soil Science, Agricultural Products Technology, Biochemistry, Plant Nutrition and Fertilizer, Applied Microbiology

Div. of Agricultural Engineering(M 6/0)

Agricultural Systems Engineering, Agricultural Machinery, Structural Engineering, Farm Land Engineering, Agricultural Hydrotechnics

Div. of Animal Husbandry(M 23/0)

Animal Breeding and Reproduction, Biochemistry and Technology of animal Products, Livestock Management, Animal Nutrition and Feeding, Grassland Science

Graduate School of Dentistry(D 68/4)

Div. of Basic Dentistry(D 9/0)

Oral Anatomy, Oral Physiology, Oral Biochemistry, Oral Pathology, Oral Microbiology, Dental Pharmacology, Dental Materials and Technology

Div. of Clinical Dentistry(D 59/4)

Preventive Dentistry, Operative Dentistry and Endodontics, Periodontology, Oral and Maxillofacial Surgery, Prosthodontics, Orthodontics, Pedodontics, Oral Radiology

Graduate School of Economics(M 12/0)

Div. of Economics(M 12/0)

Basic Theory and History, Economic Systems, Economic Analysis, Economic Policy, Management and Accounting

Graduate School of Education(M 71/0)

Div. of School Education(M 25/0)

Pedagogies of School Education, Educational Psychology, Special Education, Infant Education

Div. of School Subjects(M 46/0)

Japanese Teaching, Social Studies, English Teaching, Science Education, Music Education, Art Education, Health and Physical Education

Graduate School of Engineering(M 184/4)

Div. of Mechanical Engineering(M 36/0)

Strength of Materials, Machine Element and Dynamics of Machinery, Fluid Engineering, Thermal Engineering, Industrial Materials, Production Engineering

Div. of Precision engineering(M 12/1)

Measurement Engineering, Precision Machining, Precision Mechanics, Control Engineering

Div. of Electrical Engineering(M 29/1)

Fundamental Electrical Engineering, Electrical Measurements, Electric Power Engineering, Electrical Communication, Applied Electrical Engineering

Div. of Electronic Engineering(M 16/0)

Fundamental Electronics, Electronic Materials, Electronic Circuits, Applied Electronics

Div. of Information Engineering(M 18/0)

Biomedical Information, Information Processing, Information Processing Devices, Transmission of Information

Div. of Applied Chemistry(M 23/0)

Industrial Inorganic Chemistry, Applied Analytical Chemistry, Applied Organic Chemistry, Industrial Polymer Chemistry, Applied Physical Chemistry

Div. of Chemical Engineering(M 24/1)

Reaction Engineering, Diffusional Operations, Mechanical Operations, Process Control and Management

Div. of Civil Engineering(M 13/1)

Structural Mechanics, Soil Mechanics, Concrete Engineering, Hydraulic Engineering

Div. of Architecture(M 13/0)

Environmental and Sanitary Engineering, Architectural Planning and Design, Disaster Protection Engineering and Urban Planning, Building Materials and Structutal Engineering

Graduate School of Humanities(M 20/3)

Div. of Philosophy and Behavioral Sciences(M 4/0)

Philosophical Anthropology, Behavioral Sciences

Div. of Japanese and Oriental Culture and Civilization(M 8/3)

Japanese Culture and Civilization, Oriental Culture and Civilization

Div. of Western Culture and Civilization(M 8/0)

English and American Culture and Civilization, European Culture and Civilization

Graduate School of Law(M 20/2)

Div. of Law(M 20/2)

Basic Legal Studies, Public Law, Private Law, Criminal Law, Economic and Social Law, Political Science

Graduate School of Medicine(D 127/1)

Div. of Physiology(D 0/0)

Anatomy, Biochemistry, Neurochemistry, Physiology, Neurophysiology, Pharmacology, Neuropharmacology

Div. of Pathology(D 15/0)

Pathology, Neuropathology, Experrimental Neuropathology, Pathology (Institute of Nephrology), Immunology (Institute of Nephrology), Bacteriology, Virology, Immunology & Medical Zoology

Div. of Social Medicine(D 3/0)

Hygiene, Public Health, Forensic Medicine

Div. of Internal Medicine(D 67/1)

Internal Medicine, Neurology, Pediatrics, Dermatology, Psychiatry, Radiology, Laboratory Medicine

Div. of Surgery(D 37/0)

Surgery, Neurosurgery, Orthopedic Surgery, Urology, Otorhinolaryngology, Ophthalmology, Obstetrics & Gynecology, Anesthesiology

Gaduate School of Science(M 86/0)

Div. of Mathematics(M 14/0)

Mathematical Analysis, Functional Analysis, Algebra, Geometry, Information Mathematics

Div. of Physics(M 22/0)

Quantum Physics, Nuclear Physics, Molecular Physics, Statistical Physics, Crystal Physics, Solid–State Physics

Div. of Chemistry(M 21/0)

Analytical Chemistry, Inorganic Chemistry, Organic Chemistry, Physical Chemistry, Biophysical Chemistry

Div. of Biology(M 18/0)

Plant Morphology and Cytology, Animal Physiology and Biochemistry, Embryology and Genetics, Plant Physiology, Immunobiology

Div. of Geology and Mineralogy(M 11/0)

Geology, Mineralogy, Mineralogy and Petrology, Applied Geology

Graduate School of Science and Technology(D 99/16)

Div. of Fundamental Science and Technology(D 21/1)

Mathematical Science, Physical Science, Molecular Science, Active Material Chemistry

Div. of Biosystem Science(D 19/1)

Biomechanism, Development of Biological Functions, Plant and Animal Production

Div. of Industrial Science(D 36/6)

Material Science, Machine Design and Manufacturing, Energy Systems, Information and Electronic Systems

Div. of Environmental Science(D 23/8)

Geological Science, Regional Environment Science, Design and Construction Technology

---

信州大学
(Shinshû Daigaku)

Shinshu University

3–1–1 Asahi, Matsumoto–shi, Magano 390
☎ 0263–35–4600 FAX 0263–36–3044

Founded 1949
Professors 291
Associate Professors 251
Assistant rofessors(Tenured) 87
Assistant Professors(Non–tenured) 461
Research Assistants 237
Undergraduate Students/Foreign Students 8, 666/83
Graduate Students/Foreign Students 643/41
Library 869, 507 volumes
Contact: Student Office, Student Division, Student Affairs Section ☎ 0263–32–8257

Educational philosophy Shinshu Uiversity is engaged in training highly competent personal and carrying out research projects so as to contibute to development of scinece, culture and national economy. We aim that all students can develop their abilities in various fields.

Foreign students We hope foreign students can develop their abilities and promote mutual understanding between Japan and their own country. We are making every effort to overcome the various difficulties involved in expanding our foreign exchange programs.

Environment Shinshu University has seven campuses in different parts of Nagano Prefecture. There are four imoportant national parks in the Prefecture, which is also a mecca for the popular sports of mountain climbing, skiing and skating. The University is therefore ideally situated for students wishing to combine study with a variety of leisure activities.

Facilities Library, Health Administration Center, Center for Educational Technology, Institute of Natural Education in Shiga Heights, Hydrobiological Station, University Hospital, Institute of Cardiovascular Diseases, Institute of Experimental Animals, Research Farms, Research Forests, Institute for Highland and Cool Zone Agriculture, Institute of High Polymer Research, Computer Center, Gymnasium, Asahi University Hall, etc.

Student activities Events: Matriculation ceremony, Freshmen welcome party, Social party for foreign students, School festival, Commencement, etc.

Extracurricular activities: Symphony orchestra, Mixed chorus, Mandolin club, Climbing club, Kendo club, Soccer club, Tennis club, etc.

Academic programs for foreign students Japanese Language and Japanese Studies Courses are offered for the special benefit of foreign students at the Faculty of Liberal Arts.

In order to help newly–enrolled foreign students reduce the possible difficulties in their studies and daily lives, the university provides a Japanese student tutor for each foreign student.

Services for foreign students Shinshu University International House is established in September, 1990, for the purpose of providing living accommodations for foreign studedents and promoting international exchange programs with foreign students. Vocational Guidance, Cultural Exchange Programs, etc.

Undergraduate Programs

Faculty of Agriculture(840/7)

Dept. of Bioscience and Biotechnology(250/3)

Dept. of Crop and Animal Science(274/2)

Dept. of Forest Science(316/2)

Faculty of Arts(725/5)

Dept. of Arts(725/5)

Faculty of Economics(1, 114/50)

Dept. of Economics(1, 114/50)

Faculty of Education(1, 336/2)

Training Course for Elementary School Teachers(762/0)

Training Course for Junior High School Teachers(382/0)

Training Course for Kindergarten Teachers(110/1)

Training Course for Teachers of Retarded Chidren(82/1)

Faculty of Engineering(2, 010/12)

Dept. of Architecture and Civil Engineering(450/1)

Dept. of Chemistry and Material Engineering(367/2)

Dept. of Electrical and Electronic Engineering(453/4)

Dept. of Information Engineering(316/3)

Dept. of Mechanical Systems Engineering(424/2)
School of Medicine(635/5)
Dept. of Medicine(635/5)
Faculty of Science(814/1)
Dept. of Biology(127/0)
Dept. of Chemistry(172/1)
Dept. of Geology(124/0)
Dept. of Mathematics(214/0)
Dept. of Physics(177/0)
Faculty of Textile Science and Technology(1, 192/1)
Dept. of Applied Biology(141/0)
Dept. of Fine Materials Engineering(186/0)
Dept. of Functional Machinery Mechanics(226/0)
Dept. of Functional Polymer Science(188/0)
Dept. of Materials Creation Chemistry(208/0)
Dept. of Textile System Engineering(243/1)

Graduate Programs

Graduate School of Agriculture(M 56/2)
Div. of Agronnmy and Horticultural Science
Div. of Forestry
Div. of Animal Science
Div. of Forestry Engineering
Div. of Agricuitural Chemistry
Graduate School of Arts(M 22/10)
Div. of Region and Cultures
Div. of Language and Literature
Graduate School of Engineering(M 250/9)
Div. of Mechanical Engineering
Div. of Electrical Engineering
Div. of Electronic Engineering
Div. of Civil Engineering
Div. of Industrial Chemistry
Div. of Precision Engineering
Div. of Synthetic Chemistry
Div. of Information Engineering
Div. of Architecture and Building Engineering
Graduate School of Industrial and Social Studies(M 15/1)
Div. of Industrial and ocial Studies
Graduate School of Medicine(D 78/12)
Div. of Physiological Sciences
Div. of Pathological Sciences
Div. of Social Medicine
Div. of Internal Medicine
Div. of Surgery

One-Year Graduate Programs

Education Course
Education Major

静岡大学
(Shizuoka Daigaku)
Shizuoka University

836 Ohya, Shizuoka-shi, Shizuoka 422
☎ 054-237-1111 FAX 054-237-0146

Founded 1949
Professors 308
Associate Professors 241
Assistant Professors(Tenured) 25
Assistant Professors(Non-tenured) 267
Research Assistants 88
Undergraduate Students/Foreign Students 7, 622/44
Graduate Studetns/Foreign Students 665/47
Library 809, 589 volumes
Contact: Student Affairs Section

Educational philosophy We aim at providing our students the best educational enviroments and also contributing to the regional development of Shizuoka area.
Foreign students In this era of expanding international relations, Shizuoka University has been and is promoting its own international contacts through education and research.
Environment Shizuoka University has two prime locations; the Ohya Campus in Shizuoka City with a polulation of 475, 000, and the Hamamatsu Campus in Hamamatsu City with a population of 532, 000. The Ohya Campus commands spectacular views of Mt. Fuji to the north.
Facilities Research Institute of Electonics, Radiochemistry Research Institute, Arid Land Agricultural Research Laboratory, Laboratory of Marine Biochemical Science, University Farm and Forests, Information Processing Center, Central Library
Student activities There is a wide variety of extra curicular activities. In addition to these regular activities, there is big Students Festival which is held every autumn. For three days the students enjoy concerts, sports, parades and lots of other amusing activities.
Academic programs for foreign students Supplemental Japanese language class and Tutoring system
Services for foreign students International House, Health Clinic, Psychological counseling, Study tour

Undergraduate Programs

Faculty of Agriculture(675/4)
Dept. of Applied Biological Chemistry(182/2)
Dept. of Biological Science(266/2)
Dept. of Forest Resources Science(227/0)
Faculty of Education(2, 071/0)
Teacher Training Course for Elementary School(1, 202/0)

Teacher Training Course for Junior High School(451/0)
Teacher Training Course for Schools for the Handicapped(78/0)
Teacher Training Course for Kindergarten(98/0)
Faculty of Engineering(2, 156/17)
Dept. of Applied Chemistry(211/1)
Dept. of Chemical Engineering(202/2)
Dept. of Computer Science(193/5)
Dept. of Electrical Engineering(295/2)
Dept. of Electronic Engineering(275/3)
Dept. of Energy and Mechanical Engineering(189/1)
Dept. of Materials Science(215/0)
Dept. of Mechanical Engineering(186/3)
Dept. of Opto-Electonic and Mechanical Engineering(200/0)
Dept. of Precision Engineering(190/0)
Faculty of Humanities and Social Sciences(1, 830/21)
Dept. of Economics(591/11)
Dept. of Humanities(437/8)
Dept. of Law(588/0)
Dept. of Sociology(214/2)
Faculty of Science(846/2)
Dept. of Biology(117/1)
Dept. of Chemistry(196/0)
Dept. of Geosciences(144/0)
Dept. of Mathematics(170/0)
Dept. of Physics(219/1)

Graduate Programs

Graduate School of Agriculture(M 86/4)
Div. of Agricultural Chemistry(M 30/1)
Soil Science and Plant Nutrition, Biological Chemistry, Food Technology, Food and Nutrition, Applied Microbiology, Agricultural Geology
Div. of Agricultural Science(M 24/2)
Crop Science and Plant Breeding, Applied Entomology, Plant Pathology, Agricultural Economics, Animal Production, Reproductive Physiology
Div. of Forestry(M 7/0)
Silviculture, Forest Management and Forestry Policy, Forest Engineering, Forest Conservation
Div. of Forest Products Science(M 13/1)
Wood Technology, Wood Processing, Wood Adhesion, Wood Chemistry, Wood Industrial Chemistry
Div. of Horticultural Science(M 12/0)
Citrology, House Crops, Plant Propagation, Postharvest Science
Graduate School of Education(M 96/7)
Div. of English Education(M 11/0)
English Education, English Linguistics, English and American Literature
Div. of Fine Arts Education(M 12/0)
Fine Arts Education, Painting, Sculpture, Design and Crafts, Aesthetics of Fine Arts
Div. of Home Economics Education(M 5/1)
Homemaking Education, Science of Life, Study of Living
Div. of Japanese Language Education(M 12/1)
Japanese Education, Japanese Language, Japanese Literatue, Calligraphy
Div. of Mathematics Education(M 2/0)
Mathematical Education, Algebra and Geometry, Analysis and Applied Mathematics
Div. of Music Education(M 3/3)
Music Education, Vocal Music, Instrumental Music, Musicology
Div. of Physical Education(M 6/0)
Physical Education, Sports Science, Health and Physical Education, School Health
Div. of School Education(M 13/1)
Special Education for the Handicapped, Early Childhood Education, Pedagogy, History of Education, School Administration, Social Education, Educational Psychology, Developmental Psychology
Div. of Science Education(M 10/0)
Science Education, Physics, Chemistry, Biology, Geology
Div. of Social Studies Education(M 10/1)
Social Studies Educaion, History, Geography, Law, Economics, Philosophy and Ethics
Div. of Technology Education(M 12/0)
Technology Education, Fundamental Technology, Productive Technology
Graduate School of Engineering(M 328/12)
Div. of Applied Chemistry(M 40/0)
Applied Inorganic Chemistry, Applied Organic Chemistry
Div. of Chemical Engineering(M 27/0)
Chemical Engineering Fundamentals, Chemical Process Engineering and Biotechnology
Div. of Computer Science(M 20/5)
Artificial Intelligence and Knowledge Engineering, Computer Systems
Div. of Electrical Engineering(M 39/0)
Applied Electrical Engineering, Fundamental Electrical Engineering
Div. of Electronic Engineering(M 73/0)
Applied Mathematics, Applied Physics, Electronic Materials, Electronic Material Physics and Devices, Electronic Devices, Electronic Systems, Electronic System and Applications
Div. of Energy and Mechanical Engineering(M 28/0)
Fluid Mechanics and Control Technology, Thermodynamics
Div. of Material Science(M 38/0)
Analytical Chemistry, Inorganic Materials, Organic Materials
Div. of Mechanical Engineering(M 15/1)
Analysis of Materials, Machine Design
DIv. of Opto-Electronic and Mechanical Engineering(M 26/2)
Applied Opto-Electronic and Mechanical Engineering
Div. of Precision Engineering(M 22/3)
Manufacturing Engineering, Precision Instrument
Graduate School of Science(M 79/1)
Div. of Biology(M 17/0)

Endocrinology, Plant Ecology, Production Ecology, Plant Morphogenesis, Plant Morphology, Plant Systematics, Ecological Plant Physiology, Developmental Plant Physiology, Physiological Animal Ecology, Developmental Genetics, Function and Structure of Nucleic Acids, Enzymology in Carbohydrate Metabolism, Molecular Endocrinology, Differentiation, Energy Metabolism, Mammalian Embryology

Div. of Chemistry(M 19/0)
Molecular Structure, Electron Diffraction, Quantum Chemistry, Molecular Spectroscopy, Molecular Vibration Analysis, Computational Chemistry, Solid-State Chemistry, Chemistry of Biologically Active Natural Products and Marine Natural Products, Biochemistry of Nucleic Acids and Proteins, Enzyme Chemistry, Molecular Biology, Membrane Biochemistry, Chemistry of Coordination Compounds, Preparation and Properties of Metal Chelates, Nuclear Transformation Effects, Radiation Efffects, Radioassay, Solution, Solution Chemistry, Geochemistry of Radionuclides

Div. of Geosciences(M 15/1)
Evolutionary Geoscience, Crustal Movement, Biostratigraphy, Paleobiology, Paleoecology, Marine Geology, Sedimentology, Marine Paleoenvironment, Paleomagnetism, Isotope Geochemistry, Geochmeistry, Volcanology, Mineralogy, Economic Geology, Igneous Petrology, Physical Geoscience, Structural Geology,

Div. of Mathematics(M 10/0)
Complex Analysis, General Topology, Dimension Theory, Number Theory, Quadratic Forms, Ring Theory, Stochastic Process, Information Theory, Vector Measure, Banach Space, Mathematical Logic

Div. of Physics(M 18/0)
Mathematical Physics, Nuclear Physics, Physics on Elementary Particles, Solid State Physics, Physics on Polymers, Biophysics, Plasma Physics and Quantum Electronics

Graduate School of Electronic Science and Techogy(D 29/23)

Div. of Electronic Materials Science(D 13/2)
Solid-State Physics, Solid-State Materials Science, Surface Electronics, Inorganic Materials Science, Organic Materials Science, Energy Conversion

Div. of Electronic Engineering(D 16/21)
Semiconductor Devices, Picture Electronic Devices, Wave Electronics, Optoelectronic Metrology, Pattern Recognition, Information Processing, Systems Control, Systems Design, Instrumentation and Control, Automated Machine Engineering, Optoelectronic Machine Engineering, Biomedical Information Processing, Medical Electronics

One-Year Graduate Programs

Humanities Course
Humanities Major
Economics Major

富山医科薬科大学

(Toyama Ika Yakka Daigaku)

Toyama Medical and Pharmaceutical University

2630 sugitani, Toyama-shi, Toyama 930-01
☎ 0764-34-2281 FAX 0764-34-4545

Founded 1975
Professors 61
Associate Professors 61
Assistant Professors(Tenured) 39
Assistant Professors(Non-tenured) 197
Research Assistants 159
Undergraduate Students/Foreign Students 1, 074/2
Graduate Studetns/Foreign Students 135/27
Library 138, 203 volumes
Contact:
Undergraduate: Entrance Examination Section, Student Division ☎ ext. 2148
Graduate: Second Section of Academic Affairs, Student Division ☎ ext. 2157

Educational philosophy Our University is contributing not only to educate medical science and pharmacy characteristically and collectively, and to give expert knowledge at higher grade as a means of research and diagnosis, but to cultivate a man able to react to requirements of the times and communities and to contribute developments of medical science and welfares of the society.

Foreign students We have a system to permit on each development course to pass specially selective entrance exmination for private students sent abroad for study on faculty level and to approve on each post-graduate course to pass its entrance examination for graduated students sent abroad for study obtain the degree of Master or Doctor after experiencing lives of specialty students for 6 to 12 months.

Environment Toyama Prefecture situated in for our university, is located at the center of Japan, faced at the mountains of the Japanese Alps and the Sea of Japan, and is a splendid place rich with green woods and fresh water and gives chances to enjoy fully of seasonable natural beauties. Toyama City, town of this prefecture, is a local city of population of about 320, 000 and has a tradition to grow up the medicine manufacturing industries since 1, 600 of the Edo period and rich with nature and human feelings.

Facilities We have many kinds of facilities, such as buildings for lectures and practices, for dissections, and for laboratories used cooperatively with medical, pharmaceutical and of Wakan-Yaku, facilities for experiments of radioisotopes and for experiments of animals, botanical gardens belonging to the Faculty of the pharmacy, hospital, library, health center, gymnasium, welfare center containing restaurant, sporting ground, baseball ground, tennis courts, gymnasium for military arts, and swimming pool.

Student activities In addition to some events such as camping study for new students and training course of ski and others, many other events planned by the students such as festival of the university and sports festivals are operated by 26 groups of literary circles and 27 groups of gymnastic circles. Besides, some observing trips and party sponsored by the President are also held for the students sent abroad for syudy.

Academic programs for foreign students In the deparment course, there provides some special curriculum on the Japanese and informations on Japan. and other special programs on Japanese conversation as extracurricular supplementary lessons. In the graduated course, there provides some specific professors leading the specialized education on the pharmacy and others to give some advices on experiments, researches and others.

Services for foreign students We have international communication hall where new students sent abroad for study can stay for first one year and can join with local traditional events and homestays to intercourse with the local residents by assistance of Toyama Prefecture and volunteer parties. Furthermore, there are held a system to assist the students sent abroad for study and to receive some services such as scholarship and subsidy for medical cares from Toyama Prefecture, Toyama City and others.

Undergraduate Programs

Faculty of Medicine(635/2)
 Dept. of Medicine
Faculty of Pharmaceutical Sciences(439/0)
 Dept. of Pharmaceutical Sciences

Graduate Programs

Graduate School of Medicine(D 63/9)
 Div. of Physiology and Related Sciences(D 21/1)
 Div. of Biochemistry and Related Sciences(D 8/2)
 Div. of Morphology and Related Sciences(D 20/2)
 Div. of Environmental Medicine(D 14/4)

Anatomy, Physiology, Biochemistry, Pathology, Bacteriology & Immunology, Virology, Pharmacology, Community Medicine Public Health, Legal Medicine, Internal Medicine, Dermatology, Pediatorics, Neuropsychiatry, Radiology, Surgery, Neurosurgery, Orthopedics, Obstetrics & Gynecology, Ophthalmology, Otorinolarygology, Urology, Anesthesiology, Oral & Maxillofacial Surgery, Clinical Labolatory, Medicine, Radiological Sciences, Chemistry

Graduate School of Medicinal Sciences(M 60/4, D 12/)
 Div. of Medicinal Sciences(M 60/4, D 12/)

Pharmacy & Pharmacology, Clinical Chemistry, Medicinal Chemistry, Biological Chemistry, Medicinal Resources, Physical Pharmacy, Pharmaceutical Phisiology

富山大学
(Toyama Daigaku)
Toyama University

3190 Gohuku, Toyama-shi, Toyama 930
☎ 0764-41-1271 FAX 0764-31-1532

Founded 1949
Professors 167
Associate Professors 162
Assistant Professors(Tenured) 37
Assistant Professors(Non-tenured) 169
Research Assistants 55
Undergraduate Students/Foreign Students 6, 111/36
Graduate Studetns/Foreign Students 233/8
Library 706, 533 volumes
Contact: Admissions Office, Student Affairs Bureau

Educational philosophy Our University aims at offering a broad curriculum in many fields of study and education, contributing to regional industry and culture.

Foreign students Our university welcomes earnest students who are positive, independent and have critical minds.

Environment Our university stands to the west of Toyama city (population 320, 000) and Mt. Tateyama and the Northern Alps, near Kureha Mountain. We have good traffic facilities and can go to the center of the city in ten mimutes by bus or streetcar.

Facilities University Library, Hydrogen Isotope Research Center, Center for Cooperative Research, Gymnasium, Center for Computer and Information Services, Kurodo Hall.

Student activities Athletic Meetings, University Festival, The Hokuriku districts national university athletic meeting, Cultural Festival, Ski school, The Hokuriku districts university student art festival.

Academic programs for foreign students Tutorial System

Services for foreign students Sightseeing Trips, Talkfest.

Undergraduate Programs

Faculty of Economics(1, 841/18)
 Dept. of Business Administration(616/13)
 Dept. of Business Law(517/1)
 Dept. of Economics(708/4)
Faculty of Education(1, 016/0)
 Courses of Informatics and Education(119/0)
 Courses of Kindergarten Teachers(113/0)
 Courses of Primary School Teachers(473/0)
 Courses of Secondary School Teachers(237/0)
 Courses of Teachers of Special Education(74/0)
Faculty of Engineering(1, 559/18)
 Dept. of Chemical Engineering(145/0)

Dept. of Chemical and Biochemical Engineering(86/0)
Dept. of Electrical Engineering(120/1)
Dept. of Electronics Engineering(121/4)
Dept. of Electronics and Computer Science(272/10)
Dept. of Industrial Chemistry(166/0)
Dept. of Mechanical Engineering(176/0)
Dept. of Mechanical Engineering for Production(141/0)
Dept. of Mechanical System Engineering(102/2)
Dept. of Metallurgical Engineering(143/0)
Dept. of Materials Science and Engineering(87/1)
Faculty of Humanities(805/0)
Dept. of Humanities(400/0)
Dept. of Language and literature(405/0)
Faculty of Science(890/0)
Dept. of Biology(156/0)
Dept. of Chemistry(193/0)
Dept. of Earth Science(137/0)
Dept. of Mathematics(192/0)
Dept. of Physics(212/0)

Graduate Programs

Graduate School of Engineering(M 142/5)
Div. of Chemical Engineering(M 20/0)
Reaction Engineering, Diffusional Unit Operations, Mechanical Unit Operations, Transport Phenome
Div. of Electrical Engineering(M 24/3)
Concepts and Methods Electrical Engineering, Electrical Machinery and Apparatus, Electrical Power Engineering, Electrical Communication Engineering, Control Engineering
Div. of Electronics(M 24/0)
Fundamental Electronics, Applied Electronics, Electronics Devices, Electronics Circuits
Div. of Industrial Chemistry(M 28/0)
Industrial Organic Chemistry, Organic Synthetic Chemistry, Industrial Inorganic Chemistry, Applied Physical Chemistry, Environmental Chemistry,
Div of Mechanical Engineering(M 13/1)
Strength of Materials, Dynamics of Machines, Fluid Engineering, Thermal Engineering, Power Industrial Engineering
Div. of Mechanical Engineering for Production(M 9/0)
Metal Cutting, Industrial Measurement, Plastic Forming, Control Machinery
Div. of Metallurgical Engineering(M 24/1)
Physical Metallurgy, Materials Science, Ferrous Metallurgy, Nonferrous Metallurgy
Graduate School of Humanities(M 24/3)
Div. of Euro-American Culture and Civilization(M 8/0)
Philosophy, History of Philosophy, Occidental History, Cultural Anthropology, English Linguistics, English Literature, American Literature, German Linguistics, German Literature, Russian Linguistics and Literature, Comparative Literature
Div. of Japan-Oriental Culture and Civilzation(M 16/3)
Japanese History, Oriental History, Archaeology, Human Geography, Linguistics, Structural Study of Culture Traits, Japanese Linguistics, Japanese Literature, Korean Linguistics and Literature, Chinese Linguistics, Chinese Literature
Graduate School of Science(M 67/0)
Div. of Biology(M 14/0)
Mophology and Systematics, Cell biology, Environmental Biology, General Physiology and Plant Physiology
Div. of Chemistry(M 15/0)
Physical Chemistry, Structural Chemistry, Analytical Chemistry, Organic Chemistry, Natural Products Chemistry
Div. of Earth Science(M 67/13)
Geophysics, Geology, Hydrology and Geochemistry, Glaciology
Div. of Mathematics(M 6/0)
Algebra and Geometry, Analysis, Mathemtical Statics, Applied Analysis and Computer Science
Div. of Physics(M 19/0)
Solid State Physics, Quantum Physics, Crystal Physics, Radio and Microwave Physics, Laser Physics

One-Year Graduate Programs

Eduaction Course
Education Major
Economics Course
Business Administration and Accounting Major

豊橋技術科学大学
(Toyohashi Gijutsu Kagaku Daigaku)
Toyohashi University of Technology

1-1 Aza-Hibarigaoka, Tempaku-cho, Toyohashi-shi, Aichi 441
☎ 0523-47-0111 FAX 0532-45-0480

Founded 1976
Professors 62
Associate Professors 64
Assistant Professors(Tenured) 11
Assistant Professors(Non-tenured) 75
Research Assistants 39
Undergraduate Students/Foreign Students 1, 108/33
Graduate Studetns/Foreign Students 642/65
Library 92, 372 volumes
Contact: Administration Bureau

Educational philosophy Toyohashi University of Technology (TUT) was opened in 1978. This new type of higher education institution was established with the priority placed on graduate courses and with the specific goal of meeting the urgent social need for a new breed of engineers equipped to face the challenges of today and tomorrow.

Foreign students We believe that foreign students can enjoy a rewarding experience in our school. and can learn to culture of Japan with a field trip and the development of friendly relations.

Environment The TUT campus is located on a low hill surrounded by beautiful scenery on the outskirts of the historic city of Toyohashi, with a population of 336, 000. The Pacific Ocean is 2. 5 miles away. The city is conveniently situated in the central part of the main island of Japan.

Facilities Main Library. Language Center. Research Center of Physical Fitness, Sports, and Health. Technology Development Center. Research Center for Chemometrics. Manufacturing Technology Center. Computer Center. Gymnasium. Athletic Field. Baseball Field. Tennis Court. Swimming Pool.

Students activities Popular campus events includes Homecoming, school festival, freshmen welcome party. There is a wide variety of extra curricular activities, including volunteer work, choral groups, marching band, astronomy, tennis, baseball, football, soccer, etc.

Academic programs for foreign students Japanese language supplemetaly classes for overseas students are available as part of formal undergraduate education. Tutoring system.

Services for foreign students Health clinic, personal/Psychological counseling, College housing, Housing information, Part-time job information, cultural exchange program.

Undergraduate Programs

Faculty of Engineering(1, 108/33)

Dept. of Electrical and Electronic Engineering (160/9)

Dept. of Energy Engineering(177/3)

Dept. of Information and Computer Sciences (160/8)

Dept. of Knowledge-based Information Engineering(119/2)

Dept. of Materials Science(161/1)

Dept. of Production Systems Engineering(160/3)

Dept. of Regional Planning(171/7)

Graduate Programs

Graduate School of Engineering(M 566/38, D 76/27)

Div. of Electrical and Electronic Engineering(M 97/4)

Fundamental Research, Electric System Engineering, Electronic Devices

Div. of Energy Engineering(M 86/2)

Thermal and Fluid Engineering, Energy Conversion Engineering, Design Engineering of Energy Systems Components

Div. of Information and Computer Sciences(M 106/9)

Computer Engineering, Information Processing Engineering, Information Systems Engineering

Div. of Materials Science(M 80/5)

Industrial Analytical Chemistry, Industrial Inorganic Chemistry, Industrial Organic Chemistry

Div. of Production Systems Engineering(M 108/14)

Materials Science and Engineering, Parts-Manufacturing Technology, Production Systems Design and Control

Div. of Regional Planning(M 89/4)

Planning and Design, Environmental Engineering, Structural Engineering

Div. of Comprehensive Energy Engineering(D 23/11)

Div. of Materials System Engineering(D 19/3)

Div. of Systems and Information Engineering(D 34/13)

山梨医科大学
(Yamanashi Ika Daigaku)

Yamanashi Medical College

1110 Simokato, Tamaho-cho, Nakakoma-gun, Yamanashi 409-38
☎ 0552-73-1111

Founded 1978
Professors 35
Associate Professors 32
Assistant Professors(Tenured) 32
Assistant Professors(Non-tenured) 232
Research Assistants 132
Undergraduate Students/Foreign Students 600/0
Graduate Studetns/Foreign Students 72/7
Library 70, 406 volumes
Contact:
Undergraduate: Subsection of School Affairs, Section of Student Affairs, Division of School Affairs ☎ ext. 2095, 2096
Graduate: Subsection of Entrance Examination and Graduate School, Section of Student Affairs, Division of School Affairs ☎ ext. 2097, 2098

Educaional philosophy The College provides education for future doctors with an integrated approach. This is achieved through a general education program based on understanding of human love and a medical training program based on the ideal of respect for human life.

Foreign students It is open and accessible the graduate students for medical course, especially from Asian countries. The ultimate goal, of course, is international participation and exchange.

Environment The town of Tamaho, with a population of 5, 000 is located in center of Kofu basin, which is about 100 kilometer west of Tokyo. The surrounding view of Mt. Fuji, the Southern Alps and the Yatsugatake Mountains provide a pleasant and relaxing working atmosphere.

Facilities University Library, Center for Experiment and Practice, University Hospital, Athletic Field, Baseball Field, Tennis Courts, Gymnasium.

Student activities Popular campus events include school festival, freshmen welcome party. There is a wide variety of extracurricular activities such as choral group, orchestra, baseball, boat, soccer etc.

Academic programs for foreign students Supplementary lecturer, Tutor system

Services for foreign students Health clinic, personal/psychological counselling, Housing information, study excursion, familiar talk party

Undergraduate Programs

Faculty of Medicine(600/0)
 Dept. of Medicine

Graduate Programs

Graduate School of Medicine(D 72/7)
 Div. of Biochemistry(D 27/1)
 Div. of Ecology(D 4/0)
 Div. of Morphology(D 19/4)
 Div. of Physiology(D 22/2)

Philosophy and Ethics, Psychology, Law, Mathematics, Physics, Chemistry, Biology, English, German, Anatomy, Physiology, Biochemistry, Pharmacology, Pathology, Microbiology, Parasitology, and Immunilogy, Legal Medicine, Environmental Health, Health Sciences, Internal Medicine Pediatrics, Neuropsychiatry, Dermatology, Surgery, Orthopaedic Surgery, Neurosurgery, Anesthesiology, Obstetrics and Gynecology, Urology, Ophthalmology, Otorhinolaryngology, Radiology, Oral and Maxillofacial Surgery

---

山梨大学
(Yamanashi Daigaku)
Yamanashi University

4-37 Takeda 4, Kofu-shi, Yamanashi 400
☎ 0552-52-1111 FAX 0552-52-0583

Founded 1949
Professors 111
Associate Professors 115
Assistant Professors(Tenured) 22
Assistant Professors(Non-tenured) 320
Research Assistants 51
Undergraduate Students/Foreign Students 3, 336/20
Graduate Studetns/Foreign Students 264/14
Library 405, 786 volumes
Contact: Admissions Section, Student Affairs Bureau

Educational Philosophy We aim at producing teachers and engineers who possess both general culture and expert knowledge in some special direction so that they may unite their competence in their own field with a broad outlook on human welfare in general.

Foreign students We believe that foreign students can enjoy not only high-level academic experience in our University but also many kinds of activites organized to promote mutual understanding between them and people in the local community.

Environment Kofu City, with about 200, 000 inhabitants, can be reached within one hour and a half from Tokyo by express train. Our University is situated in a scenic environment, with Mt. Fuji to the south and snow-capped peaks of the Southern Alps of Japan to the west. The vicinity is rich historic sites.

Facilities University Library, Radioisotope Laboratory, Information Processing Center, Institute of Inorganic Synthesis, Institute of Enology and Viticulture, Educational Research Center, Attached Schools and Kindergarten, Swimming Pool, Gymnasiums, and Gym for Martial Arts.

Student activities Main campus events include university festival and freshman welcome party. There is a wide variety of extra curricular activities, including choral groups marching band, rock bands, tennis club, baseball team, karate club, etc.

Academic programs for foreign students Japanese langage class, extra curricular supplemental class, and tutorial arrangements.

Services for foreign students Health clinic, personal/psychological counselling, housing information, parttime job information, home visit, homestay, cultural exchange program, etc.

Undergraduate Programs

Faculty of Engineering(2, 319/19)
 Dept. of Applied Chemistry and Biotechnology(419/1)
 Dept. of Electrical Engineering and Computer Science(876/14)
 Dept. of Civil and Environmental Engineering(482/3)
 Dept. of Mechanical System Engineering(542/1)
Faculty of Liberal Arts & Education(1, 017/1)
 Course for Integrated Arts & Sciences(175/0)
 Kindergarten Teachers Training Course(109/0)
 Elementary School Teachers Training Course(368/0)
 Secondary School Teachers Training Course(278/1)
 Training Course for Teachers of Handicapped Children(87/0)

Graduate Programs

Graduate School of Engineering(M 264/14)
 Div. of Mechanical Engineering(M 30/0)

Physical Engineering, Production Engineering, Design System Engineering

Div. of Precision Engineering(M 35/1)
Physical Engineering, Production Engineering, Design System Engineering

Div. of Electrical Engineering(M 37/0)
Physical Science, Electromagnetics, Software Engineering and Mathematical Science, Electronics, System Engineering, Computer and Knowledge Engineering

Div. of Electronic Engineering(M 40/4)
Physical Science, Electromagnetics, Software Engineering and Mathematical Science, Electronics, System Engineering, Computer and Knowledge Engineering

Div of Computer Science(M 34/4)
Physical Science, Electomagnetics, Sofware Engineering and Mathematical Science, Electronics, System Engineering, Computer and Knowledge Engineering

Div. of Civil Engineering(M 7/0)
Structural and Geotechnical Engineering, Water Resources Engineering and Infrastructural Planning, Environmental Engineering

Div. of Environmental Engineering(M 11/1)
Structural and Geotechnical Engineering, Water Resources Engineering and Infrastructural Planning, Enviromental Engineering

Div. of Applied Chemistry(M 41/2)
Technology of Functional Substances, Chemistry of Function Design, Biotechnology

Div. of Fermentation Technology(M 29/2)
Technology of Functional Substances, Chemistry of Function Design, Biotechnology

One–Year Graduate Programs

Education Course
Education Major

Education of the Handicapped Course
Education for Mentally Retarded Children Major

Local Public Universities

愛知県立大学
(Aichi Kenritsu Daigaku)

Aichi Prefectural University

3–28 Takada–cho, Mizuho–ku, Nagoya–shi, Aichi 467
☎ 052–851–2191 FAX 052–852–5829

Founded 1947
Professors 49
Associate Professors 52
Assistant Professors(Tenured) 14
Assistant Professors(Non–tenured) 121
Undergraduate Students/Foreign Students 1, 592/7
Library 322, 816 volumes
Contact: Student Office

Education philosophy Aichi Prefectural University is a comparatively small university, admitting 360 students each year. It has a good reputation for liberal arts. One prominent feature is small classes and close teacher–student relationship.

Foreign students We believe that overseas students can enjoy their campus life, taking part in a variety of events planned by the University or its students.

Environment Our university is conveniently located in the city of Nagoya, which has a population of over 2 million and is the capital city of Aichi Prefecture. The weather is moderate all year around and the annual mean temperature is about 16 degrees centigrade.

Facilities Universtiy Library, Gymnasium, Auditorium, Computer Center, Language Laboratory, Kindergarten, Students' Cafeteria, Co–op, etc.

Student activities We have a lot of campus events such as freshmen welcome parties, a university festival, an athletic meet, besides extra–curricular activities; chorus, drama, baseball, tennis, etc.

Academic programs for foreign students Study trips (twice a year), Supplementary Japanese classes, Tutoring system, etc.

Services for foreign students Health clinic, Psychological counseling, Housing information, part-time job information, Cultural exchange program, etc.

Undergraduate Programs

Faculty of Foreign Studies(548/2)
- **Dept. of British and American Studies** (171/2)
- **Dept. of French Studies** (183/0)
- **Dept. of Spanish Studies (studies of Spain and Latin America)** (194/0)

Faculty of Literature(689/5)
- **Dept. of Child Education** (176/2)
- **Dept. of English Literature** (171/1)
- **Dept. of Japanese Literature** (176/1)
- **Dept. of Social Welfare** (166/1)

愛知県立芸術大学

(Aichi Kenritsu Geijutsu Daigaku)

Aichi Prefectural University of Fine Arts

1–1 Sagamine, Yazako, Nagakute–cho, Aichi–gun, Aichi 480–11
☎ 0561–62–1180 FAX 0561–62–0083

Founded 1966
Professors 37
Associate Professors 25
Assistant Professors (Tenured) 17
Assistant Professors (Non–tenured) 221
Research Assistants 7
Undergraduate Students/Foreign Students 692/1
Graduate Students/Foreign Students 91/6
Library 73, 903 volumes
Contact: Admission office

Educational philosophy Aichi Prefectural University of Fine Arts was founded in order to contribute to establishing and promoting the unique local culture of the Chubu Area.
Environment This Area is situated between the Tokyo and Osaka Areas with Aichi Prefecture as its center, and it has made remarkable progress in economy and industry.
Facilities General Education Building, Department of Art Buildings, Department of Music Buildings, University Hall, Library, Student Dormitory, Administration Building, Center Hall, Auditorium, Gymnasium, Art Gallery.
Student activities Art festival will be held as popular campus life on November about three days every year.

Undergraduate Programs

Faculty of Arts (350/1)
  Dept. of Ceramcs (20/0)
  Dept. of Design (145/1)
  Dept. of Japanese Painting (42/0)
  Dept. of Oil Painting (102/0)
Faculty of Arts (350/1)
  Dept. of Sculpture (41/0)
Faculty of Music (342/0)
  Dept. of Composition (21/0)
  Dept. of Instrumental Music
  (**Piano**) (108/0)
  (**Strings**) (53/0)
  (**Winds and Percussion**) (43/0)
Faculty of Music (342/0)
  Dept. of Vocal Music (117/0)

Graduate Programs

Graduate School of Arts (M 58/6)
  Div. of Design (M 17/5)
  Div. of Japanese Painting (M 9/0)
  Div. of Oil Painting (M 20/0)
  Div. of Sculpture (M 12/1)
Graduate School of Music (M 33/0)
  Div. of Composition (M 2/0)
  Div. of Instrumental Music (**Piano**) (M 11/0)
  Div. of Instrumental Music (**Strings**) (M 7/0)

岐阜薬科大学

(Gifu Yakka Daigaku)

Gifu Pharmaceutical University

5–6–1 Mitahora–higashi, Gifu–shi, Gifu 502
☎ 0582–37–3931 FAX 0582–37–5979

Founded 1934
Professors 14
Associate Professors 21
Assistant Professors (Tenured) 4
Assistant Professors (Non–tenured) 24
Research Assistants 24
Undergraduate Students/Foreign Students 597/0
Graduate Students/Foreign Students 75/2
Library 48, 000 volumes
Contact: Administration Office

Educational philosophy We aim at teaching and studying up–to–date high–level pharmaceutical science to develop intellectural, moral and applied abilities so students may contribute much to promotion of public health and public welfare.
Foreign students We believe that foreign students can enjoy a rewarding experience in our school, and can contribute a great deal to promoting mutual understanding and the development of friendly relations.
Enviroment The campus is located in the north of Gifu City (population 413, 000). The city and surroundings enjoy beautiful scenery and places of historical importance. In particular, the traditional cormorant fishing on the Nagara River is well known all over the world.
Facilities University Library, Institution of Biological Pharmacy, Institution of Manufacturing Pharmacy, RI Center, Instrumental Center, Herbal Garden, Experimental Farm, Gymnasium, Archery Range, Studen's Hall
Student activities Popular campus events includes homecoming, school festival and freshmen welcome party. There is a wide variety of extra curricular activities, including choral group, mandolin orchestra, Chinese medicine, pharmaceutical botany, baseball,

soccer, etc.

Undergraduate Programs

Faculty of Pharmaceutical Science(597/0)
Dept. of Public Health Pharmacy(295/0)
Dept. of Manufacturing Pharmacy(302/0)

Graduate Programs

Graduate School of Pharmaceutical Science(M 64/11, D 11/0)
Pharmacognosy, Pharmacology, Hygienic Chemistry, Public Health, Medicinal Chemistry, Pharmaceutics, Molecular Biology, Pharmaceutical Chemistry, Pharmaceutical Synthetic Chemistry, Pharmaceutical Analytical Chemistry, Pharmaceutical Engineering, Biochemistry, Pharmaceutical Physical Chemistry

---

金沢美術工芸大学
(Kanazawa Bijutsu Kôgei Daigaku)
Kanazawa College of Art

5-11-1 Kodatsuno, Kanazawa-shi, Ishikawa 920
☎ 0762-62-3531 FAX 0762-62-6594

Founded 1946
Professors 28
Associate Professors 25
Assistant Professors(Tenured) 3
Assistant Professors(Non-tenured) 122
Undergraduate Students/Foreign Students 579/0
Graduate Students/Foreign Students 44/3
Library 49, 000 volumes
Contact: Student's Affairs Division

Educational philosophy We aim, in respect to the fine and applied arts, at educating creative students with an artistic mind and rich humanity, and consequently to contribute to the development of art and culture of our community.
Foreign students We believe that foreign students can fully enjoy their college life with the hospitality of the Kanazawans who wish to promote mutual understanding and friendly relationship.
Environment Our college is noted for its artistic excellence and environment, especially in the field of traditional craft works as well as modern art and product design. The campus is located in the most academic and scenic area of Kanazawa which has a population of 440, 000.
Facilities Library, Research Institute of Arts and Crafts, Auditorium, Gimnasium
Student activities Popular events include College Festival, Freshmen Welcome Party, and Festival of Four College and Universities of Arts. There is a wide variety of extra curricular activities such as Drama Company, Rock Music, Tea Ceremony, Baseball, Rugby, Tennis and so on.
Services for foreign students Personal/psychological counseling, part-time job information.(grants for health insurance charges by the International Exchange Funds of Kanazawa)

Undergraduate Programs

Faculty of Art(579/0)
Dept. of Fine Arts(262/0)
Japanese Painting major, Oil Painting major, Sculpture major, Aesthetics & Art History major
Dept. of Industrial Arts(317/0)
Visual Design/Product Design/Craft Art

Graduate Programs

Graduate School of Arts and Crafts(M 44/0)
Div. of Painting and Sculpture(M 26/2)
Art Theory; Aesthetics and Science of Art Theory: Theory of Western, Japanese and Oriental History; Classical Materials Practice/Practice of Japanese Painting Technique; Japanese Painting Works; Final Works of Japanese Painting/Practice of Oil Painting Technique: Oil Painting Works; Final Works of Oil Painting/Practice of Sculpture Technique; Sculpture Works; Final Works of Sculpture
Div. of Visual Design(M 16/1)
Aesthetics and Science of Art Theory; Art History Theory; Practice of Oriental, Western and Japanese Art History; Classical, Materials Practice; Design Theory; Theory of Industrial Design History/Visual Communication Theory; Image Practice; Visual Space Practice; Color Scheme Practice; Practice of Visual Communication Design/Product Planning Theory; Morphology Practice; Human, Engineering Practice; Product Design Practice: Final Works of Product Design/Craft Design Theory; Practice of Craft Technique (Ceramics, Lacquer, Metal and Textile); Practice of Craft Design (Ceramics, Lacque, Metal and Textile); Final Works of Craft Design
Div. of Aesthetics and Art History(M 2/0)
Art Theory; Research for Art Technique/Aesthetics and Science of Art Theory; Theory of Western, Japanese and Oriental Art History: Classical Materials Practice; Theory of Craft History/Aesthetics Practice; Practice of Japanese Art History; Practice of Western Art History; Practice of Oriental Art History; Practice of Craft History; Aesthetics Thesis, Research; Thesis Research for Japanese, Western and Oriental Art History, Thesis Research for Craft History

名古屋市立大学

(Nagoya Shiritsu Daigaku)

Nagoya City University

1 Kawasumi, Mizuho-cho, Mizuho-ku, Nagoya-shi, Aichi 455

☎ 052-851-5511 FAX 052-841-7428

Founded 1950
Professors 98
Associate Professors 95
Assistant Professors(Tenured) 48
Assistant Professors(Non-tenured) 151
Research Assistants 209
Undergraduate Students/Foreign Students 1, 753/17
Graduate Students/Foreign Students 245/11
Library 380, 602 volumes
Contact: Admission Office ☎ext. 2128

Educational philosophy Aiming to contribute to further development of social culture and human welfare through providing professional education and studies.

Foreign students Nagoya is the core city of the Central Japan. The university with the sponsorship of the city can provide cozy atomosphere to make your student life fruitful.

Environment Located in the southeastern part of the city, the university has three separate campuses-Kawasumi, Tanabe-Dori, and Yamanohata within easy access.

Facilities Student hall, welfare house, three libraries, computation center, swimming pool, gymnasium, " Ryomei-so " seminar house in suburbed Tateshina area.

Student activities Welcoming Party for the freshmen and the University Festival are held annually. A wide variety of extra curricular activities, including baseball, volleyball, rugby football, orchestra, drama, etc.

Academic programs for foreign students Supplemental Japanese Language class and tutoring system are available.

Services for foreign students Housing information, part-time job information

Undergraduate Programs

Faculty of Economics(848/14)
  Dept. of Economics
Faculty of Medicine(482/0)
  Dept. of Medicine
Faculty of Pharmaceutical Sciences(423/3)
  Dept. of Pharmaceutical Sciences(198/3)
  Dept. of Pharmaceutical Technology(225/0)

Graduate Programs

Graduate School of Economics(M 65/7, D 3/0)
  Div. of Economic Policy(M 8/3, D 3/0)

Business and Accounting (Business Administration, Bookkeeping, Business Organnization, Marketing Theory, Business Finance, Accounting, Financial Statement Managerial Accounting), Economic Policy (Economic Policy, Economic History, Public Economics, Transportation Economics, Labor Economics, Socialsecurity, Industrial Economics, Aguricultural Economics, Public Finance, International Economics, Economic Development, Monetary Theory, Monetary Policy, Local Fiscal Policy), Economic Theory (Economics, Mathematics of Economics, Statistics, Marxian Economics, Operations Research, Microeconomics Theory, Contemporary Economic Theory, Information Processing, Mathematical Statistics, Economic Doctrines, History of Social Thought, Econometrics, Quantitative Economics)

  Div. of Japanese Economics and Administration(M 57/4)

Business and Accounting (Business Administration, Bookkeeping, Business Organnization, Marketing Theory, Business Finance, Accounting, Financial Statement Managerial Accounting), Economic Policy (Economic Policy, Economic History, Public Economics, Transportation Economics, Labor Economics, Socialsecurity, Industrial Economics, Aguricultural Economics, Public Finance, International Economics, Economic Development, Monetary Theory, Monetary Policy, Local Fiscal Policy), Economic Theory (Economics, Mathematics of Economics, Statistics, Marxian Economics, Operations Research, Microeconomics Theory, Contemporary Economic Theory, Information Processing, Mathematical Statistics, Economic Doctrines, History of Social Thought, Econometrics, Quantitative Economics)

Graduate School of Medicine(D 57/2)
  Div. of Medicine(D 57/2)

Anatomy, Anesthesiology, Bacteriology, Biochemistry, Dermatology, Hygiene, Internal Medicine, Legal Medicine, Medical Zoology, Neurosurgery, Obstetrics and Gynecology, Ophthalmology, Orthopedic Surgery, Otorhinolaryngology, Pathology, Pediatrics, Pharmacology, Physiology, Psychiatry, Public Health, Radiology, Surgerry, Urology

Graduate School of Pharmaceutical Sciences(M 100/2, D 20/0)
  Div. of Pharmaceutical Sciences(M 100/2, D 20/0)

Biological Chemistry, Biolpharmaceutics, Chemical Hygiene and Nutrition, Chemical Pharmacology, Pharmaceutical Analytical Chemistry, Pharmaceutical Chemistry, Pharmacognocy, Chemical and Instrumental Analysis, Chemical Reaction Engineering, Microbial Pharmacy, Pharmaceutical Industrial Chemistry, Pharmaceutics, Physical Chemistry, Cynthetic Organic Chemistry

富山県立大学

(Toyama Kenritsu Daigaku)

Toyama Prefectural University

5180 Kurokawa, Kosugi-machi, Imizu-gun, Toyama 939-03
☎ 0766-56-7500 FAX 0766-56-6182

Founded 1990
Professors 16
Associate Professors 16
Assistant Professors(Tenured) 5
Assistant Professors(Non-tenured) 9
Research Assistants 5
Undergraduate Students/Foreign Students 174/0
Library 75, 492 volumes
Contact: Instruction Section

Educational philosophy We aim at both teaching and researching deep into special fields of study and educating outstanding students in order to contribute to both cultural and academic betterment and industrial development.

Foreign students We believe that foreign students can enjoy a rewarding experience in our school, and can contribute to promoting mutual understanding and the development of friendly relations.

Environment The town of Kosugi, with a population of 30, 000, is located in the center of Toyama Prefecture, 12 kilometers west of Toyama city. The area is rich in nature and history. It also has the largest recreation park in Toyama, Taikooyama Land.

Facilities Library, Computer center, Gymnasium, Welfare Facilities such as Clinic and Cafeteria

Student activities Popular campus events includes ball games tournaments and school festival. There is a variety of extra curricular activities, including photograph, computer, orchestra, folk song, tea ceremony, badminton, soccer, ski, tennis, volleyball, etc.

Services for foreign students Toyama Prefectural Office, which founded our university, provides various research funds and scholarships for overseas students. Also, Toyama International Center organizes various activities such as international exchange gatherings and parties.

Undergraduate Programs

Faculty of Engineering(174/0)
- **Dept. of Mechanical Systems Engineering**(85/0)
- **Dept. of Electronic and Information Engineering**(89/0)

都留文科大学

(Tsuru Bunka Daigaku)

Tsuru University

3-8-1 Tahara, Tsuru-shi, Yamanashi 402
☎ 0554-43-4341

Founded 1960

Undergraduate Programs

College of Humanities
- **Dept. of Elementary Education**
- **Dept. of English**
- **Dept. of Japanese**
- **Dept. of Sociology**

静岡県立大学

(Shizuoka Kenritsu Daigaku)

University of Shizuoka

395 Yada, Shizuoka-shi, Shizuoka 422
☎ 054-264-5102 FAX 054-264-5099

Founded 1987
Professors 69
Associate Professors 46
Assistant Professors(Tenured) 31
Assistant Professors(Non-tenured) 74
Research Assistants 52
Undergraduate Students/Foreign Students 2, 019/20
Graduate Students/Foreign Students 113/2
Library 179, 078 volumes
Contact: Admission Office

Educational philosophy The aim of university is to cultivate students who can manage the problems accompanied by rapid technological adcancement, the development of our industrial economy and the advancement of society, and who can take an active part in development of Shizuoka Prefecture.

Foreign students We believe that foreign students can contribute a great deal to promoting mutual understanding and the development of friendly relations.

Enviroment Shizuoka prefecture, with a population of 3, 600, 000 is located in the middle part of Japan. It takes about on hour from Tokyo by bullet train. It is blessed with a mild climate and beautiful natural environment. Our university lies on the side of the Nihondaira Plateau, which is one of the most prominent scenic spot in Japan. In addition, one has a spectacular view of Mt. Fuji.

Facilities Library, Video Library, Audio Video Center, Computer Center, Computer Laboratory, Language Laboratory, Hall, Auditorium, Sports Training Center, Gymnasium, Tennis Coat, Ground

Student activities Events: School Festival, Freshmen welcome party, etc. Club, Circle: Basebll, Soccer, Volleyball, Jazz Dance, Judo, Wind Instrument Music, Koto, The Tea Ceremony, Art, etc.
Academic programs for foreign students Special curriculum: Things Japanese/Japanese
Services for foreign students Especially nothing, but services for students: Part–Time Job Information, Health Clinic, Housing Information

Undergraduate Programs

Faculty of Pharmaceutical Sciences(510/5)
  Dept. of Pharmacy(249/2)
  Dept. of Pharmaceutics(261/3)
Faculty of Food and Nutritional Sciences(226/0)
  Dept. of Food Science(111/0)
  Dept. of Nutrition Science(115/0)
Faculty of International Relations(856/15)
  Dept. of International Relations(285/9)
  Dept. of International Languages and Cultures(571/6)
Faculty of Administration and Informatics(427/0)
  Dept. of Administration and Informatics(427/0)

Graduate Programs

Graduate School of Pharmaceutical Sciences(M 95/2, D 18/0)
  Div. of Pharmacy(M 54/2, D 5/0)
Advanced Organic Chemistry, Pharmaceutic Analytics, Biochemistry, Hygienic Science, Pharmacognosy, Pharmaceutics, Pharmacology, Microbiology
  Div. of Pharmaceutics(M 41/0, D 13/0)
Pharmaceutic Analytics, Bio–organic Chemistry, Medicinal Chemistry, Pharmaceutical Engineering, Pharmaceutical Chemistry of Natural Product, Radio–Pharmaceutics, Industrial Hygiene

Private Universities

愛知学院大学
(Aichi Gakuin Daigaku)

Aichi Gakuin University

12 Araike, Iwasaki, Nisshin–cho, Aichi–gun, Aichi 470–01
☎ 05617–3–1111 FAX 05617–3–4449

Founded 1876
Professors 145
Associate Professors 74
Assistant Professors(Tenured) 84
Assistant Professors(Non–tenured) 456
Research Assistants 100
Undergraduate Students/Foreign Students 11, 656/55
Graduate Students/Foreign Students 171/4
Library 566, 321 volumes
Contact: Student Affairs Office

Education philosophy Aichi Gakuin University is founded on the spirit of Buddhism, in particular Zen Buddhism, which lays stress on " the unity of learning and practice ". Guided by this spirit, the University aims at cultivating in students a sense of gratitude.
Foreign students We openly welcome foreign students. We are very confident that our school will be an ideal place for foreign students to study on various aspects of Japan and the Japanese people.
Environment Our school is located in suburban Nisshin–cho, a lovely area east of Nagoya, which is the clean city of central Japan. It is an ideal campus to study and experience Japan equipped with various modern research institutes on a vast site of 500, 000 square meters.
Facilities University Library, Institute for Zen Studies, Data Processing Center, Research Institute of Law and Religion, Institute of Business Administration, Marketing Research Institute, Institute of Foreign Languages, Institute for Cultural Studies.
Student activities There are 79 sports and 85 non–sports clubs affiliated with our university. Sports clubs include Japanese archery, judo and Japanese fencing club. Non–sports clubs include flower arrangement, Japanese calligraphy and other Japanese cluture –oriented clubs.
Academic programs for foreign students We offer Japanese language and classes focusing on various aspects on Japan in our curriculum of General Education Division for foreign students to examine the Japanese culture in this internationalizing society.
Services for foreign students We provide foreign students with advisors selected by each faculty. Students can consult with their advisors on their accademics, social life and so on.

Undergraduate Programs

Faculty of Commerce(4, 888/27)
Dept. of Commerce(2, 745/10)
Dept. of Management(2, 143/17)
Faculty of Dentistry(836/3)
Dept. of Dentistry(836/3)
Faculty of Letters(2, 523/19)
Dept. of Buddhist and Religious Studies(575/2)
Dept. of History(528/1)
Dept. International Culture(500/7)
Dept. of Japanese Culture(376/7)

Dept. of Psychology(544/2)
Faculty of Law(2, 787/1)
Dept. of Law
Faculty of Management(622/5)
Dept. of Management

Graduate Programs

Graduate School of Commerce(M 47/1, D 2/0)
Div. of Commerce(M 47/1, D 2/0)
The study of:Commerce, Commercial History, Commercial policies, Commodity science, Foreign trade theories, Insurance theories, Traffic theories, Securities theories, Financial Accounting, Bookkeeping doctorines, Business Administration, Financial Management theories, Personnel Management theories, Political Policies, Money Market, International Money Market theories
Graduate School of Dentistry(D 55/0)
Div. of Dentisry(D 55/0)
Oral Anatomy, Oral Phisiology, Oral Biochemistry, Oral Pathology, Oral Microbiology, Dental Pharmacology, Dental Materials Science, Preventive Dentistry and Dental Public Health, Operative Dentistry, Prosthodontics, Oral and Maxillofacial Surgery, Orthodontics, Pedodontics, Department of Dental Radiology, Internal Medicine, Surgery
Graduate School of Law(M 61/0, D 2/0)
Div. of Law(M 61/0, D 2/0)
The study of:Civil Law, Commercial Law, Labour Law, Private International Law, Legal Philosophy, Legal History, Constitutional Law, Administrative Law, International Law, Political Science, Law Politics, Comparative Law, Religious Law, Criminal Law
Graduate School of Letters(M 48/2, D 11/1)
Div. of Buddhist and Religious Studies(M 17/1, D 4/1)
The study of: Buddhism and Buddhist History, Zen doctrines Zen thoughts' history, religion and religious history
Div. of Psychology(M 11/0, D 3/0)
The study of Social Psychology, The study of Personality Psychology, The study of Developmental Psychology, The study of Experimental Psychology, The special study of Psychology, (The study of: Social Psychology, Personality Psychology, Developmental Psychology, Experimental Psychology, Psychometrics), The study of Educational History for Handicapped Children, The study of Educational Process for Handicapped Children, The study of Nursing Training
Div. of History(M 15/1, D 4/0)
The study of Japanese History, (The study of Cultural History), (The study of Social Economical History), (The study of Political History), The study of Oriental History, (The study of Cultural History), (The study of Social Economical History), The study of Western History, (The study of Cultural History), (The study of Social Economical History), The special study of Japanese History, The special study of Oriental History, The special study of Western History, The study of Archaeology
Div. of Studies of English Speaking Cultures(M 48/2, D 11/1)
The study of English Literature, The study of cultures in English-Speaking Societies

---

愛知学泉大学
(Aichi Gakusen Daigaku)
Aichi Gakusen University

Kamikawanari, Hegoshi-cho, Okazaki-shi, Aichi 444
☎ 0564-31-6587 FAX 0564-32-3430

Founded 1966
Professors 10
Associate Professors 3
Assistant Professors(Tenured) 5
Assistant Professors(Non-tenured) 30
Research Assistants 4
Undergraduate Students/Foreign Students 268/1
Library 20, 802 volumes
Contact: instruction office, foreign student section

Edducational philosophy Through the educational philosophy-the personal development of the potential capacities -, we make it our fundamental goal to bring up such students who can contribute their share to homes and society by the peaceful but progressive minds.
Foreign students We hope foreign students can enjoy their studies and good relationship with Japanese students in our campuses, sorrounded by one big tie-human love.
Environment Okazaki city, with a population of 300, 000, is located in the suburban area of megalopolis Nagoya, 25 km from its center. This city is famous for the birth place of Ieyasu, founded Tokugawa era and rich in historic places.
Facilities Libray of Home Economics, Gymnasium with training center, Domitory for women
Student activities Main campus events: school festival, freshmanwelcome party, domestic and overseas travels student activity club:student news paper, photograph, art and painting, sa-ka-do, rock band, basketball, softball, etc.

Academic programs for foreign students tutoring system for improvement of Japanese language skill.

Undergraduate Programs

Faculty of Home Economics(268/1)
Dept. of Home Economics

愛知工業大学
(Aichi Kôgyô Daigaku)
Aichi Institute of Technology

1247 Yachigusa, Yakusa-cho, Toyota-shi, Aichi 470-03
☎ 0565-48-8121 FAX 0565-48-0277

Founded 1959
Professors 78
Associate Professors 52
Assistant Professors(Tenured) 40
Assistant Professors(Non-tenured) 173
Research Assistants 6
Undergraduate Students/Foreign Students 5, 049/0
Graduate Students/Foreign Students 57/1
Library 250, 000 volumes
Contact: Admission Office

Educational philosophy The goal of Aichi Institute of Technology is to produce graduates who are well-rounded human beings with competent technological skills. The total educational program is geared toward this aim with the hope and expectation that its graduates will contribute both to technological advancement and to society as a whole.
Foreign students The founding principles of AIT are freedom, fraternity, and sense of justice. AIT is the place for every student of technology in the world who understands those principles. Foreign students are heartily welcome and fairly treated as well as Japanse students. AIT wants to contribute to the international world through the education of foreign students.
Environment AIT is located in the city of Toyota whose population is 3, 000, 000. Toyota is near Nagoya in Aichi Prefecture in Central Japan, one hour by the bullet train from the western, oldest cities, Nara and Kyoto, two hours from the eastern, modern city, Tokyo. The region surrounding AIT on the wooded hill is the largest major industrialized in Japan as well as deeply-traditional region.
Facilities To assist students in their research and study, AIT provides up-to-date modern equipments and a library. The Computer Center has a CRAY X-MP/14 se, an IBM-3081 K and other computer equipment. The Department of civil engineering has one of the largest earthquake simulation tables in the world. The modern library contains 250, 000 books. The gymnasium has 3, 000 seats.
Student activities The academic year begins with Entrance Ceremony in April. First Semester is from April to September, Second Semester from October to February. Students enjoy AIT's Festival in May, and Summer and Winter Holidays. In addition to the academic life, students enjoy a wide variety of extra-curricular activities. Clubs play an important part in the total educational program of AIT.
Academic programs for foreign students Foreign students who passed the entrance examination of AIT, spend their academic lives under the guidance of the teachers of the Department. The teachers guide their students individually according to their capabilities and expectations. The intimate contact with the teachers is characteristic of AIT.
Services for foreign students The International Center of AIT provides the place for foreign students to stay, get contacts with each other, get advices from counselors. Besides the Center, various facilities of AIT give foreign students the chances to know how to enjoy Japanese lives.

Undergraduate Programs

Faculty of Engineering(5, 049/0)
Dept. of Applied Chemistry(546/0)
Dept. of Architecture(607/0)
Dept. of Architecture Engineering(421/0)
Dept. of Civil Engineering(603/0)
Dept. of Electrical Engineering(571/0)
Dept. of Electronics(612/0)
Dept. of Industrial Engineering(830/0)
Dept. of Information Network Engineering(273/0)
Dept. of Mechanical Engineering(586/0)

Graduate Programs

Graduate School of Engineering(M 57/1)

One-Year Graduate Programs

Industrial Engineer course

愛知医科大学
(Aichi Ika Daigaku)
Aichi Medical University

21 Yazako Karimata, Nagakute-cho, Aichi-gun, Aichi 480-11
☎ 0561-62-3311 FAX 0561-62-4866

Founded 1972
Professors 40
Associate Professors 50
Assistant Professors(Tenured) 59
Assistant Professors(Non-tenured) 149
Research Assistants 228

Undergraduate Students/Foreign Students 692/3
Graduate Students/Foreign Students 68/2
Library 120, 418 volumes
Contact: Admission Office

Educational philosophy Our University aims to train excellent medical doctors and leaders with up-to-date knowledge and advanced skills of medical science, so that they will contribute to the welfare of human society, on the basis of respect for the dignity of life and humanism.
Foreign students One of our educational philosophies is to cooperate to improve the conditions of medical care in the countries of Southeast Asia. We hope foreign students will go far toward the world medical care.
Environment Our University is situated on the eastern outskirts of Nagoya, one of the biggest cities in Japan. The surroundings with natural beauty and fresh air make our campus a best suitable place for education, study and medical care.
Facilities Hospital, Library, Gymnasium, Institute for Medical Science of Aging, Institute for Molecular Science of Medicine, Information Processing Center on Campus, and the Medical Clinic at the central part of Nagoya.
Student activities Freshmen's Orientation (April), Early Exposure Training in Hospital (July), Memorial Service for Dissection (October), Medical University Festival (November)
Extracurricular activities: Sporting clubs, 24; Non-sporting clubs, 3
Services for foreign students Some counselors are in charge of foreign students, giving advice on their school life and study. Joint excursions and socials are held for foreign students and researchers a few times a year.

Undergraduate Programs

Faculty of Medicine(692/3)
Dept. of Medicine

Graduate Programs

Graduate School of Medicine(D 68/2)
Div. of Internal Medicine(D 31/1)
Anatomy, Anesthesiology & Emergency Medicine, Biochemistry, Dermatology, Hygiene, Internal Medicine, Legal Medicine, Microbiology, Neurosurgery, Obstetrics and Gynecology, Ophthalmology, Orthopedic Surgery, Otorhinolaryngology, Parasitology, Pathology, Pediatrics, Pharmacology, Physiology, Psychiatry and Neurology, Public Health, Radiology, Surgery, Urology
Div. of Pathology(D 3/0)
Div. of Physiology(D 2/0)
Div. of Social Medicine(D 5/0)
Div. of Surgery(D 27/1)

愛知淑徳大学

(Aichi Shukutoku Daigaku)

Aichi Shukutoku University

9 Katahira, Nagakute, Nagakute-cho, Aichi-gun, Aichi 480-11
☎ 0561-62-4111 FAX 0561-62-3007

Founded 1975
Professors 42
Associate Professors 5
Assistant Professors(Tenured) 7
Assistant Professors(Non-tenured) 52
Undergraduate Students/Foreign Students 1, 468/0
Graduate Students/Foreign Students 35/0
Library 64, 273 volumes
Contact: International Center

Educational philosophy Drawing strength from the original spirit of the founder, we hope always to cherish a warmth of human relations in our community, to endow our students with a rich education in the liberal arts, and with a thorough specialist training, so that they will become productive and useful members of society.
Foreign students We hope that foreign students can enjoy a rewarding experience at Aichi Shukutoku University, and can contribute a great deal to promoting mutual understanding and the development of friendly relations among the members of our university community.
Environment The town of Nagakute, with a population of 31, 000, is located in the suburbs of Nagoya. Our campus is in a corner of the historically important Nagakute battlefield. It is only fifteen minutes from the subway line, and within 30 minutes reach from downtown Nagoya.
Facilities Library, Audio-Visual Center, International Center, Information Science Education Center, Gymnasium, Auditorium, Sports field, Affiliated campground
Student activities Popular campus events include Freshman Welcome Festival, Encounter Camp, Summer Seminar, University Festival. There is a wide variety of extra curricular activities, including tea-ceremony, flower arrangement, drama, chorus, golf, skiing, tennis, etc.

Undergraduate Programs

Faculty of Literature(1, 468/0)
Dept. of English Literature(478/0)
Dept. of Japanese Literature(501/0)
Dept. of Library and Information Science(489/0)

Graduate Programs

Graduate School of Literature(M 35/0)
Div. of English Literature(M 11/0)
English and American Literature, English Linguistics,

Comparative Literature, Translation, English as a International Language, Japanese as a foreign Language, Date Storage and Retrieval, Data/Information Management

Div. of Japanese Literature(M 12/0)
Japanese Literature (Pre-Nara, Heian, Kamakura, Edo, Post-Meiji Period), Japanese Linguisitics, ComparativeLiterature, Buddist Literature, Chinese Literature, Stylistics, Education of Japanese Language, Translation and Contrastive Linguisitics, Data Storage and Retrieval, Data/Information Management

Div. of Library and Information Science(M 12/0)
Information Storage and Retrieval, Information Technology, Information Media, Information Science, Information Systems, Data/Information Management, Structure of Information, Information Diffusion

愛知大学
(Aichi Daigaku)
Aichi University

1-1 Machihata-machi, Toyohashi-shi, Aichi 441
☎ 0532-47-4111 FAX 0532-47-4132

Founded 1946
Professors 100
Associate Professors 50
Assistant Professors(Tenured) 23
Assistant Professors(Non-tenured) 119
Undergraduate Students/Foreign Students 6, 738/48
Graduate Students/Foreign Students 50/1
Library 862, 909 volumes
Contact: International Exchange Office
☎ 0532-47-4131

Education philosophy We aim to conduct education of a high cultural and vocational standard, and to encourage people of ability to contribute to the development of society, having a wide international outlook in accordance with Article 52 of the School Education Law of Japan.

Foreign students We believe that foreign students find the University and the surrounding community an open and friendly place to live and study, and that foreign students can contribute a great deal to promoting mutual understanding in our area.

Environment Aichi Prefecture is almost in the center of Japan, and also at the center of the Japanese Car Industry, since most of the factories of Toyota Motor are situated 30 kilometers southeast of Nagoya. Toyohashi campus is full of lovely trees. As Nagoya campus was only opened in April 1, 988, it is quite new, but in time the trees and shrubs will mature.

Facilities Libraries on Toyohashi and Nagoya campuses, Comprehensive Chinese-Japanese Dictionary Editing Center, Institute of International Affairs, Community Research Institute, Research Institute of Industry in Chubu District, Managerial Research Institute, Data Processing Center, Gymnasium, etc.

Student activities Popular campus events are: freshmen welcome party, volleyball tournament, festival of the Literary Arts Union, softball game, university festival, ski-school. There are about 190 student clubs which are divided into 3 types, academic research, culture and art, and physical education.

Academic programs for foreign students In the General Education Course, general education subjects, foreign languages and physical education may be replaced by the courses in " Japanese Language and Japanese Studies. "

Services for foreign students Health clinic, personal/psychological counseling, housing information, part-time job information, vocational guidance, homestay, home visit, cultural excursion program

Undergraduate Programs

Faculty of Business Administration(1, 989/27)
Dept. of Business Administration
Faculty of Economics(1, 919/13)
Dept. of Economics
Faculty of Law(1, 439/4)
Dept. of Law
Faculty of Literature(1, 391/4)
Dept. of History(328/0)
Dept. of Literature(627/1)
Dept. of Philosophy(173/1)
Dept. of Sociology(263/2)

Graduate Programs

Gradate School of Business Administration(M 19/0, D 4/1)
Div. of Business Administration
Graduate School of Economics(M 7/0, D 2/0)
Div. of Economics
Graduate School Law(M 15/0, D 3/0)
Div. of Private Law(M 8/0, D 3/0)
Div. of Public Law(M 7/0)

One-Year Graduate Programs

Literature Course
Japanese literature Major

朝日大学
(Asahi Daigaku)
Asahi University

1851 Hozumi, Hozumi-cho, Motosu-gun, Gifu 501-02
☎ 05832-6-6131

Founded 1971

Undergraduate Programs

School of Business Administration
Dept. of Business Administration
School of Dentistry
Dept. of Dentistry
School of Law
Dept. of Law

Graduate Programs

Graduate School of Dentistry
Div. of Dental Science

中部大学
(Chûbu Daigaku)
Chubu University

1200 Matsumoto-cho, Kasugai-shi, Aichi 487
☎ 0568-51-1111 FAX 0568-51-1141

Founded 1964
Professors 101
Associate Professors 69
Assistant Professors(Tenured) 39
Assistant Professors(Non-tenured) 178
Research Assistants 6
Undergraduate Students/Foreign Students 5, 515/13
Graduate Students/Foreign Students 58/0
Library 261, 975 volumes
Contact: Center for International Programs

Educational philosophy Students are strongly disciplined to learn basic skills and knowledge in their own speciality, while developing well rounded personality. " The development of trustworthy human being, " which has been the educational doctrine of this institution, clearly defines Chubu University's educational goal.

Foreign students International students are welcome from all countries of the world. Chubu University encourages applications from students with diverse cultural backgrounds.

Environment The main campus situated about a half hour's drive from the center of Nagoya on a wooded hillside overlooking the broad Nobi Plain. The University also operates a satellite campus in Ena at the southern tip of the Japan Alps which provides supplemental research and athletic facilities.

Facilities Library, Computer Center, Language Laboratories, Audio-visual Studio, Learning Resources Center, Materials and Structures Research Center, Structural Analysis and Measurement Center, Swimming Pool, Gymnasium, Auditorium, exclusive athletic grounds, etc.

Student activities Popular campus events include homecoming, school festival, freshmen camp, music festival and overseas study trip. There are a wide variety of extra curricular activities including Choral Club, Jazz Band, Baseball Club, Handball Club, Judo Club, etc.

Academic programs for foreign students
Classes in supplemental Japanese language are available for international students. Credit for this course is converted to development. Tutoring system is also available.

Services for foreign students Health clinic, personal/psychological counseling, dormitory, housing information, part-time job information, vocational guidance, cultural exchange program, financial aid

Undergraduate Programs

Faculty of Business Administration and Information Science(1, 031/6)
Dept. of Business Administration and Information Science(1, 031/6)
Faculty of Engineering(3, 642/5)
Dept. of Architecture(521/0)
Dept. of Civil Engineering(531/0)
Dept. of Electrical Engineering(624/1)
Dept. of Electronic Engineering(606/3)
Dept. of Engineering Physics(233/0)
Dept. of Industrial Chemistry(415/0)
Dept. of Mechanical Engineering(712/1)
Faculty of International Studies(842/2)
Dept. of Comparative Cultures(414/2)
Dept. of International Relations(428/0)

Graduate Programs

Graduate School of Engineering(M 54/0, D 4/0)
Div. of Applied Physics(M 10/0, D 2/0)
Applied Nuclear Physics, Applied Properties of Matter, Instrument Engineering, Properties of Matter Engineering
Div. of Construction Engineering(M 5/0, D 0/0)
Architectural Design, Architectural Design and History, Concrete Engineering, Environmental Design, Geotechnical Engineering, Hydraulics, Structures and Bridges Engineering
Div. of Electrical Engineering(M 12/0, D 1/0)
Communication Engineering, Electric Machine Engineering, Electric Power Engineering, Electronic Engineering, Electronics Applications, Study of Physical Properties of Electronic Materials
Div. of Industrial Chemistry(M 9/0, D 1/0)
Chemical Engineering, Industrial Physical Chemistry, Inorganic Industrial Chemistry, Organic Industrial Chemistry, Organic Synthesis
Div. of Mechanical Engineering(M 18/0, D 0/0)
Applied Dinamics, Fluids Engineering, Materials and Manufacturing Engineering, Precision Engineering Laboratory, Thermal Engineering

中京大学
(Chûkyô Daigaku)
Chukyo University

101-2 Yagoto Honmachi, Showa-ku, Nagoya-shi, Aichi 466
☎ 052-832-2151 FAX 052-835-7143

Founded 1954
Professors 168
Associate Professors 70
Assistant Professors (Tenured) 20
Assistant Professors (Non-tenured) 360
Research Assistants 6
Undergraduate Students/Foreign Students 11, 336/50
Graduate Students/Foreign Students 120/26
Library 502, 044 volumes
Contact: International Affairs Section ☎, ext.340 or 341

Educational philosophy Since its founding in 1954, Chukyo University has changed with the times and with the establishment in 1990 or School of Computer and Cognitive Sciences-it now has 5 areas for post-graduate studies, 7 undergraduate schools. The spirit with which this school was founded was the determination to " be a sanctuary of earnestness for both learning and sports ".

Foreign students Chukyo University is pushing on the plan of internationalization of our campus. As a part of it, we welcome foreign studetns to our university very much. But we would like the foreign students to be sure that they have enough Japanese language ability when applying to Chukyo University.

Environment Nagoya is a vital city of industry and commerce strategically located midway between Tokyo and Osaka, the two giant metropolises of Japan, and the Nagoya campus of Chukyo University is in a hilly zone in the eastern part of the city, in an area that is called the city's most outstanding educational district.

Facilities AV Center, Sports Training Center, Swimming Pool, Gymnasium, Library, Institute for Research in Social Science, Institute for Research in Physical Education, Institute for Research into Small and Medium sized Enterprises, Institute for Advanced Studies in Artificial Intelligence.

Student activities The University has full complement of sports circles, and cultural circles. There are Japanese Calligraphy Club, Light Music Club, Photograph Club, Broadcast Club, Japanese Instrumental Music Club, Competitive Gymnastics Club, Basketball Club, Skating Club, Karate Club, Mountaineering Club and so on.

Academic programs for foreign students Japanese Language (3 levels), Japanese History, Japanese Geography, Japanese Economics and so on are the elective required subjects only for foreign students.

Services for foreign students Scholarship for foreign students, an overnight trip to University's Seminar House, College Housing in Toyota Campus, Personal/Psychological counseling and so on.

Undergraduate Programs

Faculty of Letters(1, 927/3)
- **Dept. of Japanese Language and Literature**(667/3)
- **Dept. of English Language and Literature**(671/0)
- **Dept. of Psychology**(589/0)

Faculty of Sociology(1, 222/10)
- **Dept. of Sociology**(1, 222/10)

Faculty of Law(2, 184/5)
- **Dept. of Law**(2, 184/5)

Faculty of Economics(1, 495/13)
- **Dept. of Economics**(1, 495/13)

Faculty of Commercial Sciences(2, 233/7)
- **Dept. of Commerce**(1, 164/7)
- **Dept. of Business Administration**(1, 069/0)

Faculty of Computer and Cognitive Sciences(175/1)
- **Dept. of Cognitive Sciences**(71/0)
- **Dept. of Computer Sciences**(104/1)

Faculty of Physical Education(2, 100/11)
- **Dept. of Budo (Martial Arts)** (192/0)
- **Dept. of Health Education**(391/0)
- **Dept. of Physical Education**(1, 517/11)

Graduate Programs

Graduate School of Letters(M 25/4, D 14/1)

Div. of English Literature(M 6/0, D 3/0)
English Literature, American Literature, English Language, Linguistics, English and American Juvenile Literature

Div. of Japanese Literature(M 4/3, D 9/1)
Japanese Literature, Japanese Language, Japanized Chinese Literature, History of Japanese Culture

Div. of Psychology(M 15/1, D 2/0)
Basic Psychology, Applied Psychology, Clinical Psychology, Psychological Experimentation

Graduate School of Sociology(M 4/1)

Div. of Sociology(M 4/1)
Empirical Sociology, Theoretical Sociology, Sociology of Language, Sociology of Religion, Family Sociology, Theory of Modern Society, Theory of Social Awareness, Social Anthropology, Theories on Comparative Culture, Theory of Social Welfare, Pedagogy, Theory of Social Education, Study of Technological Civilization, Developmental Psychology

Graduate School of Law(M 26/5, D 0/0)

Div. of Law(M 26/5, D 0/0)
Constitutional Law, Administrative Law, Civil Law, Commercial Law, Criminal Law, Civil Procedure Law, Criminal Procedure Law, International Private Law, Labor Law, Criminal Law, Legal Law, Legal Philosophy, Bankruptcy Law, Anglo-American Law, French Law, Soviet Law, Comparative Law, Industrial Property Law, History of European Political Ideas, International Politics, Japanese Political History and so on

Graduate School of Commercial Sciences(M 19/5, D 2/0)

Div. of Commerce(M 19/5, D 2/0)

Economic Theory, Economic Policy, Japanese Commercial History, European Commercial History, Monetary Theory, Theory of Trade, Studying of Marchandise, Accounting, Tax Accounting, Business Management

Graduate School of Physical Education(M 19/6, D 14/4)

Div. of Physical Education(M 19/6, D 14/4)

Principles of Physical Education, Sociology of Physical Education, Studying Methods of Physical Education, Physical Fitness, Exercise Physiology, Theory of Formative Development, Exercise Mechanics, Physical Dietetics, Methodology of Physical Education and Sports, Theory of Athletic Training, Social Physical Education, Modern Society and Sports, Bio-Mechanics, Exercise Mechanics, Environmental Physiology, Labor Hygienics, Dietetic Biochemistry

中京女子大学
(Chûkyô Joshi Daigaku)

Chukyo Women's University

55 Nakouyama, Yokone-cho, Obu-shi, Aichi 474
☎ 0562-46-1291 FAX 0562-48-4621

Founded 1963
Professors 24
Associate Professors 15
Assistant Professors(Tenured) 8
Assistant Professors(Non-tenured) 29
Research Assistants 1
Undergraduate Students/Foreign Students 876/2
Library 94, 951 volumes
Contact: Public Relations Section Admission Office

Educational philosophy We design to educate positive-attitude women toward life as below;

1. Women sound of mind and body.
2. Women of intelligence and creativity.
3. Mentally well-balanced women with wide prospect and interest.

Foreign students We believe that foreign students can enjoy rewarding experiences in their student life, and can contribute a great deal to promoting mutual understanding and the development of friendly relationship.

Environment Obu city, a city of health and culture, lies on the south-east of Nagoya city. Our restful campus, commanding a fine view in all directions, is on a gentle green hill with two beautiful lakes in sight. This is the ideal place for studying.

Facilities Sports Science Center, gymnasium, library, swimming pool

Student activities There are 25 sports clubs and 8 culture clubs.
sports clubs: volleyball, basketball, handball, track and field, gymnastics, ski, kendo, kyudo etc.
culture clubs: tea ceremony, flower arrangement, chorus, etc.

Academic programs for foreign students Supplemental Japanese language class

Services for foreign students Health clinic, personal/psychological counseling, College housing

Undergraduate Programs

Faculty of Home Economics(514/0)
Dept. of Child Studies(294/0)
Dept. of Food and Nutrition Science(220/0)
Faculty of Physical Education(362/2)
Dept. of Physical Education(362/2)

大同工業大学
(Daidô Kôgyô Daigaku)

Daido Institute of Technology

2-21 Daido-cho, Minami-ku, Nagoya-shi, Aichi 457
☎ 052-612-6111 FAX 052-612-5623

Founded 1964
Professors 50
Associate Professors 33
Assistant Professors(Tenured) 17
Assistant Professors(Non-tenured) 118
Research Assistants 9
Undergraduate Students/Foreign Students 2, 783/3
Graduate Students/Foreign Students 19/0
Library 116, 768 volumes
Contact: Student Affairs (Office of International Relations Activities)

Educational philosophy The name of our institution, DAIDO, signifies all of humanity for the common good. In keeping with the significance of this name, our greatest hope is to train students to take a part actively in our society and to contribute particularly to the industrial world.

Foreign students We believe that foreign students can enjoy a rewarding experience in our institution, and can contribute a great deal to promoting mutual understanding and the development of friendly relations.

Environment Our town, Daido-cho, is located in the center of Minami Ward with a population of 159, 721. Our city of Nagoya is situated in the traditional heartland of the country, midway between Tokyo and Osaka, and has been a hub of Japanese industrial technology.

Facilities Material Engineering Laboratories, Information Processing Center, Library (reconstructed in Sept. of 1989), Gymnasium, Kisokoma Seminar House (in Nagano Prefecture).

Student activities We enjoy School Festival, Sports Festival, Regatta Tournament and Ski School,

Particularly, DIT Annual Study Tour in U.S.A. and Europe is a well-known activity. As extra curricular activities there are Brass Band, Soccer, Baseball, Volleyball, Basketball, etc.
Academic programs for foreign students Academic Advising Seminar (in which foreign students take part, making a small group with a few of Japanese students) and Credits Exchange System.
Services for foreign students Health Clinic and Counseling, Housing Information, Scholarship Information, Part-Time Job Information, Vocational Guidance and Cultural Exchange Program.

Undergraduate Programs

Faculty of Engineering(2, 783/3)
Dept. of Applied Electronic Engineering(506/0)
Dept. of Construction Engineering(744/1)
(**Architecture Course**)(369/0),
(**Civil Engineering Course**)(375/1)
Dept. of Electrical Engineering(608/1)
Dept. of Mechanical Engineering(925/1)

Graduate Programs

Graduate School of Engineering(M 19/0)
Div. of Construction Engineering(M 3/0)
Structural Engineering, Foundation Materials and Transportation Engineering, Environmental and Hydraulic Engineering, Architectural History and Construction Technology
Div. of Electrical and Applied Electronic Engineering(M 6/0)
Electrical Measurement and Electrical Materials, Electrical-Magnetic Energy, System Control Engineering, Semiconductor and Material Science, Applied Microwave Engineering, Applied Electronic Circuit
Div. of Mechanical Engineering(M 10/0)
Strength of Materials, Heat and Fluid Engineering, Production Control Engineering, Mechanical Design and Drawing

---

同朋大学
(Dôhô Daigaku)
Doho University

7-1 Inabaji, Nakamura-ku, Nagoya 453
☎ 052-411-1111 FAX 052-411-1118

Founded 1921
Professors 26
Associate Professors 12
Assistant Professors(Tenured) 4
Assistant Professors(Non-tenured) 66
Research Assistants 1
Undergraduate Students/Foreign Students 1, 164/1
Library 120, 000 volumes

Educational philosophy We aim to ultimately contribute to the promotion of the welfare of human beings in the contemporary world based on Buddhism. In order to fulfill this mission, we are deeply devoted to an academic and practical education.
Foreign students We welcome students from the countries of all over the world, especialy from Asia. Studies in our school will contribute to promoting the identity of Buddhism. We hope to exchange academic works of each countries students coming from.
Environment Nagoya is located in the center of Japan. it's convenient to go Kyoto, Osaka and Tokyo. It 's very near from Nagoya Station. (20 minutes by bus). Surrounded by the quiet area of residence.
Facilities The library of Doho Institution is full of the books and materials of the fields of Buddhism, Music and several Arts of Asia countries. 3 seminar houses located in an rural area are open for students.
Student activities Extra curricular activities are lively. Campus events includes Freshman Training Camp, Sports Festival, Summer Festival, Autumn Culture Festival, etc. Many circle activities are daily vital through the year.
Academic programs for foreign students Supplemental Japanese-Culture class.
Services for foreign students Health clinic, personal/psychological counseling, Housing information, part-time job information, etc.

Undergraduate Programs

Faculty of Human Science(592/1)
Dept. of Buddhism(244/1)
Dept. of Japanese Literature(348/0)
Faculty of Social Welfare(572/0)
Dept. of Social Welfare(572/0)

藤田学園保健衛生大学
(Fujita Gakuen Hoken Eisei Daigaku)
Fujita Health University

1-98 Dengakugakubo, Kutukake-cho, Toyoake-shi, Aichi 470-11
☎ 0562-93-2000 FAX 0562-93-2649

Founded 1964
Professors 99
Associate Professors 39
Assistant Professors(Tenured) 129
Assistant Professors(Non-tenured) 136
Research Assistants 100
Undergraduate Students/Foreign Students 1, 594/0
Graduate Students/Foreign Students 169/0
Library 141, 148 volumes
Contact: Administration Center 12-1 Minamiyakata, Sakae-cho, Toyoake, Aichi 470-11 ☎ 0562-97-6131 FAX 0562-97-2463

Educational philosophy Fujita Health University

School of Medicine has unique buildings especially designed for efficient operations in each section. The university also has a school of Hygiene where medical auxiliaries and nurses are educated.

Undergraduate Programs

Faculty of Hygiene(928/0)
Dept. of Medical Technology(554/0)
Dept. of Nursing(193/0)
Dept. of Radiological Technology(181/0)
Faculty of Medicine(666/0)
Dept. of Medicine(666/0)

Graduate Programs

Graduate School of Medicine(D 169/0)
Div. of Functional Science(D 7/0)
Biochemistry, Phamacology, Physiology.
Div. of Health & Hygiene(D 4/0)
Forensic Medicine, Medical Engineering, Microbiology, Preventive Medicine, Public Health.
Div. of Internal Medicine(D 68/0)
Dermatology, Hematology, Internal Medicine, Pediatrics, Psychiatry, Radiology.
Div. of Molecular Medicine(D 8/0)
Biomedical Polymer Science, Cell Biology, Immunology, Molecular Genetics, Molecular Oncology, Neurobiology.
Div of Morphology(D 9/0)
Anatomy, Parasitology, Pathology.
Div. of Surgery(D 73/0)
Anesthesiology, Cardiovascuology, Obstetrics & Gynecology, Ophthalmology, Orthopedics, Otorhinopharyngo-laryngology, Surgery, Urology.

福井工業大学
(Fukui Kôgyo Daigaku)
Fukui Institute of Technology

3-6-1 Gakuen, Fukui-shi, Fukui 910
☎ 0776-22-8111

Founded 1965

Undergraduate Programs

Faculty of Engineering
Dept. of Applied Physics and Chemistry
Dept. of Architecture and Civil Engineering
Dept. of Electrical Engineering
Dept. of Management Science
Dept. of Mechanical Engineering

Graduate Programs

Div. of Construction Engineering
Div. of Electrical Engineering
Div. of Mechanical Engineering
Div. of Safety and Environment Engineering

岐阜経済大学
(Gifu Keizai Daigaku)
Gifu College of Economics

5-50 Kitagata-cho, Ogaki-shi, Gifu 503
☎ 0584-74-5151 FAX 0584-81-7807

Founded 1967
Professors 38
Associate Professors 12
Assistant Professors(Tenured) 8
Assistant Professors(Non-tenured) 80
Undergraduate Students/Foreign Students 3, 262/7
Library 158, 078 volumes
Contact: Admission office, Student Devision

Educational philosophy We offer students extensive knowledge as well as specific one in economics, with the purpose of turning out as many men or women of great promise as possible.
Foreign students To our regret, having not yet prepared an educational program enough to accept foreign students, we now admit students from abroad only as auditor in undergraduate class.
Environment Our college is located in Ogaki-city, with a population of 150, 000, Gifu Pref. of Mid Japan. Ogaki, with quiet atmosphere of a castle town dating back to Middle Ages in Japan, is in favorable environment of nature rich in water and green. With easy access to Nagoya, one of the big cities in Japan, it is suited for education, study and living.
Facilities By and large, we have almost all the necessary facilities such as a library with a collection of 160, 000 books, a multipurpose gymnasium, and a field of 47, 000m² in area. We also have average apparatus necessary to computer education and meet students requirements.
Student activities Athletic clubs are of activity, and so are musical ones second to them.

Undergraduate Programs

Faculty of Economics(3, 262/7)
Dept. of Economics(2, 425/5)
Dept. of Industrial management(837/2)

聖徳学園岐阜教育大学
(Shôtoku Gakuen Gifu Kyôiku Daigaku)

Gifu University for Education and Languages

2078 Takakuwa, Yanaizu-cho, Hashima-gun, Gifu 501-61
☎ 0582-79-0804 FAX 0582-79-4171

Founded 1972
Professors 45
Associate Professors 29
Assistant Professors(Tenured) 10
Assistant Professors(Non-tenured) 44
Undergraduate Students/Foreign Students 1, 625/0
Library 80, 084 volumes
Contact: Admissions Office

Educational philosophy Our motto is " flexibility of mind ", which is penetrated throughout the educational processes in teachers training and training of those internationally-minded people in the Faculty of Foreign Languages.
Foreign students The students in the Faculty of Education work toward obtaining Japanese teaching certificates, which may or may not be acceptable in other countries. The Faculty of Foreign Languages teach foreign languages as second languages. Fluency in Japanese is expected even in the Japanese language teachers training program.
Environment The university is located in the suburbs of Gifu City (pop. 420, 000) in central Japan. The environment is basically rural. It is accessible by bus in 30 minutes from downtown Gifu.
Facilities A modest size library, two computer rooms (100 sets) a gymnasium, a swimming pool, and tennis courts are available.
Student activities Freshmen welcome party in the spring and the campus festival in the fall are two main events. there are a number of clubs and circles for extracurricular activities.
Academic programs for foreign students Foreign Language requirement is substitutable by Japanese as a Second Language. Two other courses in Japanese culture and society for foreign students.
Services for foreign students Health service (nurse), counseling (psychologist: in Japnese). Student Housing facilities available.

Undergraduate Programs

Faculty of Education(1368/0)
  Dept. of Elementary Education(655/0)
  Dept. of Japanese Language(204/0)
  Dept. of Mathematics(197/0)
  Dept. of Music(106/0)
  Dept. of Social Sciences(196/0)
Faculty of Foreign Languages(267/0)
  Dept. of English(134/0)
  Dept. of Chinese(66/0)
  Dept. of Japanese(67/0)

岐阜女子大学
(Gifu Joshi Daigaku)

Gifu Women's University

80 Taromaru, Gifu-shi, Gifu 501-25
☎ 0582-29-2211 FAX 0582-29-2222

Founded 1968
Professors 29
Associate Professors 8
Assistant Professors(Tenured) 11
Assistant Professors(Non-tenured) 46
Research Assistants 6
Undergraduate Students/Foreign Students 1, 097/0
Library 70, 958 volumes
Contact: Public Relations Office

Educational philosophy Be humane, be womanly, and above all, be yourself.
Foreign students Foreign applicants must be interviewed by the faculty members concerned. Applicants' proficiency in Japanese is to be examined in this interview. Also, knowledge concerned is tested.
Environment The campuses are located at the beautiful northern tip of Gifu City, surrounded by green hills. Gifu is a medium-sized city in Central Japan with a population of approximately 410, 000. It has both urban convenience and rural natural beauty.
Facilities University library, Local Culture Research Institute, Language Laboratory, Audio Visual Room, Computer Room, Electronic Microscope Room, Gymnasium, Physical Training Room, Reading Room, Dorm.
Student activities Popular campus events includes school festival, freshmen orientation trip. There is a wide variety of extra curricular activities, including wander-Vogel, basketball, volleyball. tennis, archery, iai, calligraphy, English speaking society, drama, etc.

Undergraduate Programs

Faculty of Home Economics(582/0)
  Dept. of Home Economics(357/0)
  Dept. of Housing and Design(225/0)
Faculty of Literature(515/0)
  Dept. of English Literature(239/0)
  Dept. of Japanese Literature(276/0)

北陸大学
(Hokuriku Daigaku)
Hokuriku University

Ho-3, Kanakawa-cho, Kanazawa-shi, Ishikawa 920-11
☎ 0762-29-1161

Founded 1975

Undergraduate Programs

Faculty of Foreign Languages
  Dept. of Chinese
  Dept. of English
School of Pharmacy
  Dept. of Pharmaceutical Sciences
  Dept. of Public Health Sciences

Graduate Programs

Graduate School of Pharmacy
  Div. of Bio-functional Pharmacy
  Div. of Hygienic Environmental Sciences
  Div. of Medicinal Chemistry
  Div. of Medicinal Resources Chemistry
  Div. of Pharmacy and Pharmacology

国際大学
(Kokusai Daigaku)
International University of Japan

Yamato-machi, Minami Uonuma-gun, Niigata 949-72
☎ 0257-77-1111 FAX 0257-79-4441

Founded 1982
Professors 30
Associate Professors 15
Assistant Professors (Tenured) 13
Assistant Professors (Non-tenured) 58
Research Assistants 7
Graduate Students/Foreign Students 215/129
Library 89, 000 volumes
Contact: Admission Division 0257-77-1200 or 77-1500, Student Center 0257-77-1438 or 77-1439

Educational philosophy IR: Professional people for new age of Internationalization.
IM: The best of Japanese and western management concepts and techniques. To prepare managers for the complexities and challenges of a global business enrollments.
Foreign students Welcome to I.U.J., we all get together and study in English as common language for world peace and prosperity.
Environment I.U.J. campus is located at 200 km away from Tokyo and surrounded by mountains. In winter, we have lots of snow fall. I.U.J. has been established 8years ago. Joetsu-shinkansen is nearby at 4km distance from I.U.J. Population in Yamato town is 15, 000 only.
Facilities Dormitory, Library (Computer Center), Center for Japan-U.S. Relations The Institute of Middle Eastern Studies, International Management Reserch Institute, Gymnasium.
Student activities I.U.J. annual festival week-end party International exchange party with local people
Academic programs for foreign students Both Japanese and overseas students are equally treated in educational system.
Services for foreign students Supporting for overseas students on living affairs by Student Center Dormitory system (single students mainly)

Graduate Programs

Graduate School of International Management (M 71/31, D 0/31)
  Div. of International Management (M 71/31/)
Graduate School of International Relations (M 144/98)
  Div. of International Relations (M 144/98)

金沢経済大学
(Kanazawa Keizai Daigaku)
Kanazawa College of Economics

10-1 Ushi, Gosho-machi, Kanazawa-shi, Ishikawa 920
☎ 0762-52-2236 FAX 0762-52-2234

Founded 1967
Professors 22
Associate Professors 14
Assistant Professors (Tenured) 10
Assistant Professors (Non-tenured) 39
Undergraduate Students/Foreign Students 2, 280/2
Library 62, 972 volumes
Contact: School Affairs

Educational philosophy In order to help the students become better and more useful citizons to society we aim at: 1. acquainting the students with the vital facts of life, 2. enlarging their individual horizens and making them more aware of today's problems.
Foreign students We feel convinced that foreign students are in a position to enjoy fruitful studies and rewarding experiences during their stay in our College, so that they will be able to contribute greatly to promoting mutual understanding, respect and cooperation among the peoples of the world.

Environment Kanazawa with a population of 450, 000 is located on the Japan Sea coast. It was a castle town and center of learning in the Edo period. Today it has emerged as center of economy and industries in Hokuriku districts, having a rich cultural heritage.
Facilities Library & Reading Room, Center for Date Processing, Economics Institute, Human and Cultrual Institute, Audio-visual Room, Physical Training Center, Allweather type Teniss Court, Newly-built Auditorium, Jouzukayama Athletic Ground, Students' Hall
Student activities Popular campus events include College Festival, Freshmen Welcome Party. We have a wide variety of extra curricular activities including baseball, football, soccer, skiing, Judo & Kendo clubs, etc., and culture circles such as classic & modern music, computer, fine arts, accounting, earth science & astronomy etc.
Academic programs for foreign students There are no particular programs for foreign students. Foreign students are required to meet Standard Qualifications and tests. We are in a position to introduce Japanese language institutions to the students, if necessary.
Services for foreign students Periodic medical examination, College dormitory, housing information and job guidance available.

Undergraduate Programs

Faculty of Economics(2, 280/0)
Dept. of Economics(1, 836/2)
Dept. of Commerce(444/0)

金沢工業大学

(Kanazawa Kôgyô Daigaku)

Kanazawa Institute of Technology

7-1 Ohgigaoka, Nonoichi-machi, Ishikawa 921
☎ 0762-48-1100 FAX 0762-94-1327

Founded 1965
Professors 97
Associate Professors 51
Assistant Professors(Tenured) 38
Assistant Professors(Non-tenured) 29
Research Assistants 12
Undergraduate Students/Foreign Students 6, 401/0
Graduate Students/Foreign Students 165/0
Library 300, 000 volumes
Contact: International Affairs Office

Educational philosophy KIT's three aims are to produce well-rounded graduates, to be technologically innovative, and to respond to the needs of industry. The university emphasizes not only the acquisition of technical knowledge and skills, but also the cultivation of problem-solving capabilities, sound judgement, responsible ethics, and the broad vision needed to become contributing members of the international community.
Foreign students We believe that it is important to have foreign students for KIT to become an international institute for higher learning. Foreign applicants must take a Japanese language proficiency test, and the same entrance examination as Japanese students, consisting of written exams and an interview.
Environment Kanazawa, the home of KIT, is a 400-year-old castle town with a rich cultural history exemplified in the magnificent traditional garden of Kenrokuen. A city of 440, 000, it has a high concentration of institutions of higher learning, making for a favorable environment for education and research.
Facilities Research Institutes for Electronic Device Systems, Applied Computer and Information Science, Urban Planning, Materials Systems, and others: Library Center, Center for Information Processing Services, educational Technology Center, Anamizu Bay Seminar House, Amaike Athletic Center, etc.
Student activities Popular annual campus events are Anamizu Bay seminar, freshman orientation, and the school festival. There are ample opportunities for extracurricular activities such as traditional Japanese sports, sailing, skiing, golf, tennis, baseball, American football, photography, Jazz music, folk song, brass band, computer, automobile, Japanese traditional culture, broadcasting, and so on.
Services for foreign students The University will assist students in finding suitable lodging near the campus.

Undergraduate Programs

Faculty of Engineering(6, 401/0)
Dept. of Architecture(815/0)
Dept. of Civil Engineering(809/0)
Dept. of Electrical Engineering(806/0)
Dept. of Electronics(808/0)
Faculty of Engineering(6401/0)
Dept. of Information and Computer Engineering(823/0)
Dept. of Managerial Engineering(836/0)
Dept. of Mechanical Engineering(835/0)
Dept. of Mechanical Systems Engineering(669/0)

Graduate Programs

Graduate School of Engineering(M 175/0, D 8/0)
Div. of Architecture(M 22/0)
Structural Analysis and Construction, Earthquake Engineering, Atelier Practice of Architectural Design, Urban Planning and Housing, Environmental Engineering
Div. of Civil Engineering(M 5/0, D 0/0)
Structural Engineering, Hydraulic Engineering, Earthwork Machinery, Water Quality Control, Construction Engineering

Div. of Information and Computer Engineering(M 21/0, D 2/0)
Foundations of Information Engineering, Computer Software, Information Processing, Computers and Communication.

Div. of Electrical Engineering and Electronics(M 27/0, D 2/0)
Electrical Machines, Electric Control Engineering, Telecommunication Systems, Electronic Circuits Solid State Physics, Electronic Devices

Div. of Managerial Engineering(M 16/0)
Managerial Software Systems, Production Software Systems, Human Factors and Systems, Software Systems and Engineering

Div. of Material Design Engineering(M 15/0, D 1/0)
Material Synthesis, Molecular Design Engineering, Physical Properties of Solid Surfaces and Interfaces, Functional Materials, Dielectric Materials, Composite Materials

Div. of Mechanical Engineering(M 36/0, D 2/0)
Materials Engineering, Advanced Study of Fluids Engineering, Advanced Study of Thermal Engineering and Heat Engines, Design Engineering, Special Research for Instrument and Control Engineering, Machining and Manufacturing Systems

Div. of System Design Engineering(M 15/0, D 1/0)
Creative Design of Engineering Systems, Measurement and Transmission Systems, Control Systems, Material Forming Process Technology, Energy Systems, Biological Systems Engineering.

One-Year Graduate Programs

Engineering Course

Major in Mechanical Engineering
Major in Electrical Engineering
Major in Managerial Engineering
Major in Civil Engineering
Major in Architecture
Major in Electronics
Major in Information and Computer Engineering

金沢医科大学
(Kanazawa Ika Daigaku)
Kanazawa Medical University

1-1 Daigaku-cho, Uchinada-machi, Kahoku-gun, Ishikawa 920-02
☎ 0762-86-2211 FAX 0762-86-2373

Founded 1972
Professors 60
Associate Professors 44
Assistant Professors(Tenured) 84
Assistant Professors(Non-tenured) 106
Research Assistants 244
Undergraduate Students/Foreign Students 663/1
Graduate Students/Foreign Students 66/4
Library 145, 939 volumes
Contact: Section of General Affairs

Educational philosophy We aim to educate doctors with ethics and humanity, to cultivate a mind of making a profound study of scientific knowledge and of developing medical technology, and to make a contribution to development of medical science in Japan and medical service in the community.

Foreign students Foreign students are needed to take the same entrance examination procedures as the Japanese students.

Environment Kanazawa is an antique city in Hokuriku having left a tradition of the Kaga clan since the 16 th c. 20 min. by bus from Kanazawa to Uchinada. The campus is located on Uchinada dunes, overlooking the Sea of Japan and Kahoku Lagoon, and viewing the Tateyama and Hakusan mountain ranges.

Facilities Medical Research Institute, Academy of Nursing, Anatomy Center, Computer Center, Gym, Student Restaurant, Hospital, Annex to the Hospital

Student activities Uchinada is a mecca for the lovers of outsports and outleisure. Here is the optimal natural circumstances for marine sports. Many skiing grounds and golf courses in the suburbs. 17 atheletic and 7 cultural clubs. Students can spend a fruitful campus life.

Services for foreign students Health Clinic, Housing Information, Exchange in the community

Undergraduate Programs

Faculty of Medicine(663/1)

Graduate Programs

Graduate School of Medical Science(D 66/4)

Div. of Physiology, Pathology, Social Medicine Internal Medicine, Surgery(D 66/4)
Anatomy, Physiology, Biology, Pharmacology, Pathology, Microbiology, Medical Zoology, Hygience, Public Health, Legal Medicine, Internal Medicine, Gerontology, Neuropsychiatry, Pediatrics, Dermatology, Radiology, Clinical Pathology, Surgery, Neuro Surgery, Orthopedic Surgery, Urology, Ophthalmology, Otolaryngology, Obstetrics and Gynecology, Anesthesiology, Pediatric Surgery, Plastic and Reconstructive Surgery, Oral Surgery

金沢女子大学
(Kanazawa Joshi Daigaku)
Kanazawa Women's University

10 Sue-machi, Kanazawa-shi, Ishikawa 920-13
☎ 0762-29-1181

Founded 1987

Undergraduate Programs

Faculty of Literature
Dept. of English & American Literature
Dept. of Japanese Literature

金城学院大学
(Kinjô Gakuin Daigaku)
Kinjo Gakuin University

2-1723 Omori, Moriyama-ku, Nagoya-shi, Aichi 463
☎ 052-798-0180 FAX 052-799-2087

Founded 1889
Professors 37
Associate Professors 16
Assistant Professors (Tenured) 3
Assistant Professors (Non-tenured) 223
Undergraduate Students/Foreign Students 1, 870/3
Graduate Students/Foreign Students 25/1
Library 236, 804 volumes
Contact: Admission Office

Educational philosophy With the Christian faith in the importance of the soul, the liberating power of knowledge, and the cosmopolitan spirit, we have sought to produce creative individuals who can critically appreciate the cultural heritage and objectively see their own cultures in an international context.
Foreign students We believe that foreign students can sufficiently absorb the heritage of Kinjo accumulated over the past 100 years, and can contribute to developing mutual understanding and friendly relationship.
Environment Located in Omori, a suburban area of Nagoya. The campus is a spacious hilly area, affectionately called Kinjo-Dai (Kinjo-Heights), of 270, 000 square meters with ponds and marshy ground. It is accessible by rail or by bus 30 minutes from the mid-town of Nagoya City.
Facilities Christian Center, University Library, Auditorium, Language Laboratory, Biology Laboratory, Gymnasium, Computer Room, Open Space Plaza, Refectory, Broadcasting Studio.
Student activities Kinjo Festival (Annual School Festival) featuring exhibitions, shows, lectures, concerts, etc. American Language and Culture Program, Bible Class, Christmas Candle Service, Handbell Choir, Table Tennis, Volleyball, Mountain Climbing and other Circle activities.
Academic programs for foreign students Supplementary Japanese language class with authorization of credits for foreign students. Advisory and tutoring system.
Services for foreign students Personal/Psychological Counseling, Part-time job information, Housing information, Cultural exchange

Undergraduate Programs

Faculty of Literature(1, 134/2)
Dept. of Japanese(367/0)
Dept. of English(378/1)
Dept. of Sociology(389/1)
Faculty of Home Economics(736/1)
Dept. of Home Economics(382/1)
Dept. of Child Development(354/0)

Graduate Programs

Graduate School of Literature(M 25/1)
Div. of Japanese Literature(M 8/0)
Japanese Literature, Japanese Linguistics, Classical Chinese Literature
Div. of English Literature(M 7/1)
English Literature, American Literature, English Linguistics
Div. of Sociology(M 10/0)
Clinical Sociology, Social Pathology, Regional Cultures, Comparative Culture, Sociology of the Self. the Family, the Group.

皇學館大學
(Kôgakkan Daigaku)
Kogakkan University

1704 Kodakujimoto-cho, Ise-shi, Mie 516
☎ 0596-22-0201 FAX 0596-27-1704

Founded 1882
Professors 30
Associate Professors 20
Assistant Professors (Tenured) 7
Assistant Professors (Non-tenured) 43
Research Assistants 3
Undergraduate Students/Foreign Students 1, 668/0
Graduate Students/Foreign Students 21/1
Library 156, 000 volumes
Contact: Instruction Section

Educational philosophy We aim at elucidating the ethical ideals of the nation or what might be called our native virtues through the study of Japanese classics, and thereby contributing to a more complete development of Japanese culture from a global standpoint.

Foreign students We welcome such students as are intended to have deep and precise understanding of the Japanese culture and tradition and are able to contribute to promoting mutual understanding and friendly relationship.

Environment Our university is located in Ise City with a population of about 100, 000 and within easy access to Osaka, Kyoto, and Nagoya. Ise City is the site of the Grand Shrine of Ise, the so-called " spiritual home " of the Japanese people, and boasts long and rich history.

Facilities University Library, Shinto Institute, Historiographical Institute, Museum of Shinto and Japanese Culture, Gymnasiums, Auditorium, Audiovisual Classroom

Student activities Study tour held every year by each department unit, school festival, freshman welcome party are main popular campus events. There are some uncommon extra curricular activities, peculiar to our university, such as court music playing and shinto ritual practicing.

Services for foreign students Nothing in particular, but housing information, part-time job information, and cultural exchange program are offered.

Undergraduate Programs

Faculty of Literature(1668/0)
Dept. of Education(502/0)
Dept. of Japanese History(461/0)
Dept. of Japanese Literature(446/0)
Dept. of Shinto(259/0)

Graduate Programs

Graduate School of Literature(M 17/1, D 4/0)
Div. of Shinto Studies(M 4/0)
Shinto Studies, Comparative Religion, the History of Religions
Div. of Japanese Literature(M 6/1, D 2/0)
Japanese Literature, Japanese Language, Chinese Classics
Div. of Japanese History(M 7/0, D 2/0)
Japanese History, Special Literature, the History of Foreign Countries Concerned

---

松本歯科大学
(Matsumoto Shika Daigaku)

Matsumoto Dental College

1780 Gohbara-Hirooka, Shiojiri-Shi, Nagano 399-07
☎ 0263-52-3100 FAX 0263-53-3285

Founded 1972

Professors 26
Associate Professors 16
Assistant Professors(Tenured) 32
Assistant Professors(Non-tenured) 92
Research Assistants 83
Undergraduate Students/Foreign Students 774/5
Library 106, 871 volumes
Contact: Office of Planning and Development Hot line ☎0263-54-3210

Educational philosophy The school was opened in 1972 by Yasushi Yagasaki, his goal was to provide the young dental student with a scholary atmosphere in which to foster the true meaning of higher education, as well as to promote democratic values and an international consciousness.This combination of ideals allows M.D.C. to offer a unique environment in which there is oppotunity for well-rounded intellectual, social and cultural development.

Foreign students We believe that foreign students can enjoy a rewarding experience in our school, and can contribute a great deal to promoting mutual understanding and the development of friendly relations.

Environment Approximately 10 km. south of Matsumoto City (pop. 199, 000) in Nagano Prefecture, the school is located in the center of Japan and is easily accessible from all major cities. Express train service from Tokyo is less than three hours, from Nagoya approximately two hours, and air service from Osaka is only one hour and fifteen minutes.

Facilities Hospital, Library, Seperate Lecture and Practical buildings, Gymnasium with a heated pool, Track and Field, Baseball field, Tennis field, Institute of dental science, Computer practical room, etc.

Student activities Popular campus events, school festival, freshmen off-campus orientation. There is a wide variety of extra curricular activities, tea ceremony, flower arrangement, choral groups, baseball, football, soccer, judo, kendo, mountain-climbling, skiing, etc.

Academic programs for foreign students There are no programs specifically designed for foreign students.

Services for foreign students Health clinic, personal/College housing, Housing information, etc.

Undergraduate Programs

Faculty of Dentistry(774/5)
Dept. of Dentistry(774/5)

松阪大学
(Matsusaka Daigaku)

Matsusaka University

1846 Kubo-cho, Matsusaka-shi, Mie 515
☎ 0598-29-1122 FAX 0598-29-1014

Founded 1982

Professors 25
Associate Professors 12
Assistant Professors(Tenured) 5
Assistant Professors(Non-tenured) 34
Undergraduate Students/Foreign Students 1608/1
Library 135, 000 volumes
Contact:Admission Office

Educational philosophy " Be a sanctuary of earnestness both for learning and sports, " the founding spirit of the Umemura Group of Educational Institutions, to which our university belongs, is also the goal it tries to achieve.
Foreign students We welcome those overseas students who show zeal and eagerness to study political science and economics and experience life in Japan as it is.
Environment Matsusaka is situated in the center of Mie Prefecture, in the center of the Main Island. The area is renowned not only for its abundance of historic sites and monuments but also for its natural beauty. The university is located on a wooded low hill in the southern part of the city.
Facilities Library, Computer Training Rooms, Gymnasium, Auditorium, Institute for Regional Studies
Student activities School festival is the biggest of the campus events. Students also enjoy freshmen welcome party, Christmas party, and a large variety of extra curricular activities.
Academic programs for foreign students We offer no programs of this kind.
Services for foreign students Personal/psychological counseling, housing information and part-time job information

Undergraduate Programs

Faculty of Political Science and Economics(1, 608/1)

名城大学
(Meijô Daigaku)
Meijo University

1-501, Siogamaguchi, Tenpaku-ku, Nagoya-Shi, Aichi 468
☎ 052-832-1151 FAX 052-833-9494

Founded 1926
Professors 144
Associate Profrssors 97
Assistant Professors(Tenured) 83
Assistant Professors(Non-tenured) 558
Research Assistants 43
Undergraduate Students/Foreign Students 10, 822/36
Graduate Students/Foreign Students 182/23
Library 565, 279 volumes
Contact:Office of Admission

Educational philosophy The founding spirit of Meijo University is to develop individual trustworthiness and impartiality, and encourages personal creativity needed for the future. This educational policy has been cultivated through a tradition of academic freedom since its institutional beginning.
Foreign students Meijo University has been a proponent of international exchange since the earlist stage of its history. We can give you advice about University or studying in Japan.
Environment Nagoya, where Meijo University is located, is the fourth largest city in Japan, with its population of more than two million. It is the biggest and most influential city in the central region of Japan and greatly contributes to Japan's economy and culture.
Facilities Analytical Center, Computer laboratory, Experimental farm, Gymnasium, Library, Athletic Ground, Medical Center, Pharmaceutical Information Center, Student hall
Student activities There are many kind of club or circle activities on campus, and the fact that more than half of the entire student body joins in these activities is exceptional.
Academic programs for foreign students Meijo University has established Japanese Studies cources taught in Japanese. These cources for forreign students are alternative to the second language requirement.
Services for foreign students Foreign student domitory, Vocational guidance, Field trip, Sports festival, Sightseeing tour, Home stay, Home visit, Cultural exchange program, Welcome party

Undergraduate Programs

Faculty of Law(2, 383/13)
Dept. of Law
Faculty of Commerce(2, 471/18)
Dept. of Commerce(1, 255/16)
Dept. of Economics(1, 246/2)
Faculty of Science and Technology(3, 494/1)
Dept. of Mathematics(407/0)
Dept. of Electrical and Electronic Engineering(647/0)
Dept. of Mechanical Engineering(598/1)
Dept. of Transport Machine Engineering(570/0)
Dept. of Civil Engineering(634/0)
Dept. of Architecture(638/0)
Faculty of Agriculture(1, 195/4)
Dept. of Agricultural Science(604/2)
Dept. of Agricultural Chemistry(591/2)
Faculty of Pharmacy(1, 279/0)
Dept. of Pharmaceutical Science(866/0)
Dept. of Pharmaceutical Technology(413/0)

Graduate Programs

Graduate School of Law(M 43/7, D 6/4)
Div. of Law
Constitutional Law, Administrative Law, International Law, Criminal Law, Civil Law, Commercial Law, Civil Procedure, Social Law, Japanese Legal History, Politics,

Private International Law
Graduate School of Commerce(M 34/10)
Div. of Commerce
Commerce, Business Administration, Accounting, Economics
Graduate School of Engineering(M 31/2)
Div. of Electrical and Electronic Engineering(M 12/0)
Electrical Engineering, Electric Material Physics, Electronics, Information Transmission
Div. of Mechanical Engineering(D 4/1)
Applied Mechanics, Fluid and Heart Engineering, Manufacturing System Engineering, Materials Design System Engineering
Div. of Civil Engineering(D 5/1)
Structural Engineering, Civil Engineering Planning, River and Horbour Engineering, Materials for Civil Engineering
Div. of Architecture(M 10/0)
Architectural History, Theory and Arts, City Plannig and Architectural, Environmental Designing, Building Structure, Building Materials and Works
Graduate School of Agriculture(M 15/0, D 2/0)
Div. of Agriculture
Crop Science, Horticultural Science, Genetics and Plant Breeding, Plant Protection, Soil Science and Plant Nutrition, Applied Microbiology and Biological Chemistry, Farm Management, Food Technology and Chemistry, Science and Technology of Animal Products
Graduate School of Pharmacy(M 39/0, D 1/0)
Div. of Pharmacy
Pharmaceutical Chemistry, Analytical Chemistry, Pharmacognosy, Pharmaceutics, Organic Manufacturing, Hygienic Chemistry, Pharmacology, Microbiology, Natural Products Chemistry, Physical Pharmacy, Clinical Biochemistry, Synthetic Medicinal Chemistry, Instrumental Analytical Chemistry, Biophysical Chemistry, Chemical Phrmacology, Pharmaceutical Technology

One-Year Graduate Programs

Clinical Pharmacy Course

長野大学
(Nagano Daigaku)
Nagano University

Shimonogo, Ueda-shi, Nagano 386-12
☎ 0268-38-2350 FAX 0268-38-5887

Founded 1966
Professors 26
Associate Professors 15
Assistant Professors(Tenured) 10
Assistant Professors(Non-tenured) 46
Undergraduate Students/Foreign Students 1, 344/0
Library 78, 000 volumes
Contact:Admission Office, ☎0268-38-2386

Educational philosophy We aim to provide the students with a solid foundatin to understand society as well as professional and technical education and to encourage them to develop to their highest potential by education based on small group seminars.
Environment Nagano University is lacated in the scenic south part of Ueda City (popu. 120, 000), surrounded by many ski resorts. Ueda is also famous for many Buddist temples and Shinto shrines established in Kamakura Era.
Facilities Nagano University Library, Computer Center, Regional Society Center, Language Laboratory, Audio Visual Room, Gymnasium
Student activites Pupular campus events include Nagano University Festival, Extramural orientation for freshmen at Sugadaira. Extra curricular activities include baseball, soccer, basket, tennis, volunteer work, choral groups, drama, rock music, etc.
Services for foreign students Personal counseling, part-time job information

Undergraduate Programs

Faculty. of Social Science(1, 344/0)
Dept. of Industrial Society(467/0)
Dept. of Industry-Information Science(367/0)
Dept. of Social Work(510/0)

名古屋造形芸術大学
(Nagoya Zôkei Geijutsu Daigaku)
Nagoya College of Creative Art

6004 Nenjozaka, Okusa, Komaki-shi, Aichi 485
☎ 0568-79-1111 FAX 0568-79-1070

Founded 1990
Professors 4
Associate Professors 3
Assistant Professors(Non-tenured) 11
Undergraduate Students/Foreign Students 125/0
Library 51, 000 volumes
Contact:Admission Office

Educational philosophy The college was founded in 1990 on the basis of the teachings of Buddhist Saint Shinran. We aim at teaching and studying art and design to develop aesthetic sensibility and creative power so students can face a new age with the apirit of quest for truth and beauty.
Foreign students We are willing to receive foreign students. We belive that those who come can both study high-level art and design, and enjoy Japan's traditional culture. There are some at the Juniour College in the same campus.
Environment Our campus is located in the central part of Japan. Nagoya International Airport is in Komaki

City, adjacent to which lies Nagoya City, with a population of 2.1 million. The region is rich in good stimuli to the students of art and design.
Facilities Gallery, Studios for seramic art, metalwork, wood art, etc., Atheliers for art course and design course, Library, Language laboratory
Student activites Popular campus events include sports festival, art festival, educational visits to museums and art museums. Club activites include tennis, baseball, soccor, skateboarding, misic, glass art, travelovers, etc.
Services for foreign students Health clinic, personal/psychological counseling, housing information, part-time job information

Undergraduate Programs

Faculty. of Creative Art(125/0)
- **Dept. of Arts**(50/0)
- **Dept. of Design**(75/0)

名古屋音楽大学
(Nagoya Ongaku Daigaku)

Nagoya College of Music

7-1 Inabaji-cho, Nakamura-ku, Nagoya-shi, Aichi 453
☎ 052-411-1111 FAX 052-411-1118

Founded 1965
Professors 22
Associate Professors 16
Assistant Professors(Tenured) 12
Assistant Professors(Non-tenured) 88
Undergraduate Students/Foreign Students 1, 042/0
Graduate Students/Foreign Students 27/1
Library 131, 110 volumes
Contact:Admissions Office

Educational philosophy Nagoya College of Music is part of Doho-Gakuen, whose fundamental educational philosophy is Buddhism and we value working hand in hand with our fellows. Students are encouraged to study not only art and science of music but also the importance of harmony for human life through music.
Foreign students Music is universal, in other words, international language. We welcome such students as are excellent in music. We believe we can exchange culture through music.
Environment The city of Nagoya, located in central Japan, is the third biggest city in Japan. Nagoya College of Music is the oldest music collge in this area. It takes less than 20 minutes to get to the campus from Nagoya Station. There are various kinds of transportations available to the heart of the city.
Facilities Collection of Music books, especially of the score books published both in Japan and in other countries will assist students to study the highest lebel of art of music.
Student activities Nagoya College of Music has a full orchestra and wind-orchestra which hold annual concerts at a local auditoriums in Nagoya city. The opera group also presents an opera every year at a theater. There are students'recitals at school and at theaters.

Undergraduate Programs

Faculty of Music(1, 042/0)
- **Dept. of Composition**(15/0)
- **Dept. of Instrumental Music**(525/0)
- **Dept. of Musical Education**(255/0)
- **Dept. of Vocal Music**(247/0)

Graduate Programs

Gaduate School of Music(M 27/1)

Div. of Composition(M 3/0)
Theory of Composition, A Seminar in Composition, Composition (Special Courses 1), Composition (Special Courses 2), A Seminar in Instrumental Music, Conducting Techniques, Musicology (Special Courses), Reading the Books on Music

Div. of Instrumental Music(M 13/1)
Performance Techniques for Piano, Performance Techniques for String Instruments, Performance Techniques for Wind Instruments, Study of Music Literature, A Seminar in Performance Techniques for Piano, Performance Techniques for Piano (Special Courses), Performance Techniques for String Instruments (Special Course), Performance Techniques for Wind Instruments (Special Courses), Piano Accompanying for Songs, Performance Techniques for Cambalo, Performance Techniques for Organ, Musicology (Special Courses), Reading the Books on Music

Div. of Music Education(M 2/0)
Orientation to Music Education, A Seminar in Music Education, Music Analysis, Study of Instrumental Music, Study of Songs as Teaching Materials, Creative Writing of Music, Conducting Techniques, Study of Religious Music, Musicology (Special Courses), Reading the Books on Music

Div. of Vocal Music(M 9/0)
Study of Vocal Music, Study of Song Literature, A Seminar in Part Songs, Performance Techniques for Vocal Music, A Seminar in Instrumental Music, Study of Religious Music, Musicology (Special Courses), Reading the Books on Music

---

名古屋経済大学
(Nagoya Keizai Daigaku)

Nagoya Economics University

61-1 Uchikubo, Inuyama-shi, Aichi 484
☎ 0568-67-0511

Founded 1979
Professors 39
Associate Professors 15
Assistant Professors(Tenured) 10
Assistant Professors(Non-tenured) 11
Research Assistants 2
Undergraduate Students/Foreign Students 1, 665/0
Library 165, 500 volumes
Contact:Admission Office

Edcational philosophy Nagoya Economics University, formerly Ichimura Gakuen University, was founded in 1979 by Ichimura Educational Institute in order to educate and, more importantly, to equip students with practical business abilities.
Environment The campus is located in Inuyama City 25 kilometers north of Nagoya. In its vicinity one of the most beautiful rivers in Japan, the Kiso River; the oldest existing castle in Japan, Inuyama Castle; and the famous museum-town, Meiji Mura which collects monuments and buildings of the Meiji period. Augmenting the traditional and cultural surroundings of the University is the natural beauty of the area. The campus, covering approximately 500, 000m², is situated on the top of a hill overlooking a wide stretch of pastoral hills and vales untouched by urban life.
Facilities Research Institute for Consumer Affairs

Undergraduate Programs

Faculty of Economics(1, 665/0)
Dept. of Bussiness Administration(814/0)
Dept. of Consumer Economics(851/0)

名古屋学院大学
(Nagoya Gakuin Daigaku)
Nagoya Gakuin University

1350 kamishinano-cho, Seto-shi, Aichi 480-12
☎ 0561-42-0350 FAX 0561-41-1709

Founded 1964
Professors 54
Associate Professors 28
Assistant Professors(Tenured) 14
Assistant Professors(Non-tenured) 61
Undergraduate Students/Foreign Students 3995/20
Library 260, 000 volumes
Contact:Admission Division ☎0561-42-0339

Educational philosophy Nagoya Gakuin University (NGU) was founded as a private coeducational four-year institution, based on Christian principles as reflected in its school motto: " Awe to God-Love to Man. " The most important functions of our university is to help students develop their potencial abilities, to stimulate their aspiration, and to nurture their ethical integrity.
Foreign students NGU maintains the special entrance examination for foreign students since 1989. The University's study-abroad programs provide exchange programs for students and faculties through educational collaboration with overseas universities.
Environment Seto City, with a population of 126, 000, has been a famous ceramics center for more than one thousand years. NGU is in a naturally clean and peaceful evironment. The campus still has all the advantages of being near one of Japan's largest cities, Nagoya. A short train ride away, Nagoya offers many cultural, historical, and entertainment interests.
Facilities The University library, with the collection of over 260, 000, and the Center for Information Processing offer academic and research support for students and faculties. The chapel is a 250-seat sanctuary. A new student dining hall starts its service from the spring of 1991.
Student activities At NGU a student has much to choose from with over 50 athletic, cultural, and social organizations available. Of particular interest to the foreign students is training in the martial arts, such as karate, judo, kendo, and shorinji-kenpo. The great enthusiasm for extracurricular activities can be seen during the NGU Festival.
Academic programs for foreign sudents Japanese language courses (5 levels) are offered at the Institute for Japanese Language and Culture. Tutors are selected from NGU students and assist foreign students.
Services for foreign students Many foreign students at NGU live in the International Seminar House, built on campus in 1989. Each dorm room is air-conditioned with a bathroom, large closets, and a small kitchen. Counseling and information on remunerative activities and homestay is available.

Undergraduate Programs

Faculty of Foreign Studies(448/0)
Dept. of Chinese(122/0)
Dept. of English(326/0)
Faculty of Ecnomics(3, 547/0)
Dept. of Commerce(1, 391/0)
Dept. of Ecnomics(2, 156/0)

名古屋芸術大学
(Nagoya Geijutsu Daigaku)
Nagoya University of the Arts

280 Kumanosho, Shikatsu-cho, Nishikasugai-gun, Aichi 481
☎ 0568-24-0315 FAX 0568-24-0317

Founded 1970
Professors 41
Associate Profrssors 24
Assistant Professors(Tenured) 18
Assistant Professors(Non-tenured) 127

Undergraduate Students/Foreign Students 1, 779/2
Library 52, 672 volumes
Contact:Admission Office

Educational philosophy Our Principal object is the cultivation of creative Students especially in the fields of both Music & Fine Arts so that they can contribute much to cultural betterment.
Foreign students We believe that foreign students can enjoy our university life. Those who are 18 years or older may apply, and must have recommendations issued from their own diplomatic establishments abroad.
Environment Nagoya University of the Arts was established in 1970. The school is located in a northern suburban area of Nagoya City which is in central Japan. The Faculty of Musicd locatated in the town of Sikatsu and the Faculty of Fine Arts Nishiharu.
Facilities Auditorium, Gymnasium, two Libraries, The Training Center for Foreign Language, and a lot of trainig rooms, etc.
Student activities Popular campus events includes school festival, freshmen welcome party. There is a wide variety of extra curricular activities such as soccer, folk song, tennis, skiing, motion picture, basket ball, drama etc.

Undergraduate Programs

Faculty of Fine Arts(937/2)
  Dept. of Design(457/1)
  Dept. of Japanese paintings(102/1)
  Dept. of Oil paintings(268/0)
  Dept. of Sculpture(110/0)
Faculty of Music(842/0)
  Dept. of Instumental music(374/0)
  Dept. of Music(338/0)
  Dept. of Vocal music(130/0)

名古屋商科大学
(Nagoya Shôka Daigaku)

Nagoya University of Commerce and Business Administration

4-4 Sagamine, Nisshin-cho, Aichi-gun, Aichi 470-01
☎ 05617-3-2111 FAX 05617-3-1202

Founded 1953
Professors 43
Associate Professors 16
Assistant Professors(Tenured) 21
Assistant Professors(Non-Tenured) 61
Undergraduate Students/Foreign Students 3, 539/36
Graduate Students/Foreign Students 12/5
Library 182, 275 volumes
Contact:Admission Office

Educational philosophy Our institutions do not aim to produce academic scholars. Upon graduation, many of our students enter the business world. Accordingly, a significant part of our curriculum has been pioneered to develop in our graduates an appropriate understanding, particularly through international studies, broad language training and travel programmes.
Foreign students We believe that foreign students can enjoy a rewarding experience at our school, and can significantly help to promote mutual understanding and the development of friendly international relationships.
Environment The University, stands on a beautifully landscaped and wooded 200 acre campus, located in the countryside 40 minutes east of the center of Nagoya. Nagoya is a city of 2 million people and ranks as one of Japan's leading industrial cities. It is the center of a thriving industrial and commercial community of 6. 5 million inhabitants and firms.
Facilities Information Centre, Language Centre, Computer Centre, Intelligent School Building, Local Area Network, Seminar Centre, Gymnasium, Sports Training Centre, Community Pavilion, Swimming Pool, Shirakawa Seminar House
Student activities Outside the classroom, a wide range of opportunities is available to the students. Over 30 sports clubs are established on campus, ranging from traditional Japanese sports such as karate, aikido, judo and kendo, to tennis, rugby, baseball and golf. There are nearly as many cultural societies, encompassing just as wide a variety of interests.
Academic programs for foreign students Japanese language class, Japanese conversation class
Service for foreign students Housing information, Part-time job information, Personal/psychological counselling, Health clinic

Undergraduate Programs

Faculty of Commerce(3, 539/36)
  Dept. of Business Administration(933/17)
  Dept. of Commerce(1, 042/3)
  Dept. of Decision Sciences and Management Information Systems(877/11)
  Dept. of International Economics(687/5)

Graduate Programs

Graduate School of Business(M 12/5)
  Div. of Decision Sciences and Management Information Systems
Commerce, Marketing, Finance, Management, Production Management, Finance Management, Case Study (Marketing, Finance Management, Production Management), Accounting, Managerial Accounting, Management Science, Management Statistics, Computer Science, Computer Programing, Simulation, Data Base Applications, Systems Analysis, System Integration, Data Communication and Net Work, Economics, International Economics, Mathematical Economics, etc.

名古屋外国語大学

(Nagoya Gaikokugo Daigaku)

Nagoya University of Foreign Studies

57 Takenoyama, Iwasaki, Nisshin-cho, Aichi-gun, Aichi 470-01
☎ 05617-4-1111 FAX 05617-4-1193

Founded 1988
Professors 23
Associate Professors 7
Assistant Professors(Tenured) 11
Assistant Professors(Non-tenured) 27
Research Assistants 4
Undergraduate Students/Foreign Students 780/0
Library 24, 467 volumes
Contact:Office of Admissions and Public Relations

Educational philosophy Our educational goal is to produce graduates with both superior linguistic ability and an international perspective, people who will play active role on the world stage. At the sametime, we have as an educational goal " the harmonization of communication through language."

Foreign students We recognize the need for improving cross-cultural communication and understanding throughout the world.

Environment Both Aichi Prefecture and the City of Nagoya have recently begun to place 'Internationalization' high on their list of priorities, and the surrounding district as a whole may be seen to possess a great potential in this sense.

Facilities Library, Language Laboratory

Student activities Campus Events: School Festival, English Recitation Contest, Chinese Recitation and Oratorical Contest.

Extra Curricular Activities: English Drama, E.S.S., Baseball, Tennis, Karate, Literary, Society and so on.

Undergraduate Programs

Faculty of Foreign Studies(780/0)
- **Dept. of British and American Studies**(416/0)
- **Dept. of French Studies**(182/0)
- **Dept. of Chinese Studies**(182/0)

名古屋女子大学

(Nagoya Joshi Daigaku)

Nagoya Women's University

3-40 Shioji-cho, Mizuho-ku, Nagoya-shi, Aichi 467
☎ 052-852-1111 FAX 052-852-7470

Founded 1915
Professors 33
Associate Professors 14
Assistant Professors(Tenured) 11
Assistant Professors(Non-tenured) 62
Research Assistants 17
Undergraduate Students/Foreign Students 1, 225/1
Library 145,159 volumes
Contact:Admissions Office

Educational philosophy Based on the fundamental principle of " kindness, " the university aims at teaching science and humanities in order to cultivate women 's intelligence and vocational abilities so that they can contribute greatly to the development of society.

Foreign students International students will be heartily welcomed, since the faculty have an open eye to the rest of the world. We hope that they will develop good friendships with the Japanese as well as studying their majors.

Environment Nagoya City, with an approximate population of 2, 150, 000, is located in the central part of Japan, halfway between Tokyo and Osaka, making it convenient for transportation. Though it is a metropolitan city, Nagoya has a good natural environment, and is the center of learning and culture in the district.

Facilities Two campuses, one in Shioji (Domestic Science, Junior College) and the other in Tempaku (Literature, Research Institute of Education with Attached Kindergarten). Sports ground in Toyota, and Seminar House " Oppara-Gakusha " in rural Oku-Mino.

Student activities The university has two semesters; the first begins in April, the last in October. Freshmen's orientation is held in April, a school festival in November, the graduation ceremony in March. There are 25 cultural clubs and 11 athletic clubs. These clubs are very active.

Academic programs for foreign students Although the university does not have a special program for international students, the teaching staff give valuable advice and tutorial instruction to individual international students.

Services for foreign students The student affairs office counsels international students in health needs, housing, par-time job information, host families, etc. The students have no worries about language barriers.

Graduate Programs

Faculty of Literature(580/1)
- **Dept. of Japanese Literature**(269/1)
- **Dept. of English Language and Literature**(150/0)
- **Dept. of Child Education**(161/0)

Faculty of Domestic Science(469/0)
- **Dept. of Domestic Science**(469/0)
  - **Course of Food Science**(295/0)
  - **Course of Nutritional Science**(174/0)

南山大学
(Nanzan Daigaku)
Nanzan University

18 Yamazato-cho, Showa-ku, Nagoya-shi, Aichi 466
☎ 052-832-3111 FAX 052-833-6985

Founded 1949
Professors 97
Associate Professors 75
Assistant Professors(Tenured) 31
Assistant Professors(Non-tenured) 261
Research Assistants 1
Undergraduate Students/Foreign Students 5, 384/14
Graduate Students/Foreign Students 96/4
Library 499, 639 volumes
Contact:Admission Office

Educational philosophy Our university has four characteristics: Christian Humanism, Academic Excellence, Internatinal Spirit, and Service to the Local Commuity. All are subsumed in our motto: " Hominis Dignitati (For Human Dignity), " which is a living challenge to instill both a respect for the truth and an understanding of the dignity of all men and women in the world.

Foreing students Nanzan University accepts over 150 foreign students each year. Most of them are in the year abroad program to study Japanese language. But about one-fourth are in degree programs or special study programs.

Environment Nanzan Univeristy is atanding on a hill in the southeast of the metropolitan Nagoya, and is overlooking the whole of the city. Because there are some other universities in our neighborhood, the streets around there are crowded with students. Our university is convenient to the bus stop and the subway station.

Facilities Anthropological Institute, Nanzan Institute for Religion & Culture, Institute for Social Ethics, Center for American Studies, Center for Latin-American Studies, Center for Australian Studies, Anthropological Museum, Center for Audio-Visual Education, Physical Education Center, Information Processing Center, Library.

Student activities Popular campus events include freshmen welcome festival, intercollegiate sports festival (vs. Sophia Univ.), and school festival. Many students enjoy extra curricular activities, including international friendship club, English interpretation, choral groups, orchestra, passion play, rakugo, football, ice hockey, rugby, archery, golf, kendo, cheerleaders, etc.

Academic programs for foreign students Course substitution system

Services for foreign students Housing information, homestay, guidance and counseling by advisors, guided independent studies, cultural educational field trips, part-time job informations

Undergraduate Programs

Faculty of Arts and Letters(1, 219/2)
Dept. of Theology(20/0)
Dept. of Philosophy(108/0)
Dept. of Anthropology(153/1)
Dept. of Education(153/0)
Faculty of Arts and Letters(1, 219/2)
Dept. of English Language & Literature(295/0)
Dept. of French Language & Literature(153/0)
Dept. of German Language & Literature(154/0)
Dept. of Japanese Language & Literature(183/1)
Faculty of Foreign Languages(1, 002/1)
Dept. of British & American Studies(656/0)
Dept. of Spanish Studies(243/0)
Dept. of Japanese(103/1)
Faculty of Economics(1, 049/2)
Dept. of Economics
Faculty of Business Administration(1, 132/9)
Dept. of Business Administration(729/8)
Dept. of Information Systems & Quantitative Sciences(403/1)
Faculty of Law(982/0)
Dept. of Law

Graduate Programs

Graduate School of Arts and Letters(M 29/0, D 14/0)
Div. of Theology(M 10/0, D 6/0)
Biblical Theology, Systematic Theology, Theology of Religions
Div. of Cultural Anthropology (Ethnology and Archaeology) (M 8/0, D 2/0)
Methods in Cultural Anthropology and Archaeology, Social Anthropology, Religious Anthropology, Archaeology, Fresistory.
Div. of English Literature & Linguistics(M 5/0, D 4/0)
English Literature Seminar, English Linguistics Seminar, Special Lecture: Enlish Literature, Special Lecture: English Linguistics, Guided Research in Writers and Literary Works, Seminar in Latin/Greek
Div. of French Literature & Linguistics(M 4/0, D 2/0)
French literature, French linguistics, French thought
Div. of German Literature & Linguistics(M 2/0)
German Literature, German Linguistics, German Culture
Graduate School of Economics(M 3/2, D 2/0)
Div. of Economics
Economic Theory, History of Economics, Economic Philosophy, Econometrics, Economic Mathematics, Economic History, Economic Policy, International Economics, Public Finance, Money & Banking, Statistics, Social Policy
Graduate School of Business Administration (M 22/1, D 3/0)
Div. of Business Administration
Master's program courses

Management, Business History, Business Research Methodology, Organization and Management, Personnel Administration, Organizational Psychology, Business Finance, Investment, International Finance, Marketing, International Management, Financial Accounting, Funds Accounting, International Accounting, Comparative Accounting, Operations Research, Business Statistics, Business Mathematics, Seminar
Doctoral program courses
Management Research, Organization Research, Finance Research, Accounting Research, Organizational Research, Statistics Research, Seminar
Graduate School of Law(M 23/1)
Div. of Law
Basic Civil Law, Basic Public Law

日本福祉大学
(Nihon Fukushi Daigaku)
Nihon Fukushi University

Okuda, Mihama-cho, Chita-gum, Aichi 470-32
☎ 0569-87-2211 FAX 0569-87-1609

Founded 1957
Professors 51
Associate Professors 25
Assistant Professors(Tenured) 3
Assistant Professors(Non-tenured) 247
Undergraduate Students/Foreign Students 4, 250/3
Graduate Students/Foreign Students 16/1
Library 357, 806 volumes
Contact:Adimissoion Office

Educational philosophy Our University has been endeavoring to foster an education which is modern and scientific, supported by the social welfare faculty's humanistic spirit of respect for people. At the same time, we are responsive to the changing times and to answering the needs of people.
Foreign students From all over the world we are ready to receive whomever wishes to learn. We hope that they will enjoy various experiences and help develop mutual understanding and friendly relationships.
Environment The town of Mihama, with a population of 22, 472 is located in the South Chita Prefectual Nature Park, 50 km south of Nagoya City. One could say that the University is in a location where one can have a close contact with both city culture and natural landscape.
Facilities We have a library, the Institute of Chita Regional Development, the Psychological Research Center, the International Center, the Information Science Center, the Institute of Social Science, a Gymnasium and an Auditorium.
Student activeties Popullarcampus events include Homecoming, the school festival, and freshmen welcome party. There is a wide variety of extra curricular activities, including volunteer work, research groups, wind surfing, sailing, choral group, student news paper, etc.
Academic programs for foreign students We offer Japanesé language, Japanese history and culture, Japanese society and economics, Japanese ecology and geography. These classes are taken for credits of graduation.
Services for foreign students The International Center is in charge of the foreign students. They give Housing information, scholarship information, cultural exchange programs, personal counseling, etc.

Undergraduate Programs

Faculty of Social Welfare(2, 423/2)
Dept. of Social Welfare
Faculty of Economics(1, 827/1)
Dept. of Economics

Graduate Programs

Graduate School of Social Welfare(M 16/0)
Div. of Social Welfare(M 16/0)

新潟薬科大学
(Niigata Yakka Daigaku)
Niigata College of Pharmacy

5-13-2 Kamishin'ei-cho, Niigata-shi, Niigata 950-21
☎ 025-269-3170 FAX 025-260-1415

Founded 1977
Professors 16
Associate Professors 11
Assistant Professors(Tenured) 9
Assistant Professors(Non-tenured) 17
Research Assistants 18
Undergraduate Students/Foreign students 514/0
Libraty 27, 823 volumes
Contact:Administrative Bureau

Educational philsophy We aim at conducting research and educational activities to develop in all the students the capacity for a pharmaceutical career and to provide opportunities for as many students as possible to prepare themselves for careers in research and teaching in all fields of pharmaceutical sciences.
Foreign students We believe that foreign students, if they can speak Japanese, can enjoy a rewarding experience in our school and contribute to promoting mutural understanding and friendly relationship.
Environment The city of Niigata, with a population of 480, 000, is located on the coast of the Japan Sea and plays an important role in the various fields of industry as one of the key cities of Japan. The city is favored by scenic beauty all the year round and makes for an enjoyable learning environment.

Facilities Chemical and biomedical library, Pharmaceutical botanical garden, Radio-isotope laboratory, Genetic, engineering laboratory, Computer center, Gymnasium, Auditorium
Student activities Popular campus events include freshmen welcome party, college festival. There is a wide variety of extra-curricular activities, including choral group, light music, cinema, pharmacognosy, tea ceremony, astronomy, basketball, volleyball, badminton, tennis, archery, rugby, soccer, golf, boating, etc.
Academic programs for foreign students We are considering to set up these systems in the near future.
Services for foreign students Housing information, Part-time job information, Vocational guidance

Undergraduate Programs

Faculty of Pharmaceutical Sciences(514/0)
Dept. of Biopharmaceutical Sciences(206/0)
Dept. of Pharmaceutical Sciences(308/0)

新潟産業大学
(Niigata Sangyô Daigaku)

Niigata Sangyo University

4730 Karuigawa, Kashiwazaki-shi, Niigata 945
☎ 0257-24-6655 FAX 0257-22-1300

Founded 1988
Professors 16
Associate Professors 8
Assistant Professors(Tenured) 8
Assistant Professors(Non-tenured) 25
Undergraduate Students/Foreign Students 885/6
Library 56, 000 volumes
Contact:Admissions Office ☎ 0257-24-8436

Educational philosophy We aim at teaching and studying up-to-date and basic economics as well as liberal arts, and encourage students to become internationally-oriented men/women with a sufficient knowledge of economics and to contribute to social improvement and development.
Foreign students We believe foreign students can not only learn a lot about modern economics and Japanese culture, but also help to promote mutual understanding and to foster friendly relations.
Environment The city of Kashiwazaki, with a population of 86, 000, is located in the middle of Niigata Prefecture on the Sea of Japan, two hours from Tokyo by train. The area is full of greenery all the year, and you can enjoy swimming in summer and skiing in winter.
Facilities Library, Computer room, Gymnasium, Auditorium
Student activities Campus events: school festival, freshman welcome party
Extra-curricular activities: table tennis, basketball, volleyball, tennis, soccer, baseball, karate, kendo, Japanese archery, aikido, etc.
Services for foreign students Health clinic, personal counseling, housing information, part-time information, vocational guidance

Undergraduate Programs

Faculty of Economics(885/6)
Dept. of Economics

西東京科学大学
(Nishi Tokyo Kagaku Daigaku)

The Nishi-Tokyo University

2525 Yatsuzawa, Uenohara-machi, Kitatsuru-gun, Yamanashi 409-01
☎ 0554-63-4411 FAX 0554-63-4430

Founded 1989
Professors 35
Associate Professors 20
Assistant Professors(Tenured) 10
Assistant Professors(Non-tenured) 28
Research Assistants 8
Undergraduate Students/Foreign Students 519/0
Library 30, 321 volumes
Contact:Admissions Office

Educational philosophy We endeavour to develop in our students a raised consciousness of global issues in order to help prepare them to be aware and active individuals in our modern, scientific and technological society, not only in Japan but also world-wide.
Foreign students We believe foreign students will be provided with a rewarding experience at our university and that they, in turn, will contribute to promoting cross-cultural awareness and understanding, thereby enriching the life of our university community.
Environment The town of Uenohara, with a population of about 25, 000, is situated in the same scenic prefecture as Mt. Fuji, just over the border from Tokyo. Located in a beautiful rural area, surrounded by wonderful mountains and spectacular lakes, it is still within easy reach of Tokyo, being only about one hour from the centre.
Facilities Well-equipped library, computer center, electronics reserch center, chemical analysis center, sports training center, swimming pool, gymnasium.
Student activities Popular campus events include our freshman welcome party and university festival. There is a wide variety of extra-curricular activities such as voluntary work, choral groups, karate club, baseball, football, etc.

Undergraduate Programs

Faculty of Science and Engineering(519/0)
  Dept. of Bioscience(124/0)
  Dept. of Electronics and Infomation Science (138/0)
  Dept. of Engineering of Materials(137/0)
  Dept. of Management Engineering(120/0)

椙山女学園大学

(Sugiyama Jogakuen Daigaku)

Sugiyama Jogakuen University

17-3 Hoshigaoka-motomachi, Chikusa-ku, Nagoya-shi, Aichi 464
☎ 052-781-1186 FAX 052-781-4466

Founded 1905
Professors 51
Associate Professors 28
Assistant Professors(Tenured) 16
Assistant Professors(Non-tenured) 161
Research Assistants 14
Undergraduate Students/Foreign Students 3, 287/1
Graduate Students/Foreign Students 8/0
Library volumes 200, 064
Contact:Admissions Office, ☎ext.530, 538

Educational philosophy We aim at providing young women with both higher education and practical training to develop their intellectual, moral and applied abilities that they may contribute much to cultural and social betterment in Japan and abroad.
Environment The main Sugiyama compus is conveniently located in the eastern part of the city of Nagoya, which is situated between Tokyo and Osaka, and has a population of over 2 million. This area is rich in cultural history, especially that of the 16th and 17th century.
Facilities Audio-visual center, Auditorium, Campus Center, Computer Center, Counseling Center, Human Studies Center, Gymnasium, Student Lounge, Student Cafeteria, Travel Agency, Book Store, etc.
Student activities Popular compus events include school festival, freshman orientation trip, English festival, Study abroad, etc. There is also a wide variety of extra curricular activities, including choral group, folk song band, drama club, ESS, tea ceremony, noh performance, etc.

Undergraduate Programs

Faculty of Home Economics(1, 331/0)
  Dept. of Clothing and Textile(696/0)
  Dept. of Food and Nutrition(635/0)
Faculty of Literature(970/0)
  Dept. of English(490/0)
  Dept. of Japanese(480/0)
Faculty of Human Sciences(986/1)
  Departmetn of Human Sciences

Graduate Programs

Graduate School of Home Economics(M 8/0)
  Div. of Clothing and Textile(M 0/0)
  Div. of Food and Nutrition(M 8/0)

高岡法科大学

(Takaoka Hôka Daigaku)

Takaoka College of Law

307-3 Toidekokudai, Takaoka-shi, Toyama 939-11
☎ 0766-63-3388 FAX 0766-63-6410

Founded 1989

Undergraduate Programs

Faculty of Law
  Dept. of Law

東海女子大学

(Tôkai Joshi Daigaku)

Tokai Women's College

Kirino-cho, Naka, Kakamigahara-shi, Gifu 504
☎ 0583-89-2200 FAX 0583-89-2205

Founded 1981

Undergraduate Programs

Faculty of Liberal Arts
  Dept. of British and American Studies
  Dept. of Human Relations

常葉学園浜松大学

(Tokoha-Gakuen Hamamatsu Daigaku)

Tokoha-Gakuen Hamamatsu University

1, 230 Miyakoda-cho, Hamamatsu-shi, Shizuoka 431-21
☎ 0534-28-3511 FAX 0534-28-2900

Founded 1988
Professors 20
Associate Professors 11

Assistant Professors(Tenured) 8
Assistant Professors(Non-tenured) 23
Research Assistants 3
Undergraduate Students/Foreign Students 783/0
Library 29, 000 volumes
Contact:Adimission Office

Educational philosophy We aim at contributing to industries and the development of cultures in the community as well as fostering talented students able to cope with highly information-oriented society toward 21st century.
Foreign students We believe that foreign students can enjoy a modern and rural experience.
Environment Hamamatsu city, with a population of 520, 000, is situated in the central part of Japan, about 250 kilometer of Tokyo and within 100 kilometer of a number of the national most famous recreation areas.
Facilities Computer center, University library, University Center
Student activities Popular campus events includes, freshman camp for orientation, school festival. There is a wide variety of extra curricular activities, including base-ball, soccer, tennis, light music, camera, yachting, personal computer club, women's base-ball etc.

Undergraduate Programs

Faculty of Administration and Informatics(783/0)
Dept. of Administration and Informatics

常葉学園大学
(Tokoha Gakuen Daigaku)

Tokoha Gakuen University

1000 Sena, Shizuoka-shi, Shizuoka 420
☎ 0542-63-1125

Founded 1980

Undergraduate Programs

Faculty of Education
Dept. of Elementary Education
Faculty of Foreign Studies
Dept. of English
Dept. of Spanish

富山国際大学
(Toyama Kokusai Daigaku)

Toyama University of International Studies

65-1 Higashikuromaki, Ohyama-cho, Kaminiikawa-gun, Toyama 930-12
☎ 0764-83-8000 FAX 0764-83-8008

Founded 1990
Professors 11
Associate Professors 8
Assistant Professors(Tenured) 13
Assistant Professors(Non-tenured) 6
Undergraduate Students/Foreign Students 296/0
Library 31, 000 volumes
Contact:Instruction Section

Educational philosophy " Internationalization " is a key-note of the philosophy of the University education. The two divisions of the University: " international culture studies " and " social studies " are based on that key-note. The students educated theirin are expected to contribute something toward a realization of global village.
Foreign students Foreign students are greatly welcome to the University; they can learn Japanese culture and society through the course on the campus while contributing to cultural interchange with the students and outside comunities.
Environment The University is situated in one of the woody gently rolling hills spread out at the foot of the Northern Japan Alps; it has seven building scattered independently of one another on a specious campus; it has an easy access to Toyama air port, Toyama highway interchange, central Toyama city, Toyama JR station.
Facilities Administration offices, faculty members' offices, library, computer center, language laboratory, auditorium with audio-visual facilities, gymnasium are all housed in seven independent buildings.
Student activites The University facilities mentioned above and its natural surroundings facilitate the activities of the students on and out of the campus all though the year. Main campus events are: university festival, freshmen welcome party, sports festival; club activities are: chorus, tennis, volleyball, baseball, golf.
Academic programs for foreign students Academic programs for foreing students: Japanese language, culture, and geography courses are offered, as a substitute for other course required for Japanese students. Tutorial guidance by Japanese language instructors can be provided.
Services for foreign students Services for foreign students such as health clinic, personal counselling, housing information, part-time job information, home hospitalities, cultural exchanges information are availa-

ble in the University administration building.

Undergraduate Programs

Faculty of Humanities(296/0)
Dept. of Intercultural Studies(142/0)
Dept. of Sociology(154/0)

豊田工業大学
(Toyota Kôgyô Daigaku)
Toyota Technological Institute

2–12 Hisakata, Tempaku–ku, Nagoya–shi, Aichi 468
☎ 052–802–1111

Founded 1981

Undergraduate Programs

Faculty of Engineering
Dept. of Information and Control Engineering
Dept. of Mechanical Systems Engineering

Graduate Programs

Graduate School of Engineering
Div. of Basic Production Engineering

山梨学院大学
(Yamanashi Gakuin Daigaku)
Yamanashi Gakuin University

2–4–5 Sakaori, Kofu–shi, Yamanashi 400
☎ 0552–33–1111 FAX 0552–26–6392

Founded 1946
Professors 45
Associate Professors 24
Assistant Professors(Tenured) 21
Assistant Professors(Non–tenured) 44
Research Assistants 4
Undergraduate Students/Foreign Students 2, 533/10
Library 200, 000 volumes
Contact:Public Relations Office ☎ 0552–32–7499

Educational philosophy We aim at educating students to become globally oriented persons equipped with flexible sensibility, intelligence and creativity. We expect they can deal with and lead this world of rapid techonogical innovation, cultural encounters and exchanges, and politically, economically reshuffiling situations through their deep considerate eyes.
Foreign students We belive it is increasingly indispensable to promote a person–to–person direct communication among peoples of different cultural backgrounds. This deepens real mutual understandings and widens the scope of the worldviews.
Environment The campus is located in Kofu Basin, Surrounded by Mt. Fuji and the Japan Alps, but only 100 Kilomaters away (1 hour and half by train) from Tokyo. Kofu, population of 200, 000, is a cozy city with a history, which is now a center of high–tech industries as well.
Facilities Library, Institute of Social Science, Research Center for Administration Systems, Gymnasium, Auditorium, Language laboratory, Audiovisual rooms, 70 computer terminals, Media Room, 12 TV–Video–set rooms, etc.
Student activites The main campus event is Jutokusai (University Festival). There is a wide variety of extra curricular activities such as wrestling, rugby, skating, skiing, soccer, American football, track–and–field (distancerace, etc), drama, computer, archaeology, photography, etc.
Academic programs for foreign students Members of Committee for International Exchanges, consisting of 8 professors are available upon occasion.
Services for foreign students Health clinic, Collge housing, Vacatinal guidance. Members of Committee for International Exchanges are, as occasion demands, available for personal, psychological, cultural counselings.

Undergraduate Programs

Faculty of Commercial Science(2, 554/10)
Dept. of Commercial Science(840/7)
Dept. of Management Information(499/0)

Faculty of Law(1, 215/3)
Dept. of Administration
Dept. of Law

四日市大学
(Yokkaichi Daigaku)
Yokkaichi University

1200 Kayou–cho, Yokkaichi–shi, Mie 512
☎ 0593–65–6588 FAX 0593–65–6630

Founded 1988
Professors 22
Associate Profrssors 9
Assistant Professors(Tenured) 15
Assistant Professors(Non–tenured) 33
Research Assistants 2
Undergraduate Students/Foreign Students 1204/3
Library 30, 058 volumes
Contact:Admissions Office

Educational philosophy Individually, to help students acquire a wide awareness and a rich sense of humanity. Professionally, to produce granduates skilled in the arts of management and equipped to solve economic problems from an international perspective.

Foreign students Greater than usual importance placed on internationalism in education. Exchange agreements with universities in California, Philadelphia and Tianjin, China. Student exchanges actively promoted. A positive open doors policy towards serious applicants from overseas.

Environment Yokkaichi (pop. 270, 000) is a medium-sized industrial center and an important commercial port. Situated at the edge of the Nagoya conurbation, it forms part of the Central Japan economic region. The university is somewhat inland from tee city center, in a well forested hill area overlooking Ise Bay.

Facilities 126, 000m^2 campus, of which 9, 300m^2 occupied by buildings. Library, computer center, audio-visual lecture room, language lab, seminar rooms. Every effort made to facilitate teaching, study and research. Gymnasium planned for the very near future.

Student activities Well developed club activities. On the cultural side, 16 registered clubs from tea ceremony to international exchanges. Also, clubs connected with local traditional skills: pottery and Ise paper-cutting. For sports, 22 clubs, covering a huge variety of activities. The campus festival, 4 or 5 days each November, is a chance for meeting and socialising amid ixhibitions, concerts, bazaals and other events.

Academic programs for foreign students An elementary course in Japanese language and affairs specially for foreign students.

Services for foreign students Experienced and approachable counselors are assigned, so that problems can be about without anxiety. Lodging facilities specially for Yokkaichi University student just off campus, where the university can arrange inexpensive accomodation. Part-time job information displayed on notice board. A jobs info magazine is taken.

Undergraduate Programs

Faculty of Economics(1, 204/3)
  Dept. of Economiocs(633/1)
  Dept. of Management(571/2)

KINKI

KINKI REGION CLIMATE

- Northern District (Japan Sea side)
  Winters generally cloudy or snowy.
- Western and Inland Districts
  Light rain year-round, with broad summer-winter temperature difference.
- Southern District (Pacific Ocean side)
  Summers warm and rainy, while winters are mild.

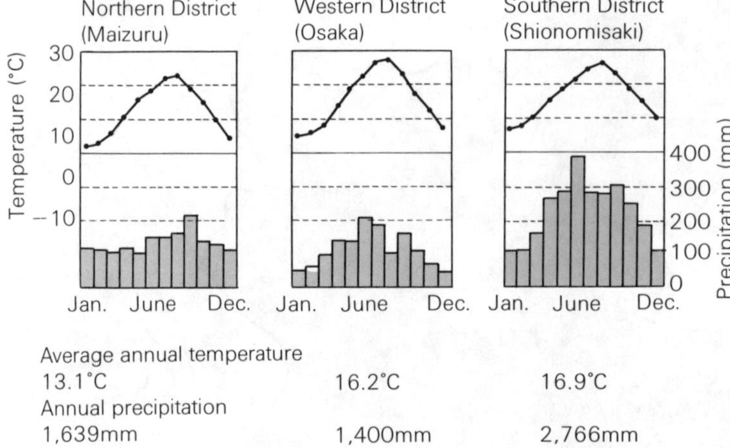

National Universities

兵庫教育大学
(Hyôgo Kyôiku Daigaku)

Hyogo University of Teacher Education

942-1 Shimokume, Yashiro-cho, Kato-gun, Hyogo 673-14
☎ 0795-44-1101 FAX 0795-44-1147

Founded 1978
Professors 79
Associate Professors 63
Assistant Professors(Tenured) 11
Assistant Professors(Non-tenured) 88
Research Assistants 21
Undergraduate Students/Foreign Students 854/5
Graduate Students/Foreign Students 521/8
Library 170, 415 volumes
Contact: Science and International Exchange Affairs official

Educational philosophy Following the amendment of the National School Establishment Law, Hyogo University of Teacher Education was founded in October 1978 as the first university devoted mainly to in-service teacher education, with an equal emphasis on theory and practice.
Foreign students We believe that foreign students can enjoy a rewarding experience in our school, and can contribute a great deal to promoting mutual understanding and the development of friendly relations.
Environment Our university is fortunate to be situated in a most desirable environment for academic research and study, in an area of great scenic beauty surrounded by green hills and woods, yet reasonably close to large international cities like Osaka and Kobe. There are two campuses, about 5km apart.
Facilities University Library, Gymnasium, Auditorium Center for School Education, Research Center for Practical Education, Research and Training, Demonstration and Research Center for The Handicapped, Data Processing Center
Student activities School Festival, Freshmen welcome party, A wide variety of extracurricular activities; news paper, drama, baseball, soccer, etc.
Academic programs for foreign students Japanese language class, Japanese educational affairs class, Japanese affairs class Tutoring system
Services for foreign students Health clinic, Personal/Psychological counselling, Students dormitory (For only regular students), Cultural exchange program, Home Visit

Undergraduate Programs

Faculty of School Education(854/5)

Graduate Programs

Graduate School of Education(M 521/8)
Div. of School Education(M 156/0)
Foundations of Education, Educational Administration, Curriculum and Instruction, Counseling and Guidance
Div. of Early Childhood Education(M 18/2)
Early Childhood Education
Div. of Education for the Handicapped(M 49/0)
Educaiton for the Handicapped
Div. of School Subject Education(M 298/6)
Language Studies, Social Sciences, Natural Sciences, Fine Arts and Music, Practical Life Studies

神戸大学
(Kôbe Daigaku)

Kobe University

1-1 Rokkodai-cho, Nada-ku, Kobe-shi, Hyogo 657
☎ 078-881-1212 FAX 078-861-6718

Founded 1902
Professors 383
Associate Professors 300
Assistant Professors(Tenured) 112
Assistant Professors(Non-tenured) 550
Research Assistants 352
Undergraduate Students/Foreign Students 11, 414/42
Graduate Students/Foreign Students 1, 615/252
Library 2, 386, 255 volumes
Contuct: International Affairs Office, General Affairs Division

Educational philosophy The main objectives of the University are to conduct research and to educate students so that they may have theoretical and practical understanding of the true meanig of education.
Foreign students Foreign students in Kobe University have many rewarding experiences, enabling the development of their full potential and contributing substantially to the promotion of mutual understanding.
Environment Kobe City which has prospered and developed mainly through foreign trade, with a population of 1.5 million, is located in the Kansai area, about 550km west of Tokyo. The city extends east and west, facing the seto Inland Sea to the south and Mount Rokko to the north.
Facilities Research Institute of Economics and Business Administration, International Center for Medical Resarch, Information Processing Center, Health Service Center, Libraries, many other centers and establishments.
Student activities Popular campus event include the university festival, and the year end party. There is a wide variety of extra-curricular activities, including for groups choral performances, drama, movies, the tea ceremony, baseball, soccer, American football, volleyball, tennis, etc.

Academic programs for foreign students Supplemental Japanese language classes, Tutoring system, Lectures on Japanese Culture, One day excursion tour, Ski tour, Freshman orientation, Year end party, Farewell party, etc.

Services for foreign students Health clinic, Personal/Psychological counseling, University dormitory, Housing information, Part-time job information, Homestays, Home visits, Cultural exchange program.

Undergraduate Programs

Faculty of Agriculture(756/1)
- **Dept. of Agriculture and Horticulture**(199/0)
- **Dept. of Agricultural Chemistry**(206/0)
- **Dept. of Agricultural Engineering**(128/1)
- **Dept. of Plant Protection**(99/0)
- **Dept. of Zootechnical Science**(124/0)

Faculty of Business Administration(1553/13)
- **Dept. of Accounting**(148/0)
- **Dept. of Business Administration**(286/3)
- **Dept. of Commercial Sceince**(224/3)

Faculty of Economics(1, 547/5)
- **Dept. of Economics**(1, 547/5)

Faculty of Education(1, 714/2)
- **Dept. of Earth Childhood Education**(100/0)
- **Dept. of Education for the Handicapped**(66/0)
- **Dept. of Education Hyginen**(31/0)
- **Dept. of Education Psychology**(38/0)
- **Dept. of Elementary School Education**(969/0)
- **Dept. of English Language and Literature**(47/0)
- **Dept. of Formative Arts**(48/2)
- **Dept. of Home Economics**(39/0)
- **Dept. of Japanese Language and Literature**(47/0)
- **Dept. of Mathematics**(47/0)
- **Dept. of Musical Arts**(47/0)
- **Dept. of Pedagogy**(49/0)
- **Dept. of Physical Education**(54/0)
- **Dept. of Science**(56/0)
- **Dept. of Social Studies**(48/0)
- **Dept. of Teaching Education**(28/0)

Faculty of Engineering(2, 639/15)
- **Dept. of Architecture**(257/0)
- **Dept. of Chemical Engineering**(213/2)
- **Dept. of Civil Engineering**(312/1)
- **Dept. of Electrical Engineering**(220/2)
- **Dept. of Electronic Engineering**(220/4)
- **Dept. of Environmental Planning**(209/0)
- **Dept. of Industrial Chemistry**(212/0)
- **Dept. of Instrumentation Engineering**(237/1)
- **Dept. of Mechanical Engineering**(325/4)
- **Dept. of Production Engineering**(214/0)
- **Dept. of System Engineering**(220/1)

Faculty of Law(1, 380/4)
- **Dept. of Law**(1, 380/4)

Faculty of Letters(515/0)
- **Dept. of History**(43/0)
- **Dept. of Literature**(128/0)
- **Dept. of Philosophy**(98/0)

Faculty of Medicine(692/0)
- **Dept. of Medicine**(692/0)

Faculty of Science(618/1)
- **Dept. of Biology**(66/0)
- **Dept. of Chemistry**(92/0)
- **Dept. of Earth Sciences**(109/0)
- **Dept. of Mathematics**(98/0)
- **Dept. of Physics**(98/1)

Graduate Programs

Graduate School of Agriculture(M 113/7)

Div. of Agriculture and Horticulture(M 30/2)

Crop Science, Plant Breeding, Tropical Economic Botany, Pomology, Floriculture and Olericulture, Preservation Technology, Agricultural Economics, Farm Management

Div. of Plant Protection(M 19/2)

Plant Pathology, Entomology, Genetics, Agricultural Chemicals

Div. of Agricultural Engineering(M 8/2)

Water Use Engineering, Land Use Engineering, Agricultural Power, Farm Equipments and Machinery, Agricultural Processing Machinery

Div. of Agricultural Chemistry(M 35/1)

Soil Science, Plant Nutrition, Biochemistry, Food and Nutritional Chemistry, Technology of Agricultural Products, Fermentation Technology

Div. of Zootechnical Science(M 21/0)

Animal Breeding, Animal Reproduction, Animal Feeding, Chemistry and Technology of Animal, Products, Animal Management, Animal Hygiene

Graduate School of Business Administration(M 59/8, D 34/16)

Div. of Business Administration(M 27/4, D 20/11)

Business Administration, Labor Management, Science of Business Management, Business Finance, Business Administration of Industry, Public Utility Management, Business Statistics, Business Mathematics, Management Information System

Div. of Commercial Science(M 26/2, D 7/3)

Marketing, Distribution System, Market Management, Securities Market, Securities, Foreign Trade, Financial Trade, Financial Institution, Transportation, International Transportation, Insurance

Div. of Accounting(M 6/2, D 7/2)

Bookkeeping, Principles of Accounting, Auditing, Cost Accounting, Management Accounting, Tax Accounting, International Accounting

Graduate School of Economics(M 24/9, D 43/15)

Div. of Economics and Economic Policy(M 40/17, D 16/7)

Theoretical Economics, National Economics, Social Economics, Mathematical Econimics, History of Economic Doctorines, Money and Banking, Principles of Economic Policy, Industrial Policy, Agricultural Policy, Social Policy, Public Finance, Economic History(Generals), Economic History(Special), Statistics, Economic Statistics, Econometrics, Public Economics, Economics of Modern Technology

Div. of International Economics(M 8/17, D 19/8)
International Economics, Foreign Trade Policy, International Finance, Economic Geography, Japanese Economy, Economic Affairs in Foreign Countries(General), Economic Affairs in Foreign Countries(Particulars), Comparative Economic Study

Graduate School of Education(M 139/19)

Div. of School Education(M 29/6)
Study of Human Development, Education Process and Method Education Planning

Div. of Japanese Language Education(M 13/2)
Method of Teaching in Education of Japanese, Japanese Philology and Literature

Div. of English Language Education(M 9/1)
Method of Teaching English, English Philology and Literature, British and American

Div. of Social Studies Education(M 12/2)
Method of Teaching Social Studies, Social Studies

Div. of Mathematics Education(M 11/1)
Method of Teaching Mathematics, Mathematics

Div. of Science Education(M 12/1)
Method of Teaching Science, Science

Div. of Technology Education(M 9/1)
Method of Teaching Technical Education, Technology

Div. of Music Education(M 15/0)
Education of Music, Music

Div. of Art Education(M 11/3)
Method of Teaching Fine Arts, Art

Div. of Health and Physical Education(M 12/2)
Method of Teaching Health and Physical Education, Science of Health and Physical Education, Health Care Education

Div. of Home Making Education(M 6/0)
Method of Teaching Home Economics, Home Economics

Graduate School of Engineering(M 436/39)

Div. of Architecture(M 34/3)
Applied Mechanics and Steel Structures, Building Materials and Construction, Structural Dynamics and Earthquake Resistant Design, History of Architecture, Architectural Design and Planning

Div. of Chemical Engineering(M 33/3)
High Pressure Chemical Engineering, Chemical Reaction Engineering, Mass Transfer Operation and Separation Engineering, Process Design and Control

Div. of Civil Engineering(M 58/7)
Structural Mechanics and Earthquake Engineering, Civil Engineering Materials and Bridge Engineering, Hydraulic Engineering, Soil Engineering, Santitary Engineering, Traffic Engineering

Div. of Electrical Engineering(M 35/2)
Fundamental Electrical Engineering, Electrical Machines and Control Systems Engineering, Information Science and Communication Systems Engineering, Electric Power Engineering

Div. of Electronic Engineering(M 34/2)
Fundamental Electronics, Electronic Circuit Engineering, Semiconductor Electronics, Computer Engineering

Div. of Environmental Planning(M 46/5)
Physical Environmental Planning, Disaster Prevention, Environmental Planning for Human Life. Analysis of Physical Environment

Div. of Industrial Chemistry(M 43/4)
Industrial Physical Chemistry, Industrial Inorganic Chemistry, Synthetic Organic Chemistry, Polymer Chemistry

Div. of Instrumentation Engineering(M 34/4)
Mechanical Instrumentation, Electronic Intrumentation, Applied Physics in Instrumentation Engineering, Automatic Control

Div. of Mechanical Engineering(M 50/4)
Solied Mechanics, Engineering Mechanics and Machine Design, Fluid Mechanics and Hydraulic Machinery, Thermodynamics and Internal Combustion Engine, Steam Power Engineering

Div. of Production Engineering(M 40/5)
Material Research for Machinery, Applied Kinematics, Production Engineering, Thermo Fluid Engineering

Div. of Systems Engineering(M 29/0)
Systems Fundamentals, Systems Design, Systems Analysis, Systems Information

Graduate School of Humanities and Social Sciences(D 75/22)

Div. of Structure of Culture(D 46/15)
Foundation of Culture, Foundation of Science, Foundation of Language and Cultures, Arts of Cultures, Japanese Language and Cultures, Foreign Language and Cultures

Div. of Culture and Society(D 29/7)
Theoretical Basis of Behavior Learning, Foundation of Social Structure, Regional Society, Theory of Regional Culture, History of Japanese Culture and Society, History of Western Cultures and Societies, History of Asian Cultures and Societies

Graduate School of Law(M 29/14, D 42/13)

Div. of Private Law(M 15/9, D 25/7)
Sociology of Law, Civil Law, Commercial Law, Social Law

Div. of Public Law(M 14/5, D 17/6)
Legal Theory and History, Public Law, Criminal Law, International Law, International Relation, Political Theory, Political Process

Graduate School of Letters(M 85/23)

Div. of Philosophy(M 8/1)
Philosophy of Europe, History of European Philosophy, History of Science

Div. of Science of Art and History of Art(M 8/3)
Science of Art, History of Art

Div. of Sociology(M 12/8)
Theoretical Sociology, Empirical Sociology, Psychology, Ethics

Div. of History(M 15/3)
Ancient and Medieval History of Japan, Modern History of Japan, Ancient and Medieval History of Asia, Modern History of Asia, Ancient and Medieval History of Europe, Modern History of Europe and America, Geography

Div. of Japanese Literature(M 24/6)
Japanese Language, Japanese Literature, Japanese Literature(Modern), Chinese Language and Literature, Philology

Div. of English and American Literature(M 18/2)
English and American Literature, English Language, German Language and Literature, French Language and Literature
Graduate School of Medicine(D 246/11)
Div. of Physiology Sciences(D 50/2)
Anatomy, Physiology, Biochemistry, Pharmacology, Radiation Biophysics
Div. of Pathologic Sciences(D 29/3)
Pathology, Microbiology, Medical Zoology
Div. of Social Medicine(D 7/1)
Hygiene, Public Health, Legal Medicine
Div. of Medical Sciences(D 72/1)
Internal Medicine, Gerontology, Pediatrics, Radiology, Neurology and Psychiatry, Dermatology, Laboratory Medicine
Div. of Surgical Sciences(D 88/4)
Surgery, Neurological Surgery, Orthopedic Surgery, Otorhinolaryngology, Obstetrics and Gynecology, Urology, Ophthalmology, Anesthesiology, Oral Surgery
Graduate School of Science(M 132/4)
Div. of Mathematics(M 16/0)
Analysis, Algebra and Topology, Geometry, Applied Mathematics
Div. of Physics(M 36/2)
Condensed Matter Spectroscopy, High Energy Physics, Elementary Particle Physics, Cosmic Nuclear Astrophysics, Solid State Physics
Div. of Chemistry(M 29/1)
Physical Chemistry, Inoganic Chemistry, Analytical Chemistry, Organic Chemistry, Structural Chemistry
Div. of Biology(M 22/1)
Physiology, Systematic Phylogency, Genetics, Cytology, Biochemistry
Div. of Earth Science(M 29/0)
Petrology and Mineralogy, Geophysics, Geology, Marine Geophysics, Geochemistry
Graduate School of Science and Technology(D 158/52)
Div. of Science of Materials(M 26/4)
Fundamental Science of Materials, Applied Science of Material Functions, Science of Material Reactions, Science of Material Differentiation
Div. of Idustrial Science(M 26/19)
Materials and Structures, Energy and Power Systems, Design and Manufacturing
Div. of Science of Biological Resources(M 25/10)
Biological Fundamentals, Biological Production, Utilization of Biological Resources
Div. of Environmental Science(M 35/5)
Nature of Earth, Environment of Greens, Regional Environment
Div. of System Science(M 24/9)
Mathematics and System Fundamentals, Information and Instrumentation, System Function and Construction
Div. of Intelligence Science(M 22/5)
Natural Intelligence, Artificial Intelligence

神戸商船大学
(Kôbe Shôsen Daigaku)
Kobe University of Mercantile Marine

5-1-1 Fukaeminami-machi, Higashinada-ku, Kobe-shi, Hyogo 658
☎ 078-453-2332

Founded 1952
Professors 40
Associate Professors 38
Assistant Professors(Tenured) 2
Assistant Professors(Non-tenred) 80
Research Assistants 16
Undergraduate Students/Foreign Students 922/4
Graduate Students/Foreign Students 57/5
Library 182, 053 volumes
Contact: Instruction Section

Educational philosophy The purpose of the University is provide students with a good knowledge of theories and technology required especially in the field of marine science and engineering, and to instill high intelligence and rich culture into the students so as to enable them to contribute to the development of sea transportation and other maritime industries.
Foreign students The University offers a very wide range of advanced undergraduate and postgraduate courses and opportunity for reseach as same condition as Japanese students. There is valuable interaction in these courses between scientific/technological training and industrial experience.
Environment Facing Osaka Bay, our school also has the Rokko Range as its hinterland and is situated at the eastern part of Kobe Port, the largest port in Japan.
Facilities University Library, Training Ship, The "Fukae-maru", Research Institute for Cargo Transportation, Marine Practice Center, Health Administration Center, Sea Training Center, Center for computer and Information Service
Student activities Orientation for the new students. University Festival. Ski School. There is a wide variety of extra curricular activities including photo section, brassband, drama, baseball, rugby, soccer, cutter, etc.
Academic programs for foreign students Supplementary class, Sightseeing trip, Tutor system.
Services for foreign students Health clinic, Housing Information, Homestay, Meeting, International Friendship Day.

Undergraduate Programs

Faculty of Mercantile Marine Science(922/4)
Dept. of Maritime Science(496/2)
Dept. of Ocean Electro Mechanical Engineering

(131/0)
Dept. of Power Systems Engineering(160/0)
Dept. of Transportation & Information Systems Engineering(135/2)

Graduate Programs

Graduate School of Mercantile Marine Science(M 57/5)
Div. of Marine Engineering(M 14/2)
Div. of Nautical Science Course(M 6/0)
Div. of Nuclear Engineering(M 13/0)
Div. of Ocean Mechanical Engineering(M 15/1)
Div. of Transportation Science(M 9/2)
Navigation Systems, Martime Science, Transportation Engineering, Information Engineering, Marine Engineering, Nuclear Engineering, Ocean Mechanical Engineering, Mechanical & Electronic Engineerng

---

京都工芸繊維大学
(Kyôto Kôgei Sen'i Daigaku)

Kyoto Institute of Technology

Hashigami-cho, Matsugasaki, Sakyo-ku, Kyoto-shi, Kyoto 606
☎ 075-791-3211 FAX 075-712-8961

Founded 1949
Professors 102
Associate Professors 95
Assistant Professors(Tenured) 15
Assistant Professors(Non-tenured) 128
Research Assistants 59
Undergraduate Students/Foreign Students 2, 921/43
Graduate Students/Foreign Students 469/56
Library 277, 084 volumes
Contact: Undergraduate Admission Student Affairs Section, Engineering and Design/Textile Science, ext. 410, 412(Engineering and Design); 708, 709(Textile Science)
Foreign Students Section, Student Affairs Division, Student Affairs Office, ext. 256
Graduate Admission Office of the Graduate School, General Affairs Division, ext. 210, 220

Educational philosophy KIT places particular emphasis on active research in basic sciences and its application in order to train students to cope with the emerging technologies wihch will surely characterize the 21st century.
Foreign students As a way to encourage and promote international exchange as well as mutual understanding, KIT welcomes qualified students from overseas. As of May 1990, sixty-seven students from twenty-two countries are studying on its campus.
Environment Kyoto, " The Ancient City, " is rich in tradition: not only in the architecture and gardens of nearly 1500 temples and 200 shrines, but also as one of the producing centers of fine silk fabrics, chinaware, and other crafts. The city also has a long tradition as a leading educational center of the country.
Facilities University Library, Museum and Archives, Information Processing Center, Radioisotope Laboratory, Experimental Farms, Design Workshop, Health Care Service Center, Tennis Court, Swimming Pool, Gymnasium, Auditorium
Student activities University Festival, Sport Festival, Extra-curricular activities such as tennis, basketball, volleyball, soccer, American football, swimming, Japanese martial arts, etc.
Academic programs for foreign students Special Orientation, Intensive Japanese Language Class, Tutoring System, Field Study(three-day tour), Substitutional Subjects.
Services for foreign students Counseling Services, Financial Aid(Scholarship Programs, Part-time Employment), Housing and Residence Information, Cultural Exchange Programs, Social Welfare Information, General Medical Services.

Undergraduate Programs

Faculty of Engineering and Design(1, 131/7)
Dept. of Architecture and Design(284/3)
Dept. of Chemistry and Meterials Technology(289/0)
Dept. of Electronics and Information Science(321/4)
Dept. of Mechanical and System Engineering(237/0)
Faculty of Textile Science(429/5)
Dept. of Applied Biology(143/2)
Dept. of Polymer Science and Engineering(286/3)

Graduate Programs

Graduate School of Technological Science(M 391/39, D 73/16)
Div. of Machanical and System Engineering(M 59/7)
Mechanical System Design, Mechanical System Development
Div. of Electronics and Information Science(M 66/9)
Communication and Systems, Electronics, Information Science
Div. of Chemistry and Materials Technology(M 81/4)
Chemical Reaction of Materials, Function of Materials, Properties and Processing of Materials
Div. of Architecture and Design(M 64/13)
Design and System, Theory and Design
Div. of Applied Biology(M 28/2)
Applied Biological Science, Biotechnology
Div. of Polymer Science and Engineering(M 93/4)
Polymer Chemistry, Polymer Engineering
Div. of Applied Science for Functionality(D 36/

8)
Art and Design, Biofunctions, Functionality of Polymers, Space and Product Design

Div. of Materials Science(D 5/3)
Science of Molecular Design, Science of Molecular, Transformation, Science of Materials Processing

Div. of Information and Production Science(D 22/5)
Information/Production and System Science, Information Science, Production Science

---

京都大学
(Kyôto Daigaku)

Kyoto University

Yoshida Honmachi, Sakyo-ku, Kyoto 606
☎ 075-753-2541 FAX 075-753-2562

Founded 1897
Professors 701
Associate Professors 678
Assistant Professors(Tenured) 152
Assistant Professors(Non-tenured) 1, 053
Research Assistants 1, 059
Undergraduate Students/Foreign Students 13, 056/93
Graduate Students/Foreign Students 4, 096/408
Library 4, 857, 375 volumes
Contact: Admission Office ☎ 075-753-2525 Foreign Student Service ☎ 075-753-2541

Educational philosophy Kyoto University was founded in oppositon to Tokyo University for the purpose of the proper independent academic activities. Therefore not only up-to-date internationally high-level scientific researches but also marked traditional individual academic spirit support our educational philosophy.
Foreign students As far as academic endeavor is concerned the receiving foreign students has become natural since the barriers between nations have already been removed or have at least become transparent.
Environment The City of Kyoto, with a population of about 1, 500, 000, is an excellent place for study.It served as the seat of the imperial Court for more than ten centuries. Due to the existence of many historical monuments and many artifacts of artistic and cultural interest, Kyoto is considered the cultural center of Japan.
Facilities International Houses, Library, Swimming pool, Gymnasium, Some recreation facilities, Some research institutes and centers, etc.
Student activities Popular campus events includes Homecoming, School festival, etc. There is a wide variety of extra curricular activities, including volunteer work, choral groups, marching band, student newspaper, drama, baseball, soccer, etc.
Academic programs for foreign students Supplemental Japanese language classes,Tutoring system, etc.
Services for foreign students Health clinic, Counselling, Housing information, Homestay system, Part-time Job information, Cultural exchange program, etc.

Undergraduate Programs

Faculty of Letters(1038(General Education 451)/0)
- **Dept. of History**(181/0)
- **Dept. of Literature**(179/0)
- **Dept. of Philosophy**(227/0)

Faculty of Education(238(Genaral education 124)/1 (General education))
- **Dept. of Education**(33/0)
- **Dept. of Educational Psychology**(86/0)
- **Dept. of Educational Sociology**(40/0)

Faculty of Law(2110/6)

Faculty of Economics(1176(General Education 522)/29(General Education 9))
- **Dept. of Business Administration**(179/6)
- **Dept. of Economics**(475/14)

Faculty of Science(1359/2)
- **Dept. of Astronomy**
- **Dept. of Biophysics**
- **Dept. of Botany**
- **Dept. of Chemistry**

Faculty of Science(1359/2)
- **Dept. of Geology and Mineralogy**
- **Dept. of Geophysics**
- **Dept. of Mathematics**
- **Dept. of Physics**
- **Dept. of Zoology**

Faculty of Medicine(708/0)

Faculty of Pharmaceutical Sciences(354/3)
- **College of Liberal Arts (General education)** (181/2)
- **Dept. of Pharmacy and Pharmacological Sciences**(87/1)
- **Dept. of Pharmaceutical Chemistry and Technology**(86/0)

Faculty of Engineering(4, 431/27)
- **Dept. of Aeronautical Engineering**(112/2)
- **Dept. of Applied Mathematics and Physics**(198/1)
- **Dept. of Architectural Engineering**(422/1)
- **Dept. of Architecture**(422/1)
- **Dept. of Chemical Engineering**(186/0)
- **Dept. of Civil Engineering**(359/1)
- **Dept. of Electrical Engineering**(603/13)
- **Dept. of Electrical Engineering Ⅱ**(603/13)
- **Dept. of Eectronics**(603/13)
- **Dept. of Engineering Science**(565/2)
- **Dept. of Environmental and Sanitary Engineering** (195/0)
- **Dept. of Hydrocarbon Chemistry**(234/0)
- **Dept. of Industrial Chemistry**(221/0)
- **Dept. of Information Science**(204/5)
- **Dept. of Mechanical Engineering**(565/2)
- **Dept. of Metallurgy**(319/1)
- **Dept. of Metal Science and Technology**(319/1)

Dept. of Mineral Science and Technology(165/0)
Dept. of Nuclear Engineering(95/0)
Dept. of Polymer Chemistry(193/1)
Dept. of Precision Mechanics(565/0)
Dept. of Synthetic Chemistry(180/0)
Dept. of Transportation Engineering(180/0)
Faculty of Agriculture(1376/3)
Dept. of Agricultural and Forestry Economics (167/0)
Dept. of Agricultural Biology(77/0)
Dept. of Agricultural Chemistry(209/2)
Dept. of Agricultural Engineering(181/0)
Dept. of Agronomy and Horticultural Science (105/0)
Dept. of Animal Science(115/0)
Dept. of Fisheries(117/0)
Dept. of Food Science and Technology(162/1)
Dept. of Forestry(101/0)
Dept. of Wood Science and Technology(142/0)

Graduate Programs

Graduate School of Letters(M 165/9, D 218/21)
Philosophy, Western Philosophy, History of Indian Philosophy, History of Chinese Philosophy, Psychology, Ethics, Aesthetics and Art History, Socilogy, Religion, Buddhist Studies, Christian Studies, Japanese History, Oriental History, European History, Contemporary History, West-Asian History, Archaeology, Human Geography, Japanese Language and Literature, Chinese Language and Literature, Sanskrit Language and Literature, French Language and Literature, English Language and Literature, American Literature, German Language and Literature, Classical Language and Literature, Italian Language and Literature, Linguistics
Graduate School of Education(M 38/2, D 46/2)
Div. of Pedagogical Studies of Education(M 8/0, D 12/0)
Pedagogy, History of Education, Compartive Education, Educational Guidance, Currculum Development
Div. of Methodological Studies of Education(M 14/2, D 25/2)
Educational Psychology, Audio-Visual Education, Library Science, Educational Administration
Div. of Clinical Studies of Education(M 16/0, D 9/0)
Clinical Pedagogy, Clinical Personality Psychology, Clinical Psychology of Education, Clinical Anthropology of Education
Graduate School of Law(M 47/14, D 52/14)
Div. of Basic Laws(M 9/1, D 10/1)
Japanese Legal History, Occidental Legal History, Roman Law, Legal Philosophy, Sociology of Law, Contemporary Foreign Law(4 chairs), Constitutional Law, General Legal Theory of State, Administrative Law, Social Security Law, Tax Law, International Law, Civil Law, Commercial Law, Maritime Law, Labour Law, Criminal Law, Criminology, Law of Civil Procedure, Law of Bankruptcy, Criminal Procedure, Privete International Law, Laws of International Trade and Transactions, Comparative Law(6 chairs), History of Political Indeas, Political History, Diplomatic History, Political and Deplomatic History of Japan, Political Theory, International Politics, Public Administration, Governmental Process, Comparative Politics
Div. of Public Laws(M 6/0, D 12/3)
Div. of Private and Criminal Laws(M 16/7, D 15/7)
Div. of Pilitical Sciences(M 16/6, D 15/3)
Graduate School of Economics(M 49/17, D 88/24)
Div. of Business Administration(M 1/1, D 9/2)
Business Administration, Business Policy, Marketing and Accounting Analysis,
Div. of Contemporary Economics(M 14/4, D 14/6)
Contemporary Economics, Japanese Economy, Applied Economics
Div. of Economic Policy(M 16/8, D 23/4)
Comparative Society and Economic Policy, Public Finance and Reaginal Economy
Div. of Economic Theory and Economic History (M 18/4, D 42/12)
Economic Theory, Statistics. Information. and Finance, Economic History and the History of Social Thought
Graduate School of Science(M 374/11, D 369/17)
Div. of Mathematics(M 34/1, D 19/1)
Algebraic Topology, Probability Theory, Number Theory, Operator Theory & Mathematical Physics, Functional Analysis, Nonlinear Partial Differential Equations, Partial Different Equations, Algebraic Geometry
Div. of Primate Research Institute(M 15/0, D 9/1)
Morphology, Neurophysiology, Psychology, Sociology Variation Research, Ecology, Physiology, Biochemistry, Systematics & Phylogeny
Div. of Mathematical Sciences(M 15/1, D 18/2)
Algebraic Analysis, Hyperfunction Theory, Functional Analysis, Partial Differential Equatnions, Mathematical Physics, Operator Algebras, Differential Equations, Theory of Computation, Numerical Analysis, Global Analysis, Analytic S-matrix Theory, Number Theory, Automorphic Functions, Stochastic Process, Mathematical Physics, Complex Geometry, Complex Analysis, Nonlinear Mechanics, Statistical Fluid Mechanics
Div. of Biophysics(M 45/1, D 46/0)
Biomembranes, Photobiology, Molecular Biology, Molecular Biology, Cell Biology, Physical Chemistry of Enzyme
Div. of Botany(M 27/0, D 16/3)
Systematic Botany & Population Biology, Plant Physiology, Plant Molecular Biology, Plant Ecology
Div. of Geology and Mineralogy(M 11/0, D 12/3)
Stratigraphy & Paleontology, Petrology, Nuclear Geology & Paleogeophysics, Sedimentology, Mineralogy
Div. of Zoology(M 33/2, D 37/2)
Ethology, Developmental Biology, Ecology, Human Evolution, Physical Anthropology, Invertebrate Zoology, Freshwater Ecology, Environmental Physiology, Radiation Biology
Div. of Chemistry(M 64/2, D 88/1)
Organic Chemistry, Physical Chemistry, Radiation

Chemistry, Solid State Chemistry, Theoretical Chemistry, Organic Solid State Chemistry, Physical & Analytical Chemistry, Biological Chemistry, Surface Science, Analytical Chemistry, Nuclear Radiation, Radiochemistry, Surface Chemistry, Crystal & Powder Chemistry, Dielectrics, Organic Unit Reaction, Molecular Biology

Div. of Geophysics(M 25/2, D 36/2)

Physics of the Solid Earth, Physical Oceanography, Meteorology, Applied Geophysics, Geomagnetism & Spese Physics, Seismology, Earthquake Ground Motions, Microearthquake, Earthquake Prediction, Applied Geomorphology, Landslide, Applied Climatology, Severe Storm, Mechanism of Volcanic Eruption

Div. of Astronomy(M 13/2, D 11/1)

Solar Physics, Astrophysics

Div. of Physics Ⅱ (M 51/0, D 40/1)

Nuclear Astrophysics, Experimental Nuclear Physics, Theory of Elemenmtary Particles, Experimental High Energy Physics, Theoretical Nuclear Physics

Div. of Physics Ⅰ (M 36/0, D 42/0)

Plasma Physics, Low Temperature Physics, Metal & Semiconductor Physics, Nonlinear Dynamics, Molecular Physics, Solid State Physics, Fluid Physics, Laser Spectroscopy, Nuclear Radiation, Theory of Elementary Particles, Solid State Physics, Non-linear Physics, Nuclear Theory, Scientific Instruments, Radiation Physics

Graduate School of Medicine(D 477/24)

Div. of Physiology(D 46/5)

Anatomy, Physiology, Medical Chemistry, Pharmacology, Experimental Radiology, Allergy,

Div. of Pathology(D 27/3)

Pathology, Microbiology, Immunobiology

Div. of Social Medicine(D 7/0)

Hygiene, Public Health, Legal Medicine

Div. of Internal Medicine(D 213/8)

Internal Medicine, Laboratory Medicine, Pediatrics, Darmatology And Syphilology. Radiology, Nuclear Medicine, Geriatric Medicine, Neurology, Psychiatry,

Div. of Surgery(D 162/6)

Surgery, Ophthalmolmology, Gynecology And Obstetrics, Orthopaedic Surgery, Urology, Otolaryngology, Oral And Mexillofacial Surgery, Neurosurgery, Anesthesia, Gardiovascular Surgery, Plastic Suegery,

Div. of Molecular Medicine(D 19/2)

Molecular Oncology, Molecular Genetics, Molecular Biology, Molecular Immunology, Molecular And Cellular Biology, Cell Biology, Tumor Virology, Clinical Molecular Biology, Molecular Diseases: Diagnosis And Treatment, Molecular Nuclear Medicine, Surgical Oncology, Molecular Radiation Therapy

Div. of Integrative Brain Science(D 3/0)

Integrative Neuroanatomy, Brain PathoPhyshiology, Cognitve Behavional Brain Science

Graduate School of Pharmaceutical Sciences(M 78/1, D 43/3)

Div. of Pharmacy and Pharmacological Sciences (M 47/0, D 35/2)

Analytical Chemistry, Organic Chemistry, Structure Chemistry, Pharmacognosy, Pharmaceutics, Pharmacology, Health Chemistry, Biofunctional Chemistry, Bioorganic Chemistry, Clinical Pharmacobiodynamics

Div. of Pharmacetuical Chemistry and Technology(M 31/1, D 8/1)

Pharmaceutical Manufacturing Chemistry, Biological Chemistry, Natural Product Chemistry, Molecular Microbiology, Physical Chemistry, Radiophamaceutical Chemistry

Graduate School of Engineering(M 1227/42, D 272/107)

Div. of Aeronautical Engineering(M 14/0, D 3/0)

Airplane Construction, Fluid Dynamics, Gas Dynamics, Propulsion Engineering, Strength of Structures, Theory of Vibration

Div. of Applied Mathematics and Physics(M 37/2, D 7/1)

Applied Mathematics, Applied Mechanics, Control Theory, Engineering Mathematics, Engineering Mechanics, Logical Systems, Operations Research

Div. of Applied Systems Science(M 68/1, D 4/1)

Applied Artificial Intelligence, Applied Informatics, Information and Communication, Image Processing Systems, Intelligent Machine Control, Robotics, Systems Science Fundamentals, Transportation Systems, Water Resources Systems Management

Div. of Architectural Engineering(M 40/3, D 14/6)

Architectural Environment Control, Area Planning, Planning of Architectural Facilities, Reinforced Concrete Construction, Soil and Foundation Engineering, Theory of Steel Structures

Div. of Architecture(M 68/5, D 15/8)

Architectural Design and Theory, Architectural Environment, Architectural Planning, Building Construction, Building Equipment, History of Architecture, Materials for Buiding Structures, Mechanics of Building Structures

Div. of Chemical Engineering(M 44/2, D 13/8)

Chemical Engineering Thermodynamics, Chemical Raction Engineering, Diffusional Unit Operations, Equipments and Materials for Chemical Processes, Mechanical Unit Operations, Process Control and Process Systems Engineering, Transport Phenomena

Div. of Civil Engineering(M 102/7, D 18/14)

Bridge Engineering, Coastal Engineering, Construction Engineering, Construction Materials Engineering, Design in Civil Enginering, Earthquake Engineering, Hydraulics, Hydrology and Water Resources Engineering, Regional Planning and Systems Analysis, River Engineering, Soil Mechanics, Structural Mechanics

Div. of Electrical Engineering(M 56/4, D 12/10)

Applied Electrical Sciences, Electrical Discharge Engineering, Electrical Machinery, Electromagnetic Theory, Engineering of Electric Power Generation, Transmission and Distribution, Fundamental Electrical Engineering, Measurement, Instrumentation and Control

Div. of Electrical Engineering Ⅱ (M 62/1, D 12/3)

Control Engineering, Digital Systems, Electrical Power System Engineering, Electric Network Theory, Energy Conversion Devices, Radio Communication Engineering, Wire Communication Engineering

Div. of Electronics(M 58/2, D 11/4)

Electron Devices, Electronic Circuit Engineering, Electron Physics, High Frequency Engineering, Quantum Electronics, Semiconductor Engineering

Div. of Engineering Science(M 29/0, D 5/1)

Atomic and Plasma Spectroscopy, Materials Science, Mechanical Behavior of Materials, Solid State Physics, Thermal Physics

Div. of Environmental and Sanitary Engineering (M 44/2, D 13/7)

Environmental Hygiene, Environmental Systems Envineering, Industrial Health Engineering, Radiological Health Engineering, Water Quality Control Engineering, Water Supply and Sewerage Engineering

Div. of Hydrocarbon Chemistry(M 40/3, D 18/6)

Catalyst Chemistry, Catalyst Engineering, Catalyst Physics, Hydrocarbon Chemistry Fundamentals, Hydrocarbon Physical Chemistry, Petrochemical Engineering, Petroleum Converion Engineering

Div. of Industrial Chemistry(M 73/0, D 11/2)

General Analytical Chemistry, General Physical Chemistry, Inustrial Analytical Chemistry, Industrial Biochemistry, Industrial Electrochemistry, Industrial Physical Chemistry, Industrial Solid-State Chemistry, Inorganic Structural Chemistry, Organic Chemistry of Natural Products, Organic Reaction Chemistry

Div. of Information Science(M 43/2, D 11/3)

Computer Software, Computer Systems, Information Processing, Information Science Fundamentals, Information Systems Engineering, Logic Circuits and Automata

Div. of Mechanical Engineering(M 56/1, D 7/7)

Applied Thermodynamics, Engineering Materials, Engineering Plasticity, Fluid Mechanics, Heat Transfer, Lubrication and Hydraulic Engineering, Mechanics of Materials, Power Engineering, Strength of Materials

Div. of Metallurgy(M 40/0, D 7/3)

Electrometallurgy, Extractive Metallurgy, Foundry and Mechanical Metallurgy, Process Metallurgy, Pyrochemical Metallurgy, Science of Metallic Materials

Div. of Metal Science and Technology(M 36/1, D 3/1)

Foundry Technology, Lattice Defects and Crystal Plasticity, Metal Physics, Science of Steels, Structural Metallurgy, Welding Engineering

Div. of Mineral Science and Technology(M 40/1, D 4/3)

Applied Geology, Applied Measurement, Equipments for Iron-Steel Making, Continuous Casting and Plastic Working Systems, Exploration Geophysics and Technology, Mineral Processing and Particulate Technology, Rock Mechanics and Excavation Technology

Div. of Molecular Engineering(M 47/0, D 19/2)

Applied Molecular Science, Applied Solid state chemistry, Molecule Design, Molecular Energy Conversion, Molecular Materials Science, Molecular Science and Technology of Catalysis, Quautum Molecular Science and Technology

Div. of Nuclear Engineering(M 41/0, D 9/3)

Atomic and Nuclear Physics, Atomic and Nuclear Reaction Engineering, Nuclear Fuel, Nuclear Instrumentation, Nuclear Material, Nuclear Reactor Enguneering

Div. of Polymer Chemistry(M 63/1, D 32/5)

Fundamental Study of Polymer Chemistry, Materials Science of Polymers, Molecular Properties of Polymers, Polymer Mechanics in the Solid-State, Polymer Physics, Polymer Synthesis, Radiation Polymer Chemistry, Structure of Polymers

Div. of Precision Mechanics(M 43/3, D 8/6)

Exact Manufacturing Sciences, Machine Elements, Measurement and Control Engineering, Production Engineering, Systems Engineering, Vibration Engineering

Div. of Synthetic Chemistry(M 43/0, D 12/1)

Free Radical Chemistry, Organic and Bioorganic Catalysis, Organometallic Chemistry, Physical Organic Chemistry, Polymerization Chemistry, Synthetic Organic Chemistry

Div. of Transportation Engineering(M 40/1, D 4/2)

Foundation Engineering, Structural Ploblems for Transportation Facilities, Terminal Facilities, Transportation and Traffic Planning, Transportation Facilitiy Planning, Urban Transportation Engineering

Graduate School of Agriculture (M 306/19, D 234/78)

Div. of Agronomy and Horticultural Science(M 24/0, D 6/3)

Crop Science, Plant Breeding, Vegetable and Ornamental Horticulture, Pomology, Weed Science

Div. of Forestry(M 15/2, D16/5)

Forest Management, Forest Ecology, Landscape Architecture, Erosion Control, Forest Engineering

Div. of Agricultural Chemistry(M 59/2, D 46/10)

Soil Science, Biogical Chemistry, Plant Nutrition, Bioplymer Chemistry, Fermentation Physiology and Applied Microbiology, Pesticide Chemistry, Chemical Biology of Pesticides, Fundamental Cell Technology, Fermentation and Metabolic Regulation, Plant Molecular Biology, Biophysical Chemistry, Plant Products Chemistry, Microbial Biochemistry, Plant Photobiochemistry (Food Production), Xenobiotic Metabolism

Div. of Agricultural Bilogy(M 19/0, D 28/8)

Plant Pathology, Entomology, Genetics, Applied Botany, Biology of Pesticides, Crop Evolution

Div. of Agricultural Engineering(M 23/1, D 18/11)

Agricultural Structure Engineering, Irigation and Drainage, Rural Planning, Water Use Engineering, Agricultural Prime Mover, Farm Machinery, Farm Processing Machinery, Radiation Control

Div. of Agricultural and Forestry Economics(M 24/6, D 22/6)

Farm Management, Farm Accounting, Agriculutral Policy, Forestry Policy, Agricultural History,the Principle of Agricultural Sciences, Accounting of Agricultural Industry, Economic Analysis and Managememt of the Farm Household

Div. of Fisheries(M 20/0, D 18/5)

Fisheries Chemistry, Fisheries Physics, Aquatic Microbiology, Aquatic Biology

Div. of Wood Science and Technology(M 38/0, D 17/12)

Wood Technology, Wood Structure, Woodworking Machinery, Forest Products Chemistry, Materials for Wood Improvements, Chemical Processing of Wood, Wood Physics, Wood Chemistry, Wood Biolgy, Composite Wood, Lignin Chemistry, High Performance Wood Products

Div. of Food Science and Technology(M 46/3, D 27/7)

Nutritional Chemistry, Bioengineeirng, Industrial Microbiology, Analysis of Agricultural Proudcts, Enzyme Chemistry, Food Processing and Preservation, Food Chemistry, Food Analysis, Applied Microbiology, Protein Food, Food Process

Div. of Animal Science(M 20/2, D 10/2)

Animal Breeding, Animal Reprodiction, Animal Nutrition, Functional Anatomy of Farm Animals

Div. of Tropical Agriculture(M 18/3, D 26/9)

Tropical Agriculture, Fishery Resources, Forestry Resources, Animla Resources, Regional Plaanig, Tropical Rice Culture, Tropical Geography, Tropical Hydeology

---

京都教育大学
(Kyôto Kyôiku Daigaku)

Kyoto University of Education

1 Fukakusa-Fujinomori-Cho, Fushimi-Ku, Kyoto-shi, Kyoto 612
☎ 075-641-9281 FAX 075-644-1394

Founded 1876
Professors 65
Associate Professors 55
Assistant Professors(Tenured) 10
Assistant Professors(Non-tenred) 166
Research Assistants 4
Undergraduate Students/Foreign Strdents 1, 853/29
Grauate Students/Foreigh Students 38/0
Library 260, 126 volumes
Contact: Admission Office(Student Division)

Educational philosophy As this is a University of Education, its main purpose is to train teacher. The Integrated Science Program of Study was established in 1988. Students belonging to this program can graduate without obtaining a teacher's certificate.

Foreign students Foreign students are expected to study hard along with Japanese students, and contribute to deepening mutual understuanding and promoting friendship, while enjoying their student lives.

Environment The campus at Fujinomori-cho is 140,724 m^2 in area-about 35 acres. Moderately hilly and with a variety of tall shade trees, it affords a most favorable atmosphere for research and education. The University has a full time faculty of academic staff for the 1, 800 students in this environment.

Facilities Faculty offices, the auditorium, laboratories, the administration building, the library, the student center, a physical training plant and other facilities.

Student activities A university sponsored swimming training, and a university festival are planned as annual events. Track-and-field, aquatic sports, soccer and other clubs are found on the physical educational part of the spectrum. As to the cultural part, there are societies for children's culture, comics and others, in which students participate in unique activities.

Academic programs for foreign students Japanese classes, supplementary Japanese classes, technical training courses, and a tutor system are provided for foreign students.

Services for foreign students Our university is equipped with a university health center, dormitories, a conversation room for foreign students. The foreign students are given assistance in finding board and lodging, part-time jobs, etc. They also go on a tour for practical study.

Undergraduate Programs

Faculty of Education(1, 853/29)

Course for Integrated Science(317/5)

Junior High School Teachers' Training Course(424/11)

Kindergarten Teachers'Training Course(105/3)

Teachers' Training Course of School for the Mentally Retarded(80/3)

Primary School Teachers' Training Course(528/0)

Teachers' Training Course for Special Subjects (Fine Arts, Industrial Arts and Crafts) (127/5)

Teachers' Training Course for Special Subjects (Health and Physical Education) (144/2)

Teachers' Training Course for Special Subjects (Science) (128/0)

Graduate Programs

Graduate School of Education(M 38/0)

Div. of Handicapped Children Education(M 1/0)

Handicapped Children Education

Div. of School Education(M 14/0)

School Education

Div. of Subject Education(M 23/0)

Social Studies Education, Science Education, Music Education, Fine Arts Education, Health and Physical Education, Home Economics Education, English Language Education

One-Year Graduate Programs

Special Education Course

Education for the mentally handicapped Major

奈良教育大学
(Nara Kyôiku Daigaku)
Nara University of Education

Takabatake, Nara-shi, Nara 630
☎ 0742-26-1101 FAX 0742-26-5040

Founded 1949
Professors 60
Associate Professors 47
Assistant Professors(Tenured) 3
Assistant Professors(Non-tenured) 131
Research Assistants 3
Undergraduate Students/Foreign Students 1, 260/14
Graduate Students/Foreign Students 121/8
Library 243, 000 volumes
Contact: Academic Affairs

Educational philosophy We aim at conducting research in education and various other fields of dicipline, as well as training the students in the theoroy and practice of their respective fields of specialization. The university tries especially to prepare students to be comptent teachers as well as good citizens, thereby contributing to the higher cultural features of the local community.

Foreign students From an international viewpoint, we intend to take an active part in receiving foreign students, For that purpose, we hold speical entrance examinations for foreign applicants, and try to prepare them to be talented and active persons aboroad.

Environment The campus is located in the eastern part of Nara, the most ancient capital of Japan, which is called the cradle of Japanese culture with many old temples and shrines. The university is only a ten-minute walk from Nara Park which includes the precincts of Todaiji Temple with the world's greatest bronze statue of Buddha.

Facilities University Library, Educational Technology Center, Experimental Farm and Forest, Swimming pool, Gymnasium, Auditorium, Judo and Kendo gymnasium, Attached Schools(Junior High School, Elementary School,and Kindergarten), Health Adminstration Center.

Student activities We have a students hall for the students to have meals and refreshments and to enjoy extra-curricular activities. The students generally choose between two sorts of club activites, cultural and athletic, which are sponsored and adminstered by the student body. School festival is held for several days in November.

Academic programs for foreign students Foreign students can study Japanese langauge in place of other languages as regular first foreign language for general subjects.We offer three special classes only for foreign students as liberal arts. Each student is assigned a tutor.

Services for foreign students Two dormitories for boys and girls, International House, Housing information, part-time Job information, cultural exchange program, study tour, party for friendly relations.

Undergraduate Programs

Faculty of Educatiion(1, 260/14)

Graduate Programs

Graduate School of Education(M 121/8)
Japanese Language, Japanese Literature, Chinese Classics, Teaching of Japanese, History, Geography, Politics, Sociology, Economics, Philosophy, Ethics, Social Studies Education, Algebra, Geometry, Analysis, Applied, Mathematics, Mathematics Education, Funametal Physics, Applied Physics, Inorganic & Physical Chemistry, Organic Chemistry, Taxonomy & Morphology, Physiology & Ecology, Astronomy, Geophysics, Geology & Mineralogy, Science Education, Vocal Music, Instrumental Music, Composition Conducting,Music Education, Painting, Sćulpture, Design, Calligraphy, Calligraphy Education, Sceince of Art, Art Education, Science of Physical Education, Biomechanics, Physiology Hygienics, Teaching Methodology of H & P. E., WoodWork,Metal Work, Electricity, Machine, Education of Industrial Arts,Food & Nutrition, Textiles & Clothing, Home Mangement, Child Development & Care, Home Economics Education,English Language, English & American Literature, English Education, Education of Handicapped Children, Infant Education, Educational Science, Educational Mehtodology, School Management, Educational Sociology, Educational Psychology, Decelopmental Psychology, Educational Clinic Psychology, Adult Education

奈良女子大学
(Nara Joshi Daigaku)
Nara Women's University

Kitauoyahigashi-machi, Nara-shi, Nara 630
☎ 0742-23-1131 FAX 0742-23-5167

Founded 1908
Professors 81
Associate Professors 65
Assistant Professors(Tenured) 10
Assistant Professors(Non-tenured) 182
Research Assistants 32
Undergraduate Students/Foreign Students 1, 849/6
Graduate Students/Foreign Students 208/29
Library 406, 183 volumes
Contact: Student Division, Student Office ext 221

Educational philosophy This university is to aim at developing women's capacity on the basis of female characteristics by offering wide knowledge through education and research on sciences and culture in each speciality.

Foreign students Foreign students who have qualifications and want to study at this university which is only one national university for women in the western Japan will be accepted positively.

Environment Nara was the center of politics and culture as the ancient capitals in Japan. There are many temples as there were which represent the glories in the past. Meanwhile, the Kansai Cultural Academic City(Kansai Bunka Gakujutsu Kenkyu Toshi)have been under construction in the area which ranges Nara, Osaka and Kyoto, so that we will enjoy the development of the area as a core place of culture and academic research in the future.

Facilities University Health Service, Auditorium, Gymnasium, Training Camp House, Dormitory, International House, Information Processing Center, Radioisotope Center, Higashiyoshino Environment Study Institution, University Library, University hall

Student activities Freshmen welcome party and school festival are popular campus events. There are 31 cultural activities, such as Music, Guitar, Fine Arts, etc., and 21 sport activities, such as Tennis, ping-pong, Kyudo(Japanese archery), etc. More than half of the students join one or more activities. Foreign students are welcomed to join these activities if their time and interests permit.

Academic programs for foreign students Each students will be assigned a tutor. Under the general direction of an academic advisor, the tutor will help the foreign students with her studies in the Japanese language and specialized fields or problem in daily life. The tutor is usually a senior student in the same field as that of the foreign students. Also, Japanese language supplementary classes are available.

Services for foreign students This university has the International House with 44 rooms. You can reside in the house if a vacant room available. Counseling on body and mental health is done at the Health Center. Home-visit or stay, participation in the exchange programs with people, and offering of scholarships are available at the Nara International Foundation commemorating the Silk Road Exposition and the other related organizations.

Undergraduate Programs

Faculty of Home Economics(623/3)
- **Dept. of Clothing Science**(157/1)
- **Domestic Science Teacher's Training Course**(0/0)
- **Dept. of Dwelling Science**(158/1)
- **Dept. of Food Science and Nutrition**(152/0)
- **Dept. of Social Science of The Family**(156/1)

Faculty of Letters(676/1)
- **Dept. of Education (Pedagogy Course)** (56/0)
- **Dept. of Education (Physical Education Course)** (53/0)
- **Dept. of English Language and English and American Literature**(65/1)
- **Dept. of Geography**(24/0)
- **Dept. of History**(42/0)
- **Dept. of Japanese Language and Japanese Literature**(62/0)
- **Dept. of Sociology**(43/0)

Faculty of Science(550/2)
- **Dept. of Biology**(124/2)
- **Dept. of Chemistry**(141/0)
- **Dept. of Mathematics**(144/0)
- **Dept. of Physics**(141/0)

Graduate Programs

Graduate School of Home Economics(M 33/6)

Div. of Clothing Science(M 9/3)

Clothing Material, Clothing Design, Clothing Care, Clothing Physiology, Clothing Life

Div. of Dwelling and Environmental Science(M 6/1)

Dwelling Style and System, Supervision of Human Settelment, Living Environment

Div. of Food Science and Nutrition(M 12/1)

Nutritional Chemistry, Food Chemistry, Cookery Science, Food Hygiene and Preservation, Nutritional Physiology

Div. of Social Sciences of the Family(M 6/1)

Household Economics, Family Relations, Home Management, Ecological Studies and Welfare

Graduate School of Human Culture(D 72/14)

Div. of Comparative Culture(D 40/7)

Society and Culture, Language and Culture

Div. of Human Life and Environmental Sciences (D 32/7)

Environmental Indicators, Human Life and Environmental Planning, Food Life Environment

Graduate School of Letters(M 60/7)

Div. of Sociology(M 5/0)

Theoretical Sociology, Empirical Sociology, Social Psychology, Philosophy

Div. of Japanese Literature(M 13/4)

Ancient Japanese Literature, Modern Japanese Literature, Japanese Linguistics, Chinese Language and Chinese Literature

Div. of English Literature(M 12/1)

English Literature, English Linguistics, Linguistic Cultre American Literature

Div. of History(M 5/0)

Japanese History, Asian History, Western History

Div. of Geography(M 0/0)

Human Geography, Phisical Geography, Regional Geography

Div. of Pedagogy(M 20/2)

Pedagogy, Education Method, Psychology

Div. of Physical Education(M 5/0)

Physical Education, Physical Education Method Exercise Physiology and Biomecanics

Graduate School of Science(M 43/2)

Div. of Mathematics(M 7/1)

Analysis, Geometry, Algebra, Probability and Statistics, Functional Analysis

Div. of Physics(M 19/0)

Elementary Particle Physics, Atomic Physics, Radiation Physics, Theoretical Solid State Physics, Experimental

Solid State Physics, High Energy Physics

Div. of Chemistry(M 6/0)

Inorganic and Analytical Chemistry, Organic Chemistry, Physical Chemistry, Polymer Chemistry, Bio Chemistry

Div. of Biology(M 11/1)

Animal Morphology, Animal Physiology and Ecology, Plant Morphology, Plant Physiology and Ecology, Cytology and Genetics, Environmental Biology

大阪教育大学
(Osaka Kyôiku Daigaku)

Osaka Kyoiku University

4-88 Minami-Kawahori-cho,Tennoji-ku,Osaka-shi,Osaka 543
☎ 06-771-8131 FAX 06-775-0591

Founded 1874
Professors 134
Associate Professors 120
Assistant Professors(Tenured) 37
Assistant Professors(Non-tenured) 218
Research Assistants 28
Undergraduate Students/Foreign Students 4, 209/0
Graduate Students/Foreign Students 274/48
Library 561, 258 volumes
Contact: Foreign Students Section, Instruction Division

Educational philosophy We aim at bringing up specially competent educators as well as erudites with rich culture who can play active parts in the areas of information and internationalization.

Foreign students We believe your student life here will help you become a capable member of the international community and bear the fruits of study unforgettable in your life.

Environment The University composed of Tennoji Campus, Ikeda Campus, and Hirano Campus, each conveniently located with an atmosphere suitable for study and research, for its repletion and development, the University will carry out removal-and integration to the new campus located in the east of the center of Osaka Prefecture, quiet and blessed with green-shrouded natural environment.

Facilities University Library, Health Control Center, The Center for Research and Guidance of Educational Practice, Data-Station, Swimming pool, Gymnasium, Practice-Farm, Mountain Lodge

Student activities Campus activities include Freshman Welcome party, University Festival, Sport Festival and Ski Class. At this University, there is a variety of activities; 41 physical circles, 6 music circles, and 42 cultural circles.

Academic programs for foreign students Welcome party, Special Lectures, Observation Tours, Farewell party, Tutoring System.

Services for foreign students Health Clinic, Living-Matters Consultation, Housing Information, Cultural Exchange Program, Scholarships Information.

Undergraduate Programs

Faculty of Education(4, 209/0)

Dept. of Arts and Sciences(1, 311/0)

Elementary School Teacher Training Course (1, 774/0)

Kindergarten Teacher Training Course(77/0)

Lower Secondary School Teacher Training Courese(590/0)

Nurse-Teacher Training Course(156/0)

Teacher Training Course for The Handicapped (301/0)

Graduate Programs

Graduate School of Education(M 274/48)

Div. of Art Education(M 24/4)

Div. of English Language Education(M 8/0)

Div. of Health and Physical Education(M 26/3)

Div. of Home Economics(M 2/0)

Div. of Japanese Language Education(M 35/11)

Div. of Mathematics Education(M 11/1)

Div. of Music Education(M 34/5)

Div. of School Education(M 43/11)

Div. of Science Education(M 25/3)

Div. of Social Studies(M 43/10)

Div. of Special Education(M 23/0)

One-Year Graduate Programs

Course in Mathematics, Course in Science, Course in Music, Course in Physical Education, Course in Painting, Course in Education for the Handicappled

大阪大学
(Osaka Daigaku)

Osaka University

1-1 Yamadaoka, Suita-shi, Osaka 565
☎ 06-877-5111 FAX 06-878-1366

Founded 1931
Professors 526
Associate Professors 463
Assistant Professors(Tenured) 210
Research Assistants 954
Undergraduate Students/Foreign Students 11, 388/56
Graduate Students/Foreign Students 3, 177/319
Library 2, 355, 431 volumes
Contact: International Relations Division, Departmant of General Affairs, Administration Bureau, Osaka University

Educatonal philosophy Osaka university is in the pioneer days at all times. Under the tradition of culture and climate in Osaka, we make it a motto not only to live in the region but to grow up together with the world.

Foreign students We hope any foreign students in our university may success in your study, enjoying Japanese life. We generously make effort for your convenient life.

Environment We have 3 campuses in Suita, Toyonaka and Osaka City in Osaka prefecture, Kinki district. The means of transportation is so convenient in these area, so one hour is enough for moving among them.

Facilities We have sufficient facilities, such as libraries, experimental equipments, gymnasium etc., so you may enough opprtunities in this sence.

Student activities There is a wide variety of extra curricular activities, so you may do anything you want to. Through any festivals and parties, you will promote friend ship with other foreigners and Japanese.

Academic programs for foreign students We have a tutorial system for every foreign students. When you wish Japanese lectures, you may choice them instead of foreign languages.

Services for foreign students We have a counselor system for your physical and mental problems. Each foreign student may be taken care of on your accmodation.

Undergraduate Programs

Faculty of Dentistry(429/0)
- **Dept. of Dentistry**(429/0)

Faculty of Economics(1, 019/13)
- **Dept. of Business Administration**(297/8)
- **Dept. of Economics**(722/5)

Faculty of Engineering(3, 766/16)
- **Dept. of Applied Chemistry**(193/0)
- **Dept. of Applied Fine Chemistry**(197/0)
- **Dept. of Applied Physics**(201/0)
- **Dept. of Architectural Engineering**(188/1)
- **Dept. of Civil Engineering**(192/0)
- **Dept. of Communication Engineering**(201/1)
- **Dept. of Electrical Engineering**(200/1)
- **Dept. of Electronic Engineering**(201/4)
- **Dept. of Environmental Engineering**(190/0)
- **Dept. of Fermentation Technology**(190/1)
- **Dept. of Information Systems Engineering**(78/0)
- **Dept. of Materials Science and Engineering**(195/1)
- **Dept. of Materials Science and Processing**(194/0)
- **Dept. of Mechanical Engineering**(195/4)
- **Dept. of Mechanical Engineering for Computer-Controlled Machinery**(170/2)
- **Dept. of Mechanical Engineering for Industrial Machinery and Systems**(191/0)
- **Dept. of Naval Architecture and Ocean Engineering**(181/1)
- **Dept. of Nuclear Engineering**(178/0)
- **Dept. of Precision Engineering**(189/0)
- **Dept. of Welding and Production Engineering**(242/0)

Faculty of Engineering Science(1, 925/15)
- **Dept. of Biophysical Engineering**(186/4)
- **Dept. of Chemical Engineering**(200/1)
- **Dept. of Chemistry**(206/0)
- **Dept. of Control Engineering**(185/3)
- **Dept. of Electrical Engineering**(214/2)
- **Dept. of Information & Computer Sciences**(310/0)
- **Dept. of Material Physics**(240/0)
- **Dept. of Mechanical Engineering**(384/5)

Faculty of Human Sciences(556/2)
- **Dept. of Human Sciences**(556/2)

Faculty of Law(943/4)
- **Dept. of Law**(943/4)

Faculty of Letters(759/2)
- **Dept. of Aesthetics**(178/0)
- **Dept. of History**(124/1)
- **Dept. of Japanese Studies**(187/0)
- **Dept. of Literature**(181/1)
- **Dept. of Philosophy**(89/0)

Faculty of Medicine(660/0)
- **Dept. of Medicine**(660/0)

Faculty of Pharmaceutical Sciences(351/2)
- **Dept. of Pharmacy**(176/2)
- **Dept. of Pharmaceutical Chemistry**(175/0)

Faculty of Science(980/2)
- **Dept. of Biology**(101/0)
- **Dept. of Chemistry**(227/1)
- **Dept. of Macromolecular Science**(131/0)
- **Dept. of Mathematics**(237/0)
- **Dept. of Physics**(284/1)

Graduate Programs

Graduate School of Dentistry(D 59/7)
- **Div. of Clinical Dentistry**(D 47/2)
- **Div. of Dental Science**(D 12/5)

Graduate School of Economics(M 27/1, D 15/4)
- **Div. of Business Administration**(M 15/1, D 6/2)
- **Div. of Economics**(M 6/0, D 5/1)
- **Div. of Public Econimics**(M 6/0, D 4/1)

Public Economics Planning for Public Expenditure, Public Welfare

Graduate School of Engineering(M 993/41, D 211/85)
- **Div. of Applied Chemistry**(M 58/2, D 15/1)
- **Div. of Applied Fine Chemistry**(M 58/2, D 15/2)
- **Div. of Applied Physics**(M 60/1, D 29/7)
- **Div. of Architectural Engineering**(M 46/7, D 9/9)
- **Div. of Chemical Process Engineering**(M 56/0, D 9/3)

Chemical Process Management, Process System Engineering, Process Design Engineering, Process Design in Solution Chemistry

- **Div. of Civil Engineering**(M 47/2, D 8/7)
- **Div. of Communication Engineering**(M 52/3, D 11/2)
- **Div. of Electrical Engineering**(M 67/4, D 9/4)
- **Div. of Electromagnetic Energy Engineering**(M 4/0, D 17/4)

Laser Engineering, Supra–High Temperature Engineering

Div. of Electronic Engineering(M 65/2, D 12/5)
Div. of Environmental Engineering(M 34/1, D 6/4)
Div. of Fermentation Technology(M 48/5, D 28/12)
Div. of Materials Science & Engineering(M 43/1, D 9/6)
Div. of Mechanical Engineering(M 37/1, D 3/1)
Div. of Mechanical Engineering for Industrial Machinery and Systems(M 38/1, D 5/2)
Div. of Metallurgical Engineering(M 36/1, D 6/2)
Div. of Naval Achitecture(M 30/3, D 9/6)
Div. of Nùclear Engineering(M 51/1, D 3/0)
Div. of Precision Engineering(M 40/0, D 1/0)
Div. of Welding Engineering(M 79/4, D 15/8)
Div. of Mechanical Engineering for Computer-Controlled Machinery(M 16/2)

Graduate School of Engineering Science(M 414/14, D 106/23)
Div. of Chemical Science(M 85/0, D 11/2)
Div. of Mathematical Science(M 4/1, D 4/1)
Div. of Physical Science(M 325/13, D 91/20)

Graduate School of Human Sciences(M 38/8, D 49/8)
Div. of Anthropology(M 15/6, D 11/2)
Div. of Education(M 9/2, D 17/4)
Div. of Psychology(M 5/0, D 14/1)
Div. of Sociology(M 9/0, D 7/1)

Graduate School of Language and Culture(M 48/3)
Div of Language and Culture(M 48/3)

Graduate School of Law(M 26/5, D 30/1)
Div. of Civil Law(M 8/3, D 4/0)
Div. of Public Law(M 18/2, D 26/1)

Graduate School of Letters(M 114/12, D 139/29)
Div. of English Literature(M 12/0, D 17/0)
Div. of French Literature(M 5/0, D 6/0)
Div. of German Literature(M 8/0, D 7/0)
Div. of History(M 18/0, D 15/3)
Div. of Japanese Literature(M 9/1, D 11/1)
Div. of Japanese Studies(M 26/10, D 43/24)
Studies of Asian Cultures
Div. of Philosophy & History of Philosophy(M 14/0, D 11/0)
Div. of Science of Arts(M 22/1, D 29/1)

Graduate School of Medicine(M 40/2, D 328/44)
Div. of Internal Medicine(D 83/6)
Div. of Medical Science(M 40/2)
Div. of Pathology(D 59/10)
Div. of Physiology(D 104/16)
Div. of Social Medicine(D 16/3)
Div. of Surgery(D 66/9)

Graduate School of Pharmaceutical Sciences(M 81/3, D 15/3)
Div. of Biological Pharmaceutical Sciences(M 41/1, D 9/2)
Div. of Chemical Pharmaceutical Sciences(M 40/2, D 6/1)

Graduate School of Science(M 262/6, D 182/20)
Div. of Biochemistry(M 28/1, D 33/4)
Div. of Inorganic & Physical Chemistry(M 40/1, D 30/2)
Dynamic Structure of Materials
Div. of Macromolecular Science(M 34/1, D 16/4)
Div. of Mathematics(M 26/0, D 12/1)
Mathematical Analysis
Div. of Organic Chemistry(M 42/0, D 14/1)
Div. of Physics(M 70/1, D 50/6)
Nuclear Matter Physics, Physics of Many Body Problems
Div. of Physiology(M 22/2, D 27/2)
Biological Dynamics

大阪外国語大学
(Osaka Gaikokugo Daigaku)

Osaka University of Foreign Studies

8-1-1 Aomatani-Higashi, Minoo-shi, Osaka 562
☎ 0727-28-3111 FAX 0727-29-4799

Founded 1921
Professors 72
Associate Professors 69
Assistant Professors(Tenured) 22
Assistant Professors(Non-tenured) 408
Research Assistants 4
Undergraduate Students/Foreign Students 4, 105/0
Graduate Students/Foreign Students 63/11
Library 439, 496 volumes
Contact: Student Division, Admissions Section

Educational philosophy We have three aims in our teaching and researches: teaching and studying foreign languages and culture, abroad in theory and practice, giving high-level education needed for international activities, and better understanding of foreign countries through languages.

Foreign students Most of the foreign students come to our school with the purpose of studying Japanese. Therefore, to serve their purpose, we are providing them with the excellent studying and living environment. Beides, most of our Japanese student speak English, and almost all the main languages of the world are taught at our school, so the foreign students will not feel lonely even at the moment of their arrival.

Environment Our university is in Minoo-City, in the northwest of Osaka Prefecture. Minoo City has about 120, 000 people. It is a residential city blessed with rich nature, and is near the International Airport and Osaka City. Because of convenience of transportation, there are a lot of educational and research institutions in Minoo and the neighboring cities.

Facilities Classrooms and Faculty Offices, Administration Building, University Library, Gymnasium, Extra Curricular Activities Facilities, University Hall, Dormitory for Students, Traning Camp, Off Campus Training Facility, Foreign Student Hall

Student activities Some of the Popular campus events are orientation study, summer festival, school festival, ski school, and freshmen welcome party. There are many variety of extra curricular activities, for example chorus, music band, art, volleyball, football, Judo, etc.

Academic programs for foreign students General Education and other subjects for foreign Students (Exceptions), Tutoring system

Services for foreign students Health clinic, personal/psychological counseling, Housing information, part-time job information, JOB Mediation

Undergraduate Programs

Faculty of Foreign studies(4, 105/0)

- **Dept. of Arabic-African studies**(208/0)
- **Dept. of Burmese studies**(72/0)
- **Dept. of Chinese studies**(273/0)
- **Dept. of Danish-Swedish Studies**(115/0)
- **Dept. of English studies**(303/0)
- **Dept. of French studies**(163/0)
- **Dept. of German studies**(160/0)
- **Dept. of Hindi-Urdu studies**(210/0)
- **Dept. of Indonesian-Filipino studies**(152/0)
- **Dept. of Italian studies**(137/0)
- **Dept. of Japanese studies**(159/0)
- **Dept. of Korean studies**(79/0)
- **Dept. of Mongolian studies**(67/0)
- **Dept. of Persian studies**(75/0)
- **Dept. of Portuguese-Brazilian studies**(129/0)
- **Dept. of Russian studies**(229/0)
- **Dept. of Spanish studies**(243/0)
- **Dept. of Thai-Vietnamese studies**(125/0)

Graduate Programs

Graduate School of Foeign Language Studies(M 63/11)

East Asian Language Studies(Chinese Language Studies, Korean Language Studies, Mongolian Language Studies), South Asian Language, Studies(Indonesian Language Studies, Thai-Vietnamese Language Studies, Burmese Language Studies), West Asian Language Studies(Hindi-Urdu Language Studies, Arabic Language Studies, Persian Language Studies), English Language Studies, German Language Studies, French Language Studies, Italian Language Studies, Spanish Language Studies, Russian Language Studies, Japanese Language Studies

One-Year Graduate Programs

Foreign Language Studies Course

Danish Language Studies Major

滋賀大学

(Shiga Daigaku)

Shiga University

1-1-1 Banba, Hikone-shi, Shiga 522

☎ 0749-22-5600 FAX 0749-23-9770

Founded 1949
Professors 83
Associate Professors 90
Assistant Professors(Tenured) 16
Assistant Professors(Non-tenured) 69
Research Assistants 9
Undergraduate Students/Foreign Students 2, 990/30
Graduate Students/Foreign Students 37/19
Library 415, 780 volumes
Contact: Admission Office

Educational philosophy We aim at teaching and studing up-to-date high-level art & sciences and professional education under the spirit of the Fundamental Law of Education, and master the profound principle of education so students may contribute a great deal to cultural betterment and social improvement in our country and abroad.

Foreign students We can offer to students from abroad the opportunities of obtaining high-level academic attainments while enjoying a homely atmosphere, traditionally maintained ever since the foundation of our school.

Environments The University campuses are located in Hikone & Otsu City. Hikone is a historic place with a population of approximately 99, 000 and can be reached in 50 minutes by train from Kyoto. Otsu is a metoropolitan city of Shiga Pref. with 250, 000 in 15 minutes by train from Kyoto. These cities face Lake Biwa, which is the largest lake in Japan.

Facilities Health and Medical Service Center, Library, Computer Center, Archives Meseum, Information Processing Center, Institute for Economics and Business Research, Institute of School Education, Research Institute for Lake Biwa, Gymnasium, Dormitories, Univesity Farm.

Student activities There are 35 cultural extra-curricular activities and 71 recreational ones, composed of students in two faculties, Education and Economics, available for anyone. University festivals are held on each campus, in October and November, in which you are advised to actively participate.

Academic programs for foreign students There is a tutorial system for foreign students to help them with their studies. It aims to assist foreign undergraduate students during their first two years and graduate students during their first year of study.

Services for foreign students Health clinic, personal/psychological counseling, College housing, Housing information, part-time job information, vocational guidance, homestay, cultural exchange propgram

Undergraduate Programs

Faculty of Economics(1, 791/10)
Dept. of Accounting(296/1)
Dept. of Business Administration(444/4)
Dept. of Economics(836/3)
Dept. of Information Processing and Management(213/1)
Faculty of Education(1, 199/20)
Elementary-School Teacher Training Course(672/3)
Handicapped-Children's-School Teacher Training Course(96/1)
Information Science Course(53/0)
Kindergarten Teacher Training Course(110/1)
Lower-Secondary School Teacher Training Course(257/12)

Graduate Programs

Graduate School of Economics(M 29/12)
Div. of Business Administration(M 12/7)
Theory of Business Organization, Business Administration, Financial Management, Personal Management, Japanese Business History, Theory of Firms, Theory of Small-to-Middle Sized companies, International Business, Marketing, Accounting, Accounting Information, Managerial Accounting, Financial Statement Analysis, International Accounting, Mechanized(Computer)Accounting, Management Information Systems, Industrial Engineering, Information Processing, Commercial Law, Economic Law and its Seminar, Reading of Foreign Literature(English, French, German)
Div. of Economics(M 17/5)
Principles of Economics, Principles of Political Economics, History of Economics Thought, Economics Policy, Industrial Economics, Public Finance, Monetary Economics, International Economic Relations, Statistics, Public Law, Commercial Law, Economic Law and its Seminar, Reading of Foreign Literature(English, French, German)

One-Year Graduate Programs

Special Education Course
Education of the mentally handicapped Major
Pedagogy Course
Podagogy Major

滋賀医科大学
(Shiga Ika Daigaku)

Shiga University of Medical Science

Seta Tsukinowa-cho, Otsu-shi, Shiga 520-21
☎ 0775-48-2111 FAX 0775-43-8659

Founded 1974
Professors 38
Associate Professors 32
Assistant Professors(Tenured) 32
Assistant Professors(Non-tenured) 252
Research Assistants 130
Undergraduate Students/Foreign Students 623/0
Graduate Students/Foreign Students 104/9
Library 91, 502 volumes
Contact: Student Division ☎ 0775-48-2071

Educational philosophy Our goal is to develop the skills, crafts, and attitudes of our students to prepare them for careers in the professional practice of medicine, with an abiding focus on the cultivation of humanity and character as a physician and researcher.
Foreign students Academic training received in basic research combined with experience in a clinical setting at our school should prepare graduates to pursue medical careers in their own countries.
Environment Otsu is a culturally sophisticated,medium-sized city, with a population of 260, 000, east of historic Kyoto and at the bottom of beautiful Lake Biwa the largest lake in Japan. Our campus is located close to the municipal library and The Museum of Modern Art, Shiga.
Facilities University campus, University Hospital, Molecular Neurobiology Research Center, University Library,gymnasium
Student activities There is a school festival,an intercollegiate match with our sister school, etc. Students enjoy belonging to athletic and/or nonathletic clubs.
Academic programs for foreign students Tutoring system
Services for foreign students Personal counseling

Undergraduate Programs

Faculty of Medicine(623/0)
Dept.of Medicine(623/0)

Graduate Programs

Graduate School of Medicine(D 104/9)
Div. of Biological Information and Control(D 24/2)
Div. of Biological Regulation of Metabolism(D 54/7)

Div. of Biological Defense Mechanism(D 7/0)
Div. of Development-Differentiation Proliferation(D 14/0)
Div. of Environment-Ecology(D 2/0)
Anatomy, Physiology, Biochemistry, Pathology, Microbiology, Pharmacology, Preventive Medicine, Health Science, Legal Medicine, Experimental Radiology, Internal Medicine, Pediatrics, Psychiatry, Dermatology, Surgery, Orthopedic Surgery, Neurosurgery, Otorhinolaryngology, Obstetrics and Gynecology Urology, Ophthalmology, Anesthesiology, Radiology, Oral and Maxillofacial Surgery

---

和歌山大学
(Wakayama Daigaku)

University of Wakayama

930 Sakaedani, Wakayama-shi, Wakayama 640
☎ 0734-54-0361 FAX 0734-54-0378

Founded 1949
Professors 75
Assosiate Professors(Tenured) 64
Assistant Professors(Non-tenured) 12
Assistant Professors 69
Research Assistants 5
Undergraduate Students/Foreign Students 2549/2
Graduate Students/Foreign Students 15/9
Library 590, 000 volumes
Contact: Student Division of Student Affair Office

Educational philosophy Our purpose is to develope well-rounded, internationally minded young men and women who have acquired a sound knowledge of the basics in their chosen field, whether that be Economics or Education, Business Admistration or Culture and Society. They will, we hope, be fully equipped to be the leaders of a society, entering the twenty first Century.
Foreign students We aim to give foreign students an opportunity to do advanced studies in subjects beneficial to themselves as well as to their home society. In addition, we hope to promote mutual understanding by bringing them into contact with Japanese people and culture.
Environment Our campus is located on a low hill, surrounded by the beauties of nature and commanding a fine view of Wakayama City, which has a population of 400, 000 and is a mere 20 km south of the new Osaka international airport which is now under construction. The area is rich in the history of Japan.
Facilities Attached Library, Institute of Economic Research, Institute of Economics and Econometrics Educational Research Center, Computer Center, gymnasium, swimming pool, student center, multi purpose grounds, running track
Student activities Popular campus events include the School festival, Dormitory festival and so on. There are many other extra curricular activities, such as popular music, Japanese classical music, drama, baseball, yachting, judo, tennis, soccer, rugby, and many other sports and clutural clubs
Academic programs for foreign students In the Education Department, the second foreign language requirement may be fulfilled by the study of Japanese language and culture. The Economics Department has a tutoring system to take care of foreign student needs.
Services for foreign students Health clinic, Personal counseling

Undergraduate Programs

Faculty of Economics(1422/1)
Dept. of Economics(643/0)
Dept. of Business Administration(608/1)
Dept. of Industrial Engineering(171/0)
Faculty of Education(1068/1)
Dept. of Culture and Society(120/1)
Dept. of Industrial Science(80/0)
Junior High School Teachers Training Course(270/0)
Primary School Teachers Training Course(554/0)
Teachers Training Course of School For Handicapped Children(44/0)

Graduate Programs

Graduate School of Economics(M 15/9)
Div. of Economics(M 2/2)
Agricultural Policy, Economic Administration, Economic History, Economic Policy, Economic Statistics, Japanese Economic History, Principles of Economics, Public Finance, Social Policy, Theoretical Economics, Western Economic History, World Economy, Businness History, Financial Accounting, International Finance, Management of Businness, Managerial Accounting, Managerial Economics, Marketing, Businness Mathematics, Industrial Engineering, Industrial Planning, Information Processing System, Office Automation, Public Law, Civil Law, Commercial Law, Social Law
Div. of Business Adoministration(M 13/7)

One-Year Graduate Programs

Economics Course
Industrial Engineering Major

Local Public Universities

姫路工業大学
(Himeji Kôgyô Daigaku)

Himeji Institute of Technology

2167 Shosha, Himeji-shi, Hyogo 671-22
☎ 0792-66-1661 FAX 0792-66-8868

Founded 1949

Undergraduate Programs

Faculty of Engineering
- **Dept. of Mechanical Engineering**
- **Dept. of Chemical Engineering**
- **Dept. of Electrical Engineering**
- **Dept. of Electronic Engineering**
- **Dept. of Applied Chemistry**
- **Dept. of Materials Science & Engineering**

Faculty of Science
- **Dept. of Life Science**
- **Dept. of Material Science**

Graduate Programs

Graduate School of Engineering
- **Div. of Applied chemistry** (M)
- **Div. of Chemical Engineering** (M)
- **Div. of Electricity and Electronics** (M)
- **Div. of Material Science** (M)
- **Div. of Mechanical Engineering** (M)
- **Div. of Productive Engineering** (D)

神戸市外国語大学
(Kôbeshi Gaikokugo Daigaku)

Kobe City University of Foreign Studies

9-1, Gakuen-higashi-machi, Nishi-ku, Kobe-shi, Hyogo 651-21
☎ 078-794-8121 FAX 078-792-9020

Founded 1949
Professors 45
Associate Professors 35
Assistant Professors(Tenured) 9
Assistant Professors(Non-tenured) 124
Research Assistants 1
Undergraduate Students/Foreign Students 1, 914/2
Graduate Students/Foreign Students 20/0
Library 242, 307 volumes
Contact: Admission Office

Educational philosophy Our university aims to study and teach foreign languages, their cultural backgrounds and international relations both in their academic and practical aspects, and to have the students acquire wide international culture and help them cultivate the ability to play an active role in international affairs.

Foreign students Since classes are generally conducted in Japanese, foreign students are required to have sufficient ability of the Japanese language.

Environment The campus is located in the center of so-called " Kobe Academic Town, " which lies in the north-west of downtwon Kobe. It is accessible by a twenty-five minute rapid train ride from downtown. Kobe is one of the largest trading ports in Japan with a population of 1, 300, 000. Its beautiful cosmopolitan environment attracts many foreign people.

Facilities The campus facilities include: the library with a spacious reading room, the audiovisual building, a computer class-room with sophisticated electronic equipments, a playground, a gymnasium, swimming pool, the students' union building, etc.

Student activities The campus life may be enjoyed by students who participate in such annual events as " star festival in July, " " autumn college festival, " and " college drama fesival, " etc. About 40 extracurricular clubs are active in the campus, such as Japanese archery club, tea ceremony club, football club, etc.

Academic programs for foreign students We have no special programs for foreign students, but the staff are eager to deal with various problems foreign students may have.

Services for foreign students Our university has no dormitory. The section for students' affairs is happy to help foreign students find an appropriate apartment house, a side-job, or give them counseling, and help them participate in extracurricular activities.

Undergraduate Programs

Faculty of Foreign Studies(1914/2)
- **Dept. of Chinese**(175/0)
- **Dept. of English-American**(540/1)
- **Dept. of International Relations**(326/1)

Faculty of Foreign studies(1914/2)
- **Dept. of Russian**(170/0)
- **Dept. of Spanish**(180/0)

Graduate Programs

Graduate School of Foreign Studies(M 20/0)
- **Div. of Chinese Linguistics**(M 1/0)
- **Div. of English Linguistics**(M 17/0)
- **Div. of Russian Linguistics**(M 0/0)
- **Div. of Spanish Linguistics**(M 2/0)

神戸商科大学
(Kôbe Syôka Daigaku)

Kobe University of Commerce

8-2-1 Gakuen-Nishimachi,Nishi-ku, Kobe-shi, Hyogo 651-21
☎ 078-794-6161 FAX 078-794-6166

Founded 1929
Professors 46
Associate Professors 38
Assistant Professors(Tenured) 14
Assistant Professors(Non-tenured) 45
Research Assistants 9
Undergraduate Students/Foreign Students 1, 972/16
Graduate Students/Foreign Students 46/17
Library 322, 721 volumes
Contact: Section of Academic Affairs

Educatonal philosophy We intend to encourage students to be intellectual and active economists who are tough enough in both theory and practice of social studies field. The ideal is thus "Caelum illuminatio mea", i. e., To learn from divine providence or truth to polish social ethics or knowledge.
Foreign students We welcome every student who work hard together with us to become leading cosmopolitans and to contribute onto his/her home country. And we shall do every effort to supplement living expenses for hard-work students.
Environment Gakuen-Nishimachi is a newly established academic town located in the westrn part of Kobe, about 20 minutes form downtown by subway. The area is surrouded by green fields and hills, yet it is convenient to downtown Osaka, the temples of Kyoto or the beaches of Suma in a short trip.
Facilities Library, Institute of Economic Research, Information Systems Center, Sports Training Center, Swimming pool, Gymnasium, Auditorium
Student activities Popular campus events includes school festival, feshmmen welcome party, inter-university tournament. There is a wide variety of extra curricular activities, including choral groups, mandolin, tennis, baseball, football, etc.
Academic programs for foreign students Tutoring system, Alternative subject system
Services for foreign students Health clinic, Personal/psycological counseling, Housing information, Part-time job information, Excursion

Undergraduate Programs

Faculty of Economics & Business Administration(1,972/16)
Dept. of Economics(666/4)
Dept. of Business Administration(587/2)
Dept. of Management Science(331/2)
Dept. of Marketing and International Business(388/8)

Graduate Programs

Graduate School of Economics(M 15/9, D 7/1)
Graduate School of Business Administration(M 14/4, D 10/3)

京都府立大学
(Kyôto Furitsu Daigaku)

Kyoto Prefectural University

1-5 Hangi-cho, Shimogamo, Sakyo-ku, Kyoto-shi, Kyoto 606
☎ 075-781-3131 FAX 075-781-1841

Founded 1895
Professors 42
Associate Professors 43
Assistant Professors(Tenured) 14
Assistant Professors(Non-tenured) 97
Research Assistants 20
Undergraduate Students/Foreign Students 1255/1
Graduate Students/Foreign Students 63/9
Library 237, 194 volumes
Contact: Office of Students Affairs

Educational philosophy The objectives of Kyoto Prefectural University shall be to further the researches in scientific therories and their practical applications in the wide-ranged perspective so that we may contribute to the advancement of learning and culture, the development of the local industries and the improvement of the local life.
Environment The campus is located on the Kamo river, the symbol of Kyoto, next to the Prefectural Botanical Garden and the Prefectural Reference Library and extends across 131, 130 square meters forming quiet and green-shrouded surroundings, in which students who gather from all over Japan are enjoying campus life.
Facilities University Library, Gymnasiums, University Farm, University Forest, Computers for Practice, University Hall, Laboratories, Tennis courts, Cooperative store and restaurant
Student activities Popular campus events include freshmen welcome party, university festival and homecoming. There is wide variety of extra curricular activities, such as volunteer work, chours club, marchig band, drama club, baseball, football, soccer, etc.

Undergraduate Programs

Faculty of Literature(544/1)
Course of Literature(220/0)
Course of History(139/0)

Course of Social Welfare(185/1)
Faculty of Living Scinece(229/0)
Course of Food Science(100/0)
Course of Housing and Design(129/0)
Faculty of Agriculture(482/0)
Course of Agriculture(177/0)
Course of Forestry(173/0)
Course of Agricultural Chemistry(132/0)

Graduate Programs

Graduate School of Living Science(M 20/6)
Food Science and Nutrition Course, Housng and Envirohmental Design Course
Graduate School of Agriculture(M 41/2, D 4/0)
Agriculture Course, Forestry Course, Agricultural Chemistry Course
Graduate School of Literature(M 2/1)
Japanese and Chinese Literature Course

京都市立芸術大学
(Kyôto Shiritsu Geijutsu Daigaku)

Kyoto City University of Arts

13-6 Kutsukake-cho, Ooe, Nishikyo-ku, Kyoto-shi, Kyoto 610-11
☎ 075-332-0701 FAX 075-332-0709

Founded 1880
Professors 49
Associate Professors 29
Assistant Professors(Tenured) 13
Assistant Professors(Non-tenured) 182
Undergraduate Students/Foreign Students 752/0
Graduate Students/Foreign Students 160/29
Library 73, 303 volumes

Educational philosophy We aim at creating a new art, based on the tradition, for the benefit of culture, arts, and the development of the society.
Foreign students We hope that foreign students can study under liberal circumstances, and enjoy the cultural and historied atmosphere of Kyoto.
Environment Kyoto traces its history and tradition back to 1,200 years ago, and is now one of the most cultured cities in the world, with a population of 1, 500, 000.
Facilities In addition to general educational facilities, we own and preserve numerous precious works of art.
Student activities Presently 19 clubs are operating in our institution. Every year a big exhibition of the Fine Art Department is held in February, and several concerts and operas are performed in the Faculty of Music.

Undergraduate Programs

Faculty of Arts(511/0)
Dept. of Crafts (Ceramics Major Dying and Weaving Major, Urushi Laquering Major) (122/0)
Dept. of Design (Environmental Design Major, Product Design Major, Visual Design Major) (101/0)
Dept. of Fine Arts (Japanese Paintings Major, Suclupture Major, Oil Paintings Major/Conceptual and Media Art Major, Printmaking Major) (288/0)
Faculty of Music(241/0)
Dept. of Music

Graduate Programs

Graduate School of Arts(M 125/25)
Graduate School of Music(M 35/4)

京都府立医科大学
(Kyôto Furitsu Ika Daigaku)

Kyoto Prefectural University of Medicine

465 Kajii-cho, Kawaramachi-dori Hirokoji-agaru, Kamigyo-ku, Kyoto-shi, Kyoto 602
☎ 075-251-5111～8 FAX 075-211-7093

Founded 1872
Professors 38
Associate Professors 34
Assistant Professors(Tenured) 50
Assistant Professors(Non-tenured) 20
Research Assistants 167
Undergraduate Students/Foreign Students 632/0
Graduate Students/Foreign Students 169/6
Library 205, 724 volumes
Contact: Instruction Section, Student Division ☎ 075-251-5227

Educational philosophy The University was founded for the purpose of giving instruction and training to its students so that they might become competent physicians and pursue advanced studies of medicine, thereby contributing to the advancement of welfare and the promotion of science.
Foreign students The University has received a number of graduate students and researchers from abroad, and been trying to make our medical programs satisfactory and useful to them.
Environment Kyoto, which was the capital of Japan for more than 1, 000 years before Tokyo, abounds not only in places of historic interest but in cultural facilities. The University is located in its central part, in an environment particularly noted for its scenic

beauty.

Facilities Central Laboratories(6 Divisions), Library, Gymnasiums, Tennis Courts, etc. Attached Units(Hospital, Children's Research Hospital, Center for Regional Health Service, School of Nursing)

Student activities The new student will find special interest groups which offer him or her a variety of cultural, athletic, and recreational opportunities for a better campus life. There are more than 50 cultural and athletic clubs.

Services for foreign students Information about cultural exchange programs, infomation about scholarships out of several funds, housing information, student health service, railroad fare discount, etc.

Undergraduate Programs

Faculty of Medicine(632/0)

Graduate Programs

Graduate School of Medicine(D 169/6)

Course I(D 9/1)

Anatomy, Physiology, Biochemistry, Pharmacology

Course II(D 6/2)

Pathology, Microbiology, Medical Zoology

Course III(D 12/3)

Hygiene, Preventive Medicine, Legal Medicine

Course IV(D 71/0)

Internal Medicine, Pediatrics, Psychiatry, Dermatology, Radiology, Laboratory Medicine, Pediatrici Medicine(Research Institute for Children's Diseases)

Course V(D 71/0)

Surgery, Neurosurgery, Orthopaedic Surgery, Obstetrics and Gynecology, Urology, Otorhinolaryngology, Ophthalmology, Anesthesiology, Pediatric Surgery(Research Institute for Children's diseases)

奈良県立医科大学

(Nara Kenritsu Ika Daigaku)

Nara Medical University

840 Shijo-cho, Kashihara-shi, Nara 634
☎ 07442-2-3051

Founded 1945

Undergraduate Programs

Faculty of Medicine

Dept. of Medicine

Basic Medicine : Anatomy, Bacteriology, Biochemistry, Hygiene, Legal Medicine, Oncological Pathology, Parasitology, Pathology, Pahrmacology, Physiology, Public Health

Clinical Medicine : Anethesiology, Clinico-Laboratory Diagnostics, Dermatology, Internal Medicine, Neurology, Obstetrics and Gynecology, Ophthalmology, Oral and Maxillofacial Surgery, Orthopedics, Otorhinolaryngology, Pediatrics, Psychiatry, Radiology, Surgery, Tumor Radiology, Urology

奈良県立商科大学

(Nara Kenritsu Shôka Daigaku)

Nara University of Commerce

10 Funahashi-cho, Nara-shi, Nara 630
☎ 0742-22-4978 FAX 0742-22-4991

Founded 1990
Professors 8
Associate Professor 9
Assistant Professors(Tenured) 1
Assistant Professors(Non-tenured) 5
Undergraduate Students/Foreign Stendents 116/0
Library 30, 982 volumes

Educational philosophy Our educational philosophy is to create able students with practical ability in buniness managemant. We aim at teaching and studying not only accademic theories but also practical theories. That's why we have only evening sessions.

Foreign students According to the order by the Immigration, any educational institution with eveing sessions are not allowed to admit foreign students.

Environments The city of Nara, with a population of 350, 000 is located in the north-western edge of Nara prefecture. There used to be a royal court in the city some twelve hundred years ago. It is also famous for so many old temples which are national treasure.

Facilities Computer Center, Library, Gymnasium, Student activity room, Auditorium, Placemert information center, etc.

Student activities Such campus events as college festival and athletic meet. There is also a wide variety of extra curricular activities including English speakig society, tea ceremony, baseball, badminton, art, Volleyball, Karate, beach volleyball, Hokke religeon study, youth hostel, etc.

Undergraduate Programs

Faculty of Commerce(116/0)

Dept. of Commerce

大阪市立大学
(Osaka Shiritsu Daigaku)
Osaka City University

3-3-138 Sugimoto, Sumiyoshi-ku, Osaka-shi, Osaka
☎ 06-605-2131 FAX 06-697-2165

Founded 1928
Professors 234
Associate Professors 198
Assistant Professors(Tenured) 147
Assistant Professors(Non-tenured) 514
Reserarch Assistants 257
Undergraduate Students/Foreign Students 6, 665/31
Graduate Students/Foreign Students 775/73
Library 1, 588, 959 volumes
Contact: Admission Office, Education Bureau

Educational philosophy As the largest municipal university in Japan, we should contribute to economic, cultural and social developments of the citizens. We make every efforts to provide excellent education and academic training both in undergraduate and graduate courses.
Foreign students We think that growing numbers of foreign students will contribute much to the mutual exchange of culture and study. We heartily wish that your student life here will be of much delight and success.
Facilities University Library, University Hospital, Toneyama Institute for Tuberculosis Reserch, Nursing School, Botanical Garden, Cosmic Ray Institute, Institute of Organic Chemistry, Institute for Economic Reserch etc.
Student sctivities Popular campus events include freshmen welcome festival, boat festival and school festival. There is a wide variety of extra curricular activities including choral groups, marching band, American football, baseball, etc.
Academic programs for foreign students Japanese launguage lesson, Tutoring system, etc.
Services for foreign students Health clinic, College housing (23 rooms, for single), cultural exchange program, summer trip, etc.

Undergraduate Programs

Faculty of Businesss(1, 042/5)
  Dept. of Businesss
Faculty of Economics(1, 140/18)
  Dept. of Economics
Faculty of Engineering(1, 102/3)
  Dept. of Applied Chemistry(153/0)
  Dept. of Applied Physics(140/0)
  Dept. of Architecture and Building Engineering(171/1)
  Dept. of Bioapplied Chemistry(29/0)
  Dept. of Civil Engineering(187/0)
  Dept. of Electrical Engineering(200/1)
  Dept. of Information and Computer Sciences(31/0)
  Dept. of Mechanical Engineering(191/1)
Faculty of Law(1, 061/4)
  Dept. of Law
Faculty of Literature(763/1)
  Dept. of History and Geography(156/0)
  Dept. of Japanese and Chinese Literature(72/0)
  Dept. of Western Literature(134/0)
  Dept. of Human Relations(205/1)
  Dept. of Philosophy(15/0)
Faculty of Medical School(510/0)
  Dept. of Medicine
Faculty of Science(495/0)
  Dept. of Mathematics(98/0)
  Dept. of Physics(123/0)
  Dept. of Chemistry(120/0)
  Dept. of Biology(93/0)
  Dept. of Geosciences(61/0)
Faculty of Science of Living(552/0)
  Dept. of Food and Nurition(26/0)
  Dept. of Enviromental Design(53/0)
  Dept. of Human Development and Welfare(47/0)

Graduate Programs

Graduate School of Business Administration(M 9/0, D 18/5)
  Div. of Business Administration(M 4/0, D 5/2)
  Div. of Business Science(M 5/0, D 13/3)
Graduate School of Economics(M 25/6, D 30/5)
  Div. of Economics Theory and Economics History(M 10/2, D 21/4)
  Div. of Economics Policy(M 15/4, D 9/1)
Graduate School of Engineering(M 150/8, D 13/3)
  Div. of Mechanical Engineering(M 27/0, D 0/0)
  Div. of Electrical Engineering(M 38/7, D 4/2)
  Div. of Applied Chemistry(M 39/0, D 5/1)
  Div. of Architecture and Building Engineering(M 9/0, D 1/0)
  Div. of Civil Engineering(M 20/1, D 0/0)
  Div. of Applied Physics(M 17/0, D 3/0)
Gracuate School of Law(M 12/4, D 20/3)
  Div. of Private Law(M 2/2, D 8/1)
  Div. of Public Law(M 10/2, D 12/2)
Graduate School of Literature(M 36/4, D 68/12)
  Div. of Chinese Language and Literature(M 5/2)
  Div. of Chinese Literautre(D 8/3)
  Div. of Education(M 1/0, D 4/1)
  Div. of English Literature(M 2/2, D 5/0)
  Div. of French Literature(M 7/1, D 8/0)
  Div. of Geography(M 2/0, D 2/0)
  Div. of German Literature(M 2/0, D 4/1)
  Div. of History of Japan(M 5/0, D 6/0)
  Div. of Japanese Literature(M 4/0, D 12/3)
  Div. of Oriental History(M 1/0, D 5/1)
  Div. of Philosohy(M 3/1, D 4/0)
  Div. of Psychology(M 1/0, D 4/0)

Div. of Sociology(M 3/0, D 6/3)
Graduate School of Medicine(D 184/3)
Div. of Internal Medicine(D 52/0)
Div. of Pathology(D 12/1)
Div. of Physiology(D 43/2)
Div. of Social Medicine(D 17/0)
Div. of Surgery(D 60/0)
Graduate School of Science(M 93/1, D 54/8)
Div. of Biology(M 17/0, D 15/3)
Div. of Chemistry(M 37/0, D 6/4)
Div. of Geosciences(M 14/1, D 8/0)
Div. of Mathematics(M 5/0, D 5/0)
Div. of Physics(M 20/0, D 20/1)
Graduate School of Science of Living(M 37/6, D 26/5)
Div. of Environmental Design(M 10/4, D 6/2)
Div. of Human Nutrition and Health Sciences(M 15/1, D 5/1)
Div. of Human Development and Welfare(M 12/3, D 15/2)

大阪女子大学
(Osaka Joshi Daigaku)

Osaka Women's University

2–1 Daisen–cho, Sakai–shi, Osaka,
☎ 0722–22–4811 FAX 0722–38–5539

Founded 1924
Professors 33
Associate Professor 21
Assistant Professors(Tenured) 11
Assistant Professors(Non–tenured) 78
Research Assistants 10
Undergraduate Students/Foreign Sudents 786/12
Graduate Students/Foreign Students 20/2
Library 223, 316 volumes
Contact: General Affairs Division.

Educational philosophy We aim to build students' character and to promote the cultural development of women through our programs of study.
Foreign students Our campus is small in size and in the number of students and staff, so students find it easy to cultivate contacts with students and teachers. We hope that foreign students will contribute to world–wide efforts for peace and human welfare.
Environment Our nuiversity is situated in Sakai City, alongside the ancient tomb of Emperor Nintoku, considered to be the greatest Imperial mausoleum in Japan. Also in the neighborhood are the public library of Sakai City, museum for local arts and products, and Daisen Park. We enjoy fine cultural and natural surroundings.
Facilities Library, Gymnasium, Auditorium, Computer center, Student activities building, Tennis court, Student dormitory.
Student activities Popular campus events includes freshmen welcome party, university festival, sports festival. There is wide variety of extra curricular activities, including university orchestra, choral groups, marching band, flower arrangement, cha–no–yu, volleyball, basketball, tennis, etc.
Academic programs for foreign students Japanese language, Japanese affairs, tutorial system
Services for foreign students Dormitory for foreign students, Housing information, Part–time job information.

Undergraduate Programs

Faculty of Arts and Sciences(786/12)
Dept. of Applied Methematics(68/1)
Dept. of English Language and Literature(191/3)
Dept. of Human Sciences(192/8)
Dept. of Japanese Language and Literature(184/0)
Dept. of Natural Sciences(151/0)

Graduate Programs

Graduate School of Literature(M 20/2)
Div. of English and American Language and Literature(M 10/0)
English Literature, American Literature, English Linguistics, English and American Literature, English and American Language and Literature, Western Classics, Comparative Literature, German Literature, French Literature
Div. of Japanese Language and Literature(M 10/2)
Japanese Literature, Japanese Linguistics, History of Japanese Language, Japanese Language and Literature, History of Japanese Language, Chinese Literature, History of Japanese Culture

---

大阪府立大学
(Osaka Furitsu Daigaku)

University of Osaka Prefecture

4–804 Mozu–Umemachi, Sakai–shi, Osaka 591
☎ 0722–52–1161 FAX 0722–52–1272

Founded 1949
Professors 168
Associate Professors 158
Assistant Professors(Tenured) 147
Assistant Professors(Non–tenured) 166
Research Assistants 232
Undergraduate Students/Foreign Students 4, 605/47
Graduate Students/Foreign Students 622/94
Library 928, 183 volumes
Contact: Student Bureau

Educational Philosophy As a center of learning connected with industry, imparting extensive knowledge, teaching and researching into special subjects of study, and cultivating promising ability with not just ample individuality and heightened culture but adequacy in both intellectual and applicative competence and practicality, thereby contributing to the enhancement of culture and development of industry.

Foreign students We would expect foreign students not only to study or make researches but to introduce to Japanese students here, as good friends to them, the culture of your nations or countries. We would also expect you to become able to understand Japanese culture properly and adequately.

Environment Sakai City, with a population of 800,000, lies south of Osaka City across the Yamato River. Its history is very old and there are many historical and cultural inheritances such as the Emperor Nintoku's Mausoleum which is claimed to be the largest grave, in area, in the world.

Facilities Library, Research Institute for Advanced Science and Technology, Computer Center, Swimming pool, Gymnasium, Conference Hall, Student Hall, Health Administitration Center, Stables and Riding-Ground

Student activities Popular campus events includes university festival, tournaments among some universities. There is a wide variety of extra curricular activities, including choral groups, orchestra, student newspaper, soccer, judo, archery, horsemanship, etc.

Academic programs for foreign students Tutoring system, Exceptional subjects: " Japanese " and " Things Japanese "

Services for foreign students Foreign students' lodging, study and training camp. Dormitory for foreign students, Exchange program, Counseling, Housing information, Part time job information.

Undergraduate Programs

Faculty of Agriculture(831/9)
- **Dept. of Agricultural Chemistry**(172/1)
- **Dept. of Agricultural Engineering**(128/0)
- **Dept. of Horticultural Science and Agronomy** (258/1)
- **Dept. of Veterinary Science**(273/7)

Faculty of Economics(1,134/16)
- **Dept. of Business Administration**(361/16)
- **Dept. of Economics**(773/7)

Faculty of Engineering(2,021/8)
- **Dept. of Aeronautical Engineering**(145/0)
- **Dept. of Applied Chemistry**(289/0)
- **Dept. of Chemical Engineering**(169/0)
- **Dept. of Electrical Engineering**(229/1)

Faculty of Engineering(2,021/8)
- **Dept. of Electronics**(242/2)
- **Dept. of Industrial Engineering**(158/1)
- **Dept. of Mathematical Sciences**(82/2)
- **Dept. of Mechanical Engineering**(334/1)

Faculty of Engineering(2,021/8)
- **Dept. of Metallurgy and Materials Sciences**(232/0)
- **Dept. of Naval Architecuture**(141/1)

Faculty of Integrated Arts and Science(417/9)
- **Dept. of Integrated Arts and Sciences**(417/9)

Faculty of Sócial Welfare(238/5)
- **Dept. of Social Welfare**(238/5)

Graduate Programs

Graduate School of Agriculture(M 91/7, D 31/15)

Div. of Horticultural Science and Agronomy(M 33/3, D 15/9)

Agricultural Politics, Crop Science, Entomology, Farm Management Economics, Floriculture, Genetics and Plant Breeding, Landscape Architecture, Plant Pathology, Pomology, Post-harvest Physiology and Storage of Horticultural Products, Vegetable Crop Science

Div. of Agricultural Engineering(M 13/3, D 4/3)

Agriculutural and Envioronmental Meteorology, Agricultural Machinery, Environmental Control in Agriculture, Land Development Engineering, Urban Landscape Design, Water Utilization in Agriculture

Div. of Agricultural Chemistry(M 45/1, D 7/2)

Applied Microbiology, Biochemistry, Biophysical Chemistry, Chemistry of Natural Products, Fermentation Chemistry, Food Chemistry, Nutrition Chemistry, Pesticide Chemistry, Soil Science, Soil Science and Plant Nutrition

Div. of Veterinary Science(D 11/1)

Laboratory Animal Science, Molecular Biology, Toxicology, Veterinary Anatomy, Veterinary Epidemiology, Veterinary Immunology, Veterinary Internal Medicine, Veterinary Microbiology, Veterinary Pathology, Veterinary Pharmacology, Veterinary Physiology, Veterinary Public Health, Veterinary Radiology, Veterinary Reproduction, Veterinary Surgery

Graduate School of Economics(M 14/9, D 9/2)

Div. of Economics(M 14/9, D 9/2)

Business Economics and Administration, Econometrics, Economic Law, Economic Theory, Economic History, Financial Accounting, Fiscal and Monetary Economics, History of Economic Thought, Industrial Economics, International Economics, Management Science, Management Accounting, Marketing, Mathematical Economics, Personnel Management and Industrial Relations, Private Law, Public Law, Public Policy

Graduate School of Engineering(M 380/29, D 36/18)

Div. of Aeronautical Engineering(M 33/2, D 3/1)

Aerodynamics, Aero-Space Systems Engineering, Instrumentation and control, Power Plant and Propulsion, Structural Mechanics

Div. of Applied Chemistry(M 63/2, D 5/1)

Analytical Chemistry, Electrochemistry, Environmental Chemistry, Industrial Organic Chemistry, Inorganic Chemistry, Organic Chemistry, Physical Chemistry, Physical Chemistry of Polymers, Polymer Chemistry, Synthetic Organic Chemistry

Div. of Chemical Engineering(M 33/0, D 2/1)

Chemical Reaction Engineering, Design and Control of Chemical Processes, Diffusional Mass Transfer, Mechanical Separation Processes, Unit Processes and Chemical Reactors

Div. of Electrical Engineering(M 48/4, D 6/3)
Electrical Engineering Materials, Electrical Machinery, Electromagneitc–Wave Communication and Information, Fundamental Theory of Electrical Engineering, Information and Communication Systems, Information Processing Theory, Material Physics, Power Engineering

Div. of Electronics(M 43/3, D 3/1)
Computer Systems Engineering, Electronic Circuit Engineering, Electronic Control Engineering, Physical Electronics, Solid–State Electronics, Vacuum and Gaseous Electronics

Div. of Industrial Engineering(M 21/7, D 7/6)
Production Engineering, Production Management, Statistical Engineering, Systems Engineering

Div. of Mathematical Science(M 16/0, D 1/0)
Applied Analysis, Applied Mechanics, Mathematical Statistics, Numerical Analysis, Quantum Mechanics, Solid State Physics

Div. of Mechanical Engineering(M 65/9, D 7/4)
Control Engineering, Engineering Design(Environmental Engineering), Fluid Mechaincs, Heat and Mass Transfer, Internal Combustion Engines, Manufacturing Processes of Machine, Measurement Engineering, Precision Machining, Strength of Materials, Thermal Energy Engineering

Div. of Metallurgy and Materials Science(M 37/1, D 2/1)
Crystal Plasticity, Extractive Metallurgy, Ferrous Materials, Functionality Materials, Metal Working, Physical Chemistry of Metals, Physical Metallurgy

Div. of Naval Architecture(M 21/1, D 0/0)
Marine Structural Mechanics, Marine–System Engineering, Ocean Development Technology, Ship Hydrodynamics

Graduate School of Integrated Arts and Sciences(M 55/14)

Div. of Culturology(M 23/13)
Language and Culture, Philosophy, Society and Culture

Div. of Materials Science(M 16/0)
Chemistry, Physics

Div. of Mathematics and Information Sciences(M 16/1)
Information System, Mathematical Science

和歌山県立医科大学
(Wakayama Kenritsu Ika Daigaku)

Wakayama Medical College

27 Kyu–Bancho, Wakayama–shi, Wakayama 640
☎ 0734–26–8302 FAX 0734–23–7794

Founded 1945
Professors 43
Associate Professors 26
Assistant Professors(Tenured) 34
Assistant Professors(Non–tenured) 140
Research Assistants 158
Undergraduate Studentes/Foreign Students 370/0
Graduate Students/Foreign Students 39/0
Library 75, 854 volumes
Contact: General Affairs Division

Educational philosophy This college, which is governed by the School Education Act in accordance with the Fundamental Law of Education, makes contributing to the improvement of cultural development and the improvement of local health care, medical care, and social welfare its goal, by teaching and researching studies relating to medical treatment.

Foreign students In compliance with the regulations of this school, those who wish to enter our school as exchange students, upon initial selection, may be admitted after a faculty conference.

Environment Our college is situated in Wakayama City, Wakayama Prefecture. This city with a population of 400, 000, centrally located in the Kansai area, is close to Kyoto, Nara and Osaka. Furthermore, since Wakayama city is near the site of the Kansai New International Airport which is due to open in 1994, it will be even more accesible in the future. This " castle town ", bordered by the sea and moutains, offers its people a mild climate.

Facilities Our college is complete, providing various facilities for its student.

Student activities The college holds an annual festival called, " The Kikyo–sai ", which sponsor cultural and physical fitness activities, available to the students of our college.

Undergraduate Programs

Faculty of Medicine(370/0)
Div. of Medicine(370/0)

Graduate Programs

Graduate School of Medicine(D 39/0)
Course of Phisiology, Anatomy, Physiology, Biochemistry, Pharmacology, Course of Pathology, Pathology, Microbiology, Course of Social Medicine, Hygiene, Public Health, Legal Medicine, Course of Internal Medicine, Internal Medicine, Pediatrics, Radiology, Neuropsychiatry, Dermatorogy, Laboratory, Medicine, Course of Surgery, Surgery, Orthopedic Surgery, Otorhinolaryngology, Obstetrics and Gynecology, Urology, Ophtalmology, Anesthesiology, Denistry and Oral Surgery

Private Universities

芦屋大学
(Ashiya Daigaku)
Ashiya University

13–22 Rokurokuso–cho, Ashiya–shi, Hyogo 659
☎ 0797–23–0661 FAX 0797–23–1901

Founded 1964
Professors 41
Associate Professors 19
Assistant Professors (Tenured) 19
Assistant Professors (Non–tenured) 72
Research Assistants 2
Undergraduate Students/Foreign Students 1, 063/0
Graduate Students/Foreign Students 39/1
Library 169, 579 volumes
Contact: Office of Administration

Educational philosophy Education is meant to guide students in discovering their life's ambitions and vocations. For this there has come into being the science of vocational guidance, the life work of Dr. Fukuyama, founder and president of the university. It constitutes integral part of the education.
Environment Overlooking the Inland Sea National Park, the University is located in a mountainous, residential area of Ashiya City, a cosmopolitan center. The campus is easily reached via public transportation.
Facilities Ashiya University Research Center, Labor Science Center, Library, Video Theater, Work Experience and Labor Science Complex, University Grove for Nature Study, Audio Visual Room, Computer Centers, Fukuyama Halls, Japanese Culture Center
Student activities Popular campus events include freshmen excursion trip, ball games competition, world grand tour, school festival. There are unique club activities such as Nagauta Music, Koto, Japanese Dancing, Kendo, Judo, Nihon Kenpo, Soccer, Golf, University Band, Choir, etc.

Undergraduate Programs

Faculty of Education(1, 063/0)
Dept. of Child Education(66/0)
Dept. of Education(61/0)
Dept. of English and English Literature Education (146/0)
Dept. of Industrial Education(790/0)

Graduate Programs

Gaduate School of Education(M 15/0, D 3/1)
Master's Program for Education
Industrial Education, Education, School Administration, History of Education, Industrial Psychology
Doctorate Program for Education
Vocational Guidance, Industrial Education, Principles on Education, Methodology of Education, Educational Psychology, History of Education, Comparative Education, School Administration, History of Theory on Economics, History of Theory on Management, Industrial Hygienics, Human Engineering, Technical Education, Technology, Industrial Psychology
Graduate School of Technical Education(M 5/0)
Mechanical Engineering, Drawing and Designing, Vocational Guidance, Electronics, Biotechnology, Thermal Mechanical Engineering, Material Studies, Material Processing, History of Science and Technology, Technical Education, Theory on the development of Technical, Education Material, Guidance of Technical Practice
Graduate School of English and English Literature Education(M 15/0)
Literature Education, English Teaching Material, English Teaching, English Language, History of English Language, Linguistics, Current English, English Teaching Method, Teaching English, English and American Literature,

梅花女子大学
(Baika Joshi Daigaku)
Baika Women's College

2–19–5 Shukunosho, Ibaraki–shi, Osaka 567
☎ 0726–43–6211 FAX 0726–41–5244

Founded 1878
Professors 29
Associate Professors 25
Assistant Professors (Tenured) 5
Assistant Professors (Non–tenured) 103
Undergraduate Students/Foreign Students 1, 861/3
Graduate Students/Foreign Students 11/0
Library 186, 695 volumes
Contact: Office of International Affairs

Educational philosophy We aim to educate young women to be independent and creative and to develop abroad academic outlook through study and research. We also provide rich character building based on Christianity while fostering a sense of freedom through various autonomous activities.
Foreign students We will welcome international students who are well versed in the Japanese language because practically all our lectures and seminars are conducted in Japanese.
Environment Our campus lies on a wooded hillside in the outskirts of Ibaraki City, and is within convenient commuting distance of Osaka, Kyoto and Kobe. Most students commute by school bus from train and subway stations.
Facilities Library, Language labs with VTR and

CAI equipment, special classroom for calligraphy practice, two cafeterias, gymnasium, auditorium, tennis courts, club houses, chapel, archery court.

Student activities Popular campus events are college festival and freshmen welcome party. There are various extra curricular activities, including calligraphy, tea ceremony, koto music, noh–song, handbell choir, archery, tennis, golf, Japanese fencing, mandolin, folk song, chorus, flower arrangement, etc.

Academic programs for foreign students Supplemental Japanese language class and tutoring system are available. There is a training course for the teaching Japanese to foreigners. International students may attend this.

Services for foreign students Living accommodations are available in the student dormitory. The International Affais Committee will sponsor meetings for international students for discussions, fellowship and counselling.

Undergraduate Programs

Faculty of Literature(1, 861/3)
  Dept. of Japanese Literature(684/0)
  Dept. of English and American Literature(788/0)
  Dept. of Children's Literature(389/3)

Graduate Programs

Graduate School of Literature(M 11/0)
  Div. of English and American Literature(M 5/0)
English Literature, American Literature, English Language, English Composition
Graduate School of Literature(M 11/0)
  Div. of Japanese Literature(M 6/0)
Japanese Literature, Japanese Language, Chinese Literature

佛教大学
(Bukkyô Daigaku)
Bukkyo University

96 Kitahananobo–cho, Muradakino, Kita–ku, Kyoto 603
☎ 075–491–2141 FAX 075–493–9040

Founded 1949
Professors 83
Associate Professors 29
Assistant Professors(Tenured) 26
Assistant Professors(Non–tenured) 278
Research Assistants 2
Undergraduate Students/Foreign Students 6, 029/16
Graduate Students/Foreign Students 102/19
Library 446, 088 volumes
Contact: Planning Division, Planning and Promotion Section

Educational philosophy The founding spirits is that of Buddhim. The most prominent characteristic of our university is the endeavor of its members to pursue their studies in the greatest possible depth and then apply the results to the benefits of society.

Foreign students We believe that foreign students can enjoy a significant life in our university. We have some sister universities in Korea, China and Taiwan. We hope foreign students to obtain good results.

Environment Kyoto City, with a population of 1,25,000, is the most famous historical and sightseeing city in Japan. Our university is located in the northwest in Kyoto City. We have many temples near our university.

Facilities Library, Research Institutes, Shijo Center (extension center), Gymnasium, Auditorium, Computer Center, Affiliated Kindergarten.

Student activities Campus events includes freshmen welcome party, school festival, Homecoming. There is a wide variety of extra curricular activities, including chorus group, Sado (tea–ceremony), the art of flower arrangement, baseball, Judo, Karate, Kendo, etc.

Academic programs for foreign students Supplemental Japanese Language Class, Tutoring system.

Services for foreign students Health clinic, exchange party, educational tour, newspaper for foreign students, College housing.

Undergraduate Programs

Faculty of Literature(2, 881/11)
  Dept. of Buddhism(798/6)
  Dept. of History(741/4)
  Dept. of Japanese Literature(612/1)
  Dept. of Chinese Literature(231/0)
  Dept. of English Literature(499/0)
Faculty of Education(679/1)
  Dept. of Education(550/1)
  Dept. of Social Education(129/0)
Faculty of Sociology(2, 469/4)
  Dept. of Sociology(1, 298/0)
  Dept. of Applied Sociology(230/1)
  Dept. of Social Welfare(941/3)

Graduate Programs

Graduate School of Literature(M 65/11, D 14/3)
  Div. of Buddhism(M 17/5, D 9/2)
Buddhism, Special Study in Buddhism, History of Buddhism, Seminar and Reading in Buddhism.
  Div. of British and American Literature(M 4/0)
English Literature, American Literature, English Linguistics, English and American Authors.
  Div. of Jodo Buddhism(M 23/3)
History of Jodo Buddhism, Jodo Sect, Seminar and Reading in Jodo Buddhism.
  Div. of Japanese History(M 9/1, D 4/1)
Japanese History, History of Cultural Exchange.
  Div. of Japanese Literature(M 11/2)
Japanese Literature, Linguistics, Japanese Linguistics.
  Div. of Oriental History(M 1/0, D 1/0)
Oriental History, History of Cultural Exchange.

Graduate School of Sociology(M 16/3, D 7/2)
Div. of Sociology(M 7/1)
Urban and Rural Sociology, Information Sociology, Industrial Sociology
Div. of Sociology and Social Welfare(D 7/2)
Sociology, Social Welfare,
Div. of Social Welfare(M 9/2)
History of Administration of Social Welfare, Welfare Sociology, Social Welfare

One-Year Graduate Programs

Buddhism Course
Buddhism Major

同志社大学
(Dôshisha Daigaku)

Doshisha University

Imadegawa-dori, Karasuma-Higashiiru, Kamigyo-ku, Kyoto-shi, Kyoto 602
☎ 075-251-3260 FAX 075-251-3057

Founded 1875
Professors 296
Associate Professors 81
Assistant Professors(Tenured) 25
Assistant Professors(Non-tenured) 706
Research Assistants 8
Undergraduate Students/Foreign Students 20, 873/165
Graduate Students/Foreign Students 606/71
Library 1, 348, 000 volumes
Contact: International Liaison Office

Educational philosophy Doshisha University was established with a lofty aim to train students on Christian principle of ethics so that they would become the conscience of the nation, being able to translate their conscience into their skill and ability.
Foreign students Doshisha University welcome well-qualified and highly motivated international students. We provide a stimulating mix of knowlege, ideas, culture and recreation.
Environment Kyoto, with its richest historical and traditional assets, is called the home of Japanese heart. It has always attracted the world-wide attention as the center of learning in Japan.
Facilities University Library, Learned Memorial Library, Audio-Visual Room, Computer Center, Student Union, Clinic, Religious Activity Center, Counseling Center, Swimming Pool, Gymnasium, Auditorium, etc.
Student activites Students' club activities are not extra-curricular at Doshisha, but are an important part of the total learning and growing experience. There are numerous autonomous groups, ranging from a highly academic study group to an outgoing " Exploration Club ".
Academic programs for foreign students Doshisha University offers the following nine classes, specifically designed to meet the need of international students. These classes are designed for the purpose of assisting studednts from overseas to make speedy adjustment to life at Doshisha and to achieve a fruitful accomplishment in Japan. Japanese language Ⅰ, Ⅱ, Introduction to Japanse Language, Jananese Literature, Contemporary Japan Ⅰ, Ⅱ, Japanese Language and Culture, Japanese Society and its Culture Ⅰ, Ⅱ
Services for foreign students Personal counseling, health care, housing arrangements, part-time job infromation, exchange programs with Japanese students, etc.

Undergraduate Programs

Faculty of Commerce(3, 872/25)
Dept. of commerce
Faculty of Economics(4, 051/13)
Dept. of Economics
Faculty of Engineering(3, 394/5)
Dept. of Applied Chemistry(597/0)
Dept. of Chemical Engineering(571/0)
Dept. of Electrical Engineering(582/1)
Dept. of Electronics(609/1)
Dept. of Mechanical Engineering(520/3)
Dept. of Mechanical Engineering Ⅱ(515/0)
Faculty of Law(4, 125/7)
Dept. of Law(3, 278/5)
Dept. of Political Science(847/2)
Faculty of Letters(5, 128/105)
Dept. of English(1, 363/1)
Dept. of Humanities(2, 337/80)
Dept. of Sociology(1, 428/24)
Faculty of Theology(303/1)
Dept. of Theology(303/1)

Graduate Programs

Graduate School of Commerce(M 13/8, D 12/3)
Div. of Commerce(M 13/8, D 12/3)
Graduate School of Economics(M 10/3, D 10/1)
Div. of Applied Economics(M 4/1, D 4/0)
Div. of Economic Theory(M 6/2, D 6/0)
Div. of Economics(D 10/1)
Graduate School of Engineering(M 224/6, D 12/1)
Div. of Applied Chemistry(M 56/1, D 1/0)
Div. of Electrical Engineering(M 56/1, D 4/1)
Div. of Mechanical Engineering(M 112/4, D 7/0)
Graduate School of Law(M 18/0, D 12/1)
Div. of Political Science(M 3/0, D 6/0)
Div. of Private Law(M 3/0, D 1/1)
Div. of Public Law(M 12/0, D 5/0)
Graduate School of Letters(M 164/28, D 79/18)
Div. of Aesthetics and Theory of Arts(M 11/5)
Div. of Cultural History(M 34/2, D 17/3)
Div. of English Literature(M 26/0, D 10/0)
Div. of Japanese Literature(M 27/12, D 16/7)
Div. of Journalism(M 13/3)
Div. of Philosophy and Ethics(M 12/1)
Div. of Philosophy and History of Philosophy(D 18/1)

Div. of Psychology(M 12/0, D 5/0)
Div. of Social Welfare(M 29/5, D 13/7)
Graduate School of Theology(M 52/1, D 15/1)
Div. of Biblical Theology(M 18/0)
Div. of Historical Theology(M 3/0, D 15/1)
Div. of Systematic Theology(M 16/1)

同志社女子大学
(Dôshisha Joshi Daigaku)
Doshisha Women's College of Liberal Arts

Tanabe campus (Faculty of Liberal Arts) Tanabe-cho, Kyoto 610-03
Imadegawa campus (Faculty of Home Economics) Kamigyo-ku, Kyoto 602
☎ 07746-5-8458 FAX 07746-3-5355

Founded 1876
Professors 57
Associate Professors 16
Assistant Professors(Tenured) 11
Assistant Professors(Non-tenured) 294
Research Assistants 5
Undergraduate Students/Foreign Students 3, 231/1
Graduate Students/Foreign Students 32/0
Library 236, 000 volumes
Contact: International Exchange Office

Educational philosophy We aim at bringing up women who can live constructively and responsibly with the international spirit, cultivating well-integrated personalities based on Christian principles.
Foreign students We give foreign students a warm welcome, but as almost all classes at this college are conducted in Japanese, the applicants should have a good command of the language.
Enviroment Tanabe campus, located between two major historical centers, Kyoto and Nara, has an ideal situation for the study of Japanese culture.

Imadegawa campus is located in the center of Kyoto, a city well known for its one-thousand-year-old history, and a center of culture and learning.
Facilities Library, Audio-visual Center, Language Laboratories, Concert Hall, Gymnasium, Auditorium
Student activities Popular campus events includes retreats, summer camp, sports festival, school festival and winter camp. There is a wide variety of extra curricular activities, including choir, Collegiate Choral Doshisha, traditional Japanese music club, tea ceremony club, tennis, volleyball and basketball club.
Academic programs for foreign students Supplemental Japanese language classes are under consideration
Services for foreign students Health clinic, personal/psychological counseling, Housing information, part-time job information

Undergraduate Programs

Faculty of Liberal Arts(2, 214/0)
Dept. of English Literature(1, 389/0)
Dept. of Japanese Language and Literature (364/0)
Dept. of Music(461/0)
Faculty of Home Economics(1, 017/1)
Dept. of Home Economics(389/0)
Dept. of Food studies (Food studeis major/Dietetics Supervision Major) (628/1)

Graduate Programs

Graduate School of Literary Studies(M 22/0, D 2/0)
Div. of English Literature(M 22/0, D 2/0)
Medieval English Literature, Modern English Literature, American Literature, English Philology, Applied Linguistics, Advanced Expository Writing in English, Classical Literature, European Literature, Classical Languages
Graduate School of Home Economics(M 8/0)
Div. of Food studies(M 8/0)
Advanced Nutritional Chemistry, Advanced Nutritional Physiology, Advanced Food Chemistry, Advanced Food Microbiology, Advanced Food Processing, Advanced Food Hygienics, Advanced Food Materials, Advanced Food Rheology, Advanced Surface Science, Advanced Cookery Science, Advanced Food Science

英知大学
(Eichi Daigaku)
Eichi University

2-18-1 Nakoji, Amagasaki-shi, Hyogo 661
☎ 06-491-5000 FAX 06-491-2591

Founded 1963
Professors 28
Associate Professors 18
Assistant Professors(Tenured) 12
Assistant Professors(Non-tenured) 32
Research Assistants 2
Undergraduate Students/Foreign Students 1, 081/0
Library 137, 832 volumes
Contact: Admission Office ☎ 06-491-5000(208)

Educational philosophy Formation of sound character through learning in the spirit of Christianity
Foreign students Our campus characteristic of colorful nationalities among the faculty indicates that this is a university open to men and women regardless of race and creed.
Enviroment The university is located between Osaka and Kobe, quite convenient to a great majority of the students presently enrolled.
Facilities Our university has a large library, gym,

computer center, etc. Our campus is large enough to admit 80 student cars with permission.
Student activities Student activities are the following; orientation ceremonies, field day, vocational guidance, oversea travels for the purpose of study, school festival, speech contest in foreign language, Chiristmas party and ski school. There are 17 sport clubs and 14 cultural clubs.
Academic programs for foreign students We are planning courses in Japanese and Japanese culture for foreign students.
Services for foreign students Our staff takes care of finding places for foreign students to live.

Undergraduate Programs

Faculty of literature(1, 081/1)
- **Dept. of English and English Literature**(637/1)
- **Dept. of Spanish and Spanish Literature**(217/0)
- **Dept. of French and French Literature**(196/0)
- **Dept. of Thoeology**(31/0)

花園大学
(Hanazono Daigaku)
Hanazono College

8-1 Tsubonouchi-cho, Nishinokyo, Nakagyo-ku, Kyoto-shi, Kyoto 604
☎075-811-5181 FAX 075-811-9664

Founded 1949

Undergraduate Programs

Faculty of Letters
- **Dept. of Buddhism**
- **Dept. of History**
- **Dept. of Japanese Literature**
- **Dept. of Social Welfare**

One-Year Graduate Programs

Course of Letters

阪南大学
(Hannan Daigaku)
Hannan University

5-4-33 Amamihigashi, Matsubara-shi, Osaka 580
☎ 0723-32-1224 FAX 0723-36-2633

Founded 1965
Professors 52
Associate Professors 35
Assistant Professors(Non-tenured) 119
Undergraduate Students/Foreign Students 4, 526/12
Library 170, 000 volumes
Contact: Admission Division

Educational philosophy Our educational objectives are to offer up-to date theories of commerce and economics and to cultivate students' abilities to use those theories for practical purposes from a global view point. In order to attain these aims, all students (including foreign students) are required to attend small tutorial classes.
Foreign students Friendship and mutual understanding between foreign students and Japanese students developing through studying and other activities will promote peaceful international relationship.
Environment Our university is situated at Matsubara-shi, the southern part of Osaka prefecture, very close to Tennoji (just fifteen minutes train journey). This area is rich in historical monuments and suitable for studying and researching.
Facilities Library, Computer Center, Institute of Industry and Economy, Students' Center.
Student activities School festival and freshmen training camp are held once a year. There is a wide variety of extra curricular activities including calligraphy, flower arrangement, historical research, baseball, football, soccer, body-building, karate, etc.
Academic programs for foreign students Supplemental Japanese language class, special English class (especially for Asian students), introductory class for Japanese culture, history and economy.
Services for foreign students Health clinic, personal counseling, housing information, part-time job information, vocational guidance.

Undergraduate Programs

Faculty of Commerce(2, 592/8)
- **Dept. of Commerce**(1, 965/5)
- **Dept. of Management Information**(627/3)

Faculty of Economics(1, 934/4)
- **Dept. of Economics**(1, 934/4)

姫路獨協大学
(Himeji Dokkyô Daigaku)
Himeji Dokkyo University

7-2-1 Kami-Ohno, Himeji-shi, Hyogo 670
☎ 0792-23-2211 FAX 0792-85-0352

Founded 1987
Professors 65
Associate Professors 38
Assistant Professors(Tenured) 22
Assistant Professors(Non-tenured) 95
Research Assistants 9
Undergraduate Students/Foreign Students 3, 475/9
Library 91, 770 volumes
Contact: School Affairs Section

Educational philosophy Himeji Dokkyo University aims at graduates who have acquired high language proficiency and deep knowledge of their special fields and are able to play important roles in today's international society.
Foreign students We hope that foreign students can enjoy their school life in our warm environment and return home with deeper understanding of each other's cultures.
Environment Himeji, a city of 450, 000 people, is located in the center of Japan, 3. 5 hours away by Shin Kansen from Tokyo, and 1. 5 hour's drive from Osaka International Airport. Historically, Himeji was a typical castle town, but it is now an international port city with modern industry and commerce.
Facilities Library, Language Laboratory, Computer practical Room, International Center, Information Science Center, Area Science Center, Human Science Center, Language Institute, Gymnasium.
Student activities There are events including University Festival, Welcome party, Invitation to city festivals and rites and a wide variety of extra-curricular acitivities such as Tea ceremony, light music, art, kendo, karate, judo, etc.
Academic programs for foreign students Language Center conducts supplemental and special language classes.
Services for foreign students Health Administration Center gives first aid and medical or personal counseling. Students Office can help them with academic guidance scholarship, homestay and others.

Undergraduate Programs

Faculty of Foreign Languages(1, 434/9)
- **Dept. of German**(252/0)
- **Dept. of English**(699/0)
- **Dept. of Chinese**(263/1)
- **Dept. of Japanese**(220/8)

Faculty of Law(1, 495/0)
- **Dept. of Law**(1, 495/0)

Faculty of Econoinformatics(534/0)
- **Dept. of Econoinformatics**(534/0)

兵庫医科大学
(Hyôgo Ika Daigaku)

Hyogo College of Medicine

1-1 Mukogawa-cho, Nishinomiya-shi, Hyogo 663
☎ 0798-45-6111 FAX 0798-45-6168

Founded 1971
Professors 45
Associate Professors 47
Assstant Professors(Tenured) 63
Assistant Professors(Non-tenured) 28
Research Assistants 216
Undergraduate Students/Foreign Students 668/0
Graduate Students/Foreign Students 90/0
Library 141, 986 volumes
Contact: General Affairs Section ☎ 0798-45-6154

Educational philosophy We aim at educating students for excellent physicians with high-leveled medical technique and good sense on the basis of the following spirits of foundation.
1. Service to the welfare of society 2. Deep love toward mankind 3. Profound scientific understanding of human beings
Foreign students We do not give special treatment in principle, including entrance examination.
Environment The college is located in Nishinomiya, an education-oriented city, with a population of 427, 000 situated between Osaka and Kobe. Besides Mt. Rokko to the west and the Muko River to the east, the college offers a splendid environment for education.
Facilities Hospital, Library, Central Research Laboratory, Animal Experimental Facilities, Center of Audio-Visual Facilities
Student activities Annual campus events include freshmen welcome party, athletic meeting and college festival. In addition, Faculty of Medicine holds a memorial service for benevolence dissection every October.
Academic programs for foreign students In case the problem in the concrete happens, we are to take suitable measures against it.
Services for foreign students We are to take measures fitting for circumstances if we receive foreign students actually.

Undergraduate Programs

Faculty of Medicine(668/0)

Graduate Programs

Graduate School of Medicine(D 90/0)
Anatomy, Physiology, Biochemistry, Pharmacology, Pathology, Bacteriology, Immunology and Medical Zoology, Public Health, Hygiene, Legal Medicine, Genetics, Science and Behavior, Internal Medicine, Pediatrics, Radiology, Clinical Psychiatry, Dermatology, Surgery, Obstetrics and Gynecology, Orthopedics, Urology, Neurosurgery, Ophthalmology, Otorhinolaryngology, Thoracic Surgery, Anesthesiology, Dentistry and Oral Surgery

---

関西医科大学
(Kansai Ika Daigaku)

Kansai Medical University

1 Fumizono-cho, Moriguchi-shi, Osaka 570
☎ 06-992-1001

Founded 1952

Undergraduate Programs

Faculty of Medicine
  Dept. of Medicine

Graduate Programs

Graduate School of Medicine
  Div. of Internal Medicine
  Div. of Pathology
  Div. of Physiology
  Div. of Social Medicine
  Div. of Surgery

関西大学
(Kansai Daigaku)
Kansai University

3-35-3 Yamate-cho, Suita-shi, Osaka 564
☎ 06-388-1121 FAX 06-330-3027

Founded 1886
Professors 357
Associate Professors 101
Assistant Professors (Tenured) 33
Assistant Professors (Non-tenured) 859
Research Assistants 40
Undergraduate Students/Foreign Students 23, 921/150
Graduate Students/Foreign Students 642/12
Library 1, 533, 573 volumes
Contact: Center for International Affairs

Educational philosophy The aim of Kansai University has been the harmonious developement of theory and practice. Our university strives for promotion of advancement in learning in a context of reality while avoiding partiality and indulgence in purely academic theory. Our motto is " To harmonize deeds with theory ".

Foreign students We believe that one of our university's most important functions is to help students develop their potential and achieve their goals. We wish them to engage in discussion with academic staff in a free atmosphere and enjoy university life to the full through mutual sharing of ideas and experience.

Environmont Kansai University is located in the center of Suita city, northern part of Osaka. Osaka, with a population of about 8.8. milion, is well known for the largest commercial city in Japan. While Kansai University is convenient to the center of Osaka, it is covered with green and in suitable surroundings to study.

Facilities Library (the best and largest of university's libraries in Japan), Information Processing Center, Research Laboratories, Sports Training Center, Indoor Swimming Pool, Gymnasium, Athletic Ground, Auditorium, Medical Center, etc.

Student activities Kansai University sponsors the following programs to promote friendly exchange: Welcome Party, Alma Mater General Meeting for Seniors, Excursion to understand the traditional culture and advanced technology of Japan, University Festival, Farewell Party. There is a wide variety of activities of students, such as judo, baseball, football, soccer, tea, calligraphy, orchestra, Japanese literature club, etc.

Academic programs for foreign students Supplemental Japanese language classes and Contemporary Japan are offered to foreign students.

Services for foreign students Health clinic, personal counseling, dormitory (International Student House), housing information, information on cultural exchange programs, scholarship (our university has our own funds for foreign students. ¥50, 000/month for 10 students for one year.), part-time job information, etc.

Undergraduate Programs

Faculty of Commerce(3, 866/74)
  Dept. of Commerce(3, 866/74)
Faculty of Economics(3, 690/24)
  Dept. of Economics(3, 690/24)
Faculty of Engineering(4, 950/11)
  Dept. of Applied Chemistry(494/1)
  Dept. of Architecture(467/3)
  Dept. of Biotechnology(80/0)
  Dept. of Chemical Engineering(519/1)
  Dept. of Civil Engineering(502/1)
  Dept. of Electrical Engineering(474/1)
  Dept. of Electronics(463/2)
  Dept. of Industrial Engineering(506/0)
  Dept. of Materials Science and Engineering(505/1)
  Dept. of Mechanical Engineering I (452/1)
  Dept. of Mechanical System Engineering(488/1)
Faculty of Law(3, 867/6)
  Dept. of Law(3, 198/3)
  Dept. of Politics(669/3)
Faculty of Letters(3, 667/7)
  Dept. of Chinese Literature(303/0)
  Dept. of Education(467/2)
  Dept. of English Literature(790/2)
  Dept. of French Literature(287/0)
  Dept. of German Literature(282/0)
  Dept. of History and Geography(741/0)
  Dept. of Japanese Literature(516/3)
  Dept. of Philosophy(281/0)
Faculty of Sociology(3, 881/28)
  Dept. of Sociology(3, 881/28)

Graduate Programs

Graduate School of Commerce(M 18/1, D 10/1)
  Div. of Commerce(M 6/1, D 7/1)
Economics of Commercial Distribution, Marketing, International Marketing, Market Problems, Merchandise, International Trade Theory, International Trede Management, International Business Communication, Foreign

exchange theory, Insurance and Risk Management, Securities Markets, Transport Economics, International Transport Economics, Public Utility Economics, Socialist Enterprise, North–South Problems, Developed Economics, History of Commerce

Div. of Financial Accounting(M 12/0, D 3/0)
Corporation Accounting, Auditing, Cost Accounting, Accounting Information Theory, International Accouting, Tax Systems, Theories of Business Adminstration, Personnel and Labor Relations, Management International Systems, Production Management, Business History, Organization Theory

Graduate School of Economics(6/0, D 2/0)

Div. of Economics(M 6/1, D 2/0)
Modern Ecomomics, Marxian Economics, History of Economics Dictrines, Econometrics, Public Finance, Social Policy, Social Security, International Economics, Economic Development, Agricultural Economics, Industrial Economics, Regional Economy, Labor Economics and International Relations, Economic History of Japan, Economic History of Europe

Graduate School of Engineering(M 372/1, D 7/0)

Div. of Applied Chemistry(M 50/0, D 1/0)
Co ordinate Chemistry, Chemistry of Organic Synthesis, Industrial Microbiology, Chemistry of Organic Reactions, Polymer Science, Stereo Organic Chemistry, Heterocyclic Chemistry, Chemistry of Functional Polymer, Bioorganic Chemistry, Polymeric Material Science

Div. of Architecture(M 31/0, D 2/0)
Technical History of Architecture, History of Building Production, Architectural Planning, Building Materials and Construction work, Building Foundation Engineering, Aseismic Structural Design, Mechanics for Building Materials

Div. of Chemical Engineering(M 31/0, D 1/0)
Exteractive Engineering, Cryo–Chemical Engineering, Mass Transfer, Advanced Process System Engineering

Div. of Civil Engineering(M 33/1, D 1/0)
Structural Mechanics, Structural Design, Coastal Engineering, Samitary Engineering, Soil Engineering, Engineering Geology, Transportation Engineering, Material for Civil Engineering and River Structure Engineering

Div. of Electrical Engineering(M 40/0, D 0/0)
Electro–Magnetic Energy Engineering, Control Circuit System, Electronic Circuits, Power Electronics

Div. of Electronics(M 41/0, D 0/0)
Microwave Electronics, Electronic Engineering Materials, Gaseous Electronics, Semiconductor Physics, Physical Electronics, Computers, Imformation Engineering, Advanced Applied Vibration Engineering

Div. of Mechanical Engineering(M 117/0, D 0/0)
Machining, Machine Design, Applied Material Science, Control Engineering, Manufacturing Systems, Theory of Plasticity, Fluid Mechanics, Applied of Material Science, Applied Fluid Mechanics, Instrumentation of Optics, Experimental Stress Analysis, Human Factors Engineering, Production Systems Engineering

Div. of Metallurgical Engineering(M 29/0, D 2/0)
Applied Physical Chemistry, Metallic Materials, Material Science of Iron and Steel, Non Ferrous Metallic Materials Science, Theory of Material Strength, Applied Material Science, Welding Engineering, Casting Materials.

Graduate School of Law(M 36/1, D 12/0)

Div. of Public Law(M 22/0, D 10/0)
Constitutinal Law, Administrative Law(General Provisions), Tax Law, Criminal Law, General Provisions Criminal Law, Law of Criminal Procedure, Labor Law, International Law(Peacetime, Wartime), Legal History(Legal History of Japan, Legal History of China), Political Theory, Political Process, Political and Governmental Organization, History of political theories, Political Philosophy

Div. of Private Law(M 14/1, D 2/0)
Civil Law(General Provisions, Real Rights, Obligations, Relatives and Succession), Commercial Law(General Provisions and Commercial Transactions, Companies, Bills and Checks, Maritime Commerce and Insurance), International Private Law, Law of Civil Procedure

Graduate School of Letters(M 72/4, D 48/1)

Div. of Chinese Literature(M 6/0, D 2/1)
Chinese Literature and its History, Chinese Philosophy and its History, Cultural History of China

Div. of Education(M 9/1)
Educational Ideas, Educational Planning, Educational Psychology, Psychology

Div. of English Literature(M 10/0, D 6/0)
English and American Literature, English Philology

Div. of French Literature(M 1/0, D 3/0)
French Literature, French Philology

Div. of Geography(M 7/0)
Physical Geography, Human Geography, Historical Geography, Regional Geography

Div. of German Literature(M 1/0, D 7/0)
German Literature, German Philology

Div. of Japanese History(M 19/2, D 24/0)
Japanese History (Ancient and Medieval, Modern and Contemporary), Cultural History of the Orient, Comparative Study of Civilizations, Japanese Archaeology

Div. of Japanese Literature(M 5/1, D 3/0)
Japanese Literature (Ancient, Early Medieval, Later Medieval, Early Modern, Later Modern and Contemporary), Japanese Philology

Div. of Philosophy(M 14/0, D 3/0)
Philosophy and History of Philosophy, Ethics and Religious Studies, Aesthetics and History of Art

Graduate School of Sociology(M 34/0, D 25/2)

Div. of Industrial Sociology(M 5/0, D 11/0)
Industrial Sociology(Theories of Industrial Society, Organizational Analysis of Enterprise), Theories of Industrial Structure, Management System

Div. of Sociology(M 12/0, D 8/1)
Sociology (General Theory, Regional Sociology, Family Sociology), Social Welfare Study, Mass Communications(Theory of Broadcasting)

Div. of Social Psycology(M 17/0, D 6/1)
Social Psychology (Basic Theories and Methodology, Cultural Behavior, Attitude), Behaviormetrics, Behavioral Apporoaches to Cognition, Industrial Psycology (Research Method and Personnel Psychology, Consumer Behavior), Clinical Psychology

関西外国語大学
(Kansai Gaikokugo Daigaku)
Kansai University of Foreign Studies

16–1 Kitakatahoko-cho, Hirakata-shi, Osaka 573
☎ 0720-56-1721 FAX 0720-55-5552

Founded 1945
Professors 73
Associate Professors 32
Assistant Professors(Tenured) 68
Assistant Professors(Non-tenured) 113
Undergraduate Students/Foreign Students 5, 150/250
Graduate Students/Foreign Students 40/1
Library 218, 542 volumes
Contact: Undergraduate and Graduate Admission: Admissions Office
Asian Studies Program Admission: Center for International Education ☎ 0720-51-6751, FAX: 0720-50-9011

Educational philosophy To provide people with the skills necessary to function in an international environment and to make contributions to international understanding. The institution provides a broad range of educational opportunities including an Asian Studies Program to help internationally minded individuals achieve their goals.

Foreign students Courses in the Asian Studies Program are designed to ensure that the credits earned will be transferable to the students' home and other institutions. Students are encouraged to enroll for a year, but one semester participation is acceptable.

Environment The campus is located in Hirakata City (population: 390, 000), midway between Osaka, Japan's second largest industrial metropolis, and Kyoto, the ancient capital of Japan, both of which are within easy access. This makes possible a wide range of opportunities from visits to traditional structures to modern facilities and institutions.

Facilities An English language Asian Studies collection (11, 000 volumes); Language Laboratories, Audio-vidual Education Center; Seminar House (international students' dormitory; coed; Japanese style rooms); Gymnasium, Auditorium, Ceramics Studio, etc.

Student activities There is a wide variety of both athletic (Karate, judo, tennis, rugby, body-building, etc.) and cultural clubs (band, flower arrangement, calligraphy, tea ceremony, etc.), all of which welcome foreign members. Many foreign students participate in the five day fall student festival.

Academic programs for foreign students Asian Studies Program: courses in Spoken and Reading & Writing Japanese from basic to advanced levels; more than 30 elective courses ranging from studio art courses to the social sciences and humanities. Non-language courses are conducted in English.

Services for foreign students Homestay, cultural orientation, health clinic, personal counseling, travel information & arrangements, Japanese language tutor program. Field trips to sites related to courses are conducted frequently.

Undergraduate Programs

Faculty of Foreign Studies(5, 150/250)
Dept. of English and American Studies(3, 960/1)
Dept. of Spanish Studies(941/0)
Dept. of Asian Studies Program(249/249)

Graduate Programs

Gaduate School of Foreign Studies Research (M 31/0, D 9/1)

Div. of English(M 13/0, D 5/0)
History of English Language, English Linguistic Seminar, Study of British and American Cultures, Comparative Literature, English Phonetics and Phonology, Advanced English Rhetoric, etc.

Div. of Languages and Cultures(M 18/0, D 4/1)
Linguistics, Cultural Anthropology, Ethnology, Folklore Study, International Relations, Comparative Literature, Comparative Study of Thought, Languages and Cultures (Rhomance, Germanic, Indian and Uralic Languages), etc.

近畿大学
(Kinki Daigaku)
Kinki University

3-4-1 Kowakae, Higashi-Osaka-shi, Osaka 577
☎ 06-721-2332 FAX 06-721-2353

Founded 1925
Professors 381
Associate Professors 269
Assistant Professors(Tenured) 194
Assistant Professors(Non-tenured) 749
Research Assistants 427
Undergraduate Students/Foreign students 24, 050/214
Graduate Students/Foreign Students 435/21
Library 1, 000, 000 volumes
Contact: International Student Center

Educatinal philosophy The motto of kinki university is to educate trustworthy, respected and well-loved persons. For this purpose effect is directed to promote not only knowledge and intellectual behaviors but also to develop the talent and health needed for better society through physical excercise and sport activities.

Foreign students Fully recognizing the different nationalities, cultural back grounds, religions and political views of foreign students, the university provide them with true international atmosphere of studying the academic excellence based upon the concept of equity.

Environment The main campus is conveniently located near the center of Osaka city, the second largest city in Japan. The university is comprehensive institution containing eight colleges and graduate schools.
Facilities In addition to normal research and educational facilities, the university is equipped with large scale library, cultural center, memorial hall, club center, joint research center, computer center, language institute and seminar houses.
Student activities Students participate in various cultural and sports events actively. Cultural activities cover some 40 sectors such as tea ceremony, orchestra and arts, and sport activities cover more than 40 sectors such as baseball, football and yacht sailing.
Academic programs for foreign students Very intensive Japanese language programme as well as the course of Jpanese culture and situation is avairable for a period of one year before foreign students move into colleges.
Services for foreign students Counselling service is avairable. Group tour (for 4/5 day) is organized to visit other part of Japan.

Undergraduate Programs

Faculty of Agriculture(2, 026/10)
  Dept. of Agriculture(498/2)
  Dept. of Agricultural Chemistry(495/1)
  Dept. of Fisheries(527/3)
  Dept. of Nutrition(506/4)
Faculty of Commerce and Economics(6, 010/165)
  Dept. of Business Administration(2, 305/99)
  Dept. of Commerce(1, 895/38)
  Dept. of Economics(1, 810/28)
Faculty of Engineering(Hiroshima)(1, 850/0)
  Dept. of Architecture(497/0)
  Dept. of Chemistry(369/0)
  Dept. of Management Engineering(506/0)
  Dept. of Mechanical Engineering(478/0)
Faculty of Engineering(Fukuoka)(1, 828/0)
  Dept. of Architecture(372/0)
  Dept. of Electrical Engineering(416/0)
  Dept. of Industrial Chemistry(355/0)
  Dept. of Industrial Design(285/0)
  Dept. of Management Engineering(285/0)
Faculty of Law(2, 387/9)
  Dept. of Business Law(1, 224/9)
  Dept. of Law(1, 163/0)
Faculty of Literature, Arts, and Cultural Studies(637/5)
  Dept. of Arts(197/2)
  Dept. of Cultural Studies(195/2)
  Dept. of Literature(245/1)
Faculty of Science and Engineering(5, 170/23)
  Dept. of Architecture(788/6)
  Dept. of Applied Chemistry(357/2)
  Dept. of Chemistry(363/0)
  Dept. of Civil Engineering(438/2)
  Dept. of Electrical Engineering(494/0)
  Dept. of Electronic Engineering(346/1)
  Dept. of Management Engineering(841/6)
  Dept. of Mechanical Engineering(532/5)
  Dept. of Metallurgical Engineering(351/1)
  Dept. of Nuclear Engineering(340/0)
  Dept. of Mathematics and Physics(320/0)
Faculty of Medicine(672/0)
Faculty of Pharmacy(565/1)

Graduate Programs

Graduate School of Agriculture(M 48/0, D 5/1)
  Div. of Agriculture(M 14/0, D 2/0)
  Div. of Agriculture Chemistry(M 24/0, D 0/0)
  Div. of Fisheries(M 10/1, D 3/1)
Graduate School of Chemistry(M 24/0, D 2/0)
  Div. of Chemistry(M 24/0, D 2/0)
Graduate School of Commerce(M 29/9, D 3/3)
  Div. of Commerce(M 29/9, D 3/3)
Graduate School of Economics(M 44/0)
  Div. of Economics(M 44/0)
Graduate School of Engineering(M 97/3, D 8/2)
  Div. of Applied Chemistry(M 40/0, D 6/1)
  Div. of Architecture(M 13/1)
  Div. of Civil Engineering(M 10/0, D 2/1)
  Div. of Electronic Engineering(M 15/0, D 0/0)
  Div. of Mechanical Engineering(M 19/2, D 0/0)
Graduate School of Law(M 13/1, D 5/1)
  Div. of Law(M 13/1, D 5/1)
Graduate School of Medicine(D 128/0)
  Div. of Internal Medicine(D 54/0)
  Div. of Pathology(D 1/0)
  Div. of Physiology(D 6/0)
  Div. of Public Health and Hygiene(D 1/0)
  Div. of Surgery(D 66/0)
Graduate School of Pharmacy(M 25/0, D 4/0)
  Div. of Pharmacy(M 25/0, D 4/0)

神戸女子大学
(Kôbe Joshi Daigaku)

Kobe Women's University

2-1 Aoyama, Higashisuma, Suma-ku, Kobe-shi, Hyogo 654
☎ 078-731-4461 FAX 078-732-5161

Founded 1966
Professors 62
Associate Professors 29
Assistant Professors(Tenured) 17
Assistant Professors(Non-tenured) 75
Research Assistants 16
Undergraduate Students/Foreign Students 2, 659/1
Graduate Students/Foreign Students 49/3
Library 112, 421 volumes
Contact: Instruction Department

Educational philosophy In recent years women in Japan have been playing remarkably important roles in various fields of the society. Therefore, our educational purpose is to bring up highly-cultured women so that they may contribute to the society with their academic achievements in their diversified fields.

Foreign students It is desirable that foreign student should at least speak and understand Japanese in their daily life as well as in lectures.

Environment Kobe is one of the most beautiful international port cities in Japan. West of the city, on a gentle hillock between the harbor and the Rokko Mountain Range lies our university; and is also a fine Suma Detached Palace Park which is blending modern and classical beauty with an elaborate fountain system. This area is also famous for one of the best classical literary works, " Genji-monogatari. "

Facilities Library, simulater for environment, C.A.D. gymnasium, seminar houses (in Hawaii, in Seto, Okayama Pre., a former residence of a foreigner in Kobe.), AV theater, Language laboratory, information center of education, domestic science research laboratory, East-West culture Research Center, dormitory.

Student activites A big welcome party for new freshmen and farewell party for the students who are going to graduate are yearly given by the president; besides, we have annual school festival days and sports days. There are 22 cultural clubs and 19 sports which are by students as their own activities.

Undergraduate Programs

Faculty of Literature(1, 995/0)

Dept. of Literature (**English Literature Section Japanese Literature Section**) (802/0)

Dept. of History(411/0)

Dept. of Pedagogy(782/0)

Faculty of Domestic Science(664/1)

Dept. of Home Economics(328/1)

Dept. of Administrative Dietitian's Section (336/0)

Graduate Programs

Graduate School of Literature Study(M 32/2)

Div. of Japanese Literature Section(M 7/1)

Japanese Literature, Japanese Literary History, Japanese Linguestics, Chinese Literature, Japanese Ethnology

Div. of English Literature Section(M 7/0)

English Literature, American Literature, English Linguestics

Div. of Japanese Historical Science Section (M 7/0)

Japanese History, Japanese Folklore, Oriental History, Occidental History

Div. of Education Science Section(M 11/1, D 7/1)

Foundation of Education, Philosophy of Education, Educational Methodology, Educational Technology, Social Education, Educational Psychology, Developmental Psychology, Clinical Psychology, Pedagogy, History of Education, Educational Sociology, Spectific Problem

Graduate School of Home Economics(M 8/0, D 2/0)

Div. of Food and Nutrition Section(M 8/0, D 2/0)

Food Chemistry, Biological Chemistry, Food Analysis, Food Technology, Science of Cookery, Food Microbiology, Nutrition Biochemistry, Nutritional Physiology, Nutrition Physiology.

神戸女学院大学

(Kôbe Jogakuin Daigaku)

Kobe College

4-1 Okadayama, Nishinomiya-shi,Hyogo 662
☎ 0798-52-0955 FAX 0798-51-1038

Founded 1875
Professors 53
Associate Professors 24
Assistant Professors(Tenured) 9
Assistant Professors(Non-tenured) 214
Research Assistants 3
Undergraduate Students/Foreign Students 2, 267/0
Graduate Students/Foreign Students 31/2
Library 255, 000 volumes
Contact: Admission Office

Educational philosophy Religious education is given based upon the Christian spirit as expressed in the motto of the college, " Love thy God, Love thy neighbour ". By fostering a democratic and independent spirit, the school, lays emphasis on the cultivation of young Christian-minded women.

Foreign students We believe that you will find yourselves being such a woman with extensive ability and good personality through our liberal education, based on Christian principle and international understanding aim.

Environment Nishinomiya city, with a population 430, 000, is located between the international port city of Kobe and the industrial megalopolis of Osaka (10 miles from both cities) .A more 90 minutes by railway separate the campus from the ancient capitals of Kyoto and Nara.

Facilities Auditorium, Chapel, Library, Gymnasium, Swimming pool, Audio-Visual center, Computer center, Seminar house

Student activities Popular campus events including freshmen camp, dormitory festival, bazzar, college festival, Christmas service. Cultural clubs: religion, I. S. A. , music, drama, art, Japanese culture, etc. Sport clubs: tennis, volleyball, basketball, skating, skiing, golf, wandervogel, etc.

Academic programs for foreign students Japanese language courses for foreign student, Tutoring system

Services for foreign students Students counseling, College housing, Part-time job information

Undergraduate Programs

Faculty of Home Ecnomics(497/0)
Dept. of Child Development Studies(262/0)
Dept. of Food and Nutrition Studies(235/0)
Faculty of Letters(1, 539/0)
Dept. of English(649/0)
Dept. of Inter-Cultural Studies(890/0)
Faculty of Music(231/0)
Dept. of Music(Instrumental Music Major/Vocal Music Major/Composition Major)(231/0)

Graduate Programs

Graduate School of Letters(M 28/2, D 1/0)
Div. of English(M 6/0, D 1/0)
English Poetry, American Poetry, English Novel, American Novel, English Drama, English Linguistics, American Literature, Linguistics, English Language, English Literature, Comparative Literature, French Language, Christian Theology
Div. of Japanese Cultual Studies(M 12/0)
Japanese Classical Literature, Japanese Modern Literature, Japanese Language, Japanese History, Japanese Thought, Japanese Culture, Comparative Religion, Comparative Thought, Comparative Literature, History of Comparative Literature, International Culture, Comparative Culture, Cultural Foundation, Christian Theology
Div. of Sociology(M 10/2)
Sociology, Study of Research Method, Social Welfare, Practice in Social Work, Comparative Culture, Cultural Foundation, Christian Theology

One-Year Graduate Programs

Music Course
Composition Major, Instrumental Music Major, Vocal Music Major

---

神戸芸術工科大学
(Kôbe Geijutsu Kôka Daigaku)

Kobe Design University

8-1-1 Gakuennishi-machi, Nishi-ku, Kobe-shi, Hyogo 651-21
☎ 078-794-2112 FAX 078-794-5027

Founded 1989
Professors 24
Associate Professors 15
Assistant Professors(Tenured) 8
Assistant Professors(Non-tenured) 7
Research Assistants 9
Undergraduate Students/Foreign Students 529/7
Library 23, 744 volumes
Contact: Admission Office: ☎ 078-794-5025, FAX 078-794-5027
International Exchanges: ☎ 078-794-5039

Educational philosophy Our principle is that design, ie. the combination of art and science is the effective approach to responding to the cultural demands of our times. And we educate students to respond positively to the changes in the social and economic environment of Japan.
Foreign students We are pleased to receive foreign students up to 10% of the total enrollment in each department. We are sure that their experience in our university will worth while.
Environment Kobe has one of the most advanced internatonal trading ports, and it is now regarded as a center of new industry such as fashion, food and high-technology. Our university is located in the west area of Kobe, where four other institutes of higher education are clustered.
Facilities Library, Computer Laboratory, Industrial Design Laboratory, Visual Communication Design Laboratory, Language Laboratory, Gymnasium, Drafting Room, Basic Design Atelier, Cafeteria
Student activities Popular campus events are School Festival, Freshmen welcome party. There are many departmental activities such as field work and on-and off-campus workshops and seminars. There is a variety of extra curricular activities, succer, drama, tennis, photo, movie, etc.
Academic programs for foreign students Tutoring by Japanese students
Services for foreign students Health clinic, Personal/psychological counseling, housing information, part-time job information, many activities presented by Kobe city or another associations.

Undergraduate Programs

Faculty of Design(529/7)
Dept. of Environmental Design(170/1)
Dept. of Industrial Design(183/3)
Dept. of Visual Communication Design(176/3)

神戸学院大学
(Kôbe Gakuin Daigaku)

Kobe-Gakuin University

518 Arise, Ikawadani-cho, Nishi-ku, Kobe-shi, Hyogo 651-21
☎ 078-974-1551 FAX 078-974-5689

Founded 1966
Professors 100
Associate Professors 50
Assistant Professors(Tenured) 20
Assistant Professors(Non-tenured) 168
Research Assistants 20
Undergraduate Students/Foreign Students 8, 256/17
Graduate Students/Foreign Students 51/2

Educational philosophy Dr. Shigeki Mori, founder

and first president of Kobe-Gakuin University, so much emphasized fondness for truth and the spirit of friendship that he made "knowledge" and "benevolence" the foundation spirit of Kobe-Gakuin University. He established the Faculty of Nutrition in 1966 aiming at "the University lasting through the future generations".

Foreign students We are very active in accepting foreign students. We accomplished a good result in each field of the foreign students' majors under the guidance of mature faculty members, and it is, indeed, noteworthy that we succeeded in achieving a mutual understanding by promoting cultural and social exchanges across the borders of countries.

Environment Kobe-Gakuin University is located on the same heights as Kobe Universiade '85 was held. This area is a picturesque place from which one can see through the Akashi Straits, Awaji Island, and the eastern part of the Inland Sea of of Japan which is internationally well-known for its scenic beauty.

Facilities The Library: A white building standing brightly in the midst of the campus. Its collection now consists of more than 410, 000 books and 4, 934 periodicals.

The Ninth Building: A gorgeous facility which has Memorial Hall, audio-visual room, a restaurant, and a lounge. Memorial Hall is a multi-purpose hall with sound and light control equipments which seats 800 spectators.

Student activities Once a year in the autumn, our students hold the '135° festival' which was named from the fact that 135 degrees east longitude passes through Akashi City near our university. They enjoy extracurricular activities. There are presently 3 independent organizations, 28 athletic clubs, 26 cultural clubs and about 26 informal circles.

Undergraduate Programs

Faculty of Law(3, 396/2)
  Dept. of Law(3, 396/2)
Faculty of Economics(3, 338/14)
  Dept. of Economics(3, 338/14)
Faculty of Nutrition(445/0)
  Dept. of Nutrition(445/0)
Faculty of Pharmaceutical Sciences(919/1)
  Dept. of pharmacy(588/1)
  Dept. of Biopharmacy(331/0)
Faculty of Humanities and Sciences(158/0)
  Dept. of Human Culture(158/0)

Graduate Programs

Gaduate School of Law(M 13/1, D 1/0)
  Div. of Law(M 13/1, D 1/0)
Constitutional Law, Administrative Law, Climinal Law, Law of Climinal Procedure, Climinology, Civil Law, Commercial Law, Law of Civil Procedure, Labor Law and Social Security Law, International Law, Political Science, Political History, International Politics, International Relations, Comparative Politics, Japanese Legal History

Graduate School of Economics(M 11/1, D 0/0)
  Div. of Economics(M 11/1, D 0/0)
Theoretical Economics, History of Economic Doctorines, Economic History, Economic Policy, International Econo-mics, Social Policy, Public Finance, Money and Banking, Statistics, Business Administration, Accounting, Commerce

Graduate School of Nutrition(M 3/0)
  Div. of Nutrition(M 3/0)
Nutritional Physiology, Nutritional Chemistry, Nutritional Pathology, Nutritional Administration, Food Chemistry, Food and Nutritional Science, Public Health and Physiology

Graduate School of Pharmaceutical Sciences(M 21/0)
  Div. of Pharmaceutical Sciences(M 21/0)
Medicinal Chemistry, Pharmacognosy and Natural Products Chemistry, Pharmaceutical Chemistry, Pharmacy Administration, Pharmaceutical Analysis, Pharmaceutics, Physiological Chemistry, Biochemistry, Chemical Hygiene and Toxicology, Pharmacology

Graduate School of Food and Medicinal Sciences(D 2/0)
  Div. of Food and Medicinal Sciences(D 2/0)

神戸海星女子学院大学

(Kôbe Kaisei Joshigakuin Daigaku)

Stella Maris Women's College

2-7-1 Aotani-cho, Nada-ku, Kobe 657
☎ 078-801-2277 FAX 078-801-5190

Founded 1965
Professors 12
Associate Professors 2
Assistant Professors(Tenured) 4
Assistant Professors(Non-tenured) 26
Research Assistants 2
Undergraduate Students/Foreign Students 562/0
Library 75, 385 volumes
Contact: Admission Office

Educational philosophy The earnest desire is to promote a trully human development, offering to all the possibility to discover the freedom given by the Gospel. The number of students is small, and general or specialized lecture allow the teaching of all the indispensable knowledge for permanent further education.

Environment The city of Kobe, with a population of 1, 473, 051, is located near Osaka (the 2nd largest city in Japan). This is a very cosmopolitan and modernized city.

Facilities The library, the Seminar Center which offers proper space for various events; such as, P.E. lessons, orientation camps for freshmen, meetings of clubs & seminars, and so on.

Student activities School Festival, Christmas Mass and Party. There is a variety of club activities, including English and French drama, music, and sports clubs.

Undergraduate Programs

Faculty of Literature(562/0)
 Dept. of English Literature(347/0)
 Dept. of French Literature(215/0)

神戸女子薬科大学
(Kôbe Joshi Yakka Daigaku)

Kobe Women's College of Pharmacy

4-19-1 Motoyamakita-machi, Higashinada-ku, Kobe-shi, Hyogo 658
☎ 078-453-0031 FAX 078-453-0205

Founded 1930
Professors 24
Associate Protrssors 16
Assistant Professors(Tenured) 19
Assistant Professors(Non-tenured) 35
Research Assistants 25
Undergraduate Students/Foreign Students 1, 183/0
Graduate Students/Foreign Students 15/1
Library 77, 496 volumes
Contact: The General Affairs Section

Educational philosophy We aim to provide women students both with professional knowledge and highly specialized techniques of pharmaceutical sciences so that they may contribute to society in many-sided fields as well-trained pharmacists or chemistry experts after they graduate.
Foreign students Foreign students are supposed to take some qualifying examinations when they apply. Applicants are required, before everything, to have full command of Japanese in order to study and to enjoy college life.
Environment The campus is situated in quiet surroundings at the eastern end of Kobe, an international port city noted for exoticism and women's new fashion, with a population of about 1.5 million. The view from the campus is splendid, with the urban areas and the Bay of Osaka far below.
Facilities Library, waste water disposal plant, botanical garden for medicinal herbs, seminar house (Mt. Rokko), gymnasium, information retrieval system via telephone network, dormitories, student union. Research laboratories are fully equipped.
Student activities Campus festival in fall. Orientation for welcoming freshmen in spring. 22 extracurricular club activities, e.g. choral society, drama, archery, marching band, tennis, photography, flower arrangement, ice-skating, tea ceremony, basketball, volleyball, fine arts, German language, badminton.
Services for foreign students Dormitory is available.

Undergraduate Programs

Faculty of Pharmacy(1, 183/0)
 Dept. of Pharmaceutical Science(621/0)
 Dept. of Biopharmaceutical Science(562/0)

Graduate Programs

Graduate School of Pharmacy(M 14/0, D 1/0)
Pharmaceutical Chemistry, Pharmacognosy, Medicinal Chemistry, Pharmaceutical Analysis, Radiation Chemistry, Hygienic Chemistry, Biological Chemistry, Pathological Biochemistry, Pharmacy, Pharmacology

光華女子大学
(Kôka Joshi Daigaku)

Koka Women's College

38 Kadono-cho, Nishikyogoku, Ukyo-ku, Kyoto 617
☎ 075-312-1783 FAX 075-321-1360

Founded 1964
Professors 17
Associate Professors 8
Assistant Professors(Tenured) 1
Assistant Professors(Non-tenured) 80
Research Assistants 2
Undergraduate Students/Foreign Students 926/0
Library 107, 119 volumes

Undergraduate Programs

Faculty of Literature(926/0)
 Dept. of English & American Literature(447/0)
 Dept. of Japanese Literature(479/0)

甲南大学
(Kônan Daigaku)

Konan University

8-9-1 Okamoto, Higashinada-Ku, Kobe 658
☎ 078-431-4341 FAX 078-413-2676

Founded 1951
Professors 130
Associate Professors 34
Assistant Professors(Tenured) 18
Assistant Professors(Non-tenured) 363
Research Assistants 2
Undergraduate Students/Foreign Students 7, 774/0
Graduate Students/Foreign Students 99/0
Library 655, 780 volumes

Contact: Konan International Exchange Center Admission Office

Educational philosophy The school motto " Virtus, Corpus, Sapientia " was originated by the school founder Hachisaburo Hirao. It encourages students to strive not only for the professional knowledge but also for the sports and cultural activities of the University life.
Foreign students Welcoming foreign students of average living standards is konan's policy, and we provide special scholarship for foreign students and developing home stay program.
Environment Konan is located in Kobe, the port city on the western Japan, close to Kyoto, Nara and Osaka, by the convenient public transportation. Kobe is the scenic city and famous for the international atmosphere with the population of 1. 4 million.
Facilities Various educational facilities to enrich classes, research activities and extra curricular activities are provided: Main Library, Gymnasium, General Study Research Center, Computer Center, etc.
Student activities Many student activities, such as orientation program for freshmen, Freshmen Camp, sports and cultural festival and other activities are organized by students. Konan is one of the leading universities in Japan in those activities.
Academic programs for foreign students Newly established Konan International Exchange Center (KIEC) provides the Japanese language and Japanology courses for foreign students who plan to transfer earned academic credits to their home university.
Services for foreign students KIEC offers various services to foreign students: orientation, placement test, homestay program, field trip, giving chances to the independent study with one of faculty members, and so forth.

Undergraduate Programs

Faculty of Letters(1, 460/0)
Dept. of English(321/0)
Dept. of German Literature and Language(10/0)
Dept. of Japanese Literature and Language(81/0)
Dept. of Sociology(347/0)
Faculty of Science(1, 346/0)
Dept. of Applied Chemistry(165/0)
Dept. of Applied Mathematics(126/0)
Dept. of Applied Physics(187/0)
Dept. of Biology(139/0)
Dept. of Chemistry(117/0)
Dept. of Information Systems and Management Science(148/0)
Dept. of Physics(136/0)
Faculty of Economics(1, 751/0)
Dept. of Economics(1, 751/0)
Faculty of Law(1, 656/0)
Dept. of Law(1, 656/0)
Faculty of Business Administration(1, 561/0)
Dept. of Business Administration(1, 561/0)

Graduate Programs

Graduate School of Humanities(M 23/1, D 17/0)
Div. of English(M 4/0, D 10/0)
Seminar, English Literature, American Literature, English Linguistics or Philology, French Literature, German Literature, Greek and Latin Literature, Literary Research (English or American Literature), English Linguistic or Philological Research
Div. of Japanese(M 6/1, D 1/0)
Japanese Literature, the Japanese Language, Chinese Literature, Literary Research (Japanese Literature),
Div. of Applied Sociology(M 13/0, D 6/0)
Applied Sociology, Sociology, Social Research, Clinical Psychology, Clinical Psychology and Psychotherapy, Philosophy, Ethics, History, Human Geography, Applied Sociological Research, Applied Psychology
Graduate School of Natural Science(M 32/0, D 5/0)
Div. of Physics(M 12/0, D 3/0)
Solid State Physics, Quantum Electronics, Topics in Nuclear Physics, Experimental Nuclear Physics, High Energy Physics, Astroparticle Physics, Topics in Quantum Mechanics, Experimental Physics, Physics, Physical Research, Research in Physics,
Div. of Chemistry(M 13/0)
Topics in Physical Chemistry, Topics in Inorganic Chemistry, Topics Analytical Chemistry, Applied Radiochemistry, Topics in Organic Chemistry, Topics in Synthetic Organic Chemistry, Topics in Biochemistry, Topics in Polymer Chemistry, Applied Polymer Chemistry, Chemical Research, Thesis Research in Chemistry
Div. of Biology(M 7/0)
Experimental Embryology, Developmental Genetics, Microbial Physiology, Molecular Genetics, Topics in Physiological Chemistry, Environmental Biology, Topics in Biochemistry, Applied Radiochemistry, Biological Research, Thesis Research in Biology
Div. of Life and Functional Materials Sciences(D 2/0)
Colloquium in Biomolecular Science, Colloquium in Environmental Materials Sciences, Colloquium in Functional Materials Sciences, Colloquium in Molecular Biology, Colloquium in Physiological Biochemistry, Life and Functional Materials Sciences
Graduate School of Social Science(M 21/0, D 1/0)
Div. of Economics(M 6/0)
Principles of Economics, History of Economic Thought, History of Japanese Economy, Western Economic History, Public Finances, Economic Policy, Social Policy, Statistics, Monetary Economics, International Economics, Economics of Transportation, Industrial Economics, Econometrics, Japanese Economy, Comparative Economic Systems, Monetary Policy, History of Social Thought, Economic Problems, Seminar
Div. of Law(M 9/0)
Civil Law, Commercial Law, Civil Procedure, Anti–Trust Law, Tax Law, Labor Law, Constitutional Law, Admin-

istrative Law, Criminal Law, Law of Criminal Procedure, Criminal Policy, International Law, Legal History, Sociology of Law, Political Theory, Political Thought, International Politics, Legal Philosophy, Law and Political Literature, Seminar

Div. of Business Adiministration(M 6/0, D 1/0)
Business Administration, Business History, Science History of Business Administration, Business Management, Business Finance, Personnel Management and Labor Relations, Management Science, Management and Organization, Industrial Management, International Business, Small Business, Principles of Accounting, Financial Accounting, Critical Issues in Accounting, Cost Accounting, Auditing Theory, the Computer Accounting, Tax Accounting, Marketing, Marketing Management, International Marketing, Financial Institutions, Theory of Securities, Insurance Science, Study in Foreign Business Literature, Seminar, Marketing Science

甲南女子大学
(Kônan Joshi Daigaku)

Konan Women's University

6-2-23 Morikitamachi, Higashinada-ku, Kobe-shi, Hyogo 658
☎ 078-431-0391 FAX 078-412-7177

Founded 1964
Professors 50
Associate Professors 15
Assistant Professors(Tenured) 3
Assistant Professors(Non-tenured) 185
Research Assistants 1
Undergraduate Students/Foreign Students 3, 467/0
Graduate Students/Foreign Students 88/16
Library 277, 431 volumes
Contact: Pubilc Relations Section

Educational philosophy We aim to teach the students the university's traditions of cultivating sincerity, respecting individuality, and instilling independence and creativity to become lofty and refined women with a noble, righteous, gengle and strong spirit.

Foreign students We accept the students from all over the world and provide them with the opportunities to exchange academic interests and achievements.

Environment The university is located on a hill at the foot of the Rokko mountins. It's in the eastern part of the international city, Kobe and overlooks beautiful Osaka Bay. School bus service is available from Okamoto station of Hankyu Railways and Settsumotoyama of Japan Railways.

Facilities Auditorium, Libraries, audio-visual education studio, psychology laboratories, language laboratoies, audio-visual rooms, computer and word processor rooms, all-weather tennis court, gymnasium, Noh stage, etc.

Student activites There are 30 cultural clubs 16 sports clubs which belong to the student association called " Seikokai ". The clubs include chorus, flower arrangement, tea ceremony, calligraphy, Noh music, koto music, Japanese archery, golf, kendo, volleyball and so on.

Academic programs for foreign students utoring system for the students who specialize in Japanese literature and education at the graduate school.

Services for foreign students Personal health clinic and counseling, University Dormitory, Cultural exchange program

Undergraduate Programs

Faculty of Letters(3, 467/0)
Dept. of English Language and Literature(1, 011/0)
Dept. of French Language and Literature(446/0)
Dept. of Human Science(1, 028/0)
Dept. of Japanese Language and Literature(982/0)

Graduate Programs

Graduate School of Letters(M 48/7, D 40/9)

Section of Education(M 8/3, D 6/3)
Education, Educational Research,

Section of English Language and Literature(M 8/0, D 7/0)
English Literature, American Literature, English Philology,

Section of French language and Literature(M 5/0, D 5/0)
French Literature, French Language, Practical Studies in French Literature by Foreign Professor

Section of Japanese Language and Literature(M 14/2, D 14/6)
Japanese Language, Japanese Literature,

Section of Psychology(M 6/0, D 6/0)
Fields of Psychology, Seminar, Advanced Studies in Psychology

Section of Sociology(M 7/2, D 2/0)
Sociology, Lecture in Specific Fields of Sociology

甲子園大学
(Kôshien Daigaku)

Koshien University

10-1 Momijigaoka, Takarazuka, Hyogo 665
☎ 0797-87-5111 FAX 0797-87-5666

Founded 1967
Professors 26
Associate Professors 12
Assistant Professors(Tenured) 14
Assistant Professors(Non-tenured) 31
Research Assistants 9

Undergraduate Students/Foreign Students 1, 500/0
Library 50, 000 volumes
Contact: General Affairs Section

Educational philosophy The philosophy of the University is to provide highly professional education with an emphasis on personality development in conformity with its motto: " Ungrudging Effort, Harmonious Cooperation, and Absolute Sincerity. "
Foreign students Warm welcome.
Environment The University is located on a picturesque hill overlooking a magnificent stretch of Takarazuka City situated between Osaka and Kobe. It is surrounded by the verdant Rokko Mountains and has easy access to Osaka, Kobe, Kyoto, Nara and other major neighbouring cities.
Facilities Excellent library, research facilities, educational facilities, information processing center, gymnasium, sports ground, etc.
Student activities University festival and other campus events. Extra curricular activities in various fields.

Undergraduate Programs

Faculty of Nutrition(487/0)
  Dept. of Nutrition(487/0)
Faculty of Business Administration and Information Science(1, 013/0)
  Dept. of Business Administration and Information Science(1, 013/0)

高野山大学
(Kôyasan Daigaku)
Koyasan University

385 Koyasan, Koya-cho, Ito-gun, Wakayama-shi, Wakayama 648-02
☎ 0736-56-2921 FAX 0736-56-2746

Founded 1886
Professors 21
Associate Professors 17
Assistant Professors(Tenured) 4
Assistant Professors(Non-tenured) 43
Research Assistants 1
Undergraduate Students/Foreign Students 1, 085/0
Graduate Students/Foreign Students 28/1
Library 245, 441 volumes

Educational philosophy Koyasan University aims to build up student's character according to a buddhist spirit.
Foreign students Applicants from abroad must take same entrance examinations as required for Japanese students.
Environment Koyasan University is located in the mount Koya, approximately 30 miles south of Osaka. The town of Koya, with a population of 6, 000, is a buddhist (Shingon sect) town. It was founded in 812 by Kobo Daishi(Kukai).
Facilities Koyasan University Library, Research Institute of Esoteric Buddhist Culture, Pra-Voga Exercise Hall
Student activites Popular campus events includes school festival, monthly buddhistic service, freshmen welcome party. There is a wide variety of extra curricular activities, including the tea ceremony, flower arrangement, calligraphy, Japanese archery, baseball, tennis, Japanese fencing, etc.

Undergraduate Programs

Faculty of Literature(1, 085/0)
  Dept. of Esoteric Buddhism(240/0)
  Dept. of Buddhism(178/0)
  Dept. of Philosophy(143/0)
  Dept. of Japanese literature(131/0)
  Dept. of English and American literature(65/0)
  Dept. of Japanese history(132/0)
  Dept. of Sociology(73/0)
  Dept. of Social welfare(123/0)

Graduate Programs

Graduate School of Literature(M 22/0, D 6/1)
  Div. of Esoteric Buddhism(M 16/0, D 4/1)
Esoteric Buddhism, India, Religion, Esoteric buddhist phenomenon, Buddhist art
  Div. of Buddhism(M 6/0, D 2/0)
Buddhism, India, Religion, Esoteric buddist phenomenon, Buddhist arts

---

京都学園大学
(Kyôto Gakuen Daigaku)
Kyoto Gakuen University

Otani Nanjo, Sogabe-cho, Kameoka-shi, Kyoto 621
☎ 07712-2-2001

Founded 1969

Undergraduate Programs

Faculty of Economics
  Dept. of Business Administration
  Dept. of Economics
Faculty of Law

京都薬科大学
(Kyôto Yakka Daigaku)

Kyoto Pharmaceutical University

5 Misasagi Makauchi-cho, Yamashina-ku, Kyoto-shi, Kyoto 400
☎ 075-581-3161 FAX 075-594-5454

Founded 1884
Professors 29
Associate Professors 17
Assistant Professors(Tenured) 6
Assistant Professors(Non-tenured) 46
Research Assistants 55
Undergraduate Students/Foreign Students 1, 439/0
Graduate Students/Foreign Students 97/2
Library 71, 380 volumes
Contact: Student Office

Educational philosophy We aim at teaching and studying basis and application of pharmaceutical sciences so that students may contribute much to promotion in research and development of pharmaceuticals and to active practices as pharmacists in hospital and community pharmacies and also in public health instituions

Foreign students We believe that foreign students can gain a great deal of knowledge and experience in pharmaceutical sciences and establish mutual understanding and friendship.

Environment Our campus is located in the eastern suburb of Kyoto, the ancient capital of Japan and now a big city with a population of one million. Student can enjoy a rewarding experiences to deepen their understanding in Japanese culture, through a great nember of historical heritages present in Kyoto.

Facilities Excellent research facilities for academic staffs and graduate students, including the Institute of molecular and Cellular Biology, Radioisotope Research Laboratory, Drug Informatin Center, Vivarium and Botanical Garden, Library, Auditorium-Gymnasium, Seminar House and Athletic Ground, etc.

Student activites Various extra-curriculum activities for students in 40 sport and culture clubs. Annual student festival. Students can also have meetings for study and cultivation of friendship in our Seminar House located at lake side of Biwa in Shiga Prefecture.

Services for foreign students Staffs in the Student Office can help foreign students obtaining necessary informations in living and studying. Academic staffs can offer proper supports and advices for studies on major subject.

Undergraduate Programs

Faculty of Pharmaceutical Science (Students are subdivided into each of 3 departments at the end of 3rd year. Numbers in the depantments are of 4th-year students only) (1, 439/0)

Dept. of Pharmaceutical Science(151(4 th-year students only)/0)

Dept. of Pharmaceutical Chemistry(131(4th-year students only)/0)

Dept. of Biological Pharmacy(92(4 th-year students only)/0)

Graduate Programs

Graduate School of Pharmaceutical Science(M 92/1, D 5/1)

General Chemistry, General biology, Organic Chemistry, Medicinal Chemistry, Natural products Chemistry, Pharmacognosy, Physical Chemistry, Analytical Chemistry, Food and environmental Chemistry, Biochemistry, Microbiology, Pharmacology, Biopharmacy, Hospital pharmacy, Molecular genetics, Molecular bioregulation, Cell biology

京都産業大学
(Kyôto Sangyô Daigaku)

Kyoto Sangyo University

Motoyama, Kamigamo, Kita-ku, Kyoto 603
☎ 075-701-2151 FAX 075-791-9422

Founded 1965
Professors 194
Associate Professors 79
Assistant Professors(Tenured) 19
Assistant Professors(Non-teured) 163
Undergraduate Students/Foreign Students 11, 225/0
Graduate Students/Foreign Students 14/0
Library 539, 026 volumes
Contact: Section for Planning and Public Relations

Educational philosophy We concentrate on adapting our educational ideas to the trends of a new age, on bringing our university closer to our ideals, and on training talented people capable of shouldering the responsibilities of tomorrow's society.

Foreign students We believe that our exchange program is to serve to promote cultural understanding between foreign countries and Japan. The number of foreign students to our university is to be increased.

Environment Our university is located in a scenic northern part of an ancient city of Kyoto. The area is rich in historical spots and very ideal for deep study. In our campus the students lead their college life actively amid the flowers of the seasons.

Facilities Central Library, Computer Center, Gymnasium, Language Laboratory Center, Seminar House

Student activities Extracurricular activities are an integral part of the University's educational programs. There are a great number of clubs and societies which grew out of the wide range of student's interests and needs.

Academic programs for foreign students Supplemental Japanese language classes are offered. A tutoring system is also available.

Services for foreign students Personal/psychological counseling, College housing, Cultural exchange program, Health Administration Center, Informtion about extracurricular activities … athletic clubs and cultural clubs. Encouraged to take part in one or two club activities.

Undergraduate Programs

Faculty of Business Adiministration(3, 084/0)
Dept. of Business Administration
Faculty of Economics(2, 937/0)
Dept. of Economics
Faculty of Engineering(200/0)
Dept. of Biotechnology(103/0)
Dept. of Information Communication Engineering(97/0)
Faculty of Foreign Languages(1, 481/0)
Dept. of Chinese(259/0)
Dept. of English(499/0)
Dept. of French(248/0)
Dept. of German(246/0)
Dept. of Linguistics(229/0)
Faculty of Law(2, 991/0)
Dept. of Law
Faculty of Science(532/0)
Dept. of Computer Sciences(191/0)
Dept. of Mathematics(170/0)
Dept. of Physics(171/0)

Graduate Programs

Graduate School of Economics(M 2/0, D 1/0)
Div. of Economics
Master's degree:
Economic Theory, Mathematical Ecnomics, National Income, Economic Growth, History of Economic Doctrines, Economic History, American Economic History, Economic Policy, Agricultural Policy, Public Finance, Fiscal Policy, Industrial Organization, Marketing, Money and Banking, International Trade Policy, International Economics, Development Economics, Economic Development, Economic Anthropology, International Investment, Economic Statistics, Business Management, International Business Administration, Labor Management, Industrial Engineering, Business History, Tax Acconting, Financial Management, Information Processing System, Readings in Foreign Publications, Research Guidance
Doctor's degree:
Economic Theory, History of Economic Doctrines, Economic History, Economic Policy, Public Finance, Markting, Industrial Location, Business Administration, Information Processing
Graduate School of Foreign Languages(M 0/0)
Div. of Chinese(M 0/0)
Chinese Linguistics, The History of Chinese, Study of Modern Chinese Grammar, Ancient Chinese, Middle and Modern Chinese, Chinese Literature, Chinese Culture, Research Guidance
Div. of Linguistics(M 0/0)
General Linguistics, Historical & Comparative Liguistics, Areal Linguistics, Linguistic Orthography & History of Letters, Phonetics, Special Studies in Languages
Indo-European family
Classical: Latin, Greek, Germanic: English, German, Romance: French, Spanish, Slavic: Russian, Czech, Polish, Others: Sanskrit
Non-Indo-European families
South Asian: Indonesian, West Asian: Arabic, Research Guidance, Courses in Related Fields, Comparative Literature, Comparative Culture, Special Studies in History (Western History, Oriental History)
Graduate School of Law(M 5/0, D 0/0)
Div. of Law
Master's degree:
Philosophy of Law, Sociology of Law, History of Japanese Law, Comparative Law, American Law, Consitutional Law, Criminal Law, International Law, Civil Law, Civil Procedure, Commercial Law, Politics, Political Systems, History of Japanese Politics, international Politics, Research Guidance, Master's Thesis
Doctor's degree:
Philosophy of Law, History of Japanese Law, Consitutional Law, Criminal Law, International Law, Civil Law, Commercial Law, Politics, Political Systems, Doctoral Dissertation
Graduate School of Science(M 4/0, D 2/0)
Div. of Mathematics(M 0/0, D 0/0)
Master's degree:
Mathematical Logic, Discrete Mathematics, Geometry, Algebra, Complex Analysis, Mathematical Analysis, Partial Differential Equations, Functional Analysis, Applied Analysis, Numerical Analysis, Computer Lanugage Theory, Computer Hardware, Information Systems, Information Processing, System Science, Mathematics, Special Research in Mathematics, Master's Thesis
Doctor's degree:
Mathematical Logic, Discrete Mathematics, Geometry, Non-Linear Analysis, Mathematical Analysis, Topology, Doctoral Dissertation
Div. of Physics(M 4/0, D 2/0)
Master's degree:
Solid State Spectoroscopy/Laboratory Work, Solid State Theory, Electronic Properties of Solids, Theoretical Nuclear Physics, Nuclear physics/Laboratory Work, Elementaly Particle physics, Geophysics/Laboratory Work, physical Geology /Laboratory Work, Celestial Mechanics Theoretical Astronomy, Condensed Matter, Surface Physics, Gravitation and Cosmology, Astrophysics, Radiation Physics, Master's Thesis
Doctor's degree:
Solid Stare Spectroscopy, Electoronic Properties of Solids, Theoretical Nuclear, Physical Nuclear Physics, Elementary Particle Physics, Geophysics-Spece Plasma Physics, Geoelectromagnetism, Physical Geology, Doc-

toral Dissertation

京都精華大学
(Kyôto Seika Daigaku)
Kyoto Seika University

137 Kino, Iwakura, Sakyo-ku, Kyoto-shi, Kyoto 606
☎ 075-791-6131 FAX 075-722-0838

Founded 1968
Professors 46
Associate Professors 19
Assistant Professors(Tenured) 21
Assistant Professors(Non-tenured) 119
Research Assistants 1
Undergraduate Students/Foreign Students 1, 740/18
Library 104, 744 volumes
Contact: Admission and Publicity ☎ 075-702-5100

Educational philosophy Kyoto Seika University seeks to foster a sense of individual freedom incorporating keen perception of personal responsibilities, and to empower students with richer understanding of their own place in the context of contemporary world culture: an essential step toward true international understanding.
Foreign students K.S.U. offers study opportunities for Japanese-proficient overseas students either as full-term degree students, research students, (usually postgraduate) or as exchange students from particular overseas institutions.
Environment K.S.U.'s pleasantly secluded location in the forested northern hills of Kyoto enables students to concentrate on their study and other on-campus activities, and makes easily available all Kyoto's immense traditional cultural heritage, including nearby points of interest such as Entsuji Temple and Kurama village.
Facilities K.S.U. recently completed a major construction, program, providing new lecture halls/classrooms, extensive video/computer/graphic architectural design facilities and ceramics studios. The Kino Papermaking workshop is unique to K.S.U.
Student activites K.S.U. gives welcome parties, holds bazaars, and sponsors an annual study trip for overseas students, who a student support group hold and ethnic food stall each year at K.S.U.'s Kinosai festival. Regular clubs and circles offer popular music, folk song, tea ceremony, kendo, and a wide variety of sports.
Academic programs for foreign students Supplementary Japanese language classes
Services for foreign students Assistance in finding accommodation, personal counseling and support, part-time job information, vocatonal guidance, cultural activities, cultural exchange.

Undergraduate Programs

Faculty of Art(1, 156/10)
Dept. of Fine Art(586/3)
Dept. of Design(570/7)
Faculty of Humanities(584/8)

京都外国語大学
(Kyôto Gaikokugo Daigaku)
Kyoto University of Foreign Studies

6 Kasame-cho, Saiin, Ukyo-ku, Kyoto 615
☎ 075-322-6012 FAX 075-311-8989

1995 - 140FT ; 270PT FAC

Founded 1947
Professors 57
Associate Professors 28
Assistant Professors(Tenured) 21
Assistant Professors(Non-tenured) 220
Undergraduate Students/Foreign Students 3, 810/36
Graduate Students/Foreign Students 37/0
Library 347, 618 volumes
Contact: Section of Entrance Examination, Department of Education Affairs ☎ 075-322-6035

Educational philosophy The motto of the University, " Pax Mundi per Linguas ", World Peace through Languages, is mirrored in the curriculum, which tresses the building of character and the heightening of potential through the medium of foreign language learning.
Environment Our university is located in the western part of the city of Kyoto, the capital of Japan in ancient times. Possessing a wealth of historic sites and cultural treasures, and bounded on three sides by mountains, Kyoto is a living museum. The university is conveniently located in the urban area.
Facilities The University Library, Data Processing Institute, Mexico Research Center, Research Center of Brazilian Culture, The International Research Institute for Studies in Language and Peace, Research Institute of Human Rights
Student activities University Events: The Freshmen Welcome Softball Game, The June Festival, The Annual Athletic Meeting
Extracurricular activities: kendo, karatedo, Shorinji kempo, judo, aikido, baseball, soccer, volunteer work, Tea ceremony, Noh drama, brass band, etc.

Undergraduate Programs

Faculty of Foreign Languages(3810/0)
Dept. of Brazilian-Portuguese Studies(329/0)
Dept. of Chinese Studies(477/0)
Dept. of English and American Studies(1, 892/0)
Dept. of French Studies(330/0)
Dept. of German Studies(340/0)
Dept. of Spanish Studies(442/0)

Graduate Programs

Gaduate School of Foreign Languages(M 37/0)
Div. of Brazilian-Portuguese Studies(M 4/0)
Brazilian-Portuguese Linguistics, Brazilian-Portuguese Literature, Brazilian-Portuguese Culture, Current Affairs of Iberoamerica
Div. of English and American Studies(M 18/0)
English Linguistics, English and American Literature, English and American Culture, Methods of American Studies
Div. of French Studies(M 1/0)
French Linguistics, French Literature, French Culture,
Div. of German Studies(M 8/0)
German Linguistics, German Literature, German Culture
Div. of Spanish Studies(M 6/0)
Spanish Linguistics, Spanish Literature, Spanish Culture, Current Affairs of Iberia, Current Affairs of Iberoamerica

---

京都橘女子大学
(Kyôto Tachibana Joshi Daigaku)
Kyoto Tachibana Women's University

34 Yamada-cho, Ohyake, Yamashina-ku, Kyoto 607
☎ 075-571-1111 FAX 075-571-5229

Founded 1967
Professors 25
Associate Professors 4
Assistant Professors(Tenured) 8
Assistant Professors(Non-tenured) 109
Undergraduate Students/Foreign Students 1, 687/5
Library 84, 875 volumes
Contact: Academic Affairs Division

Educational philosophy Our university dates back to 1902 when Takeo Nakamori founded Kyoto Girl's Handicraft School near the Imperial Palace in Kyoto. The present university was established in 1967. Under the motto of " Nobiliter et Veraciter " (Nobly and Truly) we educate our students to be independent women with nobleness in modern society.
Foreign students Our university is a small women' s institution, so in each department " face-to-face " education is put into practice. We have full-time advisors and student tutors for each foreign student in order to give individualized guidence.
Environment Our university is located in the eastern part of Kyoto, one of the most beautiful old cities in Japan. It offers students both a quiet atmosphere for study and a chance to visit numerous places of historical interest.
Facilities Our facilities include library, gymnasium, A.V. center, computer center, language laboratory, and student union.
Student activities Popular campus events include Freshman camp, campus festival, international students' party and international students' trips in Kyoto and to Karuizawa, Nagano prefecture. We have a variety of extra curricular activities from karate to Japanese fencing.
Academic programs for foreign students We have special Jananese language as well as Japanese Current Topic classes from levels 1 to 4. Foreign students review the materials covered in classes with their advisors and tutors on a regular basis.
Services for foreign students Services include college housing, housing information, part-time employment information, cultural exchange programs, health clinic, special dormitory with air conditioning and refrigerator.

Undergraduate Programs

Faculty of Liberal Arts(1, 687/5)
Dept. of English and American Literature(551/1)
Dept. of Japanese Literature(577/1)
Dept. of History (Japanese and World History)(559/3)

関西学院大学
(Kansei Gakuin Daigaku)
Kwansei Gakuin University

1-1-155 Uegahara, Nishiomiya-shi 662
☎ 0798-53-6111 FAX 0798-51-0954

Founded 1889
Professors 235
Associate Professors 38
Assistant Professors(Tenured) 13
Assistant Professors(Non-tenured) 518
Research Assistants 18
Undergraduate Students/Foreign Students 14, 067/28
Graduate Students/Foreign Students 277/9
Library 827,096 volumes
Contact: Office of International Programs ☎ 0798-51-0952

Educational philosophy With a history of over 100 years, KGU has provided unique educational curricula, which emphasize character building based on Christian principles, while maintaining high academic standards.
Foreign students We welcome international students and believe interactions between them and other KGU students will further development of vital international perspectives needed for the emerging global society.
Environment The university is located in Nishinomiya, a suburban city with a population of 430, 000, in the cultural center of Western Japan. Kyoto, Osaka, Kobe are easily accessible, because of superb public transportation systems.

Facilities Library, Institute of Industrial Research, Information Processing Center, Multi-Media Study System, LL, CAI facilities, Student Union with heated pool and sports training facilities, Gymnasium, Chapel.
Student activities About 7, 000 students participate in over 200 athletic and cultural extra-curricular activities. College Festival in November. Orientation camp, seminars, sports day, concerts, and Christmas Service.
Academic programs for foreign students Japanese language courses are offered as a first foreign language requirement. For Asian students, special English courses will be provided.
Services for foreign students Counselling, housing imformation, part-time job information, homestay, cultural exchange programs are available. Health Center is open to all.

Undergraduate Programs

School of Business Administration(2, 886/5)
School of Economics(2, 756/2)
School of Humanities(2, 733/2)
  Dept. of Aesthetics(183/0)
  Dept. of Education(233/0)
  Dept. of English(690/0)
  Dept. of French(218/0)
School of Humanities(2, 733/2)
  Dept. of German(190/0)
  Dept. of History(545/0)
  Dept. of Japanese(392/2)
  Dept. of Philosophy(103/0)
  Dept. of Psychology(179/0)
School of Law(2, 767/2)
  Dept. of Law(2, 068/0)
  Dept. of Political Science(699/2)
School of Science(596/0)
  Dept. of Chemistry(303/0)
  Dept. of Physics(293/0)
School of Sociology(2, 257/17)
School of Theology(72/2)

Graduate Programs

Graduate School of Business Administration(M 19/0, D 3/0)
  Div. of Business Administration(M 19/0, D 3/0)
Graduate School of Economics(M 5/1, D 1/0)
  Div. of Economics(M 5/1, D 1/0)
Graduate School of Humanities(M 83/3, D 63/0)
  Div. of Philosophy(M 2/0, D 6/0)
  Div. of Aesthetics(M 11/0, D 8/0)
  Div. of Psychology(M 9/0, 5/0)
  Div. of Education(M 11/0, D 9/0)
  Div. of Japanese History(M 8/0, D 5/0)
  Div. of Occidental History(M 8/0, D 4/0)
  Div. of Japanese(M 10/3, D 5/0)
  Div. of English(M 11/0, D 14/0)
  Div. of French(M 10/0, D 3/0)
  Div. of German(M 3/0, D 4/0)
Graduate School of Law(M 7/1, D 4/0)
  Div. of Political Science(M 3/0, D 1/0)
  Div. of Basic Law(M 0/0, D 1/0)
  Div. of Private and Criminal Law(M 4/1, D 2/0)
Graduate School of Science(M 49/1, D 7/0)
  Div. of Physics(M 21/0, D 6/0)
  Div. of Chemistry(M 28/1, D 1/0)
Graduate School of Sociology(M 17/1, D 5/2)
  Div. of Sociology(M 9/1, D 3/2)
  Div. of Social Work(M 8/0, D 2/0)
Graduate School of Theology(M 13/0, D 1/0)
  Div. of Biblical Theology(M 13/0, D 1/0)

京都女子大学
(Kyôto Joshi Daigaku)

Kyoto Women's University

35 Kitahiyoshi-cho, Imakumano, Higashiyama-ku, Kyoto-shi, Kyoto 605
☎ 075-531-7030

Founded 1949

Undergraduate Programs

Faculty of Home Economics
  Dept. of Food Science
  Dept. of Pedology
  Dept. of Textile and Clothing
Faculty of Literature
  Dept. of Education
  Dept. of English
  Dept. of Japanese
  Dept. of Oriental History

Graduate Programs

Graduate School of Home Economics
  Div. of Food Science
  Div. of Pedology
  Div. of Textile and Clothing
  Graduate School of Literature
  Div. of English
  Div. of Japanese
  Div. of Oriental History

明治鍼灸大学
(Meiji Shinkyû Daigaku)

Meiji College of Oriental Medicine

Hiyoshi-cho, Funai-gun, Kyoto 629-03
☎ 07717-2-1181 FAX 07717-2-0326

Founded 1983
Professors 20
Associate Professors 8
Assistant Professors(Tenured) 22
Assistant Professors(Non-tenured) 28
Research Assistants 17
Undergraduate Students/Foreign Students 502/2
Library 33, 000 volumes
Contact: General affairs office

Educational philosophy This college is one and only four-year college, with the faculty of acupuncture and moxibustion in Japan. We aim at educating practitioners in acupuncture and moxibustion with a good grounding in modern medicine, who are able to properly cooperate with physicians as medical staff of modern medicine.

Foreign students We believe that foreign student can enjoy a rewarding experience in our school, and can contribute a great deal to promoting mutual understanding and the development, of friendly relations.

Environment The campus is located in the gently-sloping Tanba Heights in a spacious natural environment.

Facilities Library, Reseach center of Oriental Medicine, Hospial, Acupuncture center, Gymnasium, Judo hall, Auditorium

Student activities Entrance ceremony, Orientation, Freshman camp, Sports day in spring, College festival in fall. There are club activities-for physical up-building: archery, tennis, golf, Judo, athletic sports, soccer, etc.; for cultural refining: tea-ceremony, light music, etc.

Undergraduate Programs

Faculty of Acupuncture and Moxibustion(502/2)

武庫川女子大学

(Mukogawa Joshi Daigaku)

Mukogawa Women's University

6-46 Ikebiraki-cho, Nishinomiya-shi, Hyogo 663
☎ 0798-47-1212 FAX 0798-47-1800

Founded 1939
Professors 107
Associate Professors 51
Assistant Professors(Tenured) 13
Assistant Professors(Non-tenured) 330
Research Assistants 72
Undergraduate Students/Foreign Students 4, 438/1
Graduate Students/Foreign Students 82/5
Library 362, 000 volumes
Contact: International Exchange Office (ext. 637)

Educational philosophy Part of Mukogawa Gakuin, a privately endowed educational institution (1939), MWU was organized by the late chancellor Kiichiro Koe in 1949 with an air to nurture intelligence, beauty, grace and self-reliance in modern women.

Foreign students Though only a small number presently, MWU intends to make its facilities available to more sutdents from abroad; proficiency in Japanese is required for studies at MWU.

Environment Educational and research facilities located in Nishinomiya (pop: 426, 808), easily accessed by rail and modern road systems between Osaka and Kobe. The community is largely residential, with some medium-sized local industries.

Facilities Main campus for 3 faculties, spacious central library, modern gymnasiums, and computerized instructions and research; 2nd campus for Pharmaceutical Sciences; and 3rd for graduate programs and an open community college. A seminar house in hills.

Student activities An academic year consists of spring semester, April-July, fall, Sept. -Dec. , and speical quarter, Jan. -Feb. to allow greater flexibility in programs for students. Diverse extracurricular activities help campus lives attain vitality.

Academic programs for foreign students All students from overseas are integrated into academic and non-academic programs for Japanese students. Coordinator is appointed to function in international exchange programs.

Services for foreign students A full range of student services available to foreign students including assistance in personal health, housing, counseling, extramural activities, and arranging financial aids.

Undergraduate Programs

Faculty of Home Economics(717/0)
- **Dept. of Food Sciences**(487/0)
- **Dept. of Textiles and Clothing Sciences**(230/0)

Faculty of Letters(2, 672/1)
- **Dept. of Education (Primary Education**) (533/0)
- **Dept. of English**(692/0)
- **Dept. of Human Relations**(234/0)
- **Dept. of Japanese**(732/0)
- **Dept. of Physical Education**(481/1)

Faculty of Music(187/0)
- **Dept. of Instrumental Study**(97/0)
- **Dept. of Voice**(90/0)

Faculty of Pharmaceutical Sciences(862/0)
- **Dept. of Bio-pharmaceutical Sciences**(142/0)
- **Dept. of Pharmaceutical Sciences**(720/0)

Graduate Programs

Graduate School of Home Economics(M 10/1, D 3/0)

Div. of Food Sciences(M 4/0, D 1/0)
Food chemistry, Food analysis and processing, Environmental science, Health care, Nutritional sciences, Cooking science, History of culinary culture.

Div. of Textile and Clothing Sciences(M 6/0, D

2/0)
Civilization and clothing, Aesthetics in clothing, Dyeing culture, Fashion in clothing, Human engineering for clothes, Clothing construction, Consumer studies, Housing and clothes.

Graduate School of Letters(M 28/0)

Div. of English Language and Literature(M 14/0)
Readings in American, English philology; Seminars on English and American literary works.

Div. of Japanese Language and Literature(M 14/3)
Japanese linguistics; Literature, ancient, early medieval, Middle ages, and early modern History of Japanese language and literature; Chinese literature; Chinese philosophy.

Graduate School of Pharmaceutical Sciences(M 9/0, D 4/1)

Div. of Pharmaceutical Sciences(M 9/0, D 4/1)
Pharmaceutical chemistry, Biochemistry, Analytical pharmacy, Biopharmacy, Hygienic chemistry, Pharmacology, Pharmaceutical physio-chemistry.

One-Year Graduate Programs

Letters Course
Education Major

Music Course
Voice Major
Instrumental Study Major

奈良産業大学

(Nara Sangyô Daigaku)

Nara Sangyo University

3-12-1 Tatsunokita, Sango-cho, Ikoma-gun, Nara 636
☎ 0745-73-7800 FAX 0745-72-0822

Founded 1984
Professors 35
Associate Professors 14
Assistant Professors(Tenured) 15
Assistant Professors(Non-tenured) 55
Undergraduate Students/Foreign Students 2, 827/0
Library 59, 600 volumes
Contact: Admission Office

Educational philosophy We aim at trainingexcellent leaders in the 21st century who are well acquaintted with information apparatus and, from an international viewpoint, can cope with information-oriented society that becomes more advanced and complicated.

Foreign students We are not yet ready to receive foreign students. We are considering receiving them in the future.

Environment The town of Sango-cho, with a population of 22, 000, is locate in scenic northwest in Nara Prefecture where is said to be the birthplace of the history of Japan and the Japanese culture.

Facilities Library, Gymnasium, Computer Center, etc.

Student activities Popular campus events includes Placement, Outdoor Activity Guidance (1st Graders), school festival, etc. There is a wide variety of extra curricular activities, including baseball, soccer, volleyball, kendo, trac-and-field events, photograhy, etc.

奈良大学

(Nara Daigaku)

Nara University

1500 Misasagi-cho, Nara-shi, Nara 631
☎ 0742-44-1251 FAX 0742-41-0650

Founded 1969
Professors 46
Associate Professors 21
Assistant Professors(Tenured) 13
Assistant Professors(Non-tenured) 88
Research Assistants 5
Undergraduate Students/Foreign Students 2, 838
Library 140, 000 volumes
Contact: Admission Office

Educational philosophy We stress, as our educational policy, harmony between tradition and modern sense, education through contact and dialogue, open university, based on our international views so that we may realize our founder's philosophy-education of international-minded people in Nara.

Foreign students We have just begun to examine positively the rules and regulations to accept students from overseas.

Environment Located in Nara (with a population of 347, 000) rich in ancient culture, our university also lies at the south end of the Kyoto-Osaka-Nara hills to be planned for the Kansai Academic and Cultural Research Cities. The nearest station is Takanohara Station on Kintetsu Line.

Facilities The institutions attached to the university are Gymnasium, Auditorium, Library, Computer Center and General Research Institute.

Student activities Main campus events are university festival and a day's study trip outside the campus. There are also events by the faculties and the departments, and extracurricular club events. The students' voluntary circles are 43 in cultural training and 34 in physical training.

Undergraduate Programs

Faculty of Letters(2, 127/0)
Dept. of Cultural Properties(294/0)
Dept. of Geography(596/0)
Dept. of History(633/0)
Dept. of Japanese Literature(604/0)

Faculty of Social Research(711/0)
Dept. of Industrial Sociology(353/0)

Dept. of Sociology(358/0)

ノートルダム女子大学

(Nôtoru damu Joshi Daigaku)

Notre Dame Women's College

1 Minami Nonogami-cho, Shimogamo, Sakyo-ku, Kyoto 606
☎ 075-781-1173 FAX 075-702-4060

Founded 1961
Professors 17
Associate Professors 17
Assistant Professors (Tenured) 6
Assistant Professors (Non-tenured) 51
Research Assistants 5
Undergraduate Students/Foreign Students 1, 163
Library 99, 893 volumes
Contact: Admission Office

Educational philosophy A most important goal at Notre Dame is aspiring to competently educate today's modern woman in order that she may lend a helping hand to the rapidly changing and complex society in which we live. We firmly belive that our education may be fully achieved with the christian spirit and virtue.

Foreign students We welcome foreign students to come to our college and to contribute a plenty of promoting mutual understanding and the development of friendly relations. We accept only female students.

Environment Our college is located in Japan's world-famous ancient capital city of Kyoto. It prides itself with its rural location in Rakuhoku in the north. Rakuhoku, architecture is highly reminiscent of the prosperous Heian culture that so broadly influenced hundreds of shrines, temples and other properties that dot Kyoto.

Facilities Library, Auditorium, A. V. center, Language Lavoratory, Cafeteria, Boarding House, Drama Studio, Music room, A. V. editing room, Sports field, Health clinic, Chemistry room, Chapel and so on.

Student activities Our campus events include freshman orientation, sports day, college festival, candle service, graduation party, There is a wide variety of extra curricular activities, including chorus club, E. S. S. , Japanese dance club, Japanese tea club, photo club, basketball, tennis, ski, youth hostel club and so on.

Undergraduate Programs

Faculty of Literature(1, 163/0)
  Dept. of Culture Living(324/0)
  Dept. of English language and literature(839/0)

大谷女子大学

(Ôtani Joshi Daigaku)

Ohtani Women's University

Shigakudai Nishikiori, Tondabayashi-shi, Osaka 584
☎ 0721-24-0381 FAX 0721-24-5741

Founded 1966
Professors 35
Associate Profrssors 26
Assistant Professors (Tenured) 11
Assistant Professors (Non-tenured) 124
Research Assistants 3
Undergraduate Students/Foreign Students 2, 391/0
Graduate Students/Foreign Students 13/0
Library 180, 000 volumes
Contact: Administrative office

Educational philosophy We make researches in literature and pedagogy, giving high-level instruction of art and science. We also aim to send out women of ability who will work for improvement of society.

Foreign students We are based on the belief in Buddhism. Students are taught in small group, which will help to develop friendship and enrich their academic experience.

Environment The city of Tondabayashi is situated in the outskirts of Osaka and abound in historic relics. It will provide a good environment for students.

Facilities Library with annex, Archaeological Museum of Kawachi Districts, Gymnasium, Swimming pool, Language laboratory, Audio-visual center.

Student activities School festival, freshmen welcome party, European tour, English training in Canada. There is a wide variety of extra curricular activities: 34 clubs in cultural activities and 20 clubs in sports.

Service for foreign students Personal/psychological counseling, boarding house, housing information, vacational guidance, academic adviser.

Undergraduate Programs

Faculty of Literature(2, 391/0)
  Dept. of Childhood Education(830/0)
  Dept. of English(782/0)
  Dept. of Japanese(779/0)

Graduate Programs

Graduate School of Literature(M 8/0, D 5/0)
  Div. of English(M 8/0, D 4/0)
Studies in English Literature, Seminar in English Literature, Special Studies in English Literature, Studies in American Literature, Seminar in American Literature, Special Studies in American Literature, Studies in English Linguistics, Seminar in English Linguistics, Special Studies in English Linguistics, the Classics (Latin).
  Div. of Japanese(M 5/0, D 4/0)

Seminar in Japanese Linguistics, Seminar in Japanese Literature, Special Studies in Japanese Linguistics, Special Studies in Japanese Literature, Special Studies in Japanese Folklore, Special Studies in Chinese Literature, Special Studies in History of Japanese Art, Special Studies in History of Japanese Buddhism

大阪音楽大学

(Osaka Ongaku Daigaku)

Osaka College of Music

1-1-8 Saiwaimachi, Shonai, Toyonaka-shi, Osaka 561
☎ 06-334-2131 FAX 06-333-0286

Founded 1915
Professors 60
Associate Professors 12
Assistant Professors (Tenured) 1
Assistant Professors (Non-tenured) 270
Research Assistants 2
Undergraduate Students/Foreign Students 1, 434/6
Graduate Students/Foreign Students 39/2
Library 85, 459 volumes
Contact: Admission Office

Educational philosophy This institution was founded by Koji Nagai with the ideals that it should be a center of music in the western area of Japan. By integrating all arts related to music, it might ulimately be a forum for creation of the source of new development of music and opera.

Foreign students Applicants from abroad are expected to speak and understand Japanese in such level that they can take lessons together with Japanese students. They have to take examinations in Japanese conversation and in major field of music.

Environment The campus is located in Osaka, the second largest city in Japan, at a commutable distance from Kyoto, Nara, and Kobe. In fact, Osaka College of Music stands where the history of Japan exists in harmony with modern civilization.

Facilities Opera House, the first and formal in Japan/Museum of musical Instruments Music library, the largest in West Japan/Music Research Institutes/Halls for chorus and instrumental ensembles/Opera studio/Acoustics laboratory/Music education laboratory etc.

Student activities Importance, is attached to students understanding of all rules and regulations. Use of the school's diverse facilities is encouraged. A well-rounded campus life is enhanced through participation in a number of extra-curricular activities.

Services for foreign students Health clinic, dormitory, housing information

Undergraduate Programs

Faculty of Music (1, 434/6)

Dept. of the Composition Course (88/0)
Dept. of the Vocal Course (466/1)
Dept. of the Instrumental Course (880/5)

Graduate Programs

Graduate School of Music (M 39/2)

Div. of Composition (M 8/1)

Composition

Composition

Special study of Composition, Advanced study of Composition, Study of Composition (Occidental), Study of Composition (Japanese), Instrumentation, Study of Electronic Music, Counterpoint

Musicology

Seminar on Musicology, Thematic study on Music, Practicum on Musicology, Science of Art

Div. of Vocal Music (M 18/0)

Opera

Opera Theater, Master Class in Operatic, Acting, Acting Class, Applied Music, Diction & Repertoire

Lied

Art Song

German Lieder Master Class, Japanese Song Master Class, Study of Religious Vocal Music, Vocal Ensemble Master Class, Diction & Repertoire

Div. of Instrumental Music (M 13/1)

Piano

Piano (studio instruction), Piano Literature, Ensemble, Concerto, Piano Accompaniment in Art Song (introduction), Piano Accompaniment in Art Song (Class instruction), Chamber Music

Wind

Study of Wind Instrumet, Chamber Music, Study of Concertos, Analysis of Wind, Works, Orchestra, Wind Orchestra, Symphonic Band, Concerto Band

String

Study of String Instrument, Chamber Music, Study of Concertos, Analysis of String Works, Orchestra

Percussion

Study of Percussion, Instrument, Chamber Music, Study of Concertos, Analysis of Percussion Works, Orchestra, Wind Orchestra, Symphonic Band, Concerto Band

One-Year Graduate Programs

Music course

Composition Major, Instrumental Music Major, Vocal Music Major

大阪体育大学

(Osaka Taiiku Daigaku)

Osaka College of Physical Education

1558-1 Noda Kumatori-cho, Sennan-gun, Osaka 590-04
☎ 0724-53-7000 FAX 0724-53-7028

Founded 1965
Professors 28
Associate Professors 20
Assistant Professors(Tenured) 13
Assistant Professors(Non-tenured) 47
Research Assistants 4
Undergraduate Students/Foreign Students 1, 539/1
Library 79, 034 volumes
Contact The Section Of General Affairs

Educational philosophy We try to develop our mental and physical activities through physical education and sports so that we may cultivate our human nature. And we aim at peace and prosperity of mankind.

Foreign students The Institute encourages the enrollment of students from abroad, and promotes international exchange programs in sports and recreation activities. In doing so, a special emphasis is placed on the relationship with China.

Environment Kumatori-cho, with a population of 38, 000, is located in southern part of Osaka, and 33km south of Tennoji Station. And this place is historical but newly developing town.

Facilities Library, Computer rooms, Research laboratories, Sports training center, Indoor swimming pool, 5 Gymnasiums, Auditorium, Athletic field, Baseball field, Football field, Soccer field, tennis court, etc.

Student activities Popular campus events include school festival, educational training outside campus. There is wide variety of extra curricular activities, including baseball, football, soccer, kendo, judo, etc.

Services for foreign students Health clinic, Housing information, part-time job information

Undergraduate Programs

Faculty of Physical Education(1, 538/1)
Dept. of Physical Education(1, 538/1)

One-Year Graduate Programs

Physical Education Course
Physical Education Major

大阪歯科大学
(Osaka Shika Daigaku)
Osaka Dental University

1-5-31 Otemae, Chuo-ku, Osaka 540
☎ 06-943-6521 FAX 06-943-8051

Founded 1911
Professors 29
Associate Professors 28
Assistant Professors(Tenured) 51
Assistant Professors(Non-tenured) 21
Research Assistants 123
Undergraduate Students/Foreign Students 906/0
Graduate Students/Foreign Students 73/1
Library 112,000 volumes
Contact: Admission Office

Educational philosophy As dental university students, our students are taught the importance of acquiring the special knowledge and skills of dentistry. They should also put great effort into studying their field of specialization. This is half of our policy. The other half of our policy is to prepare the students to assume an attitude appropriate for a life of serving people and to encourage student to be a healthy and active man or woman and to cultivate himself or herself into a person of refined and delicate sensitivity.

Environment Our school has two campus (Temmabashi campus-special and technical education and Makino campus-general education). Temmabashi campus located at center of Osaka city. Makino campus located in Hirakata city, 30 minutes from Temmabashi by keihan line.

Facilities Dental Hospital, Libraries, Research Center, Computer Center, Gymnasium, Auditorium, Sports Center.

Student activities School festival, Freshmen welcome festival. There is a wide variety of extra curricular activities, including culture groups (19 groups drama etc.) and sports groups (28 groups baseball, football, tennis etc.).

Undergraduate Programs

Faculty of Dentistry(906/0)

Graduate Programs

Graduate School of Dentistry(D 73/1)
Anatomy, Oral Anatomy, Physiology, Biochemistry, Oral Pathology, Bacteriology, Pharmacology, Biomaterials, Operative Dentistry, Endodontics, Periodontology, Prosthodontics, Oral and Maxillofaciai Surgery, Orthodontics, Oral Radiology, Pedodontics, Preventive Dentistry, Anesthesiology, Oral Diagnosis

大阪電気通信大学
(Osaka Denkitsûshin Daigaku)
Osaka Electro-Communication University

18-8 Hatsu-cho, Neyagawa-shi, Osaka 572
☎ 0720-24-1131 FAX 0720-24-0014

Founded 1961
Professors 64
Associate Professors 27
Assistant Professors(Tenured) 28
Assistant Professors(Non-tenured) 108
Undergraduate Students/Foreign Students 4, 126/1

Graduate Students/Foreign Students 7/1
Library 170, 000 volumes
Contact: Admisstrative Office

Educational philosophy Established in 1961, OECU is dedicated to the advancement of society through basic research application and education in electronics in such fields as: opto-electronics; satellite, and optical fiber communications; mechatronics; information, computer, and system control sciences; studies in electronic materials; and industrial administration
Foreign students At present we do not have any special programs for foreign students, and those who want to study at our university are required to have some fair knowledge of the Japanese language.
Environment OECU's headquarters and main campus are located a few minutes from the Keihan Railroad 's Neyagawa City Station, about 20 minutes from downtown Osaka. A second newly built campus lies 15 minutes by car on beautiful Mount Ikoma at the entrance to the Kansai Academic Park in Shijo-Nawate City.
Facilities Library, Information Science Center, Fundamental Electronics Research Center, Education Center for Information Processing. The Institute of Satellite Communication Research
Student activites Our Campus Festival is usually held in the first week of November every year. Extracarricular Activities: There are 53 sports and nonsporats clubs in all and they are active all through the year.
Services for foreign students The student's affair section of our administration is taking care of the students' needs problems.

Undergraduate Programs

Faculty of Engineering (**Freshman Enrollment 840**) (4, 126/1)
- **Dept. of Applied Electronics**(589/0)
- **Dept. of Electro-Communication Engineering** (590/0)
- **Dept. of Electro-Mechanics** (**Mechatronics**) (569/0)
- **Dept. of Electronics**(572/0)

Faculty of Engineering(4, 126/1)
- **Dept. of Management Engineering**(610/1)
- **Dept. of Precision Engineering**(578/0)
- **Dept. of Solid State Engineering**(601/0)

Graduate Programs

Graduate School of Engineering(M 7/1)
- **Div. of Electronics and Applied Physics**(M 1/0)
- **Div. of Information and Computer Science**(M 5/1)
- **Div. of Mechanical and Control Engineering**(M 1/0)

大阪学院大学
(Osaka Gakuin Daigaku)
Osaka Gakuin University

2-36-1 Kishibe-Minami, Suita-shi, Osaka 564
☎ 06-381-8434 FAX 06-382-4363

Founded 1963
Professors 116
Associate Professors 80
Assistant Professors(Tenured) 20
Assistant Professors(Non-tenured) 113
Research Assistants 1
Undergraduate Students/Foreign Students 7, 190/0
Graduate Students/Foreign Students 54/0
Library 525, 258 volumes
Contact: Admission Office, Graduate School Office

Educational philosophy This institution, by means of higher education and scholarly research, aims to develop human resources with the practical ability and broad vision to serve society at lerge as well as to contribute to the peace and welfare of mankind.
Foreign students Provide exchange students program only between sister universities.
Environment Located in Suita-shi (pop. 340, 000). It takes for 13 min. from J.R. Osaka station. Easy access to Kyoto, Nara and Kobe, which are academic and cultural center, in one hour. This location makes educational and research institutes convenient to visit. Also there are rich historic remains around the university.
Facilities Library, Research Information Center, Media Center, International Center, Career Counseling Center, Health Center, Computer Room, Word-processor Training Room, Audio Visual Room, Gymnasium (Training Room), Gakuin Island Seminar House, Aigawa Seminar House, etc.
Student activities Freshman Welcome Party, University Festival (Minazuki-sai, Kishibe-sai). Clubs; Brass Band, Newspaper, Abacus, Comic Narration, Tea Ceremony, Photopraphy, Calligraphy, Koto Music, Baseball, Golf, Volleyball, Track and Field, American Football, Archery, Judo, Kendo, etc.
Academic programs for foreign students International Exchange Program (Japanese, Japanese Affairs etc.)
Services for foreign students Providing Homestay

Undergraduate Programs

Faculty of Commerce(2, 565/0)
- **Dept. of Business Administration**(1, 271/0)
- **Dept. of Commerce**(1, 294/0)

Faculty of Economics(2, 655/0)
- **Dept. of Economics**(2, 655/0)

Faculty of Foreign Languages(850/0)
- **Dept. of English**(469/0)

Dept. of German(381/0)
Faculty of International Studies(199/0)
Dept. of International Studies(199/0)
Faculty of Law(921/0)
Dept. of Law(921/0)

Graduate Programs

Graduate School of Commerce(M 23/0)
Div. of Commerce(M 23/0)
MA: Commerce, Principles of Bookkeeping, Accounting Theory, Financial Statements, Management Accountig, Insurance, Marketing, Trust, Economic Policy, Business Administration, Theory of Finance, Theory of Trade Policy, Statistics, The Civil Code of Japan, Business History, Business Analysis, Location of Industry, Commercial Law, Cost Accounting, Reading and Commentary of English Text, Reading and Commentary of German Text, Reading and Commentary of French Text.
DR: Commerce, Accounting Theory, Financial Statements, Management Accounting, Insurance, Marketing, Trust, Economic Policy, Business Adinistration, Statistics, The Civil Code of Japan, Business History, Business Analysis, Location of Industry, Theory of Finance, Theory of Trade Policy, Commercial Law.
Graduate School of Economics(M 30/0, D 1/0)
Div. of Economics(M 31/0, D 1/0)
MA: Theoretical Economics, History of Economic Thought, Economic History, Theory of Macroeconomis Policy, Public Finance, Theory of Money and Banking, Social Policy, International Economics, Japanese Economic History, Theory of Finance, Business Fluctuations, Economic Philosophy, Manufacturing Industry, Agricultural Economics, Theory of Taxation, Economic Statistics, Economics of Business Enterprise, Regional Public Finance, Reading and Commentary of English Text, Reading and Commentary of German Text, Reading and Commentary of French Text.
DR: Theoretical Economics, History, Economic Thought, Economic History, Particular Theory of Macroeconomic Policy, Public Finance, Theory of Money and Banking, Social Policy, Japanese Economic History, International Economics, Theory of Finance, Business Fluctuations, Economic Philosophy, Manufacturing Industry Economics, Agricultural Economics, Theory of Taxation, Economic Statistics.

大阪芸術大学
(Osaka Geijutsu Daigaku)

Osaka University of Arts

Kanan-cho, Minamikawachi-gun, Osaka 585
☎ 0721-93-3781 FAX 0721-93-5587

Founded 1964
Professors 97
Associate Professors 77
Assistant Professors(Tenured) 73
Assistant Professors(Non-tenured) 337
Research Assistants 25
Undergraduate Students/Foreign Students 6, 038/72
Library 113, 208 volumes
Contact: International Student Office, ☎ 0721-93-3486, FAX 0721-93-5380

Educational philosophy Based on an orderly system and the spirit of freedom, specialization which is aimed at the over-all synthesis of art and comprehensive review of related fields are stressed in our educational ideals. We pursue Japanese traditions in arts and sciences internationally.
Foreign students We believe accepting foreign students to our university would enhance the international exchanges among the nations and contribute to the advancement of learning and arts on our campus.
Environment Our university is situated on a verdant hill southeast of Osaka City, which is the second largest in Japan, and about three and a half hours southwest of Tokyo by bullet train. Osaka offers many cultural resourses in addition to being the home of Japan's tradition.
Facilities The Art Center Library-Information Center, Audio-Visual Hall, Art Hall, Exhibition Hall.
Student activities In addition to the University Festivals and welcome party for foreign students, we have many extracurricular activities such as sports and cultural clubs on campus, and the summer seminar which is conducted every summer at one our sister schools in the U.S.A.
Academic programs for foreign students Japanese Language Class, individual counseling
Services for foreign students Individual conseling, dormitory style accommodations entrusted by our university and apartments appointed by our university, career development and placement.

Undergraduate Programs

Faculty of Arts(6, 038/65)
Dept. of Fine Arts(533/6)
Dept. of Design(568/19)
Dept. of Crafts(416/10)
Dept. of Photography(373/10)
Dept. of Architecture(437/6)
Dept. of Environmental Planning(521/0)
Dept. of Visual Concept Planning(531/7)
Dept. of Literary Arts(548/0)
Dept. of Broadcasting(506/3)
Dept. of Musicology(359/2)
Dept. of Music Education(212/0)
Dept. of Music Performance(235/0)
Dept. of Art Planning(398/0)
Dept. of Theatrical Arts(401/2)

One-Year Graduate Programs
Arts Course
Fine Arts Major
Design Major
Architecture Major

Literary Arts Major
Musicology Major
Music Performance Major
Crafts Major
Photography Major
Music Education Major

大阪工業大学
(Osaka Kôgyô Daigaku)

Osaka Institute of Technology

5-16-1 Omiya, Asahi-ku, Osaka 535
☎ 06-952-3131 FAX 06-953-9469

Founded 1949
Professors 80
Associate Professors 61
Assistant Professors(Tenured) 64
Assistant Professors(Non-tenured) 266
Research Assistants 3
Undergraduate Students/Foreign Students 8, 132/19
Graduate Students/Foreign Students 183/5
Library 332, 272 volumes
Contact: General Affairs Section

Educational philosophy Our up-to-date research and educational facilities and enjoyable campus life make it possible for us to send out into the rapidly-advancing industrial world engineers with well-developed personality and originality.

Foreign students We welcome foreign students and help them become superb engineers. In our college, they can not only enjoy their school life but also contribute a great deal by acting as goodwill envoys.

Environment Osaka City, with a population of 2, 600, 000, is the second largest city in Japan and situated at the heart of the Japanese Islands. Our Omiya Campus is on the bank of Yodo River which flows through the city, and conveniently located for commuting, being 25 minutes by bus.

Facilities Library, Central Research Laboratory, CAD Research Center, New Material Research Center, Yawata Laboratory of Engineering, Practical Machine Shops, Gymnasium, The 60 th Anniversary Memorial Halls

Student activities Popular campus events include school festival, freshmen welcome party. There is a wide variety of extra curricular activities, including, choral groups, marching band, student newspaper, drama, baseball, football, soccer, karate, judo, etc.

Academic programs for foreign students We provide special subjects for foreign students, such as Japanese Ⅰ, Japanese Ⅱ, and Japanese Culture and Society which helps them improve their ability of the Japanese language and acquire part of graduation required credits at the same time.

Services for foreign students Health clinic, personal/psychological counseling, College housing, housing information, part-time job information, observation trip, cultural exchange programs

Undergraduate Programs

Faculty of Engineering (**Daytime**) (4, 141/19)
Dept. of Applied Chemistry(589/1)
Dept. of Architecture(590/9)
Dept. of Civil Engineering(592/0)
Dept. of Electrical Engineering(606/0)
Dept. of Electronic Engineering(580/4)
Dept. of Industrial Management(596/5)
Dept. of Mechanical Engineering(588/0)

Graduate Programs

Graduate School of Engineering(M 169/4, D 14/1)
Div. of Applied Chemistry(M 28/0, D 1/0)
Master's Course Curricula
Advanced course of Applied Mathematics, Mechanics Advanced, Special Lecture on Physical Chemistry, Inorganic Chemistry (Senior Course), Organic Chemistry, Analytical Chemistry, Industrial Physical Chemistry, Inorganic Industrial Chemistry (Special Course), Applied Electrochemistry, Metal Complexes (Special Course), Chemistry of Oil. Fat and Wax Industry, Special Course on Industrial Fuel Chemistry, Special Lectures on Structure and Properties of Polymers, Engineering of High Polymers, Biological Macromolecules, Bioorganic Chemistry. Advanced, Special Lecture
Doctor's Course Curricula
Special Research on Physical Chamistry, Special Research on Inorganic Chemistry, Special Research on Organic Chemistry, Special Research on Analytical Chemistry, Special Research on Industrial Physical Chemistry, Special Research on Inorganic. Industrial Chemistry, Special Research on Structure and Propenies of Polymers, Special Research on Applied Electrochemistry, Special Research on Engineering Chemistry of High Polymers, Special Research on Industrial Fuel Chemistry, Biological Macromolecules, Special Research on Bioorganic Chemistry
Div. of Architecture(M 33/0, D 5/0)
Master's Course Curricula
Advanced Course of Applied Mathematics, Mechanics Advanced, Architectural History Advanced, Art and Art History. Advanced, Architectural Theory. Advanced, Comparatve Studies of Cultures, Architectural Planing. Advanced, Architectural Design. Advanced, City Planning. Advanced, A Planning of Residential Areas. Advanced, Urban Economy. Advanced, Architectural Design and Practical Exetcises, Architectural Environment. Advanced, Building Services Engineering, Advanced Course, Building Materials. Advanced, Structural Mechanics. Advanced, Building Construction. Advanced, Advanced Theory of Steel Structures, Advanced Theory for Reinforced Concrete Structure, Structural Planning Advanced, Selected Structural Engi-

neering. Advanced, Material Machanics. Advanced, Disaster Prevension Engineering. Advanced, Ground Hazard. Advanced, Special lecture
Doctor's Course Curricula
Architectural History, Specialized, Architectural Planning. Specialized, City Planning. Specialized, Building Materials. Specialized, Building Construction. Specialized, Structural Mechanics. Specialized, Atchitectural Environment. Specialized

Div. of Civil Engineering(M 15/0, D 2/0)
Master's Course Curricula
Advanced Course of Applied Mathematics, Mechanics. Advanced, Elastic Analysis of Structures Advanced, Plastic Analysis of Structures Advanced, Concrete Engineering. Advanced, Structural Analysis. Advanced, Civil Engineering Structures Advanced, Exercise on Civil Engineering Structures, Applied Hydraulics. Advanced, Hydraulic Engineering Advanced, Sanitary Engineering Advanced, Aquatic Chemistry Advanced, Soil Mechanics. Advance, Foundation Engineering Advanced, Ground Hazard. Advanced, Engineering Geology Advanced, Special Lecture
Doctor's Course Curricula
Special Research on Structural Machanics, Special Research on Civil Engineering Structures, Selected Topics in Sanitary Engineering, Special Research on Foundation Engineering, Special Research on Ground Hazard, Special Research on Concrete Engineering

Div. of Electrical Engineering(M 38/2, D 5/1)
Master's Course Curricula
Advanced Course of Applied Mathematics, Mechanics Advanced, Electromagnetic Theory Advanced, Special Course on Electrical Circuits, Special Course Transient Phenomena, Special Course on Electrical Instrumentation, Advanced Course on Electric Power System Engineering, Advanced Course on High Voltage Engineering, Special Course on Electrical Machinery, Special Course on Electrical Machines Control, Advanced Automiatic Control, Advanced Course on Control and Systems Engineering, Special Course on Electrical Engineering Materials, Photo-Electric Physical Engineering, Special Course on Semiconductor Electronics, Special Course on Microwave Circuits, Special Course on Electronic Circuits, Special Course on Active Circuits, Special Course on Applicd Electronics Quantum Electronics, Advance Course on Optical Wave Engineering, Intermediate Course in Telecommuications, Special Course on Radio Communication Engineering, Advanced Course on Computer Hardware, Advanced Course on Computer Software Special Lecture, Literature Research for Thesis, Special Researtch for Thesis
Doctor's Course Curriula
Topics in Electromagnetic Theory, Special Research on Electrical Circuits, Special Research on Transient Phot mana, Special Research on Electrical Instrumanation, Special Research on Electtical Power System Engineering, Special Research on Electrical Machinary, Special Research on Electrical Engineering Materials, Special Research on Semiconductor, Electronics, Special Research on Macrowave Citcuits, Special Research on Electronic Circuits, Special Research on Active Circuits, Special Research on Applied Electornics, Special Research Course of and Research on, Communication Switching System, Special Research on Commputer Hardware

Div. of Industrial Management(M 26/2)
Master's Course Curricula
Applied Mathematics Mechanics, Advanced, Organization Engineeting, Managetial Planning, Business Law, Management Information System, Marketing, Production Information System, Digital Communication System, Intelligener, Information Engineering, Software Engineering, Control Engineering, Decision Making, System, Control System, Engineering, Mathematical Programming, Economic System, Manufacturing, System
Industrial Engineering, Production, Planning, Production Management, Statistical Engineering, Quality Control, Economics, Bahaviotal Seience, Economy Engineering, Cost Engineering, Special Lectute,
Literature Research for Thesis, Special Research for Thesis

Div. of Mechanical Engineering(M 29/0, D 1/0)
Master's Course Curricula
Advanced Course of Applied Mathematics Machanics Advanced, Fluid Dynamics of a Viscous Flow, Advanced Course of Joining Technology, Advanced Study of Measuring Instruments, Mechanics of Plastic Deformation in Metal Processing, Advanced Theory of Measurement, (Scales and Weights), Safety Technology related to Mechanical Engineering, Sinteted Materials, Applied Heat Engineering, Metallurgy, Production Engineering, Heat Transfer Engineering, Power Transmission, Resistance Welding, Arc Welding, Technology for Now Materials Development, Fracture Mechanics, Air Conditioning Engineering, Statistical Engineering, Literature Research for Thesis, Special Research for Thesis
Doctor's Course Curricula
Fluid Dynamics of a Viscous Flow, Heat and Mass Transter, Measuring Instruments, Selected Topics in Welding Technology, Selected Topics in Metal Processing, Selected Topics in Measurment, Engineering, Safty Engineering, Sintered Materials Specialized Course, Metallurgy, Selected Topics in Advanced Production Engineering

---

大阪国際大学
(Osaka Kokusai Daigaku)

Osaka International University

3-50-1 Sugi, Hirakata-shi, Osaka 573-01
☎ 0720-58-1616 FAX 0720-58-0897

Founded 1988
Professors 15
Associate Professors 8
Assistant Professors(Tenured) 8

Assistant Professors(Non-tenured) 29
Research Assistants 2
Undergraduate Students/Foreign Students 801/2
Library 32, 000 volumes
Contact: International Exchange Center

Educational philosophy The liberal arts curriculum places emphasis on the mastery of foreign languages as well as exposure to a wide range of humanities and social science disciplines. The two-tier curriculum consists of liberal arts foundation courses and core courses in management.
Foreign students International students will benefit from OIU' s unique environment. As a new university with a new philosophy for higher education in Japan, students can experience a dynamism seldom found at similar institutions.
Environment Located in the center of Kansai region, the university has easy access to major urban centers as well as to a number of historic sites in Nara and Kyoto. It also adjoins the Kansai Science City, designed to provide an environment for international cultural and scientific activities.
Facilities Institute of International Relations, International Student Center, Library, Computer Center, auditorium, gymnasium, Student Activity Center, tennis courts, parking lot
Student activities Campus events include annual festival, athletic meets, freshmen welcome, party. Extra curricular activities are football, soccer, baseball, basket-ball, wandervogel, motorcycle, computer, ESS, international studies, folk song, light music, newspaper
Academic programs for foreign students JSL and supplemental Japanese language classes, full time advisors, tutoring system, career planning service
Services for foreign students Academic and personal counseling, cultural exchange program, health clinic.

Undergraduate Programs

Faculty of Management and Information Science (801/2)
Dept. of Management and Information Science (801/2)

大阪医科大学
(Osaka Ika Daigaku)
Osaka Medical College

2-7 Daigakumachi, Takatsuki-shi, Osaka 569
☎ 0726-81-1221 FAX 0726-81-3723

Founded 1927
Professors 37
Associate Professors 32
Assistant Professors(Tenured) 61
Assistant Professors(Non-tenured) 241
Research Assistants 183
Undergraduate Students/Foreign Students 638
Graduate Students/Foreign Students 120
Library 153, 802 volumes
Contact: The Instruction Section, The General Affairs Section

Educational philosophy Osaka Medical College was founded in 1927 to train high-caliber physicians and surgeons. All education and research activities are based on the college's original guiding philosophy: educational arts are the foundation of medical practice.
Environment Osaka Medical College is located in Takatuki, a residential city with many historic scenes and cultural properties. Situated between the commercial city of Osaka and historic Kyoto, Takatsuki, offers excellent transportation facilities.
Facilities college (Land 69, 340m² Floor 45, 548 m²), hospital (Land 19, 906m² Floor 60, 377m²), nurses' training school (Land 3, 489m² Floor 6, 357m²), total (Land 92, 735m² Floor 112, 282m²)
Students activities A welcome party for freshmen is held in June, and a college-wide festival is held in October with a number of lively programs. Many of the college's athletic clubs have attained good records in the Western Japan Medical Students' Athletic Association.

Undergraduate Programs

Faculty of Medicine(637/0)

Graduate Programs

Graduate School of Medicine(D 119/0)
Pathological science (Anatomy, Microbiology, Pathology)
Physiological science (Physiology, Medical chemistry, Pharmacology)
Social medicine (Hygiene and Public health, Legal medicine)
Internal Medicine (Internal medicine, Neuropsychiatry, Pediatrics, Dermatology, Radiology, Clinical pathology)
Surgery (Surgery, Orthopedic surgery, Ophthalmology, Otorhinolaryngology, Obstetrics and Gynecology, Oral surgery, Plastic surgery)

大阪産業大学
(Osaka Sangyô Daigaku)
Osaka Sangyo University

3-1-1 Nakagaito, Daito-shi, Osaka 574
☎ 0720-75-3001 FAX 0720-71-6210

Founded 1928
Professors 91
Associate Professors 60
Assistant Professors(Tenured) 19

Assistant Professors(Non-tenured) 222
Research Assistants 8
Undergraduate Students/Foreign Students 7, 642/86
Graduate Students/Foreign Students 17/3
Library 218, 682 volumes
Contact: Student Affairs Division

Educational philosophy The fundamental philosophy is well-rounded education; not only the absorption of knowledge but tireless training, good moral sense under the founding spirit, " Greatness for the Masses " We have the tradition of the education and research on transportation and industry.
Foreign students We try to come in a friendly contact with foreign students in the same manner as with Japanese students, but would respect their native customs at the minimum. A lounge for foreign students is provided.
Environment Our university is located at the foot of Mt. Ikoma. There are many time-honored buildings in the suburbs o' the university, such as Nozaki-Kannon, Ishikiri Shrine, etc. Japanese Railway (JR) is available to approach the university and buses stop within the campus.
Facilities University Library with an audio-visual corner, Academic Information Processing Center, Institute for Industrial Reseach, Gymnasium, Multi-purpose Hall, Baseball Ground with indoor training room, etc.
Student activities About 100 cultural and sports clubs are registered. Some foreign students take part in the club activities. Establishment of new clubs can be cooperated by the university. Every November, school festival is held under the auspices of each club.
Services for foreign students Bus tour for exchanging with foreign students every mid-June, including teaching staff and Japanese students. Counseling, seeking services for boarding houses and part-time jobs. No homestay service

Undergraduate Programs

Faculty of Business Management(2, 149/67)
Dept. of Business Management (Course of Business Management) (1, 109/38)
Dept. of Business Management (Course of Transportation Management) (1, 040/29)
Faculty of Economics(1, 307/10)
Dept. of Economics(1, 307/10)
Faculty of Engineering(2, 582/3)
Dept. of Mechanical Engineering(556/1)
Dept. of Mechanical Engineering for Transportation(702/1)
Dept. of Electrical Engineering and Electronics (530/1)
Dept. of Civil Engineering(518/0)
Faculty of Engineering(2, 582/3)
Dept. of Information Systems Engineering(144/0)
Dept. of Environmental Design(132/0)
Junior College(793/1)
Dept. of Automotive Engineering(793/1)

Graduate Programs

Graduate School of Engineering(M 25/3)
Div. of Mechanical Engineering(M 12/1)
Div. of Civil Engineering(M 5/1)
Div. of Electrical Engineering and Electronics(M 8/1)

大阪樟蔭女子大学

(Osaka Shôin Joshi Daigaku)

Osaka Shoin Women's College

4-2-26 Hishiya-Nishi, Higashiosaka-shi, Osaka 577
☎ 06-723-8181 FAX 06-723-8881

Founded 1917
Professors 26
Associate Profrssors 25
Assistant Professors(Tenured) 4
Assistant Professors(Non-tenured) 145
Research Assistants 12
Undergraduate Students/Foreign Students 1, 895/5
Library 204, 392 volumes
Contact: The Department of Educational Affairs

Educational philosophy OSAKA SHOIN WOMEN'S COLLEGE, as a liberal arts college, proposes to provide basic knowledge and inspriration to assist young women in gaining an understanding of the ever-shrinking would in which they live; developing their potentials and, by so doing, coping with social change they may encounter in the future.
Foreign students THE COLLEGE's curriculum is designed to assit foreign students in acquiring firsthand knowledge of Japanese culture and Japanese students in broadening their horizon through close contacts with those foreign students on and off campus.
Environment The city in which the College is located is on the verge of the Greater Osaka and has easy access to Kyoto and Nara, Japan's oldest capitals by means of public transport. Its campus is within a stone's throw of the closest railway station.
Facilities The College is making constant efforts to provide ample and most up-to-date educational facilities: Computer room, Central Library, Auditorium, Audio-Visual Center, Gymnasium, and Seminar House.
Student activities Popular campus events include Off-Campus Overnight Orientation (for Freshmen), College Festival, and Freshmen Welcome Party. There is a wide variety of extra curricular activities, both cultural and athletic and small circles.
Academic programs for foreign students Supplementary Japanese language class
Services for foreign students Health clinic; per-

sonal/psychological counselling; College Dormitory; Housing information; part-time job information

Undergraduate Programs

Faculty of Liberal Arts(1, 895/5)
Dept. of Child Study(312/4)
Dept. of Clothing Science(303/1)
Dept. of English and American Literature(486/0)
Dept. of Food Science(300/0)
Dept. of Japanese Language and Literature(494/0)

大阪商業大学
(Osaka Shôgyô Daigaku)

Osaka University of Commerce

4-1-10 Mikuriya-sakaemachi, Higashiosaka-shi, Osaka 577
☎ 06-781-0381 FAX 06-781-8438

Founded 1928
Professors 50
Associate Profrssors 26
Assistant Professors(Tenured) 16
Assistant Professors(Non-tenured) 73
Research Assistants 3
Undergraduate Students/Foreign Students 3, 997/2
Library 200, 000 volumes
Contact: The Office of Educational Affairs

Educational philosophy Our educational philosophy is to bring up persons of worth for the society. So we are endevouring to bring up persons with fine character who have professional knowledge and skill.
Foreign students We welcome foreign students; our teachers, foreign students committee and related offices work together to provide them with best facilities for study and research as well as for comfortable living.
Environment The city of Higashiosaka, with a population of 520, 000, is located in an urban area between Osaka and Nara, and is very convenient for transportation, only 20 minutes by train from Namba, the southern heart of Osaka.
Facilities Library, The Institute of Industry and Management, The Institute of Commercial History, Information Processing Center, Tanioka Memorial Hall, Gymnasium, Dormitory, Yama-no-ie (mountain house), Students' Hall
Student activities As for student activities, we have many events for students; Freshmen Welcome Party, School Festival, Language Seminar, etc. We also have many club activities; Baseball, Soccer, Rugby, ESS, Light Music, etc.

Undergraduate Programs

Faculty of Commerce and Economics(3, 997/2)
Dept. of Commerce(949/0)
Dept. of Economics(1640/0)
Dept. of Management(708/1)
Dept. of Trade(700/1)

大阪経済大学
(Osaka Keizai Daigaku)

Osaka University of Economics

2-2-8 Osumi, Higashiyodogawa-ku, Osaka-shi, Osaka 533
☎ 06-328-2431 FAX 06-370-8747

Founded 1932
Professors 62
Associate Professors 31
Assistant Professors(Tenured) 14
Assistant Professors(Non-tenured) 145
Undergraduate Students/Foreign Students 6, 492/0
Graduate Students/Foreign Students 11/0
Library 474, 421 volumes
Contact: Undergraduate and Graduate Admission
Admission Office, ☎ ext. 255～258

Educational philosophy Our educational principle is to foster personality through both learning and studing, and also a scientific critical mind together with developing intellectuality and morality so that students may be good and sound citizens who will be able to contribute a great deal to a better social and international understanding through their lives.
Foreign students Eligibility is determined on a case by case basis. Applicants are required to consult the examination office in advance.
Environment Our School is located near the center of the city of Osaka, and foreign students can enjoy a moern and pleasant city life, sometimes visiting cultural facilities or centers such as various museums, planetariums and acquariums.
Facilities School library of about 500, 000 volumes, Computation and Information Center, Institute for Research in Economic History of Japan, Institute of Small Business Research and Business Administration, Gymnasium, Sports Training Room, Student Auditorium.
Student activities Freshmen welcome events held our school and the School Festival by students themselves and Homecoming are the main yearly campus events. But There are also some other extra curricular activities as student newspaper, English speaking society, choral group, marching band, baseball, soccer, rugby football, athletics, and so on.
Academic programs for foreign students Aca-

demic programs for foreign students such as supplemental Japanese language class, tutoring systems, special curriculums including learning supporting system etc. are now under consideration.
Services for foreign students Services for foreign students will of course be considered together with academic programs mentioned above.

Undergraduate Programs

Faculty of Business Administraton(2, 679/0)
Dept. of Business Administration(2, 679/0)
Faculty of Economics(2, 776/0)
Dept. of Economics(2, 776/0)

Graduate Programs

Graduate School of Economic(M 10/0, D 1/0)
Div. of Economics(M 10/0, D 1/0)
Principles of Economics, Economic History, Economic Philosophy, Mordern Economics, Socialistic Economy, Japanese History of Economy, History of European Economy, Economic Policy, Study of International Economics, Industrial Policy, Traffic Policy, Theory of Money of Banking, Economic Fluctuation, Economic Geography, Social Security, Finance, Tax Law, Statistics, Business Administration, Business Finance, Productive Control, Distribution, Accounting Auditing, Accounting History, Economic Law, History of Social Thoughts, Study of English•Germany•French.

大阪経済法科大学
(Osaka Keizai Hôka Daigaku)

Osaka University of Economics and Law

6-10 Gakuonji, Yao-shi, Osaka 581
☎ 0729-41-8211 FAX 0729-41-4426

Founded 1971
Professors 43
Associate Professors 33
Assistant Professors(Tenured) 12
Assistant Professors(Non-tenured) 172
Undergraduate Students/Foreign Students 6, 424/68
Library 97, 039 volumes
Contact: Admission Division

Educational philosophy Our purpose is to help those who are determined to seek out their own path in today's changing society to gain a through knowledge of the world and an understanding of the international mind.
Foreign students Foreign students are only welcomed to this school but greatly expected to take active part in every field of the campus life.
Environment The university is located at the foot of Mount Ikoma in Yao city, in the suburbs of Osaka city which provides an enjoyable environment in which to study.
Facilities Institute of Economics, Institute of Legal study, Information science center, General Science Institure, Institute of Asian Studies, The Shoshukukan Gymnasium, Library.
Students activities Freshmen welome party, School festival, School softball tournament. There are lots of extra curricular activities including base-ball, light music club taekondo, Karate etc.
Academic programs for foreign students Suppllemental Japanese language class.
Services for foreign students Housing information, Part-time job information, Vocational guidance, Home visit, excursion etc.

Undergraduate Programs

Faculty of Economics(3, 297/49)
Dept. of Economics(3, 297/49)
Faculty of Law(3, 127/19)
Dept. of Law(3, 127/19)

大阪薬科大学
(Osaka Yakka Daigaku)

Osaka University of Pharmaceutical Sciences

2-10-65 Kawai, Matsubara-shi, Osaka 580
☎ 0723-32-1015 FAX 0723-32-9929

Founded 1904
Professors 27
Associate Professors 14
Assistant Professors(Tenured) 8
Assistant Professors(Non-tenured) 25
Research Assistants 43
Undergraduate Students/Foreign Students 1212/0
Graduate Students/Foreign Students 42/0
Library 54, 500 volumes
Contact: Registrar's Office, Osaka University of Pharmaceutical Sciences.

Educational philosophy As an important domain within the life sciences, pharmaceutical sciences bear a heavy social responsibility for the preservation of human life and the promotion of better health standards. Our mission is to contribute to the further advancement of pharmaceutical sciences through education and pioneering research work.
Foreign students We welcome those students, domestic or foreign, who are willing to contribute to the welfare of human being through the research work in the field of pharmaceutical sciences aimed at preserving human life.
Environment The city of Matsubara, with a population of 136, 200, is located in the southern part of

Osaka. Being situated in a suburban area with excellent transport facilities, the campus is both close to the heart of Osaka Metropolis and far from the noise and madding crowd of the city.

Facilities Library, Center for Laboratory Animals, Medical Plant Garden, Radioisotope Research Center, Gymnasium, Sewage Treatment Plant, Greenhouse for Medical Herbs, Computer Center, Student Hall, Dormitory.

Student activities Freshmen Welcome Festival in May and University Festival in November are regularly held every year. There is a variety of extra curricular activities (both cultural and physical) including chorus, research of Chinese medicine, Judo, and Rugby.

Services for foreign students Advisory system, in which each student gets proper advice about his/her student life and academic career. Housing and part-time job information.

Undergraduate Programs

Faculty of Pharmaceutical Sciences(1, 212/0)
Dept. of Pharmaceutical Sciences(608/0)
Dept. of Pharmaceutical Technology(604/0)

Graduate Programs

Graduate School of Pharmaceutical Sciences (M 38/0, D 4/0)

Organic Chemistry, Pharmacognosy, Synthetic Organic Chemistry, Hygienic Chemistry, Biochemistry, Microbiology, Pharmaceutics, Pharmacology, Analytical Chemistry, Pharmaceutical Physical Chemistry, Radiopharmaceutical Chemistry

---

大手前女子大学
(Ôtemae Joshi Daigaku)
Otemae College

6-42 Ochayasho-cho, Nishinomiya-shi, Hyogo 662
☎ 0798-34-6331 FAX 0798-23-4761

Founded 1966
Professors 28
Associate Professors 11
Assistant Professors(Tenured) 11
Assistant Professors(Non-tenured) 70
Research Assistants 3
Undergraduate Students/Foreign Students 1, 974/6
Library 71, 797 volumes
Contact: Chairman of Department of English and American Literature, Faculty of Letters

Educational philosophy We aim at cultivating virtues and accomplishments characteristic of young ladies, and, recently, in view of the progress in arts and sciences in general, a new motto: " Study for Life " has been adopted.

Foreign students Students from abroad are readily accepted. Entrance examinations are on a par with those for Japanese students. We aim at helping foreign students to contribute much to mutual understanding and cultural exchange.

Environment The College is located with five minutes' walk of Shukugawa Station, Hankyu Line. Shukugawa is well-known as high-quality residential area amidst abundant nature, which is in good harmony with the academic atomosphere of the Women's College.

Facilities Library, Gymnasium, Research Institute of History, Anglo-Norman Research Center, Art Training Center

Student activities Ist Term: April-September, 2nd Term: October-March, Enrollment in April, College Festival in November, Commencement in March, Extra-Curriculum activities: various clubs of arts and sports

Services for foreign students Services such as Health Clinic, personal/psychological counselling, part-time job information are available at the Executive office.

Undergraduate Programs

Faculty of Letters(1, 974/6)
Dept. of Aesthetics and Art History(534/2)
Dept. of British and American Literature(711/1)
Dept. of History(729/3)

大谷大学
(Ôtani Daigaku)
Otani University

Koyamakamifusa-cho, Kita-ku, Kyoto 603
☎ 075-432-3131 FAX 075-431-9117

Founded 1665
Professors 41
Associate Professors 15
Assistant Professors(Tenured) 16
Assistant Professors(Non-tenured) 155
Undergraduate Students/Foreign Students 2, 490/0
Graduate Students/Foreign Students 119/3
Library 550, 000 volumes
Contact: Publicity & Planning Office, or Admission Office

Educational philosophy The study of history, literature and Buddhist culture has a long tradition at Otani University. Students are offered a broad variety of undergraduate and graduate programs designed to foster an understanding of the vital relationship which exists between academic pursuits and living Buddhist tradition —— the Spirit of Shinran, the founder of Shin Buddhism in Japan.

Foreign students We welcome applications by students who have already received a Bachelor's Degree or its equivalent and wish to pursue research in one of the following graduate courses: Shin Buddhism, Buddhism, Philosophy, and Buddhism Culture. Students should have a command of Japanese which will allow them to follow lecture.

Environment Otani University is located in the northern part of Kyoto, a ten minute subway ride from the main Kyoto Railway Station to Kitaoji Station.

Facilities Auditorium, Gymnasium, Judo-Dojo, Archery ground and research library containing as many as 550, 000 volumes.

Student activities Students activities vivide themselves into two fields, one in the cultural field and the other is in the athletic field. Both of them are quite active in their ways.

Academic programs for foreign students We don't have a special academic program for foreign students. However, our tutorial system works quite well.

Services for foreign students Individual counseling is given by the tutor to whom the student is assigned. While there is no university housing, the student affairs section does help students locate off campus housing.

Undergraduate Programs

Faculty of Letters(2, 490/0)
Dept. of Buddhist Studies(463/0)
Dept. of History(375/0)
Dept. of Literature(392/0)
Dept. of Philosophy(328/0)
Dept. of Sociology(390/0)
Dept. of Shin Buddhist Studies(542/0)

Graduate Programs

Graduate School of Letters(M 85/3, D 34/0)
Div. of Buddhist Culture(M 21/1, D 10/0)
Japanese History, Japanese Buddhism History, East Asian history, East Asian Buddhism History, Japanese Literature, Chinese Literature
Div. of Buddhist Studies(M 21/2, D 11/0)
Buddhism, Indian Studies
Div. of Philosophy(M 11/0, D 3/0)
Western Philosophy, Ethics, Philosophy of Religion, Sociology, Education
Div. of Shin Buddhist Studies(M 32/0, D 10/0)
Shin Buddhism

追手門学院大学
(Ôtemon Gakuin Daigaku)

Otemon Gakuin University

2-1-15 Nishiai, Ibaraki-shi, Osaka 567
☎ 0726-43-5421 FAX 0726-43-5427

Founded 1966
Professors 60
Associate Professors 31
Assistant Professors(Tenured) 12
Assistant Professors(Non-tenured) 179
Research Assistants 1
Undergraduate Students/Foreign Students 5, 291/9
Graduate Students/Foreign Students 23/2
Library 208, 919 volumes
Contact: Admission Office

Educational philosophy Our university aims at producing dedicated men and women of international spirit, who are quipped with the flexibility to cope with today's fast-changing world.

Foreign students We believe that foreign students can obtain a new valuation, culture and technique in our school, and can contribute a great deal to promoting mutual understanding.

Environment Our university located close to the Meishin (Kobe-Nagoya) Expressway in Ibaraki City, and is situated on top of the lovely Shogunyama Hill.

Facilities Several Athletic fields, Gymnasium, Library, Student Hall, Language Laboratory, Dormitory, Guest House, 58 Student Clubhouse, Audio-Visual Education Center, Computer Center

Student activities Popular Campus event is university festival. There is a wide variety of extra curricular activities, including volunteer work, marching band, student news paper, drama, baseball, football, soccor, karate, aikido, flower arrangement, etc.

Academic programs for foreign students Japanese language class, English class

Services for foreign students Health clinic, Personal psychological counseling, Housing information, Part-time job information and others.

Undergraduate Programs

Faculty of Economics(3, 170/5)
Dept. of Business Administration(1, 548/4)
Dept. of Economics(1, 622/1)
Faculty of Letters(2, 121/4)
Dept. of Asian Studies(575/2)
Dept. of English and American Language and Literature(508/1)
Dept. of Psychology(518/1)
Dept. of Sociology(580/0)

Graduate Programs

Graduate School of Economics(M 12/1)
Div. of Business Administration(M 6/1)
Principles of Business Administration, Management, Mathematics for Decision Making, Accounting
Div. of Economics(M 6/0)
Theoretical Economics, Economic Policy, Labor Economics, International Economics
Graduate School of Letters(M 11/1)
Div. of Chinese Culture(M 3/1)
Chinese Philosophy, Chinese History, Chinese Literature, Chinese Culture
Div. of English Literature(M 4/0)
English Literature, American Literature, English Philology, Linguistics

Div. of Psychology(M 1/0)
System of Psychology, Clinical Psychology, Experimental Psychology, Psychology of Learning
Div. of Sociology(M 3/0)
Basic Theory of Sociology, Theory of Social Groups, Theory of Contemporary Society, Political Sociology

---

立命館大学
(Ritsumeikan Daigaku)
Ritsumeikan University

56–1 Kitamachi, Tojiin, Kita–ku, Kyoto 603
☎ 075–465–1111 FAX 075–465–8160

Founded 1900
Professors 304
Associate Professors 115
Assistant Professors(Tenured) 4
Assistant Professors(Non–tenured) 719
Research Assistants 22
Undergraduate Students/Foreign Students 21, 838/247
Graduate Students/Foreign Students 304/37
Library 1, 396, 985 volumes
Contact: International Center

Educational philosophy Built upon the characteristic ideals of freedom and innovation, Ritsumeikan University's spirit lies in peace and democracy. By incorporating these ideals into our curriculum, we hope to offer our students a rich and rewarding education.
Foreign students Boasting the largest number of international students among the private universities in Western Japan, we are making every effort to provide an ideal educational environment for them.
Environment Ritsumeikan University is located at the foot of Mt. Kinugasa in the beautiful northwestern region of Kyoto. Ryoanji, Kinkakuji, and Toji–in, some of Kyoto's most famous temples, are located adjacent to the campus, and a nice panorama of Kyoto City can be enjoyed from many of the University's buildings.
Facilities Libraries, Research Institutes of Cultural Sciences, Science & Engineering, International Relations & Area Studies, International Language & Cultural Studies, and Educational Sciences, Date Processing Center, Gymnasiums, Playing Fields, etc.
Student activities Over 200 student associations are involved in sports, art, and scholarship, and the annual School Festival is a very popular event. A Student Center and two Seminar Houses are available to students for their activities.
Academic programs for foreign students Japanese Language Courses (Reading Comprehension, Conversation, Grammar, Kanji, and Composition), English Language Courses, and Japan Studies Courses (Culture, History, Geography, Economic, Business Administration, Nature, etc.)
Services for foreign students Scholarship Information, Career Counseling, Cultural Exchange Programs (International Sports Festival, Exchange Forum, Picnic and Farewell Party for Graduating Students)

Undergraduate Programs

Faculty of Business Administration(3, 048/79)
Dept. of Business Administration(3, 048/79)
Faculty of Economics(3, 056/43)
Dept. of Economics(3, 056/43)
Faculty of International Relations(654/40)
Dept. of International Relations(654/40)
Faculty of Law(3, 212/10)
Dept. of Law(3, 212/10)
Faculty of Letters(3, 202/31)
Dept. of Geography(402/1)
Dept. of History(937/7)
Dept. of Literature(1, 282/15)
Dept. of Philosophy(581/8)
Faculty of Science and Engineering(2, 765/10)
Dept. of Chemistry(443/0)
Dept. of Civil Engineering(480/0)
Dept. of Computer Science and Systems Engineering(437/5)
Dept. of Electrical Engineering(473/5)
Dept. of Mathematics and Physics(454/0)
Dept. of Mechanical Engineering(478/0)
Faculty of Social Sciences(3, 396/34)
Dept. of Social Sciences(3, 396/34)

Graduate Programs

Graduate School of Business Administration(M 7/2, D 6/1)
Div. of Business Management(M 7/2, D 6/1)
Graduate School of Economics(M 11/2, D 6/2)
Div. of Economics(M 11/2, D 6/2)
Graduate School of Law(M 6/3, D 5/1)
Div. of Civil Law(M 2/2, D 3/0)
Div. of Public Law(M 4/1, D 2/1)
Graduate School of Letters(M 67/10, D 35/7)
Div. of East Asian Thought(M 9/3)
Div. of East Asian Thought and Literature(D 3/0)
Div. of English and American Literature(M 8/0, D 1/0)
Div. of Geography(M 6/0, D 2/0)
Div. of History(M 20/4, D 11/2)
Div. of Japanese Literature(M 14/2, D 14/5)
Div. of Philosophy(M 1/0)
Div. of Psychology(M 9/1, D 2/0)
Div. of Western Philosophy(D 2/0)
Graduate School of Science and Engineering (M 127/2, D 16/2)
Div. of Applied Chemistry(M 19/0, D 1/0)
Div. of Civil Engineering(M 17/0, D 1/0)
Div. of Electrical Engineering(M 38/1, D 4/1)
Div. of Mechanical Engineering(M 35/1, D 4/1)
Div. of Physics(M 18/0, D 6/0)
Graduate School of Sociology(M 8/3, D 10/2)
Div. of Applied Sociology(M 8/3, D 10/2)

龍谷大学
(Ryûkoku Daigaku)
Ryukoku University

67 Tsukamoto-cho, Fukakusa, Fushimi-ku, Kyoto 612
☎ 075-642-1111 FAX 075-642-8867

Founded 1639
Professors 191
Associate Professors 67
Assistant Professors(Tenured) 38
Assistant Professors(Non-tenured) 572
Research Assistants 13
Undergraduate Students/Foreign Students 11, 124/81
Graduate Students/Foreign Students 281/24
Library 1, 020, 361 volumes
Contact: Ryukoku International Center

Educational philosophy Ryukoku University was established in 1639, founded on the spirit of Buddhism for the purpose of educating and training young men of superior talent. Ryukoku ranks as one of the oldest universities in Japan.
Foreign students Ryukoku places emphasis on the differences in studens' background that assures progress and success of the future of our educational and research activities.
Environment Ryukoku is located at the center of the ancient capital of Japan, Kyoto, which is famous for being the center of traditional culture and as a " University Town " with more than 30 institutions of higher education. Nearby metropolises, Osaka, Nara and Kobe, are only one hour away.
Facilities Two Dormitories for international students (all single rooms) with four tutors, numerous reference books in English and Chinese, auditorium, gymnasium, etc.
Student activities Extra curricular activities: more than 100 student organizations including many sports, music and academic clubs.
Popular campus events: freshmen camp, school festivals, welcome party, etc.
Academic programs for foreign students Japanese Culture and Language Program (one-year intensive Japanese program), supplemental Japanese language classes for classified international students, academic advisors for foreign students, four tutors in the dormitories
Services for foreign students Two dormitories for international students (all single rooms), housing information, health clinic, personal counseling, part-time job information, employment placement, cultural exchange programs

Undergraduate Programs

Faculty of Business Administration(2, 363/28)
Faculty of Economics(2, 245/32)
Faculty of Law(2, 402/14)
Faculty of Letters(2, 869/7)
Dept. of Buddhist Studies(Shin Buddhism Course/Buddhise Studies Course) (887/0)
Dept. of History(Japanese History Course/Oriental History Course/Buddhist History Course) (731/0)
Dept. of Literature(Japanese Literature Course/English Literature Course) (259/3)
Div. of Philosophy(Philosophy Course/Education Course) (241/0)
Dept. of Sociology(Sociology Course/Social Welfare Course) (527/0)
Faculty of Science and Technology(764/0)
Dept. of Applied Mathematics and Informatics (219/0)
Dept. of Electronics and Informatics(187/0)
Dept. of Materials Chemistry(180/0)
Dept. of Mechanical and System Engineering (179/0)
Faculty of Sociology and Social Welfare(481/0)
Dept. of Sociology(277/0)
Dept. of Social Work and Welfare(204/0)

Graduate Programs

Graduate School of Business Administration(M 9/5, D 6/2)
Business Administration Criticism, Principles of Business Administration, Industrial Management, History of Business Administration, History of Business, Industrial Developments in Japan, History of American and European Business, Corporate Theory, Business Form Theory, Multinational Business Theory, Business Management Theory, Management and Labor Relations, Marketing Theory, Business Administration, Business Administration Organization Theory, Corporate Financing Theory, Research and Development Expense Management, Accounting Principles and Standards, Accounting Policy, Corporate Taxation, Cost Management, Production Analysis, Management Information Systems, Business Statistics, Behavioral Science, Literature on Business Administration, Economic Principles, Monetary Economics, Fire Insurance Contract Theory, Banking and Finance, Economic Financing Theory, Industrial Sociology, Civil Law, Commercial Law, Labor Law, Seminars
Graduate School of Economics(M 7/2, D 1/0)
Economic Theory, Quantitative Regional Analysis, History of Economics, Economic History, Regional Economic History, History of Japanese Economics, History of Social Thought, Contemporary Economic Policy, Regional Economy, Regional Commercial Economy, Regional Industrial Structure, Regional Agricultural Economy, International Economy, Economic Development, Socialist Economy, Comparative Economic Systems, Japanese Economy, Industrial Organization, Small Corporate Economy, Economic Geography, Public Finance, Regional Public Finance, Monetary Theory, Small Corporate Finance, Statistics, Labor Economics, Literature on Economics, Regional Sociology, Sociology of Religion, Civil Law, Commercial Law, Seminars

Graduate School of Law(M 14/0, D 1/0)
Philosophy of Law, Legal History, Constitution, Administrative Law, International Law, Criminal Law, Criminology, Civil Law, Commercial Law, Social Low, Civil Procedure, Criminal Procedure, Politics, Japanese Political History, Western Political History, International Politics, Foreign Laws, Jurisprudence

Graduate School of Letters(M 159/7, D 84/6)

Div. of Buddhist Studies(M 30/1, D 12/0)
Buddhism, History of Buddhist Doctrines, Indian Philosophy, Literature of Buddhism, History of Buddhism, Philosophy of Religion, Philosophy, Seminars.

Div. of English Literature(M 7/0, D 6/0)
English Literature and American Literature, English Language, Literary Works of English and American Writers, Comparative Literature, History of Western Art, Philosophy of Religion, Translations of Oriental Classics, Seminars

Div. of Japanese History(M 14/1, D 8/1)
Japanese History, History of Japanese Buddhism, History of Japanese Literature, History of Japanese Legislation, History of Chinese Buddhism, Archaeology, Ethnography, History of Art, Seminars

Div. of Japanese Literature(M 14/2, D 7/1)
Literature of Japan, Japanese Language, Works of Japanese Literature, Chinese Classics, History of Japanese Buddhism, Ethnography, History of Art, Seminars

Div. of Oriental History(M 8/0, D 10/0)
Oriental History, History of Chinese Buddhism, Literature of Oriental History, History of Chinese Legislation, History of Japanese Buddhism, Archaeology, History of Art, Seminars

Div. of Philosophy(M 10/0, D 8/0)
Philosophy, Ethics, Philosophy of Religion, Ancient and Medieval Philosophical Works, Modern Philosophical Works, Buddhism, Shin Buddhism, Education, Sociology, Seminars

Div. of Shin Buddhism Course(M 64/3, D 28/2)
Shin Buddhism, History of Doctrines in Shin Buddhism, History of Theories in Pure Land Buddhism, History of Shin Buddhism, History of Buddhism, Indian Philosophy, Buddhism, Philosophy of Religion, Philosophy, Literature of Buddhism, Seminars

Div. of Social Welfare(M 7/0, D 3/1)
Social Welfare, Social Work Research, Literature of Social Welfare, Sociology, Shin Buddhism, Buddhism, Philosophy, Japanese History, Seminars

Div. of Sociology(M 5/0, D 2/1)
Sociology, Social Survey, Literature of Sociology, Social Welfare, Shin Buddhism, Buddhism, Philosophy, Japanese History, Seminars

聖和大学
(Seiwa Daigaku)

Seiwa College

7-54 Okadayama, Nishinomiya-shi, Hyogo 662
☎ 0798-52-0724 FAX 0798-52-0974

Founded 1880
Professors 13
Associate Professors 6
Assistant Professors(Tenured) 6
Assistant Professors(Non-tenured) 68
Research Assistants 2
Undergraduate Students/Foreign Students 487/5
Graduate Students/Foreign Students 12/1
Library 108, 094 volumes
Contact: Admission Office

Educational philosophy It is the educational aim of our Seiwa College that students will be able to think for themselves based on their own deep prayer and religious practice and act with responsibility in their respective fields, not only in Japan but also in many places throughout the world.

Foreign students Students come to Seiwa not only from all over Japan but also from South East Asia and Korea. We believe Seiwa will have much to contribute to the international academic world.

Environment Nishinomiya, with a population of 427, 000, lies halfway between Osaka and Kobe, and is convenient to the traffic facilities. Seiwa college is located on a hill, in a school zone of Nishinomiya, surrounded by nature commanding a beautiful view of Osaka Bay. Students can study in this rich and calm environment.

Facilities Kindergarten, Day Care Center, Dormitory, Library, Audio-visual Room, Personal Computer System, Language Laboratory, Gymnasium, Auditorium.

Student activities Popular campus events at Seiwa includes Freshmen camp, School festival, English speech contest, Intramural sports event, Christmas celebration. Extra-curricular activities are centered around school clubs such as music clubs, sports clubs, education clubs, and communication service clubs.

Academic programs for foreign students Supplemental Japanese Language class (planning)

Services for foreign students Health, clinic, personal/psychological counseling. (Dormitory is opened for foreign students, too.)

Undergraduate Programs

Faculty of Education(487/5)

Dept. of Early Childhood Education(425/4)

Dept. of Christian Education(62/1)

Graduate Programs

Graduate School of Education(M 12/1)
Div. of Early Childhood Education(M 12/1)
Early Childhood Education, Early Childhood Psychology, etc.

摂南大学
(Setsunan Daigaku)
Setsunan University

17–8 Ikedanakamachi, Neyagawa-shi, Osaka 572
☎ 0720-26-5101 FAX 0720-26-5100

Founded 1975
Professors 108
Associate Professors 65
Assistant Professors(Tenured) 31
Assistant Professors(Non-tenured) 197
Research Assistants 27
Undergraduate Students/Foreign Students 5, 783/15
Graduate Students/Foreign Students 42/1
Library 270, 187 volumes
Contact: Admission Section

Educational philosophy Setsunan Univetsity believes that the aim of university education should be to foster personal growth in mind, body and spirit. In order to realize this aim, Setsunan University maintains a small teacher-student ratio and academic programs to meet the individual needs of each student. A strong program of extra-curricular activties is also offered. In this age of rapidly developing technology and internationalization, Setsunan University is at the forefront in striving to provide students with the education needed to be successful in today's society.
Foreign students In order to open up our study to the world, not just Japan, we are contributing to the internationalization of Setsunan University by actively encouraging the enrolment of foreign students.
There are classes in "Japanese Language" and "Japanese Affairs," to give them knowledge in such areas as Japanese culture, economics, and history.
Environment Setsunan University was established in 1975, and being developed as a university with 5 faculties, 10 departments, 11 courses, 1 master's program, and 1 doctor's program. The university has Neyagawa and Hirakata campuses situated in between Osaka and Kyoto.
Facilities Computing Center (IBM 4381, 4341), Library (270, 187 volumes and 2, 100 various of learned journals), CAD/CAM System, Reseach Laboratory for Drug Safety.
Student activities April: Entrance Ceremony, Orientations September: The First Semester Examination November: Setsunan University Festival, on-the-Bus-Trip for foreign students February: Second Semester Examination March: Graduation Ceremony
Academic programs for foreign students Japanese Courses and Personal Counseling System: Students are provided not only with instruction of the Japanese language and Japanese Studies but also personal counseling by specialists.
Services for foreign students Accommodation: The University specially provides accommodation for foreign students in Setsudai Koryu Kaikan (Setsunan University Interchange Hall). University Scholarship System: Students who study on their own payment and have a high level of attainment are to be granted 20, 000 yen or 10, 000 yen on a monthly basis. Tuition Reducation System: Students with high performance are to be provided 30 % tuition reduction.

Undergraduate Programs

Faculty of Business Administration and Information(981/6)
Dept. of Business Administration and Information(981/6)
Faculty of Engineering(2, 417/5)
Dept. of Architecture(457/1)
Dept. of Civil Engineering(466/0)
Dept. of Electrical Engineering(513/2)
Dept. of Industrial and Systems Engineering(485/2)
Dept. of Mechanical Engineering(496/0)
Faculty of International Language and Culture(947/3)
Dept. of International Language and Culture(947/3)
Faculty of Law(556/1)
Dept. of Law(556/1)
Faculty of Pharmaceutical Sciences(882/0)
Dept. of Environmental Health Sciences(573/0)
Dept. of Pharmaceutical Sciences(309/0)

Graduate Programs

Graduate School of Engineering(M 13/0)
Div. of Electricity and Electronics(M 1/0)
Solid state electrics, Control and Information Engineering, Optoelectronics and Electro dynamics
Div. of Mechanical Systems Engineering(M 4/0)
Systems and Control Engineering, Manufacturing Process and Production Engineerig, Thermo and Fluid Systems Engineering, Materials Engineering
Div. of Social Development Engineering(M 8/0)
Urban and Regional Planning, Environmental and Sanitary Engineering, Structural Engineering, Soil and Foundation Engineering
Graduate School of Pharmaceutical Sciences(M 28/0, D 1/1)
Div. of Pharmaceutical Sciences(M 28/0, D 1/1)
Pharmaceutical Chemistry, Pharmacognosy, Instrumental Analysis of Natural Products, Synthetic Chemistry, Physical Chemistry, Medical High Molecular Compound Chemistry, Biochemistry, Pharmacology, Toxicology,

Pharmacy, Drug Metabolism and Disposition, Pharmaceutical Analytical Chemistry, Clinical Biochemistry, Environmental Analytical Chemistry, Environmental Health Sciences, Food Hygienic Sciences, Microbiology, Drug Safety Assessment

親和女子大学
(Shinwa Joshi Daigaku)
Shinwa Women's College

7-13-1 Suzurandai Kita-machi, Kita-ku, Kobe-shi, Hyogo 651-11
☎ 078-591-1651 FAX 078-591-3113

Founded 1966
Professors 22
Associate Professors 14
Assistant Professors(Tenured) 9
Assistant Professors(Non-tenured) 95
Undergraduate Students/Foreign Students 1, 725/0
Library 133, 603 volumes
Contact: Admission Office

Educational philosophy As a college designed specifically for women, we hope to help the students bring an informed intelligence to bear on their personal and public concerns, and also help them in their development as educated women who are self-confident, diligent, and creative.
Foreign students Shinwa is a relatvely small college for women with a fairly limited range of courses. However, any foreign student who may be interested in studying in any of our departments will be welcome.
Environment Located in the northern part of Kobe, one of the most international cities in Japan, Shinwa is blessed with a quiet atmosphere for studying and an easy access to downtown area.
Facilities Library, Computer Center, Language Laboratory, Gymnasium, Auditorium
Student activities Annual events include freshmen orientation in spring, sports day and the college festival in autumn, and a skiing tour in winter. Mandolin club, choral group, puppet club, Japanese calligraphy, tennis, basketball, volleyball, archery, bowling are representative of the extra-curricular activities at our college.

Undergraduate Programs

Faculty of Literature(1, 725/0)
Dept. of Child Education(572/0)
Dept. of English Literature(571/0)
Dept. of Japanese Literature(582/0)

四天王寺国際仏教大学
(Shitennôji Kokusai Bukkyô Daigaku)
Shitennoji International Buddhist University

3-2-1 Gakuenmae, Habikino-shi, Osaka 583
☎ 0729-56-3181

Founded 1967

Undergraduate Programs

Faculty of Literature
Dept. of Buddhism
Dept. of Education
Dept. of Language and Culture
Arabic Studies Course
English and American Studies Course
Japanese Studies Course
Dept. of Sociology

松蔭女子学院大学
(Shôin Joshigakuin Daigaku)
Shoin Women's University

1-2-1 Shinoharaobanoyama-cho, Nada-ku, Kobe-shi, Hyogo 657
☎ 078-882-6122 FAX 078-882-5032

Founded 1966
Professors 25
Associate Professors 14
Assistant Professors(Tenured) 7
Assistant Professors(Non-tenured) 138
Undergraduate Students/Foreign Students 1, 475/0
Library 177, 445 volumes
Contact: Admission Office

Educational philosophy Sholn was founded as a mission school for girls in 1892 by English missionaries sent by the "Society for the Propagation of the Gospel," and we seek to carry on their efforts to provide a liberal education for young women of any religious affillation that emphasizes the development in students of a love of their native culture along with an awareness of and respect for foreign languages, cultures and customs.
Foreign students Foreign applicants must satisfy the Standard Qualifications Requirement and required to have passed the Japanese Language Proficiency Test (Grade 2), or show evidence of an equivalent Japanese language ability.
Environment Shoin's two campuses were united in 1980 on a site conveniently located between the internationally famed Kobe port and scenic Mount Rokko.

The new award-winning campus boasts the modern facilities and is admired for its architectural beauty and functional utility.

Facilities Shoin's facilities include a school chapel with newly built 18th century French pipe organ, a library containing 180, 000 volumes, fully-equipped language laboratories and computer/word-processing rooms, a multi-purpose gymnasium with first-class tennis courts and grounds for other sports, and two school dormitories.

Student activities Shoin students are active in such diverse activities as tennis, Naginata, lacrosse, tea ceremony, koto, chorus, calligraphy, movie club and folk singing. In addition, many students take advantage of Shoin's sister university relationships with the University of New Hampshire and Hobart and William Smith Colleges in New York State.

Academic programs for foreign students Course in Creative Computing and Computer Assisted Language Study, Course in English Language and English/American Literature, Course in Japanese Literature, Course in Teaching Japanese as a Foreign Language, One Term Intensive Program in Japanese Language and Culture for Foreign Students

Services for foreign students In addition to services provided for all undergraduates, Shoin offers students from overseas dormitory accommodation, homestay opportunities, and a variety of cultural exchange programs.

Undergraduate Programs

Faculty of Literature(1, 475/0)
- **Dept. English Language and English/American Literature**(917/0)
- **Dept. of Japanese Literature**(558/0)

種智院大学

(Shuchiin Daigaku)

Shuchiin College

545 Toji-cho, Mibudori 8-Jo sagaru, Minami-ku, Kyoto-shi, Kyoto 601
☎ 075-681-6513

Founded 1949

Undergraduate Programs

Faculty of Buddhism
- **Dept. of Buddhism**

相愛大学

(Sôai Daigaku)

Soai University

4-4-1 Nankonaka, Suminoe-ku, Osaka 559
☎ 06-612-5900 FAX 06-612-2993

Founded 1958
Professors 48
Associate Professors 14
Assistant Professors(Tenured) 2
Assistant Professors(Non-tenured) 199
Undergraduate Students/Foreign Students 1, 262/0
Library 114, 262 volumes
Contact: Kyomuka

Education philosophy Education for the whole woman in the spirit of Mahayanist Buddhism as embodied in the teachings and in the person of Shinran, founder of the Jodo-Shinshu sect, as well as development of intellectual capacities

Foreign students Foreign students are welcome, but they must possess a functional ability of the Japanese language to pursue a regular course of studies in Japanese on the college level

Environment The campus is located conveniently near the heart of metropolitan area on the man-made island of South Port in the Bay of Osaka. Osaka is the second largest city in Japan with the population of 2. 4 million.

Facilities University library, Music library, Gymnasium, Auditorium, Tennis courts, Computer rooms, etc.

Student activities Campus events includes school excursion, school festival, a series of music concerts. There is a wide variety of extra curricular activities, including tea ceremony, chorus, popular music, golf, ski, tennis, etc.

Academic programs for foreign students Academic programs for foreign students will be arranged on an individual basis

Services for foreign students Various services for foreign students will be arranged in accordance with their needs by the Committee of International Exchange at Soai University

Undergraduate Programs

Faculty of The Humanities(505/0)
- **Dept. of Anglo-American Cultural Studies**(252/0)
- **Dept. of Japanese Cultural Studies**(253/0)

Faculty of The Music(757/0)
- **Dept. of Instrumental Music**(481/0)
- **Dept. of Musical Composition**(90/0)
- **Dept. of Vocal Music**(186/0)

園田学園女子大学
(Sonoda Gakuen Joshi Daigaku)
Sonoda Gakuen Women's College

7-29-1 Minami-tsukaguchi-cho, Amagasaki-shi, Hyogo 661
☎ 06-429-1201

Founded 1966

Undergraduate Programs

Faculty of Literature
Dept. of English Literature
Dept. of Japanese Literature

桃山学院大学
(Momoyama Gakuin Daigaku)
St. Andrews University

237-1 Nishino, Sakai-shi, Osaka 588
☎ 0722-36-1181 FAX 0722-34-7276

Founded 1959
Professors 74
Associate Professors 43
Assistant Professors(Tenured) 10
Assistant Professors(Non-tenured) 116
Research Assistants 1
Undergraduate Students/Foreign Students 6, 141/41
Library 301, 436 volumes
Contact: International Center FAX 0722-36-5767

Education philosophy To achieve its primary objective, the Univetsity seeks to establish and maintain the conditions of free, independent inquiry and expression in all fields of study, with emphasis on Christian humanity, democracy and internationalism.
Foreign students Since its foundation, the University has had an international perspective. The University always welcomes international students and regards them as an indispensable constituent body of the University.
Environment Located in southern Osaka, the University has an easy access to downtown Osaka by rail. The University was established in 1959 as one of the Momoyama Gakuin's constituent institutions to commemorate the centennial of the Anglican mission in Jpan. Momoyama Gakuin is an institute founded in Osaka in 1884 by the Church Missionary Society of England.
Facilities University chapel, university library, research institute, international centre, computer center, language laboratories, audio-visual lecture theatres, library for human rights, gymnasiums, first-aid station, seminar house, guesthouse.
Student activities Momoyama festival, Christmas service, graduation ceremony, overseas programs (Australia, Britain, Canada, China, Holland, Indonesia, Korea, United States). More than 100 sports teams and clubs, and culture or social associations.
Academic programs for foreign students The International Center gives academic advice to international students. Japanese courses designed for international students.
Services for foreign students The International Center offers advice on student life, housing, and part-time jobs to international sudents. It provides them with programs for cultural and inter-student understanding.

Undergraduate Programs

Faculty of Business Administration(1, 825/27)
Dept. of Business Administration(1, 825/27)
Faculty of Economics(2, 136/1)
Dept. of Economics(2,136/1)
Faculty of Letters(393/3)
Dept. of English(156/1)
Dept. of Intercultural studies(237/2)
Faculty of Sociology(1, 787/10)
Dept. of Sociology(1, 787/10)

八代学院大学
(Yashiro Gakuin Daigaku)
St. Michael's University

5-1-1 Manabigaoka, Tarumi-ku, Kobe-shi, Hyogo 655
☎ 078-709-3851 FAX 078-707-3500

Founded 1963
Professors 18
Associate Professors 7
Assistant Professors(Tenured) 6
Assistant Professors(Non-tenured) 38
Undergraduate Students/Foreign Students 1, 922/17
Library 76, 192 volumes
Contact: International Center

Educational philosophy " Fear God, fear no man, but serve mankind."
Having this as the school motto, St. Michael's University strives to educate those who will guide Japan's economy in these changing conditions of internationalization.
Foreign students We enroll a significant number of foreign students to develop both trained leadership for neighboring countries and the international understanding of our Japanese students.
Environment Our school is conveniently situated in a suburb of the port city of Kobe rich in inrternational history and culture.
Facilities Students have the use of our modern library, extensive computer facilities, international center, martial arts buildings, religious center, and information

developed in our research center.

Student activities We have a number of sports and culture clubs to cater to the intellectual, physical and social needs of our students as well as an annual school festivel.

Academic programs for foreign students In their freshman year foreign students may take catch-up class in Japanese language and culture.

Services for foreign students Foreign faculty and administrative personnel are on band to help foreign students with their scholastic and living problems. Our International Friendship Association aids in social integration.

Unergraduate Programs

Faculty of Economics(1, 922/17)
Dept. of Economics
(the economics major, buisiness management, international trade, tourism)(1, 922/17)

宝塚造形芸術大学
(Takarazuka Zôkei Geijutsu Daigaku)

Takarazuka University of Art and Design

2-1658 Hibarigaoka, Hanayashiki, Takarzuka-shi, Hyogo 665
☎ 0727-56-1231

Founded 1986

Undergraduate Programs

Faculty of Formative Arts
Dept. of Design
Dept. of Fine Arts

帝国女子大学
(Teikoku Joshi Daigaku)

Teikoku Women's College

6-21-57 Tohda-cho, Moriguchi-shi, Osaka 570
☎ 06-902-0791 FAX 06-902-8894

Founded 1965
Professors 20
Associate Professors 11
Assistant Professors(Tenured) 6
Assistant Professors(Non-tenured) 38
Research Assistants 9
Undergraduate Students/Foreign Students 621/5
Library 79, 000 volumes
Contact: Admission Office

Educational philosophy We aim at education of young women to have knowledge and skills necessary to the effective management of domestic life, which is after all the basis of life as a Japanese. We also seek to expand the activities and ways of thinking of the students so that can assume vital roles in the various fields of society.

Foreign students We will be combining studies of the Japanese language with those of society, history and encourage to come familiar with computers. Our computer science will provide basic skills needed in modern society especially for foreign students.

Environment Moriguchi city is one of the satellite cities of Osaka, with a population of 160,000. Our college is located within easy access of Osaka and Kyoto, both of which used to be the ancient capitals of Japan. The surroundings of the college is quiet in the residential zone and is suitable for the study.

Facilities Seminar House, Library, Computer Center, Auditorium, Tennis Court, Swimming pool, Dormitory

Student activities Campus events are freshman orientation, Homestay programs in the U.S.A. and Australia, Fashion Tour to Europe, school festival, ski tour. There is a wide variety of extra curricular activities such as softball, basketball, tennis, tea ceremony, flower arrangement, chorus.

Academic programs for foreign students Supplemental Japanese language class, Word Processor, Secretarial Business Practice, Cultural history of Japan, Social Psychology, Development of Expression

Services for foreign students Foreign students will spend their days with Japanese families of students and staff and living in near-by suburbs.

Undergraduate Programs

Faculty of Domestic Science(621/5)
Dept. of Food Science(187/0)
Dept. of Clothing and Fashion(219/2)
Dept. of Juvenile Studies(Juvenile Culture course, Juvenile Psychology Course)(215/3)

天理大学
(Tenri Daigaku)

Tenri University

1050 Somanouchi, Tenri-shi, Nara 632
☎ 07436-3-1511(ext. 6430) FAX 07436-2-1965

Founded 1925
Contact: Information Section

Educational philosophy Tenri University was founded based on the doctrine of Tenrikyo Religion in order to nurture persons of international perspective to realize a world of " Joyous Life ". For this purpose, special care is being taken so that every student masters at least one foreign language with the spirit of intercultural understanding and communication.

Environment Tenri City, with a population of 70, 000, is located 10 kilometers south of Nara City.

Tenri University stands in the calm and peaceful atmosphere of Tenri City, and it is well known for Tenrikyo religion as well as the time-honored history and cultural heritage of ancient Japan.

Undergraduate Programs

Faculty of Foreign Languages
- **Dept. of Chinese Studies**
- **Dept. of English & American Studies**
- **Dept. of French Studies**
- **Dept. of German Studies**
- **Dept. of Indonesian Studies**
- **Dept. of Korean Studies**
- **Dept. of Russian Studies**
- **Dept. of Spanish Studies**

Faculty of Letters
- **Dept. of Religious Studies**
- **Dept. of Japanese Language and Literature**

Faculty of Physical Education
- **Dept. of Physical Education**

帝塚山学院大学
(Tezukayama Gakuin Daigaku)
Tezukayama Gakuin University

1823-2 Imakuma, Osakasayama-shi, Osaka 589
☎ 0723-65-0865 FAX 0723-65-5628

Founded 1961
Professors 32
Associate Professors 15
Assistant Professors(Tenured) 11
Assistant Professors(Non-tenured) 106
Research Assistants 1
Undergraduate Students/Foreign Students 1, 783/2
Library 180, 000 volumes
Contact: Admissions and Records Office

Education philosophy The aims of our university are the same as those for the whole Tezukayama Gakuin that is, to encourage the students to seek the truth, to open their eyes to the world, and to develop highly educated ladies capable of participating fully in society and the world.

Foreign students We believe that students from abroad can enjoy a rewarding life in our university, because a good many of our students are from homes comparatively rich in Japanese culture.

Environment Our university is in Osakasayama city, a suburban area with a population of 52, 000, rich in ancient Japanese historic spots. You arrive at our campus from the center of Osaka city within 50 minutes by train.

Facilities Audio-visual center; library with 180, 000 books; computer class; gymnasium; a branch class of Japan Broadcasting University.

Student activities We have sports events in June and October, and school festival in November. There is also a wide variety of extra curricular activities: golf-club, tennis club, softball club, tea cermony club, traditional Japanese music club and others.

Academic programs for foreign students We provide academic programs for foreign students, such as Japanese Grammar, Japanese History, Japanese Listening and Speech and others.

Services for foreign students Health clinic, personal & psychological counselling, housing information, home visit programs are provided for foreign students.

Undergraduate Programs

Faculty of Literature(1, 783/2)
- **Dept. of Aesthetics and Art History**(289/0)
- **Dept. of English Literature**(567/0)
- **Dept. of Intercultural Studies**(359/0)
- **Dept. of Japanese Literature**(568/0)

帝塚山大学
(Tezukayama Daigaku)
Tezukayama University

7-1-1 Tezukayama, Nara-shi, Nara 631
☎ 0742-45-4701 FAX 0742-45-7994

Founded 1964
Professors 30
Associate Professors 18
Assistant Professors(Tenured) 4
Assistant Professors(Non-tenured) 106
Undergraduate Students/Foreign Students 2, 122/3
Library 174, 630 volumes
Contact: Admission Office

Education philosophy Our university was founded in order to provide students with both breadth and depth in the study of human culture. We hope each student can take his (her) place in society as a refined modern human being with broad international views and a deep understanding of his (her) own culture.

Foreign students Now we are in the age of global world, therefore we are eager to have students from various part of the world to study at our university, and promote mutual understandings.

Environment Nara is an old capital of Japan, so there are many historic spots and national treasures. Our university is located in the western part of Nara. The campus is on the hill surrounded by deep green woods. The university is 30 minutes' by train from the center of Osaka, and 50 minutes' from Kyoto.

Facilities Library, Computer Center, Gymnasium, Language Laboratory, Archaeology Research Center

Student activities Campus Events: Freshmen Welcome Party, School Festival, Sports Festival

Club Activities: Soccer, Baseball, Rugby, American Football, Squash Tennis, Golf, Tennis, Japanese Archery, Art, Chorus, Flower Arrangement, Tea Ceremony, Broadcasting, Noh play, Cinema, Photography, etc.

Academic programs for foreign students Supplementary Japanese language class.

Services for foreign students The remission of entrance examination fee for the regular students from abroad. Financial aid: The reduction of 30% of tuition fee for regular students from abroad. International Exchange Committee, housing information, part-time job information

Undergraduate Programs

Faculty of Economics(950/2)
  Dept. of Economics(950/2)
Faculty of Liberal Arts(1, 172/1)
  Dept. of Liberal Arts(1, 172/1)

流通科学大学
(Ryûtsû Kagaku Daigaku)

University of Marketing and Distribution Sciences

3-1 Gakuen-Nishi-machi, Nishi-ku, Kobe-shi, Hyogo
651-21
☎ 078-794-3555 FAX 078-794-3510

Founded 1988
Professors 22
Associate Professors 10
Assistant Professors(Tenured) 11
Assistant Professors(Non-tenured) 58
Undergraduate Students/Foreign Students 1, 446/20
Library 37, 141 volumes
Contact: Student Affairs Section

Education philosophy UMDS cultivates human talent for scientifically elucidating the concept of distribution, and creating an ideal distribution system; these individuals will contribute to the peace and prosperity of the 21st century.

Foreign students Here is a meeting of minds that transcends nationality, profession and viewpoint.
We trust that man's insight will result from such meetings. In this spirit, our cornerstone is inscribed "Friends from afar are a welcome sight"

Environment The town of gakuen-toshi is located in west of Kobe. 5-min. walk from gakuen-toshi station which is a 22-min. ride from Sannomiya station on the Kobe Express Subway.

Facilities Lecture Building, Research Building, Library, College Hall, Community Center, Gymnasium, Fields, Yard of Meditation, Forum, Parking Lot, Tennis Courts, Club House, Institute Marketing and Distribution Sciences, Institute of Foreign Languages.

Student activities School festival, Freshman Study, Athletic meeting, Student newspaper, Light music, Basketball, Baseball, Soccer, Tennis, Field and trackevents, Rugby, etc.

Academic programs for foreign students Japanese classes for exchange students further individualize education, Things Japanese.

Services for foreign students Health clinic, Housing information, Curriculum guidance.

Undergraduate Programs

Faculty of Commece(1, 446/20)
  Dept. of Marketing and Distribution Sciences(871/16)
  Dept. of Business Administration(575/4)

CHUGOKU

CHUGOKU REGION CLIMATE

- San'in District (Japan Sea Side)
  Generally cloudy in summer.
- Seto Inland Sea Side
  Generally clear year-round, with little rain.
  Summers quite hot, with comparatively mild winters.

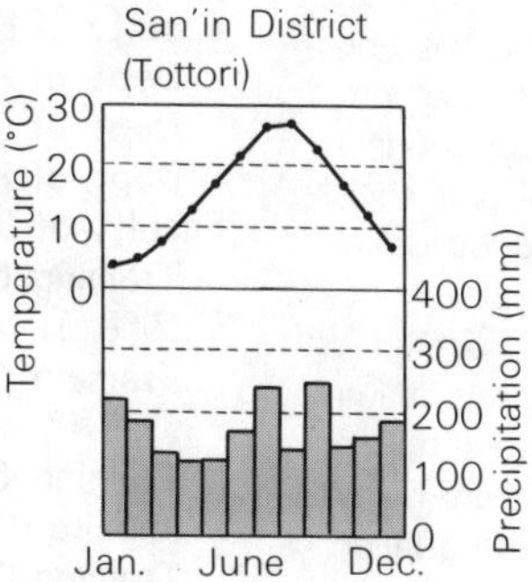

Average annual temperature
14.3°C
Annual precipitation
2,018mm

National Universities

広島大学
(Hiroshima Daigaku)
Hiroshima University

1-1-89 Higashisenda-machi, Naka-ku, Hiroshima 730
☎ 082-241-1221 FAX 082-247-2014

Founded 1949
Professors 487
Associate Professors 436
Assistant Professors(Tenured) 140
Assistant Professors(Non-tenured) 638
Research Assistants 541
Undergraduate Students/Foreign Students 12, 908/26
Graduate Students/Foreign Students 1, 865/228
Library 2, 466, 609 volumes
Contact: Foreign Students Adviser's Office

Educational philosophy Hiroshima University is a national university in an international-oriented city. It aims to provide the highest level of education and training in the teaching of Japanese as a foreign language, and encourage cultural exchanges between Japanese and foreign students. We, therefore, seek to achieve a university, which is truly international in outlook.

Foreign students The city of Hiroshima has considerable experience of international exchange programs, so foreign students will have many opportunities to participate in a wide variety of cultural and social events. We feel that they will be able to build and enjoy lasting relationships with Japanese people.

Environment The city of Hiroshima is located in the center of Chugoku-Shikoku area, facing the beautiful Seto island Sea. The population is around 1 million. It is linked with all the principal cities in Japan, by an excellent network of rail and air transportation. Hiroshima has a relatively mild climate, but there are seasonal changes. Although Hiroshima is known for the dropping of the Atomic Bomb in 1945, it has developed into a modern city.

Facilities Research Institute for Nuclear Medicine and Biology, Research Institute for Higher Education, Information Processing Center, Institute for International Education, Health Service Center, Institute for Peace Science, Gymnasium, Swimming pool, Baseball field, etc.

Student activities The University Festivals are held in the spring and autumn of every year, and in addition, each faculty organizes a College Festival. There are lots of Club activities. Sports clubs include Judo Club, Karate Club, Baseball Club, Tennis Club, etc. Cultural Circles include Calligraphy Club, Tea Geremony Study Group, The Symphony Orchestra Club, etc.

Academic programs for foreign students Supplementary courses in Japanese Language, Student advisory system

Services for foreign students Health clinic, personal/psychological counseling, Student accommodation, part-time job information

Undergraduate Programs

Faculty of Applied Biological Science(543/0)
 Dept. of Applied Biological Science
Faculty of Economics(1, 393/13)
 Dept. of Economics
Faculty of Education(1, 574/1)
 Dept. of Curriculum and Instruction(1, 069/0)
 Dept. of Education(173/0)
 Dept. of Psychology(148/0)
 Dept. of Teaching Japanese as a Second Language(184/1)
Faculty of Engineering(2, 512/11)
 Cluster I (Mechanical Engineering) (556/5)
 Cluster II (Electrical and Industrial Engineering) (700/1)
 Cluster III (Chemical-and Bio-Engineering) (575/2)
 Cluster IV (Structural Engineering Architecture) (681/3)
Faculty of Integrated Arts and Sciences(764/1)
 Dept. of Integrated Arts and Sciences
Faculty of Law(1, 373/0)
 Dept. of Law
Faculty of Letters(762/0)
 Dept. of History(148/0)
 Dept. of Literature(242/0)
 Dept. of Philosophy(372/0)
Faculty of School Education(1, 471/0)
 Training Course in Elementary School Education (908/0)
 Training Course in Junior High School Teaching (355/0)
 Training Course in the Education of the Hearing Impaired(59/0)
 Training Course in the Education of the Mentally Retarded(87/0)
 Training Course in the Education of the Visually Handicapped(62/0)
Faculty of Science(1, 155/0)
 Dept. of Biology (Botany) (56/0)
 Dept. of Biology (Zoology) (52/0)
 Dept. of Chemistry(314/0)
 Dept. of Geology and Mineralogy(73/0)
 Dept. of Materials Science(206/0)
 Dept. of Mathematics(295/0)
 Dept. of Physics(159/0)
School of Dentistry(418/0)
 Dept. of Dentistry(418/0)
School of Medicine and Institute of Pharmaceutical Science(943/0)
 Institute of Pharmaceutical Science(250/0)
 School of Medicine(693/0)

Graduate Programs

Graduate School of Biosphere Sciences(M 164/11, D 58/14)

Div. of Applied Biological Science(M 65/6, D 16/7)

Biological Oceanography, Aquaculture, Fisheries Resources Ecology, Fish Pathology and Physiology, Animal Breeding and Hygiene, Productive Physiology of Domestic Animals, Animal Nutrition and Management, Agricultural Production Economics, Utilization Research of Bio-resources, Biophysics and Food Engineering, Food Microbiology and Hygiene

Div. of Biological Sciences(M 54/4, D 20/5)

Biological Chemistry, Cell Biology, Physiology, Applied Microbiology, Applied Biochemistry, Plant Nutrition

Div. of Environment and Natural Resources (M 45/1, D 22/2)

Social Environment, Human Behavior, Community Environmental Science, Marine Science, Terrene Science, Ecosystem Science, Environmental Metrics, Physical and Chemical Methods of Measurement, Materials Science

Graduate School of Dental Science(D 57/8)

Div. of Basic Dental Science(D 6/1)

Oral Anatomy, Physiology and Oral Physiology, Biochemistry and Oral Biochemistry, Oral Pathology, Microbiology and Oral Bacteriology, Pharmacology, Dental Materials

Div. of Clinical Dental Science(D 51/7)

Preventive Dentistry, Operative Dentistry, Endodontology and Periodontology, Oral and Maxillofacial Surgery, Removable Prosthodontics, Fixed Partial Prosthodontics, Orthodontics, Pedodontics, Oral Radiology

Graduate School of Education(M 106/14, D 70/11)

Div. of Curriculum and Instruction(M 43/2, D 21/7)

Japanese Language Education, English Language Education, Social Studies Education, Mathematics Education, Science Education, Music Education, Health and Physical Education, Home Economics Education

Div. of Educational Administration(M 9/3, D 5/0)

Educational Administration and Finance, Comparative Education, Educational Management

Div. of Educational Psychology(M 12/1, D 12/0)

Educational Psychology, Developmental Psychology, Learning Psychology, Clinical Psychology and Psychology of the Handicapped

Div. of Experimental Psychology(M 3/1, D 4/0)

Experimental Psychology, Group and Social Psychology

Div. of Paedology(M 10/3, D 10/2)

Health Science of Early Childhood, Pedagogy of Early Childhood, Psychology of Early Childhood

Div. of Pedagogy(M 15/1, D 18/2)

Educational Philosophy, History of Japanese and Oriental Education, History of Western Education, Educational Sociology, Educational Methodology, Social Education

Div. of Teaching Japanese as a Second Language(M 14/3)

Teaching Japanese as a Second Language, Japanese Linguistics, Linguistics, Japanese Culture

Graduate School of Engineering(M 492/32, D 82/38)

Div. of Design Engineering(M 158/8, D 11/9)

Machine Design, Ship Design

Div. of Engineering of Transport Phenomena(M 62/0, D 9/4)

Chemical Engineering, Heat and Power Engineering, Environmental Science

Div. of Environmental Science and Engineering(M 23/2, D 2/2)

Environmental Planning and Control, Architecture

Div. of Industrial Chemistry(M 112/7, D 22/7)

Applied Chemistry, Fermentation Technology, Applied Physics and Chemistry, Environmental Science

Div. of Information Theory(M 40/2, D 8/4)

Circuits and Electrical System Engineering, Industrial and System Engineering, Applied Mathematics, Information and Behavioral Science

Div. of Materials Engineering(M 91/2, D 12/2)

Mechanical Materials, Electronics Engineering, Applied Mathematics, Applied Physics and Chemistry

Div. of Structural Engineering(M 42/3, D 8/7)

Structural Engineering, Ship Structural Engineering

Div. of Systems Engineering(M 64/8, D 10/3)

Circuits and Electrical System Engineering, Industrial and Systems Engineering, Applied Mathematics

Graduate School of Letters(M 66/1, D 82/5)

Div. of Archeology(M 3/0, D 3/1)

Archeology

Div. of Chinese and Indian Philosophy(M 8/0, D 2/0)

Philosophy of Ancient and Medieval China, Philosophy of Modern China, Indian Philosophy

Div. of Chinese Language and Literature(M 0/0, D 1/0)

Chinese Language, Chinese Literature

Div. of English Language and Literature(M 17/0, D 14/0)

English Philology, English Literature and Language, Americal Literature and Language

Div. of Ethics(M 2/0, D 5/0)

Ethics, History of Ethical Thought

Div. of French Literature(M 3/0, D 1/0)

French Literature

Div. of Geography(M 7/1, D 6/0)

Cultural Geography and Regional Geography, Physical Geography and Regional Geography

Div. of German Language and Literature(M 1/0, D 4/0)

German Language, German Literature

Div. of Japanese History(M 4/0, D 12/1)

Ancient and Medieval Japanese History, Modern Japanese History

Div. of Japanese Language and Literature(M 12/0, D 7/1)

Japanese Language, Ancient and Medieval Japanese Literature, Modern Japanese Literature

Div. of Linguistics(M 2/0, D 10/1)
General Linguistics
Div. of Oriental History(M 2/0, D 4/0)
History of China, History of Asia
Div. of Western History(M 4/0, D 8/1)
Western Social History, History of Western Thought
Div. of Western Philosophy(M 1/0, D 5/0)
Philosophy of Ancient and Medieval Europe, Philosophy of Modern Europe
Graduate School of Medical and Pharmaceutical Sciences(M 46/1, D 160/19)
Div. of Clinical Medical Soiences(M 71/4, D 0/4)
Internal Medicine, Neurology and Psychiatry, Pediatrics, Dermatology, Radiology, Clinical Pathology
Div. of Clinical Surgical Science(D 44/5)
Surgery, Neurosurgery, Orthopedic Surgery, Urology, Ophthalmology, Oto rhino Laryngology, Obstetrics and Gynecology, Anesthesiology
Div. of Medical Biological Science(D 10/4)
Anatomy, Physiology, Biochemistry, Biochemistry and Biophysics, Pharmacology, Radiation Biology
Div. of Molecular Pharmaceutical Science(M 24/1, D 3/1)
Medicinal Chemistry, Medicinal Chemistry of Natural Products, Analytical Chemistry,
Div. of Pathological Science(D 21/3)
Pathology, Cancer Research, Bacteriology, Parasitology, Hematology, Geneticopathology
Div. of Pharmacobiodynamics(M 22/0, D 7/0)
Pharmacobiodynamics, Pharmaceutics and Therapeutics, Public Health Chemistry
Div. of Social Medical Science(D 4/2)
Hygiene, Public Health, Epidemiology and Social Medicine, Biometrics, Legal Medicine
Graduate School of School Education(M 85/5)
Div. of Art Education(M 9/2)
Drawing and Painting, Sculpture and Modelling, Design and Construction, Handicraft, Science of Arts, Art Education
Div. of Education of the Handicapped(M 5/1)
Education of the Handicapped, Psychology of the Handicapped, Clinical Studies of the Handicapped
Div. of Health and Physical Education(M 7/1)
Physical Education, Biomechanics, School Health, Health and Physical Education
Div. of Language Education(M 11/1)
Linguistics, Literature, Calligraphy, Language Education
Div. of Mathematics Education(M 12/0)
Algebra, Geometry, Analysis and Statistics, Mathematics Education
Div. of Music Education(M 5/0)
Keyboard Music, Vocal Music, Composition & Conducting, Musicology, Music Education
Div. of School Education(M 14/0)
Philosophy of Education, History of Education, Educational Psychology, Developmental Psychology, School Management, Sociology of Education, Content and Method of Education, Moral Education, Adult Education
Div. of Science Education(M 15/0)
Physics, Chemistry, Biology, Earth Science, Science Education
Div. of Social Studies Education(M 7/0)
History, Geography, Political Science, Economy, Sociology, Ethics, Social Studies Education
Graduate School of Science(M 183/8, D 86/17)
Div. of Botany(M 14/0, D 13/3)
Plant Morphology, Cytogenetics, Cytology, Phytotaxonomy, Geobotany, Intermediary Metabolism, Microbial Physiology, Plant Molecular Cytology, Genetics of Eukaryotic Microbes
Div. of Chemistry(M 54/3, D 16/8)
Physical Chemistry (quantum chemistry, reaction kinetics), Colloid Chemistry (physical chemistry of molecular assemblies), Structural Chemistry (microwave spectroscopy), Polymer Chemistry (solid and solution properties of high polymers), Inorganic Chemistry (solid state chemistry, radiochemistry), Coordination Chemistry (preparation and structures of coordination compounds), Analytical Chemistry (analytical spectroscopy, metal chelates), Organic Chemistry (synthetic chemistry, stereochemistry, structural organic chemistry), Physical Organic Chemistry (organic reaction mechanism, synthetic methodology), Organic Chemistry of Natural Products (structure and synthesis), Biological Chemistry (biosynthesis, biotransformation, biological active substances)
Div. of Geology and Mineralogy(M 16/1, D 8/1)
Historical Geology, Petrology, Mineralogy, Economic Geology
Div. of Materials Science(M 39/2, D 8/2)
Magnetism, High Pressure Physics, Biopolymers, Metal Physics, Crystallography, Semiconductor Physics, Statistical Physics, Solid State Theory, Plasma Theory, Fusion Theory, Surface Science, Organic Solids, Dielectrics, Optical Properties of Solids
Div. of Mathematics(M 15/0, D 16/1)
Algebra, Number Theory, Geometry, Topology, Function Theory, Functional Analysis, Differential Equations, Applied Analysis, Probability Theory, Mathematical Statistics, Mathematical Structure
Div. of Physics(M 32/2, D 23/2)
Theory of Elementary Particles, Theoretical Nuclear Physics, Low Temperature Physics, Experimental Nuclear Physics, Hadron Physics, Intermediate and High Energy Physics, Crystal Physics (Lattice defects), Theory of Relativity, Cosmology, Field Theory, Fundamental Theory
Div. of Zoology(M 13/0, D 2/0)
Endocrinology, Embryology, Protozoology, Zootaxonomy, Animal Physiology, Animal Physiological Chemistry, Molecular Genetics, Development and Heredity of Amphibians, Evolution of Amphibians, Marine Animal Physiology, Marine Zoology
Graduate School of Social Science(M 79/27, D 49/17)
Div. of Economic Studies(M 17/11, D 7/6)
Economic Policy, Local Public Finance, Industrial Structure, Regional Development, Economic Data Analysis, Socio–economic Statistics, Modern History of Japanese Economy, Seminar in Regional Economic Studies, Pub-

lic Economics, Public Finance, Fiscal Policy, Monetary Policy, Market Economic Systems, Planned Economic Systems, Seminar in Planning Administration, Macroeconomics, Microeconomics, Dynamic Economics, International Economics, Money and Banking, International Finance, Econometrics, Information Statistics, Seminar in Quantitative Economic Studies, Business Administration, Accounting, Cost Accounting, Management Information Systems, Labor Economics, Seminar in Business Administration Studies, Political Economy, History of Economic Thought, History of American Economic Thought, Economic History of Japan, Economic History of Europe and America, Seminar in Historical Economic Studies

Div. of International and Regional Studies(M 55/13, D 33/10)

International Politics, History of International Relations, International Economics, International Management, International Development, Peace Research, Seminar in International Relations, Comparative Studies in Societies, Social Structure, Study of Law and Society, Theory of Technology, Economics of Technology, Seminar in Comparative Society, Social Anthropology, Ethnology in Latin American, Asian Anthropology, Ethnicity & Multicultural Education, Seminar in Pre-state Political Systems, Teaching & Learning in Higher Education, International Exchanges in Higher Education, Comparative Studies in University, Sociology of Higher Education, Economics of Higher Education, Higher Education Policy, Seminar in Comparative Studies on Higher Education, Political Process, History of Modern Politics, History of Political Thought, Principles of Comparative Politics, Seminar in Comparative Politics, History of Social Thought, Comparative Study of Philosophical Thought, Comparative Studies in Religion, Comparative Studies in Arts, Seminar in Comparative Thought, Japanese Studies, Japanese Socio-Economic History, History of Japanese Social Thought, Japanese Culture, Seminar in Japanese Studies, Asian Politics, Asian Society, Asian Ethnography, Asian Culture, Seminar in Asian Studies, History of European Political Thought, Russian Socio-Economic History, European Anthropology, European Culture, Seminar in European Studies, British Studies, History of British Social Thought, British Culture, Seminar in British Studies, British Society, American Studies, American Political History, History of American Economic Thought, American Culture, Seminar in American Studies, Engish, German, French, Russian, Chinese

Div. of Legal Studies(M 7/3, D 9/1)

Laws related to human affairs, Laws related to property relations, Laws related to consumers, Laws related to remedies, Laws dealing with legal disputes, Seminar in legal study in civic life relations, Laws related business associations, Laws related to business transactions, Laws related to finance and accounting, Laws related to labor-management relations, Laws related to worker welfare, Seminar in legal study in business relations, Laws related in administrative agencies, Laws related to administrative process, Laws related to public welfare, Laws related to local government, Laws related to public finance, Seminar in legal study in administrative relations, Criminal law, Laws related to criminal treatment, Studies related to criminal causes, Criminal procedure law, Seminar in criminal law and criminology, Laws related to international relations, Laws related to international organization, Laws related to international business transactions, Seminar in legal study in international relations, Laws related to systems of government, Legal theories of fundamental rights, Jurisprudence, History of law and society, Sociology of law, Anglo-American Law, Seminar in general study of law and society

---

岡山大学
(Okayama Daigaku)

Okayama University

1-1-1 Naka Tsushima, Okayama-shi, Okayama 700
☎ 0862-52-1111 FAX 0862-54-8616

Founded 1949
Professors 384
Associate Professors 304
Assistant Professors(Tenured) 132
Assistant Professors(Non-tenured) 669
Research Assistants 412
Undergraduate Students/Foreign Students 10, 083/94
Graduate Students/Foreign Students 1,321/182
Library 1, 481, 549 volumes
Contact: International Affairs Section

Educational philosophy Okayama University has the basic policy of aiming at independence and voluntary study and education corresponding flexibly changes of the times since its establishment.

Foreign students Our university is comprehensive univertity of 10 faculties and 11 graduate schools. Staffs have wide experience to accept foreign students. More than 300 foreign students enjoy studying and researching in the university.

Environment Okayama City which is located 730 km west of Tokyo is one of major commercial, educational and cultural centers of the Chyugoku-Shikoku region. Even winters the climate is mild. It has many historic sites and tourist area.

Facilities The university has Central Library and 2 Branch Libraries (about 1, 470, 000 volume of books are housed), Computer Center, Health & Medical Center, Student hall, 2 Gymnasiums and other sports facilities.

Student activities There are many campus events such as university festival (November) and Tournament of 5 National Universities of Chugoku Region. 81 clubs are set up for extracurricular activities.

Academic programs for foreign students Subjects of Japanese Language and Japanese Culture for foreign students and tutoring service by Japanese students are available.

Services for foreign students Accommodation

for foreign students (132 rooms) is established by theuniversity. Many activities such as welcome party, study excursion and homestay are planned for foreign students.

Undergraduate Programs

Faculty of Agriculture(733/1)
Dept. of Agricultural Sciences
Dental School(434/5)
Dept. of Dentistry
Faculty of Economics(916/24)
Dept. of Economics
Faculty of Education(1, 795/5)
Elementary School Teachers Training Course(840/0)
General Course for Education(134/0)
Kindergarten Teachers Training Course(120/0)
Lower Secondary School Teachers Training Course(316/0)
Special Training Course for Art and Craft Teachers(136/1)
Training Course for Nursing Teachers(165/0)
Training Course for Teachers of Handicapped Children(84/0)
Faculty of Engineering(2, 202/14)
Dept. of Applied Chemistry(370/1)
Dept. of Bioengineering Science(37/0)
Dept. of Biotechnology(168/0)
Dept. of Civil Engineering(240/0)
Dept. of Electrical and Electronic Engineering(424/7)
Dept. of Information Technology(342/0)
Dept. of Mechanical Engineering(537/6)
Faculty of Law(878/9)
Dept. of Law
Faculty of Letters(738/17)
Dept. of History(205/3)
Dept. of Literature(347/13)
Dept. of philosophy(186/1)
Medical School(698/7)
Dept. of Medicine
Faculty of Pharmaceutical Sciences(330/3)
Dept. of Pharmaceutical Science(163/3)
Dept. of Pharmaceutical Technology(167/0)
Faculty of Science(637/4)
Dept. of Biology(109/1)
Dept. of Chemistry(154/1)
Dept. of Earth Sciences(121/0)
Dept. of Mathematics(109/0)
Dept. of Physics(144/2)

Graduate Programs

Graduate School of Agriculture(M 124/12)
Div. of Agricultural Production & Technology(M 30/1)
Eco–Physiology of Crop Production, Animal Science, Agriculture Products Technology
Div. of Bioresources Science(M 29/1)
Bio–Resource Science, Applied Biology and Genetics, Genetics, Functional Biology, Environmental Biology
Div. of Rural Science(M 9/0, D 9/0)
Agricultural Technology of Integrated Land Use, Agricultural Infrastructure Development and Conservation, Environment and Resources Management
Graduate School of Dentistry(D 46/3)
Div. of Dentistry(D 46/3)
Oral Anatomy, Oral Physiology, Biochemistry, Oral Pathology, Microbiology, Pharmacology, Dental Materials, Operative Dentistry, Periodontology & Endodontology, Crown and Bridge Prosthodontics, Removable Prosthodontics, Orthodontics, Oral Radiology, Preventive Dentistry, Pediatric Dentistry, Oral and Maxillofacial Surgery
Graduate School of Economics(M 14/9)
Div. of Economics(M 14/9)
Economic Theory, Economic Measurement, Economic History, Economic Policy, Applied Economics, Industrial Administration, Accounting
Graduate School of Education(M 126/22)
Div. of Domestic Science Education(M 9/0)
Food, Clothing, Home Management, Domestic Science Education, Life Technology, Technology, Education
Div. of English Language Education(M 12/1)
English Linguistics, English & American Literature, English Language Education
Div. of Fine Arts Education(M 14/0)
Painting, Sculpture, Cubic Structure, Art & Craft, Art & Craft Education
Div. of Japanese Language Education(M 9/2)
Japanese Linguistics, Japanese Literature, Chinese Classical Literature, Calligraphy, Japanese Language Education
Div. of Mathematics Education(M 6/2)
Algebra & Geometry, Analytical Mathematics & Applied Mathematics, Mathematics Education
Div. of Music Education(M 9/0)
Vocal Music, Instrumental Music, Composition & Conducting, Music Education
Div. of Physical Education(M 13/5)
Physical Education, Kinematics, School & Public Hygiene, Health & Physical Education, Fundamental Medicine, Clinical Medicine & Science of Nursing, Education Health, School Health Nurse
Div. of School Education(M 20/6)
Pedagogics, School Management, Education Sociology, Social Education, Education Psychology, Developmental Psychology
Div. of Science Education(M 17/3)
Physics, Chemistry, Biology, Earth Science, Natural Science Education
Div. of Social Studies Education(M 17/3)
History, Geography, Law, Sociololgy, Economics, Ethics, Social Studies Education
Graduate School of Engineering(M 227/26)
Div. of Applied Mechanics(M 28/2)
Plasticity and Material Design,Machine Design and Tribology, Hear Power Engineering, Instrumentation, Engineering
Div. of Civil Engineering(M 32/3)

Analysis and Design of Structures, Soil Mechanics and Material Engineering, Sanitary Engineering, Transportation Facilities, Computational Mechanics

Div. of Electrical Engineering(M 44/4)

Basic Electrical Engineering, Electric Power Engineering, Electrical Machinery and Apparatus, Electrical Communication

Div. of Electronics(M 32/6)

Electronic Circuits, Industrial Electronics, Electron Physics, Instrumentation–Control Engineering, Applied Physics

Div. of Industrial Chemistry(M 54/3)

Physical Chemistry and Chemical Engineering, Industrial Inorganic Chemistry, Industrial Oraganic Chemistry, Organic Material Chemistry, Molecular Design & Analysis, Non–Crystalline State Chemistry, Non–Crystalline State Fundamentals

Div. of Industrial Science(M 30/3)

Industrial Management, Process Design and Control, Control Engineering, Metal Processing

Div. of Mechanical Engineering(M 30/3)

Strength of Materials, Heat Transfer Engineering, Fluid Dynamics, Precision Machining Technology

Div. of Synthetic Chemistry(M 27/2)

Polymer Chemistry, Chemical Process Engineering, Synthetic Inorganic Chemistry, Synthetic Organic Chemistry

Graduate School of Law(M 24/9, D 0/9)

Div. of Civil and Criminal Laws(M 13/6)

Civil Law, Criminal Law, Social Law, Fundamental Sciences of Law, International Law

Div. of Public Law and Political Science(M 11/3)

Public Law, International Law, Fundamental Sciences of Law, Politics

Graduate School of Letters(M 74/17)

Div. of English and American Literature(M 19/1)

English Language, English Literature, American Literature

Div. of French Literature(M 3/0)

French Language, French Literature

Div. of German Literature(M 1/0)

German Language, German Literature

Div. of History(M 16/2)

Japanese History, History of Japanese Culture, Oriental History, Occidental History, Modern History, Archaeoloqy, Geography

Div. of Japanese Literature(M 26/13)

Japanese Language, Japanese Literature, Japanese Classical Language, Chinese Language and Chinese Literature, Linguistics

Div. of Philosophy(M 5/0)

Philosophy, History of Philosophy, Ethics, Aesthetics and Art History

Div. of Psychology(M 4/1)

Psychology, Social Psychology

Graduate School of Medicine(D 248/20)

Div. of Internal Medicine(D 86/1)

Internal Medicine, Pediatrics, Neuropsychiatry, Dermatology, Radiation Medicine, Clinical Inspection Medicine, Adult Diseases, Neurobiology, Biological Psychiatry and Clinical Neurochemistry, Developmental Neuroscience and Child Neurology

Div. of Pathology(D 24/8)

Pathology, Microbiology, Virology, Parasitology, Tumor Biochemistry, Tumor Pathology, Tumor Virology, Environmental Medicine

Div. of Physiology(D 16/3)

Anatomy, Physiology, Biochemistry, Molecular Biology, Pharmacology, Neurochemistry

Div. of Social Medicine(D 14/2)

Hygiene, Public Health, Legal Medicine

Div. of Surgery(D 108/6)

Surgery, Rehabilitation Surgery, Orthopedic surgery, Neurological Surgery, Obstetrics & Gynecology, Urology, Otorhinolaryngology, Ophthalmology, Anesthesiology & Resuscitology

Graduate School of Natural Science and Technology(D 186/55)

Div. of Biopharmaceutical Science(D 37/7)

Development Drag Research, Pharmaceutical Health Science, Pharmaco–biodynamics

Div. of Bioresources Science(D 36/11)

Basic Biology, Genetic Science, Applied Bioscience and Biotechnology, Regulatory Bioengineering

Div. of Science and Technology for Materials(D 41/9)

Fundamental Science of Materials, Science of Condensed Matter, Conversion Chemistry, Materials Science, Materials Science of the Earth

Div. of Science for Engineering and Agricultural Technology(D 48/19)

Civil and Rural Engineering, Material and Design Engineering, Energy Conversion Engineering, Management of Biological Production, Biological Production Technology

Div. of System Science(D 24/9)

Mathematical Science, System Design and Control, Electronics and Information Science

Graduate School of Pharmaceutical Sciences(M 82/3)

Div. of Pharmaceutical Science(M 44/1)

Pharmaceutical Chemistry, Physiological, Chemistry, Pharmacognosy, Pharmacology, Hygienic Chemistry, Bioorganic Chemistry, Pharmaceutics

Div. of Pharmaceutical Technology(M 38/2)

Pharmaceutical Analytical Chemistry, Pharmaceutical Physical Chemistry, Microbiology, Immunochemistry, Synthetic & Medical Chemistry, Environmental Hygiene

Graduate School of Science(M 120/6)

Div. of Biology(M 23/3)

Plant Morphology, Plant Physiology, Genetics & Cytology, Animal Morphology, Animal Physiology, Marine Biology

Div. of Chemistry(M 36/0)

Physical Chemistry, Organic Chemistry, Synthetic & Physical Organic Chemistry, Inorganic Chemistry, Analytical Chemistry, High Polymer Chemistry, Fine Powders and Surface Chemistry

Div. of Earth Sciences(M 18/0)

Mineralogy, Geology, Geophysics, Geochemistry, Materials Science of the Earth's Deep Interior, Isotope Geology, Geochemical Cycle, Geochronological Studies

Div. of Mathematics(M 10/1)

Analysis, Algebra, Geometry, Topology, Applicable Mathematics

Div. of Physics(M 33/2)

Theoretical Physics, Physics of Electromagnetic Phenomena, Mathematical Physics, Nuclear Physics, Solid State Physics, Magnetism, Thin Films & Interface Physics

島根医科大学
(Shimane Ika Daigaku)
Shimane Medical University

89–1 Enya–cho, Izumo–shi, Shimane 693
☎ 0853–23–2111 FAX 0853–22–9278

Founded 1975
Professors 38
Associate Professors 33
Assistant Professors(Tenured) 28
Assistant Professors(Non–tenured) 189
Research Assistants 129
Undergraduate Students/Foreign Students 636/0
Graduate Students/Foreign Students 94/2
Library 90, 027 volumes
Contact: Student Division, ☎ ext. 2167

Educational philosophy Our educational and research activities are conducted on the principles of dedication to the ethics of medicine, cultivation of the spirit of scientific inquiry, development of medical science and community medical services and contributing to human welfare.

Foreign students We are receiving foreign students (postgraduate course) and foreign researchers, and can contribute to promoting mutual understanding and the development of friendly relations.

Environment Izumo City, on the coast of the Japan Sea, lies about 650 kilometers west of Tokyo and can be reached by plane from Tokyo in 1. 5 hours. The city is one of the homes of Japanese myth and legend, and the whole area is rich in beautiful scenery.

Facilities Library, Radioisotope research laboratory, Animal research institute, Central research laboratories, Student center, Gymnasium, Martial arts gymnasium, Swimming pool, Guesthouse

Student activities There are several annual campus events including school festival, freshman welcome party, graduation ceremony and party. There are more than 50 extra curricular activities, including rugby, basketball, yacht, ping–pong, arts, chorus, student news paper, etc.

Academic programs for foreign students Supplemental Japanese language and culture class, Tutoring system.

Services for foreign students Health clinics, personal and psychological counseling, housing information, vocational guidance, home visit, cultural exchange program.

Undergraduate Programs

Faculty of Medicine(636/0)

Dept. of Medicine

Undergraduate Programs

Graduate School of Medical Research(D 89/2)

Div. of Morphology(D 26/1)

Pathology, Surgery, Otorhinolaryngology, Radiology, Orthopaedics, Internal Medicine Oral and Maxillofacial Surgery, Anatomy, Psychiatry

Div. of Biological Functions(D 47/1)

Biochemistry, Physiology, Surgery, Urology, Internal Medicine, Obstetrics and Gynecology Laboratory, Medicine Pathology, Pediatrics, Anesthesiology, Anatomy, Pharmacology, Neurosurgery, Ophthalmology

Div. of Human Ecology(D 16/0)

Internal Medicine, Microbiology, Immunology, Dermatology, Legal Medicine, Environmental Medicine

島根大学
(Shimane Daigaku)
Shimane University

1060 Nishikawatsu–cho, Matsue–shi, Shimane 690
☎ 0852–21–7100 FAX 0852–26–7421

Founded 1949
Professors 156
Associate Professors 128
Assistant Professors(Tenured) 28
Assistant Professors(Non–tenured) 92
Research Assistants 36
Undergraduate Students/Foreign Students 4, 228/3
Graduate Students/Foreign Students 113/14
Library 587, 149 volumes
Contact: Student Affairs Department

Educational philosophy We, as the only higher education institute in the area, aim at providing students with opportunities to develop intellectual, moral and applied abilities as well as general education, and bringing up those students who may contribute greatly to society.

Foreign students We hope that students from other countries will contribute to international understanding and the development of education, art and science, after their rewarding experiences on our campus.

Environment The University is located in Matsue City, the seat of the prefectural government, with a population of about 140,000. It is a beautiful city on lake Shinji, well–known from ancient times as the town of water. The region is full of seasonal beauty and sur-

rounded by a lush, quiet atomosphere rich in historical heritage.
Facilities Health Administratipn Center, University Library, Student Union, Radioisotope Center, Center of Studies San, in Region, Information Processing Center, Handicraft and Engineering Work Center, Center of Research and Training for Educational Practice, Oki Marine Biological Station
Student activities Every year we have an enjoyable school festival in November. There are various extracurricular activities, including judo, kendo, karate, flower arrangement, tea ceremony, traditional Japanese music, all of which are very traditional.
Academic programs for foreign students Japanese language classes and Japanese culture classes are offered. Tutoring service is available.
Services for foreign students Housing information, Health clinic/counseling, Part-time job information. We help students to communicate with a wide variety of local institutions or groups who are interested in international exchange programs.

Undergraduate Programs

Faculty of Agriculture(848/1)
Dept. of Agro-forest Biology(129/0)
Dept. of Natural Resources(135/1)
Dept. of Regional Development(136/0)
Faculty of Education(1, 269/0)
Course of Social Education & Cultural Studies (157/0)
Elementary School Teachers Training Course (475/0)
Junior High School Teachers Training Course (220/0)
Kindergarten Teachers Training Course(88/0)
Training Course for Teachers of Handicapped Children(81/0)
Training Course for Teachers of Special Subject (Health and Gymnastics) (131/0)
Training Course for Teachers of Special Subject (Music) (117/0)
Subject (Music) (117/0)
Faculty of Law and Literature(1, 173/1)
Dept. of Law(733/0)
Dept. of Literature(440/1)
Faculty of Science(938/1)
Dept. of Biology(143/0)
Dept. of Chemistry(184/0)
Dept. of Geology(147/0)
Dept. of Information Science(80/1)
Dept. of Mathematics(190/0)
Dept. of Physics(194/0)

Graduate Programs

Graduate School of Research of Agriculture(M 55/8)
Div. of Agriculture(M 6/3)
Crop Science, Pomology, Vegetable and Ornamental Horticulture, Animal Science
Div. of Forestry(M 8/0)
Forestry Management, Wood Science and Engineering, Chemical and Physical Processing of Wood, Silviculture
Div. of Agricultural and Forest Economics(M 2/0)
Farm Management, Agricultural Policy, Economics of Agricultural Market, Economics of Forestry, Rural Planning and Development
Div. of Agricultural Chemistry(M 26/5)
Biological Chemistry, Food Chemistry, Applied Microbiology, Biochemical Engineering, Soil Physical Chemistry
Div. of Agricultural Engineering(M 1/0)
Irrigation and Drainage Engineering, Land Reclamation Engineering, Agricultural Structure Engineering, Agricultural Machinery and Mechanization, Cultivation Systems Control Engineering
Div. of Environmental Sciences(M 12/0)
Agro-Environmental Betterment, Plant Pathology, Insect Management, Environmental Biochemistry
Graduate School of Research of Law(M 18/2)
Div. of Law(M 18/2)
Business Law Course, Law Profession Course, Public Administration Course, Theoretical Studies Course
Graduate School of Research of Science(M 40/4)
Div. of Mathematics(M 6/0)
Algebra, Geometry, Topology and Analysis, Applied Analysis
Div. of Physics(M 3/0)
Elementary Particle Theory, Condensed Matter Physics, Solid State Physics, Applied Physics
Div. of Chemistry(M 12/1)
Physical Chemistry, Inorganic Chemistry, Organic Chemistry, Environmental Analytical Chemistry
Div. of Biology(M 6/0)
Animal Morphology and Phylogeny, Animal Physiology, Plant Physiology, Plant Ecology
Div. of Geology(M 13/3)
Petrology and Mineralogy, Historical Geology, Mineral Resources Geology, Geotectonnics

---

鳥取大学

(Tottori Daigaku)

Tottori University

4-101 Minami Koyama-cho, Tottori-shi, Tottori 680
☎ 0857-28-0321 FAX 0857-28-0378

Founded 1949
Professors 196
Associate Professors 166
Assistant Professors(Tenured) 81
Assistant Professors(Non-tenured) 215
Research Assistants 191
Undergraduate Students/Foreign Students 4, 634/2
Graduate Studetns/Foreign Students 444/36
Library 520, 715 volumes
Contact: Admission office

Educational philosophy Tottori University stresses education based on regional needs for the training of well–rounded citizens who can make a positive contribution to meeting the demands of our modern information–based, international world society.
Foreign students Tottori University provides favorable circumstances for foreign students to study their chosen fields as well as understand Japanese society through experiencing Tottori's unique location, beautiful nature and historical sites.
Environment There are two campuses in Tottori University Koyama Campus is five kilometers to the west of Tottori City, the capital of Torrori Prefecture, Yonago Campus is situated in Yonago City. Both campuses are convenient and pleasant places for foreign students to study and do research.
Facilities University Main Library, Medical Library, Data Processing Center, Radioisotope Facilities, Arid Land Research Center, Gymnasium, Swimming Pool, University Center
Student activities Popular campus events includes, school festival, long distance relay, etc. There is a wide variety of extra curricular activities, including, Tennis, Baseball, Karate, Volleyball, Tea Ceremony, Go, Japanese music, English Speaking Society.
Academic programs for foreign students Supplemental Japanese Language class, Tutoring system.
Services for foreign students Health clinic, personal/psychological counseling, College housing, Housing information, part–time job information, vocational guidance, cultural exchange program.

Undergraduate Programs

Faculty of Agriculture(1, 227/0)
Cluster of Agriculture and Forestry Sciences (955/0)
Cluster of Veterinary Sciences(212/0)
Faculty of Education(776/0)
Course For Interdisciplinary Studies(117/0)
Elementary School Teachers Training Course (358/0)
Handicapped Children's School Teachers Training Course(86/0)
Secondary School Teachers Training Course (215/0)
Faculty of Engineering(1, 963/2)
Dept. of Applied Mathematics and Physics
Dept. of Biotechnology(79/0)
Dept. of Civil Engineering(265/0)
Dept. of Electrical and Electronic Engineering (171/1)
Dept. of Information and Knowledge Engineering (122/0)
Dept. of Material Science(139/0)
Dept. of Mechanical Engineering(281/0)
Dept. of Social Systems Engineering(222/1)
Faculty of Medicine(668)
School of Medicine(628)
School of Life Science(40)

Graduate Programs

Graduate School of Agriculture(M 88/9)
Div. of Agronomy(M 23/3)
Div. of Agricultural Chemistry(M 27/1)
Div. of Forestry(M 22/3)
Div. of Agricultural Engineering(M 9/1)
Div. of Farm Economics(M 7/1)
The United Graduate School of Agricultural Science(D 35/17)
Div. of Bioproduction Science(D 10/6)
Div. of Bioenvironment Science(D 11/6)
Div. of Bioresources Science(D 14/5)
Graduate School of Engineering(M 188/4)
Div. of Mechanical Engineering Ⅰ(M 24/0)
Div. of Mechanical Engineering Ⅱ(M 25/1)
Div. of Electrical Engineering(M 21/2)
Div. of Industrial Chemistry(M 18/0)
Div. of Civil Engineering(M 19/0)
Div. of Electronics(M 22/0)
Div. of Environmental Chemistry and Techonology(M 19/0)
Div. of Ocean Civil Engineering(M 20/1)
Div. of Social Systems Engineering(M 20/0)
Graduate School of Medicine(D 133/6)
Div. of Physiology(D 24/3)
Anatomy, Physiology, Biochemistry, Pharmacology
Div. of Pathology(D 8/0)
Pathology, Bacteriology, Virology
Div. of Social Medicine(D 3/1)
Hygiene, Public Health, Medical Zoology, Legal Medicine
Div. of Internal Medicine(D 48/0)
Internal Medicine, Pediatrics, Neuropsychiatry, Radiology, Dermatology
Div. of Surgery(D 50/2)
Surgery, Orthopedic Surgery, Obsterics and Gynecology, Ophthalmology, Otorhinolaryngology, Urology, Anesthesiology

---

山口大学
(Yamaguchi Daigaku)
Yamaguchi University

1677–1 Yoshida, Yamaguchi–shi, Yamaguchi 753
☎ 0839–22–6111 FAX 0839–22–0445

Founded 1949
Professors 242
Associate Professors 197
Assistant Professors(Tenured) 89
Assistant Professors(Non–tenured) 492 1020
Research Assistants 201
Undergraduate Students/Foreign Students 7, 771/24
Graduate Students/Foreign Students 499/25
Library 1, 245, 401 volumes
Contact: International Affairs Section, General Affairs Division, Administration Bureau ☎ ext. 295

Educational philosophy Under the School Education Law of 1947, we aim at teaching and studying deeply professional learning as well as helping students to enlarge their knowledge and promoting high development of personal culture.

Foreign students At present the number of overseas students is not great but growing. We welcome foreign students from all over the world. We believe that they can enjoy a relaxed and intimate students, life in Yamaguchi. Let's study together!

Environment The University is devided into two campuses: one in Yamaguchi, a city rich in history and culture with a population of about 130, 000 people, and the other some forty kilometers away in Ube (population 180, 000), a centre of advanced medical and industrial technology.

Facilities Library, Information Processing Centre, Archeological Museum, University Hall, Student's Restaurant, Gymnasium, Sports Field, Swimming Pool, University Hospital, University Farm, Veterinary Hospital

Student activities 1st Semester April 1–September 30, 2nd Semester October 1–March 31, University Anniversary June 1, Spring Vacation April 1–April 7, Summer Vacation July 11–September 5, Winter Vacation December 25–January 7, 19 Cultural Circles, 31 Sports Clubs

Academic programs for foreign students Undergraduate may fulfill 8 or 12 of credits they are required to take in the Liberal Arts Department with courses in Japanese Language and Culture. Private tutors are available for foreign students.

Services for foreign students International House on Yamaguchi campus is a residence for non–Japanese Students and researchers. They may also enter domitories for regular students. Counselling is available at the Health Care Centre and the Students Counselling Centre.

Undergraduate Programs

Faculty of Agriculture(581/0)
- **Dept. of Agricultural Chemistry**(183/0)
- **Dept. of Agronomy**(207/0)
- **Dept. of Veterinary Medicine**(191/0)

Faculty of Economics(1, 695/11)
- **Dept. of Economics**(486/1)
- **Dept. of International Economics**(291/1)
- **Dept. of Law and Economics**(235/0)
- **Dept. of Management**(616/9)
- **Course for Commerce Teachers**(67/0)

Faculty of Education(1, 286/0)
- **Course for Elementary School Teachers**(690/0)
- **Course for Junior High School Teachers**(312/0)
- **Course for Kindergarten Teachers**(118/0)
- **Course for Teachers of Handicapped Children**(85/0)
- **General Course in Educational Culture**(81/0)

Faculty of Engineering(1, 850/12)
- **Dept. of Chemical Engineering**(198/2)
- **Dept. of Civil Engineering**(209/2)
- **Dept. of Construction Engineering**(210/0)
- **Dept. of Electrical Engineering**(176/0)
- **Dept. of Electronics Engineering**(211/3)
- **Dept. of Industrial Chemistry**(205/0)
- **Dept. of Industrial Mechanical Engineering**(223/1)
- **Dept. of Mechanical Engineering**(263/4)
- **Dept. of Mining and Mineral Engineering**(155/0)

Faculty of Humanities(844/0)
- **Dept. of Humanities**(469/0)
- **Dept. of Language and Literature**(375/0)

Faculty of Science(841/1)
- **Dept. of Biology**(127/0)
- **Dept. of Chemistry**(183/0)
- **Dept. of Mathematics**(197/0)
- **Dept. of Mineralogical Sciences and Geology**(141/0)

School of Medicine(674/0)
- **Dept. of Medicine**

Graduate Programs

Graduate School of Agriculture(M 32/1)
Agricultural Chemistry, Agronomy

Graduate School of Economics(M 25/12)
Economics

Graduate School of Engineering(M 184/4)
Chemical Engineering, Civil Engineering, Construction Engineering, Electrical Engineering, Electronics Engineering, Industrial Chemistry, Industrial Mechanical Engineering, Mechanical Engineering, Mining and Mineral Engineering

Graduate School of Humanities(M 18/2)
Language and Literary Culture, Regional Culture

Graduate School of Medicine(D 146/3)
Internal Medicine, Pathology, Physiology, Sociological Medicine, Surgery

Graduate School of Science(M 73/0)
Biology, Chemistry, Mathematics, Mineralogical Science and Geology, Physics

United Graduate School of Veterinary Sciences(D 21/3)
Veterinary Sciences

Local Public Universities

広島県立大学
(Hiroshima Kenritsu Daigaku)

Hiroshima Prefectural University

562 Nanatsuka-cho, Shobara-shi, Hiroshima 727
☎ 08247-4-1000 FAX 08247-4-0191

Founded 1989
Professors 29
Associate Professors 22
Assistant Professors(Tenured) 10
Assistant Professors(Non-tenured) 15
Research Assistants 5
Undergraduate Students/Foreign Students 466/4
Library Approx. 70, 000 volumes
Contact: Student Affairs Bureau

Educational philosophy Our University aims at promoting general learning and research in the sciences and allied fields which develop the intellectual, moral, and practical abilities of students so they may contribute to cultural betterment and economic development.

Foreign students In accordance with the Friendship Agreement which has been established between Hiroshima Prefecture and Szechwan Province, our University has been accepting students from this province.

Environment Shobara City, having a population of 23, 000, serves as a cultural center in the northern part of Hiroshima Prefecture. The University is located at Nanatsukahara, which is 6 kilometers from central Shobara and is famous for its majestic poplars standing beside green pastures. The campus is surrounded by beautiful forests and ponds.

Facilities University Library, Gymnasium and Auditorium(same building), Computer Center, Agricultural Science Center, Experimental Farms

Student activities Annual activities include the off-campus Orientation Seminars, the University Festival, and Sports Day. There is a wide variety of extracurricular activities, such as tea ceremony, music, stargazing, movies, dancing, skiing, golf, and soccer.

Services for foreign students Foreign students may live in the University dormitory. Local organizations sponsor various events for foreign students.

Undergraduate Programs

Faculty of Bioresources(231/1)
  Dept. of Bioresource Administration(96/1)
  Dept. of Bioresource Development(135/0)
Faculty of Business(235/3)
  Dept. of Business Administration(137/2)
  Dept. of Management and Information Sciences
(98/1)

広島女子大学
(Hiroshima Joshi Daigaku)

Hiroshima Women's University

1-1-71 Ujina-higashi, Minami-ku, Hiroshima-shi, Hiroshima 734
☎ 082-251-5178 FAX 082-255-7803

Founded 1920
Professors 24
Associate Professors 20
Assistant Professors(Tenured) 6
Assistant Professors(Non-tenured) 87
Research Assistants 14
Library 157, 356 volumes
Contact: Student Affairs Office Academic Affairs Section

Educational philosophy We aim to train the students to acquire the spirit of seeking truth, to develop their innate qualities and capabilities, and to equip themselves with a readiness to live useful social lives in this age of so-called globalization in an infomation-orientated society.

Foreign students We welcome foreign students who are eager to make the most of an opportunity to spend a meaningful stage of their life among our Japanese students.

Environment The campus is not far away from the center of the city but is situated in a quiet environment. Its location is convenient for going shopping or visiting museums, art galleries and public libraries.

Facilities You can use the library, the gym, the language lab, and the information processing lab.

Student activities The student body has 29 cultural and athletic clubs. The academic year begins with freshman orientation overnight away from the campus. There are the usual annual events such as the cultural festival in the autumn, Sports Day in the early summer, etc.

Academic programs for foreign students There are no special programs for foreign students, but they can receive individual attention just as the Japanese students can.

Services for foreign students Counseling, and information on accomodations and part-time jobs, etc. are offered.

Undergraduate Programs

Faculty of Letters(395/0)
  Dept. of Japanese Literature(198/0)
  Dept. of Social Welfare(197/0)
Faculty of Home Economics(571/1)
  Dept. of Child Study(170/0)

Dept. of Textiles and Clothing(134/1)
Dept. of Food and Nutrition(139/0)
Dept. of Science of Living(128/0)

下関市立大学
(Shimonoseki Shiritsu Daigaku)
Shimonoseki City University

2-1 Daigaku-cho, Shimonoseki-shi, Yamaguchi 751
☎ 0832-52-0288 FAX 0832-52-8099

Founded 1962
Professors 24
Associate Professors 15
Assistant Professors(Tenured) 10
Assistant Professors(Non-tenured) 51
Undergraduate Students/Foreign Students 1, 895/16
Library 102, 413 volumes

Educational Philosophy We aim at cultivating creativity, an independent way of college life, and a sense of internationalizaion rooted in the community. Special attention is paid to the East Asian countries such as Chiba and Korea.
Foreign students We hope that foreign students can study academic subjects, enjoying the natural beauty of Japan, and international friendship will be promoted between our faculty and students.
Environment Historically, Shimonoseki is a small international city on the Kanmon Strait, the gate to the East Asia, with a population of 263, 000. Our university is conveniently located at one of the main city centers.
Facilities Research Center(Which has library, computer lab, audiovisual room, and Shimonoseki Institute for Research of Industry and Culture), Gymnasium, Cooperative store
Student activities Annual campus events include school festival, freshmen welcome party, seniors farewell party. There is a variety of oxtra curricular activities such as drama, English speaking society, music bands, soccer, pingpong, baseball, etc.
Academic programs for foreign students Japanese language, introductory course to Japanese culture, which are elected instead of foreign languages.
Services for foreign students 50% entrance and tuition fees exemption, and part-time job information

Undergraduate Programs

Faculty of Economics(1, 895/16)
Dept. of Economics(992/2)
Dept. of International Commerce(903/14)

Private Universities

梅光女学院大学
(Baikô Jo Gakuin Daigaku)
Baiko Jo Gakuin College

365 Yoshimi-Myoji, Shimonoseki-shi, Yamaguchi 759-65
☎ 0832-86-2221 FAX 0832-31-6835
☎ 0832-23-0057(night)

Founded 1872
Professors 30
Associate Professors 4
Assistant Professors(Tenured) 10
Assistant Professors(Non-tenured) 48
Undergraduate Students/Foreign Students 908/0
Graduate Students/Foreign Students 32/3
Library 117, 385 volumes(including 29, 618 foreign books)
Contact: International Exchange Center 2-3-13 Maruyama-cho, Shimonoseki-shi, Yamaguchi 750

Educational Philosophy The Chiristian education of the College has been guides by the principle of "Walk as children of light"(Ephesian V: 8), and this ideal is reflected in the college's internationalism as it strives to realize the ideal of brotherhood of all people in the world.
Foreign students Baiko Jo Gakuin College, the oldest Christian school(founded in 1872)in the western part of Japan, has always kept her doors wide open to the students from all over the world.
Environment The city, having a population of 250,000, lies along a stretch of land between the mountains and the seas, and the campus is surrounded by the scenic beauty as well as historical interests. The proximity of the Shimonoseki school to the Continent of Asia had greatly facilitated the realization of its ideal of internationalism.
Facilities Newly-built Auditorium, Dormitory, Gymnasium, Computer Training Facilities, Language Lab., Lounge for Speaking English with Natives, International Exchange Center, Tennis Courts, Parking Space for students.
Student activities Badminton, Choral Group, College Festival, Drama, Ensemble, English Newspaper, Volleyball, many other club activities. English Speech Contest, Chinese Speech Contest, Sports Day, Field Trips, Chapel Service, Christmas activities, Volunteer work, etc.
Academic programs for foreign students Individual teaching for credit hours, Special courses offered; Japanese as a Foreign Language, Introduction to the Linguistic Study of the Japanese Language, Cultural History of Japan, Calligraphy, etc.
Services for foreign students College housing, Housing information, Home visit, Cultural Exchange Pro-

grams, Vocational information, Counseling, Financial aid, Homestay, Part-time job information.

Undergraduate Programs

Faculty of Letters(908/0)
Dept. of English and American Literature(209/0)
Dept. of English and American Language(243/0)
Dept. of Japanese Literture(456/0)

Graduate Programs

Graduate School of Letters(M 24/1, D 8/2)
Div. of Japanese Literature(M 15/1, D 6/2)
Chinese Literature, Comparative Literature, Cultural Anthropology, History of Christian Thought, Research on Japanese Literature, Seminar in Japanese Literature, Seminar in Japanese Philology.
Div. of English and American Literature(M 9/0, D 2/0)
Comparative Literature, Cultural Anthropology, History of Christian Thought, Research on English(American) Literature, Seminar in English(American)Literature, Seminar in English Philology.

エリザベト音楽大学
(Erizabeto Ongaku Daigaku)

Elisabeth University of Music

4-15 Nobori-cho, Naka-ku, Hiroshima-shi. Hiroroshima 730
☎ 082-221-0918 FAX 082-221-0947

Founded 1948
Professors 26
Associate Professors 19
Assistant Professors(Tenured) 8
Assistant Professors(Non-tenured) 73
Research Assistants 1
Undergraduate Students/Foreign Students 559/0
Graduate Students/Foreign Students 12/0
Library 81, 965 volumes
Contact: Admission Office

Educational philosophy Our goal is to form musicians whose understanding is deep, whose heart is open, and whose creativity is sentitive and powerful. For this we draw on the educational tenets of Chrisianity and the long teaching tradition of the Society of Jesus.
Foreign students An international atmosphere has been the hallmark of Elisabeth University of Music since its foundation. Of late, a special fund has been established to provide scholarships for foreign students entering our Graduate Department.
Environment Located in the very heart of Hiroshima, a city of one million peopel growing more and more international, Elisabeth Univeristy of Music is side by side to the Peace Memorial Cathedral and close to several music halls. Its quiet atmosphere is much conducive to the enjoyment and study of music.
Facilities Besides a first-class music library, a spacious music auditorium, more than seventy practice rooms, and at least six pipe organs for students' practice, Elisabeth Univ. has a new gymnasium and sports facilities in its second campus at Saijo.
Student activities Music being a most exacting metier, most of the students time is taken with musical activities both curricular and extra curricular. Among extra curricular activities there is the School Festival,and study groups,as Gregorian Chant, Liturgical Music, Madrigal singing, French and German art song, full brass orchestra, flute orchestra, etc.

Undergraduate Programs

Faculty of Music(559/0)
Dept. of Instrumental Music(239/0)
Dept. of Music Theory(129/0)
Dept. of Sacred Music(100/0)
Dept. of Vocal Music(91/0)

Graduate Programs

Graduate School of Music(M 12/0)
Div. of Instrumental Music(M 6/0)
Keyboard(includes harpischord), Strings, Winds and Percussion
Graduate School of Music(M 12/0)
Div. of Music Theroy(M 2/0)
Composition, Conducting, Musicology, Music Education.
Graduate School of Music(M 12/0)
Div. of Sacred Music(M 2/0)
Sacred Music Musicology, Sacred Vocal Music, Pipe Organ
Graduate School of Music(M 12/0)
Div. of Vocal Music(M 2/0)
Vocal Music(Opera, Art Song)

福山大学
(Fukuyama Daigaku)

Fukuyama University

985 Sanzo, Higashimura-cho, Fukuyama-shi, Hiroshima 729-02
☎ 0849-36-2111 FAX 0849-36-2213

Founded 1975
Professors 104
Associate Professor 41
Assistant Professors (Tenured) 32
Assistant Professors (Non-tenured) 66
Research Assistants 44
Undergraduate Students/Foreign Stendents 4, 757/0
Graduate Students/Foreign Students 51/0

Library 147, 363 volumes
Contact: Center for International Exchange

Educational philosophy The University aims at educating well-rounded individuals through realistic principles: 1. The search for & practice of the truth. 2. Cultivation of indomitable spirit & fine character. 3. Reverence for life & nature. 4. Development of individuality & solidarity. 5. Orientation toward the future & search for new possibilities.
Foreign students The University is ready to receive eligible students, Interviews will be arranged for eligible applicants.
Environment The University is located in the western fringe of the city of Fukuyama, which has a population of about 370, 000. The campus is easily accessible via freeway and also by railway. It is blessed with natural beauty and a cultural atmosphere. The region enjoys a mild climate throughout the seasons.
Facilities Information retrieval service is available at the University Library. Computers are installed to serve general purposes, too. Computer performance is taught both in General Education Courses and in specialized departments.
Student activities Students are active both in sports and cultural clubs. An autumnal University Festival is the culmination of the students' activities and features a traditional rice pounding ceremony. A unique program centering around rice cultivation is now traditional among the students.
Academic programs for foreign students A special internsive course of Japanese language for visiting students from U. S. A. is under preparation.
Services for foreign students Various accommondations(including " homestay " and boarding) will be arranged.

Undergraduate Programs

Faculty of Economics(1, 745/0)
　Dept. of Business Administration and Information Sciences(400/0)
　Dept. of Economics(1, 345/0)
Faculty of Engineering(?, 361/0)
　Dept. of Architecture(414/0)
　Dept. of Biotechnology(397/0)
　Dept. of Civil Engineering(341/0)
　Dept. of Electronic and Electrical Engineering(520/0)
　Dept. of Food Science and Technology(179/0)
　Dept. of Information Processing Engineering(510/0)
Faculty of Pharmacy and Pharmaceutical Sciences(651/0)
　Dept. of Bio-Pharmacy(217/0)
　Dept. of Pharmacy(434/0)

Graduate Programs

Graduate School of Engineering(M 33/0)
　Div. of Biotechnology(M 10/0)
Gene Technology, Cell Biology of Plants and Animals, Applied Microbiology, Applied Biochemistry
　Div. of Civil Engineering(M 13/0)
Infrastructure Planning, Structural Engineering, Hydraulic Engineering, Geotechnical Engineering, Safety Engineering
　Div. of Electronic and Electrical Engineering(M 10/0)
Fundamentals of Electronic and Electrical Engineering, Electric Power and Electric Machinery, Electronics and Communication, Materials
Graduate School of Phaermacy and Pharmaceutical Sciences(M 18/0)
Analytical Chemistry, Biochemistry, Biophysics, Dispensing and Manufaturing Pharmacy, Hospital Pharmacy, Hygienic Chemistry, Inorganic Chemistry, Medicinal Chemistry, Microbiology, Natural Products, Nuclear Pharmacy, Organic Chemistry, Pharmaceutics, Pharmacognosy, Pharmacology, Physical Chemistry

---

広島文教女子大学
(Hiroshima Bunkyô Joshi Daigaku)

Hiroshima Bunkyo Women's College

1-2-1 Kabehigashi, Asakita-ku, Hiroshima 731-02
☎ 082-848-3191 FAX 082-815-2097

Founded 1966
Professors 21
Associate Professors 16
Assistant Professors(Tenured) 2
Assistant Professors(Non-tenred) 56
Research Assistants 1
Undergraduate Students/Foreign Strdents 856/1
Graduate Students/Foreigh Students 10/0
Library 109021 volumes
Contact: Planning and Public Information Section

Educational philosophy Our educational aims are to produce well-mannered, cultivated and trustworthy students, as in the three school mottos, 1) Strive after truth, be just and love diligence, 2) Be a person of principle and practice, and 3) Be both modest and elegant.
Foreign students The college is small in size. This enables foreign students to maintain a close and friendly relationship with the teachers and the students in the college, which, we believe, benefits both their academic works and personal characters.
Environment The college is situated in Hiroshima city of international peace and culture. It is in a quiet residential town with the river Ota flowing nearly. With green hills behind and stream in front, we enjoy a most favorable educational environment.
Facilities Library, Language Laboratory, Computer

center, Word Processor Training Room, Gymnasium, Swimming pool, Music Laboratory, Art House, Cafeteria.

Student activities We hold such events as orientation course for freshmen, athletic sports, joint concerts, school festival. There are about thirty extra curricular activities, including flower arrangement, Japanese tea ceremony, chorus, mandolin orchestra, Japanese calligraphy, tennis, dancing, soccer, etc.

Academic programs for foreign students Tutorial system.

Services for foreign students Dormitory, housing information, health clinic, counseling, part-time job informaton.

Undergraduate Programs

Faculty of Literature(856/1)

Dept. of Japanese Literature(322/1)

Dept. of English Literature(247/0)

Dept. of Elementary Education(287/0)

Graduate Programs

Graduate School of Literature(M 10/0)

Div. of Japanese Language and Literature(M 5/0)

Japanese Language Studies, Ancient and Medival Japanese Literature, Modern Contemporary Japanese Literature, Japanese Language Education, Japanese History, Chinese Language and Literature, Chinese Calligraphy

Div. of Education(M 5/0)

Philosophy of Education, Sociology of Education, Educational Method, Educational Psychology, Developmental Psychology, Clinical Psychology, Education, Educational System, History of Japanese and Western Education

---

広島電機大学
(Hiroshima Denki Daigaku)

The Hiroshima-Denki Institute of Technology

6-20-1 Nakano, Aki-ku, Hiroshima-shi, Hiroshima 739-03
☎ 082-893-0381 FAX 082-893-3447

Founded 1967
Professors 44
Associate Professors 25
Assistant Professors(Tenured) 8
Assistant Professors(Non-tenured) 43
Undergraduate Students/Foreign Students 1822/1
Library 56, 583 volumes
Contact: Admission Office

Educational philosophy We aim at teaching and studying that up-to-date industrial technology is openly researched at the Institute and utilized in the academic curriculum. The Institute is always ready to translate the words trust, cooperation, and practice into action.

Foreign students We believe that foreign students can enjoy a rewarding experience in our school and can contribute a great deal to promoting mutual understanding and the development of friendly relations.

Environment The town of Senogawa, with a population of 30, 000, is located midway between Kure and Hiroshima, 13 kilometer east of the city of Hiroshima. Though located in a rural area, Senogawa is convenient to the area.

Facilities The Information Center, Library, Gymnasium(Auditorium), Computer Center.

Student activities Popular campus events include school festival, freshmen welcome guidance. There are a wide variety of clubs and cicles, including baseball club, golf club, and so on.

Academic programs for foreign students Tutoring system.

Services for foreign students Health clinic, part-time job information.

Undergraduate Programs

Faculty of Engineering(1822/1)

Dept. of Electrical Engineering(597/0)

Dept. of Electronic Engineering(656/0)

Dept. of Mechanical Engineering(569/1)

Automatic Control, Computer Engineering, Electrical Machinery, Solid State Electrophysics, Circuit Analysis, Computer Network and Data Base, Computer Programming Information Theory, Radar and Television, Applied Mechanics and Mechanical Vibration, Fluid Mechanics and Fluid Machinery Thermodynamics and Energy Conversion. Electric Circuits

---

広島工業大学
(Hiroshima Kôgyô Daigaku)

Hiroshima Institute of Technology

2-1-1 Miyake, Saeki-ku, Hiroshima-shi, Hiroshima 731-51
☎ 0829-21-3121 FAX 0829-23-0948

Founded 1963
Professors 76
Associate Professors 42
Assistant Professors(Tenured) 18
Assistant Professors(Non-tenured) 64
Research Assistants 2
Undergraduate Studentes/Foreign Students 3, 811/0
Graduate Students/Foreign Students 24/0
Library 155, 807 volumes
Contact: Department of Educational Information ☎ ext. 270, 271

Educational philosophy The Institute aims at nurturing and providing the society with the engineers who are keenly aware of various human concerns and would make contributions towards the development of technology and its industrial use which best meets social needs without degrading human dignity.

Foreign students At present, we do not have a program to admit foreign students. However, we are seriously studing this matter and hope to accept foreign students in a very near future.

Environment The Institute is located in Hiroshima, a metropolis of a population of 1. 1 million. The main campus is in western part of the city, on the slope of a hill with abundant greenery. It commands a spectacular view of both Seto Inland Sea and the Miyajima Island, one of the so-called three beautiful sceneries of Japan.

Facilities Library holding approximately 160, 000 volumes; Computor Center installed with HITAC 630/30 with a memory of 32 MB; Tsuru Memorial Gymnasium; Micro-computor classrooms; Research Laboratory of Engineering; Mechanical Technology Center, Numata Campus, Hiroshima Downtown Facility, etc.

Student activities Annual campus events: Athletic festival, school festival, freshmen welcome party, Extra curricular activities includes: Baseball, judo, yacht and boats, horseriding, tea-ceremony, students newspaper, music, arts, and Red Cross volunteer work.

Undergraduate Programs

Faculty of Engineering(3, 811/0)

Dept. of Architecture (Architectural Design Course, Architectural Engineering Course) (718/0)

Dept. of Civil Engineering(515/0)

Dept. of Electrical Engineering(507/0)

Dept. of Electronic Engineering(505/0)

Dept. of Industrial Enginering(525/0)

Dept. of Mechanical Engineering (Machinery Course, Electronic Machines Course) (991/0)

Graduate Programs

Graduate School of Engineering(M 24/0)

Div. of Civil Engineering(M 4/0)

Structural Engineering. Soil Mechanics and Construction. Materials Engineering. Hydraulic Engineering. Environmental Engineering and Planning. Master's Thesis. Related Subjects

Div. of Electronic Engineering(M 6/0)

Physical Electronics. Electronic Measurement Engineering. Electronic Circuits Engineering. Control and Systmes Engineering. Master's Thesis. Related Subjects

Div. of Mechanical Systems Engineering(M 14/0)

Materials Enginering. Manufacturing Systems Engineering. Energy Systems Engineering. Measurement Systems Engineering. Master's Thesis. Related Subjects

広島女学院大学

(Hiroshima Jogakuin Daigaku)

Hiroshima Jogakuin College

4-13-1 Ushita-Higashi, Higashi-ku, Hiroshima 732
☎ 082-228-0386 FAX 082-227-4502

Founded 1886
Professors 20
Associate Professors 13
Assistant Professors(Tenured) 3
Assistant Professors(Non-tenured) 25
Undergraduate Studentes/Foreign Students 949/0
Library 109, 841 volumes
Contact: Registra's Office

Educational philosophy Hiroshima Jogakuin was founded on a basis of Christianity in 1886 in cooperation with the Methodist Episcopal Church, South, in the U.S.A. Guided by the school motto " Workers Together With God ", School life is conducted in order to develop in students abroad outlook and a well-rounded personality.

Foreign students The college will welcome students from abroad. Although the lectures are given in Japanese, foreign students are assisted with various ways.

Environment The campus, some 20 ha. of green restful hill-side, surrounded by residential quarters north of down-town, is easy to access both from Hiroshima Station and from the business centers.

Facilities Library, Gymnasium, Auditorium, Mountain Retreat, Dormitory.

Student activities Main annual events includes orientation camp for freshmen, college festival and study-abroad programs. There is a wide variety of extra curricular activities, including volunteer work, choir, mandolin, " koto ", tennis, ski, etc.

Academic programs for foreign students Various kinds of programs are being made for those students from abroad.

Services for foreign students Counseling, Dormitory, " Arbeits "-introduction, Cultural exchange, etc. can be arranged.

Undergraduate Programs

Faculty of Literature(949/0)

Dept. of Japanese Literature(421/0)

Dept. of American and English Literature(528/0)

広島修道大学
(Hiroshima Shûdô University)
Hiroshima Shudo University

1717 Ohtsuka, Numata-cho, Asaminami-ku, Hiroshima 731-31
☎ 082-848-2121 FAX 082-848-6051

Founded 1960
Professors 81
Associate Professors 62
Assistant Professors(Tenured) 11
Assistant Professors(Non-tenured) 154
Undergraduate Students/Foreign Students 5, 638/31
Graduate Students/Foreign Students 55/12
Library 404, 841 volumes
Contact: International Affairs Section

Educational philosophy The name Shudo, written with two Chinese characters, comes from one of the Chinese Classics, "Chuyo". The words basically mean that Heaven has given each individual his or her own personality, and the two characters show the way that every human being should develop his or her personality. Hiroshima Shudo University strives to follow and to teach this way adequately.

Foreign students Shudo University is actively developing international contacts and exchange programs, and therefore welcomes applications from foreign students, either within the framework of university-to-university programs or as individuals. Foreign students have attended Shudo for periods of one semester, one year, and longer. Some students from abroad have also earned Shudo degrees.

Environment Shudo university occupies a wooded campus on a hill in one of the suburban districts of Hiroshima City. Hiroshima is an attractive modern city, facing the beautiful Seto Inland Sea, a national park area. The city is crossed by six rivers, and surrounded by the magnificent Chugoku Mountains. Industries include the manufacture of automobiles(Mazda)and the cultivation of oysters. These are excellent transportation facilities, both international and local. Hiroshima is responsible for promoting world peace.

Facilities Shudo university is fully equipped with all facilities necessary for academic study and research, as well as recreation. The university library collection is large and varied, in both Oriental and Western languages. The computer Center has a host computer as well as many micro-computers. There are several modern language laboratories. A full-size swimming pool has recently been built, complementing gym, tennis courts, and playing fields

Student activities Students enjoy a full extra-curricular programs, centered on more than 70 clubs. These clubs are managed by the students and subsidized by the university. A very wide range of interests is covered, including various musical tastes, and career interests. Most students belong to a club, which serves as a focus for their social lives and activities.

Academic programs for foreign students Foreign students(undergraduate), credits for general education may be satisfied, up to 22 credits, with credits earned in Japanese Language and Japanese studies courses. Each foreign student has each own superviser, an academic staff at Shudo.

Services for foreign students The International Affairs Section has special responsibility for serving the needs of foreign students at Shudo. This section provides orientation and homestay programs on arrival, and continuing counseling through the students' stay. Assistance in many practical areas is provided, including liaison with other universities, as well as city and government sevices, such as medical facilities, housing sevices, etc.

Undergraduate Programs

Faculty of Commercial Sciences(2, 881/17)
  Dept. of Business Administration(1, 079/9)
  Dept. of Business Studies(1, 043/7)
  Dept. of Mangement Science(759/1)
Faculty of Humanities and Sciences(1, 413/11)
  Dept. of Education(272/2)
  Dept. of English Language and Literature(610/4)
  Dept. of Psychology(247/0)
  Dept. of Sociology(284/5)
Faculty of Law(1, 313/3)
  Dept. of International Politics(87/2)
  Dept. of Law(1, 226/1)

Graduate Programs

Graduate School of Commercial Sciences(M 13/6, D 6/1)
  Div. of Business Administration(M 9/4, D 4/0)
Business Management, History of Business, Business Policy, Principles of Business Administration, Corporation Studies, Corporation Finance, Personnel and Labor Management, History of Japanese Business, Industrial Management, Labor Administration, Management Systems, Computer Systems, Systems Analysis, Principles of Accounting, Financial Accounting, Managerial Accounting, Business Law, Financial Analysis, Business Statistics, Financial Management
  Div. of Business Studies(M 4/2, D 2/1)
Commerce, Commercial History, Commercial Policy, Economic Geography, Economics, Business Management, Accounting, Marketing, Foreign Trade, Trade Practice Monetary Theory, Stock Market Theory, Transport Economics, Insurance Economics, Advertising, History of Asian Commerce Business Administration, International Economics, Urban Economic Geography, Theory of Economics
Graduate School of Humanities and Sciences(M 11/3, D 3/0)
  Div. of Education(M 4/0)
Foundations of Education and Educational Thought, His-

tory of Education, Methodology of Education and Instruction, Sociology of Education, Educational Systems, Social Education, Philosophy of Education, Humanistic Education, Higher Education, International Education

Div. of English Language and Literature (M 1/1, D 3/0)
English Literature, American Literature, English Language, Japanese Literature, German Literature, French Literature, Linguistics

Div. of Psychology (M 2/1)
Psychological Methods, Physiological Psychology, Sensation and Perception, Developmental Psychology, Educational Psychology, Clinical Psychology, Applied and Industrial Psychology, Experimental Psychology, Learning Psychology, Social Psychology, Comparative Psychology

Div. of Sociology (M 4/1)
Sociological Theories, Regional Study, Culture and Religion, Social Problems, Social Research, Study of Modern Society, Social Planning, Communication, Study of Social Awareness, Study of Discrimination Problems

Graduate School of Law (M 6/2)

Div. of Law (M 6/2)
Constitutional Law, Administrative Law, Criminal, Law, Civil Law, Commercial Law Criminal Procedure Act, Civil Procedure Act, Labor Law, Economic Law, International Law, International Economic Law, International Private Law, Legal Philosophy, Legal History, Political Science, International Relations

---

広島経済大学
(Hiroshima Keizai Daigaku)

Hiroshima University of Economics

5-37-1 Gion, Asaminami-ku, Hiroshima-shi, Hiroshima 731-01
☎ 082-871-1000 FAX 082-871-1005

Founded 1967
Professors 42
Associate Professors 22
Assistant Professors (Tenured) 12
Assistant Professors (Non-tenured) 64
Research Assistants 2
Undergraduate Students/Foreign Students 3, 754/5
Graduate Students/Foreign Students 13/0
Library 166, 649 volumes
Contact: Admissions Office

Educational philosophy Our institution is devoted to educating students and cultivating their character. We feel that the economists and businessmen today are required not only to have the knowledge in economics and business, but also, to have developed a "cultured" heart and mind that is flexible and adaptable to the complex society we live in today.

Foreign students As our University pursues a policy of promoting international understanding, we encourage those foreign students of high aptitude interested in business and economics to study at our University.

Environment Hiroshima University of Economics is located in the City of Hiroshima which is also known as the city of international peace and culture. With a population of over one million, the city is blessed with natural surroundings and favored by the cultural and educational environment.

Facilities Internationally approved sports facilities; Research Institute of Regional Economy; Information and Computation Center, etc.

Student activities At present, all foreign students are eligible to participate in the same extracurricular activities as the regular Japanese students on campus. Those interested should refer to the University catalogue for details.

Academic programs for foreign students At present, there are no special academic programs for foreign students. All foreign students are required to participate in the same academic programs as do the regular Japanese students.

Services for foreign students The Office of International Exchange and the Foreign Student Advisor provide for the necessary counselling and help needed during the foreign students' enrollment at the University.

Undergraduate Programs

Faculty of Economics (3, 754/5)

Dept. of Business Management (1, 851/3)

Dept. of Economics (1, 903/2)

Graduate Programs

Graduate School of Economics (M 11/0, D 2/0)
Economic Theory, Econometrics, World Economy, Statistics, European Economic History, Modern Japanese Economy, Economic Policy, Industrial Economics, Finance, International Finance, Public Finance, Accounting, Financial Management

---

川崎医科大学
(Kawasaki Ika Daigaku)

Kawasaki Medical School

577 Matsushima, Kurashiki-shi, Okayama 701-01
☎ 0864-62-1111 FAX 0864-62-1199

Founded 1970
Professors 59
Associate Professors 43
Assistant Professors (Tenured) 123
Assistant Professors (Non-tenured) 9
Research Assistants 129

Undergraduate Students/Foreign 817/0
Graduate Students/Foreign 105/0
Library 19, 257 volumes
Contact: Gakumuka Shomukakari

Educational philosophy Kawasaki Medical School was established in accordance with the following principles: liberal humanity, sound body and profound knowledge. We aim not only to train reliable clinicians, but to train medical researchers to contribute to the rapid progress taking place in medical science.
Foreign students We have no unit system to receive foreign students.
Environment The campus is located on Matsushima, in the suburbs of Kurashiki City. This city is well known as an area of historical and industrial significance. The completion of the Seto Ohashi Bridge in 1988 made this area more important and famous in Japan.
Facilities We have Library, Gymnasium, Computer Center, R. I. Center, etc. One of the outstanding institutions is the Medical Museum, which aims to facilitate the understanding of medical theories and techniques through audiovisual systems.
Student activities The most popular campus event is school festival in autumn. We have a wide variety of extra curricular activities, including ESS, drama, aikido, golf, tennis, horse-riding, and so on.

Undergraduate Programs

Faculty of Medicine(817/0)
Dept. of Medicine(817/0)

Graduate Programs

Graduate School of Medicine(D 105/0)
Div. of Morphology(D 26/0)
Div. of Physiology(D 49/0)
Div. of Biochemistry(D 20/0)
Div. of Tissue Culture and Immunology(D 5/0)
Div. of Environmental Medicine(D 5/0)

吉備国際大学
(Kibi Kokusai Daigaku)

Kibi International University

8 Iga-machi, Takahashi-shi, Okayama 716
☎ 0866-22-3517 FAX 0866-22-3476

Founded 1990
Professors 19
Associate Professors 3
Assistant Professors(Tenured) 11
Assistant Professors(Non-tenured) 12
Undergraduate Students/Foreign Students 373/1
Library 11, 000 volumes
Contact: Office of Admission, Office of International Affairs

Educational philosophy We are planning to teach students to develop their fullest potential and contribute in business fields with international passports to meet the needs of an international and industrial society.
Foreign students Our university is opened not only to Japanese students but also students from foreign countries. Foreign students will enjoy their campus life in the typical Japanese town.
Environment Takahashi City is located about 50 km north west of Okayama City with a population of 26, 000. The city is known as a traditional and cultural city. There are many cultural assets such as Raikyu-ji Temple and Takahashi Christian Church.
Facilities Library, Computer Room, Language Laboratory, Gymnasium
Student activities Campus events include sports day and campus festival. There are many students clubs for cultural and athletic activities such as music, cinema, media research, volleyball, basketball, tennis, kendo shorin-ji kenpo, etc.
Academic programs for foreign students Tutoring system, classes for Japanese society and Japanese readings
Services for foreign students Health clinic, personal/psychological counseling, housing, part-time job information, vocational guidance, cultural exchange program

Undergraduate Programs

Faculty of International and Industrial Studies(373/1)
Dept. of International-Comparative Sociology(180/1)
Dept. of Industrial Sociology(193/0)

美作女子大学
(Mimasaka Joshi Daigaku)

Mimasaka Women's College

32 Kamigawara, Tsuyama-shi, Okayama 708
☎ 0868-22-7718 FAX 0868-23-6936

Founded 1967
Professors 12
Associate Professors 9
Assistant Professors(Tenured) 7
Assistant Professors(Non-tenured) 30
Research Assistants 4
Undergraduate Students/Foreign Students 323/1
Library 92263 volumes
Contact: Registrar's Office

Educational philosophy We aim at educating students to be women of high intelligence, rich sentiments, and general virtues who are able to meet the social demand and contribute to the development of the culture of our country as well as of all human beings.

Foreign students We are ready to accept foreign students to make a profound study and make a contribution to the advance of culture.

Environment Tsuyama city is a beautiful castle town which has a history of nearly 400 years. It has been the center of politics and economy of the northern part of Okayama prefecture and has also developed as an industrial city of electronics in these days.

Facilities We have a library, Information processing center with 40 personal computers, 48 piano practicing booths, an auditorium with audiovisual equipments, a gymnasium(theater), tennis courts, etc.

Student activities Students enjoy orientation seminar, freshmen welcome party, ball game tournaments, and school festival. They can also enjoy extracurricular activities such as athletic sports, volleyball, tennis, drama, children culture study, guitar & recorder, etc.

Academic programs for foreign students Foreign students may substitute required courses for others depending on circumstances. And, special courses for foreign students may be found in case of need, especially in language.

Services for foreign students Foreign students are given as much service as Japanese students which includes housing information, part-time job information, etc.

Undergraduate Programs

Faculty of Domestic Science(323/1)
  Dept. of Child Science(216/1)
  Dept. of Food Science(107/0)

ノートルダム清心女子大学
(Nôtorudamu Seishin Joshi Daigaku)

Notre Dame Seishin University

2-16-9 Ifuku-cho, Okayama-shi, Okayama 700
☎ 0862-52-1155 FAX 0862-55-7665

Founded 1949
Professors 39
Associate Professors 18
Assistant Professors(Tenured) 21
Assistant Professors(Non-tenured) 88
Undergraduate Students/Foreign Students 1, 985/2
Library 185, 625 volumes

Educational philosophy Notre Dame Seishin University with its educational ideal based on Christianity pursues truth, goodness and beauty, fostering in each student the desire to be a real liberal person through education and research, providing opportunities to deepen the understanding of the significance of living.

Foreign students We hope that foreign students can enjoy a rewarding experience in our school, and can contribute a great deal to promoting mutual understanding and development of friendly relations.

Environment Okayama city, with a population of 600, 000, is famous for having one of the three most beautiful gardens in Japan. Our university is located near the center of the city. It takes about 10 minutes on foot from the west exit of Okayama Station, and transportation is very convenient.

Facilities Such facilities as: Library, Child Clinic Institute, Christian Research Center, Institute of Human Studies, Institute of Life Style Culture, Research Institute for Informatics and Science, Culture Center, Chapel are available.

Student activities During the four years of college life, students strive in studies and foster their ideal to be a truly liberal person. We hope that students cultivate profound aesthetic sentiments and social manners as well through the wide variety of extra curricular activities including volunteer work, college festival, club activities and other college events.

Services for foreign students Foreign students are given priority to live in the boarding school.

Undergraduate Programs

Faculty of Home Economics(1118/1)
  Dept. of Child Welfare (Course of Child Study, Course of Primary Education) (543/1)
  Dept. of Foods and Human Nutrition (Course of Food Science and Human Nutrition, Course of Dietetics Administration) (241/0)
  Dept. of Home Economics(334/0)
Faculty of Literature(867/1)
  Dept. of English Language and Literature(491/1)
  Dept. of Japanese Language and Literature(376/0)

岡山商科大学
(Okayama Shôka Daigaku)

Okayama College of Commerce

2-10-1 Tsushima, kyo-machi, Okayama-shi, Okayama 700
☎ 0862-52-0642 FAX 0862-55-6947

Founded 1965
Professors 25
Associate Professors 23
Assistant Professors(Tenured) 8
Assistant Professors(Non-tenured) 42
Research Assistants 1
Undergraduate Students/Foreign Students 2, 435/1
Library 167, 960 volumes
Contact: Admission Office

Educational Philosophy We aim at(1)training students to be persons who serve society with fairness and boad vision,(2)training students to be persons who have passion and a fighting spirit toward truth and academia,(3)training students to be persons who have a realistic interest in industry and cultural intelligence.
Foreign students We believe that foreign students can enjoy a rewarding experince in our college, and can contribute a great deal to promoting mutual understanding and the development of friendly relations.
Environment The campus is situated in the West-north section of the city of Okayama, about 4 kilometers from the center of the city and lies in the suburbs, amongst tranquil surroundings. The environment of the college is an ideal one.
Facilities Research Institutes for Economics and Management, Library, Sports Training Center, College club-house, Auditorium, Mountain Lodge, Student Hall.
Student activities Popular campus events include college festival, freshmen welcome party, etc. There is a wide variety of extra curricular activetics, including baseball, Judo, bowling, tennis, basket, Karate, E. S. S., go, shogi etc.

Undergraduate Programs

Faculty of Commerce
Dept. of Business Administration
Dept. of Commerce

岡山理科大学
(Okayama Rika Daigaku)

Okayama University of Science

1-1 Ridai-cho, Okayama-Shi 700
☎ 0862-52-3161 FAX 0862-54-8434

Founded 1964
Professors 127
Associate Professors 65
Assistant Professors(Tenured) 37
Assistant Professors(Non-tenured) 88
Research Assistants 16
Undergraduate Students/Foreign Students 5, 041/3
Graduate Students/Foreign Students 140/3
Library 210, 000 volumes
Contact: Planning & Admission Office

Educational Philosophy We encourage the students to have creatively interdisciplinary ability by connecting the study of thoughts and appliance of up-to-date technology on the international level, through their self-motivated endeavors and cooperative and reliable ties with each other.
Foreign students We open to students and researchers from abroad as seen in our programs we have now with 12 universities and colleges on the international exchange promotion, in China, Taiwan, U. S. A., Canada, Brazil and U. K.
Environment The city of Okayama, located a little east of Osaka, with a population of about 500, 000, offers a combination of rural-urban and natural-high technological stances. Also it is close to Hiroshima, Shikoku Island and kyushu. In winter people can enjoy skiing, and in summer, swimming.
Facilities Computer-controlled library, Micro-analysis Center, Ultro Low Temperature Center, High capable Computer Center(FACOM-M 380), Spaceful gymnadium and fields, Health Control Center, Environmental Resourse Center
Student activities There is a wide variety of extra Curricular activities including Karate, Kendo, Baseball, tennis, soccer, ski, other Jaoanese Martial Arts, etc. and also chorus group, brass band, photography, astronomy, etc. Campus events have May Festival, Nov. Festival, Ski Training Seminar and Mounteering.
Academic programs for foreign students Japanese language training is offered to the students from abroad, depending on the situations. Tutoring system is available.
Services for foreign students Health clinic and personal/psycholigical counseling through tutoring system, Housing information, cultural exchange program cooperated with City/Prefecture activities.

Undergraduate Programs

Faculty of Engineering(1, 937/3)
Dept. of Applied Chemistry(635/0)
Applied Chemistry Major,
Environmental Chemistry Major
Dept. of Electronic Engineering(650/3)
Electronics Engineering Major,
Information and System Engineering Major
Dept. of Mechanical Engineering(652/0)Fundamental Mechanical Engineering Major,
Industrial Mechanical Enginerring Major
Faculty of Science(3, 067/0)
Dept. of Applied Mathematics(813/0)
Applied Mathemmatics Major,
Information Processing Major
Dept. of Applied Physics(675/0)
Dept. of Applied Science(617/0)
Dept. of Biochemistry(352/0)
Faculty of Science(3, 067/0)
Dept. of Chemistry(610/0)

Graduate Programs

Graduate School of Science(M 85/0, D 24/2)
Div. of Applied Mathematics(M 15/0, D 3/1)
Doctor's, Algebra, Analysis, Computational Analysis, Geometry, Mathematical Statistics
Master's, Algebra, Analysis, Geometry, Information System, Mathematical Statistics, Numerical Analysis
Div. of Applied Physics(M 14/0)

Atomic Physics, Quantum Physics, Solid State Physics Surface Physics

Div. of Applied Science(M 21/0)

Biological Science, Earth Environmental Science, Energy Science, Mathematical Science

Div. of Chemistry(M 29/0)

Analytical Chemistry, Inorganic Chemistry, Organic Chemistry, Physical Chemistry, Solid State Chemistry

Div. of Electronic Science(M 4/0)

Electronics, Electronic Phenomina in Solids, Fundamental Theory, in Electronics, Information Science

Div. of Material Science(D 18/0)

Biological Science, Coordiantion Chemistry, Geo-material Science, Molecular Design, Natural Products Chemistry, Low Temperature Physics, Solid State Chemistry, Solid State Physics, Surface Chemistry, Radiation Physics, Theory of Condensed Matter, Quantum Physics

Div. of Mechanical Science(M 5/0)

Instrumentation and Control Engineering, Machine Design and Machining, Mathematical Analysis, Matherials Science, Thermofluid Mechanics and Energu Conversion

Div. of System Science(D 3/1)

Computer and Communication, Control System, Information Processing, Information Mathematics, Material Chemistry, Optical Machine Design, Physics at Random Systems, Process System Design, Production of Natural Products, Simulation Physics

Graduate School of Engineering(M 30/0, D 1/1)

Div. of Applied Chemistry(M 17/0)

Biological Engineering, Chemical Engineering, Inorganic Material Chemistry, Organic Material Chemistry, Synthetic Organic Chemistry

Div. of Electronic Engineering(M 4/0)

Communication Engineering, Electronics, Electrinoc Phenomena in Solids, Information Processing, Opt-Electronics, System Engineering

Div. of Mechanical Engineering(M 9/0)

Instrumentation and Control Engineering, Machine Design and Machining, Materials' Science for Machines, Mathematical Analysis, Thermofluid Mechanics and Energy Conversion

Div. of System Science(D 1/1)

Computer and Communication, Control System, Information Mathematics, Information Processing, Optical Machine Design, Solid State Physics in Electronics, Material Chemistry

One-Year Graduate Programs

Science Course

Applied Mathematics Major, Chemistry Major, Applied Chemistry Major, Applied Physics Major, Mechanical Engineering Major, Electronic Engineering Major

作陽音楽大学

(Sakuyô Ongaku Daigaku)

Sakuyo College of Music

1334-1 Yaide, Tsuyama-shi, Okayama 708
☎ 0868-24-1811 FAX 0868-24-1818

Founded 1966
Professors 21
Associate Professors 20
Assistant Professors(Tenured) 16
Assistant Professors(Non-tenured) 91
Undergraduate Students/Foreign Students 657/1
Library 42, 345 volumes
Contact: The Director of Planning and Public Relations, The School Administration, Sakuyo College of Music

Educational philosophy The idea of education of Sakuyo College of Music is to provide students with the warm-hearted, one-on-one instruction that will elevate their technical skills in music performance. As Sakuyo College is a Buddhist missionary school as well, the cultivation of human mind is added to the musical experience.

Foreign students Because of the non-urban location of Sakuyo College, we are able to attract students from all over western parts of Japan as well as America, China and Taiwan, who are welcomed by all faculties and students.

Environment Tsuyama, 60 kilometers from Okayama city, is a small but cultured city, having a population of 87, 000 and a basinlike geographical feature, which is abundant in scenic beauty and historical legacy. Express buses run Tsuyama and Osaka, the second largest city in Japan. You can reach there within two hours and a half via the Chugoku motorway.

Facilities The facilities of Sakuyo College include a library, a gymnasium, a large concert halls for symphonic concerts, several recital halls for solo or ensemble performances, practice rooms and studios.

Student activities Sakuyo 'Series Concerts', with world-recognized artists invited, are held several times a year. In-campus concerts are often held by students, besides. Of course, foreign students can participate in these performances. Such events as the college festival in November and the reception for freshmen in April are flourishing as a forum for students.

Academic programs for foreign students As our foreign students program is very young, a special curriculum for foreign students is still under development. However, foreign students are given freedom to study any subjects, including traditional Japanese music, Buddhism, as well as Japanese language.

Services for foreign students Sakuyo College will assist foreign students in adjusting life in Japan, Including the procurement of housing and any matters of daily life. The kind and generous nature of the faculty, staff and students as well as the people of tsuyama will make any foreign students feel welcome.

Undergraduate Programs

Faculty of Music(657/1)
Dept. of Music(451/0)
Dept. of Educatiional Music(206/1)

就実女子大学
(Shûjitsu Joshi Daigaku)
Shujitsu Joshi University

1-6-1 Nishigawara, Okayama-shi, Okayama 703
☎ 0862-72-3185 FAX 0862-72-2392

Founded 1979
Professors 23
Associate Professors 13
Assistant Professors(Tenured) 13
Assistant Professors(Non-tenured) 54
Undergraduate Students/Foreign Students 1348/2
Library 83, 396 volumes
Contact: Admission Office Ditto

Educational philosophy School motto is " Part from Showiness, Aim at Substantiality." SJU endeavours to Cultivate by making the best use of modern facilities women of higher culture who can contribute to the welfare and prosperity of the society.
Foreign students Foreign students will be cordially welcome to SJU. Students who are recommended by Sister Universities will get a scholarship from the University.
Environment SJU is located in the north of Korakuen Garden, which is one of the most beautiful gradens in Japan. Seto Gigantic Bridges are only about 15 miles from the campus.
Facilities Beautiful school buildings, Golf ground, Research center for Kibi culture and civilization, New gymnasium is planned.
Student activities Popular campus events include school festival, freshman camping; choral group, university band, soccer club, etc.
Academic programs for foreign students Supplemental Japanese language classes, Tutoring system, Presidential dinner party.
Services for foreign students Personal psychological counselling, College housing, Home visit, Vocational guidance.

Undergraduate Programs

Faculty of Literature(1348/2)
Dept. of English and American Literature(418/1)
Dept. of History(530/1)
Dept. of Japanese Literature(400/0)

徳山大学
(Tokuyama Daigaku)
Tokuyama University

843-4-2 Kume-kurigasako, Tokuyama-shi, Yamaguchi 745
☎ 0834-28-0411

Founded 1971

Undergraduate Programs

Faculty of Economics
Dept. of Economics
Dept. of Management

東亜大学
(Tôa Daigaku)
University of East Asia

2-1 Ichinomiyagakuen-cho, Shimonoseki-shi, Yamaguchi 751
☎ 0832-56-1111 FAX 0832-56-9577

Founded 1974
Professors 41
Associate Professors 19
Assistant Professors(Tenured) 16
Assistant Professors(Non-tenured) 13
Undergraduate Students/Foreign Students 2, 018/0
Library 49, 875 volumes
Contact: Admission Office

Educational philosophy The distinctive education and the studies are enforced in respond to the future demand of the politics, economy and culture. Practical education and studies should be carried out in order to train the men of ability.
Foreign students In principle, applicants are expected to take the same entrance examination as Japanese applicants. Then we hope that applicants will have considerable aptitude for Japanese language.
Environment Shimonoseki City where the University is located has a population of about 300, 000, and has been known for a point of traffic and commercial importance for China and Korea. The city and the surroundings are favored by natural beauty.
Facilities Library, Gymnasium, Information Processing and Science Research Center, etc.
Student activities Extra curricular activities are very popular. Especially, volleyball club often wins the victory or the second prize in the western Japan league match.
Academic programs for foreign students Special programs are put into practice according to the applicants' ability and the actual condition.
Services for foreign students Health clinic, per-

sonal/psychological counseling, Housing information, part-time job information

Undergraduate Programs

Faculty of Business Management(1, 296/0)
Dept. of Business Management(1, 296/0)
Faculty of Engineering(722/0)
Dept. of Mechanical Engineering(261/0)
Dept. of Food Technology(223/0)
Dept. of System Engineering(238/0)

山口女子大学
(Yamaguchi Joshi Daigaku)

Yamaguchi Women's University

3-2-1 Sakurabatake, Yamaguchi-shi, Yamaguchi 753
☎ 0839-28-0211 FAX 0839-28-0211

Founded 1941
Professors 31
Associate Professors 16
Assistant Professors(Tenured) 3
Assistant Professors(Non-tenured) 46
Research Assistants 14
Undergraduate Students/Foreign Students 670/0
Library 120, 000 volumes
Contact: Admission Office

Educational philosophy The university was founded as one of the few institutions of higher education for women, in Yamaguchi Prefecture. The art and science education aims to develop students' total abilities to contribute not only to local but also nationwide level.
Foreign students It is now the preparatory period for us to receive foreign students. Due to the natural environment and local history,they can surely enjoy studying the Japanese history & culture alive.
Environment The university is located in the north-east part of Yamaguchi City(also called Western Kyoto)where the Ouchi culture prospered in the Muromachi period. The city has about 130, 000 people, and the students, all female, come from the western Japan mainly.
Facilities The university library contains Terauchi Collection consisted of Japanese, Old Korean and Chinese resources; Center for Local Literature; Kindergarten; Gymnasium; Chemical Laboratory
Student activities Popuplar campus events include festivals, freshmen welcome party, commencement, etc. There is a wide variety of extra curricular activities including drama, guitar and mandolin orchestra, sports clubs, volunteer work, literature club, etc.

Undergraduate Programs

Faculty of Literature(320/0)
Dept. of Japanese Literature(160/0)
Dept. of Child and Culture(160/0)
Faculty of Home Science(320/0)
Dept. of Nutrition(120/0)
Dept. of Food Living Science(100/0)
Dept. of Living Arts(100/0)

安田女子大学
(Yasuda Joshi Daigaku)

Yasuda Women's University

6-13-1 Yasuhigashi Asaminami-ku, Hiroshima-shi, Hiroshima 731-01
☎ 082-878-8111 FAX 082-872-2896

Founded 1966
Professors 24
Associate Professors 15
Assistant Professors(Tenured) 9
Assistant Professors(Non-tenured) 51
Undergraduate Students/Foreign Students 1, 567/0
Library 82, 426 volumes
Contact: Administration

Educational philosophy " A tender, yet firm spirit " is our school motto. A tender spirit emphasizes the gentleness of a woman. It also encourages careful consideration and a graceful spirit. A firm spirit stresses the strength of wisdom: the ability to deal with circumstances without being discouraged.
Foreign students We accept foreign students under the same policies as Japanese students. An entrance examination is given at the beginning of the year, which includes Japanese, English, and a written essay. The school year begins in April.
Environment Our university is located 5 miles north of the center of Hiroshima. The city has a population of one million, and is a peaceful place. It has one of the warmest cilmates in Japan so we live comfortably surrounded by nature. The main form of transportation to the campus is the buses from downtown Hiroshima.
Facilities The Library is computer controlled and has full AV capabilities. There are Computer Rooms (CAI), an LL, Gym, Sciece Labratories, Cooking Facilities, and a Cafeteria available for student use.
Student activities Spring: Orientation Seminar; Summer: " A Summer Evening " of club performances; Autumn University Festival. Clubs: There are two types, cultural and athletic, for example, Koto, Calligraphy, Puppet, Chorus, Brass Band, Tea Ceremony, Archery, Tennis, Mountaineering, and others.

Undergraduate Programs

Faculty of Letters(1, 567/0)
- **Dept. of Japanese Literature**(620/0)
- **Dept. of English and American Language and Literature**(563/0)
- **Dept. of Primary Education**(384/0)

SHIKOKU

SHIKOKU REGION CLIMATE

- Seto Inland Sea Region

  Generally clear year-round, with light rainfall, Summers extremely hot, winters comparatively mild.

- Southern Shikoku (Pacific Ocean Side)

  Warm summers with heavy rainfall. Heavy typhoon impact, with warm winter temperatures.

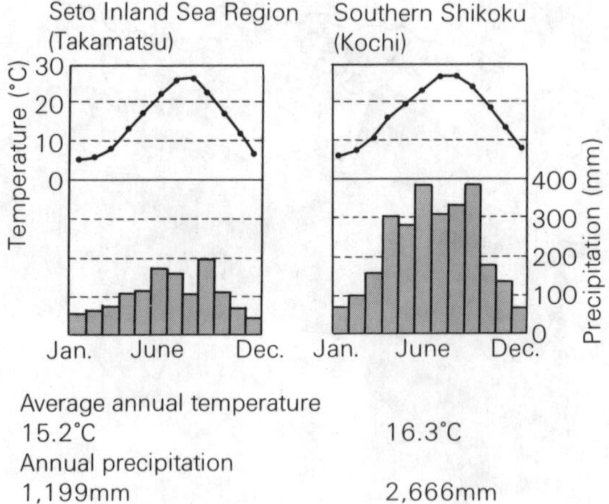

Average annual temperature

Seto Inland Sea Region (Takamatsu)	Southern Shikoku (Kochi)
15.2°C	16.3°C

Annual precipitation

Seto Inland Sea Region (Takamatsu)	Southern Shikoku (Kochi)
1,199mm	2,666mm

National Universities

愛媛大学
(Ehime Daigaku)

Ehime University

10–13 Dogo–himata, Matsuyama–shi, Ehime 790
☎ 0899–24–7111 FAX 0899–25–6474

Founded 1949
Professors 239
Associate Professors 247
Assistant Professors(Tenured) 85
Assistant Professors(Non–tenured) 542
Research Assistants 217
Undergraduate Students/Foreign Students 8, 072/32
Graduate Students/Foreign Students 438/66
Library 852, 140 volumes
Contact: Undergraduate Admission Admission Office, Ehime University, 3 Bunkyo–cho, Matsuyama–shi, Ehime 790 ☎ 0899–24–7111 ext. 2188 Graduate Admission Each Student Section of College of Agriculture(Master's degree), and United Graduate School of Agricultural Science(Doctor' s degree), Ehime University, 3–5–7 Tarumi, Matsuyama–shi, Ehime 790 ☎ 0899–41–4171 ext. 211(Master's degree), ext. 385(Doctor's degree) Each Student Section of Faculties of Engineering, and Law and Literature, Ehime University, 3 Bunkyo–cho, Matsuyama–shi, Ehime 790 ☎ 0899–24 –7111 ext. 3621(Engineering), ext. 3026(Law and Literature) Student Section, School of Medicine, Ehime University, Shitsukawa, Shigenobu–cho, Onsen–gun, Ehime 791–02 ☎ 0899–64–5111 ext. 2021 Student Section, Faculty of science, Ehime University, 2–5 Bunkyo–cho, Matsuyama–shi, Ehime 790 ☎ 0899–24–7111 ext. 3517

Educational philosophy We aim at teaching and studying up–to–date high–level art and sciences to develop intellectual, moral and applied abilities so students may contribute much to cultural betterment and social improvement.

Foreign students We believe that foreign students can enjoy a rewarding experience through their study in our school, and can contribute a great deal to promoting mutual understanding and the development of friendly relations to us.

Environment Ehime prefecture is situated along the beatutiful coast of the Seto Inland Sea on the island of Shikoku and is a famous citrus growing area of Japan. The population of Matsuyama City is approximately 450, 000 and the city has a beautiful old castle and a famous hot spring spa named Dogo Onsen.

Facilities University library, Advanced Instrumentation center for chemical analysis, Data processing Center, Health administration center, Swimming pool, Gymnasium, Auditorium

Student activities Popular campus events include regatta, swimming match, student's festival, " ekiden " race, ice–skate festival, etc. Extra curricular activities are very popular in our university. There are over 200 circles in various field; athletics, culture, technical studies, music, art, etc.

Academic programs for foreign students Japanese course for in–service foreign teacher trainees, Supplement Japanese language class, Tutoring system, Second language transfer of credits system for foreign undergraduate students

Services for foreign students Health clinic, Personal/psychological counseling, College housing, Housing information, Cultural exchange information

Undergraduate Programs

College of Agriculture(801/1)
- **Dept. of Biological Resources**(801/1)

College of Education(1504/4)
- **Course for Social and Informational Studies** (123/0)
- **Course for Training School Teachers for the Deaf**(62/0)
- **Course for Training School Teachers for the Handicapped**(82/0)
- **Lower Secondary School Teachers Training Course**(302/0)

College of Education(1504/4)
- **Preschool Teachers Training Course**(101/0)
- **Primary School Teachers Training Course**(705/0)
- **Special Subject (Music) Teachers Training Course**(129/0)

Faculty of Engineering(2125/12)
- **Dept. of Civil Engineering**(212/0)
- **Dept. of Computer Science**(165/0)
- **Dept. of Electrical Engineering**(186/2)
- **Dept. of Electronics**(207/5)
- **Dept. of Industrial Chemistry**(191/1)
- **Dept. of Materials Science and Engineering**(238/0)
- **Dept. of Mechanical and Industrial Engineering** (200/0)
- **Dept. of Mechanical Engineering**(245/4)
- **Dept. of Ocean Engineering**(269/0)
- **Dept. of Resources Chemistry**(212/0)
- **Dept. of Interdepartmental Courses**(0/0)

Faculty of Law and Literature(2178/2)
- **Dept. of Economics**(652/2)
- **Dept. of Law**(916/0)
- **Dept. of Literature**(610/0)

School of Medicine(656/3)
- **Dept. of Medicine**(656/3)

Faculty of Science(801/2)
- **Dept. of Biology**(143/0)
- **Dept. of Chemistry**(169/0)
- **Dept. of Earth Science**(143/0)
- **Dept. of Mathematics**(179/1)
- **Dept. of Physics**(167/1)

Graduate Programs

Graduate School of Agriculture(M 56/8)

Div. of Agriculture Chemistry(M 16/1)
Soil Science and Plant Nutrition, Utilization of Agricultural Products, Biological Chemistry, Pesticide Chemistry, Applied Microbiology

Div. of Agricultural Engineering(M 11/2)
Land Development Engineering, Agricultural Construction Engineering, Agricultural Hydrotechnics, Hydraulic Engineering and Poldering, Agricultural Environment Control, Agricultural Machinery

Div. of Agriculture(M 4/1)
Plant Breeding, Crop Science, Horticulture, Citriculture, Animal Science

Div. of Environmental Conservation(M 21/3)
Agricultural Meteorology, Physiology of Diseased Plants, Texone–agronomic Entomology, Environmental Microbiology, Ecotoxicology

Div. of Agricultural Managment(M 1/0)
Agricultural Land Utilization, Farm Products Marketing, Agricultural Labor Science, Farm Management

Div. of Forestry(M 3/1)
Silviculture, Forest Engineering, Wood Physics, Forest Policy, Forest Management, Wood Chemistry

United Graduate School of Agricultural Sciences(D 64/44)

Div. of Applied Bioresources Sceince(D 16/11)
Food Science, Bioresources Science for Manufacturing

Div. of Bioresource Production Sceince(D 35/27)
Plant Resource Production, Plant and Animal Production under Stucture, Aquaculture and Livestock Production, Agricultural Economics and Agribusiness

Div. of Life Environment Conservation Science(D 13/6)
Land Conservation and Irrigation Engineering, Environmental Sciences

Graduate School of Engineeing(M 151/6)

Div. of Civil Engineering(M 12/0)
Structural Engineeing, Hydraulic Engineering, Transportation Engineering, Materials of Construction

Div. of Electrical Engineering(M 23/0)
Fundamentals of Electrical Engineering, Electric Machine Engineering, Electric Power Engineering, Applied Electrical Engineering

Div. of Elctronics(M 17/0)
Fundamental Electronics, Electronic Instrument Engineering, Communication Engieering, Applied Elctronics

Div. of Industrial Chemistry(M 21/1)
Industrial Inorganic Chemistry, Industrial Organic Chemistry, Industrial Physical Chemistry, Chemical Engineeing and Polymer Chemistry

Div. of Mechanical and Industrial Engineering(M 16/0)
Materials Science and Engineering, Mechanics of Plasticity, Applied Thermal Engieering, Control Engineering

Div. of Mechanical Engineering(M 19/2)
Strength of Materials, Thermal Engineering, Fluids Engineering, Measurement Engineering, Mechanics of Machinery

Div. of Metallurgy(M 4/0)
Fundamental Materials Science, Applied Materials Science, Science of Materials Development

Div. of Ocean Engineering(M 16/1)
Coastal Oceanography, Marine Metrology, Ocean Construction Engineering, Ocean Exploitation Engineering, Marine Resource Engineering

Div. of Resources Chemistry(M 23/2)
Marine Resources Chemistry, Organic Resources Chemistry, Materials Chemistry, Resources Chemical Engineering

Graduate School of Law(M 14/3)

Div. of Law(M 14/3)
Constitutional Law, Administrative Law, Criminal Law, Law of Criminal Procedure, Civil Law, Commercial Law, Private International Law, Law of Civil Procedure, Labor Law, Economic Law, International Law, Philosophy of Law, Japanese Legal History, European Legal History, Political Science, Political History, History of Political Thought, International Relations, Public Administration, Political Culture

Graduate School of Medicine(D 80/2)

Div. of Ecological Studies(D 14/0)
Immunology and Clinical Genetics, Social and Legal Medicine, Environmental Health

Div. of Functional Studies(D 46/1)
Molecular and Cellular Physiology, Molecular Pathology, Biomedical Science, Clinical Physiology

Div. of Morphological Studies(D 20/1)
Cell Function and Structure, Organ Function and Structure, Physiology and Endocrinology, Cellular Pathology

Graduate School of Science(M 73/3)

Div. of Biology(M 17/2)
Morphology, Ecology, Physiology, Develomental Biology,

Div. of Chemistry(M 23/0)
Analytical and Inorganic Chemistry, Physics Chemistry, Organic Chemistry, Structure Chemistry

Div. of Earth Sciences(M 11/0)
Geology, Mineralogy, Geochemistry, Geophysics

Div. of Mathematics(M 6/1)
Algebra and Geometry, Analysis, Topology, Applied Mathematics

Div. of Physics(M 16/0)
Quantum Physics, Material Physics, Plasma Physics, Applied Physics

One–Year Graduate Programs

Law & Literature Course
Literature Major

Education Course
Music Major

Special Education Course
Speech impairments Major

香川医科大学
(Kagawa Ika Daigaku)
Kagawa Medical School

1750–1 Ikenobe, Miki-cho, Kita-gun, Kagawa 761–07
☎ 0878–98–5111 FAX 0878–98–6186

Founded 1978
Professors 38
Associate Professors 37
Assistant Professors(Tenured) 36
Assistant Professors(Non-tenured) 22
Research Assistants 124
Undergraduate Students/Foreign Students 631/0
Graduate Students/Foreign Students 131/8
Library 83, 212 volumes
Contact: Student Division, Department of School Affairs

Educational philosophy The basic idea behind the School's foundation is to develop a unique school of medicine in which medical research and its services are to be conducted through profound thinking about their effects upon humanity. At the same time, medicine should correspond with developments outside and render its services to the community as well as to the progress of medicine at large.

Foreign students Our School is one of the newly established national medical schools. Considering the relative size of our campus, you will find many advanced training methods and high tech research facilities normally only available at much larger schools.

Environment The campus is located on a low hill to the southeast of Takamatsu City, capital of Kagawa Prefecture. You can see the central part of the City and the Seto Inland Sea in the distance from the campus, and the campus is surrounded by beautiful ponds and greenery rich with bird and insect life. The weather is warm throughout the year. Thus the campus can offer a quiet and favorable environment for education and research.

Facilities School Hospital, School Library, Research Centers(Research Equipment Center • Experimental Animal Center • Radioisotope Research Center), Student Hall, Swimming Pool, Gymnasium, Budo Gymnasium, Baseball Field, Track and Field, etc.

Student activities There are many student clubs, such as soccer, baseball, tennis, basketball, judo, karate, popular and classical music, tea ceremony, etc. They lead active life every day fervently and intellectually.

Academic programs for foreign students Tutoring system(Your guiding professor will select one of his Japanese students as your tutor in order to help your study of specialized field and of Japanese language.)

Services for foreign students Health clinic, Personal/Psychological counseling, Housing information, Social meeting, Trip for information, etc.

Undergraduate Programs

Faculty of Medicine(631/0)
Dept. of Medicine(631/0)

Graduate Programs

Graduate School of Medicine(D 131/8)
Div. of Biological Regulation(D 104/4)
Physiology, Pharmacology, Internal Medicine, Surgery, Endocrinology, Urology, Ophthalmology, Otorhinolaryngology, Neuropsychiatry, Neurological Surgery, Anesthesiology & Emergency Medicine, Orthopedic Surgery, Pediatrics, Clinical Laboratory, Perinato-Gynecology, Radiology, Oral Surgery
Div. of Ecology and Environment(D 9/2)
Environmental Medicine, Biology, Psychology, Forensic Medicine, Immunopathology, Microbiology
Div. of Morphology and Cellular Function(D 18/2)
Anatomy, Pathology, Dermatology, Physiology, Biochemistry, Perinatology

香川大学
(Kagawa Daigaku)
Kagawa University

1–1 Saiwai-cho, Takamatsu-shi, Kagawa 760
☎ 0878–61–4141 FAX 0878–61–5466

Founded 1949
Professors 162
Associate Professors 111
Assistant Professors(Tenured) 9
Assistant Professors(Non-tenured) 67
Research Assistants 38
Undergraduate Students/Foreign Students 4, 546/1
Graduate Students/Foreign Students 78/17
Library 590, 907 volumes
Contact: Student Affairs Division

Foreign students Our University makes efforts to promote receiving foreign students and making fundamental preparations, such as building International Student House and establishing International Exchange Funds.

Environment Kagawa University is situated in Seto Inland-sea National Park. It is in beautiful and quiet environments and suitable for studying. Recently traffic facilities are much improved splendidly because of opening of Seto Ohashi Grand Bridge and New Takamatsu Air Port.

Facilities Attached schools/Center for Educational Research and Training/Computer Center/Gymnasium/Health Care Center/Marine Environment Research Center/Student Hall/Swimming Pool/University Farm/University Library, etc.

Student activities Fresh men's welcome events/ University festival, etc. There are more than 60 extracurricular circles.
Academic programs for foreign students Japanese language and culture course, Supplementary lecture, Tutoring system, etc. (Credits of Japanese language and culture course will be substituted to credits of general education and foreign language.)
Services for foreign students College housing (open in 1991), Cultural exchange program, Health clinic, Homestay/visit, Housing information, Personal/psychological counseling, etc.

Undergraduate Programs

Faculty of Agriculture(806/0)
Dept. of Agricultural Engineering(169/0)
Dept. of Agroindustrial Science(313/0)
Dept. of Bioresource Science(324/0)
Faculty of Economics(1, 657/0)
Dept. of Business Management(746/0)
Dept. of Economics(699/0)
Dept. of Information Science(212/0)
Faculty of Education(1, 234/1)
Elementary School Teachers' Training Course (489/0)
Handicapped Children's Shool Teachers' Training Course(69/0)
Integrated Arts and Sciences Courses(305/0)
Kindergarten Teachers' Training Course(115/1)
Lower Secondary School Teachers' Training Course(256/0)
Faculty of Law(849/0)
Dept. of Law(849/0)

Graduate Programs

Graduate School of Agriculture(M 61/9)
Div. of Agricultural Engineering(M 5/3)
Agricultural Civil Engineering, Regional Engineering
Div. of Agroindustrial Science(M 22/4)
Agroecosystem Management, Agronomy, Horticulture
Div. of Bioresource Science(M 34/2)
Bioresource Chemistry, Cell Biochemistry and Technology, Food Science and Technology
Graduate School of Economics(M 11/7)
Div. of Economics(M 11/7)
Economics History, Economic Policy, Monetary Economics, Public Finance, Social Policy, Statics, Theoretical, Economics
Graduate School of Law(M 6/1)
Div. of Law(M 6/1)
Foundation of Law and Political Science, Private Law, Public Law, Social and Economic Law

One-Year Graduate Programs

Education Course
Education & Science Major
Science Major
Special Education Course
Education for the mentally retarded Major

高知大学
(Kôchi Daigaku)
Kochi University

2-5-1 Akebono-cho, Kochi-shi, Kochi 780
☎ 0888-44-0111 FAX 0888-44-4011

Founded 1949
Professors 153
Associate Professors 127
Assistant Professors(Tenured) 28
Assistant Professors(Non-tenured) 141
Research Assistants 25
Undergraduate Students/Foreign Students 3, 987/10
Graduate Students/Foreign Students 125/24
Library 481, 274 volumes
Contact: The student affairs Kochi University
0888(44)0111(ext.)165 FAX 0888(44)4011

Educational philosophy Kochi Prefecture is the starting for " freedom and people's right movement ", and Japanese Democracy movement, and has produced many men who have influenced the modernization and democratization of Japan. Kochi University aims at teaching and studying unique studies and educations in the atmosphere of freedom and generosity with a cultural and regional background.
Foreign students We believe that foreign students can obtain not only general studies and knowledge but also valuable expreience with the indgenous things of the region.
Environment Kochi Prefecture faces the Pacific Ocean to the south against the backdrop of the Shikoku Mountain Range to the north, and is blessed with a mild climate of four distinct seasons. Kochi University campuses are located in and around. Kochi City, the capital city of Kochi Prefecture has a population of 320, 000, and is situated in the center of the prefecture the Kagami River running through the city. The city, blessed with historic sites, is 7 hours by train and about 1 hour by air from Tokyo. From Osaka, it is 4 hours by train and 1 hour by air.
Facilities Library, Marine Biological Research Center, Data Processing Center, Research Laboratory of Hydrothermal Chemistry, Earthquake Observatory, Reseach and Guidance Center for Teaching Practice, Attached Schools, Institute of System Horticulture, University Farm, University Forest, Health Administration Center, Dormitories, Athletic Establishments, Extracurricular Activities Center.
Student activities Our student activities include a university festival, freshmen welcoming events, and reunions as well as various events of student groups like self-governing student body, student newspaper, athletic community and volunteer activities. Students clubs

consist of 36 athletic clubs(Baseball, Soccer, Rugby, Judo, Karate etc.)and 41 cultural clubs(Chorus, Orchestra, Traditional Japanese Music, Calligraphy, Tea, Ceremony etc.)

Academic programs for foreign students Supplementary Japanese classes, various courses(Japanese and Japanese Studies), Tutoring System.

Services for foreign students Medical checkup and counselings at Health Administration Center, Dormitory and housing information, job information, consultation of Home Stay and Home Visit, International Friendship Gatherings, local cultural exchanges(group or individual)

Undergraduate Programs

Faculty of Humanities and Economics(1, 168/7)
Dept. of The Humanities(522/1)
Dept. of Department of Economics(646/6)
Faculty of Education(1, 050/1)
Dept. of Training Course for Primary School Teachers(412/0)
Dept. of Training Course for Lower Secondary School Teachers(212/1)
Dept. of Training Course for the Teachers of the School for the Mentally and Physically Handicapped(88/0)
Dept. of Special Training Course for Arts and Crafts Teachers(128/0)
Dept. of Special Training Course for Health and Physical Education Teachers(126/0)
Dept. of Division of Interdisciplinary Science(84/0)
Faculty of Science(933/1)
Dept. of Mathematics(201/0)
Dept. of Physics(189/0)
Dept. of Chemistry(196/0)
Dept. of Biology(147/1)
Dept. of Geology(155/0)
Dept. of Information Science(45/0)
Faculty of Agriculture(836/1)
Dept. of Subtropical Agriculture(150/0)
Dept. of Forestry(191/0)
Dept. of Agricultural Chemistry(148/0)
Dept. of Agricultural Engineering(202/0)
Dept. of Cultural Fisheries(145/1)

Graduate Programs

Graduate School of Science(M 50/3)
Div. of Mathematics(M 5/1)
Analysis, Geometry Algebra, statistical and Information Mathematics
Div. of Physics(M 12/0)
Dynamics and Electromagnetism, Solid State Physics, Atomic and Nuclear Physics, Geophysics
Div. of Chemistry(M 13/1)
Inorganic Chemistry, Physical Properties Chemistry, Organic Chemistry, Environmental Chemistry
Div. of Biology(M 9/1)
Taxonomy and Ecology, Developmental Biology and Cell Biology, Function Biology, Marine Biology
Div. of Geology(M 11/0)
Stratigraphy and Paleontoglogy, Petrology and Mineralogy, Marine Geology, Resources Geology
Graduate School of Agriculture(M 55/10)
Div. of Subtropical Agriculture(M 7/4)
Crop Science and Breeding, Vegetable Crop, Pomology Phytopathology and Entomology, Zootechnical Science, Farm Management
Div. of Forestry(M 6/2)
Silviculture, Forest Management, Forest Engineering, Wood Science and Technology, Erosion Control Engineering, Forest Biometrics and Econometrics, Wood Chemistry
Div. of Agricultural Chemistry(M 19/2)
Soil Science and Plant Nutrition, Chemical Technology of Agricultural products, Applied Microbiology, Biological and Nutritional Chemistry, Analytical Agricultural Chemistry, Pesticide Chemistry
Div. of Agricultural Engineering(M 4/1)
Water Utilization Engineering, Land Conservation, Construction Engineering, Water Disaster Prevention Engineering, Agricultural Machinery, Mechanical Engineeing
Div. of Cultural Fisheries(M 19/1)
Aquatic Ecology, Fish Nutrition, Fish Diseases, Aquatic Environmental Science, Fisheries Engineering, Aquatic Product Utilization
The United Graduate School of Agriculture(D 20/11)
Div. of Bioresource Production Science(D 13/7)
Plant, Resource Production, Plant and Animal Production under Structure, Aquaculture and Livestock Production, Agricultural Economics and Agribusiness
Div. of Applied Bioresource Science(D 6/4)
Food Science, Bioresource Science for Manufacturing
Div. of Life Enviornment Conservation Science(D 1/0)
Land Conservation and Irrigation Engineering, Environmental Sciences

---

高知医科大学
(Kôchi Ika Daigaku)
Kochi Medical School

Kohasu, Oko-cho, Nankoku-shi, Kochi 783
☎ 0888-66-5811 FAX 0888-66-2420

Founded 1976
Professors 38
Associate Professors 37
Assistant Professors(Tenured) 27
Assistant Professors(Non-tenured) 159
Research Assistants 132
Undergraduate Students/Foreign Strdents 622/0
Grauate Students/Foreign Students 96/4
Library 83, 418 volumes
Contact: School Affairs Section, School Adminsistration ofice

Educational philosophy The purpose of the School is to train students so that they may achieve a high level of medical knowledge and technique, and to cultivate excellent humanitarian practitioners and researchers of medicine. The Graduate School aims at developing original and up-to-date researchers.
Foreign students We believe that foreign students can enjoy a rewarding experience in our school, and can contribute a great deal to promoting mutual understanding and the development of friendly relations.
Environment The School campus, surrounded by natural beauty, is located about 10 km to the east of Kochi, the main city in southern Shikoku. The area of the school and its hospital is about 204, 000m^2.
Facilities School Library, Medical Information Center, RI Research Center & Institute for Laboratory Animals, Radioisotopic Therapy Facilities, Student Hall, Athletic Ground, Tennis Courts, Swimming Pool, Baseball Ground, Gymnasium, etc.
Student activities Popular campus events includes freshman's orientation, field day, school festival, memorial sevice for cadaver donors. There is a wide variety of extracurricular activities, including archery, golf, yacht, orchestra, tea ceremony, etc.
Academic programs for foreign students Tutoring system
Services for foreign students personal/psychological counseling, Housing information

Undergraduate Programs

Faculty of Medicine(622/0)
Dept. of Medicine(622/0)

Graduate Programs

Graduate School of Medicine(D 96/4)
Div. of Biological Function and Metabolism(D 13/0)
Anatomy, Anesthesiology and Resuscitology, Biochemistry, Clinical Laboratory Medicine, Dentistry and Oral Surgery, Dermatology, Legal Medicine, Geriatric Medicine, Hygiene, Immunology, Internal Medicine, Microbiology, Neuro-Psychiatry, Neurosurgery, Obstetrics and Gynecology, Ophthalmology, Orthopedics, Otorhinolaryngology, Parasitology, Pathology, Pediatrics, Pharmacology, Physiology, Public Health, Radiology, Surgery, Urology
Div. of Developmental and Biological Morphology(D 38/3)
Div. of Etiopathogenesis(D 16/0)
Div. of Regulatory System in the Body(D 29/1)

鳴門教育大学
(Naruto Kyôiku Daigaku)

Naruto University of Education

Takashima, Naruto-cho, Naruto-shi, Tokushima 772
☎ 0886-87-1311 FAX 0886-87-1396
FAX 0886-87-1350

Founded 1981
Professors 73
Associate Professors 51
Assistant Professors(Tenured) 20
Assistant Professors(Non-tenured) 65
Research Assistants 23
Undergraduate Students/Foreign Students 712/0
Graduate Students/Foreign Students 349/3
Library 114, 986 volumes
Contact: Department of General Affairs

Educational philosophy Naruto University of Education offers both graduate and undergraduate programs. It primarily serves to be an institution for in-service teachers to further both practical and theoretical research concerning school education. Its undergraduate program is designed to train students to become elementary or secondary school teachers.
Foreign students We wish that foreign students should have strong will and capacity to study so that they can lead a significant life in our school. So we give an entrance examination and decide acceptance or rejection of foreign students.
Environment Naruto University of Education is located in the suburbs of Naruto City with a population of 65, 000, Tokushima Prefecture, 141 kilometers southwest of Osaka and 664 kilometers west of Tokyo. It was built atop the salt fields of Takashima, today surrounded by channels, a small inland sea, and beautiful hills.
Facilities Universtisy Library, Research Center for School Education, Health Service Center, Training Center for Practical Skills, University Attached Schools(Elementary School, Lower Secondary School, School for the Handicapped, Kindergarten), Gymnasium.
Student activities Freshmen Welcome Party. School Festival, " Mei-cho Sai ", is held every autumn. There is a wide variety of extra-curricular activities, including baseball, Kendou association football, dance, tennis, sado, children's culture, etc..
Academic programs for foreign students A Japanese language follow-up course. Japanese Culture and Circumstances. Education in Japan. Tutoring system.
Services for foreign students Personal Counseling, College Housing(average rents for on-campus housing are ¥2, 780 for single, ¥10, 910 for married. Acceptance to the University does not assure students

of housing)Homestay, Cultural exchange with people of the Naruto City, etc..

Undergraduate Programs

Faculty of Education(712/0)
Dept. of Kindergarten and Elementary School Teacher Training Courses(411/0)
Dept. of Lower Secondary School Teacher Training Course(301/0)

Graduate Programs

Graduate School of Education(M 349/3)
Div. of School Education(M 137/1)
Human development, Education Administration, Methodology, School Guidance and Counseling, Early Childhood Education, Education for the Handicapped, Japanese Language Education, English Language Education, Social Sciences, Mathematics, Natural Sciences(Physics, Chemistry, Biology, Geosciences and Science Education), Music, Fine Atys, Health Physical Education, Industrial Arts, Home Economics
Div. of Education for the Handicapped(M 27/0)
Div. of Specialized Subjects(M 185/2)

徳島大学
(Tokushima Daigaku)
The University of Tokushima

2-24 Shinkura-cho, Tokushima-shi, Tokushima 770
☎ 0886-22-5131 FAX 0886-25-9090

Founded 1949
Professors 225
Associate Professors 167
Assistant Professors(Tenured) 95
Assistant Professors(Non-tenured) 739
Research Assistants 304
Undergraduate Students/Foreign Students 4, 738/9
Graduate Students/Foreign Students 435/22
Library 582, 666 volumes
Contact: Admission Office

Educational philosophy We aim at teaching and studying up-to-date high-level art and sciences to develop intellectual, moral and applied abilities in the Faculties of Integrated Arts and Sciences, Engineering, Medicine, Dentistry and Pharmaceutecal Sciences. Students may therefore contribute much to health for human being, cultural and social improvement.
Foreign students We believe that foreign students can enjoy a rewarding experience in our school, and can contribute a great deal to promoting mutual understanding and the development of friendly relations.
Environment The University of Tokushima, a large national university in the southwest of Japan, is located in the old castle town of Tokushima, at the foot of the gentle, rolling hill of Bizan. In the background are the Shikoku Mountains called the Tibet of Shikoku Island; in the foreground is the fertile delta of the Yoshino River through which the Yoshino flows into the Kii Straits.
Facilities Institute for Enzyme Research, Institute for University Extension, Computer Center, Radioisotope Center, University Hospital, University Dental Hospital, Institute for Animal Experimentation, Medicinal Plant Garden.
Student activities Popular campus events includes Homecoming, school festival, freshmen welcome party. There is a wide variety of extra curriclar activities, including symphony orchestra, art, calligraphy, flower arrangement club, mountaineering, tennis, basketball, football, baseball, etc.
Academic programs for foreign students Supplemental Japanese language class in College of General Education.
Services for foreign students Health clinic, personal/psychological counseling, Students Hall, part-time job information, Cafeteria, Tea Room, Store and Barber.

Undergraduate Programs

School of Dentistry(373/0)
Course in Dentistry(373/0)
Faculty of Engineering(2, 181/9)
Dept. of Biological Science and Technology(122/0)
Dept. of Chemical Science and Technology(357/0)
Dept. of Civil Engineering(373/0)
Dept. of Electrical and Electronic Engineering(515/4)
Dept. of Information Science and Intelligent Systems(313/4)
Dept. of Mechanical Engineerring(501/1)
Faculty of Integrated Arts and Sciences(1, 026/0)
Dept. of Integrated Arts and Sciences(1, 026/0)
School of Medicine(832/0)
Course in Medicine(635/0)
Course in Nutrition(197/0)
Faculty of Pharmaceutical Sciences(326/0)
Dept. of Pharmaceutical Sciences(161/0)
Dept. of Pharmaceutical Technochemistry(165/0)

Graduate Programs

Graduate School of Dentistry(D 46/5)
Div. of Dentistry(D 46/5)
Oral Anatomy, Physiology, Biochemistry, Oral Pathology, Microbiology, Pharmacology, Dental Engineering, Preventive Dentistry, Operative Dentistry, Periodontology and Endodontology, Removable Prosthodontics, Fixed Prosthodontics, Oral and Maxillofacial Surgery, Orthodontics, Pedodontics, Oral Radiology
Graduate School of Engineering(M 218/9)

Div. of Applied Chemistry(M 27/0)
Biological Science, Biological Technology, Synthetic and Polymer Chemistry, Physicochemical and Material Science, Chemical Process Engineering
Div. of Chemical Engineering(M 10/0)
Biological Science, Biological Technology, Synthetic and Polymer Chemistry, Physicochemical and Material Science, Chemical Process Engineering
Div. of Civil Engineering(M 26/2)
Structural Engineering and Design, Disaster Prevention and Environmental Engineering, Geotechnical Engineering, Transportation and Urban Planning
Div. of Construction Engineering(M 16/0)
Structural Engineering and Design, Disaster Prevention and Environmental Engineering, Geotechnical Engineering, Transportation and Urban Planning
Div. of Electrical Engineering(M 25/4)
Materials Science and Device Engineering, Electric Energy Engineering, Circuits, Communications, Controls and Computer Sciences
Div. of Electronic Engineering(M 26/0)
Materials Science and Device Engineering, Electric Energy Engineering, Circuits, Communications, Controls and Computer Sciences
Div. of Information Science and Systems Engineering(M 34/3)
Information and Computer Science, Intelligent Systems Engineering
Div. of Mechanical Engineering(M 29/0)
Mechanical Science, Mechanical System, Intelligent Mechanics
Div. of Precision Mechanics(M 25/0)
Mechanical Science, Mechanical System, Intelligent Mechanics
Graduate School of Medicine(D 68/5)
Div. of Basic Medicine (pathological fields) (D 4/0)
Pathology, Bacteriology, Parasitology, Virology
Div. of Basic Medicine (physiological fields) (M D 14/1)
Anatomy, Physiology, Biochemistry, Pharmacology
Div. of Clinical Medicine (internal medicine) (D 18/1)
Internal Medicine, Psychiatry and Neurology, Pediatrics, Dermatology, Radiology, Laboratory Medicine
Div. of Clinical Medicine (surgical fields) (D 31/3)
Surgery, Orthopedic Surgery, Neurosurgery, Urology, Ophthalmology, Oto-Rhino-Laryngology, Gynecology and Obstetrics, Anesthesiology
Div. of Social Medicine(D 1/0)
Hygiene, Public Health, Forensic Medicine
Graduate School of Nutrition(M 29/0, D 5/2)
Div. of Nutrition(M 34/2, D 29/2)
Nutritional Chemistry, Nutritional Physiology, Food Science, Nutrition of Particular Status, Food Microbiology, Clinico-Pathological Nutrition, Applied Nutrition
Graduate School of Pharmaceutical Sciences (M 54/1, D 15/0)
Div. of Medicinal Chemistry(M 54/1, D 15/0)
Pharmaceutical Life Science(Biochemistry, Health Chemistry, Microbial Chemistry,), Pharmacodynamics and Pharmaceutics(Chemical Pharmacology, Pharmaceutical Analytical Chemistry, Pharmaceutical Physical Chemistry, Pharmaceutics)Medicinal Material and Natural Product Chemistry(Medicinal Biochemistry, Pharmaceutical Chemistry, Pharmacognosy), Medicinal Chemistry(Chemical and Pharmaceutical Technology, Physical Pharmacy, Synthetic Pharmaceutical Chemistry)

Local Public Universities

高知女子大学
(Kôchi Joshi Daigaku)
Kochi Women's University

5–15 Eikokuji–cho, Kochi–shi, Kochi 780
☎ 0888–73–2156 FAX 0888–73–8551

Founded 1949
Professors 33
Associate Professors 19
Assistant Professors (Tenured) 1
Assistant Professors (Non–tenured) 151
Research Assistants 11
Undergraduate Students/Foreign Students 728/0
Library 133, 892 volumes
Contact: Admission Office

Educational philosophy Kochi Women's university progressed over the years from its predecessor, Kochi Women's College founded in 1947 to the present four–year public university in 1949 founded by Kochi Prefecture. Throughout its history, we have aimed at improving higher education for women in Japan.
Foreign students We are currently working on improvingour qualification process for admitting foreign students.
Environment The campus is located in the heart of Kochi City, Population 320, 000. Surrounded by the Shikoku mountains in the north and Pacific Ocean in the south, the area is famous for its natural beauty. The city has many educational institution.
Facilities Facilities within the university include library, gymnasium and computer, cooking laboratories, etc.
Student activities Popular campus events include the university festival, and the freshmen welcome party. There is a wide variety of extra curriclar activities. In particular, club demonstrations held by the mandolin club and the koto club each year are very popular among students and citizens.

Undergraduate Programs

Faculty of Home Economics(372/0)
  Dept. of Food and Nutrition(91/0)
  Dept. of Home Economics(95/0)
  Dept. of Nursing(95/0)
  Dept. of Science of Living(91/0)
Faculty of Literature(356/0)
  Dept. of English(168/0)
  Dept. of Japanese(188/0)

Private Universities

松山大学
(Matsuyama Daigaku)
Matsuyama University

4–2 Bunkyo–cho, Matsuyama–shi, Ehime 790
☎ 0899–25–7111 FAX 0899–25–1420

Founded 1949
Professors 87
Associate Professors 29
Assistant Professors (Tenured) 19
Assistant Professors (Non–tenured) 136
Undergraduate Students/Foreign Students 5, 907/12
Graduate Students/Foreign Students 17/1
Library 470, 514 volumes
Contact: Registrar's Office

Educational philosophy True to its three–fold credo of " truth, faith, and use, " the University seeks to foster research in various areas of knowledge and to relate it to current needs and future concerns of society. Above all, the University is devoted to the education of the whole person through integrated programs in general education, career preparation, and campus life.
Foreign students Since its birth 64 years ago, Matsuyama University has always been known for its intellectual vigor and its emphasis on relevant aspects of learning, its close relationship between students and faculty members, its searching examination of values, and its cohesive educational programs as solid foundations for success in personal, professional, and civic life.
Environment To meet the challenges of an ever changing world, the University attempts to develop a community in which learning and teaching will flourish and create a campus environment in which innovative student life may support academic goals.
Facilities Research Institute for Economics and as Business Administration
Services for foreign students all full–time faculty members serve advisors.

Undergraduate Programs

Faculty of Economics(1997/3)
  Dept. of Economics(1997/3)
Faculty of Business Administration(2056/4)
  Dept. of Business Administration(2056/4)
Faculty of Humanities(1126/4)
  Dept. of English(525/0)
  Dept. of Sociology(601/4)
Faculty of Law(728/1)
  Dept. of Law(728/1)

Graduate Programs

Graduate School of Economics(M 1/1, D 2/0)
Graduate School of Business Administration(M 12/0, D 2/0)

四国学院大学
(Shikoku Gakuin Daigaku)
Shikoku Christian College

3-2-1 Bunkyo-cho, Zentsuji-shi, Kagawa 765
☎ 0877-62-2111 FAX 0877-62-3961

Founded 1950
Professors 26
Associate Professors 26
Assistant Professors(Tenured) 6
Assistant Professors(Non-tenured) 133
Undergraduate Students/Foreign Students 1, 970/8
Graduate Students/Foreign Students 9/0
Library 143, 000 volumes
Contact: International Relations Section

Educational philosophy We aim at educating our students to develop in them a higher level of culture, and to encourage them to search for truth in learning, so that they may serve God and the people, following the principles laid down by Christ revealed in the Bible.
Foreign students We emphasize international relations, and enjoy having students and faculty of various nationalities. We believe that foreign students can enjoy a rewarding experience here, and can contribute a great deal to promoting mutual understanding and friendly relations.
Environment The city of Zentsuji, celebrated as the birthplace of Kukai, is a small and quiet rural city with a population of 38, 000. In spite of its locality, because of the Seto Great Bridge, Zentsuji is within one hour of Okayama, two hours of the Osaka and Kobe area.
Facilities Library, language laboratory, gymnasium, health center, chapel, student center, theater, seminar house, etc.
Student activities Campus events include college festival(called Shigakusai), freshman welcome party, play day, college picnic, religion emphasis weeks, and others. There is a wide variety of extra curricular activities, both sports and cultural.
Academic programs for foreign students Japanese, and Japan studies, and other independent studies.
Services for foreign students They are entitled to all rights given to college students: e. g. personal counseling, dormitory, housing information, part-time job information.

Undergraduate Programs

Faculty of Literature(1, 970/8)
  Dept. of English Literature(377/1)
  Dept. of Social Welfare(415/1)
  Dept. of Humanities(405/1)
  Dept. of Education(376/1)
Faculty of Sociology(397/4)

Graduate Programs

Graduate School of Social Welfare(M 9/0)

四国女子大学
(Shikoku Joshi Daigaku)
Shikoku Women's University

123-1 Ebisuno, Furukawa, Ojin-cho, Tokushima 771-11
☎ 0886-65-1300 FAX 0886-65-8037

Founded 1961
Professors 30
Associate Professors 10
Assistant Professors(Tenured) 10
Assistant Professors(Non-tenured) 65
Research Assistants 10
Undergraduate Students/Foreign Students 1, 125/1
Library 184, 064 volumes
Contact: Office of International Programs

Educational philosophy Our first aim is to provide our students with academic knowledge and technical skills in response to the needs of the changing world, as well as enjoyment of college life. Varieties of programs are designed to enrich understanding and awareness of the world around us and to develop personal growth of each students.
Foreign students We believe that our foreign students can have an academically and socially satisfactory college life in a comfortable learning environment at SWU, and will enhance cross-cultural exchange and understanding of the SWU students.
Environment Tokushima City, with a population of 260, 000 is only a thirty minute flight from Osaka. Ten minutes drive from the center of the city brings you to the SWU campus located along the River Yoshino full of greenery.
Facilities Library, Education Center for Information Processing(Computer Center), Center for Experimental Instruments, Music Hall, Research Center for Calligraphy, Gymnasium, Club House, Swimming pool, Attached Kindergarten, Workshop for Indigo Dyeing
Student activities Popular campus events includes orientation seminars for freshmen, studies abroad program, summer programs, university festival, sports meet. Club Activities: Tea ceremony, Calligraphy, Flower arrangement, Japanese music, Drama, Japanese archery, Halberd, Volleyball, Softball, Tennis, etc.

Academic programs for foreign students There is a special program for foreign students in the liberal arts course: Japanese language and culture. Some of the subjects can be replaced by other alternatives. Supplementary tutorial support will be provided.
Services for foreign students Health clinic, Personal Counseling, Dormitories, International Culture Exchange Meeting

Undergraduate Programs

Faculty of Home Economics(566/1)
- **Dept. of Home Economics Science of Clothing Course**(49/0)
- **Dept. of Home Economics Science of School-Health Course**(93/0)
- **Dept. of Pedology**(275/1)
- **Dept. of Training Administrative Dietitians**(149/0)

Faculty of Literature(559/0)
- **Dept. of English Language and Literature**(131/0)
- **Dept. of Japanses Language and Literature**
  - Calligraphy Course(289/0)
  - Japanese Literature Course(139/0)

聖カタリナ女子大学
(Sei Katarina Joshi Daigaku)

St. Catherine Women's College

660 Hojo, Hojo-shi, Ehime 799-24
☎ 0899-93-0702 FAX 0899-93-0900

Founded 1987
Professors 13
Associate Professors 4
Assistant Professors(Tenured) 6
Assistant Professors(Non-tenured) 23
Research Assistants 4
Undergraduate Students/Foreign Students 378/0
Library 65, 000 volumes
Contact: General Affairs Department or Instruction Department

Educational philosophy Educational philosophy is based on the spiritual foundation of our College which aims at teaching and studying in the idea of the Catholic humanism so that students may contribute with charity to the people in the field of social welfare.
Foreign students We hope that foreign students can have the opportunity to study academic and cultural investigation with our students and have many and useful experiences of mutual understanding and knowledge.
Environment The town of Hojo, with a population of 30, 000, is surrounded with beautiful mountains and sea, and is very peaceful to live, 30 minutes by car or train from the city of Matsuyama where is the place of historical and literary atmosphere.
Facilities College Library with AV Corner, Computer Room, Gymnasium, Cafeteria, Christian Culture Center(in course of prepartion)
Student activities Popular campus events including Freshmen Study Tour, The Blessed Mary Procession in May, Sports Day, College Festival, Speech Contest, Christmas Mass and Party. There are extra curricular activities including volunteer works, student news paper, etc.
Services for foreign students College Housing for all students who want it.

Undergraduate Programs

Faculty of Social Welfare(378/0)
- **Dept. of Social Welfare**

徳島文理大学
(Tokushima Bunri Daigaku)

Tokushima Art and Science University

1-8 Terashimahon-cho, Tokushima-shi, Tokushima 770
☎ 0886-22-0097 FAX 0886-26-2998

Founded 1895
Professors 90
Associate Professors 41
Assistant Professors(Tenured) 24
Assistant Professors(Non-tenured) 130
Research Assistants 56
Undergraduate Students/Foreign Students 2, 969/0
Graduate Students/Foreign Students 34/2
Library 243, 446 volumes
Contact: Kokusai-bu Yamashiro-cho, Tokushima-shi 770
☎ 0886-22-9611

Educational philosophy On our educational principle " Independence of human beings " which is based on the idea of Sai Murasaki, the founder, we aim at bringing up a person who has an international relationship and has an intelligence and humanity.
Foreign students We believe that foreign students can get advanced educations under favorable circumstances. We welcome foreign students as we pay attention to the international educations.
Environment Tokushima Campus: It is located at the southern part of the old Tokushima city. It covers 200, 000 square meters and has 17 lecture and research buildings. Kagawa Campus: It is on the sunny hill in Shido-cho, a town east of Takamatsu city. It covers 200, 000 square meters and has 13 intelligent buildings.
Facilities Both Tokushima and Kagawa campus have a library and a gymnasium. And we have a reserch institute for bio-medicine in Tokushima and a laboratory of comparative literature in Kagawa, and

about 900 general purpose and personal computers.

Student activities The school year is divided into two terms: the first half(Apr. 1〜Sept. 20)the second half(Sept. 21〜Mar. 31). Students activities Arts: music, tea ceremony, flower arrangement, etc. Sports: baseball, basketball, pingpong, aikido, etc.

Services for foreign students We have division of International Education and a full-time teacher who can do services for foreign students.

Undergraduate Programs

Faculty of Domestic Science(539/0)
- **Dept. of Domestic Science**(Domestic Science Course/Managerial Nutritionist Course)(322/0)
- **Dept. of Juvenile Education**(Pedagogic Course/Juvenile Education Course)(217/0)

Faculty of Enginnering(411/0)
- **Dept. of Information Science and Systems Engineering**(203/0)
- **Dept. of Mechanical-Electronic Engineering**(208/0)

Faculty of Literature(783/0)
- **Dept. of English and American Literature**(395/0)
- **Dept. of Japanese Literature**(388/0)

Faculty of Music(204/0)
- **Dept. of Music**(204/0)

Faculty of Pharmaceutical Science(1032/0)
- **Dept. of Hygienic Pharmacy**(273/0)
- **Dept. of Pharmaceutics**(759/0)

Graduate Programs

Graduate School of Pharmaceutical Science(M 24/1, D 10/1)

Pharmaceutical Chemistry, Analytical Chemistry, Pharmacognosy, Medicinal Chemistry, Phamacology, Pharmacy, Bio-organic Medicinal Chemistry, Hygienic Chemistry, Biochemistry

KYUSHU

KYUSHU REGION CLIMATE

Broad north-south temperature difference.
Region generally warm, with heavy rainy season and typhoon impact.

- Northern District
  Winters fairly cool.
- Southern District (Pacific Ocean Side)
  Heavy summer rainfall, warm winters.

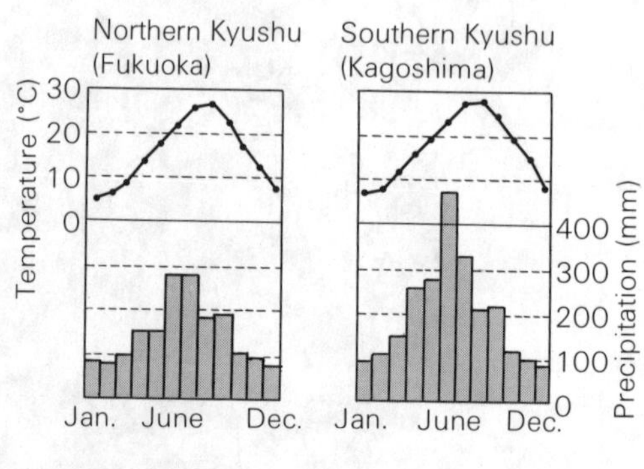

	Northern Kyushu (Fukuoka)	Southern Kyushu (Kagoshima)
Average annual temperature	16.0°C	17.3°C
Annual precipitation	1,690mm	2,375mm

National Universities

福岡教育大学
(Fukuoka Kyôiku Daigaku)

Fukuoka University of Education

729 Akama, Munakata-shi, Fukuoka 811-41
☎ 0940-32-2381 FAX 0940-32-2390

Founded 1949
Professors 106
Associate Professors 67
Assistant Professors (Tenured) 23
Assistant Professors (Non-tenured) 176
Research Assistants 15
Undergraduate Students/Foreign Students 3, 178/7
Graduate Students/Foreign Students 96/10
Library 399, 068 volumes
Contact: Student Affairs Bureau, Academic Affairs Department, Committee Administration Section

Educational philosophy The University performs mainly four functions; 1) to give research and educate special studies profoundly. 2) to develop the knowledge and technologies widely. 3) to train educational specialists of ability. 4) to contribute to the cultural development and improvement of international friendly relations among nations.

Foreign students We want to receive foreign students from all over the world according to our philosophy of education.

Environment Since ancient times, Munakata has been an important area for exchange between Kyusyu and Continent, so it is rich in history and there are many archaeological sites near the University. Munakata is located midway between 2 large cities of Fukuoka and Kitakyusyu and her population is constantly growing.

Facilities Library: The World Textbook Collection. Gymnasium: Equipemtn for Volleyball, Table tennis, Basketball, Badminton, etc. Information Processing Centei. On going computer learning operations.

Student activities April: Welcome-party for foreign students. October: Study trip (studying about society, history and culture of Japan). December: Xmas party. March: Good-bye party for foreign students.

Academic programs for foreign students Supplementary tuition: " Advanced Japanese " " Intermediate Japanese ", " Education in Japan ", " Japanese Culture " and " Comparative Studies about Educational Cultures " Student Tutorial System: (first 1 or 2 years for each kind of foreign students)

Services for foreign students Counseling for the students: held at the Health Center, Housing: Kyusyu Univ. International House, some private apartment house, etc. Home-stay, Cultural exchange events: held by invitation from the community

Undergraduate Programs

Faculty of Eucation (3, 178/7)

Primary School Teachers Course (Japanese) (251/0)
Primary School Teachers Course (Social Science) (269/0)
Primary School Teachers Course (Mathematics) (257/0)
Primary School Teachers Course (Natural Science) (198/0)
Primary School Teachers Course (Music) (98/0)
Primary School Teachers Course (Fine Arts) (127/0)
Primary School Teachers Course (Health and Physical Education) (151/0)
Primary School Teachers Course (Home Economics) (102/0)
Primary School Teachers Course (Educational Science • Educational Psychology) (201/1)
Junior High School Teachers Course (Japanese) (66/0)
Junior High School Teachers Course (Social Science) (59/0)
Junior High School Teachers Course (Mathematics) (82/0)
Junior High School Teachers Course (Natural Scinece) (83/0)
Junior High School Teachers Course (English) (65/0)
Junior High School Teachers Course (Music) (60/0)
Junior High School Teachers Course (Fine Arts) (58/1)
Junior Highe School Teachers Course (Health and Physical Education) (94/0)
Junior High School Teachers Course (Home Economics) (51/0)
Junior High School Teachers Course (Industrial Arts) (50/0)
Handicappod Children Teachers Couse (235/0)
Kindergarten Teachers Course (139/5)
Senior High School Teachers of Mathematics Course (145/0)
Senior High School Teachers of Science Course (141/0)
Senior High School Teachers of Calligraphy Course (65/0)
Senior High School Teachers of Health and Physical Education Course (131/0)

Graduate Programs

Research Divisions of Education (M 96/10)

Div. of School Education (M 18/0)

Theory of Educational, Environment and Organization, Theory of Educational Process and Practice, Theory of Human Development and Education

Div. of English Language Education(M 3/0)
English Language Teaching Methodology, English/American Literature and Linguistics
Div. of Fine Arts(M 12/3)
Arts Education, Fine Arts
Div. of Health and Physical Education(M 6/2)
Teaching Methodology of H. & P. E, Science of Physical and Biomechanics Education, Health Education
Div. of Home Economics(M 9/2)
Home Economics Education, Home Economics
Div. of Japanese(M 3/0)
Japanese Teaching Methodology, Japanese Language and Literature
Div. of Mathematics(M 7/0)
Mathematics Education, Mathematics
Div. of Music(M 15/2)
Music Education, Musicology, Music Performance
Div. of Natural Science(M 15/1)
Science Education, Natural Science
Div. of Special Education(M 8/0)
Education of Handicapped Chidren

鹿児島大学
(Kagoshima Daigaku)

Kagoshima University

1-21-24 Korimoto, Kagoshima-shi, Kagoshima 890
☎ 0992-54-7141 FAX 0992-57-2658

Founded 1949
Professors 309
Associate Professors 276
Assistant Professors(Tenured) 103
Assistant Professors(Non-tenured) 650
Research Assistants 346
Undergraduate Students/Foreign Students 8, 961/15
Graduate Students/Foreign Students 583/73
Library 1, 048, 689 volumes
Contact: Admission Office

Educational philosophy Kagoshima University offers opportunity for research and study in a wide variety of fields. Students are expected to cultivate their intellectual, moral and practical abilities so that they can contribute to the progress of science and culture.
Foreign students The University aims at helping foreign students to acquire skills needed for the promotion of mutual understanding in an international community.
Environment The campus is located in the center of Kagoshima city which has a population of about half a million. The city, surrouded by rich natural environment, is the southern gateway of Japan. Overlooking the city across Kinkoo bay is the famous volcano Mt. Sakurajima. The University serves as a focus for cultural life in Southern Kyushu.
Facilities Library, Computer center, Research center for the south pacific, Health service center, Gymnasium, Swimming pool
Student activities Campus events include school festival, welcome and farewell party. There is a wide variety of extra curricular activities, choral groups, orchestra, drama, baseball, football, soccer, etc.
Academic programs for foreign students Supplemental Japanese language courses, Tutoring system
Services for foreign students Health clinic, Personal/psychological counseling, Housing information, Part-time job information, Home stay, Home visit, and Cultural exchange program

Undergraduate Programs

Faculty of Agriculture(1, 161/2)
Dept. of Agricultural Sciences and Natural Resources(146/1)
Dept. of Biochemical Science and Technology(61/1)
Dept. of Environmental Sciences and Tecnology(65/0)
Dept. of Veterinary Medicine(192/0)
Faculty of Dentistry(492/1)
Dept. of Dentistry(492/1)
Faculty of Education(1, 544/0)
Elementary School Education Course(883/0)
Health and Physical Education Course(76/0)
Secondary School Education Course(443/0)
Special Course for Physical Education(142/0)
Faculty of Engineering(1, 895/9)
Dept. of Applied Chemistry(172/0)
Dept. of Architecture and Architectural Engineering(290/1)
Dept. of Chemical Engineergn(207/2)
Dept. of Electrical Engineering(215/0)
Faculty of Engineering(1, 895/9)
Dept. of Electronic Engineering(221/5)
Dept. of Information and Computer Science(81/1)
Dept. of Mechanical Engineering(Ⅰ)(232/0)
Dept. of Mechanical Engineering(Ⅱ)(212/0)
Dept. of Ocean Civil Engineering(265/0)
Faculty of Fisheries(674/0)
Dept. of Fisheries(674/0)
Faculty of Law and Letters(1, 686/1)
Dept. of Economics(569/1)
Dept. of Humanities(550/0)
Dept. of Law(567/0)
Faculty of Medicine(714/1)
Dept. of Medicine(714/1)
Faculty of Science(795/1)
Dept. of Biology(133/0)
Dept. of Chemistry(169/0)
Dept. of Earth Sciences(123/0)
Dept. of Mathematics(196/1)
Dept. of Physics(174/0)
School of Allied Medical Sciences(363/0)
Dept. of Nursing(238/0)
Dept. of Occupational Therapy(65/0)
Dept. of Physical Therapy(60/0)

Graduate Programs

Graduate School of Agriculture(M 54/3)

Div. of Agriculture(M 9/2)

Crop Science, Tropical Crop Science, Plant Breeding, Plant Pathology, Entomology Agricultural Economics and Policy, Agricultural Marketing, Farm Management

Div. of Forestry(M 2/0)

Siliviculture, Forest Managemant, Forest Policy, Forest Genetics and Protection, Wood Technology and Forest Product Chemistry, Forest Civil Engineering and Erosion Control

Div. of Agricultural Chemistry(M 17/0)

Soil Science, Plant Nutrition and Fertilizers, Biochemistry and Nutritional, Chemistry Applied Microbiology, Applied Starch Chemistry, Chemistry and Technology of Agricultural Products

Div. of Animal Breeding(M 22/0)

Animal Biochemistry, Animal Nutrition, Animal Products Processing Research, Animal Reproduction, Animal Breeding, Animal Management

Div. of Agricultural Engineering(M 2/1)

Lrrigation and Drainage, Engineering, Farm Land Engineering, Farm Power and Machinery, Food and Agricultural Process Engineering, Agricultural Physics

Div. of Horticulture(M 2/0)

Fruit Science, Vegetable Crops, Ornamental Horticulture and Floriculture, Postharvest Physiology and Preservation of Fruits and Vegetables

Graduate School of Cultural Science(M 23/5)

Div. of Basis of Culture(M 9/1)

Basis of Culture, Human Behaviour, Regional Relationship

Div. of Regional Cultures(M 14/4)

Japanese Culture, Asian Culture, Western Culture

Graduate School of Dental Science(M 45/2)

Div. of Dentistry(D 45/2)

Oral Anatomy, Oral Physiology, Biochemistry, Pathology, Microbiology, Pharmacology, Dental Materials Science, Preventive Dentistry, Conservative Dentistry, Prosthetic Dentistry, Oral and Maxillofacial Surgery, Orthodontics, Pediatric Dentistry, Dental Radiology

Graduate School of Engineering(M 176/7)

Div. of Mechanical Enginerring(I)(M 20/0)

Mechanics of Materials, Steam Engineering and Heat Transfer, Hydraulic Engineering, Metallurgy and Production Engineering

Div. of Mechanical Engineering(II)(M 16/0)

Engineering Materials Science, Internal Combustion Engineering, Fluid Mechanics, Presision Engineering

Div. of Electrical Engineering(M 20/0)

Fundamentals in Electrical Engineering, Electric Machinery, Electric Power Engineering, Electrical Communication

Div. of Architecture(M 26/3)

Building Materials and Construction, Structural Engineering, Structural Mechaics, Architectural Planning, History of Arichitecture and Architectural Design, Build Equipment

Div. of Applied Cheimistry(M 37/1)

Applied Physical Chemistry, Industrial Inorganic Chemistry, Industrial Organic Chemistry, Organic Synthetic Chemistry

Div. of Chemical Engineering(M 24/1)

Transport Phenomena, Industrial Physical Chemistry, Chemical Reaction Engineering, Unit Operations

Div. of Electronics Engineering(M 20/1)

Fundamentals in Electronics, Electronics Circuits, Electronics Measurements, Electronics Control Systems

Div. of Ocean Civil Engineering(M 13/1)

Fundamental Oceanography for Engineering, Marine Structural Engineering, Marine Construction, Planning of Marine Civil Engineering, Coastal and Harbor Engineering

Graduate School of Fisheries(M 44/6)

Div. of Fisheries(M 44/6)

Physical Oceanography, Engineering Oceanography, Marine Botany and Environmental Science, Marine Biology, Fish Resources, Aquacultural Physiology Marine Resources Biochemistry, Marine Resources Nutrition, Chmistry, Microbiology, Food Chmistry, Food Presevation Science, Food Analysis and Quality Control, Fishing Gear Science, Fishing Technology, Fishing Vessel Navigation, Fishing Vessel Seamanship, International Marine Policy, Fisheries Business, Economics, Fisheries Enviormental Sociology

Graduate School of Law(M 16/2)

Div. of Law(M 16/2)

Constitutuional Law, Adminstrative Law, Criminal Law and Criminal Procedure, Civil Law, Commercial Law, Law of Civil Procedure, Labor Law and Economic Law, International Law and Legal History and Legal Philosophy, Politics

Graduate School of Medical Science(D 97/8)

Div. of Physiology(D 5/1)

Anatomy, Physiology, Biochemistry, Pharmacolgy

Div. of Pothology(D 20/0)

Pathology, Bacteriology, Virology, Medical Zoology, Oncology

Div. of Social Medicine(D 5/4)

Environmental Medicine, Public Health, Legal Medicine

Div. of Internal Medicine(D 40/2)

Internal Medicine, Rehabilitation Medicine, Neuropsychiatry, Pediatrics, Dermatology, Radiology, Laboratory Medicine, Clinical Pharmacy

Div. of Surgery(D 27/1)

Surgery, Neurosurgery, Orthopedic Surgery, Urology, Ophthalmology, Otolaryngology, Obstetrics and Gynecology, Anesthesiology, Pediapric Surgery

Graduate School of Science(M 58/0)

Div. of Mathematics(M 8/0)

Analysis, Algebra, Geometry, Probability Theory and Statistics, Information Theory

Div. of Physics(M 14/0)

Atomic Physics, Solid State Physics, Applied Physics

Div. of Chemistry(M 10/0)

Physical Chemistry, Inorganic and Analytical Chemistry, Biological Chemistry, Organic Chemistry

Div. of Earth Sciences(M 11/0)

Petrology and Mineralogy, Geology and Paleontology, Applied Geology, Geophysics, Volcanology

Div. of Biology(M 15/0)

Cell Biology, Physiology, Biosystematics, Environmental Biology

Graduate School of United Agricultural Sciences(D 70/40)

Div. of Science of Bioresource Production(D 22/13)

Plant Resource Production, Animal Production, Science of Forest and Agricultural Resources

Div. of Bioresource Science for Processing(D 14/7)

Applied Biological Chemistry, Applied Resource Chemistry

Div. of Life environment Conservation Science(D 14/8)

Bioenvironment and Plant Protection Science, Agricultural Engineering

Div. of Science of Marine Resources(D 20/12)

Marine Production and Environmental Studies, Applied Science of Marine Resources

One-Year Graduate Programs

Education Course

Physical Education Major

General Education Major

Fisheries Course

Pelagic Fisheries Major

熊本大学

(Kumamoto Daigaku)

Kumamoto University

2-39-1 Kurokami, Kumamoto-shi, Kumamoto 860

☎ 096-344-2111 FAX 096-345-9562

Founded 1949
Professors 344
Associate Professors 285
Assistant Professors(Tenured) 57
Assistant Professors(Non-tenured) 875
Research Assistants 256
Undergraduate Students/Foreign Students 7, 866/14
Graduate Students/Foreign Students 833/53
Library 1, 019, 283 volumes
Contact: Student Bureau 2-40-1 Kurokami, Kumamoto-shi, Kumamoto 860 ☎ 096-344-2111 FAX 096-345-4914

Educational philosophy We seek to develop in our students a deep theoretical and practical understanding of a special field within the context of a wide range of general knowledge so that they may contribute to the intellectual, moral, and cultural welfare of society.

Foreign students Foreign students from all parts of the world currently pursue undergraduate, graduate, and research programs. They are an essential part of the university's commitment to education in a global environment.

Environment Kumamoto City, population 580, 000, is located in the center of Kyushu, one and a half hours from Tokyo and one hour from Osaka by air. It is a castle town with abundant greenery and hot springs, surrounded by the scenic Amakusa Islands and volcanic Mt. Aso.

Facilities Cooperative Research Center, University Hospital, University Library, Marine Biological Center, Engineering Research Equipment Center, Laboratory Animal Rsearch Center, Sports Training Center, Swimming Pool, etc.

Student activities Popular campus events include Homecoming, school festival, freshmen welcome party. There is a wide variety of extracurricular activities, aikido, judo, karate, kendo, kyudo(Japanese archery), sado(tea ceremony), ikebana(flower arrangement), baseball, football, soccer, tennis, etc.

Academic programs for foreign students Supplemental Japanese language class, Tutoring system (two years for undergraduates and one year for graduate students.)

Services for foreign students Health Center, personal/psychologcal counseling, College housing, Housing information, part-time job information, Homestay, Home visit, cultural exchange program

Undergraduate Programs

Faculty of Education(1, 662/2)

Elementary School Teacher's Curriculum(968/0)

Junior High School Teacher's Curriculum(365/0)

Special Education Teacher's Curriculum(85/1)

High School Nurse Teacher's Curriculum(83/1)

School Health Teacher's Curriculum(161/0)

Faculty of Engineering(2, 606/9)

Dept. of Applied Chemistry(403/1)

Dept. of Architecture and Building Science(230/1)

Dept. of Civil and Environmental Engineering(434/1)

Dept. of Electrical Engineering and Computer Science(673/6)

Dept. of Materials Science and Resource Engineering(407/0)

Dept. of Mechanical Engineering(459/0)

Faculty of Law(1, 136/0)

Dept. of Law(1, 136/0)

Faculty of Letters(776/2)

Dept. of History(192/1)

Dept. of Literature(301/1)

Dept. of Philosophy(124/0)

Dept. of Regional Science(159/0)

Faculty of Medicine (Medical School) (687/0)

Faculty of Pharmaceutical Sciences(385/0)

Faculty of Science(601/0)

Dept. of Biology(58/0)

Dept. of Biological Science(39/0)

Dept. of Chemistry(112/0)
Dept. of Geology(130/0)
Dept. of Mathematics(155/0)
Dept. of Physics(107/0)

Graduate Programs

Graduate School of Education(M 53/4)
Div. of School Education(M 13/1)
Cinical Psychology, Developmental Psychology, Educational Methodology, Educational Psychology, Educational Sociology, History of Education, Moral Education, Pedagogy, School Administration
Div. of Special Education(M 4/0)
Education of Handicapped Children, Pathology of Handicapped Children, Psychology of Handicapped Children
Div. of Teaching Methodology(M 36/3)
Algebra, Analysis, Applied Mathematics, Biology, Chemistry, Clothing, Cookery, Domestic Technology, Earth Science, Economics, Electricity, Ethics, Food, Geography, Geometry, Home Management, Japanese History, Law, Metalworking, Mechanics, Physics, Politics, Sociology, Teaching of Home Economics, Teaching of Mathermatics, Teaching of Science, Teaching of Social Studies, World History
Graduate School ov Engineering(M 276/14)
Div. of Architecture(M 23/1)
Architectural and Environmental Design, Building Structure and Construction, Environmental Control
Div. of Applied Chemistry(M 49/2)
Biorelated Chemistry, Chemistry of Industrial Materials, Fundamental Industrial Chemistry
Div. of Applied Mechanics and Mathematics
Stochastic Process, Control Theory, Fuzzy Theory and Fuzzy Systems Engineering
Div. of Civil and Invilonmental Construction Engineering(M 36/3)
Geotechnical and Disaster Prevention Engineering, Hydraulic and Coastal Engineering, River Engineering and Hydrogy, Sanitary Engineering, Environmental Engineering and Groundwater Hydrology, Structural Mechanics and Engineering, Urban Economics, Land Use, and Transportation
Div. of Electrical Engineering and Computer Science(M 62/7)
Circuits Systems and Electronic Devices, Communication Systems, Electrical Energy, Information Processing Systems, Instrumentation and Control Engineering
Div. of Mechanical Engineering(M 55/1)
Casting and Welding, Control Engineering and Instrumentation, Fluid Mechanics, High Energy Rate Laboratory, Mechanical Dynamics and Control Theory, Mechanics of Materials, Metal Cutting and Machine Tools, Metal Working and Processing, Plasticity and Metal Working Processes, Thermal Engineering
Div. of Metallrugical Engineering(M 27/0)
Materials Engineering, Physical Metallurgy, Procesa Metallurgy, Technological Metallurhy
Div. of Resource Development and Mechanical Engineering(M 24/0)
Hydrodynamics and Aerodynamics, Rock Mechanics and Mining Science
Graduate School of Law(M 16/1)
Div. of Law(M 16/1)
Criminology, Economics, Legal Theory and History, Politics, Private Law, Public Law, Social Law
Graduate School of Letters(M 45/8)
Div. of English Literature(M 12/0)
Comparative Literature(Japanese and European Literature), English Language, English Literature, French Language, French Literature
Div. of German Literature(M 0/0)
Austronesian Language, General Linguistics, German Language, German Literature, Indo-European Languages, Iranian Language
Div. of History(M 9/0)
Archaeology in Japan and East Asia, Chinese History, European History, History of Social Thought in Modern Japan and Europe, Japanese History
Div. of Japanese Literature(M 11/4)
Comparative Literature(Chinese Classics and Japanese Literature), Chinese Language, Chinese Literature, Japanese Language(9th to 16th centuries), Japanese Literature(16th to 19th centuries)
Div. of Philosophy(M 6/0)
Western Philosophy
Div. of Regional Science(M 7/4)
Family, Folklore, Geography, Medical Sociology, Migration, Social Gerontology, Sociology
Graduate School of Medicine(D 182/6)
Div. of Physiology(D 13/3)
Anatomy, Biochemistry, Medical Genetics, Bioregulation, Medical Genetics, Cytogenetics, Medical Genetics, Genetic Epidemiology, Medical Genetics, Molecular Genetics, Medical Immunology, Biochemistry, Medical Immunology, Biology, Medical Immunology, Pharmacology, Pharmacology, Physiology
Div. of Pathology(D 4/3)
Biodefence, Medical Genetics, Developmental Biology, Medical Genetics, Experimental Genetics, Medical Immunology, Pathology, Medical Immunology, Allorgy, Microbiology, Pathology, Parasitic Diseases
Div. of Social Medicine(D 1/0)
Hygiene, Legal Medicine, Public Health
Div. of Internal Medicine(D 92/0)
Cardiology, Child Development, Dermatology, Internal Medicine, Laboratory Medicine, Metabolic Medicine, Neuropsychiatry, Pediatrics, Radiology
Div. of Surgery(D 72/0)
Anesthesiology, Dentoral Surgery, Neurosurgery, Obstetrics and Gynecology, Ophthalmology, Orthopedic Surgery, Otorhinolaryngology, Surgery, Urology
Graduate School of Natural Science and Technology(D 62/9)
Div. of Industrial Science(D 21/2)
Applied Chemistry of Materials, Energy and Resources, Industrial Technology
Div. of systems Science(D 12/1)
Electric Circuits and System Engineering, Mathematical Science, Systems and Information Science

Div. of Environmental Science(D 26/9)
Disaster–Preventive Structural Engineering, Environmental Preservation Engineering, Natural Environmental Science, Regional and Environmental Design

Graduate School of Pharmaceutical Sciences(M 72/1, D 22/1)

Div. of Hygienic Chemistry(M 22/0, D 2/0)
Biochemistry, Hygienic Chemistry, Pharmaceutical Analytical Chemistry, Radiopharmaceutical Chemistry

Div. of Medicinal Chemistry(M 22/0, D 7/0)
Organic Chemistry, Pharmaceutical Engineering, Pharmacognosy, Synthetic Medicinal Chemistry

Div. of Phamaceutics(M 18/1, D 10/1)
Biopharmaceutics, Hospital Pharmacy, Physical Pharmaceutics

Div. of Pharmacological Sciences(M 12/0, D 3/0)
Chemico–Pharmacology, Medicinal Microbiology, Pharmaceutical Physical Chemistry

Graduate School of Science(M 62/4)

Div. of Biology(M 15/3)
Animal Physiology and Biochemistry, Animal Systematics and Morphology, Plant Physiology and Biochemistry, Plant Systematics and Morphology

Div. of Chemistry(M 18/1)
Analytical Chemistry, Inorganic Chemistry, Organic Chemistry, Physical Chemistry

Div. of Geology(M 10/0)
Economic Geology, Geology and Paleontology, Geotectonics, Petrology and Mineralogy

Div. of Mathematics(M 5/0)
Algebra, Analysis, Applied Analysis, Geometry, Mathematical Statistics

Div. of Physics(M 14/0)
Atomic and Molecular Physics, Elementary Particle Physics, Radiation Physics, Solid State Physics

One–Year Graduate Programs

Special Education Course
Teaching of the Mentally Retarded Major

九州芸術工科大学

(Kyûshû Geijutsukôka Daigaku)

Kyushu Institute of Design

4–9–1 Shiobaru, Minami–ku, Fukuoka–shi, Fukuoka 815
☎ 092–553–4419 FAX 092–553–4598

Founded 1968
Professors 33
Associate Professors 20
Assistant Professors(Tenured) 3
Assistant Professors(Non–tenured) 69
Research Assistants 16
Undergraduate Students/Foreign Students 691/7
Graduate Students/Foreign Students 77/6
Library 107, 392 volumes
Contact: Admission Office

Educational philosophy We aim at training students to be designers who have a good sense of art and a sufficient knowledge of not only natural sciences but also the humanities and social sciences.

Foreign students We believe that foreign students can enjoy friendly relations with academic staff because the proportion of academic staff to all students is very high(about one to seven).

Environment The campus is located in an urban area near the center of Fukuoka, which is the biggest city in Kyushu. The campus buildings and garden are beautifully arranged.

Facilities Information Processing Center, Multi–purpose Building, Design Workshop, Environmental Research Center, Biotron(Climatron), Visual Communication Design Center, Printing Workshop, Acoustic Research Center

Student activities Popular campus events includes school festival, concert, lecture meetings, exhibitions, athletic meets. There is a wide variety of extra curricular activities, including drama, orchestra, yacht, baseball, basketball, soccer, etc.

Academic programs for foreign students Japanology for overseas students(The Japanese language, introduction to Japan Ⅰ, Ⅱ), Tutoring system

Services for foreign students Health clinic, personal/psychological counseling, Dormitory(male undergraduate students only, no special dormitory for foreing students), Housing information, Home stay, Home visit, cultural exchange program

Undergraduate Programs

Faculty of Design(691/7)
Dept. of Acoustic Design(169/0)
Dept. of Environmental Design(180/1)
Dept. of Industrial Design(163/4)
Dept. of Visual Communication Design(179/2)

Graduate Programs

Graduate School of Design(M 77/6)

Div. of Living Environmental Studies(M 41/3)
Theory of Environmental Design, Environmental Design Practice, Ergonomic and Mechanic Design, Product and Interior Design

Div. of Audio and Visual Communication Studies(M 36/3)
Theory of Visual Communcation Design, Visual Communcation Design, Science of Acoustical Environment, Science of Acoustical Information

九州工業大学

(Kyûshû Kôgyô Daigaku)

Kyushu Institute of Technology

1-1 Sensui-cho, Tobata-ku, Kitakyushu-shi, Fukuoka 804
☎ 093-871-1931 FAX 093-883-1531

Founded 1907
Professors 125
Associate Professors 106
Assistant Professors (Tenured) 33
Assistant Professors (Non-tenured) 130
Research Assistants 65
Undergraduate Students/Foreign Students 4, 570/20
Graduate Students/Foreign Students 381/30
Library 345, 215 volumes
Contact: Instruction Division (Foreign Student Section)

Educational philosophy We aim at not merely imparting knowledge and technical skills but also in developing personalities of the students to contribute at their best for the betterment of the society and in the development of high technology in the 21st century.

Foreign students We have accepted many foreign students since 1917. Hereafter we are ready to welcome more excellent students from overseas.

Environment The university is located in the north of Kyushu island. Historically, this area has played a major role as a gateway in the intercourse between Japan and the Asian continent, was developed and have progressed into an important industrial area.

Facilities Information Science Center, Center for Cooperative Research, Library Microelectronic Systems Center, Health Administration Center, Memorial Auditorium Historical Materials Building, Swimming Pool, Activities House, Gymnasium

Student activities Popular various campus events includes the annual university-wide school festival, the winter long-distance relay race, and different sports festivals. There is a variety of extracurricular activities and sports clubs.

Academic programs for foreign students To the undergraduate students, we offer Japanese language classes and Japanese culture studies which can be considered as substitute to other subjects as approved by the university.

Services for foreign students Personal counseling, housing information, part-time job information, home-stay programs, home visits to the local residents, and many cultural exchange programs are available.

Undergraduate Programs

Faculty of Computer Science and Systems Engineering (1400/3)

Dept. of Artificial Intelligence (360/1)

Dept. of Biochemical Engineering and Science (158/0)

Dept. of Computer Science and Electronics (357/2)

Dept. of Control Engineering and Science (268/0)

Faculty of Mechanical System Engineering (257/0)

Faculty of Engineering (3170/17)

Dept. of Applied Chemistry, and Material Science and Engineering (1002/0)

Dept. of Civil, Mechanical and Control Engineering (1162/7)

Dept. of Electrical, Electronic and Computer Engineering (1006/10)

Graduate Programs

Graduate School of Engineering (M 324/13, D 57/17)

Div. of Applied Chemistry, and Materials Science and Engineering (M 103/1, D 17/6)

Organic and Biological Chemistry, Material Processing and Chemical Engineering, Materials Chemistry, Metal Materials

Div. of Civil, Mechanical and Control Engineering (M 133/6, D 25/6)

Construction Engineering, Material Sciences. Production Engineering, Fluid Engineering, Heat and Mass Transfer, Applied Dynamics and Control Engineering

Div. of Electrical, Electronic and Computer Engineering (M 88/6, D 15/5)

Electrical Engineering Fundamentals, Electronic Physics. Electron Device Engineering, Electric Power System, Systems and Control Engineering, Computer Engineering

九州大学

(Kyûshû Daigaku)

Kyushu University

6-10-1 Hakozaki, Higashi-ku, Fukuoka-shi, Fukuoka 812
☎ 092-641-1101 FAX 092-641-4509

Founded 1911
Professors 532
Associate Professors 484
Assistant Professors (Tenured) 110
Assistant Professors (Non-tenured) 1, 348
Research Assistants 933
Undergraduate Students/Foreign Students 40
Graduate Students/Foreign Students 278
Library 25, 290 volumes
Contact: Admission Office, International Affairs Section, Student Office, Student's Guidance Section

Educational philosophy We aim at teaching and studying the special science, contribute to compose the peaceful and democratic society, being conscious of the position that we are one of the leading figures of high–level learning, with the base on the fundamental law regarding education.

Foreign students We make every endeavor to strengthen the system for foreign students, hope that their study and life in our university grow their spiritual nourishment and the development of exchange with their countries.

Environment Fukuoka city, with a population of 1,200,000, is in the north of Kyushu, looks toward to the sea, has a variety of historic remains which is academically important. Moreover, Fukuoka is the principal point of the cultural exchange with foreign countries from ancient times to now.

Facilities Library, Institute of Language and Cultures, Institute of Health Science, Computer Center, Biotron Institute, Research Institute for Applied Mechanics, Center of Advanced Instrumental Analysis, Radiosotope Center, Research Center for Materials on Coal Mining

Student activities Orientation for freshmen, School festival, Sports festival. Besides Students' association and University newspaper, there is a great variety of extracurricular activities, such as E. S. S, science research, music, baseball, tennis, golf, yacht, etc.

Academic programs for foreign students Japanese language classes in Education center for foreign students, Tutoring system, Japanese and Japanese affairs classes in College of General Education, supplementally lesson for foreign students.

Services for foreign students Health clinic, the house for foreign students named " International House ", Housing information, part–time job information, cultural exchange program and social gathering in " Annex " which is attached to Education center for foreign students.

Undergraduate Programs

Faculty of Agriculture(1, 117/1)
Dept. of Agricultural Chemistry(86/0)
Dept. of Agricultural Economics(52/0)
Dept. of Agricultural Engineering(78/0)
Dept. of Agronomy(69/0)
Dept. of Animal Science(45/0)
Dept. of Fisheries(40/0)
Dept. of Food Science and Technology(85/1)
Dept. of Forest Products(48/0)
Dept. of Forestry(39/0)
Faculty of Dentistry(425/4)
Dept. of Dentistry
Faculty of Economics(1, 188/6)
Dept. of Business Economics(200/2)
Dept. of Economics(186/2)
Dept. of Economic Engineering(210/0)
Faculty of Education(219/0)
Faculty of Engineering(3, 633/10)
Dept. of Aeronautical Engineering(117/1)
Dept. of Applied Chemistry(91/0)
Dept. of Applied Nuclear Engineering(170/0)
Dept. of Architecture(280/2)
Dept. of Chemical Engineering(177/0)
Dept. of Civil Engineering(93/0)
Dept. of Civil Engineering Hydraulics and Soil Mechanics(110/0)
Dept. of Computer Science and Communication Engineering(135/0)
Dept. of Electrical Engineering(145/0)
Dept. of Electronics(113/1)
Dept. of Materials Science and Engineering(289/0)
Dept. of Mechanical Engineering(139/0)
Dept. of Mechanical Engineering for Power(116/0)
Dept. of Mechanical Engineering for Production(112/0)
Dept. of Mining(158/0)
Dept. of Naval Architecture(150/2)
Dept. of Organic Synthesis(89/0)
Faculty of Law(1, 133/1)
Faculty of Literature(702/4)
Dept. of History(105/1)
Dept. of Literature(135/1)
Dept. of Philosophy(107/1)
Faculty of Medicine(736/13)
Dept. of Medicine(736/13)
Faculty of Pharmaceutical Sciences(339/0)
Dept. of Pharmaceutical Sciences(82/0)
Dept. of Pharmaceutical Technology(79/0)
Faculty of Science(1, 267/1)
Dept. of Biology(246/1)
Dept. of Chemistry(334/0)
Dept. of Earth and Planetary Sciences(80/0)
Dept. of Mathematics(292/0)
Dept. of Physics(315/0)

Graduate Programs

Graduate School of Agriculture (M 198/8, D 108/39)

Div. of Agriculture Proper(M 19/1, D 28/12)
Plant Breeding, Crop Science, Horticulture, Crop Husbandry, Plant Pathology, Bntomology, Sericultural Science, Fruit Science, Environment Control in Biology

Div. of Agricultural Chemistry(M 28/1, D 11/5)
Soil Chemistry and Mineralogy, Soil Fertility and Plant Nutrition, Soil Microbiology and Biochemistry, Applied Microbiology, Biochemistry, Pesticide Chemistry, Applied Phytochemistry

Div. of Forestry(M 9/2, D 6/3)
Forest Management, Erosion Control, Silviculture, Forest Policy, Biophysics

Div. of Technology of Forest Products(M 19/1, D 6/2)
Wood Science, Wood Technology, Wood Chemistry, Industrial Chemistry of Wood, Polimer Chemistry of Woody Materials

Div. of Fishery Sciences(M 12/1, D 18/4)
Marine Biology, Fisheries Biology, Fisheries Chemisty, Fisheries, Technology, Fisheries Environmental Science

Div. of Agricultural Engineering(M 23/0, D 8/4)
Irrigation and Water Utilization, Drainageand Reclamation, Land, Land Improvement and Conservation, Agricutural Meteorology, Agricultural Machinery, Agricutural Process Engineering, Mechanics for Bio-Production

Div. of Animal Science(M 12/0, D 10/2)
Animal Breeding and Reproduction, Functional Anatomy and Physiology of Domestic Animals, Zoology, Chemistry and Technology of Animal Products, Forage Science and Animal Behaviour

Div. of Agricultural Economics(M 1/0, D 3/1)
Agricultural Economics, Agricultural Policy, Quantitative Analysis of Agricultural Economics, Farm Management, Agricultural Marketing

Div. of Food Science and Technology(M 33/0, D 18/6)
Nutrition Chemistry, Food Chemistry, Food Analysis, Food Technology, Microbial Technology, Food Hygienic Chemistry, Food Quality Control

Div. of Genetic Resources Technology(M 42/2)
Molecular Geno Technics, Protein Chemistry and Engineering, Celluar Regulation Technology, Plant Breeding, Microbial Genetic Resources, Plant Genetic Resources, Insect Genetic Resources

Graduate School of Dental Science(D 87/8)

Div. of Basic Science(D 6/1)
Oral Anatomy, Oral Physiology, Oral Biochemistry, Oral Pathology, Oral Microbiology, Dental Pharmacology, Dental Materials Engineering

Div. of Clinical Science(D 81/7)
Preventive Dentistry, Conservative Dentistry, Prosthetic Dentistry, Oral Surgery, Orthodontics, Pediatric Dentistry, Dental Radiology, Dental Anesthesiology

Graduate School of Economics(M 29/11, D 33/7)

Div. of Economics(M 11/5, D 10/4)
Economic Theory, Economic History, Economic Analysis and Policy

Div. of Business Economics(M 9/5, D 12/1)
Business Administration, Business Acounting

Div. of Economic Engineering(M 9/1, D 12/2)
Economic Mathematics, Econometrics, Industrial Planning, Management Engineering

Graduate School of Education(M 22/4, D 35/4)

Div. of Education(M 13/4, D 12/2)
Philosophy of Education, History of Education, Comparative Education, Educational Administration, Educational Sociology, Social Education, Methodology of Education

Div. of Educational Psychology(M 32/2, D 9/2)
Educational Psychology, Group Dynamics, Counselling, Science of Disabled Children

Graduate School of Engineering (M 656/20, D 126/49)

Div. of Civil Engineering(M 44/6, D 35/5)
Structural Mechanics, Bridge Engineering, Structures for Civil Engineering, Execution of Works and Concrete Engineering, Railway Engineering, Road Engineering

Div. of Civil Engineering Hydraulics and Soil Mechanics(M 38/3, D 7/3)
Applied Hydraulics, Soil Mechanics, River Engineering, Coastal Engineering, Water Supply and Water Resources Engineering, Sewage Engineering

Div. of Architecure(M 49/3, D 8/7)
Steel Structures; Structural Mechanics, Reinforced Concrete Structures; Structural Mechanics, Earthquake and Wind Engineering, Building Materials; Construction Methods, Environmental Planning in Architecture, Environmental Engineering in Architecture, Architectural Planning, Urban Design and City Planning, History and Theory of Architecture

Div. of Electrical Engineering(M 64/4, D 9/5)
Laser and Optoelectronic Devices, Solid Sate Functional Devices, Functional Material and System Engineering, System Control Engineering, Plasma Engineering, Energy Conversion Machinery, Electric Power System

Div. of Electronics(M 40/0, D 21/6)
Electronic Circuits, Computer System Electronic Measurement Engineering, Solid State Electronics, Industrial Electronics

Div. of Computer Science and Communication Enginering(M 46/3, D 9/4)
Fundamentals of Information and Networks, Computer and Comunication Systems, Wave Theory and Applications, Information Processing, Computer Hardware and Communication Devices, Electronic Elements in Computers and Communication Devices, Computer Software, Date and Knowledge Engineering, Pattern Processing

Div. of Mechanical Engineering(M 52/1, D 5/3)
Mechanics of Machinery, Machine Structure and Strength, Fluid Mechanics, Heat Transfer, Fluid Machinery, Steam Thermodynamics, Gas Thermodynamics, Combustion, Machine Design

Div. of Mechanical Engineering for Production(M 12/0, D 2/0)
Machining, Metal Processing, Tools and Machine Tools, Automatic Control, Design and Planning for Production, Precision Surface Finishing

Div. of Mechanical Engineering for Power(M 23/0, D 5/3)
Dynamics of Machinery, Thermodynamics, Air Science, Steam Power, Internal Combustion Engineering

Div. of Chemical Engineering(M 45/1, D 4/0)
Applied Physical Chemistry, Chemical Reaction Process, Unit Operations, Heat Transfer in Chemical Engineering, Fluid Flow in Chemical Engineering, Design of Chemical Appratus, Process Control

Div. of Applied Chemistry(M 45/2, D 10/2)
Structual Inorganic Chemistry and High-Temperature Chemistry, Polymer Chemistry and Material Science of Polymers, Chemical Rection Engineering, Industrial Organic Chemistry

Div. of Organic Synthesis(M 43/0, D 14/1)
Quantum Chemistry; Theoretical Organic Chemistry, Chemistry of Enzyme and Catalysis, Synthetic Chemistry of Low Molecular Compounds, Synthetic Macromolecular Chemistry, Organic Anlytical Chemistry, Chemical Process Design; Chemical Process Control

Div. of of Mining(M 19/0, D 2/1)
Minig Engineering, Mining Machinery, Mineral

Processing, Economic Geology, Exporation Geophysics, Geothemics

Div. of Metallurgy(M 21/1, D 0/0)

Technology of Metal Working, Non–Ferrous Metallugy, Material Processing, Physical Metallurgy; Non–Ferrous Alloys

Div. of Iron and Steel Metallurgy(M 22/0, D 1/1)

Ferrous Metallurgy, Physical Chemistry of Metals, Material Science of Iron and Steel, Surface Chemistry of Metals

Div. of Naval Architecture(M 20/0, D 6/2)

Strength and Vibration of Ships, Hydrodynamics and Dynamics of Ships, Structure of Ships; Design of Merchant Ships, Resistance and Propulsion of Ships, Technical Theory of Shipbuiding; Equipments of Merchant Ships, Welding Engineering for Hull Construction; Design of Welding

Div. of Applied Mechanics(M 32/1, D 6/4)

Aircraft Structure, Materials and Design, Aircraft Dynamics, Performance and Propulsion, Aircraft Strength and Vibration, Aerodynamics, Aircraft Equipment Control and Guidance, Aero–Enginers, Space Systems Engineering

Div. of Nuclear Engineering(M 32/0, D 6/2)

Nuclear Instrumentation, Radiation Measurement and Protection Engineering, Science and Technology of Radiation Effects, Nuclear Fuel Technology, Nuclear Chemical Engineering, Nuclear Mechanical Engineering

Div. of Applied Physics(M 18/0, D 2/0)

Reactor Engineering, Reactor Materials Science, Applied Mathematics, Industrial Statistics, Dynamics, Applied Physics, Physical Chemistry, Mechanics and Strength of Solids, Analytical Chemistry; Instrumental Analysis, General Electric Engineering

Graduate School of Law(M 17/3, D 20/5)

Div. of Legal Theory(M 4/1, D 2/0)

Philosophy of Law, Japanese Legal History, Western Legal History, Angro–American Law, Social Law

Div. of Public Law(M 5/2, D 5/2)

Constitutional Law, Cpmparative Constitution, Administrative Law, Theory of Public Administration, International Law

Div. of Judicial Law(M 6/0, D 6/3)

Civil Law, Commercial Law, Law of Civil Procedure, Criminal Law, Law of Criminal Procedure, Science of Judical Process, Criminal Policy, International Private Law

Div. of Social Law(M 0/0, D 2/0)

Social Law, Economic Law

Div. of Political Law(M 2/0, D 5/0)

Political Science, History of Political Science, Political History and Diplomatic History, International Political Science

Graduate School of Literature(M 95/13, D 119/23)

Div. of Philosophy and History of Philosophy(M 11/1, D 22/7)

Philosophy and History of Philoslphy, Indian Philosophy, Ethics, Aesthetics and History of Fine Arts

Div. of Sociology(M 11/0, D 8/0)

Sociology, Sociology of Regional Welfare, Science of Religion

Div. of Psychology(M 1/1, D 9/1)

Psychology

Div. of Chinese Philosophy and Literature(M 8/7, D 12/0)

Chinese Philosophy, Chinese Literature

Div. of History(M 28/4, D 34/12)

Japanese History, Oriental History, Occidental History, Korean History, Archeology, Geography

Div. of Japanese Language and Literature(M 13/0, D 6/4)

Japanese Language and Literature

Div. of English Language and Literature(M 8/0, D 11/0)

English Language and Literature

Div. of German Literature(M 6/0, D 7/0)

German Literature

Div. of French Literature(M 7/0, D 7/0)

French Literature

Div. of Linguistics(M 2/0, D 3/1)

Linguistics

Graduate School of Medical Science(D 198/36)

Div. of Physiological Science(D 11/5)

Anatomy, Physiology, Pharmacology, Clinical Pharmacology, Fundamental Radiotherapeutics

Div. of Pathological Science(D 12/6)

Pathology, Bacteriology, Virology, Parasitology

Div. of Social Medicine(D 2/0)

Public Hygiene, Hygiene, Forensic Medicine

Div. of Internal Medicine(D 56/5)

Internal Medicine, Pediatrics, Neutro–Psychiatry, Radiology, Dermatology, Psychosomatic Medicine

Div. of Surgery(D 71/9)

Surgery, Orthopedic Surgery, Gynecology and Obstetrics, Pediatric Surgery, Opthalmology, Oto–Rhino–Laryngology, Urology, Anesthesiology

Div. of Molecular Medical Sciences(M 15/5)

Cell Structure, Genetic Biochemistry, Cellular Biochemistry, Molecular Pharmacology, Molecualr Oncology, Immunogenetics, Molecular Immunology

Div. of Molecular Biology(D 31/6)

Molecular Cell Biology, Protein Engineering, Protein Chemistry, Membrane Physiology, Molecular Population, Gene Reguration

Graduate School of Pharmaceutical Sciences (M 86/2, D 33/7)

Div. of Pharmaceutical Sciences(M 45/1, D 21/4)

Pharmacognosy, Hygienic and Forensic Chemistry, Physiological Chemistry, Pharmacology, Analytical Chemistry, Chemistru of Micrrorganisms, Pharmaceutics

Div. of Pharmaceutical Technology(M 41/1, D 12/3)

Pharmaceutical Technology, Physical Chemisty, Pharmaceutical Chemistry, Plant Chemistry, Pharmaceutical Synthetic Chemistry, Radiation Chemistry

Graduate School of Science(M 232/6, D 99/7)

Div. of Mathematics(M 28/0, D 15/0)

Algebra, Geometry, Analysis, Functional Analysis, Topology, Mathematical Statistics, Mathematics of Programming and Control, Mathematics of Computation,

Mathematical Analysis

Div. of Physics(M 65/2, D 35/2)

Theory of Elementary Particles, Theoretical Nuclear Physics, Nuclear Reaction, Nuclear Spectroscopy, Statistical Theory of Matter, Low Temperature Physics, Semicouductor Physics of Magnetic Materials, Applied Physics, Geophysics, Atmospheric Physics, Seismolgy, Upper Atmosphere Dynamics

Div. of Chemistry(M 75/2, D 21/3)

Inorganic Chemistry, Organic Chemistry, Structural Chemistry, Physical Chemistry, Analytical Chemistry, Biochemistry, Synthetic Orgsnic Chemistry, Radiochemistry, Quantum Chemistry, Polymer Chemistry, Coordination Chemistry, Enzymeu Chemistry, Theortical Chemistry

Div. of Geology(M 18/1, D 5/1)

Stratigraphy, Petrology, Mineralogy, Palaeontology, Coal Geology of Nonmentallic Deposits

Div. of Biology(M 46/1, D 23/1)

Animal Physiology, Cytogentics, Developmental Biology, Plant Physiology, Ecology, Molecular Genetics, Physical Biology, Protein Chemistry, Biochemistry, Theoretical Biology

Interdisciplinary Graduate School of Enginneering Sciences(M 352/7, D 76/18)

Div. of Materials Science and Technology(M 61/1, D 13/1)

Science of Structural Materials, Strcture of Noncrystalline Materials, Functional Inorganic Materials, Functional Organic Materials, Quantum Theory of Matter. Theory of Functional Materials, Properties of Polymers, Extreme–Cicumstances Materials

Div. of Molecular Science and Technology(M 64/0, D 25/5)

Molecular Spectroscopy, Molecular Reaction Dynamics, Molecular Dersign, Chemical Reactions of Excited Molecules, Selectivity in Organic Reactions, Chemistry of Reactive Species, Technology of Functional Molecules

Div. of High Energy Engineering Science(M 36/1, D 6/0)

Fundamental Plasma Physics, Mathematical Physics of Nonlinear Systoms, High–Energy Plasma Phsics, Fusion Science and Technology, Radiation Damage of Solids, Dynamic Solid Mechanics, High Energy Science of Material Strength

Div. of Energy Conversion Engineering(M 74/0, D 10/3)

Fundamentals for Energy Comversion, Nuclear Energy Conversion Engineering, Gas Dynamics for Energy Conversion, Appliction of Atomic Energy, Inized Gas Engineering, Thermodynamics for Energy Conversion, System Control for Energy Conversion, Engineeing for Enegy Conversion Plant

Div. of Thermal Energy System(M 53/3, D 13/7)

Urban Thermal Environment, Thermal Environment of Buildings, Heat and Mass Transfer, Thermal Energy Transport, Machines and Equipments of Thermal Energy Conversion System, Utilization of Dilute Energy

Div. of Information Systems(M 48/1, D 9/2)

Information Recognition Recognition, Organization of Information, Information Transmission, Compytational Lingustics, Information Models, Information Analysis and Retrieval Systems, Phusics of Computer Elements

Div. of Earth System Science and Technology(M 16/1)

Geofluid Systems Dynamics, Ocean Environment Engineering, Ocean System Engineering, Underwater System Control, Wind Engineering, Ocean and Atmosphere Circulation Dynamics, Environmental Transpot–and Transfiguration–Processes, Dynamics of Waves in Fluids, Atmosphere–Ocean Interaction Dynamics

---

大分医科大学
(Ôita Ika Daigaku)
Medical College of Oita

1–1 Idaigaoka, Hasama–machi, Oita–gun, Oita 879–56
☎ 0975–49–4411 FAX 0975–49–3338

Founded 1976
Professors 39
Associate Professors 40
Assistant Professors(Tenured) 24
Assistant Professors(Non–tenred) 127
Research Assistants 119
Undergraduate Students/Foreign Students 617/0
Graduate Students/Foreign Students 90/1
Library 69, 514 volumes
Contact: Administration Office

Educational philosophy Our basic principles include the study of modern medical science, pursuit of advanced research, the maintenance and improvement of national health, the inculcation of the moral responsibilities in the medical field, and the instillation of a sense of community obligation.

Foreign students The presence of research students from overseas of high ability and potential helps to create a stimulating environment for the College. We believe that it can act as the focal point for mutual understanding on a global scale.

Environment The City of Oita is a fast–growing metropolis of 400, 000 with an idyllic location between the sea and mountains. It offers countless hot springs and mountain resorts. There is ample open space and the semitropical climate is ideal most of the year.

Facilities College Library, College Hospital, Research Laboratory Center, Animal Laboratory Center, Radioisotope Laboratory Center, Gymnasium, Gyms for *Kendo*, *Judo*, *Kyudo*, etc.

Student activities The main areas of student activity include clubs, societies, sport, entertainments, etc. Intercollegiate athletic meet, choral group performances, school festival, freshman welcoming party, etc, are also among them.

Academic programs for foreign students You will be allocated to your own tutor who will supervise your research and progress. Supplemental Japanese

language classes will not be available.
Services for foreign students Counseling by your own tutors. Accommodations(3 students only)at International House. Cultural exchange with local groups. Excursions, study trips, parties.

Undergraduate Programs

Faculty of Medicine(617/0)
Dept. of Medicine

Graduate Programs

Graduate School of Medicine(D 90/1)
Div. of Morphology(D 20/0)
Morphology and Function, Development, Differentiation and Oncogenesis Clinical Imaging Diagnosis
Div. of Physiology(D 22/1)
Bio–information Processing, Movement and Behavioral Control, Circulation and Respiration
Div. of Biochemistry(D 25/0)
Pharmacology and Toxicology, Metabolism and Gastro-enterology, Endocrinology and Metabolic Disorders
Div. of Ecology(D 23/0)
Pathogens and Infection, Inflammation and Immunology, Social Medicine

---

宮崎医科大学
(Miyazaki Ika Daigaku)

Miyazaki Medical College

5200 Kihara, Kiyotake–cho, Miyazaki–gun, Miyazaki 889–16
☎ 0985–85–1510 FAX 0985–85–0693

Founded 1974
Professors 34
Associate Professors 27
Assistant Professors(Tenured) 32
Assistant Professors(Non–tenured) 147
Resrarch Assistants 136
Undergraduate Students/Foreign Students 639/1
Graduate Students/Foreign Students 62/1
Libray 91, 907 volumes
Contact: Admission Office

Educational philosophy Our college offers up–to–date knowledge of medicine and aims at turning out doctors and researchers of high medical morality and integrity who place human life above all. It is our mission to contribute to the enhancement of medical standards and social welfare.
Foreign students We welcome those students who have the sufficient ability to use the Japanese language, basic knowledge needed for the study of medicine, and willingness to serve society as doctors or researchers.
Environment Our college is located in Miyazaki Prefecture at the south end of Japan. Kiyotake, where our college stands, is 6 miles from Miyazaki City. It is an academic town of scenic beauty and quietude with a population of about 20, 000.
Facilities College Library, Center for Student Health, College Hospital, Experimental Animal Center, Electron Microscope Center, RI Center, as well as such facilities as Gymnasium, Students' Common, etc.
Student activities Many students are active participants in such events as Welcome Party for Freshmen, Residential Training, College Festival, Music Festival. They also belong to one or more of 14 cultural and 20 athletic clubs and organizations.
Academic programs for foreign students Tutoring System
Services for foreign students Personal/psychiatric and medical counseling, Housing information, Part–time job information, Cultural exchange program

Undergraduate Programs

Faculty of Medicine(639/1)
Dept. of Medicine

Graduate Programs

Graduate School of Medicine(D 62/1)
Psychology, Sociology, Mathematics, Physics, Chemistry, Biology, English, German, Anatomy Physiology, Biochemistry, Pharmacology, Pathology, Microbiology, Hygiene, Public Health, Parasitology, Forensic Medicine, Internal Medicine, Psychiatry, Pediatrics, Surgery, Orthopedics, Dermatology, Urology, Ophthalmology, Otorhinolaryngology, Obstetrics and Gynecology, Radiology, Anesthesiology, Neurosurgery, Oral and Gynecology, Radiology, Anesthesiology, Neurosurgery, Oral and Maxillofacial Surgery

---

宮崎大学
(Miyazaki Daigaku)

Miyazaki University

1–1 Gakuen Kibana–Dai Nishi, Miyazaki–Shi, Miyazaki 889–21
☎ 0985–58–2811 FAX 0985–58–2865

Founded 1949
Professors 104
Associate Professors 132
Assistant Professors(Tenured) 34
Assistant Professors(Non–tenured) 111
Research Assistants 41
Undergraduate Students/Foreign Students 3, 646/13
Graduate Students/Foreign Students 135/17
Library 407, 753 volumes

Educational philosophy Miyazaki University provides the opportunity for studens to become citizens with aesthetic sensitivity who love truth and justice in a peaceful society. The University has contributed to the improvement and development of studies in specialized fields and local culture through its research and teaching.

Foreign students We believe that foreign students can enjoy a rewarding experience in our school, and can contribute a great deal to promoting mutual understanding and the development of friendly relations.

Environment The University is located in a semi-tropical climate. Its research and teaching is related to the realistic problems of the local production area. The University can also contribute to research and teaching at an international level by utilizing the local resourses.

Facilities The University Library has the function of collecting, classifying, preserving, and serving academic materials such as books, magazines, and several kinds of documents which are necessary for research and teaching.

Student activities Club activities, along with hard study, are the indispensable part of a campus life. The University encourages the students to join extra-curricular activities suitable for each student's preference and ability. Students can take the opportunity to gain many friends to make their student life more fruitful and healthy. By overcoming some hardships with their friends, students can have many lasting and happy memories of their wonderful students' life.

Academic programs for foreign students We have special academic programs for foreign students, including supplementary Japanese language classes and special lecture in the general education.

Services for foreign students Health clinic; personal/psychological counseling; student dormitory; part-time job information; cultural exchange program

Undergraduate Programs

Faculty of Agriculture(691/0)
- **Dept. of Agriculture and Forest Sciences**(241/0)
- **Dept. of Animal Grassland and Fishery Sciences** (151/0)
- **Dept. of Biological Resource Sciences**(119/0)
- **Dept. of Veterinary Science**(180/0)

Faculty of Agriculture(544/2)
- **Dept. of Agricultural Chemistry**(97/0)
- **Dept. of Agricultural Engineering**(88/0)
- **Dept. of Agronomy**(89/2)
- **Dept. of Animal Science**(67/0)
- **Dept. of Fisheries**(84/0)
- **Dept. of Forestry**(64/0)
- **Dept. of Grassland Science**(55/0)

Faculty of Education(1, 186/6)
- **Dept. of Elementary School Teachers**(431/0)
- **Dept. of Junior High School Teachers**(223/6)
- **Dept. of Kindergarten Teachers**(107/0)
- **Dept. of Teachers for the Handicapped**(74/0)
- **Dept. of Music (Training Courses by Subject)** (89/0)
- **Dept. of Science (Training Courses by Subject)** (110/0)
- **Dept. of Humanities (Miscellaneous)** (152/0)

Faculty of Engineering(1, 225/5)
- **Dept. of Mechanical Engineering**(192/1)
- **Dept. of Industrial Chemistry**(210/0)
- **Dept. of Civil Engineering**(206/1)
- **Dept. of Electrical Engineering**(220/0)
- **Dept. of Electronic Engineering**(166/2)
- **Dept. of Applied Physics**(191/1)
- **Dept. of Computer Science and Systems Engineering**(40/0)

Graduate Programs

Graduate School of Agriculture Masterse (M 48/10)

Div. of Agricultural Science(M 9/2)

Crop Science, Pomology, Forcing Culture of Vegetables and Ornamental Plants, Plant Breeding, Plant Pathology, Applied Entomology, Postharvest Horticulture, Farm Management

Div. of Forest Science(M 2/0)

Silviculture, Forest Utilization, Forest Chemistry, Forest Management, Forest Engineering, Forest Policy

Div. of Animal Science(M 14/4)

Animal Management, Animal Reproduction, Animal Breeding, Animal Nutrition and Feeding, Animal Products Science and Technology

Div. of Agricultural Chemistry(M 11/1)

Soil Science and Plant Nutrition, Biochemistry, Nutritional Chemistry, Agricultural Products Technology, Microbiology

Div. of Fishery Science(M 9/3)

Aquaculture, Aquatic Biology and Physiology, Fish Nutrition and Biochemistry, Aquatic Environment and Ecology, Fish Diseases Microbiology, Fish Disease Diagnosis and Treatment

Div. of Agricultural Engineering(M 1/0)

Agricultural Land Engineering, Agricultural Hydraulic Engineering, Agricultural Structural Engineering, Farm Work Technology, Farm Machinery

Div. of Grassland Science(M 2/0)

Forage Crops, Grassland Development, Grassland Management, Forage Utilization

Graduate School of Engineering(M 83/4)

Mechanical Engineering, Industrial Chemistry, Civil Engineering, Electrical Engineering, Electronic Engineering, Applied Physics

One-Year Graduate Programs

Course of Education (Music Education)

長崎大学
(Nagasaki Daigaku)
Nagasaki University

1–14 Bunkyo–machi, Nagasaki–shi, Nagasaki 852
☎ 0958–47–1111 FAX 0958–45–6044

Founded 1949
Professors 246
Associate Professors 229
Assistant Professors(Tenured) 106
Assistant Professors(Non–tenured) 684
Research Assistants 333
Undergraduate Students/Foreign Students 6, 735/43
Graduate Students/Foreign Students 495/47
Library 838, 305 volumes
Contact: Admission Division, Students Bureau, Academic Affairs Section of each Graduate School ☎ ext. 2507 (Pharmaceutical Sciences), 2612 (Engineering), 2902 (Marine Science and Engineering), 3109 (Fisheries). Academic Affairs Section of each Graduate School, 12–4 Sakamoto–machi, Nagasaki–shi, 852. ☎ 0958–47–2111 ext. 2021 (Medicine), 4050 (Dentistry)

Educational philosophy Four Years after the disaster of the Plutonium bomb, Nagasaki University was formed by bringing together the medical, commercial and teaching colleges and, in forty years, it has grown into a 'multiversity' exerting efforts towards an ever deeper and wider study of humanities and sciences, with an eye to the next century.

Foreign students As the University's President, I look forward with deep sincerity to the cooperation of all in helping Nagasaki University meet her worthy goals.

Environment The port town of Nagasaki, located on Western tip of the Japanese Archipelago, has had a rich history of countact and trade with other countries. The population of Nagasaki is approximately 450, 000 and the major industries are fishing, shipbuilding and tourism. It is hot and humid in summer, but it is not so cold in winter, spring and autumn are pleasantly warm. Transportation: Airway Nagasaki–Tokyo 90 min. Nagasaki–Osaka 65 min.

Facilities Main Library, Science information Center, Environmental Protection Center, Center for Instrumental Analysis, Center for Educational Research and Training, Ryugakusei center, Animal Reserch Center, University Hospitals (Medicine, Dentistry), Fishery Training Ship, Atomic Disease Institute, Institute of Tropical medicine, Radioisotope Center, Training Center, Gymnasium

Student activities Popular campus events include freshmen orientation, school festival, foreign students party. There are wide variety of extra curricular activities, orchestra, jazz band, drama, glee club, tea ceremony, baseball, football, soccer, judo, basketball, etc.

Academic programs for foreign students Supplemental Japanese language courses, Tutoring system, Undergraduate: As for foreign students in the General Education Course, general education subjects, foreign languages and physical education may be replaced, up to 26 credits, by the courses in " Japanese Language and Japanese Studies ".

Services for foreign students Health administration center, personal/psychological counseling, Ryugakusei center, International house, Housing information, part–time job information, vacational guidance Home stay, Home visit, coltural exchange program

Undergraduate Programs

Faculty of Dentistry(449/0)
Dept. of Dentistry(449/0)
Faculty of Economics(1, 317/24)
Dept. of Business(285/7)
Dept. of Economics(240/0)
Dept. of Trade(121/7)
Faculty of Education(1, 562/1)
Dept. of Primary School Teacher Training(923/0)
Dept. of Junior High School Teacher Training(435/0)
Dept. of Mentally Retarded Children Teacher Training(84/0)
Dept. of Kindergarten Teacher Training(120/1)
Faculty of Engineering(1, 865/8)
Dept. of Civil Engineering(232/0)
Dept. of Electrical Engineering and Computer Science(518/3)
Dept. of Industrial Chemistry(212/1)
Dept. of Materials Science and Engineering(231/0)
Dept. of Mechanical System Engineering(439/4)
Dept. of Structual Engineering(233/0)
Faculty of Fisheries(487/1)
Dept. of Fisheries(487/1)
Faculty of Medicine(714/8)
Dept. of Medicine(714/8)
Faculty of Pharmaceutical Sciences(341/1)
Dept. of Pharmaceutical Sciences(341/1)

Graduate Programs

Graduate School of Dentistry(D 27/1)
Div. of Dentistry(D 27/1)
Oral Anatomy, Oral Histology, Oral Physiology, Oral Biochemistry, Oral Pathology, Oral Bacteriology, Dental Pharmacology, Dental Materials Science, Preventive Dentistry, Orthodontics, Paediatric Dentistry, Endodontics and Operative Dentistry, Periodontology, Fixed Prosthodontics, Removable Prosthodontics, Maxillofacial and Oral Surgery, Oral Radiology
Graduate School of Engineering(M 169/1)
Div. of Civil Engineering(M 14/0)
Structural Engineering, Hydrography Engineering, Polymer Science and Engineering, Chemisty of Materials
Div. of Electrical Engineering(M 21/0)
Electromagnetic Fields of Energy, Control and Systems, Electric Power, Fundamentals of Electricity, Electrical

Machinery

Div. of Electronics(M 26/1)

Electronic Devices and Circuits, Electronics Communication, Information Processing Systems

Div. of Industrial Chemistry(M 28/0)

Physical Chemistry, Inorganic Chemistry, Organic Chemistry, Organic Synthesis

Div. of Material Science and Engineering(M 27/0)

Physics of Materials, Metal Science and Engineering, Polymer Science and Engineering, Chemistry of Materials

Div. of Mechanical Engineering(M 19/0)

Strength of Materials, Product Engineering, Fluid Engineering, Thermal Engineering

Div of Mechanical Engineering II(M 23/0)

Failure and Fracture of Materials, Machine Design, Automatic Control, Thermal Fluid

Div. of Structural Engineering(M 11/0)

General Dynamics of Structures, Welding Engineering and Structural Production, Design of Steel Structures and Fitting, Design and Behavior of Concrete Structures

Graduate School of Fisheries(M 40/3)

Div. of Fisheries(M 40/3)

Marine Information Science, Fishery and Oceanography, Marine Biology, Aquaculture sciences, Marine Food Sciences, Marine Chemistry

Graduate School of Marine Science and Engineering(D 67/16)

Div. of Marine Production(D 34/6)

Marine Information Control System, Marine Machinery and Engineering Materials, Marine Environmental Protection and Construction Engineering

Div. of Marine Resources(D 33/10)

Marine Biological Resources, Marine Materials Utilization, Marine Energy Resources

Graduate School of Medicine(D 133/23)

Div. of Physiology(D 9/4)

Anatomy, Physiology, Biochemistry, Pharmacology

Div. of Pathology(D 50/7)

Pathology, Bacteriology, Medical Zoology, Medical Oncology

Div. of Social Medicine(D 13/2)

Hygiene, Public Health, Forensic Medicine

Div. of Internal Medicine(D 41/6)

Internal Medicine, Neuro Psychiatry, Pediatrics, Dermatology, Radiology

Div. of Surgery(D 20/4)

Surgery, Orthopedics, Urology, Ophthalmology, Otorhinolaryngology, Obstetrics and Gynecology, Anesthesiology, Neurological Surgery, Plastic and Reconstructive Surgery, Laboratory Medicine, Cardiovsacular Surgery

Graduate School of Pharmaceutical Sciences (M 53/2, D 6/1)

Div. of Pharmaceutical Sciences(M 53/2, D 6/1)

Clinical Pharmaceutics, Medical Chemistry, Health Sciences, Natural Products Chemistry and Biotechnology

鹿屋体育大学

(Kanoya Taiiku Daigaku)

National Institute of Fitness and Sports in Kanoya

1 Shiromizu, Kanoya-shi, Kagoshima 891-23
☎ 0994-46-4111 FAX 0994-46-2516

Founded 1981
Professors 26
Associate Professors 15
Assistant Professors(Tenured) 2
Assistant Professors(Non-tenured) 20
Research Assistants 14
Undergraduate Students/Foreign Students 677/0
Graduate Students/Foreign Students 28/4
Library 47, 390 volumes
Contact: General Affairs Section

Educational philosophy Training Instructors in the field of Fitness and Sports. Promoting Budo(Japanese Traditional Sports)as Japanese Cultural Heritage. Improving Students' Athletic Capability. Promoting Marine Sports and Coastal Recreation. Promoting International Exchange Programs. Promoting Open-School Programs. Promotion of Lifetime Sports. Promotion of Scientific Research on Sports.

Foreign students The Institute encourages the enrollment of students from abroad, and promotes international exchange programs in sports and recreation activities. In doing so, we place a special emphasis on the relationship with South East Asian Nations.

Environment The City of Kanoya is the second largest city in Kagoshima with 77, 000 inhabitants and is situated in the central part of the Osumi Peninsula. Recently, Kanoya has been developing as the center of the eastern part of Kagoshima, in terms of politics, economy, culture, education, medical institutions and transportation.

Facilities Library. Health service center. Sport Hall Camplex. Budo Hall. Kyudo Hall. Indoor Experimentally Swimming Pool. Track and Field. Baseball Stadium. Tennis Courts. Rugby Football Field. Soccer Field. Field Hockey. Team Handball Field. Golf Practice Course. Marine Sports Center.

Student activities Most students belong to one of the 23 varsity teams or the equivalent organization. Track and Field, Baseball, Tennis, Soft-tennis, Badmiton, Volleyball, Basketball, Soccer, Rugby Football, Gymnastics, Swimming, Judo, Kendo, Yacht, Softball, Handball, Kyudo, Field Hockey, Karate, Climbing, Gate Ball, etc.

Academic programs for foreign students Tutor System, Supplementary Lectures.

Services for foreign students counseling, housing information, part-time job information, home visit, cultural exchange program.

Undergraduate Programs

Faculty of Physical Recreation(677/0)
Physical Education and Sports Course(431/0)
Budo Course (Japanese Traditional Sports)(246/0)

Graduate Programs

Graduate School of Physical Recreation(M 28/4)
Div. of Physical Recreation Majors
Philosophy and History of Physical Fitness, Sport and Recreation, Science of Physical Fitness, Health Education, Methodology of Sport and Recreation, Budo(Japanese Traditional Sport), Management and Administration of Physical Fitness, Sport and Recreation, Liberal Arts and Social Science.

大分大学
(Ôita Daigaku)
Oita University

700 Dannoharu, Oita-shi, Oita 870-11
☎ 0975-69-3311 FAX 0975-69-2784

Founede 1949
Professors 105
Associate Professors 103
Assistant Professors(Tenured) 28
Assistant Professors(Non-tenured) 117
Research Assistants 32
Undergraduate Students/Foreign Students 4, 312/16
Graduate Students/Foreign Students 172/9
Library 432, 804 volumes
Contact: Student Office, Section of Foreign Student

Educational philosophy Oita University aims to give its students a wide knowledge and a higher professional education, and expects them to develop into persons who are penetrating in thought, balanced in judgement, capable in practice, and competent in a changing and complex society as dynamic forces, as well as contributing to the progress of the local culture.
Foreign students We believe that foreign students can contribute an important meaning to promoting mutual understanding and friendship through their study and research.
Environment Oita University is at the base of the mountain in suburbs of Oita. It is about twenty minutes from Oita City by car. Oita city is the capital city of Oita Prefecture, with a population of about 410, 000. The campus has peaceful surroundings, ideal for study, with warm weather throughout the years.
Facilities Library, Computer Center, Reseach and Guidance Center for Classroom Teaching, Solar Energy Thermal Applications Laboratory, Marine Science Labolatory, Health Care Center, Student Hall, Gymnasiums, Welfare Facilities, International House
Student activities Campus events includes to foundation festival, school festival, bon-odori, athletic meeting, a long distance relay road race. There are 28 clubs in activites, tea ceremony, theatrical performance, light music, calligraphy. There are 30 sports activities, Japanese fencing, judo, swimming, sailling, rugby, volleyball.
Academic programs for foreign students: Lectures on Japanese language and Japanese culture, Subject Substition System, Tutor System.
Services for foreign students Apartments for Foreign Students(Internatinal House), Cultural exchange with local groups, study trips, parties.

Undergraduate Programs

Faculty of Economics(1, 504/4)
Dept. of Business Management(371/2)
Dept. of Economics(374/0)
Faculty of Education(1, 208/0)
Handicapped Children's School Teachers Training Course(75/0)
Information, Society and Culture Course(111/0)
Junior High School Teachers Training Course(317/0)
Kindergarten Teachers Training Course(85/0)
Primary School Teachers Training Course(620/0)
Faculty of Engineering(1, 600/12)
Dept. of Architectual Engineering(220/0)
Dept. of Electoric Engineering(220/4)
Dept. of Electrical Engineering(221/2)
Dept. of Energy Engineering(232/0)
Dept. of Environmental Chemistry and Engineering(240/0)
Dept. of Information Science and Systems Engineering(230/2)
Dept. of Mechanical Engineering(237/4)

Graduate Programs

Graduate School of Economics(M 5/7)
Div. of Economics(M 5/7)
Economics, History of Economic, Economics Engineering, Public Finance, Financial Theory, Economic Policy, International Economics, Economic History, Economic Geography, Statistics, Social Policy, Sociology and Social Thought, International Politics, Civil Law, Commercial Law, Social Law
Graduate School of Engineering(M 167/2)
Stregnth of Materials, Thermal Engineering, Fluid Engineering, Mechanical Technology and Dynamics, Electromagnetic Fundametals, Elctronic Fundametals, Power Engineering, Communication Engineering, Physical Electronics, Electronic Circuit, Electronic Control Systems, Applied Electronics, Information Mathematics, Computer Software and Hardware, Knowledge and Infelence Systems, Applied Intelligence Systems, Electrochemistry and Catalysis, Physical Orgainc Chemistry and Chemis-

try of Waste Water Treatment, Macromolecular Chemistry and Microbial Biochemistry, Chemical Reation Engineering, and Biological Waste Water Treatment, Fundamentals of Energy Engineering, Energy Resources Engineering, Energy Conversion Engineering, Energy Transfer Engineering, Environmental Engineering, Disaster Prevention Engineering, Architectural and Urban Plannung, Structual, Engineering,Applied Mathematics

One-Year Graduate Programs

Education Course
Education Major

佐賀医科大学
(Saga Ika Daigaku)

Saga Medical School

5-1-1 Nabeshima, Saga-shi, Saga 849
☎ 0952-31-6511 FAX 0952-30-7910

Founded 1976
Professors 39
Associate Professors 30
Assistant Professors(Tenured) 31
Assistant Professors(Non-tenured) 108
Research Assistants 133
Undergraduate Students/Foreign Students 620/0
Graduate Students/Foreign Students 44/3
Library 68, 877 volumes
Contact: Student Affairs Section, Academic Affairs Department

Educational philosophy Aspiring to the improvement and expansion of the regional medical services, Saga Medical School aims at training doctors capable of showing humanity in grasping medical problems, approaching them with creativity, and behaving with a rigorous sense of ethical conduct.
Foreign students We hope that foreign students will make friends by taking part in as many events as they can and that they will learn well and makc positive contributions to the better understanding between cultures.
Environment The campus, 235, 000m² in size, is in the suburban northwest corner of the prefectural capital city of Saga(population: about 170, 000), and offers an atmosphere conducive to serious medical education and research with its pastoral environment free of urban cacophony.
Facilities Clinical Lecture Hall; Medical School Library; Animal Experiment Lab; Radioisotope Research Center; Medical School Hall Dining Room; Gym; Martial Arts Gym; Swimming Pool; Tennis Courts; and others.
Student activities Popular campus events include get-together for freshmen and faculty; athletic and medical school festivals. There is a wide variety of extracurricular activities such as Glee Club, Light Music Society, E.S.S. as well as Baseball, Rugby, Judo, Karate, Yacht, and others.
Academic programs for foreign students Tutor system with academic advisors providing help to accommodate students' individual needs.
Services for foreign students Health Clinic; Personal/Psychological Counseling; Housing Information Service; Part-Time Job Information Service; Home Visits with Japanese Families; Friendship Parties for Foreign Students

Undergraduate Programs

Faculty of Medicine(620/0)

Graduate Programs

Graduate School of Medicine(D 44/3)
Div. of Functional anatomy and Pathology
Div. of Developmental Biology
Div. of Functional Anatomy
Div. of Pathophysiology
Div. of Bioregulation
Div. of Neural Control
Div. of Metabolism
Div. of Human Genetics
Div. of Oncology, Immunology and Infections
Div. of Biochemical Regulation and Drug Action
Div. of Human Ecology
Div. of Preventive Medicine and Epidemiology
Div. of Environmental Medicine
Div. of Legal Medicine

佐賀大学
(Saga Daigaku)

Saga University

1 Honjo-machi, Saga-shi, Saga 840
☎ 0952-24-5191 FAX 0952-23-8564

Founded 1949
Professors 145
Associate Professors 141
Assistant Professors(Tenured) 31
Assistant Professors(Non-tenured) 245
Research Assistants 48
Undergraduate Students/Foreign Students 5, 050/35
Graduate Students/Foreign Students 245/15
Library 471, 977 volumes
Contact: General Affairs Section

Educational philosophy We are making a great effort to develop our university as " a local university of marked individuality, one filled with charm and vitality " and also to make it a place every one can enjoy.
Foreign students We send hearty greetings to all of you who hope to come here to study. We are kind and warmhearted and enjoy developing friendly rela-

tionship with foreign students and visitors.

Environment Saga university is located in Saga, with a population of 170, 000, in Kyushu district which lies to the southwest of Japan, being 1, 100km distant from Tokyo. Our city is blessed with a mild climate and beautiful pastoral landscapes and is a very easy place in which to live.

Facilities Library, Health Care Center, Joint Research and Development Center, Information Processing Center, Laboratory of Radioisotopes, University Hall, International House, Sports Center, Swimming pool, Gymnasium, Athletic Ground, Baseball Ground, Tennis Courts.

Student activities Saga university foundation festival, cultural festival, welcome party for freshmen, field trip, There are 33 cultural clubs and 37 sports clubs, freshmen orientation(spring time and autumn time)

Academic programs for foreign students Japanese language class, tutoring system, foreign language and the state of affairs in Japan

Services for foreign students Health Care Center, International House, part-time job information, vocational guidance, Homestay, cultural exchange program

Undergraduate Programs

Faculty of Agriculture(674/0)
- **Dept. of Agricultural Chemistry**(57/0)
- **Dept. of Agricultural Civil Engineering**(37/0)
- **Dept. of Agricultural Sciences**(208/0)
- **Dept. of Agronomy**(47/0)
- **Dept. of Applied Biological Sciences**(287/0)
- **Dept. of Horticultural Science**(38/0)

Faculty of Economics(1, 219/13)
- **Dept. of Business Administration**(323/9)
- **Dept. of Economics**(617/3)
- **Dept. of Management Science**(279/1)

Faculty of Education(1, 052/2)
- **Arts and Crafts Course**(90/0)
- **Elementary Education Course**(520/1)
- **Integrated Culture Course**(122/1)
- **Secondary Education Course**(233/0)
- **Special Education Course**(87/0)

Faculty of Science and Engineering(2, 105/20)
- **Dept. of Applied Chemistry**(230/2)
- **Dept. of Chemistry**(153/0)
- **Dept. of Civil Engineering (I)** (194/0)
- **Dept. of Civil Engineering (II)** (191/1)
- **Dept. of Electrical Engineering**(216/3)
- **Dept. of Electronic Engineering**(209/7)
- **Dept. of Information Science**(134/4)
- **Dept. of Mathematics**(161/0)
- **Dept. of Mechanical Engineering**(227/1)
- **Dept. of Mechanical Engineering (Production Division)** (228/2)
- **Dept. of Physics**(162/0)

Graduate Programs

Graduate School of Agriculture(M 46/5)

Div. of Agronomy(M 0/2)
Crop Science, Tropical Crop Science, Plant Breeding, Plant Pathology, Agricultural Economics, Animal Science

Div. of Agricultural Chemistry(M 23/1)
Soil Science and Plant Nutrition, Food Science and Technology, Biological Chemistry, Applied Microbiology, Food Hygienic and Nutrition Chemistry

Div. of Agricultural Civil Engineering(M 5/1)
Irrigation and Drainage Engineering, Construction Engineering, Agricultural Machinery

Div. of Horticultural Science(M 9/1)
Olericulture, and Floriculture, Fruit Science, Applied Nematology and Entomology, Food Science and Horticultural Engineering

Graduate School of Science and Engineering (M 199/10)

Div. of Mathematics(M 7/1)
Algebra, Geometry, Analysis, Applied Mathematics

Div. of Physics(M 15/0)
Mathematical Physics, Electromagnetism, Quantum Physics, Solid State Physics

Div. of Chemistry(M 24/1)
Physical Chemistry, Inorganic Chemistry, Organic Chemistry, Analytical Chemistry

Div. of Mechanical Engineering(M 24/2)
Fluid Engineering, Fundamentals of Mechanical Engineering, Thermal Engineering, Machine Design and Manufacturing Technique

Div. of Mechanical Engineering (Production Division) (M 25/1)
Automatic Control Engineering, Heat and Mass Transfer Engineering, Precision Machinery, Metal Working Engineering

Div. of Electrical Engineering(M 24/2)
Fundamentals of Electrical Engineering, System Control, Electrical Machinery, Electric Power Engineering

Div. of Electronic Engineering(M 29/0)
Fundamentals of Electronics, Communication Engineering, Information Processing and Electronic Circuit, Applied Electronics

Div. of Applied Chemistry(M 36/0)
Applied Physical Chemistry, Applied Inorganic Chemistry, Applied Organic Chemistry, Chemical Engineering, Ceramic Engineering

Div. of Civil Engineering (I) (M 5/0)
Hydraulic Engineering, Structural Engineering(I), Transportation Engineering, Construction Materials and Methods

Div. of Civil Engineering (II) (M 10/3)
Planning of Infrastructure, Geotechnical Engineering, Water Resources Engineering, Structural Engineering (II)

One-Year Graduate Programs

Education Course
- Pedagogy Major
- Arts and Crafts Major

Local Public Universities

福岡女子大学
(Fukuoka Joshi Daigaku)

Fukuoka Women's University

1-1-1 Kasumigaoka, Higashi-ku, Fukuoka 813
☎ 092-661-2411 FAX 092-661-2415

Fuounded 1950
Professors 19
Associate Professors 17
Assistant Professors(Tenured) 3
Assistant Professors(Non-tenured) 98
Research Assistants 10
Undergraduate Students/Foreign Students 750/1
Library 101, 570 volumes
Contact: Division of Academic Affairs

Educational philosophy We aim at teaching and studying high level sciences and literature in order that students may develope their intellectual and moral abilities and make valuable contributions towards the improvement of society.
Foreign students We are convinced that foreign students will have a worthwhile and pleasant experience in our school and can contribute greatly to promoting mutual understanding and international friendliness.
Environment The campus is located on Kasumigaoka, (Kashii), in the north-east of Fukuoka city, a metropoplis of Western Japan in the northern part of Kyushu Island; and a place not only convenient for transporatation but also commanding a fine view of Hakata Bay.
Facilities Library, Institute of Women's Lifelong Education, Computer Room, Language Laboratory, Gymnasiam, Swimming Pool, Student Dormitory, etc.
Student activities Popular campus events include freshmen welcome party and induction tour, cultural festival, athletic meeting, etc. For extra curricular activities, we have a variety of clubs of sport and culture, such as tennis, badminton, Japanese archery, the art of tea-making, Japanese harp, calligraphy, etc.
Academic programs for foreign students Tutoring
Services for foreign students Health clinic, personal/psychological counseling, College housing, part-time job information, cultural exchange program.

Undergraduate Programs

Faculty of Home Life Science(359/1)
  Dept. of Home Life Science: Course of Food and Nutrition(117/0)
  Dept. of Home Life Science: Course of Textile and Clothing(114/0)
  Dept. of Living Science(128/1)
Faculty of Literature(391/0)
  Dept. of English Language and Literature(202/0)
  Dept. of Japanese Literature(189/0)

北九州大学
(Kitakyûshû Daigaku)

Kitakyushu University

4-2-1 Kitagata, Kokuraminami-ku, Kitakyushu-shi, Fukuoka 802
☎ 093-962-4436 FAX 093-962-1837

Founded 1946
Professors 75
Associate Professors 44
Assistant Professors(Tenured) 13
Assistant Professors(Non-tenured) 133
Research Assistants 2
Undergraduate Students/Foreign Students 3, 917/11
Graduate Students/Foreign Students 51/4
Library 319, 880 volumes
Contact: Admission Office

Educational philosophy The historical mission of Kitakyushu University is participating the culture of East and West, contributing to the culture of the world incessantly and developing our national character.
Foreign students Kitakyushu University is now organizing many facilities for international exchange, Kitakyushu University has already instituded the Japanese Language Center for foreign students.
Environment Kitakyushu University is supported by and located in Kitakyushu city, with a population of one million. The city was inaugurated in 1963 through the merger of five neighboring cities-Moji, Kokura, Yahata, Wakamatsu and Tobata on an equal footing. The climate is temperate.
Facilities Library, Gymnastics Building Auditorium, Marshal Arts building, Japanese Language Center, Language Laboratory, Audio Visual room Computer Center, Institute of Regional Studies.
Student activities Freshmen welcome party (April), School Festival(November). Students may join anyone of these clubs, baseball, Japanese fencing, Judo, Japanese archery, choral groups, marching band, etc.
Academic programs for foreign students Japanese language 4 classes a week, Introduction to Japan (Japanese society)1 class a week.
Services for foreign students Student Office will advise foreign students for part-time job. It must be remembered that the part-time job should not interfere with your purpose.

Undergraduate Programs

Faculty of Foreign Studies(885/0)
Dept. of Angro-American Studies(727/0)
Dept. of Chinese Studies(158/0)
Faculty of Economic and Business Administration(1, 419/11)
Dept. of Business Administration(726/7)
Dept. of Economics(693/4)
Faculty of Literature(718/0)
Dept. of Japanese Literature(365/0)
Dept. of English Literature(353/0)
Faculty of Law(895/0)
Dept. of Law(631/0)
Dept. of Political Science(264/0)

Graduate Programs

Graduate School of Business Administration(M 11/1)
Div. of Business Administration(M 11/1)
Accounting, Auditing, Bookkeeping, Business Administration, Business Management Corporation, Enterprise, Financial Management Industrial Control, International Business Marketing, Personnel Menagement
Graduate School of Anglo-American Languages and Cultures(M 13/1)
Div. of Anglo-American Languages and Cultures(M 13/1)
American Literature, American Studies, British Studies, English Linguistics, English Literature
Graduate School of Chiness Studies(M 6/0)
Div. of Chinese Studies(M 6/0)
Chinese Linguistics, Chinese Literature, Chinese Studies
Graduate School of Law(M 8/0)
Div. of Law(M 8/0)
Administrative Law, Civil Law, Civil Procedure, Constitutional Law, Criminal Procedure, Criminology, International Law, Social Law, The Commercial Code
Graduate School of Economics(M 13/2)
Div. of Economics(M 13/2)
Banking and Finance, Economics, Economic Policy, History of Economic theories, Monetary, Public Finance, Urban Economics

---

熊本女子大学

(Kumamoto Joshi Daigaku)

Kumamoto Women's University

2432–1 Mizuarai, Kengun-machi, Kumamoto-shi, Kumamoto 862
☎ 096-383-2929 FAX 096-384-6765

Founded 1947
Professors 24
Associate Professors 16
Assistant Professors(Tenured) 5
Assistant Professors(Non-tenured) 63
Research Assistants 10
Undergraduate Students/Foreign Students 860/2
Library 116, 470 volumes
Contact: the Instruction Section of Kumamoto Women's University

Educational philosophy As a provincial unisex university we aim at women's education in various fields of science and letters together with leadership training so that they contribute much to cultural and social improvement in the prefecture.
Foreign students Students from abroad are most welcome. We believe that studying at such a small university as ours(enrollment: 800)will offer students an ideal opportunity to pursue their goals and develop new interests in an informal and friendly atmosphere.
Environment We are located in the outskirt of Kumamoto City, one of the oldest in Japan. You can find historical embodiments(old castles, temples and shrines)all over the prefecture. The climate is mild except in the humid season of rain in mid-summer. Our cultural climate is nicknamed " moccos ", an esprit loci at once independent, self-sufficing and open to other cultures.
Facilities Libray, Language Center, Food Science Laboratory, Environmental Science Laboratory, Textile Dyes Laboratory, Computer Laboratory, Gymnasium, Auditorium. Student cafeteria, Student Club meeting rooms, Tennis courts
Student activities Annual events include Sports Day, school festival, freshmen welcome party, freshmen orientation excursion. Student extra curricular activities include: flower arrangement, tea ceremony, Koto, mandolin(orchestra), English club, bicycling, hiking, swimming, basketball, folk dance, tennis, etc.
Academic programs for foreign students The Japanese Language Program for foreign students is available.
Services for foreign students Housing information(off-campus), part-time job information, Homestay

Undergraduate Programs

Faculty of Literature(348/2)
Dept. of English Literature(165/0)
Dept. of Japanese Literature(183/2)
Faculty of Living Science(512/1)
Dept. of Science of Living Environment(170/0)
Dept. of Food Science and Nutrition(165/0)
Dept. of Science of Living(177/1)

九州歯科大学
(Kyûshû Sika Daigaku)
Kyushu Dental College

2-6-1 Manazuru, Kokurakita, Kitakyushu-shi, Fukuoka 803
☎ 093-582-1131 FAX 093-582-6000

Founded 1914
Professors 26
Associate Professors 21
Assistant Professors(Tenured) 19
Assistant Professors(Non-tenured) 84
Research Assistants 69
Undergraduate Students/Foreign Students 651/3
Graduate Students/Foreign Students 72/6
Library 72, 477 volumes
Contact: Admission Office

Educational philosophy We aim at teaching and studying up-to-date high-level art and sciences of dentistry so that students may develop their own intellectual, moral and applied abilities to contribute to national dental health care.

Foreign students We believe that receiving foreign students is one of our delightful duties, and the foreigh students can contribute to developing dental education and research in their countries.

Environment The City of Kitakyushu with a population of 1, 000, 000 is located in the northern part of Kyushu. It is the center of primary industry and trade, having many historic and scientific cultures and structures. The city is also blessed with mild climate and natural environment.

Facilities College Hospital, College Library, General Laboratory Center, Anatomy Center, Animal Research Center, School of Dental Hygiene

Student activities Student council arranges school festival and athletic meet. There is a lot of groups for extra curricular activities, 21 groups for sports, 11 groups for culture.

Services for foreign students No special services for foreign students are routinely programmed but particular attention and convenience arc circumstantially be offered through counselling.

Undergraduate Programs

Faculty of Dentistry(484/3)
Dept. of Dentistry(484/3)

Graduate Programs

Graduate School of Dentistry(D 72/6)
Div. of Fundamental Dentistry(D 5/2)
Oral Anatomy, Physiology, Biochemistry, Oral Pathology, Oral Bacteriology, Dental Pharmacology, Dental Materials Science, Oral Neuroscience
Div. of Clinical Dentistry(D 67/4)
Anatomy, Oral Histology&Embryology, Physiology, Biochemistry, Oral Pathology, Oral Bacteriology, Dental Materials Science, Oral Neuroscience

長崎県立国際経済大学
(Nagasakikenritsu Kokusai Keizai Daigaku)
Nagasaki Prefectural University of International Economics

123 Kawashimo-cho, Sasebo-shi, Nagasaki 858
☎ 0956-47-2191 FAX 0956-47-6941

Founded 1967
Professors 19
Associate Professors 5
Assistant Professors(Tenured) 12
Assistant Professors(Non-tenured) 39
Research Assistants 1
Undergraduate Students/Foreign Students 902/7
Contact: Admission Office

Educational philosophy The university offers programs with primary emphasis on the studies of economics and physical distribution and with no less emphasis on the liberal arts as well as foreign languages to help the students cultivate themselves so that they can play an active role wherever they may go.

Foreign students The presence of many foreign students on the campus will vastly help the young people widen their international outlook and strengthen the ties of friendship among the peoples of different cultures.

Environment The campus stands in the calm valley between Mt.Yumihari and the so-called Ainoura-Fuji. The Saikai National Park, dotted with numerous picturesque iles, is not very far from the campus. In short, the university is blessed with quiet environments ideal for studying and thinking.

Facilities Library, Culture & Economics Research Institute, Audio-Vidual Laboratory, Information Processing Laboratory, Gymnasium, Hall of Martial Arts, Students' Hall, Rooms for extracurricular activities

Student activities Annual Ohtori Festival held in autumn each year, Sports clubs: track-and-field, baseball, Ping-Pong, tennis, Japanes fencing, Cultural clubs: Guitar & Mandolin, folksong, brass-ensemble, art

Academic programs for foreign students The teaching of the Japanese language: 2 hours a week

Services for foreign students Advice and guidance for living and educational problems by the Committe of Foreign Student Advisors Services to find lodgings and part-time jobs

Undergraduate Programs

Faculty of Economics(902/7)

Private Universities

別府大学
(Beppu Daigaku)

Beppu University

82 Kitaishigaki, Beppu-shi, Oita 874-01
☎ 0977-67-0101 FAX 0977-67-0210

Founded 1950
Professors 22
Associate Professors 12
Assistant Professors(Tenured) 10
Assistant Professors(Non-tenured) 35
Undergraduate Students/Foreign Students 1, 258/5
Library 130, 000 volumes
Contact: Admissions and Public relations office

Educational philosophy " VERITAS LIBERAT " which means " The truth will make us free. " The creed represents the University's commitment to nurture the students' minds to seek universal truths.
Foreign students You can enhance an international atmosphere in our campus and can enjoy your campus life by communicating with our faculty members and Japanese students.
Environment The university is located in the north of Beppu City with hot spring resorts of world-wide fame. Beppu City, whose population is over 130, 000, is located in the heart of Oita Prefecture.
Facilities Library, Museum, Asian Cultural Institute of History, Early Childhood Education Research Center, Gymnasium, Martial Arts Hall, Swimming pool
Student activities Extracurricular activities are numerious and varied, including drama, movies, photography, chorus, instrumental music, judo, kendo, karate, baseball, tennis, table tennis, volleyball, badminton, volleyball, etc.
Services for foreign students Health center, counseling, housing, part-time job information

Undergraduate Programs

Faculty of Literature(1, 258/5)
Dept. of Aesthetics and History of Fine Arts(222/1)
Dept. of English Literature(228/0)
Dept. of History(492/3)
Dept. of Japanese Literature(316/1)

筑紫女学園大学

(Chikushi Jogakuen Daigaku)

Chikushi Jogakuen College

2-12-1 Ishizaka, Dazaifu-shi, Fukuoka 818-01
☎ 092-925-3511 FAX 092-924-4369

Founded 1988
Professors 15
Associate Professors 10
Assistant Professors(Tenured) 4
Assistant Professors(Non-tenured) 11
Undergraduate Students/Foreign Students 640/0
Library 18, 456 volumes
Contact: Instruction Department

Educational philosophy Chikushi Jogakuen College, founded in 1988, is the latest adittion to the Chikushi Jogakuen Group, which has a history of more than 80 years as a Buddhist school foundation dedicated to the education of women.
Environment The college is situated in Dazaifu, a small historic town to the south of Fukuoka City. The nearest railway station is Nishitetsu Dazaifu or Gojo.
Facilities Audiovisual aids in library, Buddhist Chapel, Word-processing Room, Outdoor clubhouse, Tea-Ceremony house
Student activities We have Buddhism events in addition to general campus events. There are many unique club activities, such as Japanese Archery, Folk Dancing, Tea-Ceremony, Golf, etc.

Undergraduate Programs

Faculty of Literature(640/0)
  Dept. of Japanese Language and Literature(330/0)
  Dept. of English(310/0)

第一経済大学

(Daiichi Keizai Daigaku)

Daiichi College of Economics

3-11-25 Gojo, Dazaifu-shi, Fukuoka 818-01
☎ 092-922-5131 FAX 092-921-3476

Founded 1968
Professors 35
Associate Professors 20
Assistant Professors(Tenured) 28
Assistant Professors(Non-tenured) 21
Undergraduate Students/Foreign Students 6514/2
Library 88, 323 volumes
Contact: Admission Office

Educational philosophy To contribute to the society by developing the student's individual abilities and providing the students with the most advanced economic sciences. Majors in Management, Economics and International Business are offered.
Foreign students Students not receiving a scholarship must: 1)pass entrance examination for foreign students given by Daiichi College of Economics 2)meet qualifications to apply for Japanese universities or colleges, 3)have Level 2 or higher on JLPT
Environment Located in the City of Dazaifu, population of about 60, 000 with beautiful natural surroundings, rich in history and the Dazaifu shrine. Pleasant housing and accomodation are available in the community. A short distance to metropolitan Fukuoka, the largest city in Kyushu.
Facilities Institute for Economic Research, library, student hall, 2 modern, well-equipped gymnasiums, baseball and soccer fields, tennis courts, facilities for Japanese martial arts including judo, kendo and karate.
Student activities Major campus events are: homecoming, a sports event welcoming freshmen and a autumn college festival. Student activities include: baseball, soccer, rugby, tennis, Japanese martial arts, music, cinema, various associations for the study of economics, accounting and other academic disciplines.
Academic programs for foreign students Foreign students take classes with Japanese students.
Services for foreign students Counseling is provided by Dean of Students.

Undergraduate Programs

Faculty of Economics(6514/2)
  Dept. of Business Management(2613/0)
  Dept. of Economics(2664/2)
  Dept. of Trade(1237/0)

第一薬科大学

(Daiichi Yakka Daigaku)

Daiichi College of Pharmaceutical Sciences

22-1 Tamagawa-cho, Minami-ku, Fukuoka-shi, Fukuoka 815
☎ 092-541-0161

Founded 1960

Undergraduate Programs

Faculty of Pharmaceutical Sciences
  Dept. of Industrial Pharmacy
  Dept. of Pharmacy

第一工業大学
(Dai Ichi Kôgyô Daigaku)

Dai Ichi University, College of Technology

1-10-2 Chuo, Kokubu-shi, Kagoshima 899-43
☎ 0995-45-0640 FAX 0995-47-2083

Founded 1984
Professors 43
Associate Professors 27
Assistant Professors (Tenured) 18
Assistant Professors (Non-tenured) 73
Research Assistants
Undergraduate Students/Foreign Students 3563/1
Library 34, 090 volumes
Contact: Affairs Office

Educational philosophy The purpose of Dai Ichi University, College of Technology is to train students to be competent individuals who have both technical skill and the spirit of internationalism.

Foreign students There are no special admissions requirements for foreign students wishing to enter our University. We are willing to accept foreign students who are eager to study inspite of the potential language barrier.

Environment Our University is located in Kokubu City, approximately in the center of Kagoshima Prefecture, and can be reached from Kagoshima Airport, by car, in about 20mintues. The University, surrounded by magnificent scenry, is the only private college of technology in southern Kyushu.

Facilities Our University is sufficiently furnished with the educational facilities and equipment necessary to train future technologists who will be able to deal flexibly with changes in the highly technical society of the forthcoming 21th century.

Student activities There are 26 sport clubs and 9 cultural clubs at our University. The students develop mental and physical strength, patience, frienship and relience through hard training and club activities.

Services for foreign students We have two student dormitories for single students.

Undergraduate Programs

Faculty of Technology (3563/1)
- **Dept. of Aeronautical Engineering** (824/0)
- **Dept. of Architecture** (422/1)
- **Dept. of Civil Engineering** (422/0)
- **Dept. of Electronic Engineering** (887/0)
- **Dept. of Mechanical Engineering** (1008/0)

福岡歯科大学
(Fukuoka Shika Daigaku)

Fukuoka Dental College

700 Oaza Ta, Sawara-ku, Fukuoka-shi, Fukuoka 814-01
☎ 092-801-0411 FAX 092-801-4909

Founded 1972
Professors 27
Associate Professors 25
Assistant Professors (Tenured) 22
Assistant Professors (Non-tenured) 57
Research Assistants 74
Undergraduate Students/Foreign Students 722/1
Graduate Students/Foreign Students 47/1
Library 105, 000 volumes
Contact: Fukuoka Dental College

Educational philosophy The college aims to contribute to the development of dentistry and to the welfare of Japanese society by training comeptent dentists who will have extensive professional and technical knowledge and skills, as well as moral, cultural and physical education.

Foreign students One foreign student may study at the school each year. At present, there are four foreign students: One in college, one in graduate school and two engaged in laboratory research. The college is established only for dentistry, and there is no Japanese language course for foreign students. Such students are required to sufficiently proficient in Japanese before they begin their studies at the college.

Environment The college is in Fukuoka, a city of 1.2 milion peopel on the Northwest coast of Kyushu island. 90minutes from Tokyo by air. Fukuoka is close to China and Korea and has a long history of communication and trade with countries on the Asian continent. The college is the only private dental college in the western part of Japan that is close to beautiful scenery.

Facilities The college has advanced electronic systems for the study of dentistry: these include video system in every lecture and study hall, a main frame computer for use by the instructor, and both scanning and transmission electron microscopes. The college also has an animal center for research work, a library stocked with more than 100,000 books and journals a gymnasium.

Student activities The college has two major events: At this time, the students of the school's various culture and science clubs organize displays and demonstrations of their specialities, 1) Academic Culture Week is held during June, 2) The college festival is held in October, The college's many volunteer clubs: 24 sports clubs and 7 cultural clubs, sponsor various activities, contests, concerts, etc.

Academic programs for foreign students The college has a counseling system to assist student in re-

solving their problems and to assist their academic work.
Services for foreign students The counselors for foreign students will accept foreign students' requests for couseling.

Undergraduate Programs

Faculty of Dentistry(722/1)
Dept. of Dentistry(722/1)

Graduate Programs

Graduate School of Dentistry(D 47/1)
Div. of Dentistry(D 47/1)
Oral Anatomy, Oral Physiology, Oral Biochemistry, Oral Pathology, Oral Microbiology, Pharmacolgy, Dental Materials and Devices, Preventive Dentistry, Conservative Dentistry, Endodontics and Periodontics, Removable Prosthodontics, Crown and Bridge Prosthodontics, Oral and Maxillofacial Surgery, Orthodontics, Dental Radiology, Pediatric Dentistry, Anesthesiology

---

福岡工業大学
(Fukuoka Kôgyô Daigaku)
Fukuoka Institute Of Technology

3-30-1 Wajirohigashi, Higashi-ku, Fukuoka-shi, Fukuoka 811-02
☎ 092-606-3131 FAX 092-606-8923

Founded 1963
Professors 51
Associate Professors 26
Assistant Professors(Tenured) 22
Assistant Professors(Non-tenured) 66
Research Assistants 27
Undergraduate Studentes/Foreign Students 3, 394/21
Library 117, 853 volumes
Contact: Kyoumu-ka

Educational philosophy We aim at training and bringing up humane and creative engineers who will make contribution to the society.
Foreign students We believe international exchange of students and information with schools and institutes abroad will foster internationally minded engineers. We therefore take a positive view on accepting foreign students.
Environment Fukuoka is the largest and busiest center in Kyushu for government and politics, industry and commerce, education, and air, sea, and land transportation. With a recording in an ancient Chinese history book, Fukuoka has long been active in international affairs, trade and cultural exchanges.
Facilities 7 classroom buildings, 4-9 floors high; 2 gymnasiums; an auditorium; a library Information Processing(Computer)Center; Electronics Research Center; Semi-conductor Device Laboratory; Language-Information Research Center; Machining and Tooling Center
Student activities Togetherness and Friendship is our theme. Freshman Field Trip to Mt. Aso Area; 15 clubs in Art and Culture Circle; 27 clubs in Athletic Circle.
Academic programs for foreign students Credits acquired by taking Japanese Language and Japanese Studies courses will be substituted for up to 8 units credit courses in general education subjects.
Services for foreign students Counselling three days per week; Give assistance in securing housing and part-time work

Undergraduate Programs

Faculty of Engineering(3, 394/21)
Dept. of Communication and Computer Engineering(683/7)
Dept. of Electronics Engineering(606/2)
Dept. of Electronic Materials Engineering(398/1)
Dept. of Electronic And Mechanical Engineering(598/1)
Dept. of Electrical Engineering(605/3)
Dept. of Management Engineering(504/7)

福岡女学院大学
(Fukuoka Jo Gakuin Daigaku)
Fukuoka Jo Gakuin College

2409-01 Ogori, Ogori-shi, Fukuoka 838-01
☎ 0942-73-1990 FAX 0942-73-1996

Founded 1990
Professors 10
Associate Professors 6
Assistant Professors(Tenured) 8
Assistant Professors(Non-tenured) 19
Research Assistants 3
Undergraduate Studentes/Foreign Students 242/0
Library 20, 263 volumes
Contact: Admission office

Educational philosophy Since Fukuoka Jo Gakuin was founded by missionaries, Christian education is the foundation of the school's morals. The basic aim of our college is to educate Japanese women in the humanities with emphasis on an international outlook grounded in Christian values.
Foreign students We accept foreign students and students who are educated abroad. We have several eminent non-Japanese faculty members and we are developing ties with foreign universities, giving Fukuoka Jo Gakuin College an international flavor.
Environment Our college is located in Ogori city, a quiet small town. The city is convenient to Kurume city

and Fukuoka city, so the students can enjoy the city life, too.

Facilities College library, Gymnasium, Computer room, Dining hall, Tennis courts

Student activities Popular campus events include an excursion, religious weeks, retreat, college festival. There is a wide variety of extracurricular activities, including tennis, baseball, tea ceremony, English Speaking Society, and other clubs.

Undergraduate Programs

Faculty of Humanities(242/0)
  Dept. of Japanese culture(121/0)
  Dept. of English cultures(121/0)

福岡大学

(Fukuoka Daigaku)

Fukuoka University

8-19-1 Nanakuma, Jonan-ku, Fukuoka-shi, Fukuoka
814-01
☎ 092-871-6631 FAX 092-862-4431

Founded 1934
Professors 280
Associate Professors 162
Assistant Professors(Tenured) 83
Assistant Professors(Non-tenured) 481
Research Assistants 309
Undergraduate Students/Foreign Students 22, 284/12
Graduate Students/Foreign Students 293/4
Library 1, 030, 000 volumes
Contact: International Exchange Office(Undergraduate admission) Office of Graduate Divisions(Graduate admission)

Educational philosophy Fukuoka University is committed to providing the students with an atmosphere for quality education conducive to a global perspective and to growth of the whole person, and it is also University policy to devote in the academic field through the research and educational activities to the community.

Foreign students Fukuoka University strives to open to the overseas students a broad range of academic courses which meet their academic needs and interests and lead ultimately to the baccalaureate, the master's and the doctorate's degrees.

Environment Fukuoka City developed as a major Japanese trading port and the gateway for culture from the Asian Continent coming to this country in the ancient days, and today it is one of the largest administrative, commercial, economical and culture centers in Kyushu with a population of some 1, 200, 000.

Facilities The Central Research Institute, The Computer Center, The Language Training Center, The First & The Second Memorial Gymnasiums, The Indoor Swimming Pool, The The Student Assembly Hall, The Radioisotope Center, The Libraries

Student activities The main annual events are the orientation & guidance for freshmen, the freshmen welcome picnic and the Nanakuma Festival(school & festival). The extracurricular activities are actively conducted by the student organization consisting of 40 cultural clubs and 40 athletic clubs.

Academic programs for foreign atudents Supplemental Japanese language classes

Services for foreign students Information service, Counselling & advising services including personal and interpersonal concerns and/or educational questions

Undergraduate Programs

Faculty of Commerce(5, 427/4)
  Dept. of Commerce(3, 144/1)
  Dept. of International Trade(1, 062/3)
Faculty of Economics(4, 129/1)
  Dept. of Economics(3, 077/1)
  Dept. of Industrial Economics(1, 052/0)
Faculty of Engineering(3, 346/0)
  Dept. of Architecture(551/0)
  Dept. of Chemical Engineering(544/0)
  Dept. of Civil Engineering(553/0)
  Dept. of Electrical Engineering(564/0)
  Dept. of Electronic Engineering(573/0)
  Dept. of Mechanical Engineering(561/0)
Faculty of Humanities(1, 447/1)
  Dept. of Culture(457/1)
  Dept of English Language(349/0)
  Dept. of French Language(164/0)
  Dept. of German Language(142/0)
  Dept. of History(170/0)
  Dept. of Japanese Language and Literature(165/0)
Faculty of Law(4, 234/0)
  Dept. of Business Law(1, 178/0)
  Dept. of Jurisprudence(3, 056/0)
School of Medicine(671/4)
  Dept. of Medicine(671/4)
Faculty of Pharmaceutical Sciences(911/1)
  Dept. of Pharmaceutical Chemistry(318/0)
  Dept. of Pharmaceutics(593/1)
Faculty of Physical Education(1, 197/1)
  Dept. of Physical Education(1, 197/1)
Faculty of Science(922/0)
  Dept. of Applied Mathematics(314/0)
  Dept. of Applied Physics(300/0)
  Dept. of Chemistry(308/0)

Graduate Programs

Graduate School of Commerce(M 19/0, D 4/0)
  Div. of Commerce(M 19/0, D 14/0)
Master's: Theory of Commerce, Marketing, Finance, International Finance, Foreign Trade Business, Theory of Customs, Principles of Insurance, History of Japanese Commerce, History of Foreign Trade, Business Adminis-

tration, Business Finance, Industrial Management, Financial Accounting, Accounting, Administrative Accounting, Income Tax Accounting, Doctoral: Theory of Commerce, Marketing, History of Japanese Commerce, History of Foreign Trade, Business Finance, Accounting

Graduate School of Economics(M 28/3, D 0/0)

Div. of Economics(M 28/3, D 0/0)

Master's: Theory on National Income, Markets in the Modern Economy, Theory of Money, Oriental Economic History, European Business History, Economics of Developing Countries, Theory of Economic Systems, Public Finance, Econometrics, Industrial Psychology, Social System Planning, Doctoral: Theory of National Income, Markets in the Modern Economy, Theory of Money, Theory of Economics of Systems

Graduate School of Engineering(M 39/1)

Div. of Architect and Civil Engineering(M 2/1)

Structural Analysis and Design, Theory and Design for Construction Material, Urban Environment Analysis and Design, Research and Design for Housing and Residence, Japanese Architectural History and Design

Div. of Chemical Engineering(M 7/0)

Fundamentals of Chemical Engineering, Diffusional Unit Operations, Reaction Engineering, Industrial Chemistry

Div. of Electrical Engineering(M 18/0)

Basic Electrical Engineering, Electrical Machinery, Electrical Power Engineering, Applied Electrical Engineering

Div. of Electronic Engineering(M 3/0)

Circuits and Systems, Light & Radio Wave Communications, Solid State Devices, Computer and Information Science

Div. of Mechanical Engineering(M 9/0)

Strength of Materials, Fluid Machinery, Heat Transfer, Machine Design

Graduate School of Humanities(M 8/0)

Div. of English(M 4/0)

English Linguistics, English Literture

Div. of French(M 4/0)

French Linguistics, French Literature

Graduate School of Law(M 13/0, D 5/0)

Div. of Civil and Criminal Law(M 5/0, D 4/0)

Master's: Civil Law, Commercial Law, Civil Procedure, Criminal Law, Labor Law, Social Security Law, Doctoral: Commercial Law, Civil Procedure, Criminal Law

Div. of Public Law(M 8/0, D 1/0)

Master's: Constitutional Law, Adiministrative Law, Tax Law, Political Science, History of Poltical Thought, Doctoral: Administrative Law, Political Science, History of Political Thought

Graduate School of Medical Science(D 94/0)

Div. of Human Biology(D 6/0)

Biological Structure(Gross Anatomy), Biological Structure(Microanatomy), Membrane Physiology, Cell and Organ Physiology, Biochemistry, Cell Biology

Div. of Pathogenic Biology(D 2/0)

Microbiology and Immunology, Medical Zoology, Medical Mycology

Div. of Pathological Biochemistry(D 26/0)

Immunobiochemistry, Biochemistry of the hepato-biliary and pancreatic System, Pathophysiology and Metabolism in Gastroenterogy, Cardiovascular Physiological Chemistry, Reproductive Biochemistry, Tumor Biochemistry, Clinical Chemistry and Laboratory Medicine

Div. of Pathological Bio-dynamics(D 22/0)

Neuropharmacology, Neuro-otology, Functional Kinematics, Respiratory Function, Cardiovascular Hemodynamics, Radiological Sciene, Anesthesiology

Div. of Pathomorphology(D 24/0)

Morphologic Pathology, Functional Pathology, Pathology of Central Nervous System, Pathophysiology of Visual System, Urology and Related Sciences, Pathophysiology of Castrointestinal Tract

Div. of Social Medicine and Environmental Health(D 14/0)

Epidemiology, Environmental Health, Criminal Medicine, Science of Group Health, Psychoanalysis, Science of Dental Health

Graduate School of Pharmaceutical Science(M 33/0, D 1/0)

Div. of Pharmaceutical Science(M 33/0, D 1/0)

Master's: Biochemistry, Hygienic Chemistry, Pharmacology, Microbial Chemistry, Food Chemistry, Pharmaceutics, Pharmacognosy and Plant Chemistry, Analytical Chemistry, Organic Chemistry, Medicinal Chemistry, Physical Chemistry, Hospital Pharmacy, Doctoral: Biochemistry, Hygienic Chemistry, Pharmacology, Microbial Chemistry, Food Chemistry, Pharmaceutics, Pharmacognosy and Plant Chemistry, Analytical Chemistry, Organic Chemistry, Medicinal Chemistry, Physical Chemistry

Graduate School of Physical Education(M 12/0)

Div. of Physical Education(M 12/0)

Physical education, Physical Fitness, Sports medicine, Teaching method of Physical education, Coaching method, Exercise and Health

Graduate School of Science(M 32/0, D 5/0)

Div. of Chemistry(M 16/0, D 2/0)

Master's: Physical Chemistry of Solutions, Physical Chemistry of Reactions, Inorganic Chemistry, Analytical Chemistry, Organic Chemistry, Biochemistry, Doctoral: Physical Chemistry of Solutions, Physical Chemistry of Reactions, Inorganic Chemistry, Analytical Chemistry, Organic Chemistry, Biochemistry

Graduate School of Science(M 32/0, D 5/0)

Div. of Applied Mathematics(M 8/0, D 2/0)

Master's: Fundamental Mathematics, Functional Analysis, Mathematical Analysis, Computational Mathematics, Doctoral: Fundamental Mathematics, Fundamental Analysis, Mathematical Analysis, Computational Mathematics

Div. of Applied Physics(M 8/0, D 1/0)

Master's: Polymer Physics, Crystalline Physics, Solid State Physics, Geophysics, Applied Quantum Physics, Doctoral: Polymer Physics, Crystalline Physics, Solid State Physics, Geophysics, Applied Quantum Physics

鹿児島経済大学

(Kagoshima Keizai Daigaku)

Kagoshima Keizai University

8850 Shimofukumoto-cho, Kagoshima-shi, Kagoshima 891-01

☎ 0992-61-3211 FAX 0992-61-3299

Founded 1932
Professors 30
Associate Professors 33
Assistant Professors(Tenured) 25
Assistant Professors(Non-tenured) 89
Undergraduate Students/Foreign Students 3466/0
Library 207, 113 volumes
Contact: Admission Office

Educational philosophy The university aims to develop responsible and creative students and to educate them to have independent and cooperative minds.
Foreign students Under investigation.
Environment Located on a hillside in the southwest of kagoshima city, the university campus forms an ideal educational setting. It is easily accessible to central kagoshima by train and local bus.
Facilities The university provides the necessary facilities for high-level education. Over 200, 000 volumes are housed in the university library and the gymnasium is well-equipped. The newly completed computer center offers a comprehensive system of computer facilities with an audio-visual language lab for faculty and students' use.
Student activities There is a wide variety of both athletic and cultural circles. Students are encouraged to participate in annual sport and art festivals as well as in their own circle activities.

Undergraduate Programs

Faculty of Economics(2132/0)
  Dept. of Economics(1069/0)
  Dept. of Business Administration(1063/0)
Faculty of Sociology(1334/0)
  Dept. of Industrial Sociology(680/0)
  Dept. of Social Welfare(654/0)

鹿児島女子大学

(Kagoshima Joshi Daigaku)

Kagoshima Women's College

1904 Uchi, Hayato-cho, Aira-gun, Kagoshima 899-51

☎ 0995-43-1111 FAX 0995-43-1114

Founded 1979
Professors 15
Associate Professors 11
Assistant Professors(Tenured) 10
Assistant Professors(Non-tenured) 27
Research Assistants 2
Undergraduate Students/Foreign Students 683/0
Library 58, 035 volumes
Contact: General Affairs Division

Educational philosophy In addition to our research, we aim at developing in our students necessary skills, knowledge and judgement, helping them to acquire honesty, independence and creativity, to broaden their horizons and thus to contribute to the betterment of society.
Environment Standing between the magnificent Kirishima Mountain Range and the plains of the prosperous technopolis of Kokubu and Hayato, with the spectacular expanse of Kagoshima Bay to the south, the college enjoys flowers in all seasons and superb greenery. Only 8km from Kagoshima International Airport and 10km from JR Hayato Station.
Facilities Lectures and research buildings, library, language, gymnasium, cafeteria, dormitory, etc.
Student activities Popular campus events include college festival, sports festival, interclass matches, summer camp, coming-of-the-Age ceremony, etc. Included in the extracurricular activities are athletics, tennis, volleyball, Karate, drama, music, broadcasting, chorus, calligraphy, kabuki, Noh and ESS.

Undergraduate Programs

Faculty of Literature(683/0)
  Dept. of Japanese Literature(176/0)
  Dept. of English Literature(149/0)
  Dept. of Human Relations(358/0)

熊本工業大学

(Kumamoto Kôgyô Daigaku)

The Kumamoto Institute of Technology

4-22-1 Ikeda, Kumamoto-shi, Kumamoto 860

☎ 096-326-3111 FAX 096-326-3000

Founded 1967
Professors 69
Associate Professors 59
Assistant Professors(Tenured) 26
Assistant Professors(Non-tenured) 68
Research Assistants 20
Undergraduate Students/Foreign Students 3, 479/1
Graduate Students/Foreign Students 37/0
Library 74, 685 volumes

Educational philosophy Since its establishment, the College, as a private institution, has been future ori-

entated in its research and the systematic promotion of departments and new knowledge. This will also continue to do in future.
Foreign students We believe that foreign students can enjoy a rewarding experience in our shool, and can contribute a great deal to promoting mutual understanding and the development of friendly relations.
Environment The town of Kumamoto, with a population of 570, 000, is located in the center of Kyushu. From here, one can see the volcanic smoke rising from Mt. Aso, which is the biggest caldera in the world.
Facilities Center of advanced instrumental analysis, Study centers(located in seaside and near Mt. Aso), Computer center, Library, Baseball ground, Gymnasium, Photographical center, Restaurant, etc.
Student activities Popular campus events includes school festival, sports festival, study tour for freshmen. There is a wide variety of extra curricular activities, including karate, soccer, table tennis, photo, movie, etc.

Undergraduate Programs

Faculty of Engineering(3, 479/1)
- **Dept. of Applied Microbial Technology**(400/0)
- **Dept. of Architecture**(494/0)
- **Dept. of Civil Engineering**(475/0)
- **Dept. of Electrical Engineering**(469/1)
- **Dept. of Electronic Engineering**(484/0)
- **Dept. of Industrial Chemistry**(325/0)
- **Dept. of Mechanical Engineering**(474/0)
- **Dept. of Structural Engineering**(358/0)

Graduate Programs

Graduate School of Technology(M 33/0, D 4/0)

Div. of Applied Microbiology and Technology(M 20/0, D 4/0)
Applied Microbiology, Microbial Biochemistry, Environmental Microbiology, Food and Microbial Technology, Microbial Genetics

Div. of Structural Engineering(M 4/0)
Structures Strength Vibration and Materials Engineering, Fluid Engineering, Control Engineering, Architecture

Div. of Applied Chemisty(M 9/0)
Applied Inorganic Chemistry, Applied Organic Chemistry, Applied Macromolecular Chemistry, Chemical Reaction Engineering, Environmental Chemistry and Analytical Chemistry

熊本商科大学
(Kumamoto Shôka Daigaku)
Kumamoto University of Commerce

2-5-1 Oe, Kumamoto-shi, Kumamoto 862
☎ 096-364-5161 FAX 096-363-1289

Founded 1954
Professors 57
Associate Professors 27
Assistant Professors(Tenured) 10
Assistant Professors(Non-tenured) 105
Undergraduate Students/Foreign Students 5, 496/20
Graduate Students/Foreign Students 9/4
Library 383, 138 volumes
Contact: Admissions Division

Educational philosophy Kumamoto University of Commerce has valued independence, freedom and cooperation since its foundation. Every student is taught to become a person who contribute to the local community, and to be an internationally minded person as well in this era of internationalism.
Foreign students We are very positive about accepting foreign students, since we believe that foreign students contribute to promoting mutual understanding as well as improving the level of education in our University.
Environment Kumamoto University of Commerce is located in the city of Kumamoto in Kyushu, the southernmost main island of Japan. Kumamoto City, with a population of 580, 000, is famous for its abundant greenery and the city where the Kumamoto Prefectural Office is located.
Facilities University Library, The Institute of Economics and Business, The Institute of Foreign Affairs, Computer Center, Foreign Language Training Center, Language Laboratories, Gymnasium, Swimming Pool
Student activities Popular campus events include school festival, a seminar meeting, " Sports Day " activities and freshmen welcome picnic. There is a wide variety of extracurricular activities, including volunteer work, swing band, student newspaper, drama, martial arts, etc.
Academic programs for foreign students The Faculty of General Education offers the following courses in Japanese Language and Japanese Studies for foreign students: Japanese Ⅰ through Ⅳ and Japanese Studies Ⅰ through Ⅲ.
Services for foreign students The tuition is exempted specially for foreign students by one half. Housing information, part-time job information, counseling, cultural exchange program information such as homestay and home visit

Undergraduate Programs

Faculty of Commerce(3, 555/17)
  Dept. of Commerce(1, 961/5)
  Dept. of Management(685/12)
Faculty of Economics(1, 941/3)
  Dept. of Economics(1, 753/3)
  Dept. of International Economics(188/0)

Graduate Programs

Graduate School of Commerce(M 9/4)
  Div. of Commerce(M 9/4)
Accounting, Commerce, Finance, History of Commerce and Commercial Policy, Management

---

久留米工業大学
(Kurume Kôgyô Daigaku)

Kurume Institute of Technology

2228 Kamitsu-machi, Kurume-shi, Fukuoka 830
☎ 0942-22-2345

Founded 1976

Undergraduate Programs

Faculty of Engineering
  Dept. of Architectural Equipment Engineering
  Dept. of Electronics and Information Engineering
  Dept. of Mechanical Engineering
  Dept. of Transport Mechanical Engineering

久留米大学
(Kurume Daigaku)

Kurume University

67 Asahi-machi, Kurume-shi, Fukuoka 830
☎ 0942-35-3311 FAX 0942-32-5191

Founded 1928
Professors 94
Associate Professors 64
Assistant Professors(Tenured) 118
Assistant Professors(Non-tenured) 276
Research Assistants 208
Undergraduate Students/Foreign Students 4, 596/1
Graduate Students/Foreign Students 124/17
Library 417, 219 volumes
Contact: Administrative Office of the School of Commerce and law, Kurume University, 1635 Mii-machi, Kurume-shi, Fukuoka, 830 ☎ 0942-44-2160 Administrative Office of the School of Medicine, Kurume University, 67 Asahi-machi, Kurume-shi, Fukuoka, 830 ☎ 0942-35-3311 ext. 722 or 0942-44-4259

Educational philosophy Kurume University aims to educate sincere specialists of deep refinement and expert knowledge, and to contribute to the progress of science and the advance of culture

Environment Kurume City with a population of 230, 000, the home of Kurume University, is located in the north central section of Kyushu Island. Situated at the foot of Mt, Kora. Kurume City is bounded on the north and west by the Chikugo River, the largest river in central Kyushu. Clean and beautiful, Kurume City is large enough to provide all the amenities of city life, and still small enough to retain a friendly small-town atmosphere.

Facilities Libraries, Computer Center, Sports, Training Center, Gymnasiums, Auditoriums, Instituute for Studies on Industrial Economics, Institute of comparative studies of international cultures and societies, Institute of Brain Diseases, Institute of Cardiovascular Diseases, Radioisotope Institute for Basic and Clinical Medicine, Experimental Animal Center, Institute of Life Science.

Student activities Popular campus events include homecoming, school festival, freshmen welcome party. There is a wide variety of extra curricular activities, including choral group, marching band, student newspaper, drama, various sports clubs, etc.

Undergraduate Programs

Faculty of Law(1, 244/1)
  Dept. of Law(1, 244/1)
Faculty of Commerce(2, 591/0)
  Dept. of Commercial Sciences(1, 299/0)
  Dept. of Economics(1, 292/0)
School of Medicine(761/0)
  Dept. of Medicine(761/0)

Graduate Programs

Graduate School of Comparative Studies of International Cultures and Societies(M 25/15)
  Div. of Comparative Studies of International Cultures and Societies(M 25/15)
I Theoretical Studies of Cultures and Societies, A. Comparative Studies of Structures and Functions of Cultures, a. Scientific Studies(Psychological, Antholopological, Sociological Studies, etc.), b. Historical Studies(Historical Studies of far east. Social History of China, etc.), c. Linguistic Analysis(Structural Analysis of French. Analysis of Japanese Language, Comparative Studies of Western Literature, etc.), B. Comparative studies of Law(Comparative Constitutions, Clinical Law, Civil Law, Penalty Law, Commercial Law, Social Law, etc.), C. Comparative Studies Economical Functions (Functional Analysis, Industrial Analysis, Statistical Analysis of Economy, Comparative History of Economy), D.

Comparative Studies of Life-Situations(Human Environment, Medical Study of Human Environment Ecology, etc.), II Area Studies(in Japan Asia and Europe)

Graduate School of Medicine(D 99/2)

Div. of Internal Medicine(D 51/1)

Div. of Physiological Science(D 9/0)

Div. of Pathological Science(D 22/0)

Div. of Social Medicine(D 3/0)

Div. of Surgery(D 24/1)

Anatomy, Physiology, Medical biochemistry, Pharmacology, Pathology, Immunology, Microbiology, Public health, Environmental Medicine, Parasitology, Legal Medicine, Internal Medicine, Endocrinology and Metabolism, Neuropsychiatry, Pediatrics and Child Health, Surgery, Neurosurgery, Orthopedic Surgery, Dermatology, Urology, Otorhinolaryngology-Head and Neck Surgery, Obstetrtics and Gynecology, Radiology, Anesthesiology, Oral Surgery, Plastic Surgery.

九州国際大学

(Kyûshû Kokusai Daigaku)

Kyushu International University

5-9-1 Edamitsu, Yahatahigashi-ku, Kitakyushu-shi, Fukuoka 805

☎ 093-671-8910 FAX 093-671-8995

Founded 1947
Professors 65
Associate Professors 26
Assistant Professors(Tenured) 11
Assistant Professors(Non-tenured) 87
Undergraduate Students/Foreign Students 3, 064/8
Library 234, 146 volumes
Contact: Department of Public Relations ☎ 093-671-8916

Educational philosophy The University aims to prepare students for professions which require well-balanced knowledge and specialized technology to meet the demands of society. Being small in size, the University has the advantage of keeping friendly relationships between teachers and students.

Foreign students We believe that foreign students will grow up as a generalist as well as a specialist in their field of study, and can make friendly relations.

Environment We have two campuses. The Edamitsu Campus is set high on a hill over-looking the natural beauty of the Genkai National Park. The second of these, the Hirano Campus is located in the International Village, an area set aside by the City of Kitakyushu for international exchange.

Facilities University Library, Research Center for Community, Gymnasium, Language Laboratory, Computer Room.

Student activities Our campus life begins with freshmen meeting. One of the most popular campus events is school festival in autumn. Various extracurricular activities, such as baseball, rugby and association football, track and field, Japanese archery, are carried out.

Academic programs for foreign students Japanese language class, English language class, Things Japanese class.

Services for foreign students Personal psychological counseling, Housing information, Cultural exchange program.

Undergraduate Programs

Faculty of Law and Economics(2, 677/4)

Dept. of Law(1, 334/1)

Dept. of Economics and Business Administration (1, 343/3)

Faculty of International Studies and Business(387/4)

Dept. of International Studies and Business(387/4)

九州共立大学

(Kyûshû Kyôritsu Daigaku)

Kyushu Kyoritsu University

1-1 Jiyugaoka, Yahata-nishi-ku, Kitakyushu-shi, Fukuoka 807

☎ 093-691-3331 FAX 093-603-8186

Founded 1965

Undergraduate Programs

Faculty of Economics

Dept. of Economics

Dept. of Management

Faculty of Engineering

Dept. of Architecture

Dept. of Civil Engineering

Dept. of Electric Engineering

Dept. of Environmental Chemistry

Dept. of Land Development

Dept. of Mechanical Engineering

九州産業大学

(Kyûshû Sangyô Daigaku)

Kyushu Sangyo University

2-3-1 Matsukadai, Higashi-ku, Fukuoka-shi, Fukuoka 813

☎ 092-673-5050 FAX 092-673-5599

Founded 1960
Professors 126
Associate Professors 88
Assistant Professors(Tenured) 33
Assistant Professors(Non-tenured) 340
Research Assistants 17
Undergraduate Students/Foreign Students 11, 324/21
Graduate Students/Foreign Students 73/11
Library 359, 908 volumes

Educational philosophy Founded in 1960, Kyushu Sangyo University is a private co-educational institution whose philosophy is to provide students with a well-balanced education, emphasizing both modern technical knowledge and intellectual development, which will enable students to cope successfully with today's technology-oriented world community.
Foreign students All international students who are eager to study at our university are welcome.
Environment The campus of Kyushu Sangyo University is set in an area of 500, 000 square meters of land in Fukuoka. This city, of approximately 1. 2 million inhabitants, is the largest metropolitan area and most rapidly growing city in the western part of Japan.
Facilities There are over 30 buildings on the campus, including the Central Building, the University Library, the Physical Education Center, and all the necessary facilities to accomodate comfortably more than 12, 000 students.
Student activities Special lecture to welcome new students, concerts, cultural and academic clubs open house week, school festival, orientation and introduction to extracurricular activities. 24 cultural and academic clubs. 28 athletic clubs.
Academic programs for foreign students Special subjects are provided for international students. For example: Japanese language, Japanese affairs.
Services for foreign students Student counseling, housing information, part-time job information, scholarship programs, cultural exchange programs.

Undergraduate Programs

Faculty of Art(1825/3)
Dept. of Design(816/2)
Dept. of Fine Arts(486/1)
Dept. of Photography(523/0)
Faculty of Commerce(4144/2)
Dept. of Commerce(2036/1)
Dept. of Economics(2108/1)
Faculty of Engineering(2768/1)
Dept. of Architecture(638/0)
Dept. of Civil Engineering(531/0)
Dept. of Electrical Engineering(551/0)
Dept. of Industrial Chemistry(513/0)
Dept. of Mechanical Engineering(535/1)

Graduate Programs

Graduate School of Art(M 24/10)
Div. of Fine Arts(M 11/1)
Div. of Design(M 2/1)
Graduate School of Economics(M 5/1)
Div. of Economics(M 5/1)
Graduate School of Engineering(M 44/0)
Div of Industrial Chemistry(M 21/0)
Div. of Mechanical Engineering(M 6/0)
Div. of Civil Engineering(M 10/0)
Div. of Architecture(M 4/0)
Div. of Electrical Engineering(M 3/0)

九州東海大学
(Kyûshû Tôkai Daigaku)
Kyushu Tokai University

223 Toroku, Kumamoto-shi, Kumamoto 862
☎ 096-382-1141 FAX 096-381-7956

Founded 1973
Professors 75
Associate Professors 45
Assistant Professors(Tenured) 26
Assistant Professors(Non-tenured) 98
Research Assistants 5
Undergraduate Students/Foreign Students 3094/4
Graduate Students/Foreign Students 19/3
Library 172, 586 volumes

Educational philosophy We aim to educate the students to become well-rounded and creative leaders who are well versed not only in their special scientific fields but in the humanities. We dedicate ourselves to contribute to development of the regional society and also to take the initiative to play an important role towards the prosperity of the world.
Foreign students We are promoting active academic exchanges with foreign institutes. We are also well prepared to accept researchers and students from abroad.
Environment Kumamoto campus is located in the center of Kumamoto which plays a leading role in various fields in Kyushu. Being about 30 kilometers to the east away from Kumamoto, Aso campus is located halfway up Mt. Aso which is the largest composite volcano in the world.
Facilities Library 172, 586 volumes, Institute of Science and Technical Research, Agricultural Research Institute, Information Development Techonlogy Center, Electronic Computer Center, Space Information Center
Student activities April: Orientation, Welcome Field Trip for Freshmen, October 31-November 5: School Festival(Kengkusai), Extracurricular activities: 36 Athletic clubs, 11 Academic clubs
Academic programs for foreign students Intensive Japanese Language Program(1 year, pre-college) Foreign Students Course with special curriculum. Special Japanese Language Course for Exchange Students.

Undergraduate Programs

Faculty of Agriculture(680/1)
Dept. of Agronomy(380/0)
Dept. of Animal Science(300/1)
Faculty of Engineering(2414/3)
Dept. of Architecture(397/0)
Dept. of Civil Engineering(387/0)
Dept. of Electrical Engineering(295/0)
Dept. of Electronics and Information Technology(288/0)
Faculty of Engineering(2414/3)
Dept. of Information and System Engineering(287/1)
Dept. of Management Engineering(378/2)
Dept. of Mechanical Engineering(382/0)

Graduate Programs

Graduate School of Agriculture(M 17/1, D 5/2)
Div. of Agronomy(M 10/0, D 2/1)
Plant Resources and Crop Science, Plant Breeding and Genetics, Horticultural Science, Plant Protection, Agricultural Economics
Div. of Animal Science(M 7/1, D 3/1)
Animal Breeding, Animal Reproduction, Animal Nutrition and Management, Functional Anatomy and Biochemistry, Grassland Science, Chemistry and Technology of Animal Products
Graduate School of Engineering(M 2/0)
Div. of Production Engineering(M 2/0)
Energy Engineering, Materials Engineering, Manufacturing Engineering
Div. of Information Engineering(M 0/0)
Computer Science and Engineering, Communication and Information Engineering

---

九州女子大学
(Kyûshû Joshi Daigaku)

Kyushu Women's University

1-1 Jiyugaoka, Yahata-nishi-ku, Kitakyushu-shi, Fukuoka 807
☎ 093-691-0591 FAX 093-691-6468

Founded 1962
Professors 22
Associate Professors 15
Assistant Professors(Tenured) 6
Assistant Professors(Non-tenured) 43
Research Assistants 12
Undergraduate Students/Foreign Students 723/3
Library 73, 000 volumes

Educational philosophy Three virtues such as " discipline ", " deligence " and " good manners " are mentioned as the spirit of foundation. Its practice is to deal with things and do good while disciplining himself. We aim at bringing up women with deep perspective and high sensitivity according to the educational philosophy.

Foreign students Overseas students are required to have a command of Japanese to meet the studies and have a guarantee in Japan. Now we have students from China and Formosa. They are supposed to learn Japanese culture besides professional education.

Environment The campus is located on a hill within 15 minutes' walk of Orio Station in Kitakyushu City of one million people. The academy is rich in greenery and natural beauty covering 500, 000 m^2. Nippon Steel Co. as the symbol of Japaneses modern industry and many other historic places are in its vicinities.

Facilities Facilities include a library with a spacious reading room, a gym with training and dancing rooms, the management of information rooms with personal computers, and word processors. Dormitories housing 600 students lie within and outside the campus.

Student activities University festival organrized by students is held on a large scale every November. They are 19 sport clubs such as a basketball club which actively joins a national meet, an amateur golf club and so on as well as 20 cultural clubs like a new etiquette club to study about Japanese mind.

Academic programs for foreign students Lectures are given on Japanese language and Japanese affairs for overseas students. Tutor system is to be introduced in 1991.

Services for foreign students Full-time lecturers are in charge of counselling students from abroad. Classmates are ready to show them around to historic places in the city and help them to have a good valuable time.

Undergraduate Programs

Faculty of Home Economics(237/2)
Dept. of Home Economics(237/2)
Faculty of Liberal Arts(495/1)
Dept. of English Literature(225/0)
Dept. of Japanese Literature(270/1)

活水女子大学
(Kassui Joshi Daigaku)

Kwassui Women's College

1-50 Higashi-Yamate-machi, Nagasaki-shi, Nagasaki 850
☎ 0958-22-4107 FAX 0958-28-3702

Founded 1879
Professors 17
Associate Professors 10
Assistant Professors(Tenured) 4
Assistant Professors(Non-tenured) 18
Undergraduate Students/Foreign Students 488/0
Library 135, 640 volumes

Contact: International Section

Educational philosophy The name of Kwassui means living water and is a symbol of the living power of Christ in human lives, sending us out to serve. Our purpose is to send out each student as an independent and responsible woman under God, with a broad outlook, an international mind, willing to serve the community.
Foreign students We hope foreign students will recognize our educational philosophy, and contribute to our international exchange program. Please enjoy your campus life at Kwassui.
Environment Nagasaki city, with a population of 450, 000, is located in the west of Japan. There are mountains, slopes and a historical harbor, the only window to the outside world from 1639 till 1859. Our college is built on the hill looking down on the harbor, 2 miles south of Nagasaki station. It is convenient for transportation and for studying one aspect of Japanese history and culture.
Facilities Chapel, Library, Gymnasium, Dormitory and Refectory.
Student activities Popular campus events include chapel services, retreats, the school festival, sports day, ski tours and the special Christmas service. There is a variety of extracurricular activities including YMCA, the art of flower arrangement, the tea ceremony, volleyball, tennis, etc.
Academic programs for foreign students We are planning supplemental Japanese language classes, the tutoring system, etc.
Services for foreign students We are planning counseling services, a health clinic, part-time job information, cultural exchange program, etc

Undergraduate Programs

Faculty of Literature(488/0)
Dept. of English Literature(245/0)
Dept. of Japanese Literature(243/0)

宮崎産業経営大学
(Miyazaki Sangyô-Keiei Daigaku)

Miyazaki Sangyo-Keiei University

100 Maruo, Furujo-cho, Miyazaki-shi, Miyazaki 880
☎ 0985-52-3111 FAX 0985-51-0859

Founded 1987
Professors 29
Associate Professors 5
Assistant Professors(Tenured) 23
Assistant Professors(Non-tenured) 37
Research Assistants 2
Undergraduate Students/Foreign Students 1, 040/1
Library 43, 810 volumes
Contact: Miyazaki Sangyo-Keiei University ☎ ext. 113

Educational Philosophy We seek to broaden our students' mind, new creations, and rich humanities, and to read them to make practical contributions to both Japanese society and to the world at large through our education.
Foreign students We believe that foreign students can enjoy a rewarding experience in our school, and we also believe contribute a great deal to promoting mutual understanding and the development of friendly relations.
Environment Our university is located close to downtown Miyazaki City with a population of 300, 000, (You can commute to our school by bus within five minute from the Miyazaki central bus station)and it is surrounded by woods and ponds. It is an ideal environment for studing.
Facilities An affiliated library, on the campus we have a computer room, an audio-visual classroom, and a sports training center.
Student activities School festival is held over thrre days during November every year. There is a wide variety of extra curricular activities, including ESS, a flower arrangement group, a brass band, a baseball, a soccer, a tennis, and a Japanese archery, etc.
Academic programs for foreign students A special program on foreign students is under review among a committee.
Services for foreign students Psychological counseling, part-time job information, vocational guidance

Undergraduate Programs

Faculty of Law(511/0)
Dept. of Law
Faculty of Business Administration(529/1)
Dept. of Business Administration

南九州大学
(Minami Kyûshû Daigaku)

Minami Kyushu College

11609 Minamitakanabe-Oaza, Takanabe-cho, Koyu-gun, Miyazaki 884
☎ 0983-23-0793 FAX 0983-22-3444

Founded 1967
Professors 22
Associate Professors 14
Assistant Professors(Tenured) 14
Assistant Professors(Non-tenured) 43
Undergraduate Students/Foreign Students 1, 509/0
Library 49, 354 volumes
Contact: Admission Office

Educational Philosophy We aim to have the students master professional knowledge in the field of agriculture and provide them with a wide range of knowledge to prepare for the world of future.
Foreign students Althogh we have been considering, we are presently not in a position to receive foreign students due to lack of proper facilities.
Environment Takanabe Town has a population of 23, 000, located 25 km north of Miyazaki City. It is an old castle town eager to promote learning.
Facilities Computer Laboratory, Cell Biotechnology Laboratory, Research Farm, X–ray Radiation Facility, Gymnasium, School Library, Japanese–style Garden.
Student activities Annual College Festival and Freshmen–Welcome Sports Festival are held. We have 25 sports clubs and 20 cultural clubs.

Undergraduate Programs

Faculty of Horticulture(1509/0)
Dept. of Horticulture(431/0)
Dept. of Landscape Gardening(363/0)
Dept. of Agricultural Economics(330/0)
Dept. of Food Science and Technology(385/0)

長崎総合科学大学
(Nagasaki Sôgô Kagaku Daigaku)

Nagasaki Institute of Applied Science

536 Aba–machi, Nagasaki–shi, Nagasaki 851–01
☎ 0958–39–3111 FAX 0958–39–0584

Founded 1965
Professors 38
Associate Professors 33
Assistant Professors(Tenured) 12
Assistant Professors(Non–tenured) 101
Research Assistants 13
Undergraduate Students/Foreign Students 2, 213/35
Graduate Students/Foreign Students 14/1
Library 98, 812 volumes
Contact: Admission Office, ext. 2222, 2223, Graduate Admision Office, ext. 3027

Educational philosophy We train our students and further expect them to acquire information techniques and methods outside of their own specialities. We are proud of being a rare private college that sends excellent engineers into the highly technological, information–based Japanese society.
Environment Nagasaki Institute of Applied Sciences is in Nagasaki Prefecture, located in the western extremity of Japan. Nagasaki is one of the most famous tourist cities in Japan, retaining its exotic atmosphere and offering many historical sights.
Facilities Computer Science Center, Nagasaki Institute for Peace Culture, Technical Research Laboratory, The Institute of Regional Sciences.
Student activities We have school festival and sports festival. And We have many activities, baseball, soccer, boxing, basketball, tennis, youth hostel club, light music, cinema, art, etc.
Academic programs for foreign students " Japanese Culture ", " Japan Today "
Services for foreign students We help male students to find private lodgings. Our college provides a dormitory for female students.

Undergraduate Programs

Faculty of Engineering(2213/35)
Dept. of Administrative Technology(450/16)
Dept. of Architecture(494/3)
Dept. of Electrical Engineering(451/5)
Dept. of Mechanical Engineering(565/9)
Dept. of Naval Architectural Engineering(258/2)

Graduate Programs

Graduate School of Engineering(M 14/1)
Fluid Engineering, Structural Engineering

中村学園大学
(Nakamura Gakuen Daigaku)

Nakamura Gakuen College

5–7–1 Befu, Jonan–ku, Fukuoka–shi, Fukuoka 814–01
☎ 092–851–2531 FAX 092–841–7762

Founded 1965
Professors 26
Associate Professors 14
Assistant Professors(Tenured) 4
Assistant Professors(Non–tenured) 30
Research Assistants 17
Undergraduate Students/Foreign Students 1, 049/1
Graduate Students/Foreign Students 5/1
Library 108, 170 volumes
Contact: Admission Office

Educational philosophy We aim at educating specialists devoted to the improvement of nutrition and domestic life and cultivating educators dedicating themselves to child education.
Foreign students We believe the improvement of nutrition and education is a universal theme of the human race. Foreign students who agree with our belief will be made very welcome.
Environment Our college is located in Fukuoka city, Kyushu Island, the westernmost of the four main islands of Japan. The college has the student body over 1, 000 whose majority are females. Some students commute from home and others live in the three dormitories.
Facilities Newly developed library, Music Hall,

Gymnasium, Animal Center, Research Center of Nutrition and Health, Seminar House, Electron Microscope Room, Computer Center and a big lecture hall, etc.
Student activities Our college provides 47 club activities, including small groups and circles. Several music clubs hold concerts every year. Other students participate in the other various activities, such as Naginata, basketball, archery, baseball, flower arrangement, tea ceremony, calligraphy, etc.
Academic programs for foreign students We highly value our " tutorial " system for personal guidance to all students including those from abroad.
Services for foreign students College dormitories, housing information, homestay, part-time job service, cultural exchange programs, personal/psychological counseling, etc.

Undergraduate Programs

Faculty of Home Economics(1, 049/1)
Dept. of Child Education(607/0)
Dept. of Food and Nutrition(442/1)

Graduate Programs

Graduate School of Health and Nutrition Sciences (M 5/1)
Div. of Health and Nutrition Sciences(M 5/1)
Nutritional Biochemistry, Nutrition Physiology and Morphology, Food Science, Health Promotion Science, Clinical Nutrition, Environment and Nutrition

One-Year Graduate Programs

Course of Food Science, Course of Nutrition, Course of Child Study, Course of Primary Education

---

日本文理大学
(Nippon Bunri Daigaku)
Nippon Bunri University

1727 Ichigi, Oita-Shi, Oita 870-03
☎ 0975-92-1600 FAX 0975-93-2071

Founded 1967
Professors 67
Associate Professors 22
Assistant Professors(Tenured) 17
Assistant Professors(Non-tenured) 59
Research Assistants 1
Undergraduate Students/Foreign Students 4, 865/47
Library 170, 000 volumes

Educational philosophy We aim at teaching both academic and industrial education to develop intellectual and applied abilities so that students could contribute much to the era of internationalization.
Foreign students Nearly 70 students from various countries in the world are studying at our university. We made friendship and fidelity our motto.
Environment The city of Oita, with a population of 400, 000, is located in the east of Kyushu, blessed with abundant beautiful historic scenes.
Facilities The Research Institute for the Pacific Region, Library, Video-Library, Traininig Center, Gymansium, Auditorium, Swimming pool, Computer Center, Information center, etc.
Student activities Popular campus events includes school festival, freshman welcome party, etc. There is a wide variety of extra curricular sport's activities.
Academic programs for foreign students Japanese language is a compulsory subject instead of a second language.
Services for foreign students Both the resiedents who live in this town and the Oita Committee for Economic Development, have been supporting the students in cooperation with our university.

Undergraduate Programs

Faculty of Engineering(2855/25)
Dept. of Mechanical Engineering(467/2)
Dept. of Electrical Engineering(371/4)
Dept. of Civil Engineering(339/1)
Dept. of Architecture(516/2)
Dept. of Industrial Engineering(355/11)
Dept. of Industrial Chemistry(361/3)
Dept. of Aeronautics(445/2)
Faculty of Business and Economics(2010/22)
Dept. of Business Administration(934/15)
Dept. of Economics(1076/7)

西九州大学
(Nishikyûshû Daigaku)
Nishikyushu University

4490-9 Hirayama, Osaki, Kanzaki-machi, Kanzaki-gun, Saga 842
☎ 0952-52-4191

Founded 1968

Undergraduate Programs

Faculty of Home Economics
Dept. of Food and Nutrition
Dept. of Social welfare

西日本工業大学
(Nishinippon Kôgyô Daigaku)
Nishinippon Institute of Technology

1633 Aratsu, Kanda-cho, Miyako-gun, Fukuoka 800-03
☎ 09302-3-1491 FAX 09302-4-7900

Founded 1967
Professors 18
Associate Professors 30
Assistant Professors(Tenured) 5
Assistant Professors(Non-tenured) 57
Research Assistants 9
Undergraduate Students/Foreign Students 2, 079/0
Library 95, 301 volumes
Contact: The instruction department

Educational philosophy We are consistent in aiming at the development of creative activity based on a complete mastery of fundamental technical skill, through courses of study extended in accordance with the ability and aptitude of individual students, placing as much emphasis on the formation of character, the cultivation of an independent spirit and a well-balanced mind.

Foreign students Since there is a harmonius and close teamwork between the faculty and the student body prevailing on the campus, the will assuredly lead to helpful academic and private counselling and suggestion readily extended to foreign students by Japanese teachers/students.

Environment The campus, covering approximately 160,000, is situated on a low rise in a pastoral and tranquil area along the Nippo Line(JR Kyushu). Rich in historical sites, the town of Kanda, where the campus is located, is adjacent to the Kitakyushu Industrial District, and is converted to an industrial area, swarmed with big plants on its reclaimed coastland.

Facilities an information processing center equipped with computers comparable in size with those of private college in Japan, a geotechnical research institution, a libraty with a collection of 100,000 volumes and over a thousand different kinds of magazines

Student activities The annual campus events under the auspices of the student Council include the cultural festival, the sports day as well as the campus festival, so attractive to the townspeople, reputed as being among the town's big events. In the extracurricular activities the campus has 31 clubs, both cultural and sporting, including the dancing circle.

Academic programs for foreign students Constant guidance is designed for the improvement of foreign student's studying and living conditions. No special courses are offered to them and they must take same classes as Japanese students. A tutor is ready to be in contact with them.

Services for foreign students No residential facilities are available to foreign students within the campus, but the appropriate section will help them to find suitable off-campus living accomodation. Partial or total exemption from tution fees is granted to foreign students.

Undergraduate Programs

Faculty of Engineering(2, 079/0)
Dept. of Architecture Engineering(461/0)
Dept. of Civil Engineering(443/0)
Dept. of Electrical Engineering(598/0)
Dept. of Mechanical Engineering(577/0)

西南学院大学
(Seinan Gakuin Daigaku)
Seinan Gakuin University

6-2-92 Nishijin, Sawara-ku, Fukuoka-shi, Fukuoka 814
☎ 092-841-1311 FAX 092-823-3227

Founded 1949
Professors 115
Associate Professors 44
Assistant Professors(Tenured) 12
Assistant Professors(Non-tenured) 256
Undergraduate Students/Foreign Students 7, 447/3
Graduate Students/Foreign Students 46/1
International Division Students
(One Year Study Abroad) 18
Library 585, 175 volumes
Contact: Undergraduate Admission: Admission Office ☎ 092-823-3324,3297
Graduate Admission: Graduate School Office ☎ 092-823-3368
International Division Adimission: International Exchange Office ☎ 092-823-3345,3346

Educational philosophy Seinan Gakuin University, founded in 1916 as an academy for boys by Charles K. Doziei, a Southern Baptist missionary from the United States, is part of Seinan Gakuin Educational Foundation. All through its history, Seinan Gakuin has aimed at a high academic quality of education and character education based on Christian principles, to produce internationally-minded graduates.

Foreign students Over the years, Seinan Gakuin has accepted, besides exchange students in the International Division, other foreign students, mainly from Asia. To be admitted, they must have a certain level of academic standing and competency in Japanese to cope with regular courses taught in Japanese.

Environment The University is conveniently located in the residential and academical area of Fukuoka City, which has a population of 1.2 million, and which is the center of politics and industries in Kyushu island. Students can enjoy easy access to the scenic mountains and to the beautiful sea.

Facilities United Nations Depository Library, European Documentation Centre, Computer Center, Language Laboratory and Video Library, Audio-visual Classrooms, Gymnasium, Outdoor Swimming Pool, Athletic Fields, Auditorium, Seminar House.

Student activites Popular campus events include the University Festival Freshmen Welcome Parties, Musical events. There are various academical and sports clubs and circles such as Government Examinations Preparation groups, Literary and Choral groups, Symphony Orchestra, Marching Band, Baseball, Rugby, American Football, and many others.

Academic programs for foreign students Educational field trips to historical areas, Japanese language tutoring to encourage language studies and fellowship with Japanese students.

Services for foreign students Furnished apartments, counseling, health clinic information, homestay information, part-time language teaching job opportunities upon request, friendship gathering opportunities by local organizations

Undergraduate Programs

Dept. of Commerce(1, 680/0)
  Div. of Business Administration(791/0)
  Div. of Commerce(889/0)
Dept. of Economics(1, 495/0)
  Economics Course(1,159/0)
  International Economics Course(336/0)
Dept. of Law(1, 718/0)
  Div. of Law
Dept. of Literature(2, 522/3)
  Div. of Childhood Education(554/1)
  Div. of English Literature(545/0)
  Div. of Foreign Languages(733/1)
    English Course(481/1)
    French Course(252/0)
  Div. of International Cultures(690/1)
Dept. of Theology(32/0)
  Div. of Theology(32/0)
International Division (One Year Study Abroad Program) (/18)

Graduate Programs

Graduate School of Business Administration(M 5/1, D 6/1)
  Course in Business Administration
Principles of Business Administration, Principles of Business Management, Personnel Management & Labor Relations, Financial Management, Organizational Psychology, Economic Theory of Corporation, Industrial Sociology, Economics of Public Enterprise, Business History, Theory of Medium and Small Enterprises, Advanced Theories in Marketing, Theory of Foreign Trade, Distribution System Theory, Theory of Securities market, Theory of Money and Banking, Financial Accounting, Management Accounting, Cost Accounting, Tax Accounting, Theory of Audit, Principles of Acconting, Financial Analysis

Graduate School of Economics(M 1/0)
  Couse in Economics(M 1/0)
Economics, History of Economics, Occidental Economic History, Economic Policy, World Economy, Public Finance, International Financial Management, Statistics, Social Policy

Graduate School of Law(M 14/0, D 3/0)
  Course in Law
Constitutional Law, Administrative Law, Civil Law, Commercial Law, Criminal Law, Civil Procedure Law, International Law, Social Law, Economic Law, International Private law, Phylosophy of Law, History of Law, Sociology of Law, Political Science, Political and Diplomatic History, International Politics

Graduate School of Literature(M 11/0, D 6/0)
  Course in English Literature(M 8/0, D 5/0)
Research in English Literature, Research in American Literature, Research in English Philology
  Course in French Literature(M 3/0, D 1/0)
Research in French Literature, Research in French Philology

One-Year Graduate Programs

Theology Course
  Theology Major
Commerce Course
  Cmmerce Major
Economics Course
  Economics Major
Literature Course
  International Cultures Major

尚絅大学
(Shôkei Daigaku)
Shokei College

2155-7 Nirenoki, Shimizu-machi, Kumamoto-shi, Kumamoto 860
☎ 096-338-8840 FAX 096-338-9301

Founded 1975
Professors 17
Associate Professors 3
Assistant Professors(Tenured) 8
Assistant Professors(Non-tenured) 14
Undergraduate Students/Foreign Students 523/1
Library 44, 499 volumes
Contact: The Instructions Department

Educational philosophy The aims of the education in our college are five: virtue of modesty, constancy, love and integrity, diligence and gratitude. By developing these aims we contribute to the culture of our society and of the world. We expect our students to develop intellectual abilities as well as moral abilities to use them for their self-realization.

Foreign students Our belief is that the true love of the contry and tradition comes from knowing other cultures and peoples. In order to be able to accept foreign students, we are going to improve our system of curriculum and equipment to facilitate their life here.
Environment Our college is in the north of Kumamoto Ciyt, the seat of prefectural office. The school building are on a low hill surrounded by the suburban residential area, about 15 kilometers from downtown and 15 minutes' walk from the nearest JR station. The site commands views of Kumamoto plains and volcano Aso.
Facilities School library, Language Laboratory, Japanese Calligraphy Laboratory, Word Processor Center, Gymnasium, Swimming Pool, Auditorium.
Student activities Campus events include school festival, freshmen welcome excursion, sports festival, extra curricular activities e. g. music, drama, poetry, Japanese poetry(Tanka), art, Koto(a kind of musical instrument), tea-ceremony, flower arrangement, Japanese calligraphy, comics, mountaineering, badminton, tennis, etc.
Academic programs for foreign students As for supplemental Japanese language class, we are to consider about it.
Services for foreign students College dormitory is available to foreign students. Personal counseling and homestay are ready to be in service.

Undergraduate Programs

Faculty of Literature(523/1)
Dept. of Japanese Literature(305/1)
Dept. of English Literature(218/0)

東和大学
(Tôwa Daigaku)
Towa University

1-1-1 Chikushigaoka, Minami ku, Fukuoka-shi, Fukuoka 815
☎ 092-541-1511 FAX 092-552-2707

Founded 1967
Professors 22
Associate Professors 13
Assistant Professors(Tenured) 12
Assistant Professors(Non-tenured) 69
Research Assistants 9
Undergraduate Students/Foreign Students 2, 091/7
Library 44, 425 volumes
Contact: Student's Affairs Office

Educational philosophy We aim teaching and studying up-to-date high-level art and sciences to develop intellectual, moral and applied abilities so students may contribute much to cultural betterment and social improvement.
Foreign students We believe that foreign students can enjoy a rewarding experience in our university.
Environment The town of Chikushigaoka is located in the south of Fukuoka city, 4 miles south of the heart of the city, Tenjin. Though located in a big city, Chikushigaoka is in the suburbs.
Facilities Library, Computer Center, Research Center, Gymnasium
Student activities Popular campus events include, a school festival and orientation for freshmen, There is a wide variety of extra curricular activities, including American football, Judo, Cheerleading, Photography, Computer Club, and more.
Academic programs for foreign students Supplemental Japanese language classes.

Undergraduate Programs

Faculty of Technology(2091/7)
Dept. of Chemical Engineering(226/0)
Dept. of Electric Engineering(842/0)
Dept. of Constructional Engineering (Civil Engineering Major/Architecture Major) (577/0)
Dept. of Industrial Engineering(446/0)

産業医科大学
(Sangyô Ika Daigaku)
University of Occupational and Environmental Health, Japan

1-1 Iseigaoka, Yahatanishi-ku, Kitakyushu-shi, Fukuoka 807
☎ 093-603-1611 FAX 093-602-5482

Founded 1978
Professors 56
Associate Professors 55
Assistant Professors(Tenured) 37
Assistant Professors(Non-tenured) 114
Research Assistants 139
Undergraduate Students/Foreign Students 631/0
Graduate Students/Foreign Students 64/1
Library 90, 933 volumes
Contact: Admission Office, ☎ ext. 2219(Undergraduate) ext. 2273(Graduate)

Educatonal philosophy The University will educate medical and health professionals to educate themselves and to have as their lifelong philosophy a devotion to serving the health needs of humanity, aiming to become a pioneer in the field of health sciences in the 21st century.
Foreign students The foreign students will enjoy not only training themselves in the field of health sciences but also the beautiful natural environment in which historical sitis abound.
Environment The City of Kitakyushu, with a popu-

lation of 1, 034, 000, is located in northwest part of Kyushu. To reach, UOEH Univetsity in the case of the Super Express(Shinkansen), get off at Kokura, change to the Kagoshima Line for Hakata and get off at Orio.

Facilities Library, University Hospital, Institute of Industrial Ecological Sciences, Reserch Center for Common Use, Animal Reserch Center, Radio Isotope Reserch Center, Information Service Center, Audiovisual Education Center.

Student activities The school festival is one of the main events of the school year. There are also a large variety of extra curricular activities, such as, choral groups, cinema, photograph, students newspaper, baseball, soccer, golf, tennis, wandervogel club, yachting.

Undergraduate Programs

Faculty of Medicine(631/0)
Dept. of Medicine(631/0)

Graduate Programs

Graduate School of Medical Science(D 64/1)
Div. of Clinical/Biomedical Informatics(D 20/0)
Second Department of Internal Medicine, Radiology, Systems Physiology, Hyperbaric Medicine, Ergonomics, Neurosurgery, Ophthalmology, Oto-rhino-laryngology, Anesthesiology, Pediatrics, Obstetrics, Central Clinical Laboratory,

Div. of Medical/Occupational Health Science(D 29/1)
Pathology and Oncology, Microbiology, First Department of Internal Medicine, General and Abdominal Surgery, Thoracic and Cardiovascular Surgery, Orthopedic Surgery, Rehabilitation Medicine, Third Department of Internal Medicine, Dermatology, Oral Surgery, Urology,

Div. of Applied Health Science(D 10/0)
Environmental Health, Environmental Health Engineering, Radiation Biology and Health, Environmental Epidemiology, Human Ecology, Medical Zoology, Medical and Hospital Administration, Clinical Epidemiology, Health Policy and Management, Neurology, Psychiatry, Environmental Toxicology,

Div. of Fundamental Life Science(D 5/0)
Anatomy and Anthropology, Anatomy and Histology, Forensic Medicine, Biochemistry, Molecular Biology, Immunology, Physiology, Pharmacology, Pathology and Surgical Pathology

OKINAWA

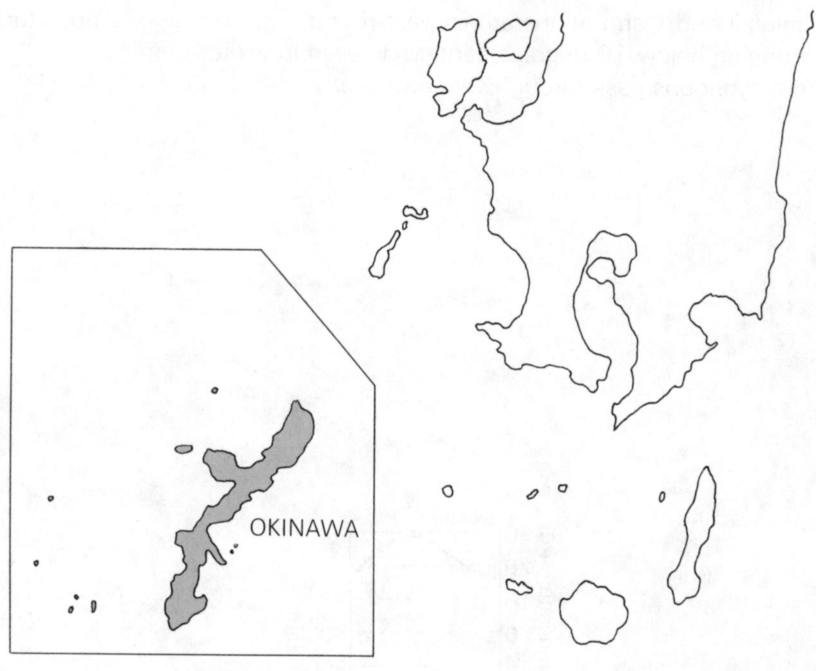

OKINAWA REGION CLIMATE

Heavy rainfall and warm temperatures year-round, with average temperature never dropping below 10 degrees centigrade even in winter.
Numerous typhoons pass through Okinawa yearly.

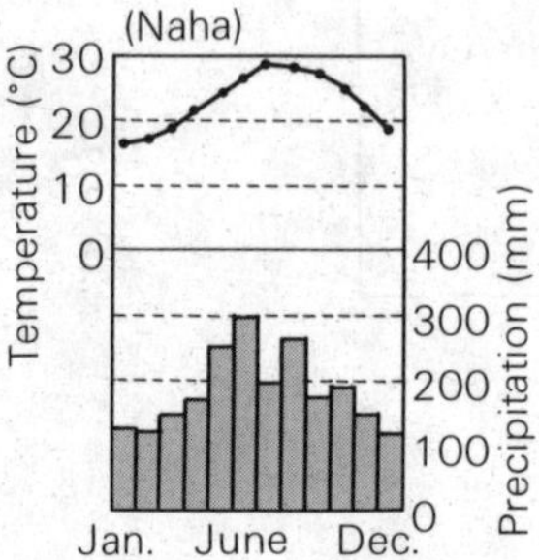

Average annual temperature
22.4°C
Annual precipitation
2,128mm

National Universities

琉球大学
(Ryûkyû Daigaku)

University Of The Ryukyus

1 Senbaru, Nishihara-cho, Okinawa 903-01
☎ 09889-5-2221 FAX 09889-5-4586

Founded 1950
Professors 245
Associate Professors 212
Assistant Professors(Tenured) 76
Assistant Professors(Non-tenured) 333
Research Assistants 227
Undergraduate Students/Foreign Students 6, 074/19
Graduate Students/Foreign Students 363/47
Library 678, 644 volumes
Contact: International Affairs Section, Department Of General Affairs ☎ ext. 2127

Educational philosophy Our University, as the institution for higher education, aims to cultivate persons of ability, pursue the truth, and contribute to the development of economy, society, education, and culture in Okinawa region, ultimately to the world peace and the welfare of the humans.

Foreign students The University aspires to be an international university toward the 21st century and has made a great effort at the promotion of international exchange. We heartily welcome to have students from countries all over the world.

Environment Okinawa, where the University is located in, is the southernmost prefecture and in the sub-tropical zone. Surrounded by the East China Sea and the Pacific Ocean, it has a population of 1.2 million and its climate is temperate all the year round.

Facilities Library, Marine Science Center, Health Administration Center, R.I. Facility, Information Processing Center, Language Laboratory, Research Institure of Tropical Agriculture, Extracurricular Activities Facilities, Gymnasium, University Hospital

Student activities Main campus events include orientation for foreign students, welcome and farewell parties for foreign students, university festival, Halloween party, Japanese speech contest by foreign students, etc. In addition, many students participate in various kinds of club as extracurricular activities

Academic programs for foreign students Supplemental Japanese classes for foreign students, Tutoring system, Tour of study, Extracurricular program for foreign students

Service for foreign students Counseling for foreign students, International House (dormitory for foreign students), Student dormitories, Homestay, Cultural exchange program, Health administration Center, Part-time job information

Undergraduate Programs

College of Law and Letters(1, 586/7)
Dept. of Law and Political Science(429/0)
Dept. of Economics(508/5)
Dept. of Literature(269/1)
Dept. of History(162/0)
Dept. of Sociology(218/1)
College of Education(956/2)
Elementary School Teachers Training Course(420/0)
Lower Secondary School Teachers Training Course(372/0)
Special School Teachers Training Course(81/0)
General Science Course(83/2)
College of Science(763/0)
Dept. of Mathematics(138/0)
Dept. of Physics(146/0)
Dept. of Chemistry(140/0)
Dept. of Biology(146/0)
Dept. of Marine Science(193/0)
Faculty of Medicine(888/2)
Dept. of Medicine(617/2)
Dept. of Health Sciences(271/0)
College of Engineering(1, 251/8)
Dept. of Mechanical Engineering(248/1)
Dept. of Civil Engineering(208/0)
Dept. of Architectural Engineering(210/0)
Dept. of Electrical Engineering(212/2)
Dept. of Electrical Engineering Information Engineering(203/5)
Dept. of Energy and Mechanical Engineering(170/0)
College of Agriculture(630/0)
Dept. of Agriculture(148/0)
Dept. of Agricultural Chemistry(145/0)
Dept. of Agicultural Engineering(118/0)
Dept. of Animal Science(118/0)
Dept. of Forestry(101/0)

Graduate Programs

Graduate School of Law(M 25/3)
Div. of Law(M 25/3)
Constitutional law and Administrative Law, Labor Law and Social Securities Law, Criminal Law and Criminal Procedure Law, Civil Law, Commercial Law, International Law and Phylosophy of Law, Civil Procedure Law, Political Science and Political History, Public Administration and History of Political Ideas, International Politics and Diplomatic History
Graduate School of Education(M 24/0)
Div. of School Education(M 9/0)
School of Education, Mathematics, Arts and Crafts, Technical Education, Home Economics, English
Div. of Subject Education(M 15/0)
School of Education, Mathematics, Arts and Crafts, Technical Education, Home Economics, English
Graduate School of Science(M 86/22)

Div. of Mathematics(M 7/0)
Div. of Physics(M 15/2)
Div. of Chemistry(M 13/3)
Div. of Biology(M 19/5)
Div. of Marine Science(M 15/12)
Algebra, Geometry, Analysis, Applied Mathematics, Mechanics, Electromagnetics, Solid State Physics, Quantum Physics, Physical Chemistry, Analytical Chemistry, Organic Chemistry, Inorganic Chemistry, Ecology, Phytotaxonomy snd Phytomorphology, Structural Zoology, Physiology and Biochemistry, Marine Biology, Marine Environmental Science, Marine Environmental Science, Coral Reef Science, Sedimentology, Geology
Graduate School of Medicine(D 73/4)
Div. of Bioregulation Study(D 62/3)
Pathophysiology, Artificial Organ, Hyperbaric, Medicine Anesthesiology and Physiological Monitoring, Oncolgy and Physiological Monitoring
Div. of Environmental Medicine–Ecology(D 11/1)
Social Medicine, Pathogen–Immunity, Tropical Medicine
Graduate School of Health Sciences(M 30/3)
Div. of Health Sciences(M 30/3)
Health Administration: Human Ecology, Epidemiology, Nutrition, Community Health Administration, Sanitary Zoology, Health Sociology
Health Care: Mental Health, Adult Health, Senile Health, Maternal Health, Child Health, Medical Rehabilitation, Nursing
Health Technology: Microbiology, Clinical Pathology, Pathologic Biochemistry, Morphological Pathology, Physiological Pharmacology
Graduate School of Engineering(M 62/7)
Div. of Mechanical Engineering(M 16/2)
Mechanics and Machine Elements, Engineering Materials and Manufacturing Processes, Fluid Engineering, Thermal Engineering
Div. of Architectural and Civil Engineering(M 17/0)
Structural Analysis, Structural Engineering, Architectural Planning, Environmental Engineering for Regional Planning, Disaster Prevention Engineering, Environmental Engineering for Architecture
Div. of Electrical and Information Engineering(M 29/5)
Electromagnetic Engineering, Information Network Engineering, Electrical Machinery and Power Systems, Electronic Computer System, Electronics Engineering
Graduate School of Agriculture(M 48/7)
Div. of Agriculture(M 14/3)
Crop Science, Plant Breeding, Horticultural Science, Phytopathology, Entomology, Farm Management
Div. of Agricultural Chemistry(M 17/2)
Soil Science and Plant Nutrition, Biological Chemistry and Nutritional Chemistry, Applied Microbiology, Agricultural Product Processing and Pesticide Chemistry, Sugar Technological Chemistry
Div. of Agricultural Engineering(M 7/2)
Irrigation Engineering and Agricultural Hydrology, Hydraulic Structures Engineering, Agricultural Land Engineering, Agricultural Process Engineering, Farm Machinery
Div. of Animal Science(M 5/0)
Animal Breeding and Reproduction, Livestock Feeding and Management, Chemistry and Technology of Animal Products and Tropical Grassland Science, Animal Anatomy and Physiology, Animal Environmental Science and Hygiene
Div. of Forestry(M 5/0)
Tropical Silviculture, Forest Products Processing, Forest Protection and Engineering, Forest Management and Policy

One–Year Graduate Programs

Special Education Course
Mental Retardation Education Major

Local Public Universities

沖縄県立芸術大学
(Okinawa Kenritsu Geijutsu Daigaku)

Okinawa Prefectural College of Arts

1–4 Tonokura Shuri, Naha–shi, Okinawa 903
☎ 0988–31–5000

Founded 1986

Undergraduate Programs

Faculty of Arts and Design
- **Dept. of Craft & Design**
- **Dept. of Fine Arts**

Faculty of Music
- **Dept. of Vocal Music**
- **Dept. of Instrumental Music**
- **Dept. of Musicology**
- **Dept. of Japanese Music**

Private Universities

沖縄国際大学
(Okinawa Kokusai Daigaku)

Okinawa Kokusai University

276–2 Aza–Ginowan, Ginowan–shi, Okinawa 901–22
☎ 09889–2–1111 FAX 09889–3–3271

Founded 1972
Professors 60
Associate Professors 21
Assistant Professors(Tenured) 21
Assistant Professors(Non–tenured) 102
Research Assistants 1
Undergraduate Students/Foreign Students 4, 886/36
Library 135, 768 volumes
Contact: Academic Affairs Division

Educational philosophy We strive to provide a well–rounded education in the commercial, liberal and fine arts and sciences, to equip our students, practically, morally and intellectually for creative and satisfying lives in the highly internationalized world of tomorrow.

Foreign students Our steadily growing foreign student population enjoy rewarding educational experiences. And they contribute to mutual, cross–cultural understanding and friendly relations among the entire academy.

Environment Ginowan City, population 70, 000, is only 10 km from Naha in the geographic and academic center of Okinawa. Public transportation is convenient to the nearby national and Christian universities, the International Center and to the beaches of scenic Okinawa Island.

Facilities Library, personal computer room, language laboratory room, Southern Island Cultural Institute, Gymnasium, University union, students activities building, book store, cafeteria, coffee shop, meeting room, etc

Student activities Orientation for foreign students, freshman's welcome party, Japanese speech contest, There are wide vareity of cultural or athletic clubs, shodo calligraphy, Ryukywan dance, excursion, koto music, flower–arrangements & tea ceremony, kendo, judo, etc.

Academic programs for foreign students There are credit courses that can be substituted for various required general education course. Japanese, Japanese Expression, culture, society, nature, special lecture, etc.

Services for foreign students Health clinic, personal/psychological counseling, scholarships, housing information, foreign student's association.

Undergraduate Programs

Faculty of Law(890/0)

Dept. of Law(890/0)
Faculty of Commerce and Ecocomics(1, 748/16)
Dept. of Economics(878/1)
Dept. of Commerce(870/15)
Faculty of Letters(1, 126/10)
Dept. of Japanese Literature(264/3)
Dept. of English Literature(344/5)
Dept. of Sociology(518/2)

沖縄大学
(Okinawa Daigaku)

The University of Okinawa

747 Kokuba, Naha-shi, Okinawa 902
☎ 0988-32-1768

Founded 1958

Undergraduate Programs

Faculty of Law and Economics
Dept. of Economics
Business Administration Course, Economics Course
Dept. of Law

Appendix

Scholarships for Foreign Students

I. Japanese Government Scholarships (See pp 456)

1. Overview

Japanese government scholarships are available in six different types, varying by the educational institute of study.

Application may be made through the local Japanese embassy or the host university in Japan. In either case, applicants will undergo an initial screening process. A secondary screening of written materials is conducted by the Ministry of Education, Science and Culture, with the recipients then selected.

2. Application Procedures

(1) Embassy Recommendation
(Application Through Japanese Embassies)

Recruiting covers all scholarship categories. However, because recruiting targets will differ by country and region, potential applicants should check closely with the Japanese Embassy in their own specific country or region.

The initial screening is comprised of a document inspection, a written test and an interview. Subjects of the written test vary somewhat by country and region, but generally consist of the following.

Category	Test
Research Student	Japanese (limited to students with previous study of Japanese)
In-Service Training for Teachers	
Special Training School Student	
Undergraduate Student	Japanese, English, Mathematics, World History or Science
College of Technology Student	Mathematics, Physics or Chemistry
Japanese Studies Student	Japanese

The local Japanese embassies conduct their screening on the basis of these test results, and then make their recommendations to the Ministry of Education, Science and Culture. The Ministry of Education, Science and Culture confers with the selection committee, deliberates with the host schools, and then makes it final selections. While candidates may express their preferences for specific schools of study, the final decision will be made by the Ministry of Education, Science and Culture.

(2) University Recommendation
(Application Through Japanese Universities)

1) Overseas Selection (Selection of New Applicants Before They Arrive in Japan)

Based on the university exchange agreement, Japanese universities conduct their examinations of the foreign student candidates, with recommendations made to the Ministry of Education, Science and Culture as research students or Japanese studies students. The Ministry of Education, Science and Culture confers with the selection committee, and then makes its selections. For further details, candidates should contact their current school of enrollment or a Japanese university.

2) Domestic Selection (Selection of Privately Financed Students Already in Japan)

Targeted under this category are privately financed students currently studying at Japanese universities. Qualified are third-year undergraduates expected to advance to fourth-year regular student status (sixth-year status in the case of medical or dental students), fourth-year students expected to advance to regular Master's program student status, or Master's or Doctoral students expected to remain as regular students for one year or longer. Applicants with excellent academic records are chosen to attend from the new school year as undergraduate or research students.

Fourth-year undergraduates will lose their qualification if they fail to advance into a Master's degree program (cancellation of selection). For further details, candidates should contact their current school of enrollment.

3. Extension of Scholarship Duration

(1) Research Students, Undergraduate Students, College of Technology Students

Research students normally attend school as non-degree students. When applying for entrance to a Master's or Doctoral program, it is necessary to maintain that status for six months or more, and then pass the entrance examination given by that university. Upon passing, an extension of the scholarship may be approved for the remaining period necessary to obtain the degree (two years for a Master's, three years for a Doctorate). If failing to pass, the candidate will continue to study under nondegree student status.

Furthermore, undergraduate students receiving permission to enroll in a graduate school Master's program or technical college students receiving permission to enroll in a university undergraduate program may both quality for scholarship extensions of up to two years.

(2) Post-Graduate Training and Practical Training for Undergraduate Students

Students who graduate from medical school may receive practical training for up to one year until such time that they pass the national medical examination. Those who pass the national test, meanwhile, may undergo two years of internee training.

Students majoring in science, engineering or fisheries may engage in practical plant training for up to three months.

In either case, Japanese government scholarships will be furnished during the period in question.

4. Recruiting, Arrival in Japan

The recruiting period will differ by country and region, although the following timing normally applies.

	Category	Recruiting period	Arrival in Japan (scholarship payment start-up)
Embassy Recommendation	Research student	Mar.-Sep.	April or October of following year
	Undergraduate student		April of following year
	In-service training for teachers	Mar.-Apr.	October of same year
	College of technology student		
	Special training school student		
	Japanese studies student		
University Recommendation	Research student (Overseas selection)	Jan.-Feb.	October of same year or January of following year
	Japanese studies student		October of same year
	Research student (Domestic selection)	Dec.-Jan.	April of same year

II. Local Government Scholarships (See pp 457)

III. Private Foundation Scholarships (See pp 466)

1. Overview

Differing from Japanese government scholarships, the majority of these grants are furnished to persons at the university level and above. The scholarships are provided by local governments and private foundations.

The local governments target residents of the particular region or students attending schools in their districts. The grants vary widely in content. Besides the general pattern of covering school and living expenses, there are also housing assistance or national health insurance aid types, where in some cases support is supplied in the form of transportation passes, book coupons and other modes.

As these examples indicate, because most local government scholarships seek to improve the life style conditions of the recipients, there is a trend for the amounts to be comparatively smaller.

Recipients of private foundation scholarships qualify through various different means, with these requirements in most cases reflecting the objectives and character of the bodies furnishing the grants. In some cases the grants target students attending schools in the same district as the group. If the group itself was established for purposes of communication and exchange with a specific country or region, meanwhile, the grants may go to students from that country or region. In the same spirit, the scholarships may be awarded to fields of specialization related to the company or companies which set up the group. While the amount of private foundation scholarships exceed those offered by local governments, there appear to be few examples of such grants being sufficient to singularly cover all the expenses of studying in Japan.

2. Application Procedure

With the exception of local government sister city relationships, the majority of scholarships target (recruit)

students who have previously arrived in Japan and have decided where they will reside, or have been accepted by a school included in the scholarship category. Because the applicant's performance or research attitude at the school in question is used as a point of reference, there are many groups which recruit applicants from the autumn on.

The screening process normally consists of a document examination, a written test (general education, knowledge in the field of major, Japanese-language proficiency, etc.), and an interview. Evaluations of the individual applicants are a major factor. Letters of recommendation from academic advisors are another important judgement standard, while consideration is also given to the question of whether applicants are likely to contribute to cultural exchange between Japan and their native country and region.

3. Reading the chart

* Qualifier

The academic level of grantees are indicated.

- University Japanese Programs—Refers to the "Preparatory Japanese language programs" established by private universities ("College Student" status).
- Japanese Language Schools—Refers to Japanese language courses other than the above.

Note that this chart does not include information on researchers.

* Plural Grants and Limits

Groups which allow their grants to overlap with other funding are marked in this column with "O." In cases when limits are imposed on scholarships received from other sources, the maximum funding permitted is listed.

* Reapplication, Other

Cases when a recipient from the previous year is permitted to reapply are marked with "O." Limits on district of residence and other conditions are also listed in this column.

* Contents, Duration, Application Period/Deadline

The figures are those implemented in 1990. Information from 1991 should be obtained from the specific scholarship source.

* Duration

Cases when it is possible to extend the scholarship duration are marked with "O."

* Applicants for the Previous Year

Numbers are actual numbers for 1989.

The "—" indicates that the program was started up in 1990.

* Contact

This is the column for questions and applications. In cases when application is made directly to the funding body, a "O" appears in the "LG" column for local government scholarships and in the "F" column for private foundation scholarships. When the "O" appears in the "S" column, the school currently being attended should be consulted directly.

A small number of scholarship systems permit application from overseas. Of these, programs which make their selections prior to the applicant's arrival in Japan are marked with "●" while those for which screening is performed after coming to Japan are indicated by "◎."

IV. Scholarships by Colleges and Universities

The student affairs sections of universities provide information on various forms of economic assistance for outstanding students and for students who for some reason face economic hardship. At these sections it is possible to apply for the AIEJ's subsidy system, by which the association offers to pay 30% of the tuition fees of foreign students enrolled in regular courses at private universities.

In addition, some universities offer scholarships for their own students and subsidize tuition fees, the subsidy rate varying from 30% to 100%.

The forms of economic assistance listed here are those offered by universities for foreign students or for all students, including foreign students, and those offered by private organizations for students at certain universities. Inquiries should be made directly to the university concerned.

I. Japanese Government Scholarships

Type of Scholarship	Eligibility			Specifications				Duration	Number of Grantees
	Age	Fields of Study	Other Requirements	Monthly Allowance	Yearly Research Allowance	Japanese Language Training	Other		
Research Student (Graduate School Student & Research Student)	Under 35	(1) Humanities and Social Sciences: Literature, History, Aesthetics, Law, Politics, Economics, Commerce, Pedagogy, Psychology, Sociology, Music, Fine Arts, etc. (2) Natural Sciences: Pure Science, Engineering, Agriculture, Fisheries, Pharmacology, Medicine, Dentistry, Home Science.	University or college graduates (or prospect)	¥180,500	Up to ¥40,000/ year	6 months (those with sufficient Japanese ability are exempted)	*Transportation: One round-trip ticket	2 years	2,295
In-Service Training for Teachers		Education	University or teacher training college graduates who have over 5 years of experience as (1) teachers in active service of primary or secondary schools, or (2) teachers in teacher training service, or (3) staff of educational administration services				*Housing assistance: ¥9,000 (local cities) ¥12,000 (major cities) *Tuition: Remission for national universities	18 months	145
Undergraduate Student	17~22	(1) Social Science and Humanities: Law, Politics, Economics, Business Administration, Education, Sociology, Literature, History, Japanese Language and Others (2) Natural Sciences A: Science (Mathematics, Physics, Chemistry), Electric & Electronic Studies (Electronics, Electrical Eng., Information Eng.), Mechanical Studies (Mechanical Eng., Naval Architecture, Agricultural Eng.), Civil Eng., and Architecture (Civil Eng., Architecture, Environmental Eng.,). Chemical Studies (Applied Chemistry, Chemical Eng., Industrial Chemistry, Textile Eng.), and other fields (Merallurgical Eng., Mining Eng., Mercantile Marine, Biotechnology) B: Agricultural studies (Agriculture, Agricultural Chemistry, Animal Science, Veterinary Medicine, Forestry, Food Science, Fisheries), Hygienic studies (Pharmacy, Hygienics, Nursing), Science (Biology) C: Medicine, Dentistry	Those who have completed secondary school, and are eligible for entering university in their country	¥137,500	¥40,000 for final school year	1 year	Local public & private university fees paid by the Ministry of Education, Science and Culture *Arrival allowance: ¥25,000 *Medical fee reimbursement: 80% of actual cost	5 years (7 years: Medicine, Dentistry, Animal Husbandry)	235
College of Technology Student		Mechanical Eng., Electrical Eng., Electronics, Electronic Control Eng., Information Eng., Industrial Chemistry, Civil Eng., Architecture, Mercantile Marine			×	6 months		$3^{1}/_{2}$yrs (4 yrs: Marine Eng.)	55
Senshu-gakko Student (Special Training School Student)	18~22	Civil Eng., Architecture, Electrical Eng., Electronics, Nutrition, Telecommunication, Infant Education, Secretarial Studies, Tourism, Hotel Management, Fashion, Dress Making, Design, Photography, Others						$2^{1}/_{2}$yrs	55
Japanese Studies Student	18~30	Japanese Language, Japanese Culture, Japanese Affairs	3rd or 4th year university students		Up to ¥40,000	×		1 school year	180

II. Scholarships by Local Government

*1 Qualifier
CT: College of technology students
ST: Special training school students
JL: Japanese language school students
UJ: University Japanese program students
JC: Junior college students
A: Auditors (Undergraduate)
U: Undergraduate students
R: Research students (Graduate)
M: Master's program students
D: Doctor's program students

*2 Plural grants permitted=○
*3 Reapplication permitted=○
*4 MYR: Minimum years required for graduation/completion
UTG: Up to graduation/completion
Renewable=○

*5 LG: Local government
S: School currently ennolled in Japan
Locally adopted=●
Overseas application=◎

Name of Local Government (Foundation) Name of Scholarship	Address Telephone	Eligibility *1 Qualifier	School Year Age Limit	Designated Countries	Designated School in Japan	Designated Field of Study	*2 Plural Grants and Limits (¥1,000)	*3 Reapplication and Other Eligibility (¥1,000)	Contents (¥1,000)	*4 Duration	Application Period/ Deadline	Grantees	Applicants for the Previous Year	*5 Contact LG	Contact S
Obihiro-shi Foreign Student Scholarship	8 Minami, Nishi-Gojo, Obihiro-shi, Hokkaido 080 (0155-24-4111)	JC U M D						○ Those living in Obihiro over a year	20/yr.	1yr.			24		○
Iwate-ken Foreign Student Scholarship	10-1 Uchimaru, Morioka-shi, Iwate 020 (0196-51-3111) Ext.2139	JC A U R M D			Schools in Iwate pref.			○	10/mo.	1yr. (Apr ~ Mar)	Jun 11~22		6		○
Miyagi-ken Foreign Student Scholarship	3-8-1 Hon-machi, Aoba-ku, Sendai-shi, Miyagi 980 (022-211-2276)	CT U R M D			Schools in Miyagi pref.		○	Privately financed students attending a school in Miyagi Pref. over a year	10/mo.	1yr. (Apr ~ Mar)	May 1~31	60	101		○
Sendai-shi Foreign Student's Bus Coupons Project	3-7-1 Kokubun-cho, Aoba-ku, Sendai-shi, Miyagi 980 (022-261-1111) Ext.2653	CT UJ JC A U R M D					○	○ Privately financed students in Sendai-shi	5/mo.	1yr. (Apr ~ Mar)	Apr		373	○	○

Name of Local Government (Foundation) Name of Scholarship	Address Telephone	Eligibility							Contents (¥1,000)	Duration	Application Period/ Deadline	Grantees	Applicants for the Previous Year	Contact	
		Qualifier School Year · Age Limit		Designated Countries	Designated School in Japan	Designated Field of Study	Plural Grants and Limits (¥1,000)	Reapplication and Other Eligibility (¥1,000)						LG	S
Akita-shi Educational Expense Assistance Policy for Foreign Students	1-1-1 Sanno, Akita-shi, Akita 010 (0188-63-2222)	JC A U R M D			Schools in Akita-shi			○	5/mo.	6mo.	May Oct		33	○ ●	
Tsukuba-shi Foreign Student Scholarship	4711 Yatabe, Oaza, Tsukuba-shi, Ibaraki 305 (0298-37-1666)	U R M D			Universities in Tsukuba-shi			○ Residents in Tsukuba-shi	10/mo.	1yr.	Apr	50	120		○
Chiba-shi Foreign Student Scholarship	1-1 Chibaminato, Chiba-shi, Chiba 260-91 (0472-41-1111)	JC A U R M D			Schools in Chiba-shi		○	○ Privately financed students in Chiba-shi attending a school as of Oct. 1	10/yr. in book coupons	1yr.	Sep		215		○
Taito-ku Foreign Student Scholarship	4-5-6 Higashi-Ueno, Taito-ku, Tokyo 110 (03-3842-5311) Ext.363	JC U R M D					○ 20/mo.	○ Privately financed students in Taito-ku	20/mo.	1yr.	Jul 2~22	31	40	○	
Musashino Shimin Shakai Fukushi Kyogikai Foreign Student Scholarship	2-2-28 Midori-machi, Musashino-shi, Tokyo 180 (0422-51-5131) Ext.2641	JC U R M D					○	Privately financed students in Musashino-shi	5/mo.	UTG			215	○	
Hino-shi Foreign Student Scholarship	1-12-1 Shinmei, Hino-shi, Tokyo 191 (0425-85-1111) Ext.433	JC U R M D					○	Privately financed students in Hino-shi	10/mo.	6mo.			37	○	

Name of Local Government (Foundation) Name of Scholarship	Address Telephone	Eligibility: Qualifier School Year	Eligibility: Age Limit	Eligibility: Designated Countries	Eligibility: Designated School in Japan	Eligibility: Designated Field of Study	Eligibility: Plural Grants and Limits (¥1,000)	Eligibility: Reapplication and Other Eligibility (¥1,000)	Contents (¥1,000)	Duration	Application Period/ Deadline	Grantees	Applicants for the Previous Year	Contact: LG	Contact: S
Hachioji-shi Foreign Student Scholarship	3-24-1 Motohongo-machi, Hachioji-shi, Tokyo 192 (0426-26-3111)	CT UJ JC U R M D			Schools in Hachioji-shi		○	○ Privately financed students in Hachioji-shi	8/mo.	1yr.	May	160	140		○
Yokohama Ryugakusei Shien Suishin Kyogikai Foreign Student Scholarship	3F Sangyo Boeki Center Bldg., Yamashita-machi, Naka-ku, Yokohama-shi, Kanagawa 231 (045-671-7189)	JC U R M D			Schools in Yokohama-shi		○ 45/mo.	Residents in Yokohama-shi living in non-university housing	10/mo.	~Mar	Jun ~ Nov	175	165		○
Kawasaki-shi Foreign Student Scholarship	1 Miyamoto-machi, Kawasaki-ku, Kawasaki-shi, Kanagawa 210 (044-200-2121)	JC A U R M D					○	Privately financed students in Kawasaki-shi	10/mo.	~Mar 1992			263	○	
Niigata-ken Foreign Student Scholarship ①	4-1 Shinko-cho, Niigata-shi, Niigata 950 (025-285-5511)	A R	~29	Korea	Niigata Univ. Prefectural research institute, etc.				Part of the expenses	1yr.	Oct	2	2	○	
				Brasil								3	2	●	
②			20~	Heilon-jiang, China	Niigata Univ. Prefectural research institute, etc. Nagaoka University of Technology					1mo.~12mo. (Apr ~)		within 8	8		
③					Niigata Cancer Center Hospital					1yr.		1	2		
										1mo. ~6mo.		2			
Saitama International Association Foreign Student Scholarship	4F Sonic City Bldg., 1-7-5 Sakuragi-machi, Omiya-shi, Saitama 331 (048-647-4175)	JC U M D					○	○ Privately financed students in rented housing (10/mo. and above)	5/mo.	~Mar		300	309	○	○

Name of Local Government (Foundation) Name of Scholarship	Address Telephone	Eligibility: Qualifier School Year	Age Limit	Designated Countries	Designated School in Japan	Designated Field of Study	Plural Grants and Limits (¥1,000)	Reapplication and Other Eligibility (¥1,000)	Contents (¥1,000)	Duration	Application Period/ Deadline	Grantees	Applicants for the Previous Year	Contact: LG	S
The Toyama International Center Foundation ①Toyama International Exchange Scholarship	1-1-61 Sakura-machi, Toyama-shi, Toyama 930 (0764-45-4591)	CT:4·5 JC U R M D			Schools in Toyama pref.		○ 142.85 /mo.	○ Privately financed students in Toyama pref. attending a school in Toyama pref. over 6 months	10/mo.	3mo.	May, Aug, Nov, Feb		62		○
②Toyama Research Fund to Enhance International Understanding							○	Privately financed students in Toyama pref. attending a school in Toyama pref. over 6 months	5/mo. in book coupons				95		
③Toyama Prefecture's Financial Support-Getting National Health Insurance							○	the same as above	Assistance for insurance		Jul, Oct, Jan, Mar		35		
④Toyama City's Financial Support-Getting National Health Insurance for Foreign Students								○ Residents in Toyama-shi attending a school in Toyama pref. over 6 months					29		
Kosugi-machi Foreign Student Scholarship ①	1511 Hibari, Kosugi-machi, Imizu-gun, Toyama 939-03 (0766-56-1511)	ST			Schools in Kosugi-machi		○ 133.1 /mo.	Privately financed students in Kosugi-machi	5/mo. in merchandise coupon	UTG	May, July, Oct, Jan		12		○
②							○	Residents in Kosugi-machi	2.5/mo. in merchandise coupon						
③								Privately financed students in Kosugi-machi			Sep		9		

Name of Local Government (Foundation) Name of Scholarship	Address Telephone	Eligibility: Qualifier School Year Age Limit	Eligibility: Designated Countries	Eligibility: Designated School in Japan	Eligibility: Designated Field of Study	Eligibility: Plural Grants and Limits (¥1,000)	Eligibility: Reapplication and Other Eligibility (¥1,000)	Contents (¥1,000)	Duration	Application Period/ Deadline	Grantees	Applicants for the Previous Year	Contact: LG	Contact: S
Ishikawa-ken Foreign Student Scholarship	2-1-1 Hirosaka, Kanazawa-shi, Ishikawa 920 (0762-23-9108)	CT UJ JC A U R M D		Schools in Ishikawa pref.		○	Privately financed students in Ishikawa pref.	120/yr.	UTG	Apr 1~30 Oct 1~31		62 74		○
Gifu-shi Foreign Student Scholarship	39-1 Kakigase, Gifu-shi, Gifu 500 (0582-34-1166)	CT ST JL UJ JC A U R M D				○	○ Residents in Gifu-shi	City bus commuter's pass	1yr. (May 1 ~Apr 30)			194	○	
Shizuoka-ken Foreign Student's Studying Material Subsidy	9-6 Otemachi, Shizuoka-shi, Shizuoka 420 (0542-21-3310)	JC A U R M D		Schools in Shizuoka pref.				60/mo.	1yr.			227		○
International Student Center Foreign Student Scholarship	2-2-29 Minato-Sakae, Minato-ku, Nagoya-shi Aichi 455 (052-054-3511)	JC A U R M D					○ Residents in Aichi Pref.	10/mo.	1yr. (Apr ~ Mar)	Jul 14	220	255	○	
Shiga International Friendship Association Foreign Student Scholarship	4-1-1 Kyo-machi, Otsu-shi, Shiga 520 (0755-26-0931)	JC U M D / A R		Schools in Shiga pref.		○ 20/mo.	Privately financed students	20/mo.	MYR / UTG	Jun 20 ~ Jul 8		15	○	○

Name of Local Government (Foundation) Name of Scholarship	Address Telephone	Eligibility							Contents (¥1,000)	Duration	Application Period/ Deadline	Grantees	Applicants for the Previous Year	Contact	
		Qualifier School Year	Age Limit	Designated Countries	Designated School in Japan	Designated Field of Study	Plural Grants and Limits (¥1,000)	Reapplication and Other Eligibility (¥1,000)						LG	S
Osaka Foundtion of International Exchange The Osaka Prefectural Government Scholarships for Privately Funded Foreign Students	14F Twin 21 MID Tower, 2-1-61 Shiromi, Chuo-ku, Osaka-shi, Osaka 540 (06-945-6071)	CT:4·5 ST JL JC			Schools in Osaka pref. & Kansai International Students Institute		○ 20/mo.	○ Privately financed students attending a school over a year (JL: over 6mo.)	20/mo.	1yr. (Apr 1 ~ Mar 31)	Apr	200	228	○	○
		U M D							40/mo.	6mo. (Oct 1 ~ Mar 31)					
Osaka International House Foundation Foreign Students Scholarship ①	8-2-6 Uehonmachi, Tennoji-ku, Osaka-shi, Osaka 543 (06-772-5931)	ST JL JC	2~		Schools in Osaka-shi		○	○ Privately financed students	20/mo.	1yr.	Apr	125	104		○
		U M D							40/mo.						
②		ST JL JC U R M D					○ R·M·D 178.5 /mo. Others 135.5 /mo.	○ Privately financed students in Osaka-shi	within 300 for housing deposit	UTG		30	9	○	
②								○ Privately financed students or those attending a school in Osaka-shi	Assistance for National Health Insurance fee	~Mar	Jun 1~20 Nov 1~20		—		○
Ibaraki-shi Kokusai Shinzen Toshi Kyokai Foreign Student Scholarship	3-8-13 Ekimae, Ibaraki-shi, Osaka 567 (0726-22-8121)	U	~34		Universities in Ibaraki-shi		○ 100/mo.	○ Residents in Ibaraki-shi	5/mo.	1yr.		5	3		○
Itami-shi Foreign Student Scholarship	1-1 Senzo, Itami-shi, Hyogo 644 (0727-83-1234)	JC U	18~ 29	Hasselt, Belgium Foshan, China	Schools in Itami-shi and its environs				Air fare, Living cost (Within 5/day), Tuition, etc.	UTG		0 1		●	

Name of Local Government (Foundation) Name of Scholarship	Address Telephone	Eligibility: Qualifier School Year	Age Limit	Designated Countries	Designated School in Japan	Designated Field of Study	Plural Grants and Limits (¥1,000)	Reapplication and Other Eligibility (¥1,000)	Contents (¥1,000)	Duration	Application Period/ Deadline	Grantees	Applicants for the Previous Year	Contact: LG	S
Hyogo-ken Kokusai Koryu Kyokai Foreign Student Scholarship	6-1-1 Nakayamatedori, Chuo-ku, Kobe-shi, Hyogo 650 (078-341-7402)	ST JL CT JC U M D			Schools designated by Hyogo pref. Schools in Hyogo pref.			○	30/mo.	1yr.	Jun 1~30	110	115		○
Kobe International Association ① Kobe International Scholarship	6-9-1 Naka-machi, Minatojima, Chuo-ku, Kobe-shi, Hyogo 650 (078-302-5200)	U M D		Developing countries, etc.	Universities in Kobe-shi			○	80/mo.	1yr.	Apr	50	100		○
② Kobe Asian Center Housing-Deposit Loan		JC U M D					○	Residents in Kobe-shi	within 500			10	7		
③ Kobe Asian Center Subsidies for National Health Insurance Premiums		U R M D					○ 135.5 /mo.	○ Residents in Kobe-shi whose incomes do not exceed 136/mo.	Assistance for National Health Insurance fee	1yr.	Jul		57		
Himeji-shi Foreign Student Scholarship	4-1 Yasuda, Himeji-shi, Hyogo 670 (0792-21-2762)	JC U			Schools in Himeji-shi		○	Residents in Himeji-shi	10~30 /mo.	UTG	Apr, Oct.	20	5		○
Okayama-shi Foreign Student Scholarship	2-4-6 Uchiyamashita, Okayama-shi, Okayama 700 (0862-52-4211)	JC A U R M D			Schools in Okayama pref.			○	20/mo.	1yr.	Jun	20	5	○	

Name of Local Government (Foundation) Name of Scholarship	Address Telephone	Eligibility: Qualifier School Year	. Age Limit	Designated Countries	Designated School in Japan	Designated Field of Study	Plural Grants and Limits (¥1,000)	Reapplication and Other Eligibility (¥1,000)	Contents (¥1,000)	Dura-tion	Appli-cation Period/ Dead-line	Gran-tees	Appli-cants for the Previ-ous Year	Contact: LG	S
Hiroshima Kokusai Center Foreign Student Scholarship ①	10-52 Moto-machi, Naka-ku, Hiroshima-shi, Hiroshima 730 (082-222-3063)	JC U R M D			Schools in Hiroshima pref.			○	20/mo.	1yr.	May 15~26	30	65		○
										6mo.	Nov 1~17	20	35		
②								Residents in Hiroshima pref.	Assist-ance for National Health Insurance fee		May 1~15 Nov 1~15		314		
③								○ Privately fianced students in a rented housing in Hiroshima pref.	Within 100 for housing-deposit				3		
Hiroshima International Relations Organization Hiroshima Scholarship	Hiroshima Kokusai Kaigijo, 1-5 Nakajima-cho, Naka-ku, Hiroshima-shi, Hiroshima 730 (082-247-8007)	JC U R M D	~34		Schools in Hiroshima-shi			○	20/mo.	1yr.	Apr	25	50		○
											Oct		10		
Fukuoka International Exchange Foundation Foreign Student Scholarship	8F Nihon Seimei Hakata Minami Bldg., Hakataeki-minami, Hakata-ku, Fukuoka-shi, Fukuoka 812 (092-451-4411)	CT JC A U R M D			Schools in Fukuoka pref. (Excluding those in Fukuoka metro-politan area)			○ Privately financed students in Fukuoka pref.	20/mo.	1yr.	Apr ~ Mid-May	20	–		○
International Research Exchange Foundation for Japanese Studies (財)国際日本文化研究交流財団	4F Rakusei Center Bldg., 2-5-9 Sakaidani-cho, Oharano-higashi, Nishikyo-ku, Kyoto-shi, Kyoto 610-11 (075-332-1868)	D				Japanese Psychology, Geography, Sociology, Political science, Anthropology, History, Philosophy, Literature, Economics, etc.			150/mo.	2yr.	Apr 10	12	44		○

Name of Local Government (Foundation) Name of Scholarship	Address Telephone	Eligibility: Qualifier School Year	Age Limit	Designated Countries	Designated School in Japan	Designated Field of Study	Plural Grants and Limits (¥1,000)	Reapplication and Other Eligibility (¥1,000)	Contents (¥1,000)	Duration	Application Period/ Deadline	Grantees	Applicants for the Previous Year	Contact: LG	S
Fukuoka International Association Foreign Student Scholarship	8F Imuzu Bldg., 1-7-11 Tenjin, Chuo-ku, Fukuoka-shi, Fukuoka 810 (092-733-2220)	JC A U R M D			Schools in Fukuoka-shi and its environs		○ Single 20/mo. Family 40/mo.	○	20/mo.	1yr.	Apr～May	60	120		○
Nagasaki-Asia Foundation Foreign Student Scholarship	2-13 Edo-machi, Nagasaki-shi, Nagasaki 850 (0958-24-1111) Ext. 2087	U R					○	Privately financed students	10 for National Health Insurance fee	UTG	Apr～May		7		○
Kumamoto Prefectural Government Scholarships for Foreign Student	6-18-1 Suizenji, Kumamoto-shi, Kumamoto 862 (096-383-1502)	JC A U R M D			Schools in Kumamoto pref.			○	30/mo.	1yr.	Jun～Jul	20	–		○
Kagoshima-shi Foreign Student Scholarship	11-1 Yamashita-cho, Kagoshima-shi, Kagoshima 892 (0992-24-1111)	JC A U R M D			Schools in Kagoshima-shi			○ Residents in Kagoshima-shi	Car fare 18/yr. 30/yr. in book coupons	1yr.	May		80 80		○
Okinawa-ken Okinawa Overseas Students Scholarship Program	1-2-2 Izumizaki, Naha-shi Okinawa 900 (0988-66-2479)	A	～29	Korea, Taiwan, Singapore, Phillip-pines, Thailand, Malaysia, Indonesia	Universities or research institutes in Okinawa pref.	Except medicine			Round-trip fare, Tuition, Living cost (95/mo.) Insurance (23.49/yr) Others (68/yr)	1yr.	Sep 30	9		○ ●	

III. Scholarships by Private Foundations

*1 Qualifier
- CT: College of technology students
- ST: Special training school students
- JL: Japanese language school students
- UJ: University Japanese program students
- JC: Junior college students
- A: Auditors (Undergraduate)
- U: Undergraduate students
- R: Research students (Graduate)
- M: Master's program students
- D: Doctor's program students

*2 Plural grants permitted=○
*3 Reapplication permitted=○
*4 Renewable=○
MYR=Minimum years required for graduation/completion
UTG=Up to graduation/completion

*5 F: Foundation
S: School currently enrolled in Japan
Locally adopted=●
Overseas application=◎

Name of Foundation Name of Scholarship	Address Telephone	Eligibility *1 Qualifier School Year	Age Limit	Designated Countries	Designated School in Japan	Designated Field of Study	*2 Plural Grants and Limits (¥1,000)	*3 Reapplication, Others (¥1,000)	Contents (¥1,000)	*4 Duration	Application Period/Deadline	Grantees	Applicants for the Previous Year	*5 Contact F	S
Asahi Glass Company Scholarship Society (財)旭硝子奨学会	2-1-2 Marunouchi, Chiyoda-ku, Tokyo 100 (03-3218-5282)	M D		Indonesia, Thailand	25 schools				80/mo.	2yr.	Feb 10 ~ Apr 10	6	10		○
Asia 21 Foundation (財)アジア21世紀奨学財団	5-17 Kamiyama-cho, Shibuya-ku, Tokyo 150 (03-3460-2100)	U M D		Korea, China, Taiwan, Hong Kong, Philippines, Malaysia, Thailand, Indonesia, Singapore					50/mo.	1yr.	Apr 1~30	20~25	300	○	
Association for Asian Educational Exchange (AEE) (財)アジア教育文化交流協会	6-6-2 Nishi-shinjuku, Shinjuku-ku, Tokyo 160 (03-3342-6661)	M	35	China	10 schools	Social Science			100/mo.	1yr. ~ 2yr.	Dec 5 ~ Jan 25	15	42	○	○
Association of International Education, Japan Honors Scholarship (財)日本国際教育協会	4-5-29 Komaba, Meguro-ku, Tokyo 153 (03-3467-3521 ext.58)	ST:2·3 JC U R M D	30 35				○ 45.5/mo. ○ 66/mo.	○ ○	45.5/mo. 66/mo.	1yr.	Mar 31 ~ May	300 200 3,300 1,200	428 228 4,086 2,693		○

Name of Foundation Name of Scholarship	Address Telephone	Eligibility							Contents (¥1,000)	Duration	Application Period/ Deadline	Grantees	Applicants for the Previous Year	Contact	
		Qualifier School Year	Age Limit	Designated Countries	Designated School in Japan	Designated Field of Study	Plural Grants and Limits (¥1,000)	Reapplication, Others (¥1,000)						F	S
Better Home Association Better Home Goodwill Scholarship (財)ベターホーム協会	1-15-12 Shibuya, Shibuya-ku, Tokyo 150 (03-3407-0471)	U M D	30		Yes		O only small amounts		40/mo.	UTG	Apr	30			O
Bijutsu Kogei Shinko Sato Kikin (財)美術工芸振興佐藤基金	408 Jomyoji, Kamakura-shi, Kanagawa 248 (0467-23-0118)	R M D				Arts & crafts, Cultural history		O	80/mo. Dormitory	1yr. ~ 3yr.	Apr ~ Dec	As vacancy arises	3	◎	
Fujisawa Foundation, The (財)医薬資源研究振興会	Ebisu Bldg., 3-2-9 Awaji-cho, Chuo-ku, Osaka-shi, Osaka 541 (06-201-5894)	M	30	China		Discovery and development of medicinal resources			Total: 2,000	1yr.	Dec Jun	10	24	O	
Fukuoka Nanotsu Lions Club Scholarship 福岡那の津ライオンズクラブ	1-7-11 Tenjin, Chuo-ku, Fukuoka 810 (092-733-2220)	M D							50/m	MYR	Apr ~ May	2	13		O
Fulbright Foundation (財)日本教育交流振興財団	6 Sanbancho, Chiyoda-ku, Tokyo 102 (03-3221-1841)	R								12 mo.				O	
Hakumon Shogakkai (財)白門奨学会	3-11-5 Surugadai, Kanda, Chiyoda-ku, Tokyo 112 (03-3219-6175)	U M			Universities in Tokyo				within 500/yr.	1yr.	Apr ~ May31	20	52	O	
Hashimoto Jun Kinen-kai (財)橋本循記念会	Kyoto Chuo Shin'yo Kinko 91 Kankoboko-cho, Higashi-iru, Muromachi, Shijo-dori, Shimogyo-ku, Kyoto-shi, Kyoto 600 (075-223-2525)	U R		Eastern Asia (China, etc.)	Universities in Kyoto pref.	Humanities	O		80/mo. 100/mo.	MYR	Mar20 ~ Apr19	10	—	O	
Hashiya Scholarship Foundation (財)橋谷奨学会	3-17-9 Higashi Kasai, Edogawa-ku, Tokyo 134 (03-3689-3111 ext.260)	ST JC U R M D		Indonesia					30/mo. 60/mo.	UTG	Mar 1 ~ May10	14		O	

Name of Foundation Name of Scholarship	Address Telephone	Eligibility: Qualifier School Year	Age Limit	Designated Countries	Designated School in Japan	Designated Field of Study	Plural Grants and Limits (¥1,000)	Reapplication, Others (¥1,000)	Contents (¥1,000)	Duration	Application Period/ Deadline	Grantees	Applicants for the Previous Year	Contact F	Contact S
Hattori Kaigai Ryugakusei Ikueikai (財)服部海外留学生育英会	5-12 Suemoridori, Chigusa-ku, Nagoya-shi, Aichi 464 (052-751-1103)	U R M D		Asia	Universities in Aichi pref.				50/mo.	UTG	Jan15 ~ Feb15	10			○
Hitachi Scholarship Foundation, The Hitachi Scholarship (財)日立国際奨学財団	1-5-1 Marunouchi, Chiyoda-ku, Tokyo 100 (03-3215-3761)	M D	30 35	Designated schools in Thailand, Singapore, Indonesia, Malaysia, Philippines		Science & technology			180/mo. Tuition, Housing assistance, Round-trip ticket	24 mo. ~30 mo. 36 mo. ~ 42 mo.	Sep ~ Dec	6~8	40		●
Hokkaido Kankokujin Shogakukai (財)北海道韓国人奨学会	Minami 9, Nishi 3, Chuo-ku, Sapporo Hokkaido 064 (011-562-4133)	ST JC A U R M			Schools in Hokkaido pref.				30/mo.	1yr.	Feb	7	11		○
IBM IBM Asia Fellowship	International House of Japan 5-11-16 Roppongi, Minato-ku, Tokyo 106 (03-3470-3211)	M	30	HongKong, Indonesia, Korea, Malaysia, Philippines, Singapore, Taiwan, Thai		Mathematics, Science, Engineering			200/mo. Insurance fee	w/in 24 mo.	Nov20	8	–	◎	
Ichikawa International Scholarship Foundation (財)市川国際奨学財団	1-20-5 Tenma, Kita-ku, Osaka-shi, Osaka 530 (06-356-2357)	CT U R M D		Asian countries	Osaka, Kyoto, Kobe, Wakayama, Osaka City, U of Osaka Pref., Kansai, Kwansei Gakuin, Doshisha, Ritsumeikan, Kinki, Ryukoku, Kobe U. of Commerce				100/mo.	2yr.	Oct ~ Dec20	30	29		○
Inner Trip Foundation (財)インナートリップ国際交流協会	1-9-8 Azabudai, Minato-ku, Tokyo 106 (03-3585-2533)	U:3·4 M D	30 35	Southeast Asia, Latin America	Yes (names not given)		○ 40/mo.	○	100/mo.	2yr. 2yr. ○	Apr19 ~ May20	6	20	○	

Name of Foundation Name of Scholarship	Address Telephone	Eligibility: Qualifier School Year	Eligibility: Age Limit	Eligibility: Designated Countries	Eligibility: Designated School in Japan	Eligibility: Designated Field of Study	Eligibility: Plural Grants and Limits (¥1,000)	Eligibility: Reapplication, Others (¥1,000)	Contents (¥1,000)	Duration	Application Period/ Deadline	Grantees	Applicants for the Previous Year	Contact F	Contact S
Inoac International Educational Scholarship Foundation (財)イノアック国際教育振興財団	2-13-4 Minami, Meieki, Nakamura-ku, Nagoya-shi, Aichi 450 (052-581-5665)	U M D			Universities in Aichi pref.			Students in Aichi	38/mo.	2yr.	May 1 ~ Jun 30	25			○
INPEX Foundation INPEX Scholarships (財)インドネシア石油教育交流財団	3-5-1 Toranomon, Minato-ku, Tokyo 105 (03-5470-1302)	M	30	Indonesia		Natural science			150/mo. Tuition, Round-trip fare, Insurance, etc.	32 mo.	Aug 1 ~ Nov15	6	31	●	
Interchange Association (財)交流協会 (Application in Taiwan)	Taipei Office 台北市済南路二段43号 (02-351-7250~3)	R M D	35	Taiwan	National universities				179/mo. Round trip ticket, Tuition, etc.	2yr. ○	Oct 2~12	56	312	●	
(Application in Japan)	NP Onarimon 3-25-33 Nishi-Shinbashi, Minato-ku, Tokyo 105 (03-3437-1501~5)	M D							179.5/mo. One way air ticket, Tuition, etc.		Sep ~ Oct	4	61	○	
International Information Science Foundation (財)情報科学国際交流財団	2-4-14 Hirakawa-cho, Chiyoda-ku, Tokyo 102 (03-3261-7661)	R M D				Information science	○	○	Air fare/ Living cost assistance	Lump sum	Dec~Jan Feb~Mar Jul~Aug	50	80	◎	●
International Research Exchange Foundation for Japanese Studies (財)国際日本文化研究交流財団	2-5-9 Higashi Sakaidanicho, Ooharano, Nishigyo-ku, Kyoto-shi, Kyoto 610-11 (075-332-1868)	D				Psychology, Geography, Sociology, Politics, Humanities, History of scientific technology, Philosophy, History, Literature			150/mo.	2yr.	Apr10	12	44		○

Name of Foundation Name of Scholarship	Address Telephone	Eligibility							Contents (¥1,000)	Duration	Application Period/ Deadline	Grantees	Applicants for the Previous Year	Contact	
		Qualifier School Year	Age Limit	Designated Countries	Designated School in Japan	Designated Field of Study	Plural Grants and Limits (¥1,000)	Reapplication, Others (¥1,000)						F	S
Isetan Foundation (財)伊勢丹奨学会	3-14-1 Shinjuku, Shinjuku-ku, Tokyo 160 (03-3352-1111)	M D	30 35	Asia, Europe	Waseda, Keio University	Commerce, Economics, Business administration			100/mo.	2yr.	Apr ~ May	2	2		O
Ishizaka Foundation (財)国際文化教育交流財団	1-9-4 Otemachi, Chiyoda-ku, Tokyo 100 (03-3279-1411 ext.282)	M D			Hokkaido, Tohoku, Tsukuba, Chiba, U of Tokyo, Tokyo Institute of Technology, Nagoya, Kyoto Sangyo, Tokyo National U of Fine Arts and Music, Hiroshima, Kyushu, ICU, Keio, Hitotsubashi, Tokyo U of Foreign Studies, Sophia, Waseda, International U of Japan, Kyoto, Doshisha, Osaka, Kobe University				100/mo.	2yr.	Feb 22 ~ Apr 21	12	28		O
Seiho Scholarship		U:3		East & Southeast Asia	Tsukuba, Chiba, Tokyo Institute of Technology, Keio, Hitotsubashi, Tokyo U of Foreign Studies, Sophia, Waseda, ICU		O 40/mo.		50/mo.	2yr.	Mar ~ May 31	12	—		O
Isono Ikuei Shogakukai (財)磯野育英奨学会	1-12-14 Muro-machi, Nihonbashi, Chuo-ku, Tokyo 103 (03-3241-0561)	U:1			ICU, Waseda, Tokyo U of Agriculture and Technology, Hitotsubashi, Tokyo Institute of Technology, Keio, Aoyama, Tokyo Metropolitan, Sophia, U of Tokyo				15/mo.	MYR	May	20			O
Iwaki Scholarship Foundation (財)岩城留学生奨学会	4-8-2 Honcho, Nihonbashi, Chuo-ku, Tokyo 103 (03-3242-5890)	U R M		Asian countries	Universities in Kanto, Chubu region	Medical sciences, Pharmaceutics, Organic chemistry		O	100/mo.	2yr.	Nov 1 ~ Dec 31	10	48		O

Name of Foundation Name of Scholarship	Address Telephone	Eligibility Qualifier School Year	Age Limit	Designated Countries	Designated School in Japan	Designated Field of Study	Plural Grants and Limits (¥1,000)	Reapplication, Others (¥1,000)	Contents (¥1,000)	Duration	Application Period/ Deadline	Grantees	Applicants for the Previous Year	Contact F	Contact S
Iwatani Naoji Foundation, The Iwatani International Scholarship (財)岩谷直治記念財団	2-10-2 Nagata-cho, Chiyoda-ku, Tokyo 100 (03-3580-2251)	M D	30 35	East Asia, Southeast Asia		Natural science			1,200/yr. Other	1yr.	Dec16 ~ Jan 15	11~12	278		○
Japan Dental Association (社)日本歯科医師会	4-1-20 Kudan Kita, Chiyoda-ku, Tokyo 102 (03-3262-9213)	U R D		Asia, West pacific nations		Dentistry	○		150/mo.	1mo. ~ 12 mo.	Jun Dec	14	20	◎	
Japan Foundation, The Fellowship (特)国際交流基金	3-6 Kioi-cho, Chiyoda-ku, Tokyo 102 (03-3263-4497/8)	D	35	All countries except North Korea		Humanities, Social science		Ph.D. Candidate	180/mo. Air fare, Housing, etc.	4mo. ~ 14 mo.	Sep ~ Nov	110	599	● ○ ◎	
Japan Oceania Society for Cultural Exchanges Scholarship for Oceania Students (任)日本オセアニア交流協会	1-24-16 Minami tsukaguchi-cho, Amagasaki-shi, Hyogo 661 (06-427-8006)	U JC		South Pacific University	Sonoda Gakuen Women's College/Junior College				Total US$3,000	3mo.	Sep ~ Oct	4	130		●
Japan Securities Schlarship Foundation, The Educational Awards for Overseas Students (財)日本証券奨学財団	1-5-8 Kayaba-cho, Nihonbashi, Chuo-ku, Tokyo 103 (03-3664-7113)	M	30	Thailand, Malaysia, Singapore, Indonesia, Philippines, China, Hong Kong, Taiwan, Korea		Social science, Humanities			180/mo. Air fare, Tuition, etc.	3yr.	Jan ~ Jul 31	7		●	
Kaiseikai Foundation. The Grants Subsidy (財)偕成会	13-2 Kabutocho, Nihonbashi, Chuo-ku, Tokyo 103 (03-3666-2022)	R M D							Total budget 3,000	1yr.	Apr 1 ~ Apr30	3~6	100	○	
Kamei Memorial Foundation Kamei Scholarship (財)亀井記念財団	3-1-18 Kokubuncho, Aoba-ku, Sendai-shi, Miyagi 980 (022-264-6239)	U M D			Tohoku University				25/mo. 30/mo.	MYR	Apr21 ~ May31	10	12		○

Name of Foundation Name of Scholarship	Address Telephone	Eligibility: Qualifier School Year	Eligibility: Age Limit	Eligibility: Designated Countries	Eligibility: Designated School in Japan	Eligibility: Designated Field of Study	Eligibility: Plural Grants and Limits (¥1,000)	Eligibility: Reapplication, Others (¥1,000)	Contents (¥1,000)	Duration	Application Period/ Deadline	Grantees	Applicants for the Previous Year	Contact: F	Contact: S
Kamiyama Shogaku Zaidan (財)上山奨学財団	4-16-29 Sakae, Naka-ku, Nagoya-shi, Aichi 460 (052-262-5031)	U R M D			4-year universities in Aichi pref.		○	○	200/yr.	1yr.	Apr25 ~ May20	Within 30	195	○	
Kanbayashi Scholarship Foundation Scholarship	1 Funamachi, Shinjuku-ku, Tokyo 160 (03-3350-4504)	U M D		East & Southeast Asia	Graduate schools in Kanto district		○ 50/mo.	○	100/mo.	1yr. ○	Apr 1~20	35	151	○	○
Grants-in-aid for Study (財)神林留学生奨学会						East & Southeast Asian studies			within 1,000/yr.	1yr.		7	5	○	
Kanehara Ichiro Kinen Igaku Iryo Shinko Zaidan (財)金原一郎記念医学医療振興財団	2-18-12 Hongo, Bunkyo-ku, Tokyo 113 (03-3815-7801)	M D				Basic medical science			100/mo.		Nov 1 ~ Dec20	3	0	○	
Kaneko Foundation for International Cultural Communication (財)金子国際文化交流財団	4-8-4 Takadanobaba, Shinjuku-ku, Tokyo 169 (03-3371-2174)	U:3·4 M D		Pacific rim countries	Yes (names not given)				50/mo.	10 mo.	Apr 10 ~ May15	12	11		○
Kashiyama Scholarship Foundation (財)樫山奨学財団	3-10-5 Nihonbashi, Chuo-ku, Tokyo 103 (03-3272-2336)	M:1 D:2	30 35	Asia, Pacific area	7 universities				100/mo.	w/in 2yr.	Apr 1 ~ May15	7	7		○
Kawakami Memorial Foundation, The Kawakami Scholarship (財)河上記念財団	1-11-1 Marunouchi, Chiyoda-ku, Tokyo 100 (03-3216-1538)	M	35		International U of Japan				100/mo.	2yr.	Sep ~ Oct	4	2		○
Kawamura Scholarship Foundation (財)川村育英会	3-7-20 Nihonbashi, Chuo-ku, Tokyo 103 (03-3272-4511)	M D		China, Taiwan	5 universities	Science, Technology, Chemistry	○		50/mo.	2yr.	Mar ~ Apr	5	10	○	
Kinoshita Kinen Jigyodan (財)木下記念事業団	2-10-15 Kano-cho, Chuo-ku, Kobe-shi, Hyogo 650 (078-222-2551)	U M D		Southeast, Asia, Taiwan, ASEAN countries	Kobe, Kobe U of Commerce, Kwansei Gakuin, Konan University				360/yr. 480/yr. 600/yr.	MYR	Apr	1	2		○
Kiwanis Foundation キワニス奨学基金	5-3-68 Nakanoshima, Kita-ku, Osaka-shi, Osaka 530 (06-448-3870)	U M D		Southeast Asia	Osaka, Osaka City, U of Osaka prefecture, Kansai, Kinki University				20/mo.	1yr. ~ 2yr.	Apr 1~25	5	8		○

Name of Foundation Name of Scholarship	Address Telephone	Eligibility: Qualifier School Year	Eligibility: Age Limit	Eligibility: Designated Countries	Eligibility: Designated School in Japan	Eligibility: Designated Field of Study	Eligibility: Plural Grants and Limits (¥1,000)	Eligibility: Reapplication, Others (¥1,000)	Contents (¥1,000)	Duration	Application Period/ Deadline	Grantees	Applicants for the Previous Year	Contact F	Contact S
Kobayashi Foundation for Students from Abroad (財)小林外来留学生奨学財団	1-4-16 Kadotayashiki, Okayama-shi, Okayama 703 (0862-72-0447)	A U R M D		Asia, Africa, Latin America	Universities in Okayama pref.		○ 40/mo.		40/mo.	2yr.	Apr ~ May31	38	66		○
Kokusai Kyowa Foundation (財)国際協和奨学会	2-4-7-201 Nagata-cho, Chiyoda-ku, Tokyo 100 (03-3580-2469)	ST:2·3 U:3·4 R D D:1·2			Schools in Tokyo	Science & technology			80/mo.	1yr. ~ 2yr.	Dec	10	50	○	
Korean Scholarship Foundation, The (財)朝鮮奨学会	1-8-1 Nishi Sinjuku, Shinjuku-ku, Tokyo 160 (03-3343-5757)	U M D		Korea			○ U:20 G:40	○	20/mo. 30/mo.	1yr.	Apr 1 ~ May10	242		○	
Kumahira Scholarship Foundation (財)熊平奨学会	2-4-34 Higashi, Ujina, Minami-ku, Hiroshima-shi, Hiroshima 730 (082-251-2111)	U R M D			Universities in Hiroshima pref.		○	○	50/mo.	1yr.	Jan ~ Mar31	50	118		○
Kumamoto Lions Club (任)熊本ライオンズクラブ在熊外国人留学生奨学会	5-1-3 Shimazaki, Kumamoto-shi, Kumamoto 860 (096-366-2339)	A U R M D			Universities in Kumamoto pref.				10/mo.	1yr.	Jun	10			○
Kuraoka Foundation Scholarship (A) (財)倉岡奨学会	4-12 Nishinomaru-cho, Takamatsu-shi, Kagawa 760 (0878-22-3720)	U:3·4		Developing countries	Universities in Kagawa pref.				100/mo.	2yr.	Apr15 ~ May13	1	15	○	
(B)		R M D							50/mo. or 25/mo.	1yr.		5			
Kyoshin-Kizo Sakakida Memorial Scholarship Foundation, The (財)京信榊田喜三記念育英会	1-2 Tokumaru-cho, Umezu, Ukyo-ku, Kyoto-shi, Kyoto 615 (075-872-3044)	U	30		10 universities			○ Privately financed students	50/mo.	1yr.	Feb 7 ~ Apr25	10			○

Name of Foundation Name of Scholarship	Address Telephone	Eligibility: Qualifier School Year	Eligibility: Age Limit	Eligibility: Designated Countries	Eligibility: Designated School in Japan	Eligibility: Designated Field of Study	Eligibility: Plural Grants and Limits (¥1,000)	Eligibility: Reapplication, Others (¥1,000)	Contents (¥1,000)	Duration	Application Period/Deadline	Grantees	Applicants for the Previous Year	Contact: F	Contact: S
Lions supporting activity plan for foreign students LISA LISA奨学会	2-1-11 Nakayamatedori, Chuo-ku, Kobe-shi, Hyogo 650 (078-321-0108)	U M D			Universities in Kobe-shi				Within 80/mo.	UTG	any time	5			○
Maeda Masuzo Kinen Shogaku Kikin (公益信託)前田増三記念奨学基金	2-1-1 Muromachi, Nihonbashi, Chuo-ku, Tokyo 103 (03-3270-9511 ext.4335)	M:1	30		Tokyo, Chiba, Keio, Waseda, Tokyo U of Foreign Studies	Humanities, Social science	○ 100/mo.		50/mo.	2yr.	Apr ~ May	3~4	4		○
Maezawa Ikuei Zaidan (財)前沢育英財団	1-3-3 Kyobashi, Chuo-ku, Tokyo 104 (03-3281-5521 ext.300)	U			Keio, Kogakuin, Chuo, U of Tokyo, Tokyo Denki, Tokyo U of Technology, Tokyo Kasei, Nihon, Hosei, Meiji, Rikkyo, Waseda			Students/parents living in Tokyo	20/mo.	MYR	Apr ~ May	10	13		○
Makita Scholarship Foundation (財)牧田国際育英会	2-18 Agebacho, Shinjuku-ku, Tokyo 162 (03-3260-2788)	U:3·4 M D	30		Yes (names not given)		○ small amount		100/mo.	w/in 2yr.	Nov10 ~ Jan31	29	161	○	○
Meitetsu Internatinal Scholarship Association (財)名鉄国際育英会	1-2-4 Meieki, Nakamura-ku, Nagoya-shi, Aichi 450 (052-571-2111 ext.3431)	U M D		Pacific rim countries	Universities in Aichi pref.				80/mo.	2yr.	Nov ~ Dec	12~13	88		○
Mitsubishi Trust Yamamuro Memorial Scholarship Foundation The Special Scholarship for Students from Abroad	2-2-4 Nihonbashi, Chuo-ku, Tokyo 103 (03-3275-2215)	U:2~	30		ICU, Tokyo U of Foreign Studies, Sophia, Doshisha University		○		50/mo.	MYR	Mar ~ Apr	5			○
		M D			Waseda, Tokyo, Kyoto, Keio, Kobe, Tsukuba				70/mo.			11			
Scholarship (財)三菱信託山室記念奨学財団奨学会		U:2~4 M D	35		International U of Japan, etc.				100/mo. Tuition, Air fare, etc.	MYR		3		○	

Name of Foundation Name of Scholarship	Address Telephone	Eligibility							Contents (¥1,000)	Duration	Application Period/Deadline	Grantees	Applicants for the Previous Year	Contact	
		Qualifier School Year	Age Limit	Designated Countries	Designated School in Japan	Designated Field of Study	Plural Grants and Limits (¥1,000)	Reapplication, Others (¥1,000)						F	S
Morita Scholarship Foundation, The (財)盛田国際教育振興財団	1-4-30 Sakae, Naka-ku, Nagoya, Aichi 460 (052-204-1231)	JC U M D			Schools in Aichi pref.				1,000/yr.	1yr.	May20 ~ Jul 31	4	36		○
Moritani Scholarship Foundation, The (財)守谷育英会	1-4-22 Yaesu, Chuo-ku, Tokyo 103 (03-3271-2734)	CT JC U M D			Schools in Tokyo		○	○	15/mo. 20/mo. 25/mo.	MYR	Apr ~ May	30~40	480		○
Moriya Foundation Moriya Scholarship (財)守屋留学生交流協会	3-29 Jinbo-cho, Kanda, Chiyoda-ku, Tokyo 101 (03-3263-7952)	U:3	30	Asia	Yes (names not given)	Transferred students are not eligible.			45/mo.	2yr.	Apr 1~30	30	29		○
Nagasaki-ken Asia Koryu Zaidan (財)長崎県アジア交流財団	2-13 Edomachi, Nagasaki-shi, Nagasaki 850 (0958-24-1111-2084)	ST JL JC A U R M D	30 30 30 30 30 30 30 30	Asia	Schools in Nagasaki pref.				104/mo.	1yr.	Nov	5	9		○
Nagasaki Kita Rotary Club 長崎北ロータリークラブ	6-38 Manzaimachi, Nagasaki-shi, Nagasaki 850 (0958-25-6485)	U R M D			Universities in Nagasaki pref.				30/mo.	UTG	Dec ~ Jan	5	18	●	
Nagoya Lions Club 名古屋ライオンズクラブ	3-8-14 Nishiki, Naka-ku, Nagoya 460 (052-581-1711)	U M D			Universities in Aichi pref.		○ 20/mo.	○	500/yr.	1yr.	Jul 30	25~30	27		○

Name of Foundation Name of Scholarship	Address Telephone	Eligibility: Qualifier School Year	Eligibility: Age Limit	Eligibility: Designated Countries	Eligibility: Designated School in Japan	Eligibility: Designated Field of Study	Eligibility: Plural Grants and Limits (¥1,000)	Eligibility: Reapplication, Others (¥1,000)	Contents (¥1,000)	Duration	Application Period/ Deadline	Grantees	Applicants for the Previous Year	Contact: F	Contact: S
Nagoya Zonta Club 国際ゾンタ名古屋クラブ	2-16-7 Niban, Atsuta-ku, Nagoya-shi, Aichi 456 (052-653-0310)	U R M D			Universities in Aichi pref.			Women	30/mo.	1yr.	Jun 20 ~ Jul 20	2	22		○
Nakauchi Ikueikai (財)中内育英会	4-1-1 Minatojimanakamachi Chuo-ku, Kobe-shi, Hyogo 650 (078-302-8408)	U M D			Universities in Hyogo pref.	Commerce			80/mo.	2yr.		2~3			○
21 Seiki Bunka Gakujutsu Zaidan Gakujutsu Shoreikin 二十一世紀文化学術財団	1-4-6 Marunouchi, Chiyoda-ku, Tokyo 100 (03-3211-1271)	ST JC A U R M D				Social science			Total 5,000	1yr. ~ 2yr.	Oct ~ Dec	not fixed	70	○	
Nihon Han Taiheiyo Tonan Ajia Fujin Kyokai 日本汎太平洋東南アジア婦人協会	2-20-2 Higashi Nakano, Nakano-ku, Tokyo 164 (03-3361-1490)	U M D		Pan-Pacific Asian nations	Waseda, Keio University	Social & cultural improvement, Improvement on women's position	○	Women	10/mo.	1yr.	Apr ~ Mar	4			○
Nissho Iwai Foundation (財)日商岩井国際交流財団	2-4-5 Akasaka, Minato-ku, Tokyo 107 (03-3588-2115)	U:3·4 - - - M D	30 - - - 35		Yes (names not given)				30/mo. - - - 50/mo.	w/in 2yr.	Apr 1 ~ May 20	10	341	○	
Nihon Life Insurance Foundation Scholarship for Privately Financed Students (財)日本生命財団	4F Nihon Life Insurance Imahashi Bldg., 3-1-7, Imahashi, Chuo-ku, Osaka-shi, Osaka 541 (06-204-4014)	D	40	China, Taiwan, Hong Kong, ASEAN, Korea	Tokyo, Waseda, Hitotsubashi, Keio, Sophia, Kyoto, Osaka, Kobe, Osaka Pref., Osaka City, Doshisha, Nagoya, Kyushu, Kwansei Gakuin	Law, Economics, Management		○	Within 100/mo.	1yr.	Nov 1 ~ Dec 20	80	108	○	

Name of Foundation Name of Scholarship	Address Telephone	Eligibility							Contents (¥1,000)	Duration	Application Period/ Deadline	Grantees	Applicants for the Previous Year	Contact	
		Qualifier School Year	Age Limit	Designated Countries	Designated School in Japan	Designated Field of Study	Plural Grants and Limits (¥1,000)	Reapplication, Others (¥1,000)						F	S
Nomura Cultural Foundation (財)野村国際文化財団	1-9-1 Nihonbashi, Chuo-ku, Tokyo 103 (03-3271-2330)	U:3·4 M D	35		Tokyo, Keio, Kyoto, Waseda, Hitotsubashi	Humanities, Social sciences	○ Within 50/mo.		100/mo. 150/mo.	2yr.	Jan 31	10	—	○	
Okumura Shogakukai (財)奥村奨学会	1-5-13 Doshin, Kita-ku, Osaka-shi, Osaka 503 (06-357-2994)	U M D		Asia, Pacific area	Universities in Osaka pref.		○	○Non-doctrate holder in Osaka pref.	40/mo. 50/mo.	1yr. ○	Apr 1 ~ May10	10	77		○
Osaka Nagahoribashi Lions Club 大阪長堀橋ライオンズクラブ	1-21-22 Shimanouchi, Chuo-ku, Osaka-shi, Osaka 542 (06-245-5963)	M			Osaka University				75/mo.	2yr.	Feb	2			○
Osaka Nishi Rotary Club 大阪西ロータリークラブ	1-13-13 Umeda, Kita-ku, Osaka-shi, Osaka 530 (06-348-8436)	U R M D		Countries without Rotary Club (China etc.)	Universities in Osaka pref.				100/mo.	2yr.	May ~ Jun	1			○
Park Yong Koo Scholarship Foundation (財)朴龍九育英会	3-8-6 Nihonbashi, Chuo-ku, Tokyo 103 (03-3271-3414)	M D	30 35	Korea		Natural science			70/mo.	1yr.	Mar ~ Apr	35	124	○	
Rotary Yoneyama Memorial Foundation. Ict. (財)ロータリー米山記念奨学会奨学金	2-6-3 Shiba Koen, Minato-ku, Tokyo 105 (03-3435-1828)	U:3·4 M D	40	Countries with Rotary Club					120/mo. 150/mo.	w/in 2yr.	Oct 1~15	350~ 370	1,000	○	○
Rural Asia Solidarity Association Financial Assistance for Asian Students (任)RASA	7-14 Kawatacho, Shinjuku-ku, Tokyo 162 (03-3359-7655)	CT ST JC U A R M D		Asia				○	Total 100	lump sum	Apr 1 ~ May12	11	564	○	

Name of Foundation· Name of Scholarship	Address Telephone	Eligibility							Contents (¥1,000)	Duration	Application Period/ Deadline	Grantees	Applicants for the Previous Year	Contact	
		Qualifier School Year Age Limit		Designated Countries	Designated School in Japan	Designated Field of Study	Plural Grants and Limits (¥1,000)	Reapplication, Others (¥1,000)						F	S
Sagawa Scholarship Foundation Sagawa scholarship (財)佐川留学生奨学会	678 Ohmandokorocho, Bukkoji Sagaru, Karasumadori, Shimogyo-ku, Kyoto-shi, Kyoto 600 (075-371-0818)	U:3 M:1 D:2	27 35	Indonesia, Singapore, Malaysia, Thailand, Burnei, Cambodia, Myanma, Vietnam, Philippines, Laos				○	100/mo.	2yr.	Feb 3 ~ Apr18	15	65	○	
Sakaguchi International Scholarship Foundation (財)坂口国際育英奨学財団	1-12-2 Sotokanda, Chiyoda-ku, Tokyo 101 (03-3257-1951)	U:3·4 M D	30 35		Yes (names not given)	Humanities, Social science			80/mo.	2yr.	Oct 1 ~ Dec20	5	10		○
Sakai Ooizumi Rotary Club Nakagami Memorial Foundation 堺おおいずみロータリークラブ奨学会	1-1-20 Ryujinbashicho, Sakai-shi, Osaka 590 (0722-23-0770)	U M D	40		Universities in Osaka pref.				50/mo.	1yr.	Dec 1~23	3	5	○	
Saneyoshi Scholarship Foundation (財)實吉奨学会 Grant for Post-Graduate Students from Abroad	2-6-2 Otemachi, Chiyoda-ku, Tokyo 100 (03-3241-2907)	M D	35		25 schools	Science & technology (except Medical science, Pharmaceutics, Dentistry)	○	○	90/mo.	1yr.	Apr ~ May	10			○
Grant for Students from Abroad							○	○	50/mo.	1yr.		Over25			○
Sankei Shimbun, The Sankei Grants for Non-Japanese Students 産経新聞社	Sankei Media Service 1-7-2 Otemachi, Chiyoda-ku, Tokyo 100-77 (03-3275-8696)						○		Sum1,000 Sum 500	lump sum	Sep ~ Jan	1 24	382	○	

Name of Foundation Name of Scholarship	Address Telephone	Eligibility: Qualifier School Year	Eligibility: Age Limit	Eligibility: Designated Countries	Eligibility: Designated School in Japan	Eligibility: Designated Field of Study	Eligibility: Plural Grants and Limits (¥1,000)	Eligibility: Reapplication, Others (¥1,000)	Contents (¥1,000)	Duration	Application Period/ Deadline	Grantees	Applicants for the Previous Year	Contact: F	Contact: S
Sanwa Kokusai Kikin Scholarship (財)三和国際基金	1-1-1 Otemachi, Chiyoda-ku, Tokyo 100 (03-3211-7870)	U:3-4		Asia		Medical science, Japanese				w/in 2yr.	Jul			○	
		M		America, Europe, Australia		Economics, Business administration, Commerce, Trade, History					Jul				
Seiwa International Students Scholarship Foundation (財)清和国際留学生奨学会	6-4-14 Higashi Ueno, Taito-ku, Tokyo 110 (03-3843-7311)	U M D	30	Asia, Pacific countries	Tokyo, Kyoto, Kyushu, Akita, Tokyo U of Foreign Studies, Tsukuba, Tokyo Institute of Technology, Muroran Institute of Technology, Kyoto U of Foreign Studies, Chiba Institute of Technology, Musashi Institute of Technology, Waseda, Takushoku, Chuo, Nihon, Reitaku, Sophia, Tokai, Keio, Hosei, Nippon Institute of Technology				50/mo. 70/mo. 70/mo.	2yr.	Dec	5 5	56		○
Sendai Riverside Scholarship Association 仙台リヴァサイド奨学会	1-13-15 Sakuragaoka, Aoba-ku, Sendai-shi, Miyagi 981 (022-278-1304)	U M D			Miyagi Kenritsu Hobo Senmon Gakuin, Tohoku, Miyagi U of Education			○	60/yr.	1yr.	Mar 5 ~ Apr 28	7	17	○	
Shundoh International Foundation (財)俊道国際奨学会	2-17-3 Shibuya, Shibuya-ku, Tokyo 150 (03-3407-8511 ext.222)	M D			U of Tokyo, Tokyo Insutitute of Technology, Kyoto, Tsukuba, Yokohama National, Tohoku, Waseda, Keio, Sophia, Int'l U of Japan			○	100/mo.	2yr.	Mar 1~31	5	29		○

Name of Foundation Name of Scholarship	Address Telephone	Eligibility: Qualifier School Year	Eligibility: Age Limit	Eligibility: Designated Countries	Eligibility: Designated School in Japan	Eligibility: Designated Field of Study	Eligibility: Plural Grants and Limits (¥1,000)	Eligibility: Reapplication, Others (¥1,000)	Contents (¥1,000)	Duration	Application Period/ Deadline	Grantees	Applicants for the Previous Year	Contact: F	Contact: S
Soroptimist International of Nara 国際ソロプチミスト奈良	c/o Hiroko Yasukawa 202 Minami-mitsubo, Shinjo-cho, Kita-katsuragi-gun, Nara 639-21	U R M	1	Asia	Universities in Nara pref.				20/mo.	1yr.		5～6	7		○
Sponsors Association of Aichi Foreign Students Association Urgent Relief Money 愛知留学生会後援会	International Student Center 2-2-29 Koei, Minato-ku, Nagoya-shi, Aichi 455 (052-654-3511 ext. 531)	UJ A JC U R M D			Schools in Aichi pref.			○	Total: 50	Lump sum	Jun Nov	100～150	170	○	
Takaku Foundation (財)高久国際奨学財団	1-5-22 Shimo Ochiai, Shinjuku-ku, Tokyo 161 (03-3366-6727)	U ----- R M D					○ 30/mo.		70/mo. ----- 100/mo.	1yr.	Dec 1 ～ Jan 10	40	1,160	○	
Takamura Foundation 高村育英会	Tokyo Roki Co. Ltd. 2-14-10 Shin-yokohama, Kohoku-ku, Yokohama-shi, Kanagawa 222 (045-473-3120)	U ----- M D	30 ----- 35		Yokohama National, Yokohama City, Tokyo, Keio, Tokyo Institute of Technology, etc.				50/mo.	MYR	Apr16 ～ May10	3 ----- 3	16		○
Takugin Shogakkai (財)たくぎん奨学会	3-7 Ohdohri Nishi, Chuo-ku, Sapporo-shi, Hokkaido 060 (011-271-2111 ext.3425)	U R M D		Asia Africa	Universities in Hokkaido		○	○	60/mo.	1yr.	May	5	0		○
Theater Company Hikosen International Scholarship (A) (B) (任)劇団飛行船国際奨学会	2-15-1-617 Dogenzaka, Shibuya-ku, Tokyo 150 (03-3464-5476)	ST U A R M D		Korea, Taiwan, China, Hong Kong	Nihon, Meiji, Senshu, Tamagawa, Waseda, Musashino Art University			Students interested in maskplay musical	(A) 20/mo. ----- (B) 50/mo.	1yr.	Nov ～ Feb	15	15		○

Name of Foundation Name of Scholarship	Address Telephone	Eligibility Qualifier School Year	Age Limit	Designated Countries	Designated School in Japan	Designated Field of Study	Plural Grants and Limits (¥1,000)	Reapplication, Others (¥1,000)	Contents (¥1,000)	Duration	Application Period/ Deadline	Grantees	Applicants for the Previous Year	Contact F	Contact S
Toka Kyoiku Bunka Koryu Zaidan (財)東華教育文化交流財団	8-2-12 Ginza, Chuo-ku, Tokyo 104 (03-3571-7613)	U:3·4 R M D		China					80/mo.	w/in 2yr. ○	Oct 15 ~ Nov15 /Apr 1~15	10		○	
Tokyu Foundation for Inbound students (財)とうきゅう外来留学生奨学財団	26-20 Sakuragaoka-cho, Shibuya-ku, Tokyo 150 (03-3461-0844)	R M D	30 35	Asia, Pacific nations					110/mo. Medical fee, etc.	2yr. ○	Oct 1 ~ Dec 5	20	491	○	
Tonen International Scholarship Foundation (財)東燃国際奨学財団	1-1-1 Hitotsubashi, Chiyoda-ku, Tokyo 100 (03-3286-5072)	J:3·4 M:1·2 D:	35 35 35		Yes (names not given)				100/mo. 120/mo. 120/mo.	2yr. 2yr. 1yr.	Apr	10	–	○	
Toyobo Biotechnology Foundation Long-term Research Grants 東洋紡百周年記念バイオテクノロジー研究財団	17-9 Koamicho, Nihonbashi, Chuo-ku, Tokyo 103 (03-3660-4890)	M D	40			Biotechnology			Total 2,000 ~3,000	1yr.	Aug	5~6		○	
Toyota Tsusho International Scholarship Foundation (財)豊田通商国際育英会	4-7-23 Meieki, Nakamura-ku, Nagoya-shi, Aichi 450 (052-584-5600)	U M D			Universities in Aichi pref.			Students in Aichi pref.	70/mo.	MYR	Apr ~ May	6	62		○
Tsurukame Corporation ツルカメコーポレーション	1-19-32 Nishiki, Naka-ku, Nagoya-shi, Aichi 460 (052-221-6507)	JC U R M D			Universities in Aichi, Gifu, Mie pref.		○ Self-financed students	○	Total 400	Lump sum	May22 ~ Jun30	25	128		○
Watanuki International Scholarship Foundation 綿貫国際奨学財団	Keiyo Bank 1-11-11 Fujimi, Chiba-shi, Chiba 280 (0472-22-2121)	U:3·4 M D		Asian and the Pacific rim countries	Yes (names not given)			○	120/mo. 150/mo.	○ 1yr.	Mar15	8 22	–		○

Name of Foundation Name of Scholarship	Address Telephone	Eligibility							Contents (¥1,000)	Duration	Application Period/Deadline	Grantees	Applicants for the Previous Year	Contact	
		Qualifier School Year	Age Limit	Designated Countries	Designated School in Japan	Designated Field of Study	Plural Grants and Limits (¥1,000)	Reapplication, Others (¥1,000)						F	S
Yamaha Motor International Friendship (公益信託)ヤマハ発動機国際友好基金	2-1-1 Muromachi, Nihonbashi, Chuo-ku, Tokyo 103 (03-3270-9511 ext. 4335)	M:1	30		Tokyo, Tokyo Institute of Technology, Chiba, Waseda, Yokohama National, Keio, U of Electro-communications	Engineering			100/mo.	2yr.	Dec ~ Mar	5	14		○
Yamaoka Scholarship Foundation (財)山岡育英会	1-32 Chayamachi, Kita-ku, Osaka-shi, Osaka 530 (06-376-6281)	M D	35	East & Southeast Asia	11 universities	Science, Technology	○ 50/mo.		80/mo.	2yr.	Mar10 ~ May20	6	10		○
Yokoyama Kokusai Shogaku Zaidan (財)横山国際奨学財団	3-12 Kioi-cho, Chiyoda-ku, Tokyo 102 (03-3238-2913)	U R UJ M D	35 40	Australia		All except Medical science, Dentistry		○	120~150/mo. Tuition, Housing assistance	MYR	Mar 31	10~15			● ◎
Yoshida Ikueikai (財)吉田育英会 Scholarship (A)	200 Yoshida, Kurobe-shi, Toyama 938 (0765-57-1111 ext.2181~2183)	U M D			29 universities		○		50/mo.	12 mo.	May ~ Jun	50	51		○
Scholarship (B)		U M D		U.S., Europe	9 universities		○		150/mo.			10	10		○
Yoshimoto Shoji Shogakukai (財)吉本章治奨学会	2-2-11 Hakata Ekimae, Hakata-ku, Fukuoka-shi, Fukuoka 812 (092-431-7771)	U M D			Universities in Fukuoka pref.				40/mo.	w/in 2yr.	May	8	89		○
Yumoto Ikueikai (財)湯本育英会	4-17-7 Asakusabashi, Taito-ku, Tokyo 111 (03-3861-2311)	U:1			Waseda, Keio, Meiji, Aoyama, Seijo, Tokyo Women's University		○		15/mo.	MYR	Apr ~ Jun	10	18	○	○
ZONTA International Kyoto 国際京都ZONTAクラブ	30 Kamimiyanomaecho, Sakyo-ku, Shishigadani, Kyoto-shi, Kyoto 606 (075-771-4794)	U M D		Asia				Women in Kyoto-shi	70/mo.	1yr.	Jan 1 ~ Mar 1	2			○

IV. Scholarships by Colleges and Universities

*1 Qualifier
A: Auditors (Undergraduate)
U: Undergraduate Students
R: Research Students (Graduate)
M: Master's Program Students
D: Doctor's Program Students
SC: Special Course Students
SA: Study Abroad Program Students

*2 Plural grants permitted=○
*3 Reapplication permitted=○

*4 Renewable=○
MYR=Minimum years required for graduation/completion
UTG=Up to graduation/completion

*5 Locally adopted=●
Overseas application=◎

Name of University	Name of Scholarship	Eligibility *1 Qualifier	School Year	Age Limit	Designated Countries	Designated Field of Study	Plural Grants and Limit (¥1,000) *2	Reapplication, *3	and Other Eligibility (¥1,000)	Contents (¥1,000)	Duration *4	Application Period/ Deadline	Grantees	Applicants for the Previous Year	Notes *5
Hokkaido Region															
Muroran Institute of Technology	The Foundation for Academic Advancement and International Exchange	U R M D					○	○	Foreign students without any scholarship have priority	50/mo.	○	Not fixed	A certain number of students		●
Fuji Women's College	Bishop Kinold Memorial Scholarship 1) scholarship 2) student loan	U					○	○	(not during the same year)	1) 50/yr. 2) 20/mo. (for those living at home) 25/mo. (for those not living at home)	1) 12mo. 2) until graduation	1) any time 2) Apr. 22 ~ May 12	1) 10* 2) 15* *These numbers include those from Fuji Women's Junior College.	1) 0 2) 23*	
Hokkaido Tokai University	Graduate School Scholarship	M	1~2						Excellent Academic Standing	All expenses equivalent to admission fee, tuition fees, facility use, etc.	12mo.		1		
Rakuno Gakuen University	Rakuno Educational Scholarship	U R								30/mo. 50/mo.					

Name of University	Name of Scholarship	Eligibility: Qualifier School Year Age Limit			Designated Countries	Designated Field of Study	Plural Grants and Limit (¥1,000)	Reapplication, and Other Eligibility (¥1,000)		Contents (¥1,000)	Duration	Application Period/ Deadline	Grantees	Applicants for the Previous Year	Notes
Sapporo Gakuin University	Meiwa Gakuen Scholarships	U	1~4					○		300/yr.	10mo.	Apr. 9 ~ Apr. 26	85	165	●
Tohoku Region															
Hirosaki Gakuin College	Hirosaki Gakuin Scholarship	U	1~4				○	○		32/mo.	12mo.	May 1 ~ May 30	10	25	●
Tohoku Institute of Technology	Tohoku Institute of Technology Scholarship	U	1~4				○			10/mo.	12mo.		59	60	
Tohoku Living Culture College	The Japan Scholarship Foundation	U	1~4					○		35~ 48/mo.	45mo. ~ 48mo.	Apr. 20 ~ May 30	14	26	
Kanto Region															
Hitotsubashi University	Josuikai	U M D	1~4 1~2 1~3				○ 50/mo.	○		360/yr.	12mo.		30	33	
Ochanomizu University	Mayako Ikeda Memorial Fund Tadashi Ikeda Memorial Fund	U M D	4 2 3				○	○		100/yr.		~Oct.31		5	
University of Tsukuba	Fund for International Exchange	U M D						○		300/yr.	1yr.	Dec. 10 ~ Jan. 31	4	13	
	Tien Lo Fund for International Academic Research	U M D						○		300/yr.	1yr.	Jul. 20 ~ Sep. 12	10	23	
	Saneyoshi Scholarship Foundation	R						○		500/yr.	1yr.	Jun. 15 ~ Jul. 5	1	1	
Ashikaga Institute of Technology	Scholarship	U	2~4							Tuition	12mo.		15	0	

Name of University	Name of Scholarship	Eligibility: Qualifier School Year Age Limit			Designated Countries	Designated Field of Study	Plural Grants and Limit (¥1,000)	Reapplication, and Other Eligibility (¥1,000)		Contents (¥1,000)	Duration	Application Period/ Deadline	Grantees	Applicants for the Previous Year	Notes
Bunkyo University	Bunkyo University Foreign Student Scholarship	U	2~4							100/yr.~ 50/yr.		Apr. Jun.			
Chuogakuin University	Chuogakuin University Scholarship	U	1~4				○	○		Tuition	12mo. ○	May 1 ~ May 15	30	100	
Chuo University	Scholarship for Foreign Students	U M D	2~4 1~2 1~3				○	○	Excludes Monbusho Scholarship students	Half tuition & laboratory fees	1yr.	Jun.	Unfixed	59	
	Special Scholarship for Foreign Undergraduate Students	U	2~4		Asian Countries		○ 30/mo.	○	Excludes Monbusho Scholarship students	50/mo.	12mo.	Apr.	5	37	
Daito Bunka University	Daito's Special (NISHU) Scholarship	U M D	1~4 1~2 1~3					○		Tuition exemption	12mo.	Jun. 10 ~ Jun. 30	3 3	22	
	Daito's Study Incentive (Actual Reduction of Tuition Fee)	U M D	1~4 1~2 1~3					○		180/yr.	12mo.	Apr. 1 ~ May 30	285	237	
		SC	1					○		100/yr.	12mo.	Apr. 1 ~ May 30	32	32	
Dokkyo University	International Scholarship	U	1~4				○	○		240/yr.	1yr.	Apr. 26 ~27	21	51	
	Scholarship for Graduate students	M D	1~5				○	○		190/yr. or 380/yr.	1yr.	Apr. 12 ~17	29	38	

Name of University	Name of Scholarship	Eligibility: Qualifier	School Year	Age Limit	Designated Countries	Designated Field of Study	Plural Grants and Limit (¥1,000)	Reapplication,	and Other Eligibility (¥1,000)	Contents (¥1,000)	Duration	Application Period/ Deadline	Grantees	Applicants for the Previous Year	Notes
Dokkyo University School of Medicine	Parents' Benefit Association Scholarships	U	3~6						Granted to students who face great difficulty in continuing their studies because of a parent's death or disablement.	Amount depends on the economic situation of the students	Not specified				●
Gakushuin University	Gakushuin Scholarship	U M D	1~4				○	○		Tuition	12mo. ○				
	Yoshishige Abe Commemorative Education Fund Awards for Academic Achievements at Graduate Level	M D	1~3				○			450/yr.	12mo.				
	Yoshishige Abe Commemorative Education Fund Awards for Academic Achievements at Undergraduate Level	U	1~4				○			Tuition	12mo.				
	Seki Ikuei Scholarship Fund					Physical Sciences related to Electrical Engineering, Electronics and Nuclear Energy	○			360/yr.	12mo.		1		
	Gakushuin Scholarship Fund Grants for Research/Study Plans Characterized by Unique Qualifies	U M D					○				○				
	Scholarship and Awards for Foreign Students	U M D					○			100/yr.	12mo. ○				

Name of University	Name of Scholarship	Eligibility: Qualifier School Year Age Limit			Eligibility: Designated Countries	Eligibility: Designated Field of Study	Eligibility: Plural Grants and Limit (¥1,000)	Eligibility: Reapplication, and Other Eligibility (¥1,000)		Contents (¥1,000)	Duration	Application Period/ Deadline	Grantees	Applicants for the Previous Year	Notes
Hakuoh University	International Exchange Scholarship	U	2~4	18~30			○ 45/mo.	○	Housing under 50/mo. Allowance under 80/mo.	45/mo.	12mo.	May 1~ May 19	2~3	4	●
Hosei University	Hosei International Fund Foreign Students' Scholarship	U	1~4				○		University's nomination	Tuition, admission, facilities and laboratory fees.	1yr. ○		8		●
	Special Hosei University Centtennial Scholarship	U M D	2~4				○	○		150~ 450/yr.	1yr.	Apr.~ May		174	●
	Hosei University Scholarship	U M D	1~4				○	○		80~ 200/yr.	1yr.	Apr.~ May		174	●
International Christian University	ICU Non-Japanese Student Scholarship	U M D	1~4 1~2 1~2				○	○	registration of at least 2 terms at ICU before application	1/3, 1/2 or 2/3 of tuition	1yr.	mid. Apr.~ May		17	
International University of Japan	I.U.J. Scholarship Fund	M								Tuition Admission Stipend	12mo. ○	mid. Jan.			◎ ●
Japan College of Social Work	Japan College of Social Work Scholarship	U R	1~4				○	○		Tuition		Jul. 1~ Jul. 20 (freshmen) Jan. 1~ Jan. 31 (other students)	10~15	62	
Japan Women's College of Physical Education	Nikaido Scholarship	U	1~4	18~			○	○		180/yr.	12mo.	May 1~ May 15	some students		

Name of University	Name of Scholarship	Eligibility: Qualifier School Year Age Limit			Designated Countries	Designated Field of Study	Plural Grants and Limit (¥1,000)	Reapplication, and Other Eligibility (¥1,000)		Contents (¥1,000)	Duration	Application Period/ Deadline	Grantees	Applicants for the Previous Year	Notes
Kanagawa Institute of Technology	Arai Scholarship	U	3~4				○			200/yr.					
Kanagawa University	Kanagawa University's Tuition Reduction Scholarship	U M D	1~4 1~2 1~3				○ ○ ○	○ ○ ○		30% Tuition	12mo.	May 16 ~ May 18		11	
Kanto Gakuin University	Kanto Gakuin University Graduate School Scholarship	M					○			180/yr.	12mo.	Apr. 9 ~13	5	18	●
		D					○			120/yr., tuition exemption	12mo.	Apr. 9 ~13	a few	3	●
	Saito Koshiro Scholarship	U	3, 4							100/yr.	Jul.	Jun.	6	9	●
Keio University	Keio U. Scholrship for Self-funding International Undergrad. Students	U	1~4				○	○		Type I: Tuition Type II: Half tuition	1yr.	Apr.	34	58	
	Keio U. Scholarship for Int'l Graduate Students	M D	1~2 1~3				○	○		Type I: Admission, Facilities, Equipment, & Lab. costs reduction and Book Allowance Type II: Admission fee; Book Allowance	1yr.	Ibid.	15	new	

Name of University	Name of Scholarship	Eligibility: Qualifier School Year Age Limit			Designated Countries	Designated Field of Study	Plural Grants and Limit (¥1,000)	Reapplication, and Other Eligibility (¥1,000)		Contents (¥1,000)	Duration	Application Period/ Deadline	Grantees	Applicants for the Previous Year	Notes
Keio University	Yamaoka Memorial Fund Scholarships for International Students	U	1		Asia	Letters, Economics, Business & Commerce, Science & Technology	○		Applicants for Keio University Graduate School	Total expenses required at entrance		same as exam. d'line	5	27	
		D	3			Letters, Economics, Law, Human Relations, Business & Commerce, Science & Technology	○		expected to be enroled at Doctral course for the 4th year and to complete dissertation by extending enrollment	Tuition fees and Lab. costs		Mar.	2	4	
Keisen Jogakuen College	Asian Students Scholarship	U			Asian Countries		○	○		Tuition	12mo.				
	Keisen Jogakuen International Educational Fund	U					○	○		Tuition	12mo.				
	College Scholarship	U					○	○		Tuition	12mo.				
Kogakkan University	Shinoda Fund for Advancement of Science	U A M D R				Shinto	○			Tuition, Housing, 50~100/mo.	UTG	Not fixed	Several students	2	
Kokushikan University	Foreign Students	U M D SA					○	○		30/mo.	12mo.	Jan. 8 ~ Feb. 12	Not Fixed	150	

Name of University	Name of Scholarship	Eligibility: Qualifier School Year Age Limit			Eligibility: Designated Countries	Eligibility: Designated Field of Study	Eligibility: Plural Grants and Limit (¥1,000)	Eligibility: Reapplication, and Other Eligibility (¥1,000)		Contents (¥1,000)	Duration	Application Period/ Deadline	Grantees	Applicants for the Previous Year	Notes
Komazawa University	Komazawa Univ. Special Scholarship	U	1~4				○	○		200/yr.	1yr.	Jul.	45	140	
	Komazawa Univ. Centenary Commemoration Scholarship	U M D	1~4					○		240/yr.	1yr.	Apr.	70	91	
	Komazawa Univ. Educational Scholarship for Freshmen	U	1				○			Admission Tuition Maintenance fees	4yr.		7		
Meiji College of Pharmacy	Meiji College of Pharmacy Scholarship	R M D		22~		Course of Pharmaceutical Sciences	○	○		Tuition 500/yr. 400/yr. 450/yr.	12mo.	Apr. 25 May 15	15	21	
Meiji Gakuin University	Type One Scholarships A	U	2~4						Scholarstic attainments must be upper 20%	150/yr. (50 in the form of book token)		Oct. 1 ~3		98	
	Type One Scholarships B									100/yr. (50 in the form of book token)					
	Type Two Scholarship	U	1~4						Must have applied for Japan Student Aid Association Scholarship	The upper limit is half of the tuition and miscellaneous fees		Apr. 16 ~20 Oct. 4 ~8		100	
	Scholarships for Students to Study abroad	U	3~4						Both scholastic attinments and characters must be good	Travelling subsidies		Jul. 9 ~ Jul. 11		12	

Name of University	Name of Scholarship	Eligibility: Qualifier	School Year	Age Limit	Designated Countries	Designated Field of Study	Plural Grants and Limit (¥1,000)	Reapplication,	and Other Eligibility (¥1,000)	Contents (¥1,000)	Duration	Application Period/ Deadline	Grantees	Applicants for the Previous Year	Notes
Meiji Gakuin University	Scholarships for Foreign Students	U	1~4						When/If recognized as financial support is necessary in order to pursue studies			Oct. 4 ~ Oct. 8		11	
	Scholarships for Short-term Exchange Students	U	2~4						Hope College summer seminar participant	200/yr.		Jun. 4 ~ Jun. 6	No limit	15	
	Meiji Gakuin University Parents' Association Scholarship	U	1~4							The upper limit is half of the tuition		Oct. 4 ~ Oct. 8	No limit	31	
Musashi University	Musashi University Student Loans	U								530/yr.	48mo.	Apr. 10~ May 10	10	19	
	Musashi University Graduate Student Loans	M D								660/yr. 760/yr.	24mo. 36mo.	Apr. 10 ~27	10	0	
Musashino Art University	Musashino Art University Scholarship	U M	1~4 1~2				O	O		250/yr.	1yr.	Apr. 30	3		
Musashino Women's College	M.W.C. Anniversary scholarship	U	1~4				O	O		120/yr.	12mo.	Apr.~ May	30	45	
	Friends of M.W.I. scholarship	U	1~4				O	O		20/mo.~ 30/mo.	12mo.	On occasion	15~20	19	
Nippon Institute of Technology	Nippon Institute of Technology Scholarship	U M D	2~4				O	O		20/mo.	36m	Apr. 16 ~ May 16	No Limit	30	

Name of University	Name of Scholarship	Eligibility: Qualifier School Year Age Limit			Eligibility: Designated Countries	Eligibility: Designated Field of Study	Eligibility: Plural Grants and Limit (¥1,000)	Eligibility: Reapplication, and Other Eligibility (¥1,000)		Contents (¥1,000)	Duration	Application Period/ Deadline	Grantees	Applicants for the Previous Year	Notes
Nippon Veterinary and Animal Science University	Nippon Medical School Scholarship for Foreign researchers	D					○ 80/mo.	○		960/yr.	6mo.	Dec. 1~ Jan. 31 Jul. 1~ Aug. 31	10	1	
Nishogakusha University	Special scholarship for foreigners	U	2~4				○	○		50/mo.	12mo.	May		1	
Reitaku University	Reitaku University Foreign Students Scholarship	U SC	1~4							Tuition	12mo.	Sep. 6 ~ Oct. 4	15	25	
Rikkyo University	Rikkyo University International Scholarship	U M D SA					○		exchange Student	100~ 130/mo.	4~ 11mo.	Oct.~ Dec.	8	14	◎
	St. Paul's Lions Club Scholarship	U M D SA			Asian Countries		○			200/yr.		Apr.~ May	1	2	
	St. Paul's Ladies Club Scholarship	U M D SA					○		women	300/yr.		Oct.~ Dec.	1	5	
	Ogata-Heim Scholarship	U M D SA			U.S.A.		○			400/yr.		Jan.~ Feb.	1	1	
	Almini Association Scholarship	U M D			Asian Countries		○			500/yr.		Sep.~ Oct.	a few	2	
	Rikkyo University Scholarship	U	2~				○	○		100/yr.		Apr.~ May	No limit (depends on budget)	0	
		M D					○	○		120~ 180/yr.				18	
	Rikkyo University Loans	U M D					○	○		300~ 470/yr.		Apr.~ May	No limit (depends on budget)	13	

Name of University	Name of Scholarship	Eligibility								Contents (¥1,000)	Duration	Application Period/ Deadline	Grantees	Applicants for the Previous Year	Notes
		Qualifier School Year Age Limit			Designated Countries	Designated Field of Study	Plural Grants and Limit (¥1,000)	Reapplication, and Other Eligibility (¥1,000)							
Rissho University	Rissho tachibana Scholarship	U M D					○	○		U: 400/yr. G: 500/yr.	1yr.	May 10 ~ May 21	81	237	
SANNO College	SANNO College Ueno Scholarships for Foreign Students														
	1. TOKUBETSU (Special) Scholarship	U	2~4					○		Half tuition		Appoint by Col.	Up to 2	1	
	2. IKUEI (Educational) Scholarship	U	1~4					○		150~ 200/yr.		Recom-mend by Col.	Up to 3	4	
	3. KOKUSAI (International) Scholarship	U	1~4		Southeast Asia			○	Those admitted through recommendation by the College designated public organizations	Full tuition plus fees, plus 300/yr.		As designated by	Up to 2	0	
Seikei University	Seikei Graduate Schools Scholarship	M D					○	○		Tuition, one half or one quarter	12mo.	Apr. 1 Apr. 20		52	
	Tuition Waiver Program	M D					○	○		Tuition Waiver, up to 100%	12mo.	Apr.		3	
Senshu University	Type 1 Type 2	U U	2~4 2							Tuition Tuition and Fees, 15/yr.	1yr. 3yr.				
	Type 3-A Type 3-B Type 3-C	U U U								10/mo. Tuition 100					

Name of University	Name of Scholarship	Eligibility								Contents (¥1,000)	Duration	Application Period/ Deadline	Grantees	Applicants for the Previous Year	Notes
		Qualifier School Year Age Limit			Designated Countries	Designated Field of Study	Plural Grants and Limit (¥1,000)	Reapplication, and Other Eligibility (¥1,000)							
Shibaura Institute of Technology	S.I.T. College Scholarship	U					85/mo.		In case of high financial needs caused by difficulties at home country.	Tuition 510/6mo.	6mo.	Apr. 1 ~ Mar. 31			●
Showa Academia Musicae	Tosei Gakuen Scholarship	U	1～4					○		Tuition (latter term) 445/yr.		When applying for admission		15	
Showa University	Showa University Visiting fellow Scholarship	R				Medicine, Dentistry, Pharmaceutical Science				100/mo.	1yr.	Apr. 1～ Mar. 31	20		
Shukutoku University	Shukutoku University Scholarship	U	1～4		Foreign Student			○		Tuition, 550/yr.	1yr.	May	2	2	
		M	1～2		Japanese & Foreigen Student			○		Tuition, 400 or 165/yr.	1yr.	Jul.	Some students	9	
	Shukutoku University Foundation Scholarship	U	1～4		Japanese			○		Tuition, 275/yr.	1yr.	U: 2～4 May U: 1 Oct.	16	8	
Soka University	International Scholarship	SC U M D	1～4				○	○		120/yr.	12mo.	Jul. 1 ～31		75	●
Sophia University	New Students' Scholarships	U M D	New Students							Amount equivalent to tuition	1yr.	At the time of application for admission		102	◎

Name of University	Name of Scholarship	Eligibility: Qualifier School Year Age Limit			Eligibility: Designated Countries	Eligibility: Designated Field of Study	Eligibility: Plural Grants and Limit (¥1,000)	Eligibility: Reapplication, and Other Eligibility (¥1,000)		Contents (¥1,000)	Duration	Application Period/ Deadline	Grantees	Applicants for the Previous Year	Notes
Sophia University	Type I Scholarship	U	2~4				○			A book coupon equivalent to 50/yr.	1yr.		105		
	Type II Scholarship	U	New Students & Seniors 1~3				○	○			1yr.	May October		611	
	Type III Scholarship ①Lemos	U				Comparative Culture				1/3 of tuition	1yr.	May	a few	27	
	②Teilhard de Chardin	M D								50~200/yr.	1yr.	Oct.			
	③Adachi	U M D			Asian Students					633.6~953.3/yr.	1yr.	Oct.	a few	64	
	④Oizumi	U				Faculty of Humanities				55/yr.	1yr.	May	a few		
	⑤St. Louis Fund	U				French Lit.				50/yr.	1yr.	May	a few		
	⑥Russell Briens	U	3~4			Journalism				125/yr.	1yr.	May	1		
	⑦Sophia Britanica	U				Eng. Lang.				40~80/yr.	1yr.	Jun.			
	⑧Numata Takumi	U				Chemistry				60/yr.	1yr.	Jul.	2		
	⑨Atom Physics International	M D								100/yr.	1yr.	May			
	⑩Foreign Students	U M D			Asian Students					200/yr.	1yr.	Oct.	a few		
	⑪Nishimura	U				Spanish Lang	○			50/yr.	1yr.	Jul.	a few		
	⑫Sophia Sci-Tech Association	M D				Division of Sci. & Tech.				216.3/yr.	1yr.		a few		

Name of University	Name of Scholarship	Eligibility: Qualifier School Year Age Limit			Eligibility: Designated Countries	Eligibility: Designated Field of Study	Eligibility: Plural Grants and Limit (¥1,000)	Eligibility: Reapplication, and Other Eligibility (¥1,000)		Contents (¥1,000)	Duration	Application Period/ Deadline	Grantees	Applicants for the Previous Year	Notes
Taisho University	Scholarship of Taisho University	U SA						○	Excellent Students	Proportional to the tuition 430/yr.	Lump sum				
	Scholarship of the parents' Association of Taisho University	U R M						○	Excellent Students	50/yr. 70/yr.	Lump sum Lump sum				
	Scholarship of the Foreign Student Studying Abroad at private expense	SA M D								Proportional to the tuition's 40%	Lump sum				
Takachiho College of Commerce	Takachiho Fund	U	1~4	18~			○ 80/yr.	○		150/yr.				0	
	Takachiho Scholarship (Top 10/grade)	U	1~4	18~			○ 150/yr.	○		80/yr.				0	
Takushoku University	International Student Scholarship	U	2~4				○ Under 250/mo.	○		Tuition, Housing, 250/yr.	12mo.	Jun. 15 ~30	20	85	
Tama Art University	Tama Art University Scholarship	U M	2~4				○	○		200/yr.	12mo.	May	6	15	
Tokai University	Tokai University Foreign Student Scholarship Class one	U	1~4				○ 45/mo.			Tuition Educational operating fee Educational facilities fee	12mo.		44		●
	Class two									Tuition					

Name of University	Name of Scholarship	Eligibility: Qualifier School Year Age Limit			Eligibility: Designated Countries	Eligibility: Designated Field of Study	Eligibility: Plural Grants and Limit (¥1,000)	Eligibility: Reapplication, and Other Eligibility (¥1,000)		Contents (¥1,000)	Duration	Application Period/ Deadline	Grantees	Applicants for the Previous Year	Notes
Tokyo Christian University	Scholarship	U					○	○		Full Tuition 309/yr. Half Tuition 154.5/yr.		Apr. 15 ~ May 15	1 1	0 0	
	International Students Scholarship	U					○	○		30% Tuition 92.7/yr.		Apr. 15 ~ May 15		4	
Tokyo Denki University	T.D.U. Alumni Association Shin Denki Scholarship	U	1~4				○		1 loan throughout 4 years	the amount corresponding to the fees of one term		1yr.	a few	8	
	T.D.U. Special Scholarship	U	2~4				○	○	The academic record	a part or tuition	1yr.	Apr. ~ May	a few	48	
Tokyo Dental College	Tokyo Dental College Scholarship	U	1~6				○		a good school good character, healthful and respectable	Tuition & others	1yr.				●
Tokyo Kasei University	Watanabe Gakuen Scholarship	U	1~4					○		10/mo.	12mo.	Apr. 11 ~ Apr. 20	7	24 (total)	
	W.G. Endou Scholarship	U	1~4					○		10/mo.	12mo.		5		
	W.G. Ryokusokai Scholarship	U	1~4					○		10/mo.	12mo.		4		
	W.G. Tsuruta Scholarship	U	1~4					○		10/mo.	12mo.		2		
	W.G. Aihara Scholarship	U	1~4					○		75	Lump sum		1		
	W.G. Aoki Scholarship	U	1~4					○		50			1		
	W.G. Kisoyama Scholarship	U	1~4					○		50			1		

Name of University	Name of Scholarship	Eligibility: Qualifier School Year Age Limit			Designated Countries	Designated Field of Study	Plural Grants and Limit (¥1,000)	Reapplication, and Other Eligibility (¥1,000)		Contents (¥1,000)	Duration	Application Period/ Deadline	Grantees	Applicants for the Previous Year	Notes
Tokyo Keizai University	Scholarship for graduate students	M D	1~2 1~3					○		360/yr.	1yr.	May	a few	11	
	Scholarship for foreign independent students	U	1~4					○		300/yr.	MYR	Apr.	a few	1	
Tokyo Medical and Dental University	Shouichi Kobashi Scholarship	D				Morphology, Physiology, and Social Medicine				600/yr.	12mo. ~ 24mo.	Mar. 31	a few	0	
Tokyo Union Theological Seminary	Scholarships for Tuition Fee	U M	2~4 1~2				○	○		50~80/ Half year	6mo.	Feb. 28 Jun. 30	all students	64	
	Scholarhips for Admission Fee	U	4				○			60~70		Feb. 28	all students	15	
Tokyo University of Art and Design	The University Scholarship	U	3~4							Tuition 1.50% 2.33%	1yr.	Oct.	Authorized by University	26	
Tokyo University of Information Sciences	Scholarship for International Students	U	1~4				○			Tuition 225/yr.	12mo.				
Tokyo Woman's Christian University	Tokyo Woman's Christian University Foreign Scholarship	M							Students currently enrolled or prospective students	Tuition	1yr.	Final date of application		7	◎
Tokyo Women's Medical College	Tokyo Women's Medical College Special Scholarship Student	U	1~6				○	○	·Special Student ·She lost her parents and had to pay herself	Tuition 2,625	1yr.	Apr. 1 ~ Apr. 20		1	
	Campbell Scholarship	U	1~6				○	○	·Special Student ·Top Student	70	1yr.		1/class	6	

Name of University	Name of Scholarship	Eligibility: Qualifier	School Year	Age Limit	Designated Countries	Designated Field of Study	Plural Grants and Limit (¥1,000)	Reapplication, and Other Eligibility (¥1,000)		Contents (¥1,000)	Duration	Application Period/ Deadline	Grantees	Applicants for the Previous Year	Notes
Toyo Eiwa Women's University	Toyo Eiwa Women's University Scholarship Type A: Type B:	U					○	○	student loan	Tuition 1/2 Tuition	1yr.	Apr.	Unfixed	9	
Toyo University	Tuition support for foreign students studying at their own expenses	U M D					○		Students on Japanese government scholarship excluded	20% of tuition	1yr.	1) Continuing students (April) 2) Newly enrolled students (May)	Applicable to all registered students from overseas	247	
Tsuda College	Foreign Scholarships	U M	2~					○	Exchange students only	A part of study expenses		Jun. & Nov.		2	
	International Exchange Scholarships	U M			U.S.A. Australia Philippines R.O.K.					Tuition, Dorm rent, 80/mo.	10mo.		5	5	◎
		U M			U.S.A.					Tuition, Dorm rent	10mo.		4	2	◎
Waseda University	Okuma Memorial Scholarships	U	2~4					○		Tuition	12mo.	Apr. 14 ~ May 12	11	43	
		M	1~2					○		Tuition Admission Fee 150~180/yr.	12mo.	Apr. 14 ~ May 12	11	42	
		D	1~3					○		Tuition Admission Fee 360/yr.					
	Azusa Ono Memorial Scholarships	U	1~4					○		80% of Tuition for the 2nd Semester	12mo.	Apr. 14 ~ May 12	10		

Name of University	Name of Scholarship	Eligibility: Qualifier School Year Age Limit			Eligibility: Designated Countries	Eligibility: Designated Field of Study	Eligibility: Plural Grants and Limit (¥1,000)	Eligibility: Reapplication, and Other Eligibility (¥1,000)		Contents (¥1,000)	Duration	Application Period/ Deadline	Grantees	Applicants for the Previous Year	Notes
Waseda University	Scholarships for Doctoral Course Students	D	1~3			Humanities & Social Sciences	○	○		90/yr.	12mo.		Qualified students		
						Science and Engineering Major	○	○		150/yr.					
Women's College of Fine Arts	Fine Arts Scholarship	U	2~4				○	○		165/yr.	12mo.	Apr.	30	42	
	Alumni Association Scholarship	U	1~4				○	○		10/mo.	12mo.	Jul.	6	12	
	Loan Scholarship	U	1~4					○		70% of Tuition		Jul.	10	4	
Yokohama City University	exemptions in tuition	U	1~4				○	○		Half tuition		3 times a year	17	30	
Yokohama National University	Yokohama Kogyokai Scholarship	D				Engineering		○		40/mo.	12mo.	Sep. 1 ~ Sep. 15	4	5	
Kanto Gakuen University	International Exchange Scholarship	U	1~4		Thailand	Economics Business Management				Tuition 700/yr.	4yr.		2	3	
Tokyo Institute of Technology	The Fund Funded in the Memory of the Centennial of T.I.T.	U M						○		480/yr.	1yr.			22	●

Name of University	Name of Scholarship	Eligibility: Qualifier	School Year	Age Limit	Designated Countries	Designated Field of Study	Plural Grants and Limit (¥1,000)	Reapplication,	and Other Eligibility (¥1,000)	Contents (¥1,000)	Duration	Application Period/ Deadline	Grantees	Applicants for the Previous Year	Notes
Asia University	Private paying International Students-Scholarship	U M D	1～4 1～2 1～3				○	○	Outstanding Academic Achievement	Tuition Equivalent	1yr.	Early-May	12	14	
	Tokyu Scholarship	SC U M D	1 2～4 1～2 1～3				○	○	Outstanding Accademic Achievement	150/yr. 150/yr. 150/yr. 150/yr.	1yr. 1yr. 1yr. 1yr.	Mar. Early-May	1 7		
	Ohta Scholarship Fund (International Students Invitation Scholarship)	SC U M D	1 1 1 1		Asian Countries		○	○	Outstanding Accademic Achievement	180/yr. 180/yr. 180/yr. 180/yr.	1yr. 4yr. 2yr. 3yr.	Apr. ～ Mar.	a few		
Utsunomiya University	Utsunomiya University Scholarship for Foreign Students at Private Expense	U M D					○ U 70/mo. M,D 90/mo.			Bank Transfer 60/yr.	12mo.	Apr. 20 ～ May 15	10	24	●
The Jikei University School of medicine	Jikei University Scholarship	U	1～6			medicine	○	○		Tuition and living expense 900/yr.	1yr.	End of Apr.	a few	15	
Chubu Region															
University of Shizuoka	Fujikawa-cho Scholarship For Foreign Students	U M D	1～4 2 2～3							100/yr.	1yr.	Apr. 15 ～ Apr. 30	10	20	
Aichi Gakuin University	Aichi Gakuin University Scholarship for foreign students	U M D								100/yr.	UTG				
Aichi Shukutoku University	Award for Financial Aid	U	1～4					○		Tuition, 38/mo.	12mo.	May Oct.	a few	0	
		M	1～2					○		72/mo.	12mo.	May	a few	5	
Aichi University	Scholarship to cover foreign students' private-expenses	U M D	1～4 1～2 1～3							Half tuition			All Foreign Students		

Name of University	Name of Scholarship	Eligibility: Qualifier School Year Age Limit			Eligibility: Designated Countries	Eligibility: Designated Field of Study	Eligibility: Plural Grants and Limit (¥1,000)	Eligibility: Reapplication, and Other Eligibility (¥1,000)		Contents (¥1,000)	Duration	Application Period/ Deadline	Grantees	Applicants for the Previous Year	Notes
Chubu University	International Student Scholarship	U M D	2~4 2 2~3					O		Tuition 300/yr.	1yr.	Apr.	10	7	
Chukyo University	Chukyo University Foreign Student's Scholarship	U M D	2~4 1~2 1~3					O		45/mo. 65/mo.	12mo.		6 9	25	
Kanazawa Institute of Technology	Kanazawa Institute of Technology Scholarship Type 1 Type 2	U	2~4							Full tuition Half tuition					
	Kanazawa Institute of Technology Scholarship	M D								Half tuition					
Nagoya College of Creative Art	Nagoya College of Creative Art Scholarship	U	1~4				O	O		Half tuition	12mo. O	May 1 ~ Jun. 30	some	5	
Nagoya Gakuin University	Nagoya Gakuin University Scholarship A	U						O	depend on the financial condition	Tuition/ Half Tuition	12mo.	Apr.	about 30	98	
	Scholarship B	U						O	depend on the academic records	200/ 100	12mo.	Apr.	about 15	38	
	IJLC (Institute for Japanese Language & Culture) Scholarship	SC					O	O		250/yr. 125/yr. 65/yr.	one term	Spring/ Fall	not fixed	23	
Nagoya University of Commerce & Business Administration	Education Scholarship (Kurimoto-Gakuen Kyoiku Shorei-kin)	U					O			Tuition, Housing, 550/yr. Tuition, Housing, 360/yr.	4yr.	Jan. 7 ~ Feb. 8		263	◎

Name of University	Name of Scholarship	Eligibility								Contents (¥1,000)	Duration	Application Period/ Deadline	Grantees	Applicants for the Previous Year	Notes
		Qualifier School Year Age Limit			Designated Countries	Designated Field of Study	Plural Grants and Limit (¥1,000)	Reapplication, and Other Eligibility (¥1,000)							
Nanzan University	Hirschmeier Scholarship	SC U M D								Full or Half Tuition	One Semester 1yr.	May Nov. Apr.	depend on the budget	47	
Nihon Fukushi University	Tuition Reduction Grant	U M	1~4 1~2				○	○		Tuition Reduction	12mo.	Apr. 23 ~ Apr. 28	Limited	4	●
Toyama University		U M					○	○		10/mo.	12mo.	May 1 ~ May 10	12	41	●
Yamanashi Gakuin University		U	1~4							Half Tuition			All students		
Kinki Region															
Kobe College	Kobe College Scholarships	U	2~4	18~			○	○		Full, 1/2 or 1/3 tuition	12mo.	Jan. 15 ~ Feb. 17	25	30	●
	Kobe College Scholarships for Foreign Students (graduate school)	M	1~2	24~	Asian and African Countries		○	○		1,200/yr.	12mo.	Apr. 1 ~ Apr. 15	3	1	●
Kyoto University	Sano Scholarship	U R M D			Asian Countries			○		30/mo.	1yr.	May 31	7~8	28	
Shiga University	The Education and Research Bounty for Foreign Student (private expense) of Shiga University	U R M					○ 65/mo.	○		20/yr.					
Osaka Women's University	Scholarship by the Society for the Support of Foreign Students at the University of Osaka Prefecture & Osaka Women's University	U M	1~2 1							20/mo.	12mo.	Sep.	4	16	

Name of University	Name of Scholarship	Eligibility: Qualifier	School Year	Age Limit	Designated Countries	Designated Field of Study	Plural Grants and Limit (¥1,000)	Reapplication, and Other Eligibility (¥1,000)		Contents (¥1,000)	Duration	Application Period/ Deadline	Grantees	Applicants for the Previous Year	Notes
University of Osaka Prefecture	Scholarship by the Society for the Support of Foreign Students at the University of Osaka Prefecture & Osaka Women's University	U M	1~2 1							20/mo.	12mo.	Sep.	4	16	
Baika Women's College	Baika Women's College Scholarship	U M	1~4 1~2				○	○		1/4~1/2 Tuition	12mo.	Jun. 1 ~ Jun. 14	18 7	35 4	
Bukkyo University	Bukkyo University Foreign Student Special Scholarship	U M D	2~4 2 2~3					○		50/mo. 100/mo. 100/mo.	1yr. 1yr. 1yr.	Apr. 1 ~ Apr. 15	} 5	8 8 4	
	Bukkyo University Foreign Student Fee Remission	U M D						○		1/2 or 2/3 Fee	1yr.	Apr. 1 ~ Apr. 15	6~7	24	
Doshisha University	Scholarship for International Students	U	1~4					○		60/yr. 120/yr.	12mo.	Sep. 20 ~ Sep. 26	30	18	
Kansai University	K.U. Scholarship for International Students	U M D								50/mo.	12mo.	Oct. 1 ~ Oct. 30	10	40	
Kansai University of Foreign Studies	Merit Scholarship	SC				Asian Studies Program	○	○	3.0 G.P.A. or above on 4.0 scale	Tuition Deduction 3·6/yr.	○	May 15 (Fall) Nov. 1 (Spring)			◎ ●
	English Teaching Assistantship	SC				Asian Studies Program	○	○	Native English Speaker 3.0 G.P.A. or above on 4.0 scale	Tuition Deduction 5.7/yr.	○	May 15 (Fall) Nov. 1 (Spring)	10~15	31	◎ ●

Name of University	Name of Scholarship	Eligibility: Qualifier School Year Age Limit			Designated Countries	Designated Field of Study	Plural Grants and Limit (¥1,000)	Reapplication, and Other Eligibility (¥1,000)		Contents (¥1,000)	Duration	Application Period/ Deadline	Grantees	Applicants for the Previous Year	Notes
Kobe Women's College of Pharmacy	Kobe Women's College of Pharmacy's Graduate School-Scholarship	M D					○		Students in financial difficulties are given priority	(A) 10/mo. or 15/mo. (B) Within the equivalent amount of annual tuition	24mo. 36mo.	Apr.～ May		1	
Konan Women's University	Konan Women's University Graduate School Special Scholarship	R M D								1,200/yr.					
Konan University	Konan Scholarships For Undergraduates	U					○	○		Tuition at the latter term + 100	1yr.	Jul.	280	232	
	Konan Scholarships For Graduates	M D					○	○		A 720/yr. B 480/yr.	1yr.	Apr.	15 10	15	
Kyoto University of Foreign Studies	Scholarship for foreign students on exchange program	SC				the course in Japanese Studies for Overseas Students				Matriculation Fee, Tuition Fee 538/yr.	1yr.			8	◎
Kwansei Gakuin University		U M D					○ ○ ○	○ ○ ○		Half Tuition	lump sum	Jun. 18 ～ Jul. 6	} 14	23 5 2	
Kyoto Pharmaceutical University	Science Foundation	U M D								A part of tuition	1yr.	Nov. 30	Not fixed	2	

Name of University	Name of Scholarship	Eligibility: Qualifier School Year Age Limit			Designated Countries	Designated Field of Study	Plural Grants and Limit (¥1,000)	Reapplication, and Other Eligibility (¥1,000)		Contents (¥1,000)	Duration	Application Period/ Deadline	Grantees	Applicants for the Previous Year	Notes
Kyoto Institute of Technology	International Cultural Exchange Promotion Fund	U M D						○		60/yr.	1yr.	~Oct. 31	25~30	30	
Kyoto Seika University	K.S.U. O/S Scholarship	U	1~4				○	○		20% of tuition	4yr.	After enrol-ment	All stu-dents	18	
	K.S.U. O/S Special Scholarship	U	1~4				○	○		50% of tuition	1yr. ○	After enrol-ment	2 per grade in each faculty	18	
Meiji College of Oriental Medicine	Meiji Institute of Oriental Medicine Scholarship	U	1~4				○			38~48 /mo.	1yr.~	Apr. 15 ~ Apr. 30	21	7	
Mukogawa Women's University	Foreign Student Scholarship	U	1~4				○ 45/mo.	○		Admission fee Tuition, etc.	48mo.	Apr. Sep.		0	
		M	1~2			Liberal arts Home eco-nomics Pharma-ceutical	○ 65/mo.	○		Admision fee Tuition, etc. 303/yr. 423/yr. 453/yr.	24mo.	Apr., Sep.		3	
		D	1~3				○ 65/mo.	○			36mo.	Apr., Sep.		0	
Notre Dame Women's College	Marian Scholarship Theresian Scholarship	U U					○			Tuition	6mo.	Oct. 1 ~ Oct. 20	1 2~5	2 4	
Osaka Institute of Technology	Osaka Institute of Technology Scholarship For Foreign Students	U M D					○	○		20/mo.~ 10/mo.	12mo.		19	11	●
Osaka International University	Scholarship for Foreign Students	U	2~4				○			500/yr.	1yr.	Apr.	Few		

Name of University	Name of Scholarship	Eligibility: Qualifier School Year Age Limit			Eligibility: Designated Countries	Eligibility: Designated Field of Study	Eligibility: Plural Grants and Limit (¥1,000)	Eligibility: Reapplication, and Other Eligibility (¥1,000)		Contents (¥1,000)	Duration	Application Period/ Deadline	Grantees	Applicants for the Previous Year	Notes
Osaka University of Economics and Law		U	1~4				○			Entrance Fee Half Tuition				30	
Osaka University of Pharmaceutical Sciences	Parent Association of Osaka University of Pharmaceutical Sciences	U M D	1~4 1~2 1~3				○ ○ ○			240/yr. 240/yr. 240/yr.	12mo. 12mo. 12mo.	Jun. Jun. Jun.	11 } 3	19 } 5	
Otani University	Otani Daigaku Ikuei Shougakukin								Regular Student Only	584/yr.	12mo.	Apr. 30	24		●
Ritsumeikan University	Ritsumeikan University Honors Scholarship for International Students	U	1 2~4				○	○		Half Tuition		Dec. 14 ~Jan. 7 Apr. 13 ~18	10	66	
Ryukoku University	Numata Fellowships and Scholarships	U M D	1~4			Buddhist Studies				179.5/mo. 45/mo.	12mo.	Dec. 20	a few	0	●
Setsunan University	Setsunan Daigaku Gaikokujin ryugakusei Gakunai Shougakukin	U M D	1~4					○		Scholar in University Interchange Hall 120/yr. Others 240/yr.	12mo.	Apr.	13 ('90)	8	
St. Andrew's University	St. Andrew's University International Student Award	U	1~4					○		25/mo.	12mo.	Oct. 10 ~ Oct. 15	9	6	●
St. Michael's University (Yashirogakuin University)	Yashiro Gakuin daigaku scholarship	U	1~4					○		240/yr.	12mo.	May	30	45	●

Name of University	Name of Scholarship	Eligibility: Qualifier School Year Age Limit			Eligibility: Designated Countries	Eligibility: Designated Field of Study	Eligibility: Plural Grants and Limit (¥1,000)	Eligibility: Reapplication, and Other Eligibility (¥1,000)		Contents (¥1,000)	Dura-tion	Appli-cation Period/ Deadline	Gran-tees	Appli-cants for the Previous Year	Notes
Chugoku Region															
Hiroshima University	Hiroshima University Scholarship	U R M D						○	Excludes Monbusho Scholar's spouse	20/mo.	12mo.	Oct.～ Nov.	25	42	
Okayama University	Okayama University International Foundation Scholarship	A U R M D								30/mo.	6mo.	May 28 ～ Jun. 20 Oct. 5 ～ Nov. 20	20	27	
Baiko Jo Gakuin College	International Exchange Scholarship	U	1～4	18～	U.S.A.	Japanese Literature (including Japanese Language)		○		Admission fee, Tuition etc.	10mo.	Dec. 1 ～ Feb. 28	5～10	0	◎ ●
	Special Scholarship for International graduate students	R M D		over 20～	U.S.A.	Japanese Literature (intensive study under the graduate programs)				Said above, housing and 150/mo.	12mo.	Oct. 1 ～ Dec. 31	1～2	3	◎ ●
Elisabeth University of Music	Loyola International Exchange Fund	M	1～2		Asian Countries	Music		○		Tuition, Living stipend	12mo.	Mar. 1～ Apr. 15	2	0	◎
	Honor Student Award	U	1			Music	○	○		800/yr.	12mo.		4	4	
			2～4							240/yr.	12mo.		12	12	
	Xavier Grants	U M	1～4 1～2			Music Music	○ ○	○ ○		According to need	12mo.	Apr. 1	According to need	1	◎
Hiroshima Shudo University	University Scholarship	A U R M D						○		1/2 or 4/5 of Tuition 150～ 600/yr.		Apr. 10 ～ Apr. 25	52	40	
	Alumni Association Scholarship	A U R M D								70/mo.	12mo.	May 25 ～ Jun. 10	1	5	

Name of University	Name of Scholarship	Eligibility: Qualifier School Year Age Limit			Designated Countries	Designated Field of Study	Plural Grants and Limit (¥1,000)	Reapplication, and Other Eligibility (¥1,000)		Contents (¥1,000)	Duration	Application Period/ Deadline	Grantees	Applicants for the Previous Year	Notes
Notre Dame Seishin University	Foreign Students Scholarship	U	1～4			○	○		Non Cuvilly Scholar	Tuition (partial or full)	1yr.	Apr.	limited number	1	
	Cuvilly Scholarship	U	2～4			○	○		Non foreign students scholar	Tuition (full or half)	1yr.	late Nov.～ mid Dec.	limited number	0	
Shujitsu Joshi University	International Sister College Scholarship	U	1～4				○		Students recommended by sister universities or by foreign government	Tuition exemption or/and 360/yr.	4yr.			2	
Shikoku Region															
Kagawa Nutrition College	Yokomaki Nobu's Memorial Scholarship	U R M	2～4				○ 80/mo.	○		Tuition	6mo.	Apr. 1～30 Nov. 1～30	3～4	1	
The University of Tokushima	Fujii-Otsuka Fellowship for international exchange program	A U R M D					○ 50/mo.	○		30/mo.	12mo.	Apr. 1 ～ Apr. 30	a few	2	
	The fellowship for international exchange program in The University of Tokushima	A U R M D					○ 50/mo.	○		30/mo.	12mo.	Apr. 1 ～ Apr. 30	a few	5	
Matsuyama University	Matsuyama University Foreign Student Scholarship	U M D	1～4				○	○		The maximum amount being equal to the tuition	1yr.	Apr. 20 ～ Apr. 30	a few	1	

Name of University	Name of Scholarship	Eligibility: Qualifier School Year Age Limit			Designated Countries	Designated Field of Study	Plural Grants and Limit (¥1,000)	Reapplication, and Other Eligibility (¥1,000)		Contents (¥1,000)	Duration	Application Period/ Deadline	Grantees	Applicants for the Previous Year	Notes
Shikoku Christian College		A			Korea				Sister College students	Tuition Housing 840/yr.	12mo.	Apr. 1 ~ Apr. 15	2	2	
Shikoku Women's University	SWU Scholarship	U	1 2~4				○	○	Applicants should be in the upper ten percent of the course in respect of school records For students in need of financial aid	Half tuition		Oct. 1~ Oct. 30 Apr. 1~ Apr. 30	One out of every 200 Students	22	
St. Catherine Women's College	St. Catherine Scholarship	U	1~4							Tuition 750/yr.	4yr.	Nov.	2~3	2~3	
Kyushu Region															
Fukuoka University of Education	Fukuoka Overseas Students Scholarship									20/mo.	12mo.	May 15	60	14	
Kyushu Institute of Design		U R M					○	○		30/yr.			All applicants		
Kyushu Institute of Technology	Uemura	U M D			Asian		○ 20/mo.	○		240/yr.	12mo.	Apr. 1 ~ Apr. 30	5	7	●
National Institute of Fitness and Sports in Kanoya		U M	1~4 1~2	Under 30 Under 35			○ 20/mo.	○		20/mo. 20/mo.	12mo.	Apr. ~ May		2	● ●

Name of University	Name of Scholarship	Eligibility: Qualifier	School Year	Age Limit	Designated Countries	Designated Field of Study	Plural Grants and Limit (¥1,000)	Reapplication, and Other Eligibility (¥1,000)		Contents (¥1,000)	Duration	Application Period/ Deadline	Grantees	Applicants for the Previous Year	Notes
Saga University	Kinoshita Commemoration Wako Scholarship	U M					○ 45/mo.	○		35/mo.	1yr.	Apr. 12 ~ Apr. 30	3	4	
	Saga University Scholarship	U M	2~4 1~2				○	○	Expense Students who have already studied more than one year at Saga University	50/yr.	1yr.	Apr. 12 ~ Apr. 30	6	20	
Kyushu Dental College	Nagamatsu Scholarship	U	1				○			15/mo.	72mo.	Sep. 10 ~30	5	2	
		D	1~4				○	○		30/mo.	12mo. ~ 48mo.	Sep. 10 ~30	5	0	
Fukuoka Institute of Technology	International Exchange Scholarship	U	1~4	Under 35				○		45/mo.	12mo.	Apr. 10 ~ May 18			
Kagoshima Women's College		U	1~4												
Kurume University	Kurume University Scholarship	M	1~2					○		600/yr.	7mo.	May 1 ~7	24	4	
Kyushu International University	Kyushu International University General Scholarship	U	2~4				○	○		100/yr.	12mo.	Apr. 16 ~ Apr. 23	some	1	
	Kyushu International University Special Scholarship	U	3							Equivalent to school expence	24mo.		some		
Kyushu Sangyo University	Scholarship by alumni association (Nanpu-kai)	U					○	○		120/yr.	1yr.	May 1 ~31	5	10	

Name of University	Name of Scholarship	Eligibility								Contents (¥1,000)	Duration	Application Period/ Deadline	Grantees	Applicants for the Previous Year	Notes
		Qualifier School Year Age Limit			Designated Countries	Designated Field of Study	Plural Grants and Limit (¥1,000)	Reapplication, and Other Eligibility (¥1,000)							
Kyushu Tokai University	Scholarship for Foreign Students in the Undergraduate Program	U	1~4					○		Tuition & Fees / Tuition	12mo.				
	Scholarship for Foreign Students in the Graduate Program	M D	1~5					○		Tuition & Fees / Tuition	12mo.				
Miyazaki Sangyo-Keiei University	Scholarship for student studing abroard	U		Under 30			○	○		45/mo.	12mo.	May 11		0	●
	Korea Foundational Scholarship	U			Koreans		○ 20/mo.	○		20/mo.	12mo.	Apr. 2~ May 10		0	●
	Scholarship for Koreans	U			Koreans			○			12mo.	Apr. 10 ~ May 15		0	●
Nagasaki Institute of Applied Science	Kihara Scholarship	SC U M					○	○		According to individual needs	lump sum	Jun. (U, M) Feb. (SC)	Not limited	11	
	Special Scholarship for Foreign Students	U M					○	○		60% tuition	lump sum	May	Not limited	10	
Okinawa Region															
Okinawa Kokusai University	Okinawa Kokusai University Scholarship	U	2~4				○	○		Tuition	12mo.	May	10	45	●
	Special Scholarship for Foreign Students	U	2~4					○		45/mo.	12mo.	May	6	6	●
	San-A Compay Scholarship	U	3~4					○		40/mo.	12mo.	May	5	16	●
	Buntaro Taira Scholarship	U	3~4			English Literature	○	○		100/yr.	12mo.	May	1	1	●
	Okinawa Kokusai University Alumni association Scholarship	U	2~4				○	○		50/yr.	12mo.	May	10	10	●
	Okinawa Kokusai University Alumni association Special Scholarship for Foreign Student	U	2~4		China, South America		○	○		100/yr.	12mo.	Dec.			●

Preparatory Japanese Language Programs at Universities (For 1991 Academic Year)

School Program	Address Telephone	Year Program Established	Faculty: Full-time	Faculty: Part-time	Eligibility *1	Program Length	Application Deadline	Program Starting Date	Program Size	Class Size	Classes/Week × Number of Weeks *2	Other Subjects Available in Preparation for University Entrance Exam: English	Mathematics	Natural Science	Social Science	Application Fee (¥1,000)	Admission Fee (¥1,000)	Tuition (¥1,000)	Other Fees (¥1,000)	3 Largest Ethnic Groups *3	Guarantor System	Dormitory *4
Aichi University Junior College Japanese Language Program	1 Machihatamachi, Toyohashi-shi, Aichi 441 0532-47-4162	1988	2	10		1yr.	Oct. 15	Apr.	30	15	16 × 30	○	—	—	—	10	60	370	31.2	CH KO TH	—	—
Asia University Special Course for Foreign Students	5-24-10 Sakai, Musashino-shi, Tokyo 180 0422-54-3111	1953	6	6	○	1yr.	Oct. 25	Apr.	40	20	22 × 30	○	—	—	—	20	120	420	36	TA KO HK CH	○	W
Beppu University Japanese Language Course	82 Kita-Ishigaki, Beppu-shi, Oita 874-01 0977-67-0101	1989	5	3		1yr.	Dec. 25	Apr.	30	10	16 × 34	—	—	—	—	25	150	500	30	TA KO CH	○	—
Daito Bunka University Japanese Language Program for Overseas Students	1-9-1 Takashimadaira, Itabashi-ku, Tokyo 175 03-3935-1111	1977	8	10	○	1yr.	Oct. 29	Apr.	20	20	19 × 30	—	—	—	—	30	154.5	420	—	CH KO HK	—	—
Iwaki Junior College Japanese Language Section for Foreign Students	2-37-1 Taira, Iwaki-shi, Fukushima 970 0246-25-9185	1986	2	5		1yr.	Oct. ~ Mar.	Apr.	30	15	20 × 36	○	—	—	—	10	100	380	30	TA CH PH	○	W
Josai University Japanese Language Course	1-1 Keyakidai, Sakado-shi, Saitama 350-02 0492-86-2233	1990	3	8		1yr.	Aug. 21*5 Feb. 1*6	Apr.	50		17 × 30	—	—	—	—	25	200	320	100	CH TA MA	—	—
Keio University Japanese Language Program	2-15-45 Mita, Minato-ku, Tokyo 108 03-3453-4511	1964	14	27		1yr.	Oct. 31 Apr. 30	Apr. Sep.	180	20	15 × 30	—	—	—	—	10	103	450	20	US KO TA	—	—
Kyorin University Special Japanese Training Course for Overseas Students	476 Miyashita-cho, Hachioji-shi, Tokyo 192 0426-91-0141	1988	8	3		1yr.	Jan. 19	Apr.	20	20	22 × 30	○	○	○	—	25	100	450	25	CH KO TA	—	—

School Program	Address Telephone	Year Program Established	Faculty: Full-time	Faculty: Part-time	Eligibility	Program Length	Application Deadline	Program Starting Date	Program Size	Class Size	Classes/Week × Number of Weeks	Other Subjects Available in Preparation for University Entrance Exam: English	Mathematics	Natural Science	Social Science	Application Fee (¥1,000)	Admission Fee (¥1,000)	Tuition (¥1,000)	Other Fees (¥1,000)	3 Largest Ethnic Groups	Guarantor System	Dormitory
Kyoto University of Foreign Studies The Course in Japanese Students for Overseas Students	Saiin, Ukyo-ku, Kyoto-shi, Kyoto 615 075-322-6043	1981	10	9		1yr.	Oct. 31	Apr.	30	16	20 × 30	–	–	–	–	1.5	103	435	–	US CH TA	–	–
Meikai University The Japanese Language Course for Overseas Students	8 Meikai, Urayasu-shi, Chiba 279 0473-55-5111	1991	2	5		1yr.	Dec. 15	Apr.	35	20	32 × 37	O	O	–	O	20	200	400	–	CH KO TA	–	–
Nagasaki Institute of Applied Science Japanese Language Course	536 Aba-machi, Nagasaki-shi, Nagasaki 851-01 0958-39-3111	1979	6	9		1yr.	Oct. 31 Jan. 16	Apr.	10	10	20 × 33	O	O	O	O	10	60	360	30	MA CH TA	–	W
Reitaku University Course of Japanese Language	2-1-1 Hikarigaoka, Kashiwa-shi, Chiba 277 0471-73-3690	1976	8	9		1yr.	Nov. 30	Apr.	60	20	16 × 30	O	O	O	O	30	150	420	160	TA CH KO	–	O
Ryukoku University The Japanese Culture and Language Program	67 Tsukamoto-cho, Fukakusa, Fushimi-ku, Kyoto-shi, Kyoto 612 075-642-1111	1960	8	13		1yr.	Dec. 5 June	Apr. Oct.	20 20	15	13 × 31	–	–	–	–	30	51.5	487	–	CH KO TA	–	O
Sanno Junior College Japanese Language Section for Foreign Students	6-39-15 Todoroki, Setagaya-ku, Tokyo 158 03-3704-1110	1989	5	14		1yr.	Nov. 30	Apr.	50	15	15 × 32	O	O	–	O	20	123.6	500	40.6	TA KO CH	–	O
Soka University Institute of the Japanese Language	1-236 Tangi-cho, Hachioji-shi, Tokyo 192 0426-91-2206	1976	5	2	O	1yr.	Nov. 30	Apr.	20	10	30 × 30	O	–	–	–	28	103	370	58.5	US TA KO	–	–
Takushoku University Japanese Language Section for Foreign Students	3-4-14, Kohinata, Bunkyo-ku, Tokyo 112 03-3947-2261	1972	13	41		1yr.	Oct. 31	Apr.	130	20	20 × 36	O	O	O	O	25	125	400	30	TA CH KO	–	O
Teikyo University The Foreign Student's Program	359 Otsuka, Hachioji-shi, Tokyo 192-03 0426-76-8211 Ext. 644	1990	5	2		1yr.	Nov. 30	Apr.	60	20	20 × 30	–	–	–	–	30	51.5	420	90.6	CH SR	–	–

School / Program	Address / Telephone	Year Program Established	Faculty		Eligibility	Program Length	Application Deadline	Program Starting Date	Program Size	Class Size	Classes/Week × Number of Weeks	Other Subjects Available in Preparation for University Entrance Exam				Application Fee (¥1,000)	Admission Fee (¥1,000)	Tuition (¥1,000)	Other Fees (¥1,000)	3 Largest Ethnic Groups	Guarantor System	Dormitory
			Full-time	Part-time								English	Mathematics	Natural Science	Social Science							
Tokai University Japanese Language Course	1117 Kitakaname, Hiratsuka-shi, Kanagawa 259-12 0463-58-1211	1963	11	17	O	1yr.	Nov. 15	Apr.	60	15	20 × 35	O	O	O	O	30	40	393	161.61	CH TA KO	–	O
Tokyo International University The Preparing Program for Entering a Japanese College or University	1-13-1 Matoba-kita, Kawagoe-shi, Saitama 350 0492-32-1111	1982	3	9	O	1yr.	Nov. 22	Apr.	40	20	35 × 30	–	–	–	–	20	130	450	60	CH TA KO	O	–
Tsuchiura Junior College Japanese Language Course for Foreign Students	6-7-10 Manaba, Tsuchiura-shi, Ibaragi 300 0298-21-6125	1989	5	2	O W	1yr.	Dec. 31	Apr.	15	15	14 × 35	O	–	–	–	28	180	470	74	KO TA CH	–	O
Waseda University Intensive Japanese Language Program	1-6-1 Nishiwaseda, Shinjuku-ku, Tokyo 169-50 03-5273-3142	1962	11	31	●	1yr.	Sep. 30	Apr.	20	13	12 × 33	–	–	–	–	–	51.5	305	20	CH KO	–	–

*1 O=In principle, only open to students seeking entrance into the same university
W=Women
●=University graduates of Japanese major
*2 90 min./class (60 min./class at TIU, 50 min. at Meikai, 45 min. at Soka)
*3 CH=China HK=Hong Kong KO=Korea MA=Malaysia PH=Phillipines SR=Sri Lanka TA=Taiwan TH=Thailand US=United States
*4 W=Women only
*5 For overseas applicants
*6 For domestic applicants

JAPAN STUDIES PROGRAM (STUDY ABROAD PROGRAM)

(For 1991 Academic Year)

University Program	Contact	Year Program Established	Faculty Full-time	Faculty Part-time	Program Length	Application Deadline	Program Starting Date	Program Size	Application Fee (¥1,000)	Admission Fee (¥1,000)	Tuition (¥1,000)	Other Fees (¥1,000)	Guarantor System	Dormitory	Home Stay Program	Scholarship Program	Language of Instruction*[1]	Classes Available 1. Classes for Foreign Students 2. Classes for All Students
Doshisha University Associated Kyoto Program	P.O. Box 6608 Connecticut Collge New London, CT 06320 U.S.A.	1972	9	3	9mo.	#	Sep.	50	#	#	#	#	—	—	—	—	Jpn. Eng.	1. Japanese*[2] Japan related elective classes for Spring 1991, included Culture & Society, Japan & Western Music, Religion, Tanizaki Junichiro, The Pacific War & the Atomic Bomb, Land Reform in Asia, Theater, Introduction to the World of Tea
Himeji Dokkyo University Non-Japanese Students (One-Year Students)	Admissions Section Education Affairs Office Himeji Dokkyo University 7-2-1 Kamiohno, Himeji-shi, Hyogo 670 Japan 0792-23-6504	1987	4	1	1yr.	July 15	Oct.	#	25	129	350	78	—	—	—	—	Jpn. & Eng.	1. Elementary Japanese
International Christian University One-Year-Regular Students	Admissions Office International Christian Univ. 3-10-2 Osawa, Mitaka-shi, Tokyo 181 Japan 0422-33-3058 or ICU Committee for Hong Kong Educated Students Box 35241 King's Road Post Office Hong Kong	1953	159	87	1yr.	Apr. 15	Sep.	30	20	140	1,031	—	○	○	—	—	Eng. & Jpn.	1. Japanese (Elementary to Advanded) 2. All classes are available Art, Archeology, Modern Literature, Business, History, Society, Religion, Education, Values & Ethics, Social Structure, Philosophy, Politics, Economics, International Relations, Music, etc.

University Program	Contact	Year Program Established	Faculty		Program Length	Application Deadline	Program Starting Date	Program Size	Application Fee (¥1,000)	Admission Fee (¥1,000)	Tuition (¥1,000)	Other Fees (¥1,000)	Guarantor System	Dormitory	Home Stay Program	Scholarship Program	Language of Instruction*1	Classes Available 1. Classes for Foreign Students 2. Classes for All Students
			Full-time	Part-time														
Josai University Japanese Culture Course	Center for Inter-Cultural Studies and Education Josai University 1-1 Keyaki-dai, Sakado-shi, Saitama 350-02 Japan 0492-86-2233	1990	3	8	1yr.	Aug. 21*3 Feb. 1*4	Apr.	20	25	200	320	100	–	–	–	–	Jpn.	1. Japanese*2 Philosophy & Lifestyle, Society & Economics, Resources & Industry, Business & Technology, Current Affairs, English Conversation, Business English, Practicum in Commerce, OA Systems, Computer Operation, Word Processing, Computers and Mathematics, Basic Mathematics, Business Internship, Observation Trip
Kansai University of Foreign Studies Asian Studies Program	Center for International Education Kansai University of Foreign Studies 16-1 Kitakatahoko-cho, Hirakata-shi, Osaka 573 Japan 0720-51-6751	1972	21	3	6mo.	May 15 Nov. 1	Aug. Jan.	150 150	US$ 30	US$ 200	US$ 4,500	US$	–	○	○	○	Jpn. Eng.	1. Japanese (Elementary to Advanced) Pacific Rivalry, Politics, Economics, Trading, Marketing, Management, Law, Women, Society, Intercultural Communication, History, Literature, Art, Foreign Relations, Ceramics, Brush Painting, etc.
Konan University Year in Japan Program	Center for East & Pacific Studies University of Illinois 1208 West California, Urbana, IL 61801 U.S.A.	1975	1	7	1yr.	#	Sep.	30	#	#	#	#	○	–	○	○	Jpn. Eng.	1. Japanese*2 Literature, Religion, Law & Politics, Japanese Art, etc.
Kwansei Gakuin University International Programs	Office of International Programs Kwansei Gakuin University Uegahara, Nishinomiya, Hyogo 662 Japan 0798-53-6111	1979	10	6	1yr. or 4mo.	May 15	Sep. 3	20	#	#	#	#	○	○	○	–	Jpn. Eng.	1. Japanese (Elementary to Advanced) Early History, Religion, Psychology, Society, Social Welfare Issues, Literature, Art, Economy, Business, Government & Politics Public Policy & Political Economy, Introduction to Japanese Studies

University Program	Contact	Year Program Established	Faculty: Full-time	Faculty: Part-time	Program Length	Application Deadline	Program Starting Date	Program Size	Application Fee (¥1,000)	Admission Fee (¥1,000)	Tuition (¥1,000)	Other Fees (¥1,000)	Guarantor System	Dormitory	Home Stay Program	Scholarship Program	Language of Instruction*1	Classes Available 1. Classes for Foreign Students 2. Classes for All Students
Nagoya Gakuin University	Insitute for Japanese Language and Culture Nagoya Gakuin University 1350 Kamishinano-cho, Seto-shi, Aichi 480-12 Japan 0561-42-0737	1989	8	9	1yr.	May 30 Nov. 30	Sep. Apr.	30	10	30	500	60	—	○	○	○	Jpn. Eng. & Jpn.	1. Japanese (Elementary to Advanced) Politics, Economics, Art, Religion, International Relations, Business, Sociology, Literature, History, etc.
Nanzan University	Center for Japanese Studies Nanzan University 18 Yamazato-cho, Showa-ku, Nagoya-shi, Aichi 466 052-832-3123	1974	5	12	1yr.	Apr. 15	Sep.	40	10	—	630	30	○	—	○	○	Jpn. & Eng. Eng.	1. Japanese (Elementary to Advanced) Business, Economy, Folklore, History, Religions, Linguistics, Literature, Politics, Society, International Relations, Translation, Shodo, Classical Japanese, Ikebana, Sumie, Hanga, etc.
Obirin University Reconnaissance Japan Program	Center for International Studies Obirin University 3758 Tokiwa-machi, Machida-shi, Tokyo 194-02 Japan 0427-97-2661 Ext. 353	1991	38	4	1yr.	Apr. 1	Sep.	30	10	—	915	600 (for home-stay) 480 (for dormitory)	○	○	○	—	Eng. Jpn.	1. Japanese (Elementary to Advanced) History, Culture, Politics, Economy, Society, Education, etc. 2. All classes offered by the School of International Studies
Ritsumeikan University One Year Program	The International Center Ritsumeikan University 56-1 Tojiin Kitamachi, Kita-ku, Kyoto-shi, Kyoto 603 Japan 075-465-8230	1988	2	4	1yr.	Feb. 1	May	20	—	—	500	50 (refundable)	○	○	○ *5	—	Jpn.	1. Japanese*2 Japan Studies 2. All classes are available
Seinan Gakuin University	International Division Seinan Gakuin University 6-2-92 Nishijin, Sawara-ku, Fukuoka-shi, Fukuoka 814 Japan 092-841-1311	1973	16	3	1yr.	Mar. 31	Sep.	30	10	—	510	60	—	—	—	—	Eng.	1. Japanese (Elementary to Advanced) Literature, History, Comparative Religions, Traditional Culture, Intercultural Communication, Business Management, Economy, Government, Psychology and Society, Foreign Policy

University Program	Contact	Year Program Established	Faculty Full-time	Faculty Part-time	Program Length	Application Deadline	Program Starting Date	Program Size	Application Fee (¥1,000)	Admission Fee (¥1,000)	Tuition (¥1,000)	Other Fees (¥1,000)	Guarantor System	Dormitory	Home Stay Program	Scholarship Program	Language of Instruction*1	Classes Available 1. Classes for Foreign Students 2. Classes for All Students
Shoin Women's University Japan Study Program	Hobart & William Smith Colleges Geneva, New York 14456-3397 U.S.A.	1989	2	10	14w.	#	Sep.	30	Total Fee: US$4,500 (not including air fare)				O	O	O	—	Jpn.	1. Japanese (Elementary to Advanced)
																	Eng.	Art & Religion in Traditional Japan, Economic & Social Institutions in Contemporary Japan
Sophia University	Admissions Office Sophia University 7-1 Kioicho, Chiyoda-ku, Tokyo 102 Japan 03-3238-4018	1967	47	37	1yr.	Nov. 22 Mar. 29	Apr. Oct.	40 80	30	107	920 (10 classes)	79	—	O	—	—	Eng.	1. Japanese (Elementary to Advanced) 2. Anthropology & Sociology, Art History, History, International Business & Economics, Literature, Japanese Studies, Philosophy & Religion, International Relations & Politics
Waseda University	International Division Waseda University 1-6-1 Nishi-Waseda, Shinjuku-ku, Tokyo 169-50 Japan 03-3203-4141	1963	3	48	1yr.	Mar. 31	Sep.	100 ~ 120	5	—	540	50	—	—	O	O	Jpn.	1. Japanese (Elementary, Intermediate)
																	Eng.	Politics, Economics, Society, Business, Law, International Trade, Industrial Structure, Geography, Legal Institution, Foreign Policy, History, Religions, Art, Literature, Language & Culture, Islam, etc.

For detailed information, please contact respective school directly.
*1 Eng.: English
Jpn.: Japanese
*2 Japanese language ability required
*3 For overseas applicants
*4 For domestic applicants
*5 During vacation only

How to Use the Index of Majors

Introduction

The three most important factors that students should take into account when choosing a university are the programs of study available, the type of institution, and the location. The index of majors helps prospective students learn which universities offer the specific field of study that interests them ; whether these universities are national, local public, or private ; and whether they are in the desired location. In this edition, the index is based on up-to-date information on curricula and academic programs provided by the universities themselves. Students are advised to contact the universities that interest them to confirm the information and obtain more details.

Major fields of study

Under " Major Fields of Study by Discipline", specific majors are grouped into general categories and are listed alphabetically under each discipline. The index is divided into undergraduate and graduate programs. For the graduate programs, the levels at which the universities offer specific majors are shown by the letter M(master's degree) or D (doctorate) after the university's name. The universities are listed by region from northern to southern Japan and are grouped by type, with the letter N(national), L(local public), or P(private) given before the university's name.

Some universities listed here do not offrer majors in the traditional sense but provide in-depth specialization that approximates the course work usually required for a degree. Universities were provided with the list of fields and requested to use it to report their majors, even though their own titles for some of the programs might not match the titles on the list. Universities could and often did add the names of other programs that they felt did not conform closely enough to any of the titles listed. These additional fields have not been included in the index of majors, but they can be found in the " Institutional Profiles " section.

Major Fields of Study

Aeronautics
Agricultural Economics
Agricultural Sciences
Animal Sciences
Architecture
Astronomy
Biology
Business and Management
Chemistry
Civil Engineering
Communication
Computer and Information Sciences
Crafts and Design
Dentistry
Economics
Education(General)
Education(School Level)
Education(Special Education)
Education(Specific Subjects)
Engineering(Micellaneous)
Electrical Engineering
Energy Engineering
Environmental Sciences
Fine Arts
Fisheries and Marine Engineering
Food Science
Forest Science
Geography
Geology
Health Science
History
Home Science
Horticulture
Humanities(Miscellaneous)
International Studies
Law
Library and Information
Literature, Linguistics and Area Studies
Materials Science and Engineering
Mathematics
Mechanical Engineering
Medicine
Metal Engineering
Music
Natural Science(Miscellaneous)
Nursing
Nutrition
Pharmaceutical Sciences
Philosophy
Physical Education
Physics
Political Science
Psychology
Religion
Social Sciences(Miscellaneous)
Social Welfare
Sociology
Systems Science and Engineering
Transportation
Visual and Performing Arts
Zoology

Undergraduate Program

Aeronautics

• Aeronautical Engineering
N–Nagoya University
N–Kyoto University
N–Kyushu University
L–University of Osaka Prefecture
P–Dai Ichi University, College of Technology

• Aeronautics
N–The University of Tokyo
P–Tokai University
P–Nippon Bunri University

• Aerospace Engineering
L–Tokyo Metropolitan Institute of Technology
P–Nihon University

Agricultural Economics

• Agricultural and Forestry Economics
N–Kyoto University

• Agricultural Economics
N–Hokkaido University
N–Utsunomiya University
N–The University of Tokyo
N–Kyushu University
P–Rakuno Gakuen University
P–Tokyo University of Agriculture
P–Nihon University
P–Meiji University
P–Minami Kyushu College

• Food Industrial Economics
P–Nihon University

• Horticultural Economics
N–Chiba University

• Land Development
P–Nihon University
P–Kyushu Kyoritsu University

• Regional development
N–Shimane University

Agricultural Science

• Agricultural Biology
N–Hokkaido University
N–Kyoto University

• Agricultural Chemistry
N–Hokkaido University
N–Iwate University
N–Tohoku University
N–Yamagata University
N–Utsunomiya University
N–Chiba University
N–The University of Tokyo
N–Niigata University
N–Shinshu University
N–Nagoya University
N–Kyoto University
N–Kobe University
N–Yamaguchi University
N–Kochi University
N–Kyushu University
N–Miyazaki University
N–University of the Ryukyus
L–Kyoto Prefectural University
L–University of Osaka Prefecture
P–Tamagawa University
P–Tokyo University of Agriculture
P–Nihon University
P–Meiji University
P–Meijo University
P–Kinki University

• Agricultural Engineering
N–Hokkaido University
N–Iwate University
N–Yamagata University
N–Utsunomiya University
N–The University of Tokyo
N–Niigata University
N–Kyoto University
N–Kobe University
N–Kagawa University
N–Kochi University
N–Kyushu University
N–Miyazaki University
N–University of the Ryukyus
L–University of Osaka Prefecture
P–Tokyo University of Agriculture
P–Nihon University

• Agricultural Machinery
N–Iwate University

• Agricultural Production
N–Tokyo University of Agriculture and Technology

• Agricultural Science
N–Hirosaki University
N–Saga University
P–Meijo University

• Agricultural Science and Natural Resources
N–Okayama University
N–Kagoshima University

• Agricultural System Engineering
N–Hirosaki University

• Agriculture
N–Iwate University
N–Yamagata University
N–Utsunomiya University
N–Kyoto University
N–Yamaguchi University
N–University of the Ryukyus
L–Kyoto Prefectural University
P–Tamagawa University
P–Tokyo University of Agriculture
P–Nihon University
P–Meiji University
P–Kinki University

• Agriculture and Forestry
N–University of Tsukuba
N–University of Tottori
N–Miyazaki University

• Agriculture and Horticulture
N–Kobe University
L–University of Osaka Prefecture

• Agrobiology
N–The University of Tokyo
N–Kyoto University

• Agro–Forest Biology
N–Shimane University

• Agroindustrial Science
N–Naruto University of Education

• Agronomy
N–Hokkaido University
N–Tohoku University
N–Niigata University
N–Nagoya University
N–Kyushu University
N–Miyazaki University
P–Kyushu Tokai University

• Agronomy and Horticultural Science
N–Kyoto University

• Applied Biological Science
N–Hiroshima University
N–Saga University
P–Ishinomaki Senshu University

• Biochemical Science and Technology
N–Kagoshima University

• Bioproduction
N–Hiroshima University
P–Tokyo University of Agriculture

• Bioproduction System
N–Gifu University

• Bioresource Development
L–Hiroshima Prefectural University

• Bioresource Management
L–Hiroshima Prefectural University

• Bioresource Production
N–Gifu University

• Bioresources
N–Hirosaki University
N–Ibaraki University
N–Shinshu University
N–Gifu University
N–Mie University
N–Kagawa University
N–Ehime University
N–Miyazaki University

• Brewing and Relative Studies
P–Tokyo University of Agriculture

• Fermentation Technology
N–Osaka University

• Natural Resources
N–Shimane University

• Plant Protection
N–Kobe University

• Subtropical Agriculture
N–Kochi University

Animal Sciences

• Agro-environmental Science
N–Obihiro University of Agriculture and Veterinary Medicine

• Animal Environment and Production
P–Azabu University

• Animal Grassland and Fishery Sciences
N–Miyazaki University

• Animal Husbandry
N–Iwate University
N–Niigata University
N–Shinshu University
N–University of the Ryukyus
P–Kitasato University
P–Ibaraki Christian College
P–Nihon University
P–Nippon Veterinary and Zootechnical College
P–Azabu University

• Animal Husbandry and Management
P–Nippon Veterinary and Zootechnical College

• Animal Production and Agricultural Economics
N–Obihiro University of Agriculture and Veterinary Medicine

• Animal Science
N–Hokkaido University
N–Tohoku University
N–Utsunomiya University
N–Nagoya University
N–Kyoto University
N–Kyushu University
N–Miyazaki University
P–Nihon University
P–Kyushu Tokai University

• Bioresource Chemistry
N–Obihiro University of Agriculture and Veterinary Medicine

• Dairy
P–Rakuno Gakuen University

• Engineering for Animal Husbandry
P–Kitasato University

• Grassland Science
N–Miyazaki University

• Veterinary Medicine
N–Hokkaido University
N–Obihiro University of Agriculture and Veterinary Medicine
N–Iwate University
N–The University of Tokyo
N–Tokyo University of Agriculture and Technology
N–Gifu University
N–University of Tottori
N–Yamaguchi University
N–Miyazaki University
N–Kagoshima University
L–University of Osaka Prefecture
P–Rakuno Gakuen University
P–Kitasato University
P–Nihon University
P–Nippon Veterinary and Zootechnical College
P–Azabu University

Architecture

• Architectual and Building Science
L–Tokyo Metropolitan University

• Architectual Engineering
N–Kyoto University
N–Osaka University
N–Oita University
N–University of the Ryukyus
L–Tokyo Metropolitan University
P–Hachinohe Institute of Technology
P–Kokushikan University
P–Tokyo Denki University
P–Nihon University
P–Fukui Institute of Technology
P–Aichi Institute of Technology
P–Towa University

• Architectual Environment Engineering
P–Tokyo University of Art and Design
P–Kanto Gakuin Universtiy

• Architectual Equipment Engineering
P–Kanto Gakuin Universtiy
P–Kurume Institute of Technology

• Architecture
N–Hokkaido University
N–Tohoku University
N–Chiba University
N–The University of Tokyo
N–Nagoya University
N–Mie University
N–Kyoto University
N–Kobe University
N–Hiroshima University
N–Kyushu University
N–Kagoshima University
L–Osaka City University
P–Hokkai Gakuen University
P–Hokkaido Tokai University
P–Tohoku Institute of Technology
P–Ashikaga Institute of Technology
P–Nippon Institute of Technology
P–Chiba Institute of Technology
P–Kogakuin University
P–Shibaura Institute of Technology
P–Tokai University
P–Tokyo University of Art and Design
P–Tokyo Denki University
P–Science University of Tokyo
P–Toyo University
P–Nihon University
P–Hosei University
P–Musashi Institute of Technology
P–Musashino Art University
P–Meiji University
P–Waseda University
P–Kanagawa University
P–Kanto Gakuin Universtiy
P–Tokyo Institute of Polytechnics
P–Kanazawa Institute of Technology
P–Fukui Institute of Technology
P–Aichi Institute of Technology
P–Daido Institute of Technology
P–Chubu University
P–Meijo University
P–Osaka University of Arts
P–Osaka Institute of Technology
P–Kansai University
P–Kinki University
P–Setsunan University
P–Hiroshima Institute of Technology
P–Fukuyama University

P–Kyushu Kyoritsu University
P–Kyushu Sangyo University
P–Towa University
P–Nishinippon Institute of Technology
P–Fukuoka University
P–Nagasaki Institute of Applied Sciences
P–Kyushu Tokai University
P–The Kumamoto Institute of Technology
P–Nippon Bunri University
P–Dai Ichi University , College of Technology

• Architecture and Building Engineering
N–Tokyo Institute of Technology
N–Kumamoto University
P–Shibaura Institute of Technology

• Architecture and Civil Engineering
N–Utsunomiya University

• Architecture and Design
N–Kyoto Institute of Technology

• Architecture, Urban Engineering and Civil Engineering
N–Nagoya Institute of Technology

Astronomy

N–Tohoku University
N–The University of Tokyo
N–Kyoto University

Biology

• Applied Biochemistry
N–University of Tsukuba
N–Shizuoka University

• Applied Biological Science
N–Tokyo University of Agriculture and Technology
P–Nihon University

• Applied Biology
N–University of Tsukuba
N–Kyoto Institute of Technology

• Applied Microbital Technology
P–The Kumamoto Institute of Technology

• Basic Biology
N–University of Tsukuba

• Bioapplied Chemistry
L–Osaka City University

• Biochemical Engineering and Science
N–Kyushu Institute of Technology

• Biochemistry
N–Yamagata University
N–Ibaraki University
N–Saitama University
N–Toyama University
N–Kanazawa University
N–Fukui University
N–Shinshu University
N–Nagoya University
N–Kochi University
N–University of the Ryukyus
L–Tokyo Metropolitan University
L–Osaka City University
P–Meisei University
P–Rikkyo University
P–Waseda University
P–Okayama University of Science

• Biochemistry and Engineering
N–Tohoku University

• Biochemistry and Technology
L–Osaka City University

• Bioengineering
N–Tokyo Institute of Technology
N–Nagaoka University of Technology
N–Okayama University
N–Hiroshima University
N–The University of Tokushima

• Biological and Chemical Engineering
N–Gunma University

• Biological Environment Creation
N–University of Tsukuba

• Biological Resource Sciences
N–Miyazaki University

• Biological Resources and Production
N–University of Tsukuba

• Biological Science
N–University of Tsukuba
N–Tokyo Institute of Technology
N–Shinshu University
N–Kumamoto University
L–Osaka City University
P–Saitama Medical College
P–Josai University
P–Sophia University
P–Science University of Tokyo
P–Rikkyo University
P–Kanagawa University

• Biology
N–Hokkaido University
N–Hirosaki University
N–Tohoku University
N–Yamagata University
N–Ibaraki University
N–Chiba University
N–The University of Tokyo
N–Ochanomizu University
N–Niigata University
N–Toyama University
N–Kanazawa University
N–Shinshu University
N–Shizuoka University
N–Nagoya University
N–Osaka University
N–Kobe University
N–Nara Women's University
N–Shimane University
N–Okayama University
N–Hiroshima University
N–Yamaguchi University
N–Ehime University
N–Kochi University
N–Kyushu University
N–Kumamoto University
N–Miyazaki University
N–Kagoshima University
N–University of the Ryukyus
L–Tokyo Metropolitan University
L–Osaka City University
P–International Christian University
P–Teikyo University
P–Toho University
P–Japan Women's University
P–Kwansei Gakuin University
P–Konan University

• Biomolecular Engineering
N–Tokyo Institute of Technology

• Biomolecular Science
P–Toho University

• Biophysical Engineering
N–Osaka University

• Biophysics
N–Kyoto University

• Biophysics and Biochemistry
N–The University of Tokyo

• Bioproduction Engineering
P–Ishinomaki Senshu University
P–Tokyo University of Agriculture

• Biosciences
P–Kitasato University
P–Teikyo University

• Bioscience and Biotechnology
N–Shinshu University
P–The Nishi–Tokyo University

• Biosciences and Technology
N–The University of Tokushima
P–Hokkaido Tokai University
P–Science University of Tokyo

• Biotechnology
N–Tokyo University of Agriculture and Technology
N–Yamanashi University
N–University of Tottori
N–Okayama University
P–Tokyo University of Agriculture
P–Kyoto Sangyo University
P–Kansai University
P–Fukuyama University

• Botany
N–Kyoto University

• Life and Functional Materials Science
P–Konan University

• Life Science
N–Tokyo Institute of Technology
L–Himeji Institute of Technology

• Molecular Biology
N–Nagoya University

• Regulation Biology
N–Saitama University

Business and Management

• Accounting
N–Yokohama National University
N–Shiga University
N–Kobe University
P–Tokyo International University
P–Asia University
P–Senshu University
P–Chuo University
P–Nihon University
P–Tokoha–Gakuen Hamamatsu University

• Administration and Informatics
L–Shizuoka Prefectural University

• Administrative Technology
P–Nagasaki Institute of Applied Sciences

• Business Administration
N–Hokkaido University
N–The University of Tokyo
N–Yokohama National University
N–Nagoya University
N–Shiga University
N–Kyoto University
N–Osaka University
N–Kobe University
N–Saga University
L–Yokohama City University
L–Kobe University of Commerce
L–Hiroshima Prefectural University
L–Kitakyushu University
P–Tokiwa University
P–Ryutsu Keizai University
P–Asia University
P–International Christian University
P–Takushoku University
P–Chuo University
P–Toyo University
P–Nihon University
P–Hosei University
P–Meiji University
P–Aichi University
P–Chukyo University
P–Chubu University
P–Nagoya Economics University
P–Nagoya University of Commerce and Business Administration
P–Nanzan University
P–Kyoto Sangyo University
P–Ritsumeikan University
P–Otemon Gakuin University
P–St . Andrew's University
P–Kwansei Gakuin University
P–Konan University
P–Fukuyama University
P–Seinan Gakuin University
P–Miyazaki Sangyo–Keizai University

• Business Administration and Information
P–Setsunan University

• Business Economics
N–Kyushu University
P–Tokyo University of Agriculture
P–Wako University
P–Kyushu International University

• Business Management
N–Tohoku University
N–Fukushima University
N–Saitama University
N–Hitotsubashi University
N–Toyama University
N–University of Wakayama
N–Yamaguchi University
N–Kagawa University
N–Nagasaki University
N–Oita University
L–Takasaki City University of Economics
L–University of Osaka Prefecture
P–Sapporo University
P–Hokkai Gakuen University
P–Hokkaido Information University
P–Aomori University
P–Ishinomaki Senshu University
P–Tokiwa University
P–Sakushin Gakuin University
P–Hakuoh University
P–Kanto Gakuen University
P–Josai University
P–Tokyo International University
P–Dokkyo University
P–Chiba University of Commerce
P–Tokyo University of Information Sciences
P–Aoyama Gakuin University
P–Gakushuin University
P–International Christian University
P–Kokushikan University
P–Komazawa University
P–Sophia University
P–Seikei University
P–Seijo University
P–Senshu University
P–Soka University
P–Daito Bunka University
P–Takachiho University of Commerce
P–Tokai University
P–Tokyo Keizai University
P–Tokyo University of Agriculture
P–Musashi University
P–Rikkyo University
P–Rissho University
P–Kanto Gakuin Universtiy
P–Sanno College
P–Asahi University
P–Aichi Gakuin University
P–Aichi Gakusen University
P–Chukyo University
P–Yokkaichi University
P–Kyoto Gakuen University
P–Ryukoku University
P–Osaka Gakuin University
P–Osaka University of Economics
P–Osaka Sangyo University
P–Kinki University
P–University of Marketing and Distribution Sciences
P–Nara Sangyo University
P–Hiroshima University of Economics
P–Hiroshima Shudo University
P–Tokuyama University
P–The University of East Asia
P–Matsuyama University
P–Kyushu Kyoritsu University
P–Daiichi College of Commerce and Industry
P–Kagoshima Keizai University

• Commerce
N–Otaru University of Commerce
N–Hitotsubashi University
L–Osaka City University
P–Sapporo Gakuin University
P–Hakodate University
P–Hokkai Gakuen Kitami University
P–Hachinohe University
P–Tohoku Gakuin University
P–Jobu University
P–Tokyo International University
P–Chiba University of Commerce
P–Chuo Gakuin University
P–Obirin University
P–Keio University
P–Komazawa University
P–Senshu University
P–Takachiho University of Commerce
P–Toyo University
P–Nihon University
P–Hosei University
P–Meiji University
P–Meiji Gakuin University
P–Waseda University
P–Yokohama College of Commerce
P–Kanazawa College of Economics
P–Yamanashi Gakuin University
P–Aichi Gakuin University
P–Chukyo University
P–Nagoya Gakuin University
P–Nagoya University of Commerce and Business Administration
P–Meijo University
P–Doshisha University
P–Osaka Gakuin University
P–Osaka University of Commerce
P–Kansai University
P–Kinki University
P–University of Hannan
P–Okayama College of Commerce
P–Hiroshima Shudo University
P–Kyushu Sangyo University
P–Kurume University
P–Seinan Gakuin University
P–Fukuoka University
P–Kumamoto University of Commerce
P–Nippon Bunri University
P–Okinawa Kokusai University

• Control Engineering
N–Tokyo Institute of Technology

N–Tokyo University of Marcantile Marine
N–Osaka University
P–Tokai University

• **Distribution**
P–Tokyo International University
P–University of Marketing and Distribution Sciences

• **Foreign Trade**
P–Takushoku University

• **Foreign Trade and Tourism**
P–Yokohama College of Commerce

• **Industrial Administration**
P–Meiji University

• **Industrial and Systems**
P–Ashikaga Institute of Technology

• **Industrial and Systems Engineering**
P–Chuo University
P–Setsunan University

• **Industrial Engineering**
N–University of Wakayama
P–Hokkaido Institute of Technology
P–Seikei University
P–Kansai University

• **Industrial Engineering and Management**
N–Tokyo Institute of Technology

• **Industrial Management**
P–Chiba Institute of Technology
P–Shibaura Institute of Technology
P–Tokyo University of Agriculture
P–Nihon University
P–Waseda University
P–Kanagawa University
P–Gifu College of Economics
P–Nagoya University of Commerce and Business Administration
P–Osaka Institute of Technology
P–Okayama College of Commerce
P–Hiroshima Institute of Technology
P–Kyushu Sangyo University
P–Fukuoka Institute of Technology

• **Industrial Relations**
P–Rikkyo University
P–Doshisha University

• **Industrial Science**
N–University of Wakayama

• **International Business Management**
L–Kobe University of Commerce
P–Tokyo International University
P–Aoyama Gakuin University
P–International Christian University
P–Kanagawa University
P–Kyushu Sangyo University

• **International Commerce**
L–Shimonoseki City College
P–Tokyo International University
P–Kyushu International University

• **Life Science**
N–University of Tottori

• **Management**
P–Osaka University of Commerce
P–Kumamoto University of Commerce

• **Management and Information Science**
L–Hiroshima Prefectural University
P–Jobu University

• **Management and Public Aadministration**
P–Nihon University

• **Management Engineering**
N–Tokyo Institute of Technology
L–University of Osaka Prefecture
P–Aoyama Gakuin University
P–Keio University
P–Tamagawa University
P–Tokai University
P–Tokyo Denki University
P–Science University of Tokyo
P–Musashi Institute of Techonology
P–Fukui Institute of Technology
P–The Nishi–Tokyo University
P–Aichi Institute of Technology
P–Osaka Electro–Communication University
P–Kinki University
P–Towa University
P–Fukuoka Institute of Technology
P–Kyushu Tokai University
P–Nippon Bunri University

• **Management Information**
L–Hiroshima Prefectural University
P–Hokusei Gakuen University
P–Hokkaido Information University
P–Jobu University
P–Surugadai University
P–Tokyo International University
P–Bunkyo University
P–Teikyo University of Technology
P–Tama Institute of Management and Information
P–Sanno College
P–Yokohama College of Commerce
P–Yamanashi Gakuin University
P–Tokoha–Gakuen Hamamatsu University
P–Chubu University
P–Nagoya University of Commerce and Business Administration
P–Osaka International University
P–University of Hannan
P–Koshien University

• **Management Science**
N–Otaru University of Commerce
N–Yokohama National University
N–Kagawa University
N–Saga University
L–Kobe University of Commerce
P–Konan University
P–Hiroshima Shudo University

• **Management Studies**
N–University of Tsukuba

• **Management Systems Engineering**
L–Tokyo Metropolitan Institute of Technology

• **Managerial Engineering**
P–Kanazawa Institute of Technology

• **Marketing and Trade**
P–Tokyo International University
P–Chuo University

• **Marketing and International Business**
L–Kobe University of Commerce

• **Tourism**
P–Rikkyo University

• **Trade**
N–Nagasaki University
P–Tokyo International University
P–Kanagawa University
P–Osaka University of Commerce
P–Daiichi College of Commerce and Industry
P–Fukuoka University

• **Trade and Commerce**
P–Asahikawa University
P–Tokyo International University

• **Transportation Business Administration**
P–Osaka International University

Chemistry

• **Applied Chemical Engineering**
N–The University of Tokushima

• **Applied Chemistry**
N–Hokkaido University
N–Muroran Institute of Technology
N–Iwate University
N–Yamagata University
N–Utsunomiya University
N–Gunma University
N–Saitama University
N–Chiba University
N–Tokyo University of Agriculture and Technology
N–Yamanashi University
N–Gifu University
N–Shizuoka University
N–Nagoya University
N–Nagoya Institute of Technology
N–Osaka University
N–Okayama University
N–Kyushu University
N–Saga University
N–Kumamoto University
N–Kagoshima University
L–Osaka City University
L–University of Osaka Prefecture
L–Himeji Institute of Technology
P–Keio University

P–Sophia University
P–Chuo University
P–Science University of Tokyo
P–Toyo University
P–Waseda University
P–Kanagawa University
P–Aichi Institute of Technology
P–Osaka Institute of Technology
P–Kansai University
P–Kinki University
P–Konan University
P–Okayama University of Science

• Applied Chemistry and Materials
N–Kyushu Institute of Technology

• Applied Fine Chemistry
N–Osaka University

• Chemistry and Materials Technology
N–Kyoto Institute of Technology

• Chemical Engineering
N–Yamagata University
N–The University of Tokyo
N–Tokyo University of Agriculture and Technology
N–Tokyo Institute of Technology
N–Kanazawa University
N–Shizuoka University
N–Nagoya University
N–Kyoto University
N–Osaka University
N–Kobe University
N–Hiroshima University
N–Yamaguchi University
N–Kyushu University
N–Kagoshima University
L–University of Osaka Prefecture
P–Kogakuin University
P–Doshisha University
P–Kansai University
P–Fukuoka University

• Chemical Engineering for Resource
N–Akita University

• Chemical Process Engineering
N–Hokkaido University

• Chemical Science and Technology
N–The University of Tokushima

• Chemistry
N–Hokkaido University
N–Hirosaki University
N–Tohoku University
N–Ibaraki University
N–University of Tsukuba
N–Gunma University
N–Saitama University
N–Chiba University
N–The University of Tokyo
N–Tokyo Institute of Technology
N–Ochanomizu University
N–Niigata University
N–Toyama University
N–Kanazawa University
N–Shinshu University
N–Shizuoka University
N–Nagoya University
N–Kyoto University
N–Osaka University
N–Shimane University
N–Okayama University
N–Hiroshima University
N–Yamaguchi University
N–Ehime University
N–Kochi University
N–Kyushu University
N–Saga University
N–Kumamoto University
N–Kagoshima University
N–University of the Ryukyus
L–Osaka City University
P–Josai University
P–International Budo University
P–Chiba Keizai University
P–Aoyama Gakuin University
P–Gakushuin University
P–Kitasato University
P–Keio University
P–International Christian University
P–Shibaura Institute of Technology
P–Sophia University
P–Tokai University
P–Science University of Tokyo
P–Toho University
P–Nihon University
P–Japan Women's University
P–Meisei University
P–Rikkyo University
P–Waseda University
P–Ritsumeikan University
P–Kinki University
P–Kwansei Gakuin University
P–Konan University
P–Okayama University of Science
P–Fukuoka University

• Fuel Engineering
N–Akita University

• Hydrocarbon Chemistry
N–Kyoto University

• Industrial Chemistry
N–Kitami Institute of Technology
N–The University of Tokyo
N–Kyoto University
N–Kobe University
N–Yamaguchi University
N–Ehime University
N–Nagasaki University
N–Miyazaki Universit
L–Tokyo Metropolitan University
P–Chiba Institute of Technology
P–Kogakuin University
P–Shibaura Institute of Technology
P–Seikei University
P–Tokai University
P–Science University of Tokyo
P–Nihon University
P–Meiji University
P–Kanagawa Institute of Technology
P–Kanto Gakuin Universtiy
P–Tokyo Institute of Polytechnics
P–Chubu University
P–Doshisha University
P–Kinki University
P–Kyushu Sangyo University
P–Towa University
P–The Kumamoto Institute of Technology
P–Nippon Bunri University

• Materials Chemistry
N–Fukui University
P–Ryukoku University

• Molecular Chemistry and Engineering
N–Tohoku University

• Organic Synthesis
N–Kyushu University

• Polymer Chemistry
N–Yamagata University
N–Gunma University
N–Kyoto University

• Polymer Materials Engineering
N–Yamagata University

• Polymer Science and Engineering
N–Hokkaido University
N–Kyoto Institute of Technology

• Pure and Applied Sciences
N–The University of Tokyo

• Reaction Chemistry
N–The University of Tokyo

• Resource Chemistry
N–Iwate University
N–Ehime University

• Synthetic Chemistry
N–Gunma University
N–The University of Tokyo
N–Shinshu University
N–Nagoya University
N–Kyoto University

Civil Engineering

• Civil and Environmental Engineering
N–Yamanashi University
N–Kumamoto University

• Civil Engineering
N–Hokkaido University
N–Kitami Institute of Technology
N–Iwate University
N–Tohoku University
N–Akita University
N–Gunma University
N–The University of Tokyo
N–Tokyo Institute of Technology
N–Nagaoka University of Technology
N–Kanazawa University
N–Gifu University

N–Nagoya University
N–Kyoto University
N–Osaka University
N–Kobe University
N–University of Tottori
N–Okayama University
N–Hiroshima University
N–Yamaguchi University
N–The University of Tokushima
N–Ehime University
N–Kyushu University
N–Saga University
N–Nagasaki University
N–Miyazaki University
N–University of the Ryukyus
L–Tokyo Metropolitan University
L–Osaka City University
P–Hokkaido Institute of Technology
P–Hachinohe Institute of Technology
P–Tohoku Gakuin University
P–Tohoku Institute of Technology
P–Ashikaga Institute of Technology
P–Chiba Institute of Technology
P–Kokushikan University
P–Shibaura Institute of Technology
P–Chuo University
P–Tokai University
P–Science University of Tokyo
P–Toyo University
P–Nihon University
P–Hosei University
P–Musashi Institute of Techonology
P–Meisei University
P–Waseda University
P–Kanto Gakuin Universtiy
P–Kanazawa Institute of Technology
P–Fukui Institute of Technology
P–Aichi Institute of Technology
P–Daido Institute of Technology
P–Chubu University
P–Meijo University
P–Ritsumeikan University
P–Osaka Institute of Technology
P–Osaka Sangyo University
P–Kansai University
P–Kinki University
P–Setsunan University
P–Hiroshima Institute of Technology
P–Fukuyama University
P–Kyushu Kyoritsu University
P–Kyushu Sangyo University
P–Towa University
P–Nishinippon Institute of Technology
P–Fukuoka University
P–Kyushu Tokai University
P–The Kumamoto Institute of Technology
P–Nippon Bunri University
P–Dai Ichi University, College of Technology

• Civil Engineering and Architecture
N–Niigata University

• Civil Engineering, Architecture and Marine Technology
N–Yokohama National University

• Civil Engineering Hydraulics and Soil Mechanics
N–Kyushu University

• Construction Engineering
N–Saitama University
N–Hiroshima University
N–Yamaguchi University
N–Saga University
N–University of the Ryukyus
P–Tokyo Denki University

• Construction System Engineering
N–Muroran Institute of Technology

• Development Engineering
N–Kitami Institute of Technology

• Foundation Engineering
N–Saitama University

• Regional Planning
N–Toyohashi University of Technology

• Social Development
N–Shinshu University

• Social Engineering
N–Tokyo Institute of Technology

• Structural Engineering
N–Nagasaki University
P–The Kumamoto Institute of Technology

• Traffic and Civil Engineering
P–Nihon University

• Urban and Civil Engineering
N–Ibaraki University

• Urban Engineering
N–The University of Tokyo
N–University of Tottori

• Urban Planning
N–University of Tsukuba

Communication

• Broadcasting
P–Nihon University
P–Osaka University of Arts

• Journalism/Masscommunication
P–Tokiwa University
P–Bunkyo University
P–Edogawa University
P–International Christian University
P–Sophia University
P–Seijo University
P–Tokai University
P–Tokyo Women's Christian University
P–Nihon University
P–Doshisha University
P–Kansai University

• Visual Communication
P–Tokiwa University
P–Tokyo University of Art and Design

• Visual Communication Design
N–Kyushu Institute of Design
P–Tokyo University of Art and Design
P–Nihon University
P–Musashino Art University
P–Kobe Design University

Computer and Information Sciences

• Applied Mathematics and Informatics
P–Ryukoku University

• Artificial Intelligence
N–The University of Tokushima
N–Kyushu Institute of Technology
P–Tokyo International University

• Computer Science
N–Gunma University
N–Shizuoka University
N–Ehime University
L–Nara Medical University
L–Wakayama Medical College
L–Shimonoseki City College
L–Tokyo Metropolitan University
L–Tokyo Metropolitan Institute of Technology
P–Tokyo International University
P–Science University of Tokyo
P–Meiji University
P–Sanno College
P–Chukyo University
P–Kyoto Sangyo University

• Communication and Computer Engineering
P–Fukuoka Institute of Technology

• Communication Engineering
N–Osaka University
P–Tohoku Institute of Technology
P–Shibaura Institute of Technology
P–Tokai University
P–Osaka Electro–Commucation University

• Computer Science and Communication Engineering
N–Kyushu University

• Computer Science and Electronics
N–Kyushu Institute of Technology

• Computer Science and Engineering
P–Kanagawa Institute of Technology
P–Sanno College

• Computer Science and Information Mathematics
N–The University of Electro–Communications
P–Tokyo International University

• Computer Science and Systems Engineering
P–Ritsumeikan University

• Electrical and Communication Engineering
P–Tokyo Denki University

• Electrical Communications
N–Tohoku University

• Electronic Communication Engineering
P–Musashi Institute of Techonology
P–Meiji University
P–Waseda University

• Electrical and Information Engineering
N–Yamagata University

• Electrical and Computer Engineering
N–Nagoya Institute of Technology

• Electrical Engineering and Computer science
N–Nagasaki University
N–Kumamoto University

• Electric Information Engineering
N–Kanazawa University
N–Nagasaki University

• Electronics and Information Engineering
N–Tokyo University of Agriculture and Technology
N–The University of Electro–Communications
N–Toyama University
N–Yamanashi University
N–Gifu University
N–University of theRyukyus
L–Toyama Prefectural University
P–Hokkai Gakuen University
P–Hokkaido Tokai University
P–The Nishi–Tokyo University
P–Ryukoku University
P–Kurume Institute of Technology
P–Kyushu Tokai University

• Electronics and Information Science
N–Kyoto Institute of Technology

• Electronics and Information Technology
P–Kyushu Tokai University

• Environmental Information
P–Keio University

• Information and Computer Engineering
P–Kanazawa Institute of Technology

• Information and Computer Sciences
N–Chiba University
N–Tokyo University of Mercantile Marine
N–Toyohashi University of Technology
N–Osaka University
N–Kagoshima University
P–Tokyo University of Information Sciences
P–Toyo University
P–Tokoha–Gakuen Hamamatsu University

• Information and Control Information
P–Toyota Technological Institute

• Information and Environmental Science
N–Tokyo Gakugei University

• Information and Knowledge Engineering
N–University of Tottori

• Information and System Engineering
P–Kyushu Tokai University

• Information Control
N–Shiga University
P–Senshu University

• Information Engineering
N–Hokkaido University
N–Muroran Institute of Technology
N–Kitami Institute of Technology
N–Tohoku University
N–Akita University
N–Yamagata University
N–Gunma University
N–Saitama University
N–Tokyo University of Mercantile Marine
N–The University of Electro–Communications
N–Niigata University
N–Fukui University
N–Shinshu University
N–Nagoya University
N–Mie University
N–Okayama University
N–Miyazaki University
L–Osaka City University
P–Chiba Institute of Technology
P–Teikyo University of Technology
P–Takushoku University
P–Tokyo Kasei University
P–Tokyo Engineering University
P–Shonan Institute of Technology
P–Sanno College

• Information Processing Engineering
P–Tokyo International University
P–Sanno College
P–Kanazawa Institute of Technology
P–Fukuyama University

• Information Science
N–Hirosaki University
N–Iwate University
N–Ibaraki University
N–University of Tsukuba
N–Utsunomiya University
N–Saitama University
N–The University of Tokyo
N–Tokyo Institute of Technology
N–Shiga University
N–Kyoto University
N–Shimane University
N–Oita University
N–Saga University
P–Hokkaido Information University
P–Tohoku Gakuin University
P–Tokyo International University
P–International Christian University
P–Teikyo University
P–Tokyo Denki University
P–Toho University
P–Kanagawa University
P–Sanno College
P–Chukyo University
P–Fukuyama University

• Information Science and Systems Engineering
N–Oita University

• Information System
P–Bunkyo University
P–Teikyo University of Technology
P–Osaka Sangyo University
P–Okayama University of Science

• Information System Engineering
N–Tokyo University of Mercantile Marine
N–Osaka University
P–Tokushima Bunri University
P–Kyushu Tokai University

• Information Systems and Quantitative Sciences
P–Nanzan University

• Information Technology
N–University of Tsukuba

• Information and Communication
P–Chuo University

• Information and Communication Engineering
P–Tamagawa University
P–Tokyo Denki University
P–Aichi Institute of Technology
P–Kyoto Sangyo University

• Information Science
N–Ibaraki University
N–Toyama University
N–Fukui University
N–Mie University
N–Shiga University
N–Ehime University
N–Oita University

• Information–Society and Culture
N–Oita University

• Information Sciences
N–Ochanomizu University
P–Chubu University

• Knowledge-Based Information Engineering
N–Toyohashi University of Technology

• Mathematical Engineering
L–University of Osaka Prefecture
P–Nihon University

Crafts and Design

• Acoustic Design
N–Kyushu Institute of Design

• Architectural Design
N–Tokyo National University of Fine Arts and Music
P–Dohto University
P–Tama Art University
P–Tokyo University of Art and Design
P–Musashino Art University
P–Osaka University of Arts

• Calligraphy
P–Shikoku Women's University

• Ceramics
L–Aichi Prefectural University of Fine Arts
L–Kyoto City University of Arts

• Crafts
N–Tokyo National University of Fine Arts and Music
L–Okinawa Prefectural College of Arts
P–Women's College of Fine Arts
P–Tokyo Kasei University
P–Nagoya University of the Arts
P–Osaka University of Arts

• Crafts and Culture
P–Tokyo Kasei Gakuin University

• Craft Design
L–Kanazawa College of Art

• Design
N–University of Tsukuba
N–Tokyo National University of Fine Art
L–Aichi Prefectural University of Fine Arts
L–Okinawa Prefectural College of Arts
P–Dohto University
P–Hokkaido Tokai University
P–Women's College of Fine Arts
P–Tama Art University
P–Tokyo Kasei University
P–Tokyo University of Art and Design
P–Musashino Art University
P–Nagoya University of the Arts
P–Nagoya College of Art and Design
P–Osaka University of Arts
P–Kyushu Sangyo University

• Display and Fashion
P–Tokyo Kasei University

• Dying and Weaving
L–Kyoto City University of Arts

• Environmental Design
L–Kyoto City University of Arts
P–Women's College of Fine Arts
P–Tokyo University of Art and Design
P–Osaka University of Arts
P–Kobe Design University

• Graphic-Product and Interior Design
P–Women's College of Fine Arts

• Industrial Design
N–Chiba University
N–Kyushu Institute of Design
L–Kanazawa College of Art
P–Tohoku Institute of Technology
P–Chiba Institute of Technology
P–Takushoku University
P–Tokyo University of Art and Design
P–Kinki University
P–Kobe Design University
P–Takarazuka University of Art and Design

• Industrial-Interior and Craft Design
P–Musashino Art University

• Product Design
L–Kyoto City University of Arts
P–Tokyo University of Art and Design

• Science of Design
P–Musashino Art University

• Scenography, Display and Fashion Design
P–Musashino Art University

• Textile Agriculture
N–Shinshu University

• Textile Engineering
N–Shinshu University

• Textile Engineering Chemistry
N–Shinshu University

• Textile System Engineering
N–Shinshu University

• Urushi Lacquering
L–Kyoto City University of Arts

• Visual Communication Design
N–Kyushu Institute of Design
P–Musashino Art University

• Visual Concept Planning
P–Tokyo University of Art and Design
P–Osaka University of Arts

• Visual Design
L–Kanazawa College of Art
L–Kyoto City University of Arts

Dentistry

• Dentistry
N–Hokkaido University
N–Tohoku University
N–Tokyo Medical and Dental University
N–Niigata University
N–Osaka University
N–Okayama University
N–Hiroshima University
N–The University of Tokushima
N–Kyushu University
N–Nagasaki University
N–Kagoshima University
L–Kyushu Dental College
P–Higashi Nippon Gakuen University
P–Iwate Medical University
P–Ohu University
P–Meikai University
P–Tokyo Dental College
P–Showa University
P–Nihon University
P–The Nippon Dental University
P–Kanagawa Dental College
P–Tsurumi University
P–Matsumoto Dental College
P–Asahi University
P–Aichi Gakuin University
P–Osaka Dental University
P–Fukuoka Dental College

Economics

• Applied Economics
P–Hosei University

• Consumer Economics
P–Tokyo International University
P–Nagoya Economics University

• Econoinformatics
P–Himeji Dokkyo University

• Economic Engineering
N–Kyushu University

• Economics
N–Hokkaido University
N–Otaru University of Commerce
N–Hirosaki University
N–Tohoku University
N–Yamagata University
N–Fukushima University
N–University of Tsukuba
N–Saitama University
N–The University of Tokyo
N–Hitotsubashi University
N–Yokohama National University
N–Niigata University
N–Toyama University
N–Kanazawa University
N–Shinshu University
N–Shizuoka University
N–Nagoya University
N–Shiga University
N–Kyoto University
N–Osaka University
N–Kobe University
N–University of Wakayama
N–Okayama University
N–Hiroshima University
N–Yamaguchi University
N–Kagawa University
N–Ehime University
N–Kochi University
N–Kyushu University
N–Saga University

N–Nagasaki University
N–Oita University
N–Kagoshima University
N–University of the Ryukyus
L–Kushiro Public University of Economics
L–Takasaki City University of Economics
L–Tokyo Metropolitan University
L–Yokohama City University
L–Nagoya City University
L–Osaka City University
L–University of Osaka Prefecture
L–Kobe University of Commerce
L–Shimonoseki City College
L–Kitakyushu University
L–Nagasaki Prefectural University of International Economics
P–Asahikawa University
P–Sapporo University
P–Sapporo Gakuin University
P–Hokusei Gakuen University
P–Hokkai Gakuen University
P–Fuji College
P–Tohoku Gakuin University
P–Akita University of Economics and Law
P–Ryutsu Keizai University
P–Kanto Gakuen University
P–Josai University
P–Surugadai University
P–Tokyo International University
P–Dokkyo University
P–Meikai University
P–Keiai University
P–Chiba Keizai University
P–Chiba University of Commerce
P–Aoyama Gakuin University
P–Asia University
P–Obirin University
P–Gakushuin University
P–Keio University
P–Kokugakuin University
P–International Christian University
P–Kokushikan University
P–Komazawa University
P–Sophia University
P–Seikei University
P–Seijo University
P–Senshu University
P–Soka University
P–Daito Bunka University
P–Takushoku University
P–Chuo University
P–Teikyo University
P–Tokai University
P–Tokyo Keizai University
P–Toyo University
P–Nihon University
P–Hosei University
P–Musashi University
P–Meiji University
P–Meiji Gakuin University
P–Meisei University
P–Rikkyo University
P–Rissho University
P–Wako University
P–Waseda University
P–Kanagawa University
P–Kanto Gakuin Universtiy
P–Niigata Sangyo University
P–Kanazawa College of Economics
P–Gifu College of Economics
P–Aichi University
P–Chukyo University
P–Nagoya Gakuin University
P–Nanzan University
P–Nihon Fukushi University
P–Meijo University
P–Yokkaichi University
P–Kyoto Gakuen University
P–Kyoto Sangyo University
P–Doshisha University
P–Ritsumeikan University
P–Ryukoku University
P–Osaka Gakuin University
P–Osaka University of Economics
P–Osaka University of Economics and Law
P–Osaka Sangyo University
P–Osaka University of Commerce
P–Otemon Gakuin University
P–Kansai University
P–Kinki University
P–University of Hannan
P–St. Andrew's University
P–Kwansei Gakuin University
P–Konan University
P–Kobe Gakuin University
P–St. Michael's University
P–Tezukayama University
P–Nara Sangyo University
P–Hiroshima University of Economics
P–Fukuyama University
P–Tokuyama University
P–Matsuyama University
P–Kyushu Kyoritsu University
P–Kyushu Sangyo University
P–Kurume University
P–Seinan Gakuin University
P–Daiichi College of Commerce and Industry
P–Fukuoka University
P–Kumamoto University of Commerce
P–Nippon Bunri University
P–Kagoshima Keizai University
P–The University of Okinawa
P–Okinawa Kokusai University

• Economic Politics
P–Asia University

• Economics and Business Administration
N–Chiba University

• Economic Theories
P–Asia University

• Finance
P–Asia University

• Food Economics
P–Nihon University

• History of Economics and Thoughts
P–Asia University

• Industrial Economics
P–Chuo University
P–Fukuoka University

• International Economics
N–Yokohama National University
N–Yamaguchi University
P–Tokyo International University
P–Aoyama Gakuin University
P–Asia University
P–Chuo University
P–Nagoya University of Commerce and Business Administration
P–Seinan Gakuin University
P–Kumamoto University of Commerce

• Labor Economics
P–Asia University

• Money
P–Asia University

• Social and Economic Analysis
N–University of Tsukuba

• Social-Economic Planning Statics
N–University of Tsukuba
P–Asia University

Education (General)

• Arts and Science
N–Osaka Kyoiku University

• Comprehensive Education
N–Utsunomiya University

• Child Education
L–Aichi Prefectural University
P–Morioka College
P–Ibaraki Christian College
P–Otsuma Women's University
P–Kunitachi College of Music
P–Soka University
P–Tokyo Kasei University
P–Ohtani Women's University
P–Ashiya University
P–Shinwa Women's College
P–Seiwa College
P–Yasuda Women's University
P–Tokushima Bunri University
P–Seinan Gakuin University

• Christian Education
P–Seiwa College

• Curriculum and Instruction
N–Hiroshima University

• Education
N–Hokkaido University
N–Tohoku University
N–University of Tsukuba
N–Utsunomiya University
N–The University of Tokyo
N–Ochanomizu University
N–Shizuoka University
N–Nagoya University
N–Kyoto University
N–Nara Women's University
N–Okayama University

N–Hiroshima University
N–Kyushu University
L–Tokyo Metropolitan University
L–Osaka City University
P–Tokiwa University
P–Aoyama Gakuin University
P–Keio University
P–International Christian University
P–Kokushikan University
P–Sophia University
P–University of the Sacred Heart
P–Soka University
P–Daito Bunka University
P–Tamagawa University
P–Chuo University
P–Teikyo University
P–Toyo University
P–Nihon University
P–Japan Women's University
P–Hosei University
P–Meisei University
P–Rikkyo University
P–Wako University
P–Waseda University
P–Sugiyama Jogakuen University
P–Nanzan University
P–Kogakkan University
P–Doshisha University
P–Bukkyo University
P–Ryukoku University
P–Kansai University
P–Shitennoji International Buddhist University
P–Ashiya University
P–Kwansei Gakuin University
P–Hiroshima Shudo University
P–Shikoku Christian College

• Educational Administration
N–The University of Tokyo
P–Mukogawa Women's University

• Educational Culture
N–Yamaguchi University

• Educational Psychology
N–Nagoya University
N–Kyoto University

• Educational Sociology
N–Kyoto University

• Elementary Education
L–Tsuru University
P–Bunkyo University
P–Kokushikan University
P–University of the Sacred Heart
P–Teikyo University
P–Tokyo Kasei University
P–Tokoha Gakuen University
P–Kyoto Women's University
P–Mukogawa Women's University

• Life-long Education
N–Kochi University
P–Tohoku Fukushi University
P–Mukogawa Women's University

• Life-long Integrated Education
N–Yokohama National University

• Primary Education
P–Nakamura Gakuen College

• Psychology and Education
N–Tohoku University
N–The University of Tokyo
N–Hiroshima University
L–Osaka City University
P–University of the Sacred Heart
P–Tokyo Kasei University

• School Education
N–The University of Tokyo

• Social Education
P–Bukkyo University

• Social Education and Cultural Studies
N–Shimane University

Education (School Level)

• Elementary School Teachers
N–Hokkaido University of Education
N–Hirosaki University
N–Iwate University
N–Miyagi University of Education
N–Akita University
N–Yamagata University
N–Fukushima University
N–Ibaraki University
N–Utsunomiya University
N–Gunma University
N–Saitama University
N–Chiba University
N–Tokyo Gakugei University
N–Yokohama National University
N–Niigata University
N–Joetsu University of Education
N–Toyama University
N–Kanazawa University
N–Fukui University
N–Yamanashi University
N–Shinshu University
N–Gifu University
N–Shizuoka University
N–Aichi University of Education
N–Mie University
N–Shiga University
N–Kyoto University of Education
N–Osaka Kyoiku University
N–Hyogo University of Teacher Education
N–Kobe University
N–Nara University of Education
N–University of Wakayama
N–University of Tottori
N–Shimane University
N–Okayama University
N–Hiroshima University
N–Yamaguchi University
N–Naruto University of Education
N–Kagawa University
N–Ehime University
N–Kochi University
N–Fukuoka University of Education
N–Saga University
N–Nagasaki University
N–Kumamoto University
N–Oita University
N–Miyazaki University
N–Kagoshima University
N–University of the Ryukyus
P–Bunkyo University
P–Shotoku Academy Gifu College of Education
P–Mukogawa Women's University
P–Notre Dame Seishin University
P–Hiroshima Bunkyo Women's College

• High School Teachers
P–Sakushin Gakuin University
P–Mukogawa Women's University

• Junior High School Teachers
N–Hokkaido University of Education
N–Hirosaki University
N–Iwate University
N–Miyagi University of Education
N–Akita University
N–Yamagata University
N–Fukushima University
N–Ibaraki University
N–Utsunomiya University
N–Gunma University
N–Saitama University
N–Chiba University
N–Tokyo Gakugei University
N–Yokohama National University
N–Niigata University
N–Toyama University
N–Kanazawa University
N–Fukui University
N–Yamanashi University
N–Shinshu University
N–Gifu University
N–Shizuoka University
N–Aichi University of Education
N–Mie University
N–Shiga University
N–Kyoto University of Education
N–Osaka Kyoiku University
N–Kobe University
N–Nara University of Education
N–University of Wakayama
N–University of Tottori
N–Shimane University
N–Okayama University
N–Hiroshima University
N–Yamaguchi University
N–Naruto University of Education
N–Kagawa University
N–Ehime University
N–Kochi University
N–Fukuoka University of Education
N–Saga University
N–Nagasaki University
N–Kumamoto University
N–Oita University
N–Miyazaki University
N–Kagoshima University
N–University of the Ryukyus
P–Shotoku Academy Gifu College of Education
P–Mukogawa Women's University

• Kindergarten Teachers
N–Hokkaido University of Education
N–Hirosaki University
N–Miyagi University of Education
N–Akita University
N–Fukushima University
N–Saitama University
N–Chiba University
N–Tokyo Gakugei University
N–Niigata University
N–Joetsu University of Education
N–Toyama University
N–Yamanashi University
N–Shinshu University
N–Shizuoka University
N–Aichi University of Education
N–Mie University
N–Shiga University
N–Kyoto University of Education
N–Osaka Kyoiku University
N–Kobe University
N–Nara University of Education
N–Shimane University
N–Okayama University
N–Yamaguchi University
N–Kagawa University
N–Ehime University
N–Fukuoka University of Education
N–Nagasaki University
N–Oita University
N–Miyazaki University
P–Mukogawa Women's University

• School Health Teachers
N–Kumamoto University

• School Nurses
N–Hokkaido University of Education
N–Hirosaki University
N–Ibaraki University
N–Chiba University
N–Aichi University of Education
N–Osaka Kyoiku University
N–Okayama University
N–Kumamoto University

Education (Special Education)

• Special Education
N–University of Tsukuba
N–Kumamoto University

• Teachers for the Deaf
N–Tokyo Gakugei University
N–Kanazawa University
N–Hiroshima University
N–Ehime University

• Teachers for the Handicapped
N–Hokkaido University of Education
N–Hirosaki University
N–Iwate University
N–Miyagi University of Education
N–Akita University
N–Yamagata University
N–Fukushima University
N–Ibaraki University
N–Gunma University
N–Saitama University
N–Chiba University
N–Tokyo Gakugei University
N–Yokohama National University
N–Toyama University
N–Kanazawa University
N–Fukui University
N–Yamanashi University
N–Shinshu University
N–Gifu University
N–Shizuoka University
N–Aichi University of Education
N–Mie University
N–Shiga University
N–Kyoto University of Education
N–Osaka Kyoiku University
N–Kobe University
N–Nara University of Education
N–University of Wakayama
N–University of Tottori
N–Shimane University
N–Okayama University
N–Yamaguchi University
N–Kagawa University
N–Ehime University
N–Kochi University
N–Fukuoka University of Education
N–Saga University
N–Nagasaki University
N–Oita University
N–Miyazaki University
N–Kagoshima University
N–University of the Ryukyus

• Teachers for the Mentally Retarded
N–Utsunomiya University
N–Hiroshima University

• Teachers for the Speech Handicapped
N–Miyagi University of Education
N–Tokyo Gakugei University
N–Kanazawa University

• Teachers for the Visual Handicapped
N–Miyagi University of Education
N–Hiroshima University

• Teachers of Retarded Children
N–Niigata University

Education (Specific Subjects)

• Arts
N–Gunma University
N–Tokyo Gakugei University

• Arts and Crafts
N–Hokkaido University of Education
N–Iwate University
N–Tokyo Gakugei University
N–Kyoto University of Education
N–Okayama University
N–Kochi University
N–Saga University
N–University of the Ryukyus
P–Tokyo Kasei University

• Business
N–Otaru University of Commerce
N–University of Wakayama
N–Yamaguchi University

• Calligraphy
N–Tokyo Gakugei University
N–Niigata University
N–Aichi University of Education
N–Nara University of Education
N–Fukuoka University of Education
P–Mukogáwa Women's University

• Dancing
P–Mukogawa Women's University

• Dancing and Music Education
N–Ochanomizu University

• English
N–University of the Ryukyus

• English Language and Literature Education
P–Ashiya University

• Fisheries
N–Tokyo University of Fisheries
N–Kagoshima University

• General Science
N–University of the Ryukyus

• Health and Physical Education
N–Hokkaido University of Education
N–Fukushima University
N–Tokyo Gakugei University
N–Kyoto University of Education
N–Nara Women's University
N–Shimane University
N–Kochi University
N–Fukuoka University of Education
N–Kagoshima University
P–Mukogawa Women's University

• Home Economics
N–University of the Ryukyus

• Home Science
N–Kyoto University of Education
N–Nara Women's University
P–Tokyo Kasei University

• Industry
N–Kanazawa University
P–Ashiya University

• Integrated arts and Sciences
N–Hokkaido University of Education
N–Yokohama National University

• Integrated Culture
N–Saga University

• Japanese

N–University of the Ryukyus
P–Tokyo International University
P–Shotoku Academy Gifu College of Education

• Japanese Language and Literature
N–Gunma University
N–University of the Ryukyus

• Mathematics
N–Miyagi University of Education
N–Gunma University
N–Tokyo Gakugei University
N–Aichi University of Education
N–Fukuoka University of Education
N–University of the Ryukyus
P–Tokyo International University
P–Shotoku Academy Gifu College of Education

• Music
N–Yamagata University
N–Gunma University
N–Tokyo Gakugei University
N–Niigata University
N–Shimane University
N–Ehime University
N–Miyazaki University
N–University of the Ryukyus
P–Bunkyo University
P–Kunitachi College of Music
P–Tokyo College of Music
P–Musashino Academia Musicae
P–Senzoku Gakuen College of Music Academy
P–Shotoku Academy Gifu College of Education
P–Nagoya College of Music
P–Nagoya University of the Arts
P–Kyoto Women's University
P–Osaka University of Arts
P–Mukogawa Women's University
P–Sakuyo College of Music

• Music Theory and History
N–University of the Ryukyus

• Natural Sciences
N–University of the Ryukyus

• Nurse
N–Hirosaki University
N–Kumamoto University

• Science
N–Miyagi University of Education
N–Gunma University
N–Tokyo Gakugei University
N–Gifu University
N–Aichi University of Education
N–Kyoto University of Education
N–Nara University of Education
N–Fukuoka University of Education
N–Miyazaki University
P–Waseda University

• Social Education
N–Hokkaido University of Education

• Social Science
N–Gunma University
N–University of the Ryukyus
P–Waseda University
P–Shotoku Academy Gifu College of Education

• Teaching Japanese as A Second Language
N–Hiroshima University

• Technical Education
N–Gunma University
N–University of the Ryukyus

• Vocal Music
N–University of the Ryukyus

Engineering (Micellaneous)

• Engineering Sciences
N–University of Tsukuba
N–Kyoto University

Electrical Engineering

• Applied Electronic Engineering
P–Tokyo Denki University
P–Science University of Tokyo
P–Daido Institute of Technology
P–Osaka Electro-Commucation University

• Applied Electronics
P–Hokkaido Institute of Technology

• Control and System Engineering
N–Tokyo University of Mercantile Marine
P–Toin University of Yokohama

• Control Engineering and Science
N–Kyushu Institute of Technology

• Electrical and Computer Engineering
N–Yokohama National University
N–Kanazawa University

• Electrical and Electronic Engineering
N–Muroran Institute of Technology
N–Ibaraki University
N–Utsunomiya University
N–Chiba University
N–Tokyo University of Agriculture and Technology
N–Tokyo Institute of Technology
N–Niigata University
N–Shinshu University
N–Toyohashi University of Technology
N–University of Tottori
N–Okayama University
N–The University of Tokushima
P–Nippon Institute of Technology
P–Aoyama Gakuin University
P–Sophia University
P–Chuo University
P–Hosei University
P–Musashi Institute of Techonology
P–Kanagawa Institute of Technology
P–Meijo University
P–Osaka Sangyo University
P–Fukuyama University

• Electrical and Electronics System Engineering
N–Nagaoka University of Technology
P–Teikyo University

• Electrical Engineering
N–Hokkaido University
N–Kitami Institute of Technology
N–Iwate University
N–Tohoku University
N–Akita University
N–Yamagata University
N–Gunma University
N–Saitama University
N–The University of Tokyo
N–Shizuoka University
N–Nagoya University
N–Mie University
N–Kyoto University
N–Osaka University
N–Kobe University
N–Hiroshima University
N–Yamaguchi University
N–Ehime University
N–Kyushu University
N–Saga University
N–Oita University
N–Miyazaki University
N–Kagoshima University
N–University of the Ryukyus
L–Tokyo Metropolitan University
L–Osaka City University
L–University of Osaka Prefecture
L–Himeji Institute of Technology
P–Hokkaido Institute of Technology
P–Hachinohe Institute of Technology
P–Tohoku Gakuin University
P–Ashikaga Institute of Technology
P–Chiba Institute of Technology
P–Keio University
P–Kogakuin University
P–Kokushikan University
P–Shibaura Institute of Technology
P–Seikei University
P–Tokai University
P–Tokyo Denki University
P–Science University of Tokyo
P–Toyo University
P–Nihon University
P–Hosei University
P–Meiji University
P–Meisei University
P–Waseda University
P–Kanagawa University
P–Kanto Gakuin Universtiy
P–Shonan Institute of Technology
P–Kanazawa Institute of Technology
P–Fukui Institute of Technology
P–Aichi Institute of Technology
P–Daido Institute of Technology
P–Chubu University

P–Doshisha University
P–Ritsumeikan University
P–Osaka Institute of Technology
P–Kansai University
P–Kinki University
P–Setsunan University
P–Hiroshima Institute of Technology
P–The Hiroshima–Denki Institute of Technology
P–Kyushu Kyoritsu University
P–Kyushu Sangyo University
P–Towa University
P–Nishinippon Institute of Technology
P–Fukuoka University
P–Fukuoka Institute of Technology
P–Nagasaki Institute of Applied Sciences
P–Kyushu Tokai University
P–The Kumamoto Institute of Technology
P–Nippon Bunri University

• Electrical, Electronic and Computer Engineering
N–Kyushu Institute of Technology

• Electronic Systems Engineering
L–Tokyo Metropolitan Institute of Technology

• Electronic and Mechanical Engineering
N–Tokyo University of Mercantile Marine

• Electronic Engineering
N–Hokkaido University
N–Kitami Institute of Technology
N–Iwate University
N–Tohoku University
N–Akita University
N–Yamagata University
N–Gunma University
N–Saitama University
N–The University of Tokyo
N–The University of Electro–Communications
N–Nagaoka University of Technology
N–Fukui University
N–Shizuoka University
N–Mie University
N–Kyoto University
N–Osaka University
N–Kobe University
N–Hiroshima University
N–Yamaguchi University
N–Ehime University
N–Saga University
N–Oita University
N–Miyazaki University
N–Kagoshima University
L–University of Osaka Prefecture
L–Himeji Institute of Technology
P–Tohoku Institute of Technology
P–Iwaki Meisei University
P–Saitama Institute of Technology
P–Chiba Institute of Technology
P–Kogakuin University
P–Shibaura Institute of Technology
P–Takushoku University
P–Tamagawa University
P–Tokai University
P–Tokyo Engineering University
P–Tokyo Denki University
P–Nihon University
P–Tokyo Institute of Polytechnics
P–Kanazawa Institute of Technology
P–Fukui Institute of Technology
P–Aichi Institute of Technology
P–Chubu University
P–Doshisha University
P–Osaka Institute of Technology
P–Osaka Electro–Commucation University
P–Kinki University
P–Okayama University of Science
P–Hiroshima Institute of Technology
P–The Hiroshima–Denki Institute of Technology
P–Fukuoka University
P–Fukuoka Institute of Technology
P–The Kumamoto Institute of Technology
P–Dai Ichi University, College of Technology

• Electronic Machinery
P–Koshien University

• Electronic Machinery Engineering
N–Tokyo University of Mercantile Marine

• Electronic Materials Engineering
P–Ishinomaki Senshu University
P–Fukuoka Institute of Technology

• Electronics
N–Nagoya University
N–Kyoto University
N–Kyushu University
P–Kansai University

• Electronics and Communication
P–Meiji University

• Electronics and Informatics
P–Ryukoku University

• Electron Optics
P–Tokai University

• Electro Photo Optics
P–Tokai University

• Opto–Electronic and Mechanical Engineering
N–Shizuoka University

• Physical Electronics
N–Tokyo Institute of Technology

• Solid State Electronics
N–The University of Electro–Communications
P–Osaka Electro–Commucation University

Energy Engineering

• Energy and Mechanical Engineering
N–Shizuoka University
N–University of the Ryukyus

• Energy Engineering
N–University of Tsukuba
N–Toyohashi University of Technology
N–Oita University
P–Hachinohe Institute of Technology

Environmental Sciences

• Environmental and Technology
N–Kagoshima University

• Environmental Science and Resources
N–Tokyo University of Agriculture and Technology

• Environmental Studies for Open Space
N–Chiba University

• Environmental Chemistry
P–Kyushu Kyoritsu University

• Environmental Chemistry and Engineering
N–Oita University

• Environmental Design
N–Kyushu Institute of Design
P–Osaka Sangyo University

• Environmental Planning
N–Kobe University
P–Tokyo University of Art and Design

• Environmental and Sanitary Engineering
N–Kyoto University

• Environmental Design
P–Kobe Design University

• Environmental Engineering
N–Kitami Institute of Technology
N–Saitama University
N–Fukui University
N–Osaka University
P–Saitama Institute of Technology
P–Fukui Institute of Technology
P–Osaka University of Arts

Fine Arts

• Aesthetics
N–Osaka University
P–Kwansei Gakuin University

• Aesthetics and Art History
L–Gunma Prefectural Women's College
L–Kanazawa College of Art
P–Atomi Gakuen Women's College
P–Keio University
P–Jissen Women's University
P–Doshisha University
P–Tezukayama Gakuin University
P–Otemae College
P–Beppu University

• Art and Design
P–Musashino Art University

• Art Planning
P–Osaka University of Arts

• Arts
N–Tokyo National University of Fine Arts and Music
N–Shinshu University
L–Okinawa Prefectural College of Arts
P–Kyoritsu Women's University
P–International Christian University
P–Women's College of Fine Arts
P–Seijo University
P–Tamagawa University
P–Tama Art University
P–Tokai University
P–Tokyo Kasei University
P–Tokyo University of Art and Design
P–Nihon University
P–Wako University
P–Nagoya College of Art and Design
P–Osaka University of Arts
P–Kinki University
P–Takarazuka University of Art and Design
P–Kyushu Sangyo University

• Art Studies
P–Meiji Gakuin University

• Constructive Art
N–University of Tsukuba

• Fine Arts
N–University of Tsukuba
P–Nippon University
P–Musashino Art University

• Formative Arts
P–Women's College of Fine Arts
P–Kyoto Seika University

• History and Philosophy of Art
N–University of Tsukuba

• Japanese Paintings
N–Tokyo National University of Fine Arts and Music
L–Kanazawa College of Art
L–Aichi Prefectural University of Fine Arts
L–Kyoto City University of Arts
P–Women's College of Fine Arts
P–Musashino Art University
P–Nagoya University of the Arts

• Oil Paintings
N–Tokyo National University of Fine Arts and Music
L–Kanazawa College of Art
L–Aichi Prefectural University of Fine Arts
L–Kyoto City University of Arts
P–Women's College of Fine Arts
P–Tokyo Kasei University
P–Musashino Art University
P–Nagoya University of the Arts

• Printmaking
L–Kyoto City University of Arts

• Sculpture
N–Tokyo National University of Fine Arts and Music
L–Kanazawa College of Art
L–Aichi Prefectural University of Fine Arts
L–Kyoto City University of Arts
L–Okinawa Prefectural College of Arts
P–Tama Art University
P–Tokyo University of Art and Design
P–Musashino Art University
P–Nagoya University of the Arts

• Science of Arts
P–Women's College of Fine Arts

Fisheries and Marine Engineering

• Aquacultural Sciences
P–Kitasato University

• Aquatic Bioscience
N–Tokyo University of Fisheries

• Biology and Aquaculture
N–Hokkaido University

• Cultural Fisheries
N–Kochi University

• Fisheries
N–Hokkaido University
N–Tohoku University
N–The University of Tokyo
N–Kyoto University
N–Kyushu University
N–Nagasaki University
N–Kagoshima University
P–Tokai University
P–Nihon University
P–Kinki University

• Fisheries Resources Management
N–Tokyo University of Fisheries

• Fishing Science
N–Hokkaido University

• Marine Civil Engineering
P–Tokai University

• Marine Electronics
N–Tokyo University of Marcantile Marine

• Marine Engineering
N–The University of Tokyo
N–Tokyo University of Marcantile Marine
N–Osaka University
N–Kobe University of Marcantile Marine
N–Hiroshima University
L–University of Osaka Prefecture
P–Tokai University

• Marine Food Chemistry
P–Kitasato University

• Marine Mineral Resources
P–Tokai University

• Marine Science
N–University of the Ryukyus
P–Tokai University

• Marine Science and Technology
N–Tokyo University of Marcantile Marine
N–Tokyo University of Fisheries
P–Hokkaido Tokai University

• Marine System Engineering
N–Tokyo University of Marcantile Marine

• Naval Architectural Engineering
P–Nagasaki Institute of Applied Sciences

• Naval Architecture
N–Kyushu University
P–Tokai University

• Naval Architecture and Ocean Engineering
N–The University of Tokyo
N–Osaka University

• Oceanic Architecture and Engineering
P–Nippon University

• Oceanic Civil Engineering
P–Komazawa University
P–Tokai University

• Maritime Science
N–Kobe University of Marcantile Marine

• Nautical Engineerig
N–Tokyo University of Marcantile Marine
P–Tokai University

• Nautical Science
N–Tokyo University of Marcantile Marine

• Navigation
N–Tokyo University of Marcantile Marine

• Ocean Electro–Mechanical Engineering
N–Kobe University of Marcantile Marine

• Ocean Engineering
N–Ehime University
P–Tokai University

Food Science

• Food
L–Kyoto Prefectural University
P–Wayo Women's University
P–Jissen Women's University
P–Showa Women's University
P–Tokyo University of Agriculture
P–Kyoto Women's University
P–Osaka Shoin Women's College
P–Teikoku Women's University
P–Mukogawa Women's University
P–Mimasaka Women's College

• Food and Human Nutrition
P–Notre Dame Seishin University

• Food and Nutrition
P–Koriyama Women's College
P–Nakamura Gakuen College

• Food and Nutrition Science
N–Ochanomizu University
N–Nara Women's University
L–Osaka City University
L–Hiroshima Women's University
L–Yamaguchi Women's University
L–Kochi Women's University
L–Fukuoka Women's University
L–Kumamoto Women's University
P–Koriyama Women's College
P–Showa Women's University
P–Japan Women's University
P–Gifu Women's University
P–Sugiyama Jogakuen University
P–Chukyo Women's University
P–Kinki University
P–Kobe College
P–Nishikyushu University

• Food Chemistry
N–Tohoku University

• Food Engineering
P–Nihon University
P–Fukuyama University
P–The University of East Asia

• Food Living Science
L–Yamaguchi Women's University

• Food Science
L–Shizuoka Prefectural University
P–Rakuno Gakuen University
P–Otsuma Women's University
P–Tokyo University of Agriculture
P–Nagoya Women's University
P–Doshisha Women's College of Liberal Arts
P–Mukogawa Women's University
P–Nakamura Gakuen College

• Food Science and Technology
N–Tokyo University of Fisheries
N–Nagoya University
N–Kyoto University
N–Kyushu University
P–Tokyo University of Agriculture
P–Nippon Veterinary and Zootechnical College
P–Minami Kyushu College

• Food Technology
P–Nihon University

Forest Science

• Forestry
N–Hokkaido University
N–Iwate University
N–Yamagata University
N–Utsunomiya University
N–The University of Tokyo
N–Niigata University
N–Shinshu University
N–Nagoya University
N–Kyoto University
N–Kochi University
N–Kyushu University
N–University of the Ryukyus
L–Kyoto Prefectural University
P–Tokyo University of Agriculture
P–Nihon University

• Forest Production
N–The University of Tokyo
N–Kyushu University
N–Miyazaki University

• Forest Products
N–Hokkaido University
N–Nagoya University

• Forest Resources Science
N–Shizuoka University

• Wood Science and Technology
N–Shinshu University
N–Kyoto University

Geography

• Geography
N–Tohoku University
N–Ochanomizu University
N–Nara Women's University
P–Kokushikan University
P–Komazawa University
P–Nihon University
P–Hosei University
P–Rissho University
P–Ritsumeikan University
P–Nara University

Geology

• Applied Earth Science
P–Nihon University

• Applied Geology
P–Nihon University

• Earth and Planetary Science
N–Kyushu University

• Earth Sciences
N–Yamagata University
N–Ibaraki University
N–Okayama University

• Earth Sciences
N–Hirosaki University
N–Chiba University
N–Kanazawa University

• Geology
N–The University of Tokyo
N–Kanazawa University
N–Shinshu University
N–Shimane University
N–Kochi University
N–Kumamoto University
N–Kagoshima University
L–Osaka City University

• Geology and Mineralogy
N–Hokkaido University
N–Niigata University
N–Kyoto University
N–Hiroshima University
N–Yamaguchi University

• Geology and Paleontology
N–Tohoku University

• Geophysics
N–Hokkaido University
N–Tohoku University
N–The University of Tokyo
N–Kyoto University

• Geoscience–Earth Science
N–Hirosaki University
N–Yamagata University
N–University of Tsukuba
N–Shizuoka University
N–Nagoya University
N–Ehime University

• Geosciences
N–Shizuoka University

• Geosciences, Mining Engineering and Materials Processing
N–Akita University

• Mineral Engineering
N–Yamaguchi University
P–Waseda University

• Mineralogy–Petrology and Economic Geology
N–Tohoku University

• Mineral Resources Development Engineering
N–Hokkaido University
N–Iwate University
N–The University of Tokyo

• Mineral Science and Technology
N–Kyoto University

• Mining
N–Kyushu University

• Mining Engineering
N–Akita University

• Mining Geology
N–Akita University

Health Science

• **Applied Health Sciences**
N–Tokyo Medical and Dental University

• **Environmental Health**
P–Azabu University
P–Setsunan University

• **Health Education**
N–University of Tsukuba
P–Juntendo University
P–Nippon College of Physical Education

• **Health and Nutrition**
P–Kagawa Nutrition College

• **Hygienic Technology**
P–Kitasato University
P–Azabu University

• **Industrial Hygiene**
P–Kitasato University

• **Health Science**
N–The University of Tokyo
N–University of the Ryukyus
P–Kyorin University
P–Waseda University
P–Chukyo University

• **Hygienic Technology**
P–Kitasato University

• **Industrial Hygiene**
P–Kitasato University

• **Sanitary Engineering**
N–Hokkaido University

• **School–Health**
P–Shikoku Women's University

History

• **Archaeology**
P–Tokai University

• **Archaeology and Ethnology**
P–Keio University

• **Archaeology and Folklore**
N–University of Tsukuba

• **Civilization and Social History**
N–Hitotsubashi University

• **East Asian History**
P–Ritsumeikan University

• **European and American History**
P–Ritsumeikan University

• **Historical Science**
N–Chiba University

• **History**
N–Hokkaido University
N–Tohoku University
N–University of Tsukuba
N–The University of Tokyo
N–Ochanomizu University
N–Kanazawa University
N–Kyoto University
N–Osaka University
N–Kobe University
N–Nara Women's University
N–Okayama University
N–Hiroshima University
N–Kyushu University
N–Kumamoto University
N–University of theRyukyus
L–Tokyo Metropolitan University
L–Kyoto Prefectural University
P–Tohoku Gakuin University
P–Kawamura Gakuen Women's University
P–Aoyama Gakuin University
P–Gakushuin University
P–Kokugakuin University
P–International Christian University
P–Komazawa University
P–Sophia University
P–University of the Sacred Heart
P–Taisho University
P–Teikyo University
P–Tokyo Women's Christian University
P–Toyo University
P–Nihon University
P–Japan Women's University
P–Hosei University
P–Rikkyo University
P–Rissho University
P–Aichi University
P–Aichi Gakuin University
P–Otani University
P–Kyoto Tachibana Women's University
P–Doshisha University
P–Hanazono College
P–Bukkyo University
P–Otemae College
P–Kwansei Gakuin University
P–Kobe Women's University
P–Nara University
P–Shujitsu Joshi University
P–Fukuoka University
P–Beppu University

• **History and Geography**
N–Nagoya University
L–Osaka City University
P–Kokushikan University
P–Meiji University
P–Kansai University

• **Japanese History**
P–Keio University
P–Kokugakuin University
P–Kokushikan University
P–Chuo University
P–Tokai University
P–Waseda University
P–Kogakkan University
P–Ritsumeikan University
P–Ryukoku University
P–Koyasan University

• **Oriental History**
P–Keio University
P–Kokushikan University
P–Chuo University
P–Tokai University
P–Kyoto Women's University
P–Ryukoku University

• **Western History**
P–Keio University
P–Kokushikan University
P–Chuo University
P–Tokai University

Home Science

• **Child Studies**
N–Ochanomizu University
L–Hiroshima Women's University
P–Tohoku Women's College
P–Seitoku University
P–Otsuma Women's University
P–Tokyo Kasei University
P–Japan Women's University
P–Kamakura Women's Universtiy
P–Kinjo Gakuin University
P–Chukyo Women's University
P–Kyoto Women's University
P–Osaka Shoin Women's College
P–Teikoku Women's University
P–Kobe College
P–Notre Dame Seishin University
P–Mimasaka Women's College
P–Tokushima Bunri University
P–Nakamura Gakuen College

• **Clothing**
N–Ochanomizu University
N–Nara Women's University
L–Hiroshima Women's University
L–Yamaguchi Women's University
L–Fukuoka Women's University
P–Wayo Women's University
P–Otsuma Women's University
P–Kyoritsu Women's University
P–Jissen Women's University
P–Sugino Women's College
P–Tokyo Kasei University
P–Japan Women's University
P–Bunka Women's University
P–Sugiyama Jogakuen University
P–Kyoto Women's University
P–Osaka Shoin Women's College
P–Teikoku Women's University
P–Mukogawa Women's University
P–Shikoku Women's University

• **Domestic Science**
P–Tohoku Living Culture College
P–Nagoya Women's University
P–Kobe Women's University

• **Dwelling Science**
N–Nara Women's University

• **Human Life**
P–Koriyama Women's College

• Home Economics
P–Kyushu Women's University

• Home Life Administration
N–Ochanomizu University

• Home Science
L–Kochi Women's University
L–Fukuoka Women's University
P–Tohoku Women's College
P–Miyagi Gakuin Women's College
P–Tokyo Kasei University
P–Tokyo Kasei Gakuin University
P–Japan Women's University
P–Kamakura Women's Universtiy
P–Gifu Women's University
P–Aichi Gakusen University
P–Kinjo Gakuin University
P–Nagoya Women's University
P–Doshisha Women's College of Liberal Arts
P–Notre Dame Seishin University
P–Tokushima Bunri University

• Household Economics
P–Japan Women's University

• Housing and Living Design
N–Nara Women's University
L–Kyoto Prefectural University
P–Tokyo Kasei Gakuin University
P–Japan Women's University
P–Gifu Women's University

• Living
P–Tokai University
P–Notre Dame Women's College

• Living Arts
L–Yamaguchi Women's University
P–Tohoku Living Culture College
P–Kyoritsu Women's University
P–Showa Women's University
P–Bunka Women's University

• Living System
P–Showa Women's University

• Pedology
P–Shikoku Women's University

• Science of Living
L–Hiroshima Women's University
L–Kochi Women's University
L–Fukuoka Women's University
L–Kumamoto Women's University
P–Showa Women's University

• Science of Living Environment
L–Osaka City University
L–Kumamoto Women's University

• Social Sciences of the Family
N–Nara Women's University

Horticulture

• Horticultural Science
N–Chiba University

• Horticulture
N–Yamagata University
N–Chiba University
N–Shinshu University
P–Minami Kyushu College

• Landscape Architecture
P–Tokyo University of Agriculture
P–Minami Kyushu College

Humanities (Miscellaneous)

• Human Development
P–Tokai University

• Humanities
N–Hirosaki University
N–Iwate University
N–Ibaraki University
N–University of Tsukuba
N–Toyama University
N–Shizuoka University
N–Mie University
N–Yamaguchi University
N–Miyazaki University
N–Kagoshima University
P–International Christian University
P–Senshu University
P–Soka University
P–Tokyo Kasei University
P–Kyoto Seika University
P–Shikoku Christian College

• Humanity and Cultures
P–Japan Women's University

• Humanities and Social Sciences
N–Yokohama National University

• Human Relations
P–Tokiwa University
P–Tokyo International University
P–University of the Sacred Heart
P–Tokai Women's College
P–Mukogawa Women's University
P–Kagoshima Women's College

• Human Sciences
N–Tokyo Gakugei University
L–Osaka Women's University
P–Sapporo Gakuin University
P–Tohoku Gakuin University
P–Tokiwa University
P–Bunkyo University
P–Edogawa University
P–Keio University
P–Waseda University
P–Toyo Eiwa Women's University
P–Tokai University
P–Meiji Gakuin University
P–Doshisha University
P–Osaka Gakuin University
P–Konan Women's University

• Liberal Arts
N–Saitama University
L–Yokohama City University
P–Tezukayama University

International Studies

• International Social Studies
P–Kibi International University

• International Studies
P–Tokyo International University
P–Bunkyo University
P–Obirin University

• International Relations
N–University of Tsukuba
N–Hitotsubashi University
L–Shizuoka Prefectural University
L–Kobe City University of Foreign Studies
P–Asia University
P–Obirin University
P–International Christian University
P–Daido Bunka University
P–Tsuda College
P–Nihon University
P–Chubu University
P–Ritsumeikan University

Law

• Basic Law
P–Asia University

• Business Law
N–Otaru University of Commerce
N–Toyama University
P–Tokyo International University
P–Toyo University
P–Nihon University
P–Kinki University
P–Fukuoka University

• Civil Law
P–Asia University

• Criminal Law
P–Asia University

• International Comparative Law
P–Rikkyo University

• International Legal Studies
P–Tokyo International University
P–Sophia University

• Law
N–Hokkaido University
N–Tohoku University
N–Yamagata University
N–University of Tsukuba
N–Niigata University
N–Kanazawa University

N–Shizuoka University
N–Nagoya University
N–Kyoto University
N–Osaka University
N–Kobe University
N–Shimane University
N–Okayama University
N–Hiroshima University
N–Kagawa University
N–Ehime University
N–Kyushu University
N–Kumamoto University
N–Kagoshima University
L–Tokyo Metropolitan University
L–Osaka City University
L–Kitakyushu University
P–Sapporo University
P–Sapporo Gakuin University
P–Hokkai Gakuen University
P–Tohoku Gakuin University
P–Akita University of Economics and Law
P–Kanto Gakuen University
P–Surugadai University
P–Dokkyo University
P–Chuo Gakuin University
P–Asia University
P–Gakushuin University
P–Keio University
P–Kokugakuin University
P–International Christian University
P–Kokushikan University
P–Komazawa University
P–Sophia University
P–Seikei University
P–Seijo University
P–Senshu University
P–Soka University
P–Daido Bunka University
P–Chuo University
P–Teikyo University
P–Tokai University
P–Toyo University
P–Nihon University
P–Nippon Bunka University
P–Hosei University
P–Meiji University
P–Meiji Gakuin University
P–Rikkyo University
P–Rissho University
P–Waseda University
P–Kanagawa University
P–Takaoka College of Law
P–Yamanashi Gakuin University
P–Asahi University
P–Aichi University
P–Aichi Gakuin University
P–Chukyo University
P–Nanzan University
P–Meijo University
P–Kyoto Gakuen University
P–Kyoto Sangyo University
P–Doshisha University
P–Ritsumeikan University
P–Ryukoku University
P–Osaka Gakuin University
P–Osaka University of Economics and Law
P–Kansai University
P–Kinki University
P–Setsunan University
P–Kwansei Gakuin University
P–Konan University
P–Kobe Gakuin University
P–Himeji Dokkyo University
P–Nara Sangyo University
P–Hiroshima Shudo University
P–Matsuyama University
P–Kyushu International University
P–Kurume University
P–Seinan Gakuin University
P–Fukuoka University
P–Miyazaki Sangyo–Keizai University
P–The University of Okinawa
P–Okinawa Kokusai University

• Law and Administration
N–Fukushima University
P–Tokyo International University
P–Yamanashi Gakuin University

• Law and Economics
N–Yokohama National University
N–Yamaguchi University
P–Tokyo International University

• Law and Politics
N–Chiba University
N–University of the Ryukyus

• Private Law
N–The University of Tokyo
N–Hitotsubashi University
P–Aoyama Gakuin University

• Public Law
N–The University of Tokyo
N–Hitotsubashi University
P–Aoyama Gakuin University

• Public Law and Political Science
P–Asia University

Library and Information

• Library and Information
N–The University of Library and Information Science
P–Keio University
P–Chuo University
P–Aichi Shukutoku University

Literature, Linguistics and Area Studies

• Anglo American Culture
P–Soai University

• Anglo–American Studies
N–Tokyo University of Foreign Studies
L–Kitakyushu University

• Arabic–African Studies
N–Osaka University of Foreign Studies

• Arabic Studies
N–Tokyo University of Foreign Studies
P–Tokyo International University
P–Shitennoji International Buddhist University

• Asian Studies
P–Tokyo International University
P–Tokai University
P–Otemon Gakuin University

• British and American Studies
N–Tokyo University of Foreign Studies
L–Aichi Prefectural University
L–Kobe City University of Foreign Studies
P–Tokyo International University
P–Meikai University
P–Keisen Jogakuen University
P–Tokoha Gakuen University
P–Nagoya University of Foreign Studies
P–Nagoya Gakuin University
P–Nanzan University
P–Kyoto University of Foreign Studies
P–Shitennoji International Buddhist University
P–Tenri University

• British and American Culture
P–Seitoku University
P–Tokai Women's College
P–Soai University

• Burmese Studies
N–Osaka University of Foreign Studies

• Child and Culture
L–Yamaguchi Women's University
P–Shirayuri Women's College

• Children's Literature
P–Shirayuri Women's College
P–Baika Women's College

• Chinese Language
P–Tokyo International University
P–Kanda University of International Studies
P–Reitaku University
P–Kyorin University
P–Soka University
P–Daido Bunka University
P–Takushoku University
P–Kanagawa University
P–Hokuriku University
P–Shotoku Academy Gifu College of Education
P–Kyoto Sangyo University
P–Himeji Dokkyo University
P–Mukogawa Women's University

• Chinese Language and Literature
P–Bunkyo University
P–Obirin University

• Chinese Literature
L–Tokyo Metropolitan University
P–Kokushikan University
P–Daido Bunka University
P–Nisho –Gakusha University
P–Nihon University
P–Bukkyo University
P–Ritsumeikan University
P–Kansai University

• **Chinese Studies**
N–Tokyo University of Foreign Studies
N–Osaka University of Foreign Studies
L–Kobe City University of Foreign Studies
L–Kitakyushu University
P–Tokyo International University
P–Meikai University
P–Keio University
P–Nagoya University of Foreign Studies
P–Nagoya Gakuin University
P–Kyoto University of Foreign Studies
P–Tenri University

• **Christian Culture**
P–Seisen Women's College

• **Comparative Culture**
N–University of Tsukuba
P–Hokkaido Tokai University
P–Sophia University
P–Chubu University

• **Comparative Literature**
N–University of Tsukuba

• **Cultural History**
P–Seijo University
P–Doshisha University

• **Cultural Properties**
P–Nara University

• **Cultural Sciences**
P–Seikei University

• **Culture and Civilizatioin**
N–Niigata University

• **Culture and Society**
N–University of Wakayama

• **Culture Living**
P–Notre Dame Women's College

• **Culture Studies**
P–Atomi Gakuen Women's College
P–Tokyo Women's Christian University
P–Kinki University
P–Kobe College
P–Fukuoka University

• **Danish-Swedish Studies**
N–Osaka University of Foreign Studies

• **English**
P–Tohoku Gakuin University

• **English and American Language**
P–Kanda University of International Studies
P–Kyorin University
P–Takushoku University
P–Hokuriku University
P–Shotoku Academy Gifu College of Education
P–Kyoto Sangyo University
P–Kansai University of Foreign Studies
P–Baika Jo Gakuin College

• **English and American Language and literature**
N–Nara Women's University
P–Sapporo Gakuin University
P–Tokyo International University
P–Bunkyo University
P–Tokyo Women's Christian University
P–Japan Women's University
P–Doshisha Women's College of Liberal Arts
P–Otemon Gakuin University
P–Konan University

• **English and American Literature**
P–Fuji Women's College
P–Hirosaki Gakuin College
P–Morioka College
P–Iwaki Meisei University
P–Wayo Women's University
P–Aoyaman akuin University
P–Gakushuin University
P–Keio University
P–International Christian University
P–Komazawa University
P–Showa Women's University
P–Seikei University
P–Senshu University
P–Daito Bunka University
P–Tamagawa University
P–Chuo University
P–Toyo University
P–Musashino Women's College
P–Rikkyo University
P–Rissho University
P–Kanto Gakuin Universtiy
P–Sagami Women's University
P–Tsurumi University
P–Kanazawa Women's University
P–Koka Women's College
P–Ritsumeikan University
P–Osaka Shoin Women's College
P–Kinki University
P–Baika Women's College
P–Otemae College
P–Kobe College
P–Mukogawa Women's University
P–Koyasan University
P–Shujitsu Joshi University
P–Hiroshima Jogakuin College
P–Baika Jo Gakuin College
P–Tokushima Bunri University

• **English Cultures**
P–Fukuoka Jo Gakuin University

• **English Language**
P–Sapporo University
P–Dokkyo University
P–Reitaku University
P–Sophia University
P–Daito Bunka University
P–Kanagawa University
P–Osaka Gakuin University
P–Himeji Dokkyo University
P–Mukogawa Women's University
P–Seinan Gakuin University
P–Chikushi Jogakuen College
P–Fukuoka University

• **English Language and English and American Literature**
P–Sapporo Gakuin University
P–Ibaraki Christian College
P–Obirin University
P–Hosei University
P–Meisei University
P–St. Andrew's University
P–Shoin Women's University
P–Yasuda Women's University
P–Matsuyama University

• **English Language and Literature**
L–Osaka Women's University
L–Fukuoka Women's University
P–Ohu University
P–Kawamura Gakuen Women's University
P–University of the Sacred Heart
P–Taisho University
P–Tsuda College
P–Tokyo Kasei University
P–Waseda University
P–Chukyo University
P–Nagoya Women's University
P–Nanzan University
P–Kyoto Tachibana Women's University
P–Notre Dame Women's College
P–Eichi University
P–Konan Women's University
P–Notre Dame Seishin University
P–Hiroshima Shudo University
P–Shikoku Women's University

• **English Literature**
L–Gunma Prefectural Women's College
L–Tokyo Metropolitan University
L–Tsuru University
L–Aichi Prefectural University
L–Kochi Women's University
L–Kitakyushu University
L–Kumamoto Women's University
P–Hokusei Gakuen University
P–Hirosaki Gakuin College
P–Morioka College
P–Sophia University
P–Shirayuri Women's College
P–Seijo University
P–Seisen Women's College
P–Teikyo University
P–Tokai University
P–Nihon University
P–Meiji Gakuin University
P–Gifu Women's University
P–Aichi Shukutoku University
P–Doshisha University
P–Bukkyo University
P–Ryukoku University
P–Ohtani Women's University
P–Kansai University
P–Tezukayama Gakuin University
P–Kwansei Gakuin University
P–Kobe Kaisei Stella Maris College
P–Kobe Women's University
P–Shinwa Women's College
P–Hiroshima Bunkyo Women's College
P–Kyushu Women's University
P–Seinan Gakuin University
P–Kwassui Women's College
P–Shokei College

P–Beppu University
P–Kagoshima Women's College
P–Okinawa Kokusai University

• **English Studies**
N–Osaka University of Foreign Studies

• **European Culture**
P–Seijo University

• **European Studies**
P–Tokai University

• **Foreign Language**
P–Tamagawa University

• **Foreign Literature**
N–Ochanomizu University

• **French Language**
P–Tokyo International University
P–Dokkyo University
P–International Christian University
P–Sophia University
P–Kyoto Sangyo University
P–Fukuoka University

• **French Language and Literature**
P–Ohu University
P–Nanzan University
P–Eichi University
P–Konan Women's University

• **French Literature**
L–Tokyo Metropolitan University
P–Aoyama Gakuin University
P–Gakushuin University
P–Keio University
P–Sophia University
P–Shirayuri Women's College
P–Chuo University
P–Meiji Gakuin University
P–Rikkyo University
P–Kansai University
P–Kwansei Gakuin University
P–Kobe Kaisei Stella Maris College
P–Mukogawa Women's University

• **French Studies**
N–Tokyo University of Foreign Studies
N–Osaka University of Foreign Studies
L–Aichi Prefectural University
P–Nagoya University of Foreign Studies
P–Kyoto University of Foreign Studies
P–Tenri University

• **General Culture**
N–Yamaguchi University
N–Saga University

• **German Language**
P–Tokyo International University
P–Dokkyo University
P–Reitaku University
P–Keio University
P–Sophia University
P–Kyoto Sangyo University
P–Osaka Gakuin University
P–Himeji Dokkyo University
P–Fukuoka University

• **German Language and Literature**
P–Nanzan University

• **German Literature**
L–Tokyo Metropolitan University
P–Gakushuin University
P–Sophia University
P–Chuo University
P–Nihon University
P–Rikkyo University
P–Kansai University
P–Kwansei Gakuin University
P–Konan University
P–Mukogawa Women's University

• **German Studies**
N–Tokyo University of Foreign Studies
N–Osaka University of Foreign Studies
P–Kyoto University of Foreign Studies
P–Tenri University

• **Hindi- Urdu Studies**
N–Osaka University of Foreign Studies

• **Human Culture**
P–Kobe Gakuin University

• **Indochinese Language**
N–Tokyo University of Foreign Studies

• **Indonesian- Malaysian Studies**
N–Tokyo University of Foreign Studies

• **Indonesian Studies**
P–Tenri University

• **Indonesian- Filipino Studies**
N–Osaka University of Foreign Studies

• **Indo- Pakistani Studies**
N–Tokyo University of Foreign Studies

• **Intercultural Studies**
P–Hokkaido Tokai University
P–Kyoritsu Women's University
P–Tsuda College
P–Teikyo University
P–Nihon University
P–Ferris Women's College
P–Toyama University of International Studies
P–Aichi Gakuin University
P–Tezukayama Gakuin University
P–St. Andrew's University

• **International Cultures**
P–Daido Bunka University
P–Seinan Gakuin University

• **International Education and Cultures**
N–Tokyo Gakugei University

• **International Languages and Cultures**
L–Shizuoka Prefectural University
P–Setsunan University

• **Italian Studies**
N–Tokyo University of Foreign Studies
N–Osaka University of Foreign Studies

• **Japanese and Chinese Literature**
L–Kyoto Prefectural University

• **Japanese Culture**
P–Tokyo International University
P–Seitoku University
P–Tokyo Kasei Gakuin University
P–Musashi University
P–Aichi Gakuin University
P–Soai University
P–Fukuoka JoGakuin University

• **Japanese Language**
N–Tohoku University
P–Tokyo International University
P–Reitaku University
P–Kyorin University
P–International Christian University
P–Shotoku Academy Gifu College of Education
P–Himeji Dokkyo University
P–Mukogawa Women's University

• **Japanese Language and Culture**
N–University of Tsukuba
P–Nanzan University
P–Kansai University of Foreign Studies

• **Japanese Language and Literature**
N–Nara Women's University
L–Osaka Women's University
P–Ohu University
P–Bunkyo University
P–Gakushuin University
P–Kokushikan University
P–University of the Sacred Heart
P–Soka University
P–Tokyo Women's Christian University
P–Japan Women's University
P–Waseda University
P–Nanzan University
P–Doshisha Women's College of Liberal Arts
P–Konan Women's University
P–Tenri University
P–Notre Dame Seishin University
P–Chikushi Jogakuen College
P–Fukuoka University

• **Japanese Literature**
N–Ochanomizu University
L–Gunma Prefectural Women's College
L–Tokyo Metropolitan University
L–Tsuru University
L–Aichi Prefectural University
L–Hiroshima Women's University
L–Yamaguchi Women's University
L–Kochi Women's University
L–Kitakyushu University
L–Fukuoka Women's University
L–Kumamoto Women's University
P–Fuji Women's College
P–Hirosaki Gakuin College
P–Morioka College
P–Miyagi Gakuin Women's College
P–Iwaki Meisei University

P–Wayo Women's University
P–Aoyama Gakuin University
P–Otsuma Women's University
P–Keio University
P–Komazawa University
P–Jissen Women's University
P–Sophia University
P–Showa Women's University
P–Shirayuri Women's College
P–Seikei University
P–Seijo University
P–Seisen Women's College
P–Senshu University
P–Taisho University
P–Daido Bunka University
P–Chuo University
P–Teikyo University
P–Tokai University
P–Toyo University
P–Nisho– Gakusha University
P–Nihon University
P–Hosei University
P–Musashino Women's College
P–Rikkyo University
P–Rissho University
P–Sagami Women's University
P–Tsurumi University
P–Ferris Women's College
P–Kanazawa Women's University
P–Gifu Women's University
P–Aichi Shukutoku University
P–Kinjo Gakuin University
P–Sugiyama Jogakuen University
P–Chukyo University
P–Doho University
P–Nagoya Women's University
P–Kogakkan University
P–Kyoto Women's University
P–Kyoto Tachibana Women's University
P–Koka Women's College
P–Doshisha University
P–Hanazono College
P–Bukkyo University
P–Ritsumeikan University
P–Ryukoku University
P–Osaka Shoin Women's College
P–Ohtani Women's University
P–Kansai University
P–Kinki University
P–Tezukayama Gakuin University
P–Baika Women's College
P–Kwansei Gakuin University
P–Konan University
P–Kobe Women's University
P–Shoin Women's University
P–Shinwa Women's College
P–Sonoda Gakuen Women's College
P–Mukogawa Women's University
P–Nara University
P–Koyasan University
P–Shujitsu Joshi University
P–Hiroshima Jogakuin College
P–Hiroshima Bunkyo Women's College
P–Yasuda Women's University
P–Baika JoGakuin College
P–Shikoku Women's University
P–Tokushima Bunri University
P–Kyushu Women's University
P–Kwassui Women's College
P–Shokei College
P–Beppu University
P–Kagoshima Women's College
P–Okinawa Kokusai University

• Japanese Studies

N–Tokyo University of Foreign Studies
N–Osaka University
N–Osaka University of Foreign Studies
P–Meikai University
P–Keisen Jogakuen University
P–Sophia University
P–Shitennoji International Buddhist University

• Korean Language

P–Kanda University of International Studies

• Korean Studies

N–Tokyo University of Foreign Studies
N–Osaka University of Foreign Studies
P–Tenri University

• Language and Culture

P–Tokyo Women's Christian University

• Language and Literature

N–The University of Tokyo

• Linguistics

N–University of Tsukuba
P–International Christian University
P–Kyoto Sangyo University

• Linguistics and Literature

N–Toyama University
N–Yamaguchi University

• Linguistics Science

P–Tohoku Gakuin University

• Literary Art

P–Nihon University
P–Osaka University of Arts

• Literature

N–Hokkaido University
N–Tohoku University
N–Yamagata University
N–Chiba University
N–Kanazawa University
N–Nagoya University
N–Kyoto University
N–Osaka University
N–Kobe University
N–Shimane University
N–Okayama University
N–Hiroshima University
N–Ehime University
N–Oita University
N–Kyushu University
N–Nagasaki University
N–Kumamoto University
N–University of the Ryukyus
P–Kyoritsu Women's University
P–Keio University
P–Kokugakuin University
P–Meiji University
P–Wako University
P–Waseda University
P–Aichi University
P–Otani University
P–Kinki University

• Liberal Arts

N–The University of Tokyo

• Modern Thought

N–University of Tsukuba

• Mongolian Studies

N–Tokyo University of Foreign Studies
N–Osaka University of Foreign Studies

• Nordic Studies

P–Tokai University

• Persian Studies

N–Tokyo University of Foreign Studies
N–Osaka University of Foreign Studies

• Portuguese– Brazilian Studies

N–Tokyo University of Foreign Studies
N–Osaka University of Foreign Studies
P–Kyoto University of Foreign Studies

• Portuguese Language

P–Sophia University

• Russian Language

P–Sapporo University
P–Tokyo International University
P–Sophia University
P–Soka University

• Russian Studies

N–Tokyo University of Foreign Studies
N–Osaka University of Foreign Studies
L–Kobe City University of Foreign Studies
P–Tokyo International University
P–Tenri University

• Scandinavian Literature

P–Tokai University

• Spanish Language

P–Tokyo International University
P–Kanda University of International Studies
P–Sophia University
P–Takushoku University
P–Kanagawa University
P–Kansai University of Foreign Studies

• Spanish Language and Literature

P–Seisen Women's College
P–Eichi University

• Spanish Studies

N–Tokyo University of Foreign Studies
N–Osaka University of Foreign Studies
L–Aichi Prefectural University
L–Kobe City University of Foreign Studies
P–Tokoha Gakuen University
P–Nanzan University
P–Kyoto University of Foreign Studies
P–Tenri University

• Thai–Vietnamese Studies

N–Osaka University of Foreign Studies

• Western Culture
P–Musashi University

• Western Literature
L–Kyoto Prefectural University
L–Osaka City University

Materials Science and Engineering

• Fine Materials Engineering
N–Shinshu University

• Material Chemistry
P–Ryukoku University

• Material and Chemical Engineering
N–Niigata University

• Material Engineering
N–University of Tsukuba
N–Shinshu University
N–University of Tottori
N–Ehime University
P–Science University of Tokyo
P–Waseda University
P–Shonan Institute of Technology
P–Toin University of Yokohama
P–The Nishi–Tokyo University

• Material Physics
N–Osaka University

• Material Science and Processing
N–Osaka University

• Materials Creation Chemistry
N–Shinshu University

• Materials Engineering and Applied Chemistry
N–Akita University

• Materials Processing
N–Tohoku University

• Materials Processing Engineering
N–Nagoya University

• Material Science
N–Hiroshima University
L–Himeji Institute of Technology
P–Iwaki Meisei University

• Materials Science and Engineering
N–Nagoya Institute of Technology
N–Osaka University
N–Kyushu University
N–Nagasaki University

• Materials Science and Resource Engineering
N–Kumamoto University

• Materials Science and Technology
N–Nagaoka University of Technology
N–Toyama University

• Material Systems Engineering
N–Tokyo University of Agriculture and Technology

• Metallurgical Engineering
P–Tokai University

• Molecular Materials Engineering
N–Mie University

• Organic and Polymeric Materials
N–Tokyo Institute of Technology

• Polymer Material Engineering
N–Yamagata University

• Resources Engineering
N–Tohoku University

• Functional Polymer Science
N–Shinshu University

• Inorganic Materials
N–Tokyo Institute of Technology

• Material Science and Chemical Engineering
N–Yokohama National University

• Material Science and Engineering
N–Yamagata University
N–Fukui University
N–Nagoya University
P–Teikyo University
P–Kansai University

• Materials Science
N–Tohoku University
N–The University of Tokyo
N–Toyohashi University of Technology
P–Kanagawa University

• Materials Science Engineering
N–Muroran Institute of Technology

Mathematics

• Applied Mathematics
L–Osaka Women's University
P–Science University of Tokyo
P–Nihon University
P–Konan University
P–Okayama University of Science
P–Fukuoka University

• Applied Mathematics and Physics
N–Kyoto University

• Mathematics
N–Hokkaido University
N–Hirosaki University
N–Tohoku University
N–Yamagata University
N–Ibaraki University
N–University of Tsukuba
N–Saitama University
N–Chiba University
N–The University of Tokyo
N–Tokyo Institute of Technology
N–Ochanomizu University
N–Niigata University
N–Toyama University
N–Kanazawa University
N–Shinshu University
N–Shizuoka University
N–Nagoya University
N–Kyoto University
N–Osaka University
N–Kobe University
N–Nara Women's University
N–Shimane University
N–Okayama University
N–Hiroshima University
N–Yamaguchi University
N–Ehime University
N–Oita University
N–Kyushu University
N–Saga University
N–Kumamoto University
N–Miyazaki University
N–Kagoshima University
N–University of the Ryukyus
L–Tokyo Metropolitan University
L–Osaka City University
P–Josai University
P–Gakushuin University
P–Keio University
P–International Christian University
P–Sophia University
P–Chuo University
P–Tsuda College
P–Tokai University
P–Tokyo Women's Christian University
P–Tokyo Denki University
P–Science University of Tokyo
P–Nihon University
P–Japan Women's University
P–Meiji University
P–Rikkyo University
P–Waseda University
P–Meijo University
P–Kyoto Sangyo University
P–Kwansei Gakuin University

• Mathematical Engineering and Instrumentation Physics
N–The University of Tokyo

• Mathematics and Computer Science
P–Tokai University

• Mathematics and Informatics
P–Ryukoku University

• Mathematics and Physics
P–Ritsumeikan University
P–Kinki University

Mechanical Engineering

• Applied Mechanical Engineering
N–Kitami Institute of Technology
N–Tokyo University of Agriculture and Tech-

nology

• **Civil, Mechanical and Control Engineering**
N–Kyushu Institute of Technology

• **Electronic Mechanical Engineering**
N–Tokyo University of Marcantile Marine
N–Nagoya University
P–Fukui Institute of Technology
P–Osaka Electro–Commucation University
P–Tokushima Bunri University
P–Fukuoka Institute of Technology

• **Engineering Mechanics**
N–University of Tsukuba

• **Functional Machinery and Mechanics**
N–Shinshu University

• **Fundamental Mechanical Engineering**
N–Tokyo University of Agriculture and Technology
P–Okayama University of Science

• **Industrial Mechanical Engineering**
P–Tokyo Denki University
P–Okayama University of Science

• **Instrument and Control Engineering**
P–Hosei University

• **Instrumentation Engineering**
N–Kobe University
P–Keio University

• **Mechanical and Control Engineering**
N–The University of Electro–Communications
P–Tokyo engineering University

• **Mechanical and System Engineering**
N–Kyoto Institute of Technology

• **Mechanical Engineering**
N–Hokkaido University
N–Kitami Institute of Technology
N–Iwate University
N–Tohoku University
N–Akita University
N–Yamagata University
N–Ibaraki University
N–Gunma University
N–Saitama University
N–Chiba University
N–The University of Tokyo
N–Tokyo Institute of Technology
N–Tokyo University of Marcantile Marine
N–Niigata University
N–Fukui University
N–Shinshu University
N–Gifu University
N–Shizuoka University
N–Nagoya University
N–Nagoya Institute of Technology
N–Mie University
N–Kyoto University
N–Osaka University
N–Kobe University
N–University of Tottori
N–Okayama University
N–Hiroshima University
N–Yamaguchi University
N–The University of Tokushima
N–Ehime University
N–Kyushu University
N–Saga University
N–Kumamoto University
N–Oita University
N–Miyazaki University
N–Kagoshima University
N–University of the Ryukyus
L–Tokyo Metropolitan University
L–Osaka City University
L–University of Osaka Prefecture
L–Himeji Institute of Technology
P–Hokkaido Institute of Technology
P–Hachinohe Institute of Technology
P–Ishinomaki Senshu University
P–Tohoku Gakuin University
P–Iwaki Meisei University
P–Ashikaga Institute of Technology
P–Saitama Institute of Technology
P–Nippon Institute of Technology
P–Chiba Institute of Technology
P–Aoyama Gakuin University
P–Keio University
P–Kogakuin University
P–Kokushikan University
P–Shibaura Institute of Technology
P–Sophia University
P–Seikei University
P–Tamagawa University
P–Tokyo Denki University
P–Science University of Tokyo
P–Toyo University
P–Nihon University
P–Hosei University
P–Musashi Institute of Techonology
P–Meiji University
P–Meisei University
P–Waseda University
P–Kanagawa University
P–Kanagawa Institute of Technology
P–Kanto Gakuin Universtiy
P–Shonan Institute of Technology
P–Kanazawa Institute of Technology
P–Fukui Institute of Technology
P–Aichi Institute of Technology
P–Daido Institute of Technology
P–Chubu University
P–Meijo University
P–Doshisha University
P–Ritsumeikan University
P–Osaka Institute of Technology
P–Osaka Sangyo University
P–Kansai University
P–Kinki University
P–Setsunan University
P–Okayama University of Science
P–Hiroshima Institute of Technology
P–The Hiroshima–Denki Institute of Technology
P–The University of East Asia
P–Kyushu Kyoritsu University
P–Kyushu Sangyo University
P–Kurume Institute of Technology
P–Nishinippon Institute of Technology
P–Fukuoka University
P–Nagasaki Institute of Applied Sciences
P–Kyushu Tokai University
P–The Kumamoto Institute of Technology
P–Nippon Bunri University
P–Dai Ichi University, College of Technology

• **Mechanical Engineering and Material Science**
N–Yokohama National University
N–Mie University

• **Mechanical Engineering for Computer–Controlled Machinery**
N–Osaka University

• **Mechanical Engineering for Industrial Machinery and Systems**
N–Osaka University

• **Mechanical Engineering for Power**
N–Kyushu University

• **Mechanical Engineering for Production**
N–Akita University
N–The University of Tokyo
N–Tokyo Institute of Technology
N–Kyushu University

• **Mechanical Engineering Science**
N–Tokyo Institute of Technology

• **Mechanical Systems Engineering**
N–Muroran Institute of Technology
N–Yamagata University
N–Utsunomiya University
N–Tokyo University of Agriculture and Technology
N–Nagaoka University of Technology
N–Toyama University
N–Kanazawa University
N–Yamanashi University
N–Kyushu Institute of Technology
N–Nagasaki University
L–Tokyo Metropolitan Institute of Technology
L–Toyama Prefectural University
P–Tokushoku University
P–Kanagawa Institute of Technology
P–Kanazawa Institute of Technology
P–Toyota Technological Institute
P–Ryukoku University
P–Kansai University

• **Mechanical and Precision System**
P–Teikyo University

• **Planning and Production Engineering**
N–Nagaoka University of Technology

• **Power Mechanical Engineering**
P–Tokai University

• **Precision Engineering**

N–Hokkaido University
N–Tohoku University
N–Yamagata University
N–Shinshu University
N–Shizuoka University
N–Kyoto University
N–Osaka University
P–Chiba Institute of Technology
P–Chuo University
P–Teikyo University
P–Tokai University
P–Tokyo Denki University
P–Meiji University
P–Osaka Electro–Commucation University

• Precision Mechanical Engineering
P–Nihon University

• Precision Machinery Engineering
N–The University of Tokyo

• Production Machinery Engineering
N–Osaka University
N–Kobe University
N–Yamaguchi University
N–Ehime University
N–Saga University
L–Himeji Institute of Technology
P–Kogakuin University
P–Tokai University
P–Tokyo Denki University

• Production Systems Engineering
N–Shinshu University
N–Toyohashi University of Technology

• Power Systems Engineering
N–Kobe University of Marcantile Marine

Medicine

• Acupuncture and Moxibustion
P–Meiji College of Oriental Medicine

• Clinical Laboratory Science
N–Kanazawa University

• Medical Technology
P–Kyorin University
P–Fujita–Gakuen Health Unive University

• Medicine
N–Hokkaido University
N–Asahikawa Medical College
N–Hirosaki University
N–Tohoku University
N–Akita University
N–Yamagata University
N–University of Tsukuba
N–Gunma University
N–Chiba University
N–The University of Tokyo
N–Tokyo Medical and Dental University
N–Niigata University
N–Toyama Medical and Pharmaceutical University
N–Kanazawa University
N–Fukui Medical School
N–Yamanashi Medical College
N–Shinshu University
N–Gifu University
N–Hamamatsu University School of Medicine
N–Nagoya University
N–Mie University
N–Shiga University of Medical Science
N–Kyoto University
N–Osaka University
N–Kobe University
N–University of Tottori
N–Shimane Medical University
N–Okayama University
N–Hiroshima University
N–Yamaguchi University
N–The University of Tokushima
N–Kagawa Medical School
N–Ehime University
N–Kochi Medical School
N–Kyushu University
N–Saga Medical School
N–Nagasaki University
N–Kumamoto University
N–Oita Medical College
N–Miyazaki Medical College
N–Kagoshima University
N–University of the Ryukyus
L–Sapporo Medical College
L–Fukushima Medical College
L–Yokohama City University
L–Nagoya City University
L–Kyoto Prefectural University of Medicine
L–Osaka City University
L–Nara Medical University
L–Wakayama Medical College
P–Iwate Medical University
P–Jichi Medical School
P–Dokkyo University School of Medicine
P–Saitama Medical College
P–Kitasato University
P–Kyorin University
P–Keio University
P–Juntendo University
P–Showa University
P–Teikyo University
P–Tokai University
P–Tokyo Medical College
P–Jikei University School of Medicine
P–Tokyo Women's Medical College
P–Toho University
P–Nihon University
P–Nippon Medical School
P–St. Marianna University School of Med
P–Kanazawa Medical University
P–Aichi Medical University
P–Fujita–Gakuen Health Unive University
P–Osaka Medical College
P–Kansai Medical University
P–Kinki University
P–Hyogo College of Medicine
P–Kawasaki Medical School
P–Kurume University
P–University of Occupational and Environmental Health, Japan
P–Fukuoka University

• Medical Science
N–Yamagata University

• Radiological Technology
N–Kanazawa University

Metal Engineering

• Metal Engineering
N–Iwate University
L–University of Osaka Prefecture
P–Chiba Institute of Technology
P–Kinki University

• Metal Engineering for Materials
N–Akita University

• Metallurgical Engineering
N–Hokkaido University
P–Shibaura Institute of Technology

• Metallurgy
N–Tohoku University
N–Akita University
N–The University of Tokyo
N–Kyoto University

• Metallurgy Engineering
N–Tokyo Institute of Technology

• Metal Material Engineering
L–Himeji Institute of Technology
P–Tokai University

• Metal Science and Technology
N–Kyoto University

• Welding and Production Engineering
N–Osaka University

Music

• Conducting
N–Tokyo National University of Fine Arts and Music
P–Toho Gakuen School of Music

• Instrumental Music
N–Tokyo National University of Fine Arts and Music
L–Okinawa Prefectural College of Arts
P–Ueno Gakuen College
P–Kunitachi College of Music
P–Tokyo College of Music
P–Toho Gakuen School of Music
P–Musashino Academia Musicae
P–Showa Academia Musicae
P–Senzoku Gakuen College of Music Academy
P–Ferris Women's College
P–Nagoya College of Music
P–Nagoya University of the Arts
P–Osaka College of Music
P–Osaka University of Arts
P–Soai University
P–Kobe College
P–Mukogawa Women's University

P–Elisabeth University of Music

• Keyboard Instruments
L–Aichi Prefectural University of Fine Arts

• Japanese Music
N–Tokyo National University of Fine Arts and Music
L–Okinawa Prefectural College of Arts

• Music
L–Kyoto City University of Arts
P–Miyagi Gakuin Women's College
P–Toho College of Music
P–Ueno Gakuen College
P–Nihon University
P–Doshisha Women's College of Liberal Arts
P–Osaka University of Arts
P–Kobe College
P–Sakuyo College of Music
P–Elisabeth University of Music
P–Tokushima Bunri University

• Musical Composition
N–Tokyo National University of Fine Arts and Music
L–Aichi Prefectural University of Fine
P–Kunitachi College of Music
P–Toho Gakuen School of Music
P–Musashino Academia Musicae
P–Showa Academia Musicae
P–Senzoku Gakuen College of Music Academy
P–Nagoya College of Music
P–Osaka College of Music
P–Soai University

• Musicology
N–Tokyo National University of Fine Arts and Music
L–Okinawa Prefectural College of Arts
P–Kunitachi College of Music
P–International Christian University
P–Toho Gakuen School of Music
P–Musashino Academia Musicae
P–Ferris Women's College

• Percussions
L–Aichi Prefectural University of Fine

• Religious Music
P–Elisabeth University of Music

• Vocal and Instrumental Music
P–Osaka University of Arts

• Vocal Music
N–Tokyo National University of Fine Arts and Music
L–Aichi Prefectural University of Fine
L–Okinawa Prefectural College of Arts
P–Ueno Gakuen College
P–Kunitachi College of Music
P–Tokyo College of Music
P–Toho Gakuen School of Music
P–Musashino Academia Musicae
P–Showa Academia Musicae
P–Senzoku Gakuen College of Music Academy
P–Ferris Women's College
P–Nagoya College of Music
P–Nagoya University of the Arts
P–Osaka College of Music
P–Soai University
P–Mukogawa Women's University
P–Elisabeth University of Music

• Winds
L–Aichi Prefectural University of Fine Arts

Natural Science (Miscellaneous)

• Applied Science
P–Tokyo University of Art and Design
P–Tokyo Denki University
P–Fukui Institute of Technology
P–Okayama University of Science

• Fundamental Science
P–Ishinomaki Senshu University
P–Iwaki Meisei University

• Integrated Science
N–Kanazawa University
N–Yamanashi University
N–Aichi University of Education
N–Kyoto University of Education
N–University of Tottori
N–Hiroshima University
N–The University of Tokushima
N–Kagawa University
N–University of the Ryukyus
L–University of Osaka Prefecture

• Natural Science
N–University of Tsukuba
N–Yokohama National University
L–Yokohama City University
L–Osaka Women's University
P–International Christian University

Nursing

• Midwifery
N–Kanazawa University

• Nursing
N–Chiba University
N–Kanazawa University
N–Kagoshima University
L–Kochi Women's University
P–Kitasato University
P–St. Luke's College of Nursing
P–The Japanese Red Cross College of Nursing
P–Fujita–Gakuen Health University

• Occupational Theraphy
N–Kanazawa University

• Physical Theraphy
N–Kanazawa University

Nutrition

• Administrative Dietitian
P–Kobe Women's University
P–Shikoku Women's University

• Nutrition
N–The University of Tokushima
L–Yamaguchi Women's University
P–Kagawa Nutrition College
P–Kyoritsu Women's University
P–Tokyo Kasei University
P–Tokyo University of Agriculture
P–Sagami Women's University
P–Tokoha–Gakuen Hamamatsu University
P–Doshisha Women's College of Liberal Arts
P–Osaka Shoin Women's College
P–Koshien University
P–Kobe Gakuin University
P–Kobe College
P–Mukogawa Women's University

• Nutrition Administrator Training
P–Miyagi Gakuin Women's College
P–Wayo Women's University
P–Otsuma Women's University
P–Kyoritsu Women's University
P–Jissen Women's University
P–Showa Women's University
P–Tokyo Kasei University
P–Tokyo Kasei Gakuin University
P–Kamakura Women's Universtiy
P–Sagami Women's University
P–Sugiyama Jogakuen University
P–Doshisha Women's College of Liberal Arts
P–Mukogawa Women's University
P–Notre Dame Seishin University
P–Tokushima Bunri University
P–Kyushu Women's University
P–Nishikyushu University

• Nutrition and Food
P–Kyushu Women's University

• Nutritional Science
L–Shizuoka Prefectural University
P–Nagoya Women's University

• Radiological Technology
P–Fujita–Gakuen Health Unive University

Pharmaceutical Sciences

• Biological Pharmacy
P–Hokkaido Institute of Pharmaceutical Sciences
P–Kyoritsu College of Pharmacy
P–Showa University
P–Showa College of Pharmaceutical Sciences
P–Teikyo University
P–Kyoto Pharmaceutical University
P–Mukogawa Women's University

• Biopharmacy
P–Tokyo University of Agriculture

P–Nihon University
P–Meiji College of Pharmacy
P–Kobe Gakuin University
P–Fukuyama University
P–Daiichi College of Pharmaceutical Sciences

• Hygienic Pharmaceutical Science
P–Higashi Nippon Gakuen University
P–Tohoku College of Pharmacy
P–Tokyo College of Pharmacy
P–Toho University
P–Hoshi University
P–Niigata College of Pharmacy
P–Hokuriku University
P–Setsunan University
P–Kobe Women's College of Pharmacy
P–Tokushima Bunri University

• Manufacturing Pharmacy
L–Gifu Pharmaceutical University

• Pharmaceutical Chemistry
N–Hokkaido University
N–The University of Tokyo
N–Kanazawa University
N–Kyoto University
N–Osaka University
N–The University of Tokushima
P–Tohoku College of Pharmacy
P–Meiji College of Pharmacy
P–Kyoto Pharmaceutical University
P–Fukuoka University

• Pharmaceutical Science
N–Hokkaido University
N–Tohoku University
N–Chiba University
N–The University of Tokyo
N–Toyama Medical and Pharmaceutical University
N–Kanazawa University
N–Kyoto University
N–Okayama University
N–Hiroshima University
N–The University of Tokushima
N–Kyushu University
N–Nagasaki University
N–Kumamoto University
L–Shizuoka Prefectural University
L–Nagoya City University
P–Higashi Nippon Gakuen University
P–Hokkaido Institute of Pharmaceutical Sciences
P–Tohoku College of Pharmacy
P–Josai University
P–Kitasato University
P–Kyoritsu College of Pharmacy
P–Showa University
P–Showa College of Pharmaceutical Sciences
P–Teikyo University
P–Tokyo College of Pharmacy
P–Science University of Tokyo
P–Toho University
P–Nippon University
P–Hoshi University
P–Meiji College of Pharmacy
P–Niigata College of Pharmacy
P–Hokuriku University
P–Meijo University
P–Kyoto Pharmaceutical University
P–Osaka University of Pharmaceutical Sciences
P–Kinki University
P–Setsunan University
P–Kobe Gakuin University
P–Kobe Women's College of Pharmacy
P–Mukogawa Women's University
P–Tokushima Bunri University
P–Daiichi College of Pharmaceutical Sciences
P–Fukuoka University

• Pharmaceutical Technochemistry
N–The University of Tokyo
N–Kyushu University

• Pharmaceutical Technology
N–Tohoku University
N–Okayama University
L–Nagoya City University
P–Kitasato University
P–Science University of Tokyo
P–Meijo University
P–Osaka University of Pharmaceutical Sciences

• Pharmaceutics
L–Shizuoka Prefectural University

• Pharmacy
N–Osaka University
L–Shizuoka Prefectural University
P–Nihon University
P–Fukuyama University

• Public Health Pharmacy
L–Gifu Pharmaceutical University

Philosophy

• Chinese Philosophy and Literature
P–Toyo University

• Ethics
P–Keio University

• Indian Philosophy
P–Toyo University

• Philosophy
N–Hokkaido University
N–Tohoku University
N–University of Tsukuba
N–The University of Tokyo
N–Ochanomizu University
N–Nagoya University
N–Kyoto University
N–Osaka University
N–Kobe University
N–Okayama University
N–Hiroshima University
N–Kyushu University
N–Kumamoto University
L–Tokyo Metropolitan University
L–Osaka City University
P–Gakushuin University
P–Keio University
P–Kokugakuin University
P–International Christian University
P–Sophia University
P–University of the Sacred Heart
P–Taisho University
P–Chuo University
P–Tokyo Women's Christian University
P–Toyo University
P–Nihon University
P–Hosei University
P–Rissho University
P–Waseda University
P–Aichi University
P–Nanzan University
P–Otani University
P–Doshisha University
P–Ritsumeikan University
P–Ryukoku University
P–Kansai University
P–Kwansei Gakuin University
P–Koyasan University

• Philosophy and Behavioral Sciences
N–Niigata University

Physical Education

• Group Sports
N–University of Tsukuba

• Individual Sports
N–University of Tsukuba

• Judo and Kendo
N–National Institute of Fitness and Sports in Kanoya
P–International Budo University
P–Kokushikan University
P–Tokai University
P–Nippon College of Physical Education
P–Chukyo University

• Martial Arts
N–University of Tsukuba

• Physical and Health Education
N–The University of Tokyo

• Physical Education
N–University of Tsukuba
N–Gunma University
P–Sendai College
P–International Budo University
P–Kokushikan University
P–Juntendo University
P–Tokai University
P–Tokyo Women's College of Physical Education
P–Nihon University
P–Japan Women's College of Physial Education
P–Nippon College of Physical Education
P–Chukyo University
P–Chukyo Women's University
P–Osaka College of Physical Education
P–Mukogawa Women's University

P–Tenri University
P–Fukuoka University

• Physical Education and Sports Science

N–National Institute of Fitness and Sports in Kanoya
P–Mukogawa Women's University

• Physical Recreation

P–Tokai University
P–Nippon College of Physical Education

• Sports Science

N–Kanazawa University
P–Waseda University
P–Mukogawa Women's University

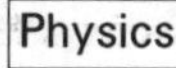

Physics

• Applied Nuclear Engineering

N–Kyushu University

• Applied Physics

N–Hokkaido University
N–Tohoku University
N–University of Tsukuba
N–The University of Tokyo
N–Tokyo Institute of Technology
N–Tokyo University of Agriculture and technology
N–Toyama University
N–Fukui University
N–Nagoya University
N–Osaka University
L–Osaka City University
P–Tohoku Gakuin University
P–Seikei University
P–Tokai University
P–Science University of Tokyo
P–Nihon University
P–Waseda University
P–Konan University
P–Okayama University of Science
P–Fukuoka University

• Engineering Physics

P–Chubu University

• Nuclear Engineering

N–Hokkaido University
N–Tohoku University
N–The University of Tokyo
N–Nagoya University
N–Kyoto University
N–Osaka University
P–Tokai University
P–Kinki University

• Physics

N–Hokkaido University
N–Hirosaki University
N–Tohoku University
N–Yamagata University
N–Ibaraki University
N–University of Tsukuba
N–Saitama University
N–Chiba University
N–The University of Tokyo
N–Tokyo Institute of Technology
N–Ochanomizu University
N–Niigata University
N–Toyama University
N–Kanazawa University
N–Shinshu University
N–Shizuoka University
N–Nagoya University
N–Kyoto University
N–Osaka University
N–Kobe University
N–Nara Women's University
N–Shimane University
N–Okayama University
N–Hiroshima University
N–Yamaguchi University
N–Ehime University
N–Oita University
N–Kyushu University
N–Saga University
N–Kumamoto University
N–Kagoshima University
N–University of the Ryukyus
L–Tokyo Metropolitan University
L–Osaka City University
P–Aoyama Gakuin University
P–Gakushuin University
P–Keio University
P–Chuo University
P–Tokai University
P–Science University of Tokyo
P–Toho University
P–Nihon University
P–Japan Women's University
P–Meiji University
P–Meisei University
P–Rikkyo University
P–Waseda University
P–Kyoto Sangyo University
P–Kwansei Gakuin University
P–Konan University

Political Science

• International Politics

P–Aoyama Gakuin University
P–International Christian University
P–Hiroshima Shudo University

• Political Science

N–University of Tsukuba
N–The University of Tokyo
N–Nagoya University
L–Tokyo Metropolitan University
L–Kitakyushu University
P–Gakushuin University
P–Keio University
P–International Christian University
P–Kokushikan University
P–Komazawa University
P–Seikei University
P–Daido Bunka University
P–Takushoku University
P–Chuo University
P–Tokai University
P–Hosei University
P–Meiji University
P–Meiji Gakuin University
P–Waseda University
P–Doshisha University
P–Kansai University
P–Kwansei Gakuin University

• Political Science and Economics

P–Seigakuin University
P–Yachio International University
P–Nihon University
P–Matsusaka University

Psychology

• Industrial Psychology

P–Tokyo International University
P–Kansai University

• Psychology

N–The University of Tokyo
L–Tokyo Metropolitan University
P–Tokiwa University
P–Tokyo International University
P–Kawamura Gakuen Women's University
P–Gakushuin University
P–Keio University
P–International Christian University
P–Sophia University
P–Chuo University
P–Teikyo University
P–Tokyo Women's Christian University
P–Nihon University
P–Japan Women's University
P–Meiji Gakuin University
P–Meisei University
P–Rikkyo University
P–Wako University
P–Aichi Gakuin University
P–Sugiyama Jogakuen University
P–Chukyo University
P–Doshisha University
P–Ritsumeikan University
P–Otemon Gakuin University
P–Kwansei Gakuin University
P–Hiroshima Shudo University

• Welfare Psychology

P–Tohoku Fukushi University

Religion

• Buddhism

P–Komazawa University
P–Taisho University
P–Rissho University
P–Doho University
P–Otani University
P–Shuchiin College
P–Hanazono College
P–Bukkyo University
P–Ryukoku University
P–Shitennoji International Buddhist University
P–Koyasan University

• Buddhistic History
P–Ryukoku University

• Christianity
P–Ibaraki Christian College
P–International Christian University
P–Tokyo Christian University
P–Tokyo Union Theological Seminary
P–Japan Lutheram Theological College
P–Rikkyo University
P–Doshisha University
P–Eichi University
P–Kwansei Gakuin University

• Christian Studies
P–Tohoku Gakuin University

• Esoteric Buddhism
P–Koyasan University

• Nichiren Buddhism
P–Rissho University

• Religion
P–Aichi Gakuin University
P–Tenri University

• Shin Buddhism
P–Ryukoku University

• Shinto
P–Kokugakuin University
P–Kogakkan University

• Theology
P–Sophia University
P–Nanzan University
P–Seinan Gakuin University

• True Pure Land Buddhism
P–Otani University

• Zen
P–Komazawa University

Social Sciences (Miscellaneous)

• Administrations of Human Organization
P–Tokiwa University

• Anthropology
P–International Christian University
P–Nanzan University

• Behavioral Science
N–Hokkaido University
N–Chiba University
N–Kanazawa University

• Policy Management
P–Keio University

• Regional Science
N–Kumamoto University

• Social Problems and Social Policy
N–Hitotsubashi University

• Social Sciences
N–Tohoku University
N–Ibaraki University
N–University of Tsukuba
N–Mie University
P–Kyorin University
P–International Christian University
P–Waseda University
P–Toyo Eiwa Women's University
P–Ritsumeikan University

• Social Theory
N–Hitotsubashi University

Social Welfare

• Child Welfare
P–Japan College of Social Work

• Industrial Welfare
P–Tohoku Fukushi University

• Social Welfare
L–Tokyo Metropolitan University
L–Aichi Prefectural University
L–Kyoto Prefectural University
L–Osaka City University
L–University of Osaka Prefecture
L–Hiroshima Women's University
P–Dohto University
P–Hokusei Gakuen University
P–Tohoku Fukushi University
P–Shukutoku University
P–Sophia University
P–Taisho University
P–Japan College of Social Work
P–Japan Women's University
P–Japan Lutheram Theological College
P–Meiji Gakuin University
P–Nagano University
P–Doho University
P–Nihon Fukushi University
P–Doshisha University
P–Hanazono College
P–Bukkyo University
P–Ryukoku University
P–Koyasan University
P–Shikoku Christian College
P–St. Catherine Women's College
P–Nishikyushu University
P–Kagoshima Keizai University

Sociology

• Applied Sociology
P–Edogawa University
P–Toyo University
P–Bukkyo University

• Appleid Sociology and Social Sciences
N–Fukushima University

• Contemporary Sociology
P–Japan Women's University

• Industrial Sociology
P–Tokyo International University
P–Rikkyo University
P–Nagano University
P–Ritsumeikan University
P–Kansai University
P–Nara University
P–Kibi International University
P–Kagoshima Keizai University

• International–Comparative Sociology
P–Kibi International University

• Sociology
N–University of Tsukuba
N–The University of Tokyo
N–Shizuoka University
N–Mie University
N–Nara Women's University
N–University of the Ryukyus
L–Tokyo Metropolitan University
L–Tsuru University
P–Aomori University
P–Iwaki Meisei University
P–Tokiwa University
P–Ryutsu Keizai University
P–Keio University
P–International Christian University
P–Komazawa University
P–Sophia University
P–Soka University
P–Taisho University
P–Chuo University
P–Teikyo University
P–Tokyo Women's Christian University
P–Toyo University
P–Nihon University
P–Hosei University
P–Musashi University
P–Meiji Gakuin University
P–Meisei University
P–Rikkyo University
P–Rissho University
P–Wako University
P–Kanto Gakuin Universtiy
P–Toyama University of International Studies
P–Aichi University
P–Kinjo Gakuin University
P–Sugiyama Jogakuen University
P–Chukyo University
P–Otani University
P–Doshisha University
P–Bukkyo University
P–Ryukoku University
P–Otemon Gakuin University
P–Kansai University
P–Shitennoji International Buddhist University
P–St. Andrew's University
P–Kwansei Gakuin University
P–Konan University
P–Nara University
P–Koyasan University
P–Hiroshima Shudo University
P–Shikoku Christian College
P–Matsuyama University

P–Okinawa Kokusai University

System Sciences and Engineering

• Systems Engineering
N–Tokyo University of Mercantile Marine
N–Kobe University
N–Hiroshima University
P–Nippon Institute of Technology
P–Hosei University
P–The University of East Asia

• Systems Engineering
N–Ibaraki University
N–Nagoya Institute of Technology

Trasportation

• Transportation Engineering
N–Tokyo University of Marcantile Marine
N–Kyoto University

• Transportation and Information Systems Engineering
N–Kobe University of Marcantile Marine

• Transportation Science
N–Tokyo University of Marcantile Marine

• Transport Machine Engineering
P–Meijo University
P–Osaka Sangyo University
P–Kurume Institute of Technology

Visual and Performing Arts

• Cinema
P–Tokyo University of Art and Design
P–Nihon University

• Conceptual and Media Art
L–Kyoto City University of Arts

• Drama
P–Nihon University
P–Kinki University

• Image Science
N–Chiba University

• Image Science and Technology
P–Tokyo Institute of Polytechnics

• Imaging Arts and Sciences
P–Musashino Art University

• Imaging Engineering
P–Tokyo Institute of Polytech

• Photographic Engineering
P–Tokyo Institute of Polytechnics

• Photography
P–Tokyo University of Art and Design
P–Nihon University
P–Osaka University of Arts
P–Kyushu Sangyo University

Zoology

• Zoology
N–Kyoto University

• Zootechnical Science
N–Kobe University

Graduate Program

Aeronautics

• Aeronautical Engineering
N-Nagoya University *M, D*
N-Kyoto University *M, D*
L-University of Osaka Prefecture

• Aeronautics
N-The University of Tokyo *M, D*

• Aeronautics and Astronautics
P-Tokai University *M, D*

• Aerospace Engineering
P-Nihon University *M, D*

Agricultural Economics

• Agricultural and Forest Economics
N-Kyoto University *M, D*
N-Shimane University *M*

• Agricultural Economics
N-Hokkaido University *M, D*
N-Obihiro University of Agriculture and Veterinary Medicine *M*
N-Utsunomiya University *M*
N-The University of Tokyo *M, D*
N-Kyushu University *M, D*
P-Tokyo University of Agriculture *M, D*
P-Nihon University *M, D*
P-Meiji University *M, D*

• Agricultural Management
N-Ehime University *M*

• Farm Economics
N-University of Tottori *M*

• Horticultural Economics
N-Chiba University *M*

Agricultural Science

• Agricultural Biology
N-Hokkaido University *M, D*
N-Kyoto University *M, D*

• Agricultural Chemistry
N-Hokkaido University *M, D*
N-Obihiro University of Agriculture and Veterinary Medicine *M*
N-Iwate University *M*
N-Tohoku University *M, D*
N-Yamagata University *M*
N-Ibaraki University *M*
N-Utsunomiya University *M*
N-Chiba University *M*
N-The University of Tokyo *M, D*
N-Tokyo University of Agriculture and Technology *M*
N-Niigata University *M*
N-Shinshu University *M*
N-Gifu University *M*
N-Shizuoka University *M*
N-Nagoya University *M, D*
N-Kyoto University *M, D*
N-Kobe University *M*
N-University of Tottori *M*
N-Shimane University *M*
N-Yamaguchi University *M*
N-Ehime University *M*
N-Kochi University *M*
N-Kyushu University *M, D*
N-Saga University *M*
N-Miyazaki University *M*
N-Kagoshima University *M*
N-University of the Ryukyus *M*
L-University of Osaka Prefecture *M, D*
P-Tokyo University of Agriculture *M, D*
P-Nihon University *M, D*
P-Meiji University *M, D*
P-Kinki University *M, D*

• Agricultural Civil Engineering
N-Saga University *M*

• Agricultural Engineering
N-Hokkaido University *M, D*
N-Obihiro University of Agriculture and Veterinary Medicine *M*
N-Hirosaki University *M*
N-Iwate University *M*
N-Yamagata University *M*
N-Ibaraki University *M*
N-Utsunomiya University *M*
N-The University of Tokyo *M, D*
N-Tokyo University of Agriculture and Technology *M*
N-Niigata University *M*
N-Gifu University *M*
N-Kyoto University *M, D*
N-Kobe University *M*
N-University of Tottori *M*
N-Shimane Universityu *M*
N-Kagawa University *M*
N-Ehime University *M*
N-Kochi University *M*
N-Kyushu University *M, D*
N-Miyazaki University *M*
N-Kagoshima University *M*
N-University of the Ryukyus *M*
L-University of Osaka Prefecture *M, D*
P-Tokyo University of Agriculture *M*
P-Nihon University *M*

• Agricultural Machinery
N-Iwate University *M*

• Agricultural Production
N-Ibaraki University *M*
N-Mie University *M*

• Agricultural Production & Technology
N-Okayama University *M*

• Agricultural Science
N-Gifu University *M*
N-Shizuoka University *M*
N-Miyazaki University *M*
P-Tokyo University of Agriculture *M, D*

• Agriculture
N-Yamagata University *M*
N-Ibaraki University *M*
N-Utsunomiya University *M*
N-Tokyo University of Agriculture and Technology *M*
N-Shimane University *M*
N-Ehime University *M*
N-Kyushu University *M, D*
N-Kagoshima University *M*
N-University of the Ryukyus *M*
P-Nihon University *M, D*
P-Meiji University *M, D*
P-Meijo University *M, D*
P-Kinki University *M, D*

• Agriculture and Forestry
N-University of Tsukuba *M, D*

• Agricultural and Forestry Engineering
N-University of Tsukuba *M, D*

• Agriculture and Horticulture
N-Kobe University *M*

• Agrobiology
N-The University of Tokyo *M, D*

• Agro-environmental Chemistry
N-Obihiro University of Agriculture and Veterinary Medicine *M*

• Agroindustrial Science
N-Kagawa University *M*

• Agronomy
N-Hokkaido University *M, D*
N-Hirosaki University *M*
N-Iwate University *M*
N-Tohoku University *M, D*
N-Niigata University *M*
N-Nagoya University *M, D*
N-University of Tottori *M*
N-Yamaguchi University *M*
N-Saga University *M*
P-Kyushu Tokai University *M, D*

• Agronomy and Horticultural Science
N-Shinshu University *M*
N-Kyoto University *M, D*

• Applied Bioresources Science
N-Ehime University *D*
N-Kochi University *D*

• Biochemical Regulation
N-Nagoya University *M, D*

• Bioregulation Studies
P-Tokyo University of Agriculture *D*

• Bioproduction
N-Iwate University *D*
N-Mie University *M*
N-University of Tottori *D*

• Bioresource Production
N-Ehime University *D*
N-Kochi University *D*
N-Kagoshima University *D*

• Bioresource Sciences
N-Iwate University *D*
N-Okayama University *M*
N-University of Tottori *D*
N-Kagawa University *M*
N-Kagoshima University *D*

• Brewing and Fermentation
P-Tokyo University of Agriculture *M*

• Exploitation of Bioresources
N-Mie University *M*

• Fermentation Technology
N-Yamanashi University *M*
N-Osaka University *M, D*

• Genetic Resources Technology
N-Kyushu University *M, D*

• Resource Biology
N-Ibaraki University *M*

• Sericulture
N-Tokyo University of Agriculture and Technology *M*

• Subtropical Agriculture
N-Kochi University *M*

• Tropical Agriculture
N-Kyoto University *M, D*

Animal Sciences

• Animal Breeding
N-Kagoshima University *M*

• Animal Husbandry
N-Iwate University *M*
N-Niigata University *M*
P-Kitasato University *M*

• Animal Science
N-Hokkaido University *M, D*
N-Obihiro University of Agriculture and Veterinary Medicine *M*
N-Tohoku University *M, D*
N-Utsunomiya University *M*
N-Shinshu University *M*
N-Nagoya University *M, D*
N-Kyoto University *M, D*
N-Kyushu University *M, D*
N-Miyazaki University *M*
N-University of the Ryukyus *M*
P-Kitasato University *M, D*
P-Nihon University *M, D*
P-Kyushu Tokai University *M, D*

• Dairy Science
P-Rakuno Gakuen University *M*

• Poultry and Animal Science
N-Gifu University *M*

• Morphology-Function
N-Hokkaido University *D*

• Prophylaxis-Therapeutics
N-Hokkaido University *D*

• Veterinary Medicine
N-The University of Tokyo *D*
N-Gifu University *D*
P-Rakuno Gakuen University *D*
P-Kitasato University *D*
P-Nihon University *D*

• Veterinary Science
N-Yamaguchi University *D*
L-University of Osaka Prefecture *D*
P-Azabu University *D*
P-Nippon Veterinary and Zootechnical College *D*

Architecture

• Architectural Engineering
N-Chiba University *M*
N-Kyoto University *M, D*
N-Osaka University *M, D*
N-Oita University *M*

• Architecture
N-Hokkaido University *M, D*
N-Tohoku University *M, D*
N-Utsunomiya University *M*
N-Chiba University *M*
N-The University of Tokyo *M, D*
N-Tokyo National University of Fine Arts and Music *M*
N-Niigata University *M*
N-Fukui University *M*
N-Nagoya University *M, D*
N-Mie University *M*
N-Kyoto University *M, D*
N-Kobe University *M*
N-Kyushu University *M, D*
N-Kumamoto University *M*
N-Kagoshima University *M*
P-Hokkaido Institute of Technology *M*
P-Nippon Institute of Technology *M, D*
P-Science University of Tokyo *M, D*
P-Toyo University *M, D*
P-Nihon University *M, D*
P-Meiji University *M, D*
P-Kanto Gakuin University *M, D*
P-Kanazawa Institute of Technology *M*
P-Aichi Institute of Technology *M*
P-Meijo University *M*
P-Osaka Institute of Technology *M, D*
P-Kansai University *M, D*
P-Kinki University *M*
P-Kyushu Sangyo University *M*

• Architecture and Architectural Engineering
P-Nihon University *M, D*

• Architecture and Building Engineering
N-Tokyo Institute of Technology *M, D*
N-Shinshu University *M*
L-Tokyo Metropolitan University *M, D*
P-Tokai University *M, D*
P-Science University of Tokyo *M,D*
P-Kanagawa University *M, D*

• Architectural and Civil Engineering
N-University of the Ryukyus *M*
P-Shibaura Institute of Technology *M*
P-Waseda University *M, D*
P-Fukuoka University *M*

• Architecture, Urban Egnineering and Civil Engineering
N-Nagoya Institute of Technology *M, D*

Astronomy

• Astronomy
N-Tohoku University *M, D*
N-The University of Tokyo *M, D*
N-Kyoto University *M, D*

• Astrophysics
N-Nagoya University *M, D*

Biology

• Applied Biochemistry
N-University of Tsukuba *M, D*

• Applied Biological Science
N-Hiroshima University *M, D*
P-Science University of Tokyo *M, D*

• Applied Biology
N-Kyoto Institute of Technology *M*

• Applied Microbiology and Technology
P-The Kumamoto Institute of Technology *M, D*

• Biochemistry
N-Saitama University *M*
N-Osaka University *M, D*
P-Kobe Women's College of Pharmacy *M, D*

• Biochemistry and Biotechnology
N-Tokyo University of Agriculture and Technology *D*

• Bioengineering
N-Tokyo Institute of Technology *M*

• Biological & Chemical Engineering
N-Gunma University *M*

• Biological and Environmental Sciences
N-Saitama University *D*

• Biological Resources
N-Kobe University *D*

• **Biological Sciences**
N-Hiroshima University *M, D*
P-Sophia University *M, D*

• **Biology**
N-Hirosaki University *M*
N-Tohoku University *M*
N-Yamagata University *M*
N-Ibaraki University *M*
N-University of Tsukuba *M, D*
N-Chiba University *M*
N-Ochanomizu University *M*
N-Niigata University *M*
N-Toyama University *M*
N-Kanazawa University *M*
N-Shizuoka University *M*
N-Nagoya University *M, D*
N-Kobe University *M*
N-Nara Women's University *M*
N-Okayama University *M*
N-Shimane University *M*
N-Yamaguchi University *M*
N-Ehime University *M*
N-Kochi University *M*
N-Kumamoto University *M*
N-Kagoshima University *M*
N-University of the Ryukyus *M*
L-Tokyo Metropolitan University *M, D*
P-Toho University *M, D*
P-Konan University *M*

• **Biomedical Engineering**
N-Hokkaido University *M, D*

• **Biophysics**
N-Kyoto University *M, D*

• **Biophysics and Biochemistry**
N-University of Tsukuba *M, D*
N-The University of Tokyo *M, D*

• **Bioresources Science**
N-Okayama University *D*

• **Biosystem Science**
N-Niigata University *M, D*

• **Biotechnology**
N-The University of Tokyo *M, D*
P-Fukuyama University *M*

• **Genetics**
N-The Graduate University for Advanced Studies *D*

• **Life and Functional Materials Sciences**
P-Konan University *D*

• **Life Chemistry**
N-Tokyo Institute of Technology *M, D*

• **Life Science**
N-Tokyo Institute of Technology *M*
N-Kanazawa University *D*

• **Molecular Biology**
N-Nagoya University *M, D*

• **Molecular Biomechanics**
N-The Graduate University for Advanced Studies *D*

• **Physiology**
N-The Graduate University for Advanced Studies *D*
N-Osaka University *M, D*

• **Regulation Biology**
N-Saitama University *M*

Business and Management

• **Accounting**
N-Kobe University *M, D*
P-Tokyo International University *M, D*
P-Nihon University *M, D*

• **Administration Engineering**
P-Keio University *M, D*

• **Business**
P-Seikei University *M, D*

• **Business Administration**
N-Hokkaido University *M, D*
N-Otaru University of Commerce *M*
N-The University of Tokyo *M, D*
N-Yokohama National University *M*
N-Nagoya University *M, D*
N-Shiga University *M*
N-Kyoto University *M, D*
N-Osaka University *M, D*
N-Kobe University *M, D*
N-University of Wakayama *M*
L-Yokohama City University *M*
L-Kobe University of Commerce *M, D*
L-Kitakyushu University *M*
P-Tokyo International University *M, D*
P-Aoyama Gakuin University *M, D*
P-Asia University *M, D*
P-Keio University *M*
P-Komazawa University *M, D*
P-Seijo University *M*
P-Senshu University *M, D*
P-Tokyo Keizai University *M, D*
P-Toyo University *M*
P-Nihon University *M, D*
P-Meiji University *M, D*
P-Aichi University *M, D*
P-Nanzan University *M, D*
P-Otemon Gakuin University *M*
P-Ryukoku University *M, D*
P-Kwansei Gakuin University *M, D*
P-Konan University *M, D*
P-Hiroshima Shudo University *M, D*
P-Matsuyama University *M, D*
P-Seinan Gakuin University *M, D*

• **Business and Commerce**
P-Tokyo International University *M, D*

• **Business Economics**
N-Kyushu University *M, D*

• **Business Management**
N-Tohoku University *M, D*
P-Ritsumeikan University *M, D*

• **Business Management and Accounting**
N-Hitotsubashi University *M, D*

• **Business Science**
N-Fukushima University *M*

• **Business Studies**
P-Hiroshima Shudo University *M, D*

• **Commerce**
N-Hitotsubashi University *M, D*
N-Kobe University *M, D*
P-Chiba University of Commerce *M*
P-Keio University *M, D*
P-Komazawa University *M, D*
P-Senshu University *M, D*
P-Takushoku University *M, D*
P-Chuo University *M, D*
P-Nihon University *M, D*
P-Meiji University *M, D*
P-Meiji Gakuin University *M, D*
P-Waseda University *M, D*
P-Aichi Gakuin University *M, D*
P-Chukyo University *M, D*
P-Meijo University *M*
P-Osaka Gakuin University *M, D*
P-Kansai University *M, D*
P-Kinki University *M, D*
P-Doshisha University *M, D*
P-Fukuoka University *M, D*
P-Kumamoto University of Commerce *M*

• **Control Engineering**
N-Tokyo Institute of Technology *M, D*

• **Decision Sciences and Management Information Systems**
P-Nagoya University of Commerce and Business Administration *M*

• **Financial Accounting**
P-Kansai University *M, D*

• **Industrial Administration**
P-Science University of Tokyo *M, D*

• **Industrial and Systems Engineering**
P-Aoyama Gakuin University *M, D*

• **Industrial and Social Studies**
N-Shinshu University *M*

• **Industrial Engineering**
L-University of Osaka Prefecture *M, D*

• **Industrial Engineering and Management**
N-Tokyo Institute of Technology *M, D*

• **Industrial Management**
P-Osaka Institute of Technology *M*

• **International Business**
P-Aoyama Gakuin University *M, D*

• **International Management**
P-International University of Japan *M*

• **Management**
P-Gakushuin University *M, D*

• **Management and Accounting**
P-Keio University *M, D*

• **Management Engineering**
P-Tokai University *M, D*
P-Nihon University *M, D*
P-Kanazawa Institute of Technology *M*

• Management Sciences and Public Policy Studies
N-University of Tsukuba *M*

Chemistry

• Applied Chemistry
N-Hokkaido University *M, D*
N-Muroran Institute of Technology *M*
N-Iwate University *M*
N-Tohoku University *M, D*
N-Yamagata University *M*
N-Gunma University *M*
N-Saitama University *M, D*
N-Niigata University *M*
N-Fukui University *M*
N-Yamanashi University *M*
N-Shizuoka University *M*
N-Nagoya University *M, D*
N-Osaka University *M, D*
N-The University of Tokushima *M*
N-Kyushu University *M, D*
N-Saga University *M*
N-Kumamoto University *M*
N-Kagoshima University *M*
L-University of Osaka Prefecture *M, D*
P-Keio University *M, D*
P-Sophia University *M, D*
P-Toyo University *M, D*
P-Waseda University *M, D*
P-Kanagawa University *M, D*
P-Aichi Institute of Technology *M*
P-Osaka Institute of Technology *M, D*
P-Kansai University *M, D*
P-Kinki University *M, D*
P-Doshisha University *M, D*
P-Ritsumeikan University *M, D*
P-Okayama University of Science *M*
P-The Kumamoto Institute of Technology *M*

• Applied Chemistry, and Materials Science and Engineering
N-Kyushu Institute of Technology

• Applied Fine Chemistry
N-Osaka University *M, D*

• Chemical and Biological Science and Technology
N-Tokyo University of Agriculture and Technology *M, D*

• Chemical and Materials Engineering
N-Muroran Institute of Technology *D*

• Chemistry and Materials Technology
N-Kyoto Institute of Technology *M*

• Chemical Engineering
N-Akita University *M*
N-Tohoku University *M, D*
N-Yamagata University *M*
N-Gunma University *M*
N-The University of Tokyo *M, D*
N-Tokyo Institute of Technology *M, D*
N-Niigata University *M*
N-Toyama University *M*
N-Shizuoka University *M*
N-Nagoya University *M, D*
N-Kyoto University *M, D*
N-Kobe University *M*
N-Yamaguchi University *M*
N-The University of Tokushima *M*
N-Kyushu University *M, D*
N-Kagoshima University *M*
L-University of Osaka Prefecture *M, D*
P-Kansai University *M, D*
P-Fukuoka University *M*

• Chemical Environmental Engineering
N-Kitami Institute of Technology *M*

• Chemical Process Engineering
N-Hokkaido University *M, D*
N-Osaka University *M, D*

• Chemical Science
N-Osaka University *M, D*

• Chemical Technology
P-Kanagawa Institute of Technology *M*

• Chemistry
N-Hokkaido University *M, D*
N-Hirosaki University *M*
N-Tohoku University *M, D*
N-Yamagata University *M*
N-Ibaraki University *M*
N-University of Tsukuba *M, D*
N-Gunma University *D*
N-Saitama University *M*
N-Chiba University *M*
N-The University of Tokyo *M, D*
N-Tokyo Institute of Technology *M, D*
N-Ochanomizu University *M*
N-Niigata University *M*
N-Toyama University *M*
N-Kanazawa University *M*
N-Shizuoka University *M*
N-Nagoya University *M, D*
N-Kyoto University *M, D*
N-Kobe University *M*
N-Nara Women's University *M*
N-Shimane University *M*
N-Okayama University *M*
N-Hiroshima University *M, D*
N-Yamaguchi University *M*
N-Ehime University *M*
N-Kochi University *M*
N-Kyushu University *M, D*
N-Saga University *M*
N-Kumamoto University *M*
N-Kagoshima University *M*
N-University of the Ryukyus *M*
L-Tokyo Metorpolitan University *M, D*
P-Aoyama Gakuin University *M, D*
P-Gakushuin University *M, D*
P-Keio University *M, D*
P-Sophia Universityu *M, D*
P-Tokai University *M, D*
P-Science University of Tokyo *M, D*
P-Toho University *M, D*
P-Meisei University *M, D*
P-Rikkyo University *M, D*
P-Waseda University *M, D*
P-Kansai Gakuin University *M, D*
P-Kinki University *M, D*
P-Konan University *M*
P-Okayama University of Science *M*
P-Fukuoka University *M, D*

• Chemistry and Chemical Engineering
N-Kanazawa University *M*

• Chemistry of Resources
N-Mie University *M*

• Electronic Chemistry
N-Tokyo Institute of Technology *M, D*

• Fuel Chemistry
N-Akita University *M*

• Hydrocarbon Chemistry
N-Kyoto University *M, D*

• Industrial Chemistry
N-Ibaraki University *M*
N-Utsunomiya University *M*
N-Chiba University *M*
N-The University of Tokyo *M, D*
N-Toyama University *M*
N-Fukui University *M*
N-Shinshu University *M*
N-Gifu University *M*
N-Mie University *M*
N-Kyoto University *M, D*
N-Kobe University *M*
N-Okayama University *M*
N-University of Tottori *M*
N-Hiroshima University *M, D*
N-Yamaguchi University *M*
N-Ehime University *M*
N-Nagasaki University *M*
N-Miyazaki Universityu *M*
L-Tokyo Metropolitan University *M, D*
P-Shibaura Institue of Technology *M*
P-Seikei University *M, D*
P-Chuo University *M, D*
P-Tokai University *M, D*
P-Science University of Tokyo *M, D*
P-Nihon University *M, D*
P-Meiji University *M, D*
P-Kanto Gakuin University *M*
P-Chubu University *M, D*
P-Kyushu Sangyo University *M*

• Inorganic & Physical Chemistry
N-Osaka University *M, D*

• Materials Chemistry
N-Tohoku University *M, D*

• Molecular Science and Technology
N-Kyushu University *M, D*

• Organic Chemistry
N-Osaka University *M, D*

• Organic Synthesis
N-Kyushu University *M, D*

• Polymer and Textile
N-Gunma University *M*

• Polymer Chemistry
N-Yamagata University *M*
N-Gunma University *M*
N-Tokyo Institute of Technology *M, D*
N-Kyoto University *M, D*

• Polymer Science and Engineering
N-Kyoto Iustitute of Technology *M*

• Reaction Chemistry
N-The University of Tokyo *M, D*

• Resources Chemistry
N-Iwate University *M*
N-Ehime University *M*

• Synthetic Chemistry
N-Gunma University *M*
N-Chiba University *M*
N-The University of Tokyo *M, D*
N-Shinshu University *M*
N-Gifu University *M*
N-Nagoya University *M, D*
N-Kyoto University *M, D*
N-Okayama University *M*

• Transport Phenomena
N-Hiroshima University *M, D*

Civil Engineering

• Civil and Environmental Engineering
N-Muroran Institute of Technology *D*

• Civil and Environmental Construction Engineering
N-Kumamoto University *M*

• Civil and Structural Engineering
P-Tokyo Denki University *M*

• Civil Engineering
N-Hokkaido University *M, D*
N-Iwate University *M*
N-Tohoku University *M, D*
N-Akita University *M*
N-Utsunomiya University *M*
N-Gunma University *M*
N-The University of Tokyo *M, D*
N-Tokyo Institute of Technology *M, D*
N-Niigata University *M*
N-Nagaoka University of Technology *M*
N-Kanazawa University *M*
N-Yamanashi University *M*
N-Shinshu University *M*
N-Gifu University *M*
N-Nagoya University *M, D*
N-Kyoto University *M, D*
N-Osaka University *M, D*
N-Kobe University *M*
N-University of Tottori *M*
N-Okayama University *M*
N-Yamaguchi University *M*
N-The University of Tokushima *M*
N-Ehime University *M*
N-Saga University *M*
N-Nagasaki University *M*
N-Miyazaki University *M*
L-Tokyo Metropolitan University *M*
P-Tohoku Gakuin University *M*
P-Ashikaga Institute of Technology *M*
P-Chuo University *M, D*
P-Tokai University *M, D*
P-Science University of Tokyo *M, D*
P-Toyo University *M, D*
P-Nihon University *M, D*
P-Meisei University *M*
P-Kanto Gakuin University *M, D*
P-Kanazawa Institute of Technology *M, D*
P-Aichi Institute of Technology *M*
P-Meijo University *M*
P-Ritsumeikan University *M, D*
P-Osaka Institute of Technology *M, D*
P-Osaka Sangyo Universityu *M*
P-Kansai University *M, D*
P-Kinki University *M, D*
P-Hiroshima Institute of Technology *M*
P-Fukuyama University *M*
P-Kyushu Sangyo University *M*

• Construction Engineering
N-Ibaraki University *M*
N-Saitama Universityu *M*
N-Gifu University *M*
N-Yamaguchi University *M*
N-The University of Tokushima *M*
P-Chubu University *M, D*
P-Hosei University *M, D*
P-Daido Institute of Technology *M, D*

• Developmental Civil Engineering
N-Kitami Institute of Technology *M*

• General Construction Engineering
N-Fukui University *M*

• Regional Planning
N-Toyohashi University of Technology *M*

• Social Development Engineering
P-Setsunan University *M*

• Social Engineering
N-Tokyo Institute of Technology *M, D*

• Social Systems Engineering
N-University of Tottri *M*

• Structural Engineering
N-Hiroshima University *M, D*
N-Nagasaki University *M*
P-Nagasaki Institute of Applied Sciences *M*
P-The Kumamoto Institute of Technology *M*

• Urban and Regional Planning
N-University of Tsukuba *M, D*

• Urban Engineering
N-The University of Tokyo *M, D*

Communication

• Audio and Visual Communication Studies
N-Kyushu Institute of Design *M*

• Communication Studies
P-Seijo University *M, D*

• Journalism
P-Sophia University *M, D*
P-Doshisha University *M*

• Journalism and Communication
N-The University of Tokyo

• Mass Communications
P-Tokai University *M, D*

Computer and Information Sciences

• Communications and Systems
N-University of Electro-Communications *M, D*

• Communication Engineering
N-Osaka University *M, D*

• Computer Science
N-Iwate University *M*
N-Gunma University *M*
N-Tokyo Institute of Technology *M, D*
N-Yamahashi University *M*
N-Shizuoka University *M*
P-Keio University *M, D*

• Computer and Communication
N-Gunma University *D*
N-Kyushu University *M, D*

• Computer Science and Information Mathematics
N-The University of Electro-Communications *M, D*

• Computer Science and Systems Engineering
N-Muroran Institute of Technology *M*

• Information and Communication Engineering
P-Tokyo Denki University *M*

• Information and Computer Engineering
P-Kanazawa Institute of Technology *M, D*

• Information and Computer Sciences
N-Toyohashi University of Technology *M*
P-Osaka Electro-Communication University *M*

• Information and Production Science
N-Kyoto Institute of Technology *D*

• Information Engineering
N-Hokkaido University *M, D*
N-Tohoku University *M, D*
N-Yamagata University *M*
N-The University of Tokyo *M, D*
N-Niigata University *M*
N-Shinshu University *M*
N-Nagoya University *M, D*
P-Kyushu Tokai University *M*

• Information Processing
N-Tokyo Institute of Technology *M, D*

• Information Science
N-Ibaraki University *M*
N-Utsunomiya University *M*
N-The University of Tokyo *M, D*
N-Tokyo Institute of Technology *M, D*
N-Fukui University *M*
N-Kyoto University *M, D*
P-Seikei University *M, D*

P-Tokyo Denki University M
P-Science University of Tokyo M, D

• Information Science and Control Engineering
N-Nagaoka University of Technology D

• Information Science and Systems Engineering
N-The University of Tokushima M
N-Oita University M

• Information Systems
N-Kyushu University M, D

• Information Theory
N-Hiroshima University M, D

• Intelligence Science
N-Kobe University D

• Production and Information Sciences
N-Saitama University D

Crafts and Design

• Architecture and Design
N-Kyoto Institute of Technology M

• Ceramics
N-Tokyo National University of Fine Arts and Music M
P-Tama Art University M

• Crafts
N-University of Tsukuba M, D
N-Tokyo National University of Fine Arts and Music M
L-Kyoto City University of Arts M

• Crafts and Design
P-Tokai University M
P-Kyushu Sangyo University M

• Design
N-University of Tsukuba M
N-Tokyo National University of Fine Arts and Music M
L-Aichi Prefectural University of Fine Arts M
L-Kyoto City University of Arts M
P-Hokkaido Tokai University M
P-Tama Art University M
P-Musashino Art University M
P-Kyushu Sangyo University M

• Design Engineering
N-Hiroshima University M, D

• Industrial Design
N-Chiba University M

• Living Environmental Studies
N-Kyushu Institute of Design M

• Textile and Clothing Sciences
N-Ochanomizu University M
P-Mukogawa Women's University M, D
P-Tokyo Kasei University M

• Textile Engineering
M-Gifu University M

• Visual Design
L-Kanazawa College of Art M

Dentistry

• Dentistry
N-Hokkaido University D
N-Tohoku University D
N-Tokyo Medical and Dental University D
N-Niigata University D
N-Osaka University D
N-Okayama University D
N-Hiroshima University D
N-The University of Tokushima D
N-Kyushu University D
N-Nagasaki University D
N-Kagoshima University D
L-Kyushu Dental College D
P-Higashi Nippon Gakuen University D
P-Iwate Medical University D
P-Ohu University D
P-Meikai University D
P-Showa University D
P-Tokyo Dental College D
P-Nihon University D
P-The Nippon Dental University D
P-Kanagawa Dental College D
P-Tsurumi University D
P-Aichi Gakuin University D
P-Osaka Dental University D
P-Fukuoka Dental College D

Economics

• Applied Economics
N-The University of Tokyo M, D
P-Tokai University M, D
P-Waseda University M, D
P-Doshisha University M

• Economics
N-Hokkaido University M, D
N-Tohoku University M, D
N-Fukushima University M
N-University of Tsukuba M, D
N-Chiba University M
N-Yokohama National University M
N-Niigata University M
N-Kanazawa University M
N-Nagoya University M, D
N-Shiga University M
N-Kyoto University M, D
N-Osaka University M, D
N-University of Wakayama M
N-Okayama University M
N-Hiroshima University M, D
N-Yamaguchi University M
N-Kagawa University M
N-Kyushu University M, D
N-Oita University M
L-Tokyo Metropolitan University M, D
L-Yokohama City University M
L-University of Osaka Prefecture M, D
L-Kobe University of Commerce M, D
L-Kitakyushu University M
P-Tohoku Gakuin University M, D
P-Ryutsu-keizai University M
P-Josai University M
P-Dokkyo University M
P-Chiba University of Commerce M
P-Aoyama Gakuin University M, D
P-Asia University M, D
P-Gakushuin University M, D
P-Keio University D
P-Kokugakuin University M, D
P-Kokushikan University M, D
P-Komazawa University M, D
P-Shphia University M, D
P-Seikei University M, D
P-Seijo University M, D
P-Senshu University M, D
P-Soka University M, D
P-Daito Bunka University M, D
P-Chuo University M, D
P-Tokyo Keizai University M, D
P-Toyo University M, D
P-Nihon University M, D
P-Hosei University M, D
P-Meiji Gakuin University M, D
P-Musashi University M, D
P-Meiji University M, D
P-Rikkyo University M, D
P-Rissho University M
P-Kanagawa University M, D
P-Kanto Gakuen University M
P-Aichi University M, D
P-Nanzan University M, D
P-Kyoto Sangyo University M, D
P-Doshisha University D
P-Ritsumeikan University M, D
P-Ryukoku University M, D
P-Osaka Gakuin University M, D
P-Osaka University of Economics M, D
P-Otemon Gakuin University M
P-Kansai University M, D
P-Kansai Gakuin University M, D
P-Kinki University M
P-Kobe Gakuin University M, D
P-Konan University M
P-Matsuyama University M, D
P-Seinan Gakuin University M
P-Fukuoka University M, D

• Economics and Economic Policy
N-Kobe University M, D

• Economic Engineering
N-Kyushu University M, D

• Economic History
P-Keio University M
P-Kanto Gakuin University D

• Economic History and Economic Policy
N-Hitotsubashi University M, D

• Economic Policy
N-Kyoto University M, D
L-Nagoya City University M, D
P-Hokkaigakuen University M
P-Josai University M
P-Keio University M

• Economic Systems and Organization
P-Sophia University M, D

• Economic Theory
P-Doshisha University M

• Economic Theory and Economic History
N-The University of Tokyo M, D
N-Kyoto University M, D

• International Economics
N-Yokohama National University M
N-Kobe University M, D
P-Aoyama Gakuin University M, D
P-Takushoku University M, D

• Japanese Economics and Administration
L-Nagoya City University M

• Public Economics
N-Osaka University M, D

• Social History
P-Kanto Gakuin University D

• Theoretical Economics and Economic History
P-Waseda University M, D

• Theoretical Economics and Statistics
N-Hitotsubashi University M, D

Education (General)

• Curriculum and Instruction
N-Hiroshima University M, D

• Developmental Clinical Studies
N-Nagoya University M

• Early Childhood Education
N-Hyogo University of Teacher Education M
N-Hiroshima University M, D
N-Joetsu University of Education M
P-Seiwa College M

• Education
N-Hokkaido University M, D
N-Akita University M
N-University of Tsukuba M, D
N-The University of Tokyo M, D
N-Ochanomizu University M
N-Joetsu University of Education M
N-Nagoya University M, D
N-Kyoto University M, D
N-Osaka University M, D
N-Kyushu University M, D
P-Aoyama Gakuin University M, D
P-Keio University M, D
P-International Christian University M, D
P-Sophia University M, D
P-Soka University M, D
P-Nihon University M, D
P-Japan Women's University M, D
P-Rikkyo University M, D
P-Waseda University M
P-Kansai University M
P-Ashiya University M, D
P-Kobe Women's University M, D
P-Kwansei Gakuin University M, D
P-Konan Women's University M, D
P-Hiroshima Shudo University M
P-Hiroshima Bunkyo Women's College M

• Educational Administration
N-Hokkaido University M, D
N-The University of Tokyo M, D
N-Joetsu University of Education M
N-Hiroshima University M, D

• Educational Methods
N-Joetsu University of Education M
N-Kyoto University M, D
N-Kumamoto University M
P-International Christian University M, D

• Educational Psychology
N-Tohoku University M, D
N-The University of Tokyo M, D
N-Nagoya University M, D
N-Hiroshima University M, D
N-Kyushu University M, D

• Pedagogy
N-Tohoku University M, D
N-Kyoto University M, D
N-Nara Women's University M
N-Hiroshima University M, D
L-Tokyo Metropolitan University M, D
P-Meisei University M, D
P-Waseda University M, D

• School Education
N-Miyagi University of Education M
N-Fukushima University M
N-Ibaraki University M
N-University of Tsukuba M, D
N-Utsunomiya University M
N-Gunma University M
N-Saitama University M
N-Chiba University M
N-The University of Tokyo M, D
N-Tokyo Gakugei University M
N-Yokohama National University M
N-Niigata University M
N-Kanazawa University M
N-Shizuoka University M
N-Aichi University of Education M
N-Mie University M
N-Kyoto University of Education M
N-Osaka Kyoiku University M
N-Hyogo University of Teacher Education M
N-Kobe University M
N-Okayama University M
N-Hiroshima University M
N-Naruto University of Education M
N-Fukuoka University of Education M
N-Kumamoto University M
N-University of the Ryukyus M

• Student Guidance
N-Joetsu University of Education M

• School Management
N-Nara University of Education M

Education (Special Education)

• Education of the Handicapped
N-Miyagi University of Education M
N-Ibaraki University M
N-University of Tsukuba M, D
N-Tokyo Gakugei University M
N-Yokohama National University M
N-Joetsu University of Education M
N-Mie University M
N-Kyoto University of Education M
N-Aichi University of Education M
N-Osaka Kyoiku University M
N-Hyogo University of Theacher Education M
N-Hiroshima University M
N-Naruto University of Education M
N-Fukuoka University of Education M
N-Kumamoto University M
P-Kanazawa University M

Education (Specific Subjects)

• Art Education
N-Miyagi University of Education M
N-Ibaraki University M
N-Utsunomiya University M
N-Gunma University M
N-Saitama University M
N-Chiba University M
N-Tokyo Gakugei University M
N-Yokohama National University M
N-Niigata University M
N-Joetsu University of Education M
N-Shizuoka University M
N-Aichi University of Education M
N-Kanazawa University M
N-Mie University M
N-Kyoto University of Education M
N-Osaka Kyoiku University M
N-Hyogo University of Teacher Education M
N-Kobe University M
N-Nara University of Education M
N-Okayama University M
N-Hiroshima University M
N-Fukuoka University of Education M
N-University of the Ryukyus M

• Dance and Music Education
N-Ochanomizu University M

• English Education
N-Miyagi University of Education M
N-Akita University M
N-Fukushima University M
N-Ibaraki University M
N-Utsunomiya University M
N-Saitama University M
N-Chiba University M
N-Tokyo Gakugei University M
N-Yokohama National University M
N-Niigata University M
N-Kanazawa University M
N-Shizuoka University M
N-Aichi University of Education M
N-Kyoto University of Education M
N-Osaka Kyoiku University M
N-Kobe University M
N-Nara University of Education M
N-Okayama University M
N-Fukuoka University of Education M
N-University of the Ryukyus M
P-Waseda University M
P-Ashiya University M

• Heatlh Education
N-University of Tsukuba M

• Health and Physical Education,
N-Miyagi University of Education M
N-Ibaraki University M
N-Utsunomiya University M
N-Chiba University M
N-Tokyo Gakugei University M
N-Yokohama National University M
N-Kanazawa University M
N-Niigata University M
N-Aichi University of Education M

N-Mie University *M*
N-Kyoto University of Education *M*
N-Osaka Kyoiku University *M*
N-Kobe University *M*
N-Hiroshima University *M*
N-Fukuoka University of Education *M*

• Home Economics Education
N-Fukushima University *M*
N-Ibaraki University *M*
N-Gunma University *M*
N-Tokyo Gakugei University *M*
N-Yokohama National University *M*
N-Kanazawa University *M*
N-Shizuoka University *M*
N-Aichi University of Education *M*
N-Kyoto University of Education *M*
N-Osaka Kyoiku University *M*
N-Kobe University *M*
N-Nara University of Education *M*
N-Okayama University *M*
N-Fukuoka University of Education *M*
N-University of the Ryukyus *M*

• Japanese Education
N-Miyagi University of Education *M*
N-Fukushima University *M*
N-Ibaraki University *M*
N-Utsunomiya University *M*
N-Gunma University *M*
N-Saitama University *M*
N-Chiba University *M*
N-Tokyo Gakugei University *M*
N-Niigata University *M*
N-Kanazawa University *M*
N-Shizuoka University *M*
N-Aichi University of Education *M*
N-Mie University *M*
N-Osaka Kyoiku University *M*
N-Kobe University *M*
N-Nara University of Education *M*
N-Okayama University *M*
N-Fukuoka University of Education *M*
P-Waseda University *M*

• Language Education
N-Joetsu University of Education *M*
N-Hyogo University of Teacher Education *M*
N-Hiroshima University *M*

• Mathematics Education
N-Miyagi University of Education *M*
N Akita University *M*
N-Gunma University *M*
N-Mie University *M*
N-Saitama University *M*
N-Chiba University *M*
N-Tokyo Gakugei University *M*
N-Yokohama National University *M*
N-Kanazawa University *M*
N-Shizuoka University *M*
N-Aichi University of Education *M*
N-Osaka Kyoiku University *M*
N-Kobe University *M*
N-Nara University of Education *M*
N-Okayama University *M*
N-Hiroshima University *M*
N-Fukuoka University of Education *M*
N-University of the Ryukyus *M*

• Music Education
N-Miyagi University of Education *M*
N-Utsunomiya University *M*
N-Gunma University *M*
N-Saitama University *M*
N-Chiba University *M*
N-Tokyo Gakugei University *M*
N-Yokohama National University *M*
N-Niigata University *M*
N-Joetsu University of Education *M*
N-Shizuoka University *M*
N-Aichi University of Education *M*
N-Kyoto University of Education *M*
N-Osaka Kyoiku University *M*
N-Hyogo University of Teacher Education *M*
N-Kobe University *M*
N-Nara University of Education *M*
N-Okayama University *M*
N-Hiroshima University *M*
N-Fukuoka University of Education *M*
P-Nagoya College of Music *M*

• Physical Education
N-Gunma University *M*
N-Saitama University *M*
N-The University of Tokyo *M, D*
N-Joetsu University of Education *M*
N-Shizuoka University *M*
N-Nara University of Education *M*
N-Nara Women's University *M*
N-Okayama University *M*

• Science Education
N-Miyagi University of Education *M*
N-Akita University *M*
N-Fukushima University *M*
N-Ibaraki University *M*
N-Utsunomiya University *M*
N-Gunma University *M*
N-Saitama University *M*
N-Chiba University *M*
N-Tokyo Gakugei University *M*
N-Yokohama National University *M*
N-Niigata University *M*
N-Joetsu University of Education *M*
N-Kanazawa University *M*
N-Shizuoka University *M*
N-Aichi University of Education *M*
N-Mie University *M*
N-Kyoto University of Education *M*
N-Osaka Kyoiku University *M*
N-Hyogo University of Teacher Education *M*
N-Kobe University *M*
N Nara University of Education *M*
N-Okayama University *M*
N-Hiroshmia University *M*
N-Fukuoka University of Education *M*
N-Akita University *M*
N-Fukushima University *M*
N-Utsunomiya University *M*
N-Ibaraki University *M*
N-Gunma University *M*
N-Saitama University *M*
N-Chiba University *M*
N-Tokyo Gakugei University *M*
N-Yokohama National University *M*
N-Niigata University *M*
N-Joetsu University of Education *M*
N-Kanazawa University *M*
N-Aichi University of Education *M*
N-Shizuoka University *M*
N-Mie University *M*
N-Kyoto University of Education *M*
N-Osaka Kyoiku University *M*
N-Hyogo University of Teacher Education *M*
N-Kobe University *M*
N-Nara University of Education *M*
N-Okayama University *M*
N-Hiroshima University *M*
P-Waseda University *M*

• Specialized Subjects
N-Naruto University of Education *M*

• Teaching Japanese as a Second Language
N-Yokohama National University *M*
N-Hiroshima University *M*

• Technical Education
N-Utsunomiya University *M*
N-Gunma University *M*
N-Chiba University *M*
N-Tokyo Gakugei University *M*
N-Yokohama National University *M*
N-Kanazawa University *M*
N-Aichi University of Education *M*
N-Shizuoka University *M*
N-Mie University *M*
N-Kobe University *M*
N-Nara University of Education *M*
N-University of the Ryukyus *M*
P-Ashiya University *M*

Electrical Engineering

• Applied Electronic Engineering
P-Tokyo Denki University *M*

• Applied Electronics
N-Tokyo Institute of Technology *M, D*
P-Hokkaido Institute of Technology *M*

• Electrical and Applied Electronic Engineering
P-Daido Institute of Technology *M*

• Electrical and Communication Engineering
N-Tohoku University *M, D*

• Electrical and Computer Engineering
N-Yokohama National University *M, D*
N-Nagoya Institute of Technology *M, D*

• Electrical and Electronic Engineering
N-Muroran Institute of Technology *M*
N-Kitami Institute of Technology *M*
N-Tokyo Institute of Technology *M, D*
N-Toyohashi University of Technology *M*
P-Sophia University *M, D*
P-Meijo University *M*

• Electrical and Electronic Systems Engineering
N-Nagaoka University of Technology *M*

• Electrical and Information Engineering
N-University of the Ryukyus *M*

• Electrical, Electronic and Computer Engineering
N-Kyushu Institute of Technology *M, D*

• Electrical Engineering

N-Hokkaido University *M, D*
N-Iwate University *M*
N-Akita University *M*
N-Yamagata University *M*
N-Ibaraki University *M*
N-Utsunomiya University *M*
N-Gunma University *M*
N-Saitama University *M*
N-Chiba University *M*
N-The University of Tokyo *M, D*
N-Niigata University *M*
N-Toyama University *M*
N-Fukui University *M*
N-Yamanashi University *M*
N-Shinshu University *M*
N-Gifu University *M*
N-Shizuoka University *M*
N-Nagoya University *M, D*
N-Mie University *M*
N-Kyoto University *M, D*
N-Osaka University *M, D*
N-Kobe University *M*
N-University of Tottori *M*
N-Okayama University *M*
N-Yamaguchi University *M*
N-The University of Tokushima *M*
N-Ehime University *M*
N-Kyushu University *M, D*
N-Saga University *M*
N-Nagasaki University *M*
N-Oita University *M*
N-Miyazaki University *M*
N-Kagoshima University *M*
L-Tokyo Metropolitan University *M*
L-University of Osaka Prefecture *M, D*
P-Hokkaido Institute of Technology *M*
P-Tohoku Gakuin University *M, D*
P-Ashikaga Institute of Technology *M*
P-Nippon Institute of Technology *M, D*
P-Keio University *M, D*
P-Shibaura Institute of Technology *M*
P-Seijo University *M, D*
P-Chuo University *M, D*
P-Tokai University *M, D*
P-Tokyo Denki University *M, D*
P-Science University of Tokyo *M, D*
P-Toyo University *M, D*
P-Nihon University *M, D*
P-Hosei University *M, D*
P-Meiji University *M, D*
P-Meisei University *M, D*
P-Waseda University *M, D*
P-Kanagawa University *M, D*
P-Kanto Gakuin University *M*
P-Aichi Institute of Technology *M*
P-Chubu University *M, D*
P-Doshisha University *M, D*
P-Ritsumeikan University *M, D*
P-Osaka Institute of Technology *M, D*
P-Kansai University *M, D*
P-Kyushu Sangyo University *M*
P-Fukuoka University *M*
N-Kumamoto University *M*
P-Kanazawa Institute of Technology *M, D*
P-Osaka Sangyo University *M*

• Electricity and Electronics

P-Setsunar University *M*

• Electromagnetic Energy Engineering

N-Osaka University *M, D*

• Electronics

N-Toyama University *M*
N-Fukui University *M*
N-Nagoya University *M, D*
N-Kyoto University *M, D*
N-University of Tottori *M*
N-Okayama University *M*
N-Ehime University *M*
N-Kyushu University *M, D*
N-Nagasaki University *M*
L-University of Osaka Prefecture *M, D*
P-Tokai University *M, D*
P-Kansai University *M, D*

• Electronics and Applied Physics

P-Osaka Electro-Communication University *M*

• Electronics and Electrical Engineering

P-Aoyama Gakuin University *M, D*
P-Kanagawa Institute of Technology *M*
P-Fukuyama University *M*

• Electronic and Information Engineering

N-Tokyo University of Agriculture and Technology *M, D*

• Electronics and Information Science

N-University of Tsukuba *M, D*
N-Kyoto Institute of Technology *M*
L-Tokyo Metroplitan Institute of Technology *M*

• Electronics Engineering

N-Hokkaido University *M, D*
N-Iwate University *M*
N-Tohoku University *M, D*
N-Akita University *M*
N-Yamagata University *M*
N-Ibaraki University *M*
N-Utsunomiya University *M*
N-Gunma University *M*
N-Saitama University *M*
N-Chiba University *M*
N-The University of Tokyo *M, D*
N-The University of Electro-Communications *M, D*
N-Niigata University *M*
N-Nagaoka University of Technology *M*
N-Yamanashi University *M*
N-Shinshu University *M*
N-Gifu University *M*
N-Shizuoka University *M*
N-Mie University *M*
N-Osaka University *M, D*
N-Kobe University *M*
N-Yamaguchi University *M*
N-The University of Tokushima *M*
N-Saga University *M*
N-Oita University *M*
N-Miyazaki University *M*
N-Kagoshima University *M*
P-Tokyo Denki University *M*
P-Nihon University *M, D*
P-Kinki University *M, D*
P-Okayama University of Science *M*
P-Hiroshima Institute of Technology *M*
P-Fukuoka University *M*

• Electronic Materials Science

N-Shizuoka University *D*

• Electronic-Mechanical Engineering

N-Nagoya University *M, D*

• Electronic Science

P-Okayama University of Science *M*

• Electro Photo Optics

P-Tokai University *M, D*

• Opto-Electronic and Mechanical Engineering

N-Shizuoka University *M*

• Physical Electronics

N-Tokyo Institute of Technology *M, D*

Energy Engineering

• Chemical Energy Engineering

N-The University of Tokyo *M, D*

• Comprehensive Energy Engineering

N-Toyohashi University of Technology *D*

• Energy and environment science

N-Nagaoka University of Technology *D*

• Energy and Mechanical Engineering

N-Shizuoka University *M*

• Energy Conversion Engineering

N-Kyushu University *M, D*

• Energy Engineering

N-Oita University *M*
N-Toyohashi University of Technology *M*

• Energy Sciences

N-Tokyo Instutite of Technology *M, D*

• High Energy Engineering Science

N-Kyushu University *M, D*

• Thermal Energy System

N-Kyushu University *M, D*

Engineering (Micellaneous)

• Applied Engineering Sciences

L-Tokyo Metropolitan Institute of Technology *M*

• Engineering and Agricultural Technology

N-Okayama University *D*

• Engineering Science

N-Nagoya Institute of Technology *M, D*
N-Kyoto University *M, D*

• Foundation Engineering

N-Saitama University *M*
N-Niigata University *D*
N-Kobe University *D*
N-Okayama University *M*
N-Kumamoto University *D*

• Polymer Engineering

N-Fukui University *M*

Environmental Sciences

• Atmosphere and Hydrosphere
N-Nagoya University *M, D*

• Bioenvironment Science
N-University of Tottori *D*

• Biotic Environment
N-Iwate University *D*

• Environmental and Sanitary Engineering
N-Kyoto University *M, D*

• Environmental Chemistry
N-Utsunomiya University *M*
N-Saitama University *M*

• Environmental Chemistry and Engineering
N-Tokyo Institute of Technology *M, D*
N-Oita University *M*

• Environmental Chemistry and Technology
N-University of Tottori *M*

• Environmental Conservation
N-Hokkaido University *M, D*
N-Ehime University *M*

• Environmental Engineering
N-Tokyo Institute of Technology *M, D*
N-Yamanashi University *M*
N-Osaka University *M, D*

• Environmental Planning
N-Hokkaido University *M, D*
N-Kobe University *M*

• Environmental Sciences
N-University of Tsukuba *M*
N-Chiba University *D*
N-Niigata University *D*
N-Kobe University *D*
N-Shimane University *M*
N-Kumamoto University *D*

• Environmental Science and Conservation
N-Tokyo University of Agriculture and Technology *M*

• Environmental Science and Engineering
N-Hiroshima University *M, D*

• Environmental Structure
N-Hokkaido University *M, D*

• Environmental Studies for Open Space
N-Chiba University *M*

• Environment and Natural Resources
N-Hiroshima University *M, D*

• Human Environment
N-Ochanomizu University *D*

• Human Life and Environmental Sciences
N-Nara Women's University *D*

• Life Environment Conservation Science
N-Ehime University *D*
N-Kochi University *D*
N-Kagoshima University *D*

• Rural Science
N-Okayama University *M*

• Social Environment
N-Hokkaido University *M, D*

Fine Arts

• Aesthetics
N-University of Tsukuba *M, D*
N-The University of Tokyo *M, D*
N-Osaka University *M, D*
N-Kobe University *M*
L-Kyoto City University of Arts *M*
P-Tokai University *M*
P-Kwansei Gakuin University *M, D*
P-Kyushu Sangyo University *M*

• Aesthetics and Art History
N-Tohoku University *M, D*
N-Tokyo National University of Fine Arts and Music *M*
N-Kyoto University *M, D*
L-Kanazawa College of Art *M*
P-Seijo University *M, D*

• Aesthetics and Theory of Arts
P-Doshisha University *M*

• Art History
N-University of Tsukuba *M, D*
N-The University of Tokyo *M, D*
N-Osaka University *M, D*
N-Kobe University *M*
L-Kyoto City University of Arts *M*
P-Tokai University *M*
P-Waseda University *M, D*
P-Kyushu Sangyo University *M*

• Japanese Paintings
N-University of Tsukuba *M, D*
N-Tokyo National University of Fine Arts and Music *M*
L-Kanazawa College of Art *M*
L-Aichi Prefectural University of Fine Arts *M*
L-Kyoto City University of Arts *M*
P-Tama Art University *M*
P-Musashino Art University *M*
P-Kyushu Sangyo University *M*

• Oil Paintings
N-University of Tsukuba *M, D*
N-Tokyo National University of Fine Arts and Music *M*
L-Kanazawa College of Art *M*
L-Aichi Prefectural University of Fine Arts *M*
L-Kyoto City University of Arts *M*
P-Tama Art University *M*
P-Tokai University *M*
P-Kyushu Sangyo University *M*

• Sculpture
N-Tokyo National University of A Fine Arts and Music *M*
L-Kanazawa College of Art *M*
L-Aichi Prefectural University of Fine Arts *M*
L-Kyoto City University of Arts *M*
P-Tama Art University *M*
P-Tokai University *M*
P-Musashino Art University *M*
P-Kyushu Sangyo University *M*

Fisheries and Marine Engineering

• Aquatic Biosciences
N-Tokyo University Fisheries *M, D*

• Biology & Aquaculture
N-Hokkaido University *M, D*

• Control Engineering
N-Tokyo University of Mercantile Marine *M*

• Cultural Fisheries
N-Kochi University *M*

• Fisheries
N-The University of Tokyo *M, D*
N-Kyoto University *M, D*
N-Nagasaki University *M*
N-Kagoshima University *M*
P-Nihon University *M, D*
P-Kinki University *M, D*

• Fishery Sciences
N-Tohoku University *M, D*
N-Kyushu University *M, D*
N-Miyazaki University *M*
P-Kitasato University *M, D*

• Fisheries Science and Marine Biological Production
N-Mie University *M*

• Fishing Science
N-Hokkaido University *M, D*

• Fluid Engineering
P-Nagasaki Institute of Applied Sciences *M*

• Living Marine Resources
P-Tokai University *M, D*

• Marine Engineering
N-The University of Tokyo *M, D*
N-Tokyo University of Mercantile Marine *M*
N-Kobe University of Mercantile Marine *M*
P-Tokai University *M, D*

• Marine Production
N-Nagasaki University *D*

• Marine Resources
N-Nagasaki University *D*
N-Kagoshima University *D*

• Marine Science
N-University of the Ryukyus *M*

P-Tokai University *M, D*

• Marine Science and Technology
N-Tokyo University of Fisheries *M, D*

• Nautical Science
N-Kobe University of Mercantile Marine *M*

• Naval Architecture
N-Osaka University *M, D*
N-Kyushu University *M, D*
L-University of Osaka Prefecture *M, D*

• Naval Architecture and Ocean Engineering
N-The University of Tokyo *M, D*

• Navigation
N-Tokyo University off Mercantile Marine *M*

• Nuclear Engineering
N-Kobe University of Mercantile Marine *M*

• Ocean Civil Engineering
N-University of Tottori *M*
N-Kagoshima University *M*

• Ocean Engineering
N-Ehime University *M*

• Oceanic Architecture and Engineering
P-Nihon University *M, D*

• Ocean Mechnanical Engineering
N-Kobe University of Mercantile Marine *M*

• Transportation Science
N-Kobe University of Mercantile Marine *M*

• Transportation Engineering
N-Tokyo University of Mercantile Marine *M*

Food Science

• Food and Medicinal Sciences
P-Kobe Gakuin University *D*

• Food and Nutrition
N-Ochanomizu University *M*
P-Showa Women's University *M*
P-Tokyo Kasei University *M*
P-Tokyo University of Agriculture *M*
P-Japan Women's University *M*
P-Sugiyama Jogakuen University *M*
P-Kobe. Women's University *M, D*

• Food Chemistry
N-Tohoku University *M, D*

• Food Science
P-Otsuma Women's University *M*
P-Mukogawa Woman's University *M, D*

• Food Science and Nutrition
L-Kyoto Prefectural University *M*
P-Jissen Women's University *M*
N-Nara Joshi Daigaku *M*

• Food Science & Technology
N-Hokkaido University *M, D*
N-Tokyo University of Fishenies *M, D*
N-Nagoya University *M, D*
N-Kyoto University *M, D*

• Food Studies
P-Doshisha University *M*

• Food Technology
P-Nihon University *M, D*
N-Kyushu University *M, D*

Forest Science

• Botany
N-Hokkaido University *M, D*
N-The University of Tokyo *M, D*
N-Kyoto University *M, D*
N-Hiroshima University *M, D*

• Forest Products
N-Hokkaido University *M, D*
N-The University of Tokyo *M, D*
N-Tokyo University of Agiculture and Technology *M*
N-Shizuoka University *M*
N-Nagoya University *M, D*

• Forest Products Technology
N-Kyushu University *M, D*

• Forest Resources
N-Mie University *M*

• Forest Science
N-Hokkaido University *M, D*
N-Iwate University *M*
N-Yamagata University *M*
N-Utsunomiya University *M*
N-The University of Tokyo *M, D*
N-Tokyo University of Agriculture and Technology *M*
N-Niigata University *M*
N-Shinshu University *M*
N-Gifu University *M*
N-Shizuoka University *M*
N-Nagoya University *M, D*
N-Kyoto University *M, D*
N-University of Tottori *M*
N-Shimane University *M*
N-Ehime University *M*
N-Kochi University *M*
N-Kyushu University *M, D*
N-Miyazaki University *M*
N-Kagoshima University *M*
N-University of the Ryukyus *M*

• Forestry Engineering
N-Shinshu University *M, D*

• Grassland Science
N-Obihiro University of Agriculture and Veterinary Medicine *M*
N-Miyazaki University *M*

• International Agricultural Development
P-Tokyo University of Agriculture *M*

• Plant and Animal Production
N-Tokyo University of Agriculture and Technology *D*

• Plant Protection
N-Tokyo University of Agriculture and Techinology *M*
N-Kobe University *M*

• Resources and Environment
N-Tokyo University of Agriculture and Technology *D*

• Wood Science and Technology
N-Kyoto University *M.D*

Geography

• Geography
N-Tohoku University *M, D*
N-The University of Tokyo *M, D*
N-Ochanomizu University *M*
N-Kyoto University *M, D*
N-Nara Women's University *M*
N-Hiroshima University *M, D*
L-Tokyo Metropolitan University *M, D*
P-Komazawa University *M, D*
P-Nihon University *M, D*
P-Hosei University *M, D*
P-Meiji University *M, D*
P-Rikkyo University *M, D*
P-Rissho University *M, D*
P-Ritsumeikan University *M, D*
P-Kansai University *M*

• Geography and Hydrology
N-University of Tsukuba *M, D*

Geology

• Earth Science
N-Hirosaki University *M*
N-Yamagata University *M*
N-Ibaraki University *M*
N-Chiba University *M*
N-Toyama University *M*
N-Kanazawa University *M*
N-Nagoya University *M, D*
N-Kobe University *M*
N-Okayama University *M*
N-Ehime University *M*
N-Kagoshima University *M*

• Earth System Science and Technology
N-Kyushu University *M, D*

• Geology
N-University of Tsukuba *M, D*
N-The University of Tokyo *M, D*
N-Shimane University *M*
N-Kochi University *M*
N-Kyushu University *M, D*

• Geology
N-Kumamoto University *M*

• Geology & Mineralogy
N-Hokkaido University *M, D*
N-Niigata University *M*
N-Kyoto University *M, D*
N-Hiroshima University *M, D*

• **Geology and Paleontology**
N-Tohoku University *M, D*

• **Geophysics**
N-Hokkaido University *M, D*
N-Tohoku University *M, D*
N-The University of Tokyo *M, D*
N-Kyoto University *M, D*

• **Geosciences**
N-Shizuoka University *M*

• **Geotechnical Engineering**
N-Nagoya University *M, D*

• **Mineral Development Engineering**
N-Iwate University *M*
N-The University of Tokyo *M, D*

• **Mineral Industry and Materials Engineering**
P-Waseda University *M, D*

• **Mineral Resources Development Engineering**
N-Hokkaido University *M, D*

• **Mineral Science and Technology**
N-Kyoto University *M, D*

• **Mineralogical Sciences and Geology**
N-Yamaguchi University *M*

• **Mineralogy**
N-The University of Tokyo *M, D*

• **Petrology and Economic Geology**
N-Tohoku University *M, D*

• **Mining**
N-Kyushu University *M, D*

• **Mining and Mineral Engineering**
N-Yamaguchi University *M*

• **Mining Engineering**
N-Akita University *M*

• **Mining Geology**
N-Akita University *M*

• **Resources Engineering**
N-Tohoku University *M, D*

• **Resource Development and Mechanical Engineering**
N-Kumamoto University *M*

Health Sciences

• **Adult Health**
P-Kyorin University *M, D*

• **Environmental Health**
P-Jichi Medical School *D*
P-Juntendo University *M*

• **Health Administration**
P-Kyorin University *M, D*

• **Health & Hygiene**
P-Fujita-Gakuen Health University *D*

• **Health and Nutrition Sciences**
P-Nakamura Gakuen College *M*

• **Health and Sport Sciences**
N-University of Tsukuba *M, D*

• **Health Care Administration**
P-Juntendo University *M*

• **Health Sciences**
N-University of Tokyo, The *M, D*
N-University of the Ryukyus *M*
P-Kitasato University *D*

• **Hygienic Sciences**
P-Kitasato University *M*

• **Sanitary Engineering**
N-Hokkaido University *M, D*

History

• **Archaeology**
N-The University of Tokyo *M, D*
N-Kyoto University *M, D*
N-Hiroshima University *M, D*

• **Asian History**
N-Hokkaido University *M, D*
P-Chuo University *M, D*

• **European History**
N-Tohoku University *M, D*

• **Historical Science**
N-Chiba University *M*

• **History**
N-University of Tsukuba *M, D*
N-Ochanomizu University *M*
N-Kanazawa University *M*
N-Osaka University *M, D*
N-Kobe University *M*
N-Nara Women's University *M*
N-Okayama University *M*
N-Kyushu University *M, D*
N-Kumamoto University *M*
L-Tokyo Metropolitan University *M, D*
P-Aoyama Gakuin University *M, D*
P-Gakushuin University *M, D*
P-Keio University *M, D*
P-University of the Sacred Heart *M*
P-Taisho University *M, D*
P-Tokai University *M, D*
P-Tokyo Woman's Christian University *M*
P-Sophia University *M, D*
P-Meiji University *M, D*
P-Rikkyo University *M, D*
P-Rissho University *M, D*
P-Waseda University *M, D*
P-Aichi Gakuin University *M, D*
P-Ritsumeikan University *M, D*

• **History and Geography**
N-Nagoya University *M, D*

• **Japanese History**
N-Hokkaido University *M, D*
N-Tohoku University *M, D*
N-The University of Tokyo *M, D*
N-Kyoto University *M, D*
N-Hiroshima University *M, D*
P-Kokugakuin University *M, D*
P-Komazawa University *M, D*
P-Chuo University *M, D*
P-Toyo University *M*
P-Nihon University *M, D*
P-Hosei University *M, D*
P-Kogakkan University *M, D*
P-Bukkyo University *M, D*
P-Ryukoku University *M, D*
P-Kansai University *M, D*
P-Kwansei Gakuin University *M, D*
P-Kobe Women's University *M*

• **Occidental History**
N-The University of Tokyo *M, D*
P-Kwansei Gakuin University *M, D*

• **Oriental History**
N-Tohoku University *M, D*
N-The University of Tokyo *M, D*
N-Kyoto University *M, D*
N-Hiroshima University *M, D*
P-Nihon University *M, D*
P-Bukkyo University *M, D*
P-Ryukoku University *M, D*

• **Western History**
N-Hokkaido University *M, D*
N-Kyoto University *M, D*
N-Hiroshima University *M, D*
P-Chuo Universityu *M*

Home Science

• **Clothing**
P-Japan Women's University *M*

• **Clothing and Textile**
P-Sugiyama Jogakuen University *M*

• **Clothing Environment**
P-Otsuma Women's University *D*
P-Bunka Women's University *D*

• **Clothing Science**
N-Nara Women's University *M*
P-Otsuma Women's University *M*
P-Jissen Women's University *M*
P-Bunka Women's University *M*

• **Child Study**
N-Ochanomizu University *M*
P-Japan Women's University *M*

• **Dwelling and Environmental Science**
N-Nara Women's University *M*

• **Home Life Administration**
N-Ochanomizu University *M*

• **Housing**
P-Japan Women's University *M*

• **Housing and Planning**
L-Kyoto Prefectural University *M*

• **Living Design**
P-Showa Women's University *M*

• **Living System**
P-Showa Women's University *D*

• Pedology
P-Otsuma Women's University *M*

• Social Sciences of The Family
N-Nara Women's University *M*

Horticulture

• Horticultural Chemistry
N-Hirosaki University *M*

• Horticultural Science
N-Hirosaki University *M*
N-Yamagata University *M*
N-Chiba University *M*
N-Shizuoka University *M*
N-Saga University *M*
N-Kagoshima University *M*

• Horticultural Science and Agronomy
L-University of Osaka Prefecture *M, D*

• Landscape Architecture
N-Chiba University *M*
P-Tokyo University of Agriculture *M*

Humanities (Miscellaneous)

• Human Development
N-Ochanomizu University *D*

• Human Science
P-Tokiwa University *M*

International Studies

• International Relations
N-The University of Tokyo *M, D*
P-Sophia University *M, D*
P-Nihon University *M*
P-International University of Japan *M*
P-Tokyo International University *M*
P-Meiji Gakuin University *M*

• International and Cultural Studies
P-Tsuda College *M, D*

Law

• Anglo-American Law
P-Chuo University *M*

• Basic Laws
N-Kyoto University *M, D*
P-Kwansei Gakuin University *M, D*
N-The University of Tokyo *M, D*

• Business Law
P-Tokai University *M*

• Civil and Criminal Law
N-The University of Tokyo *M, D*
N-Okayama University *M*
P-Rikkyo University *M, D*
P-Fukuoka University *M, D*

• Civil Law
N-Osaka University *M, D*
P-Keio University *M, D*
P-Senshu University *D*
P-Meiji University *M, D*
P-Waseda University *M, D*
P-Ritsumeikan University *M, D*

• Comparative Law
P-Rikkyo University *M, D*

• Criminal Law
P-Chuo University *M, D*

• Economic and Private Law
N-Hitotsubashi University *M, D*

• Economic Relations Law
N-Yokohama National University *M*

• Foundations of Law
N-Tohoku University *M, D*

• Fundamental Legal Studies
P-Waseda University *M*

• International and Comparative Law
P-Tokai University *M*

• International Relations Law
N-Yokohama National University *M*

• Judicial Law
N-Kyushu University *M, D*

• Law
N-University of Tsukuba *M, D*
N-Chiba University *M*
N-Niigata University *M*
N-Kanazawa University *M*
N-Shimane University *M*
N-Kagawa University *M*
N-Ehime University *M*
N-Kumamoto University *M*
N-Kagoshima University *M*
N-University of the Ryukyus *M*
L-Tokyo Metropolitan University *M, D*
L-Kitakyushu University *M, D*
P-Hokkaigakuen University *M*
P-Tohoku Gakuin University *M*
P-Ashiya University *M, D*
P-Gakushuin University *M, D*
P-Kokugakuin University *M, D*
P-Sophia University *M, D*
P-Seikei University *M, D*
P-Seijo University *M*
P-Soka University *M, D*
P-Daito Bunka University *M*
P-Dokkyo University *M, D*
P-Meiji Gakuin University *M, D*
P-Kanagawa University *M*
P-Aichi Gakuin University *M, D*
P-Chukyo University *M*
P-Nanzan University *M*
P-Meijo University *M, D*
P-Kyoto Sangyo University *M*
P-Ryukoku University *M, D*
P-Kinki University *M, D*
P-Kobe Gakuin University *M, D*
P-Konan University *M*
P-Hiroshima Shudo University *M*
P-Seinan Gakuin University *M, D*

• Legal Studies
N-Hiroshima University *M, D*

• Legal Theory
N-Kyushu University *M, D*

• Political Law
N-Kyushu University *M, D*

• Private and Criminal Law
N-Nagoya University *M, D*
N-Kyoto University *M, D*
P-Kwansei Gakuin University *M, D*

• Private Law
N-Hokkaido University *M, D*
N-Tohoku University *M, D*
N-Kobe University *M, D*
P-Aoyama Gakuin University *M, D*
P-Komazawa University *M, D*
P-Senshu University *M*
P-Chuo University *M, D*
P-Toyo University *M, D*
P-Nihon University *M, D*
P-Hosei University *M, D*
P-Aichi University *M, D*
P-Doshisha University *M, D*
P-Kansai University *M, D*

• Public Law
N-Hokkaido University *M*
N-Tohoku University *M, D*
N-The University of Tokyo *M, D*
N-Kyoto University *M, D*
N-Osaka University *M, D*
N-Kobe University *M, D*
N-Kyushu University *M, D*
P-Aoyama Gakuin University *M, D*
P-Keio University *M, D*
P-Komazawa University *M, D*
P-Senshu University *M, D*
P-Chuo University *M, D*
P-Tokai University *M*
P-Toyo University *M*
P-Nihon University *M, D*
P-Meiji University *M, D*
P-Waseda University *M, D*
P-Aichi University *M*
P-Doshisha University *M*
P-Ritsumeikan University *M, D*
P-Kansai University *M, D*
P-Fukuoka University *M, D*

• Public Law and International Relations
N-Hitotsubashi University *M, D*

• Public Law and Political Science
N-Okayama University *M*

• Social Law
N-Kyushu University *M, D*

Library and Information Sciences

• Library and Information Science
N-The University of Library and Information Science *M*
P-Keio University *M, D*
P-Aichi Shukutoku University *M*

Literature, Linguistics and Area Studies

• American and English Literature
N-Kanazawa University *M*

• American Literature
N-Tokyo University of Foreign Studies *M*

• Arabic Language and Literature
N-Tokyo University of Foreign Studies *M*

• Arabic Language Studies
N-Osaka University of Foreign Studies *M*

• Area Literature
N-University of Tsukuba *M, D*

• Area Studies
N-Iwate University *M*
N-University of Tsukuba *M*
N-The University of Tokyo *M, D*

• Basis of Culture
N-Kagoshima University *M*

• Brazilian-Portuguese Studies
P-Kyoto University of Foreign Studies *M*

• British and American Literature
P-Bukkyo University *M*

• Burmese Language and Literature
N-Tokyo University of Foreign Studies *M*

• Burmese Language Studies
N-Osaka University of Foreign Studies *M*

• Children's Literature
P-Shirayuri Women's College *M*

• Chinese
P-Waseda University *M, D*
P-Kyoto Sangyo University *M*

• Chinese Culture
P-Otemon Gakuin University *M*

• Chinese Language
N-Tokyo University of Foreign Studies *M*

• Chinese Language and Literature
N-The University of Tokyo *M, D*
N-Kyoto University *M, D*
N-Hiroshima University *M, D*
L-Tokyo Metropolitan University *M, D*

• Chinese Language Studies
N-Osaka University of Foreign Studies *M*

• Chinese Linguistics
L-Kobe City University of Foreign Studies *M*

• Chinese Literature
N-Hokkaido University *M, D*
N-Tokyo University of Foreign Studies *M*
N-Ochanomizu University *M*
N-Nagoya University *M, D*
P-Keio University *M, D*
P-Daito Bunka University *M, D*
P-Nihon University *M, D*
P-Kansai University *M, D*

• Chinese Literature and Philosophy
P-Nisho-Gakusha University *M, D*

• Chinese Studies
N-Tohoku University *M, D*
L-Kitakyushu University *M*

• Civilization Studies
P-Tokai University *M, D*

• Comparative Culture
N-Ochanomizu University *D*
N-Nara Women's University *D*
P-International Christian University *M, D*
P-Sophia University *M*

• Comparative Literature and Culture
N-The University of Tokyo *M, D*

• Comparative Studies
N-The graduate University for Advanced Studies *D*

• Comparative Studies of International Cultures and Societies
P-Kurume University *M*
N-The University of Tokyo *M, D*

• Cultural History
P-Doshisha University *M, D*

• Culture and Society
N-Kobe University *D*

• Culturology
L-University of Osaka Prefecture *M*

• Dutch Language and Literature
N-Tokyo University of Foreign Studies *M*

• English
P-Dokkyo University *M, D*
P-Tokyo Woman's Christian University *M*
P-Waseda University *M, D*
P-Ohtani Women's College *M, D*
P-Kansai University of Foreign Studies *M, D*
P-Kwansei Gakuin University *M, D*
P-Konan University *M, D*
P-Kobe College *M, D*
P-Fukuoka University *M*

• English and American Language
N-Tokyo University of Foreign Studies *M*

• English and American Language and Literature
L-Osaka Women's University *M*

• English and American Languages and Cultures
L-Kitakyushu University *M*

• English and American Literature
N-Hokkaido University *M, D*
N-Kyoto University *M, D*
N-Kobe University *M*
N-Okayama University *M*
P-Aoyama Gakuin University *M, D*
P-Keio University *M, D*
P-Sophia University *M, D*
P-Showa Women's University *M, D*
P-Seikei University *M*
P-Daito Bunka University *M*
P-Chuo University *M, D*
P-Toyo University *M, D*
P-Meiji University *M, D*
P-Meisei University *M, D*
P-Rikkyo University *M, D*
P-Rissho University *M, D*
P-Tsurumi University *M*
P-Ritsumeikan University *M, D*
P-Baika Women's College *M*
P-Baiko Jo Gakuin College *M, D*

• English and American Studies
P-Kyoto University of Foreign Studies *M*

• English language
N-Kyoto University *M, D*

• English Language and British & American Literature
P-Musashi University *M*

• English Languages and Literature
N-The University of Tokyo *M, D*
N-Hiroshima University *M, D*
N-Kyushu University *M, D*
L-Tokyo Metropolitan University *M, D*
P-Tohoku Gakuin University *M, D*
P-Gakushuin University *M, D*
P-Tsuda College *M, D*
P-Japan Women's University *M, D*
P-Konan Women's University *M, D*
P-Mukogawa Women's University *M*
P-Hiroshima Shudo University *M, D*

• English Language Studies
N-Osaka University of Foreign Studies *M*

• English Linguistics
L-Kobe City University of Foreign Studies *M*

• English Literature
N-Tokyo University of Foreign Studies *M*
N-Ochanomizu University *M*
N-Nagoya University *M, D*
N-Osaka University *M, D*
N-Nara Women's University *M*
N-Kumamoto University *M*
P-Kobe Women's University *M*
P-Otsuma Women's University *M*
P-Komazawa University *M, D*
P-Jissen Women's University *M*
P-University of the Sacred Heart *M*
P-Senshu University *M, D*
P-Soka University *M, D*
P-Tokai University *M, D*
P-Nihon University *M, D*
P-Hosei University *M, D*
P-Meiji Gakuin University *M, D*
P-Aichi Shukutoku University *M*
P-Kinjo Gakuin University *M*
P-Chukyo University *M*
P-Doshisha University *M, D*
P-Doshisha Women's College of Liberal Arts *M, D*

P-Ryukoku University *M, D*
P-Otemon Gakuin University *M*
P-Kansai University *M, D*
P-Seinan Gakuin University *M, D*
P-Nanzan University *M, D*

• English Literature, English Linguistics, and Linguistics
N-Tohoku University *M, D*

• English Speaking Cultures
P-Aichi Gakuin University *M*

• English Studies
P-Seijo University *M, D*

• Euro-American Culture and Civilization
N-Toyama University *M*

• Euro-American Languages and Cultures
N-Chiba University *M*

• European Culture
P-Seijo University *M, D*

• French
P-Dokkyo University *M*
P-Waseda University *M, D*
P-Kwansei Gakuin University *M, D*
P-Fukuoka University *M*

• French Language Studies
N-Osaka University of Foreign Studies *M*

• French Language and Literature
N-The University of Tokyo *M, D*
N-Kyoto University *M, D*
L-Tokyo Metropolitan University *M, D*
P-Gakushuin University *M, D*
P-Musashi University *M*
P-Konan Women's University *M, D*

• French Literature
N-Nagoya University *M, D*
N-Osaka University *M, D*
N-Okayama University *M*
N-Hiroshima University *M, D*
N-Kyushu University *M, D*
P-Keio University *M, D*
P-Sophia University *M, D*
P-Chuo University *M, D*
P-Meiji University *M, D*
P-Rikkyo University *M, D*
P-Kansai University *M, D*
P-Seinan Gakuin University *M, D*

• French Literature and Linguistics
N-Tohoku University *M, D*
P-Aoyama Gakuin University *M, D*
P-Nanzan University *M, D*

• French Studies
P-Kyoto University of Foreign Studies *M*

• Fundamentals of Culture
N-Hirosaki University *M*

• German
P-Dokkyo University *M, D*
P-Waseda University *M, D*
P-Kwansei Gakuin University *M, D*

• German Language
N-Tokyo University of Foreign Studies *M*
N-The University of Tokyo *M, D*
N-Kyoto University *M, D*
N-Hiroshima University *M, D*
L-Tokyo Metropolitan University *M, D*
P-Gakushuin University *M, D*
P-Musashi University *M*

• German Language Studies
N-Osaka University of Foreign Studies *M*

• German Literature
N-Hokkaido University *M, D*
N-Tokyo University of Foreign Studies *M*
N-Kanazawa University *M*
N-Nagoya University *M, D*
N-Osaka University *M, D*
N-Okayama University *M*
N-Kyushu University *M, D*
N-Kumamoto University *M*
P-Keio University *M, D*
P-Sophia University *M, D*
P-Chuo University *M, D*
P-Nihon University *M, D*
P-Meiji University *M, D*
P-Rikkyo University *M, D*
P-Kansai University *M, D*

• German Literature and German Linguistics
N-Tohoku University *M, D*
P-Nanzan University *M, D*

• German Studies
P-Kyoto University of Foreign Studies *M*

• Hindi Language and Literature
N-Tokyo University of Foreign Studies *M*

• Hindi-Urdu Language Studies
N-Osaka University of Foreign Studies *M*

• Indic Philology
N-Kyoto University *M, D*

• Indology and History of Buddhism
N-Tohoku University *M, D*

• Indonesian Language and Literature
N-Tokyo University of Foreign Studies *M*

• Indonesian Language Studies
N-Osaka University of Foreign Studies *M*

• International and Area Studies
N-Hirosaki University *M*

• Islamic Studies
N-The University of Tokyo *M, D*

• Italian Languages and Literature
N-The University of Tokyo *M, D*

• Italian Language Studies
N-Osaka University of Foreign Studies *M*

• Japanese
P-Waseda University *M, D*

P-Ohtani Women's College *M, D*
P-Kwansei Gakuin University *M, D*
P-Konan University *M, D*

• Japanese and Chinese Literature
L-Kyoto Prefectural University *M*

• Japanese and Oriental Culture and Civilization
N-Niigata Universityu *M*

• Japanese Cultual Studies
P-Kobe College *M*

• Japanese Folk Culture
P-Seijo University *M, D*

• Japanese Language
N-Tokyo University of Foreign Studies *M*

• Japanese Language and Culture
N-Nagoya University *M, D*
P-Waseda University *M, D*

• Japanese Language and Literature
N-The University of Tokyo *M, D*
N-Kyoto University *M, D*
N-Hiroshima University *M, D*
N-Kyushu University *M, D*
L-Tokyo Metropolitan University *M, D*
L-Osaka Women's University *M*
P-Gakushuin University *M, D*
P-Japan Women's University *M, D*
P-Musashi University *M*
P-Konan Woman's University *M, D*
P-Mukogawa Women's University *M*
P-Hiroshima Bunkyo Women's College *M*

• Japanese Language Studies
N-Osaka University of Foreign Studies *M*

• Japanese Literature
N-Hokkaido University *M, D*
N-Chiba University *M*
N-Ochanomizu University *M*
N-Kanazawa University *M*
N-Nagoya University *M, D*
N-Osaka University *M, D*
N-Kobe University *M*
N-Nara Women's University *M*
N-Okayama University *M*
N-Kumamoto University *M*
P-Otsuma Women's University *M*
P-Keio University *M, D*
P-Kokugakuin University *M, D*
P-Komazawa University *M, D*
P-Jissen Women's University *M, D*
P-Sophia University *M, D*
P-Showa Women's University *M, D*
P-Seikei University *M*
P-Seijo University *M, D*
P-University of the Sacred Heart *M*
P-Senshu University *M, D*
P-Taisho University *M, D*
P-Daito Bunka University *M, D*
P-Chuo University *M, D*
P-Tokai University *M, D*
P-Tokyo Woman's University *M*
P-Toyo University *M, D*
P-Nisho-Gakusha University *M, D*
P-Nihon University *M, D*

P-Hosei University *M, D*
P-Meiji University *M, D*
P-Rikkyo University *M, D*
P-Rissho University *M*
P-Tsurumi University *M*
P-Aichi Shukutoku University *M*
P-Kinjo Gakuin University *M*
P-Chukyo University *M, D*
P-Kogakkan University *M, D*
P-Doshisha University *M, D*
P-Bukkyo University *M*
P-Ritsumeikan University *M, D*
P-Ryukoku University *M, D*
P-Kansai University *M, D*
P-Baika Women's College *M*
P-Kobe Women's University *M*
P-Baiko Jo Gakuin College *M, D*

• Japanese Literature and Language
P-Aoyama Gakuin University *M, D*

• Japanese Literature, Japanese Linguistics, and History of Japanese Thoughts
N-Tohoku University *M, D*

• Japanese Studies
N-Osaka University *M, D*

• Japano-Oriental Culture and Civilization
N-Toyama University *M*

• Korean Language and Literature
N-Tokyo University of Foreign Studies *M*

• Korean Language Studies
N-Osaka University of Foreign Studies *M*

• Language and Culture
N-Osaka University *M*
P-Kansai University of Foreign Studies *M, D*

• Language and Literature
N-Shinshu University *M*

• Linguistics
N-Hokkaido University *M, D*
N-University of Tsukuba *M, D*
N-The University of Tokyo *M, D*
N-Kyoto University *M, D*
N-Hiroshima University *M, D*
N-Kyushu University *M, D*
P-Sophia University *M, D*
P-Kyoto Sangyo University *M*

• Linguistic and Literary Culture
N-Yamaguchi University *M*

• Linguistic Culture
N-Saitama University *M*

• Literary Arts
P-Nihon University *M*

• Literature
N-University of Tsukuba *M, D*

• Malaysian Language and Literature
N-Tokyo University of Foreign Studies *M*

• Mongolian Language and Literature
N-Tokyo University of Foreign Studies *M*

• Mongolian Language Studies
N-Osaka University of Foreign Studies *M*

• Persian Language
N-Tokyo University of Foreign Studies *M*

• Persian Language Studies
N-Osaka University of Foreign Studies *M*

• Persian Literature
N-Tokyo University of Foreign Studies *M*
N-Nagoya University *M, D*

• Regional Culture
N-Yamaguchi University *M*
N-Kagoshima University *M*

• Regional Studies
N-The Graduate University for Advanced Studies *D*

• Region and Cultures
N-Shinshu University *M*

• Romance Language
N-Tokyo University of Foreign Studies

• Russian
P-Waseda University *M, D*

• Russian Languages and Literature
N-The University of Tokyo *M, D*

• Russian Language Studies
N-Osaka University of Foreign Studies *M*

• Russian Linguistics
L-Kobe City University of Foreign Studies *M*

• Slavic Languages
N-Tokyo University of Foreign Studies *M*

• Social Culture
N-Saitama University *M*

• Spanish Language Studies
N-Osaka University of Foreign Studies *M*

• Spanish Linguistics
L-Kobe City University of Foreign Studies *M*

• Spanish Studies
P-Kyoto University of Foreign Studies *M*

• Structure of Culture
N-Kobe University *D*

• Thai Language and Literature
N-Tokyo University of Foreign Studies *M*

• Thai-Vietnamese Language Studies
N-Osaka University of Foreign Studies *M*

• Urdu Language and Literature
N-Tokyo University of Foreign Studies *M*

• Vietnamese Language and Literature
N-Tokyo University of Foreign Studies *M*

• Western Civilization
P-Seikei University *M*

• Western Culture and Civilization
N-Niigata University *M*

Materials Science

• Crystalline Materials Science
N-Nagoya University *M, D*

• Inorganic Materials
N-Tokyo Institute of Technology *M, D*

• Materials Science and Technology
N-Nagaoka University of Technology *M*

• Materials Engineering
N-Hiroshima University *M, D*

• Materials Processing
N-Tohoku University *M, D*
N-University of Tsukuba *M, D*
N-Gunma University *M*
N-Saitama University *D*
N-The University of Tokyo *M, D*
N-Nagaoka University of Technology *D*
N-Shizuoka University *M*
N-Toyohashi University of Technology *M*
N-Kyoto Institute of Technology *D*
N-Kobe University *D*
N-Hiroshima University *M, D*
L-University of Osaka Prefecture *M*
P-Keio University *M, D*
P-Okayama University of Science *D*

• Materials Science and Chemical Engineering
N-Yokohama National University *M, D*
N-Muroran Institute of Technology *M*
N-Tokyo Institute of Technology *M, D*
N-Nagoya Institute of Technology *M, D*
N-Osaka University *M, D*
N-Nagasaki University *M*
N-Kyushu University *M, D*

• Materials System Engineering
N-Toyohashi University of Technology *D*

• Polymer Materials Engineering
N-Yamagata University *M*

• Science and Technology for Materials
N-Okayama University *D*

• Material Design Engineering
P-Kanazawa Institute of Technology *M, D*

Mathematics

• Applied Mathematics
P-Okayama University of Science *M, D*
P-Fukuoka University *M, D*

• Applied Mathematics and Physics
N-Kyoto University *M, D*

• Mathematical Engineering
P-Nihon University *M, D*

• Mathematical Engineering and Information Physics
N-The University of Tokyo *M, D*

• Mathematical Sciences
N-Kyoto University *M, D*
N-Osaka University *M, D*
L-University of Osaka Prefecture *M, D*
P-Tokyo Denki University *M, D*

• Mathematics
N-Hokkaido University *M, D*
N-Hirosaki University *M*
N-Tohoku University *M, D*
N-Yamagata University *M*
N-Ibaraki University *M*
N-University of Tsukuba *M, D*
N-Saitama University *M*
N-Chiba University *M*
N-The University of Tokyo *M, D*
N-Tokyo Institute of Technology *M, D*
N-Ochanomizu University *M*
N-Niigata University *M*
N-Toyama University *M*
N-Kanazawa University *M*
N-Shizuoka University *M*
N-Nagoya University *M, D*
N-Kyoto University *M, D*
N-Osaka University *M, D*
N-Kobe University *M*
N-Nara Women's University *M*
N-Shimane University *M*
N-Okayama University *M*
N-Hiroshima University *M, D*
N-Yamaguchi University *M*
N-Ehime University *M*
N-Kochi University *M*
N-Kyushu University *M, D*
N-Saga University *M*
N-Kumamoto University *M*
N-Kagoshima University *M*
N-University of the Ryukyus *M*
L-Tokyo Metropolitan University *M, D*
P-Gakushuin University *M, D*
P-Keio University *M, D*
P-Sophia University *M, D*
P-Tsuda College *M, D*
P-Tokai University *M, D*
P-Tokyo Women's Chistian University *M*
P-Science University of Tokyo *M, D*
P-Nihon University *M, D*
P-Rikkyo University *M, D*
P-Waseda University *M, D*
P-Kyoto Sangyo University *M, D*

• Mathematics and Information Sciences
L-University of Osaka Prefecture *M*

• Mathematics and Physical Sciences
N-Chiba University *D*

• Statistical Science
N-The Graduate University for Advanced Studies *D*

Mechanical Engineering

• Applied Mechanics
N-Okayama University *M*
N-Kyushu University *M, D*

• Civil, Mechanical and Control Engineering
N-Kyushu Institute of Technology *M, D*

• Engineering Mechanics
N-University of Tsukuba *M, D*

• Industrial Mechanical Engineering
N-Yamaguchi University *M*

• Instrumentation Engineering
N-Kobe University *M*
P-Keio University *M, D*

• Mechanical and Control Engineering
N-The University of Electro-Communications *M, D*
P-Osaka Electro-Communication University *M*

• Mechanical and Industrial Engineering
N-Fukui University *M*
N-Ehime University *M*

• Mechanical and Materials Engineering
N-Mie University *M*

• Mechanical and System Engineering
N-Kyoto Institute of Technology *M*

• Mechanical Engineering
N-Hokkaido University *M, D*
N-Kitami Institute of Technology *M*
N-Iwate University *M*
N-Tohoku University *M, D*
N-Akita University *M*
N-Yamagata University *M*
N-Ibaraki University *M*
N-Utsunomiya University *M*
N-Gunma University *M*
N-Chiba University *M*
N-The University of Tokyo *M, D*
N-Tokyo Institute of Technology *M, D*
N-Niigata University *M*
N-Toyama University *M*
N-Fukui University *M*
N-Yamanashi University *M*
N-Shinshu University *M*
N-Gifu University *M*
N-Shizuoka University *M*
N-Nagoya University *M, D*
N-Mie University *M*
N-Kyoto University *M, D*
N-Osaka University *M, D*
N-Kobe University *M*
N-University of Tottori *M*
N-Okayama University *M*
N-Yamaguchi University *M*
N-The University of Tokushima *M*
N-Ehime University *M*
N-Kyushu University *M, D*
N-Saga University *M*
N-Nagasaki University *M*
N-Kumamoto University *M*
N-Oita University *M*
N-Miyazaki University *M*
N-Kagoshima University *M*
N-University of the Ryukyus *M*
L-Tokyo Metropolitan University *M, D*
L-University of Osaka Prefecture *M, D*
P-Tohoku Gakuin University *M, D*
P-Ashikaga Institute of Technology *M*
P-Nippon Institute of Technology *M, D*
P-Aoyama Gakuin University *M, D*
P-Keio University *M, D*
P-Shibaura Institute of Technology *M*
P-Sophia University *M, D*
P-Seikei University *M, D*
P-Tokai University *M, D*
P-Tokyo Denki University *M*
P-Science University of Tokyo *M, D*
P-Toyo University *M, D*
P-Nihon University *M, D*
P-Hosei University *M, D*
P-Meiji University *M, D*
P-Meisei University *M, D*
P-Waseda University *M, D*
P-Kanagawa University *M, D*
P-Kanagawa Institute of Technology *M*
P-Kanto Gakuin University *M, D*
P-Kanazawa Institute of Technology *M, D*
P-Aichi Institute of Technology *M*
P-Daido Institute of Technology *M*
P-Chubu University *M, D*
P-Meijo University *M*
P-Doshisha University *M, D*
P-Ritsumeikan University *M, D*
P-Osaka Institute of Technology *M, D*
P-Osaka Sangyo University *M*
P-Kansai University *M, D*
P-Kinki University *M, D*
P-Okayama University of Science *M*
P-Kyushu Sangyo University *M*
P-Fukuoka University *M*

• Mechanical Engineering and Materials Science
N-Yokohama National University *M, D*

• Mechanical Engineering for Computer-Controlled Machinery
N-Osaka University *M, D*

• Mechanical Engineering for Industrial Machinery and Systems
N-Osaka University *M, D*

• Mechanical Engineering for power
N-Kyushu University *M, D*

• Mechanical Engineering for Production
N-Akita University *M*
N-The University of Tokyo *M, D*
N-Tokyo Institute of Technology *M, D*
N-Toyama University *M*
N-Kyushu University *M, D*
N-Saga University *M*

• Mechanical Engineering Science
N-Tokyo Institute of Technology *M, D*

• Mechanical Science
P-Okayama University of Science *M*

• Mechanical Systems Engineering
N-Muroran Institute of Technology *M*
N-Tokyo University of Agriculture and Technology *M, D*
N-Nagaoka University of Technology *M*
P-Kanagawa Institute of Technology *M*
P-Kanazawa University *M*
P-Setsunan University *M*
P-Hiroshima Institute of Technology *M*

• Planning and Production Engineering
N-Nagaoka University of Technology *M*

• Precision Engineering
N-Hokkaido University *M, D*
N-Tohoku University *M, D*
N-Yamagata University *M*
N-Ibaraki University *M*
N-Utsunomiya University *M*
N-Niigata University *M*
N-Yamanashi University *M*
N-Shinshu University *M*
N-Gifu University *M*
N-Shizuoka University *M*
N-Osaka University *M, D*

• Precision Machinery Systems
N-Tokyo Institute of Technology *M, D*
N-The University of Tokyo *M, D*
P-Chuo University *M, D*
P-Nihon University *M, D*

• Precision Mechanics
N-Kyoto University *M, D*
N-The University of Tokushima *M*

• Production and Information Systems Engineering
N-Muroran Institute of Technology *D*

• Production Engineering
N-Gunma University *D*
N-Kobe University *M*
P-Kyushu Tokai University *M*

• Production Science and Technology
N-Chiba University *D*

• Production Systems Engineering
N-Toyohashi University of Technology *M*

Medicine

• Medicine
N-Hokkaido University *D*
N-Asahikawa Medical College *D*
N-Hirosaki University *D*
N-Tohoku University *D*
N-Akita University *D*
N-Yamagata University *D*
N-Gunma University *D*
N-Chiba University *D*
N-University of Tsukuba *D*
N-The University of Tokyo *D*
N-Tokyo Medical and Dental University *D*
N-Niigata University *D*
N-Toyama Medical and Pharmaceutical University *D*
N-Kanazawa University *D*
N-Fukui Medical School *D*
N-Yamanashi Medical College *D*
N-Shinshu University *D*
N-Gifu University *D*
N-Hamamatsu University School of Medicine *D*
N-Nagoya University *D*
N-Mie University *D*
N-Shiga University of Medical Science *D*
N-Kyoto University *D*
N-Osaka University *D*
N-Kobe University *D*
N-University of Tottori *D*
N-Shimane medical University *D*
N-Okayama University *D*
N-Hiroshima University *D*
N-Yamaguchi University *D*
N-The University of Tokushima *D*
N-Kagawa Medical School *D*
N-Ehime University *D*
N-Kochi Medical School *D*
N-Kyushu University *D*
N-Saga Medical School *D*
N-Nagasaki University *D*
N-Kumamoto University *D*
N-Oita Medical College *D*
N-Miyazaki College *D*
N-Kagoshima University *D*
N-University of the Ryukyus *D*
L-Sapporo Medical College *D*
L-Yokohama City University *D*
L-Nagoya City University *D*
L-Kyoto Prefectural University of Medicine *D*
L-Wakayama Medical College *D*
P-Iwate Medical University *D*
P-Dokkyo University School of Medicine *D*
P-Saitama Medical College *D*
P-Saitama Medical College *D*
P-Kitasato University *D*
P-Kyorin University *D*
P-Keio University *D*
P-Showa University *D*
P-Tokai University *D*
P-Jikei University School of Medicine *D*
P-Tokyo Women's Medical College *D*
P-Toho University *D*
P-Nihon University *D*
P-Kanazawa Medical University *D*
P-Aichi Medical University *D*
P-Fujita Gakuen Health University *D*
P-Osaka Medical College *D*
P-Kinki University *D*
P-Hyogo College of Medicine *D*
P-Kawasaki Medical School *D*
P-Kurume University *D*
P-University of Occupational and Environmental Health, Japan *D*
P-Fukuoka University *D*

Metal Engineering

• Iron and Steel Engineering
N-Nagoya University *M, D*
N-Kyushu University *M, D*

• Metallurgical Engineering
N-Hokkaido University *M, D*
N-Iwate University *M*

• Metallurgy
N-Tohoku University *M, D*
N-Akita University *M*
N-Ibaraki University *M*
N-The University of Tokyo *M, D*
N-Tokyo Institute of Technology *M, D*
N-Toyama University *M*
N-Nagoya University *M, D*
N-Kyoto University *M, D*
N-Osaka University *M, D*
N-Ehime University *M*
N-Kyushu University *M, D*
N-Kumamoto University *M*
P-Shibaura Institute of Technology *M*
P-Tokai University *M, D*
P-Kansai University *M, D*

• Metallurgy and Materials Science
L-University of Osaka Prefectuure *M, D*

• Metal Science and Technology
N-Kyoto University *M, D*

• Metallic Engineering for Metallics
N-Akita University *M*

• Organic and Polymeric Materials
N-Tokyo Institute of Technology *M, D*

• Welding Engineering
N-Osaka University *M, D*

Music

• Conducting
N-Tokyo National University of Fine Arts and Music *M*

• Composition
N-Tokyo National University of Fine Arts and Music *M*
L-Aichi Prefectural University of Fine Arts *M*
L-Kyoto City University of Arts *M*
P-Nagoya College of Music *M*
P-Osaka College of Music *M*

• Instrumental Music
N-Tokyo National University of Fine Arts and Music *M*
L-Aichi Prefectural University of Fine Arts *M*
L-Kyoto City University of Arts *M*
P-Nagoya College of Music *M*
P-Osaka College of Music *M*
P-Elisabeth University of Music *M*

• Japanese Music
N-Tokyo National University of Fine Arts and Music *M*

• Music
P-Tokai University *M*

• Musicology
N-Tokyo National University of Fine Arts and Music M

• Music Theory
P-Elisabeth University of Music M

• Sacred Music
P-Elisabeth University of Music M

• Vocal Music
N-Tokyo National University of Fine Arts and Music M
L-Kyoto City University of Arts M
P-Nagoya College of Music M
P-Osaka College of Music M
P-Elisabeth University of Music M

Natural Science (Micellaneous)

• Applied Science
P-Tokai University M, D
P-Okayama University of Science M

• Applied Science for Functionality
N-Kyoto Institute of Technology D

• Coordinated Sciences
N-The University of Tokyo M, D

• Functional Molecular Science
N-The Graduate University for Advanced Studies D

• Fundamental Science and Technology
N-Niigata University D

• History and Philosophy of Science
N-The University of Tokyo M, D

• Integrated Basic Science
P-International Christian University M

• Macromolecular Science
N-Osaka University M, D

• Molecular Engineering
N-Kyoto University M, D

• Polymer Science
N-Hokkaido University M, D

• Science and Engineering
N-University of Tsukuba M

• Structural Molecular Science
N-The Graduate University for Advanced Studies D

Nursing

• Nursing
N-Chiba University M
P-Kitasato University M
P-St. Luke's College of Nursing M, D

Nutrition

• Nutrition
N-The University of Tokushima M, D
P-Kobe Gakuin University M

• Nutrition Sciences
P-Kagawa Nutrition College M, D

Pharmaceutical Sciences

• Pharmaceutical Sciences
N-Hokkaido University M, D
N-Tohoku University M, D
N-Chiba University M, D
N-The University of Tokyo M, D
N-Kanazawa University M
N-Kyoto University M, D
N-Osaka University M, D
N-Okayama University M
N-Hiroshima University M, D
N-The University of Tokushima M, D
N-Kyushu University M, D
N-Nagasaki University M, D
N-Kumamoto University M, D
L-Shizuoka Prefectural University M, D
L-Nagoya City University M, D
L-Gifu Pharmaceutical University M, D
P-Hokkaido Institute of Pharmaceutical Science M, D
P-Higashi Nippon Gakuen University M, D
P-Tohoku College of Pharmacy M, D
P-Josai University M, D
P-Kitasato University M, D
P-Kyoritsu College of Pharmacy M, D
P-Showa University M, D
P-Science University of Tokyo M, D
P-Toho University M, D
P-Hoshi University M, D
P-Meiji College of Pharmacy M, D
P-Meijo University M, D
P-Kyoto Pharmaceutical University M, D
P-Osaka University of Pharmaceutical Science M, D
P-Setsunan University M, D
P-Kobe Women's College of Pharmacy M, D
P-Kobe Gakuin University M
P-Kinki University M, D
P-Mukogawa Women's University M, D
P-Fukuyama University M
P-Tokushima Bunri University M, D
P-Fukuoka University M, D

Philosophy

• Chinese Philosophy
N-The University of Tokyo M, D
P-Toyo University M

• Chinese and Indian Philosophy
N-Hiroshima University M, D

• Chinese Philosophy and Literature
N-Kyushu University M, D

• Classical Philology
N-The University of Tokyo M, D

• East Asian Thought
P-Ritsumeikan University M

• East Asian Thought and Literature
P-Ritsumeikan University D

• Eastern Philosophy
N-Hokkaido University M, D

• Ethics
N-University of Tsukuba M, D
N-The University of Tokyo M, D
N-Hiroshima University M, D

• Indian Philosophy and Literature
N-The University of Tokyo M, D

• Oriental Philosophy
N-Nagoya University M, D
P-Waseda University M, D

• Philosophy
N-Hokkaido University M, D
N-Tohoku University M, D
N-University of Tsukuba M, D
N-The University of Tokyo M, D
N-Ochanomizu University M
N-Kanazawa University M
N-Nagoya University M, D
N-Kyoto University M, D
N-Kobe University M
N-Okayama University M
N-Kumamoto University M
L-Tokyo Metropolitan University M, D
P-Gakushuin University M, D
P-Keio University M, D
P-Sophia University M, D
P-Senshu University M, D
P-Chuo University M, D
P-Tokyo Woman's Christian University M
P-Toyo University M, D
P-Nihon University M, D
P-Hosei University M, D
P-Rissho University M
P-Waseda University M, D
P-Otani University M, D
P-Ritsumeikan University M
P-Ryukoku University M, D
P-Kansai University M, D
P-Kwansei Gakuin University M, D

• Philosophy and Behavioral Sciences
N-Niigata University M

• Philosophy and Ethics
P-Doshisha University M

• Philosophy & History of Philosophy
N-Osaka University M, D
N-Kyushu University M, D
P-Doshisha University D

• Practical Philosophy
N-Tohoku University M, D
N-Hiroshima University M, D
P-Ritsumeikan University D

Physical Education

• Athletic Coaching
N-University of Tsukuba M

• Methodology of Physical Education
N-University of Tsukuba *M*

• Physical Education
P-Tokai University *M*
P-Japan College of Physical Education *M*
P-Chukyo University *M, D*
P-Fukuoka University *M*

• Physical Recreation
N-National Institute of Fitness and Sports in Kanoya *M*

Physics

• Accelerator Science
N-The Graduate University for Advanced Studies *D*

• Applied Physics
N-Hokkaido University *M, D*
N-Tohoku University *M, D*
N-University of Tsukuba *M, D*
N-The University of Tokyo *M, D*
N-Tokyo Institute of Technology *M, D*
N-Fukui University *M*
N-Nagoya University *M, D*
N-Osaka University *M, D*
N-Kyushu University *M, D*
N-Miyazaki University *M*
P-Tohoku Gakuin University *M, D*
P-Chubu University *M, D*
P-Okayama University of Science *M*
P-Fukuoka University *M, D*

• Applied Physics and Chemistry
N-The University of Electro-Communications *M, D*

• Atomic Physics
P-Rikkyo University *M, D*

• Nuclear Engineering
N-Hokkaido University *M, D*
N-Tohoku University *M, D*
N-The University of Tokyo *M, D*
N-Tokyo Institute of Technology *M, D*
N-Nagoya University *M, D*
N-Kyoto University *M, D*
N-Osaka University *M, D*
N-Kyushu University *M, D*

• Nuclear Physics
N-Tohoku University *M, D*

• Physical Sciences
N-Kanazawa University *D*
N-Osaka University *M, D*

• Physics
N-Hokkaido University *M, D*
N-Hirosaki University *M*
N-Tohoku University *M, D*
N-Yamagata University *M*
N-Ibaraki University *M*
N-University of Tsukuba *M, D*
N-Saitama University *M*
N-Chiba University *M*
N-The University of Tokyo *M, D*
N-Tokyo Institute of Technology *M, D*
N-Ochanomizu University *M*
N-Niigata University *M*
N-Toyama University *M*
N-Kanazawa University *M*
N-Shizuoka University *M*
N-Nagoya University *M, D*
N-Kyoto University *M, D*
N-Osaka University *M, D*
N-Kobe University *M*
N-Nara Women's University *M*
N-Shimane University *M*
N-Okayama University *M*
N-Hiroshima University *M, D*
N-Yamaguchi University *M*
N-Ehime University *M*
N-Kochi University *M*
N-Kyushu University *M, D*
N-Saga University *M*
N-Kumamoto University *M*
N-Kagoshima University *M*
N-University of the Ryukyus *M*
L-Tokyo Metropolitan University *M, D*
P-Aoyama Gakuin University *M, D*
P-Keio University *M, D*
P-Gakushuin University *M, D*
P-Sophia University *M, D*
P-Chuo University *M*
P-Tokai University *M, D*
P-Science University of Tokyo *M, D*
P-Toho University *M, D*
P-Nihon University *M, D*
P-Meisei University *M, D*
P-Kyoto Sangyo University *M, D*
P-Ritsumeikan University *M, D*
P-Kansai Gakuin University *M, D*
P-Konan University *M, D*

• Pure and Applied Physics
P-Waseda University *M, D*

• Synchrotron Radiation Science
N-The Graduate University for Advanced Studies *D*

• Superconductivity Engineering
N-The University of Tokyo *M*

Political Science

• International Politics
P-Aoyama Gakuin University *M, D*

• Political Science
N-Tohoku University *M, D*

• Policy Science
N-Saitama University *M*
N-The University of Tokyo *M, D*

• Political Science and Public Law
N-Nagoya University *M, D*
N-Kyoto University *M, D*
L-Tokyo Metropolitan University *M, D*

• Politics
P-Gakushuin University *M, D*
P-Keio University *M, D*
P-Kokushikan University *M, D*
P-Seikei University *M, D*
P-Chuo University *M, D*
P-Tokai University *M, D*
P-Nihon University *M, D*
P-Hosei University *M, D*
P-Meiji University *M, D*
P-Waseda University *M, D*
P-Doshisha University *M, D*
P-Kwansei Gakuin University *M, D*

• Public Administration
D-International Christian University *M*

• Quantitative Policy Analysis
N-University of Tsukuba *M, D*

Psychology

• Clinical Social Psychology
P-Tokyo International University *M*

• Developmental Psychology
P-Shirayuri Women's College *M*

• Experimental Psychology
N-Hiroshima University *M, D*

• Psychology
N-Tohoku University *M, D*
N-University of Tsukuba *M, D*
N-The University of Tokyo *M, D*
N-Nagoya University *M, D*
N-Kyoto University *M, D*
N-Osaka University *M, D*
N-Okayama University *M*
L-Tokyo Metropolitan University *M, D*
P-Aoyama Gakuin University *M, D*
P-Gakushuin University *M, D*
P-Keio University *M, D*
P-Komazawa University *M, D*
P-Nihon University *M, D*
P-Meisei University *M, D*
P-Rikkyo University *M, D*
P-Waseda University *M, D*
P-Aichi Gakuin University *M, D*
P-Chukyo University *M, D*
P-Doshisha University *M, D*
P-Ritsumeikan University *M, D*
P-Otemon Gakuin University *M*
P-Kwansei Gakuin University *M, D*

• Section of Psychology
P-Konan Women's University *M, D*
P-Hiroshima Shudo University *M, D*

• Social Psychology
N-The University of Tokyo *M, D*
P-Kansai University *M, D*

Religion

• Biblical Theology
P-Tokyo Union Theological Seminary *M, D*
P-Doshisha University *M*
P-Kwansei Gakuin University *M, D*

• Buddhism
P-KomazawaUniversity *M, D*
P-Toyo University *M, D*
P-Bukkyo University *M, D*
P-Koyasan University *M, D*

• Buddhist Culture
P-Otani University *M, D*

• Buddhist Studies
P-Taisho University *M, D*
P-Rissho University *M, D*

P-Otani University M, D
P-Ryukoku University M, D

• Buddhist and Religious Studies
P-Aichi Gakuin University M, D

• Esoteric Buddhism
P-Koyasan University M, D

• Historical Theology
P-Doshisha University M, D

• Jodo Buddhism
P-Bukkyo University M

• Religion
N-Kyoto University M, D

• Religious Studies
P-Taisho University M, D

• Religion and Comparative Thought
N-University of Tsukuba M, D

• Shin Buddhist Studies
P-Otani University M, D

• Shin Buddhism
P-Ryukoku University M, D

• Systematic Theology
P-Sophia University M, D
P-Tokyo Union Theological Seminary M, D
P-Doshisha University M

• Science and History of Religion
N-The University of Tokyo M, D

• Shinto Studies
P-Kogakkan University M

• Shinto
P-Kokugakuin University M, D

• Theology
P-Rikkyo University M, D
P-Nanzan University M, D

Social Sciences

• Anthropology
N-University of Tsukuba M, D
N-The University of Tokyo M, D
N-Osaka University M, D

• Behavioral Science
N-Hokkaido University M, D
N-Chiba University M

• Cultural Anthropology
N-The University of Tokyo M, D
P-Nanzan University M, D

• International and Regional Studies
N-Hiroshima University M, D

• Regional Science
N-Kumamoto University M

• Social Anthropology
L-Tokyo Metropolitan University M, D

• Social Relations
N-The University of Tokyo M, D

• Social Sciences
N-Iwate University M
P-Komazawa University M, D

Social Welfare

• Social Welfare
P-Tohoku Fukushi University M
P-Shukutoku University M
P-Toyo University M, D
P-Japan College of Social Work M
P-Japan Women's University M, D
P-Nihon Fukushi University M
P-Bukkyo University M
P-Doshisha University M, D
P-Ryukoku University M, D
P-Shikoku Christian College M

• Social Work
P-Meiji Gakuin University M
P-Kwansei Gakuin University M, D

Sociology

• Applied Sociology
P-Rikkyo University M, D
P-Ritsumeikan University M, D
P-Konan University M, D

• Industrial Sociology
P-Tokyo International University M
P-Kansai University M, D

• Socio-Cultural Area Studies
N-Hitotsubashi University M, D

• Social Problems and Social Policies
N-Hitotsubashi University M, D

• Sociology
N-Tohoku University M, D
N-University of Tsukuba M, D
N-The University of Tokyo M, D
N-Hitotsubashi University M, D
N-Nagoya University M, D
N-Kyoto University M, D
N-Kobe University M
N-Osaka University M, D
N-Nara Women's University M
N-Kyushu University M, D
L-Tokyo Metropolitan University M, D
P-Keio University M, D
P-Sophia University M, D
P-Soka University M, D
P-Chuo University M, D
P-Toyo University M, D
P-Nihon University M, D
P-Hosei University M, D
P-Meiji Gakuin University M
P-Meisei University M, D
P-Rikkyo University M
P-Rissho University M, D
P-Waseda University M, D
P-Chukyo University M
P-Otemon Gakuin University M
P-Kansai University M, D
P-Bukkyo University M
P-Ryukoku University M, D
P-Kobe Women's University M
P-Kwansei Gakuin University M, D
P-Konan Women's University M, D
P-Kinjo Gakuin University M
P-Hiroshima Shudo University M

• Sociology and Social Welfare
P-Bukkyo University M

• Sociology and Social Work
P-Meiji Gakuin Universityu D

Systems Science

• Applied Systems Engineering
P-Tokyo Denki University D

• Applied Systems Science
N-Kyoto University M, D

• General Systems Studies
N-The University of Tokyo M, D

• System Design Engineering
P-Kanazawa Institute of Technology M, D

• Systems and Information Engineering
N-Toyohashi University of Technology D

• System Science and Technology
N-Kanazawa University D

• Systems Engineering
N-Nagoya Institute of Technology M, D
N-Kobe University M
N-Hiroshima University M, D
P-Tokyo Denki University M
P-Hosei University M, D

• Systems Science
N-Tokyo Institute of Technology M, D
N-Kobe University D
N-Kumamoto University D
P-Okayama University of Science D

Transportation

• Transport Civil Engineering
P-Nihon University M, D

• Transportation Engineering
N-Kyoto University M, D

Visual and Performing Arts

• Drama
P-Meiji University M, D

• Dramatic Arts
P-Waseda University M, D

• Image Science and Engineering
N-Chiba University M

• Image Science and Technology
N-Chiba University M

• Motion pictures
P-Waseda University M, D

• Photography

P-Tokai University *M*

Zoology

• Zoology

N-Hokkaido University *M, D*
N-The University of Tokyo *M, D*
N-Kyoto University *M, D*
N-Hiroshima University *M, D*
N-Kobe University *M*
P-Tokyo University of Agriculture *M, D*

Japanese and English Name List of Colleges and Universities

Ehime Daigaku
Ehime University 391
Eichi Daigaku
Eichi University 318
Erizabeto Ongaku Daigaku
Elisabeth University of Music 376
Fuerisu Jogakuin Daigaku
Ferris University 120
Fuji Daigaku
Fuji College 57
Fuji Joshi Daigaku
Fuji Women's College 35
Fujita-Gakuen Hoken Eisei Daigaku
Fujita Gakuen Health University 266
Fukui Daigaku
Fukui University 230
Fukui Ika Daigaku
Fukui Medical School 230
Fukui Kôgyô Daigaku
Fukui Institute of Technology 267
Fukuoka Daigaku
Fukuoka University 430
Fukuoka Jo Gakuin Daigaku
Fukuoka Jo Gakuin College 429
Fukuoka Joshi Daigaku
Fukuoka Women's University 423
Fukuoka Kôgyô Daigaku
Fukuoka Institute of Technology 429
Fukuoka Kyôiku Daigaku
Fukuoka University of Education 405
Fukuoka Shika Daigaku
Fukuoka Dental College 428
Fukushima Daigaku
Fukushima University 45
Fukushima Kenritsu Ika Daigaku
Fukushima Medical College 56
Fukuyama Daigaku
Fukuyama University 376
Gakushûin Daigaku
Gakushuin University 120
Gifu Daigaku
Gifu University 231
Gifu Joshi Daigaku
Gifu Women's University 268
Gifu Keizai Daigaku
Gifu College of Economics 267
Gifu Yakka Daigaku
Gifu Pharmaceutical University 254
Gunma Daigaku
Gunma University 72
Gunma Kenritsu Joshi Daigaku
Gunma Prefectural Women's College 102
Hachinohe Daigaku
Hachinohe University 57
Hachinohe Kôgyô Daigaku
Hachinohe Institute of Technology 58
Hakodate Daigaku
Hakodate University 35
Hakuô Daigaku
Hakuoh University 121
Hamamatsu Ika Daigaku
Hamamatsu University School of Medicine 233
Hanazono Daigaku
Hanazono College 319
Hannan Daigaku
Hannan University 319
Higashi Nippon Gakuen Daigaku
Higashi-Nippon-Gakuen University 36
Himeji Dokkyô Daigaku
Himeji Dokkyo University 319
Himeji Kôgyô Daigaku
Himeji Institute of Technology 307
Hirosaki Daigaku
Hirosaki University 46
Hirosaki Gakuin Daigaku
Hirosaki Gakuin College 58
Hiroshima Bunkyô Joshi Daigaku
Hiroshima Bunkyo Women's College 377
Hiroshima Daigaku
Hiroshima University 364
Hiroshima Denki Daigaku
The Hisoshima-Denki Institute of Technology 378
Hiroshima Jogakuin Daigaku
Hiroshima Jogakuin College 379
Hiroshima Joshi Daigaku
Hiroshima Women's University 374
Hiroshima Keizai Daigaku
Hiroshima University of Economics 381
Hiroshima Kenritsu Daigaku
Hiroshima Prefectural University 374
Hiroshima Kôgyô Daigaku
Hiroshima Institute of Technology 376
Hiroshima Shûdô Daigaku
Hiroshima Shudo University 380
Hitotsubashi Daigaku
Hitotsubashi University 73
Hokkaidô Daigaku
Hokkaido University 25
Hokkaidô Jôhô Daigaku
Hokkaido Information University 36
Hokkaidô Kôgyô Daigaku
Hokkaido Institute of Technology 37
Hokkaido Kyôiku Daigaku
Hokkaido University of Education 29
Hokkaidô Tôkai Daigaku
Hokkaido Tokai University 38
Hokkaidô Yakka Daigaku
Hokkaido Institute of Pharmaceutical Sciences 37
Hokkaigakuen Daigaku
Hokkaigakuen University 39
Hokkaigakuen Kitami Daigaku
Hokkai-gakuen University of Kitami 39
Hokuriku Daigaku
Hokuriku University 269
Hokusei Gakuen Daigaku
Hokusei Gakuen University 40
Hôsei Daigaku
Hosei University 121
Hoshi Yakka Daigaku
Hoshi University 123

Meijô Daigaku
Meijo University 274
Meikai Daigaku
Meikai University 156
Meisei Daigaku
Meisei University 156
Mie Daigaku
Mie University 236
Mimasaka Joshi Daigaku
Mimasaka Women's College 382
Minami Kyûshû Daigaku
Minami Kyushu College 438
Miyagi Gakuin Joshi Daigaku
Miyagi Gakuin Women's College 60
Miyagi Kyôiku Daigaku
Miyagi University of Education 49
Miyazaki Daigaku
Miyazaki University 416
Miyazaki Ika Daigaku
Miyazaki Medical College 416
Miyazaki Sangyô-Keiei Daigaku
Miyazaki Sangyo-Keiei University 438
Momoyama Gakuin Daigaku
St. Andrews University 358
Morioka Daigaku
Morioka College 61
Mukogawa Joshi Daigaku
Mukogawa Women's University 337
Muroran Kôgyô Daigaku
Muroran Institute of Technology 30
Musashi Daigaku
Musahi University 159
Musashi Kôgyo Daigaku
Musashi Institute of Technology 158
Musashino Bijutsu Daigaku
Musashino Art University 158
Musashino Joshi Daigaku
Musashino Women's College 159
Musashino Ongaku Daigaku
Musashino Academia Musicae 158
Nagano Daigaku
Nagano University 275
Nagaoka Gijutsukagaku Daigaku
Nagaoka University of Technology 238
Nagasaki Daigaku
Nagasaki University 417
Nagasaki Kenritsu Kokusai Keizai Daigaku
Nagasaki Prefectural University of International Economics 425
Nagasaki Sôgô Kagaku Daigaku
Nagasaki Institute of Applied Science 439
Nagoya Daigaku
Nagoya University 240
Nagoya Gaikokugo Daigaku
Nagoya University of Foreign Studies 279
Nagoya Gakuin Daigaku
Nagoya Gakuin University 277
Nagoya Geijutsu Daigaku
Nagoya University of the Arts 277
Nagoya Joshi Daigaku
Nagoya Women's University 279
Nagoya Keizai Daigaku
Nagoya Economics University 276
Nagoya Kôgyô Daigaku
Nagoya Institute of Technology 239
Nagoya Ongaku Daigaku
Nagoya College of Music 276
Nagoya Shiritsu Daigaku
Nagoya City University 256
Nagoya Shôka Daigaku
Nagoya University of Commerce and Business Administration 278
Nagoya Zôkei Geijutsu Daigaku
Nagoya College of Creative Art 275
Nakamura Gakuen Daigaku
Nakamura Gakuen College 439
Nanzan Daigaku
Nanzan University 280
Nara Daigaku
Nara University 338
Nara Joshi Daigaku
Nara Women's University 299
Nara Kenritsu Ika Daigaku
Nara Medical University 309
Nara Kenritsu Shôka Daigaku
Nara University of Commerce 309
Nara Kyôiku Daigaku
Nara University of Education 299
Nara Sangyô Daigaku
Nara Sangyo University 338
Naruto Kyôiku Daigaku
Naruto University of Education 396
Nihon Daigaku
Nihon University 160
Nihon Fukushi Daigaku
Nihon Fukushi University 281
Nihon Joshi Daigaku
Japan Women's University 128
Nihon Joshi Taiiku Daigaku
Japan Women's College of Physical Education 127
Nihon Jûichikusan Daigaku
Nippon Veterinary and Animal Science University 168
Nihon Rûteru Shigaku Daigaku
Japan Lutheran Theological College 127
Nihon Sekijuji Kango Daigaku
The Japanese Red Cross College of Nursing 127
Nihon Shakaijigyo Daigaku
Japan College of Social Work 126
Niigata Daigaku
Niigata University 243
Niigata Sangyô Daigaku
Niigata Sangyo University 282
Niigata Yakka Daigaku
Niigata College of Pharmacy 281
Nippon Bunka Daigaku
Nippon Bunka University 160
Nippon Bunri Daigaku
Nippon Bunri University 440

Saga Daigaku
Saga University 421
Saga Ika Daigaku
Saga Medical School 421
Sagami Joshi Daigaku
Sagami Women's University 175
Saitama Daigaku
Saitama University 77
Saitama Ika Daigaku
Saitama Medical College 176
Saitama Kôgyo Daigaku
Saitama Institute of Technology 175
Sakushin Gakuin Daigaku
Sakushin Gakuin University 176
Sakuyô Ongaku Daigaku
Sakuyo College of Music 385
Sangyô Ika Daigaku
University of Occupational and Environmental Health, Japan 443
Sannô Daigaku
Sanno College 177
Sapporo Daigaku
Sapporo University 41
Sapporo Gakuin Daigaku
Sapporo Gakuin University 41
Sapporo Ika Daigaku
Sapporo Medical College 34
Seigakuin Daigaku
Seigakuin University 178
Seijô Daigaku
Seijo University 179
Sei Katarina Joshi Daigaku
St. Catherine Women's College 401
Seikei Daigaku
Seikei University 180
Sei Marianna Ika Daigaku
St. Marianna University School of Medicine 192
Seinan Gakuin Daigaku
Seinan Gakuin University 441
Seiruka Kango Daigaku
St. Luke's College of Nursing 191
Seisen Joshi Daigaku
Seisen Women's College 181
Seishin Joshi Daigaku
University of the Sacred Heart 221
Seitoku Daigaku
Seitoku University 182
Seiwa Daigaku
Seiwa College 354
Sendai Daigaku
Sendai College 62
Senshû Daigaku
Senshu University 182
Senzoku Gakuen Daigaku
Senzoku Gakuen College 183
Setsunan Daigaku
Setsunan University 355
Shibaura Kogyo Daigaku
Shibaura Institute of Technology 184
Shiga Daigaku
Shiga University 304
Shiga Ika Daigaku
Shiga University of Medical Science 305
Shikoku Gakuin Daigaku
Shikoku Christian College 400
Shikoku Joshi Daigaku
Shikoku Women's University 400
Shimane Daigaku
Shimane University 370
Shimane Ika Daigaku
Shimane Medical University 370
Shimonoseki Shiritsu Daigaku
Shimonoseki City College 375
Shinshû Daigaku
Shinshu University 245
Shinwa Joshi Daigaku
Shinwa Women's College 356
Shirayuri Joshi Daigaku
Shirayuri Women's College 185
Shitennôji Kokusai Bukkyô Daigaku
Shitennoji International Buddhist University 356
Shizuoka Daigaku
Shizuoka University 246
Shizuoka Kenritsu Daigaku
University of Shizuoka 257
Shôin Joshigakuin Daigaku
Shoin Women's University 356
Shôkei Daigaku
Shokei College 442
Shônan Kôka Daigaku
Shonan Institute of Technology 185
Shôtoku Gakuen Gifu Kyôiku Daigaku
Gifu University for Education and Languages 268
Shôwa Daigaku
Showa University 186
Shôwa Joshi Daigaku
Showa Women's University 187
Shôwa Ongaku Daigaku
Showa Academia Musicae 186
Shôwa Yakka Daigaku
Showa College of Pharmaceutical Sciences 186
Shuchiin Daigaku
Shuchiin College 357
Shûjitsu Joshi Daigaku
Shujitsu Joshi University 386
Shukutoku Daigaku
Shukutoku University 188
Sôai Daigaku
Soai University 357
Sôgô Kenkyû Daigakuin Daigaku
The Graduate University for Advanced Studies 70
Sôka Daigaku
Soka University 188
Sonoda Gakuen Joshi Daigaku
Sonoda Gakuen Women's College 358
Sugino Joshi Daigaku
Sugino Women's College 192
Sugiyama Jogakuen Daigaku
Sugiyama Jogakuen University 283

Index

Japanese Colleges
and Universities 1991

平成 3 年 3 月 30 日発行

監　修　文　部　省
編　者　財団法人 日本国際教育協会

発行者　海 老 原 熊 雄

発行所　丸 善 株 式 会 社
郵便番号 103　東京都中央区日本橋二丁目 3 番10号

印刷・製本　大日本印刷株式会社

Published by **MARUZEN COMPANY, LTD.**
Tokyo, Japan
ISBN4-621-03599-1 C1502